MW00791449

Tide Tables 2021   HIGH AND LOW WATER PREDICTIONS

East Coast of North America

Issued 2020

2021 COMMERCIAL EDITION

IMPORTANT INFORMATION ABOUT THIS EDITION

In 2020, NOAA announced that it will eliminate paper publications of the annual Tide Tables and Tidal Current Tables beginning in 2021. In order to provide a similar printed resource for those who prefer a physical copy, Paradise Cay Publications has prepared this edition, it is designed to emulate the format and content of the official NOAA tide table books as closely as possible. Some significant exceptions are indicated below.

- NOAA was previously able to include tide and current predictions for foreign ports in the annual Tide Tables and Tidal Current Tables publications as part of an International Hydrographic Organization (IHO) agreement. This international data previously provided to NOAA and disseminated in the Tide Tables and Tidal Current Table is not available to the public and are therefore not offered in this publication.

- Some of the stations included in previous years have different naming conventions or have been replaced with more relevant reporting stations. As a result, some of the Tidal Differences (Table 2) may reference stations that are not included in the current edition.

- The USNO has historically provided the moonrise/moonset date, however the USNO website is down for extended maintenance throughout 2020, and as a result the moonrise/moonset data is currently not available and omitted from this edition. Should this data become available we will add it to future tide and tidal current publications.

- The sunrise/sunset times are obtained directly from NOAA, but the format of this data has changed. Rather than using a "local mean time" format, we have provided data from select cities in the areas covered in the publication. This data was obtained from NOAA directly.

- Some formatting has changed in both data and text content, relative to previous editions. We have noted as many of these changes as possible both in this disclaimer, and within the book where the change has occurred.

- The index format has been changed. The data we've compiled has been presented as accurately as possible but is to be used for reference purposes only - this volume does not fulfill any carriage requirements. We welcome any feedback, suggestions, or corrections as we continue to develop and refine this series of tide table books.

Paradise Cay Publications, Inc.
paracay.com

SOURCES OF ADDITIONAL INFORMATION

THE NATIONAL OCEAN SERVICE IS NO LONGER PRINTING AND DISTRIBUTING THE TIDE AND TIDAL CURRENT TABLES

Tide and Tidal current data continue to be updated, generated and published by the NOAA/ National Ocean Service; however, the printing and distribution in book-form is now done by several private companies working from information provided by NOS.

NOS now offers two vehicles for obtaining predictions. First, the complete set of Tables as camera-ready page-images will be available on CD-ROM. The CD-ROM vehicle is primarily intended for use by federal or private printers who wish to print in book-form the full set of Tables for distribution to resellers and the general public. Second, for domestic tide stations, predictions are available on the NOS, Center for Operational Oceanographic Products and Services (CO-OPS), website, (http://tidesandcurrents.noaa.gov/).

In addition to predictions, the website provides updated information on the status of the Tables as they are finalized each year. Notices concerning the most recent Table updates and publication cut-off dates are included.

For the names of companies printing and distributing the Tables, please call or write to:

National Ocean Service
Oceanographic Division, N/OPS3
1305 East-West Highway
Silver Spring, MD 20910
(301) 713-2815, fax (301) 713-4500

A list of authorized sales agents is published in the Nautical Chart Catalogs or may be obtained on request from the National Ocean Service.

TECHNICAL ASSISTANCE:

Technical questions relating to **tide and current predictions,** as well as requests for **special predictions**, should be addressed to:

National Ocean Service
Oceanographic Division, N/OPS3
1305 East-West Highway
Silver Spring, MD 20910
(301) 713-2815

Technical questions relating to **actual tide observations, tidal datums, and other information necessary** for **engineering projects** should be addressed to:

National Ocean Service
Oceanographic Division, N/OPS3
1305 East-West Highway
Silver Spring, MD 20910
(301) 713-2815

Technical questions relating to *other publications and nautical charts* should be addressed to:

National Ocean Service
Navigation Services Division
1315 East-West Highway
Silver Spring, MD 20910
(888) 990-NOAA (6622)

SOURCES OF ADDITIONAL INFORMATION

WEBSITES

Center for Operational Oceanographic Products and Services
(PORTS® * Predictions * Observations * Bench Marks * Tides Online * Great Lakes Online)
https://tidesandcurrents.noaa.gov

Marine Chart Division - https://www.nauticalcharts.noaa.gov

Office for Coastal Management - https://www.coast.noaa.gov

Ocean Predictions Center - https://ocean.weather.gov

National Center for Environmental Information - https://www.ncei.noaa.gov

National Centers for Environmental Predictions - https://www.ncep.noaa.gov

National Climatic Data Center - https://www.ncdc.noaa.gov

National Data Buoy Center - https://www.ndbc.noaa.gov

National Geodetic Survey - https://www.ngs.noaa.gov

National Geophysical Data Center - https://www.ngdc.noaa.gov

National Ocean Service - https://www.oceanservice.noaa.gov

National Oceanic and Atmospheric Administration - https://www.noaa.gov

National Oceanographic Data Center - https://www.nodc.noaa.gov

National Weather Service - https://www.weather.gov

U.S. Coast Guard - https://www.uscg.mil

U.S. Geological Survey - https://www.usgs.gov

U.S. Naval Observatory - https://www.usno.navy.mil

U.S. Naval Oceanographic Office - https://www.usno.navy.mil/NAVO

CORRECTIONS:

Corrections to this publication, after the date of printing, may appear in the Notice to Mariners. They may also appear in the Local Notice to Mariners, published weekly, by the various United States Coast Guard Districts.

CONTENTS

IMPORTANT NOTICES

For the most part, tide predictions for U.S. reference stations are based upon analyses of tide observations for periods of at least one year. Since the extremes of meteorological conditions have been excluded from the analyses and predictions, the predicted tidal heights should be considered as those expected under average weather conditions. During times when weather conditions differ from what is considered average for the area, the mariner must take note of the corresponding differences between predicted levels and those actually observed. Generally, prolonged onshore winds or a low barometric pressure can produce higher levels than predicted, while the opposite can result in lower levels than those predicted.

Exclusive of weather conditions, the astronomical tide is subject to range variations which should be noted. Decreased ranges may be expected near the times when the Moon is in apogee (apogean tides) or in quadrature (neap tides), and increased ranges may be expected when the Moon is in perigee (perigean tides) or in a new or full position (spring tides). A larger diurnal range may also result when the Moon is in its maximum declination (tropic tides). The actual range will depend upon the extent to which combinations of these positions reinforce or detract one from the other. The effect of these astronomical lineups is included in the predictions and may be apparent upon inspection.

The mariner may be kept aware of the times of these astronomical events by referring to the astronomical data listed in this book. He should realize, however, that there is generally a time lag from a few hours to several days from the time of the astronomical event to the time of the resultant tide. During times of storm surges or when extreme weather conditions are imminent, the mariner should closely follow local weather forecasts as they relate to the effects upon the tide levels.

Effective January 1, 1989, the chart datum and tidal datum chart, for all nautical charts, bathymetric maps, and tide tables covering the east coast of the United States and areas of the Caribbean Islands were changed from mean low water (MLW) to mean lower low water (MLLW). Notice of changes in tidal datums established through the "National Tidal Datum Convention of 1980" Federal Register, vol. 45, No. 207, Thursday, October 23, 1980, p. 70296-70297.

DAYLIGHT-SAVING TIME IS NOT USED IN THIS PUBLICATION. All daily tide predictions and predictions compiled by the use of Table 2 data are based on the standard time meridian indicated for each location. Predicted times may be converted to daylight saving times, where necessary, by adding 1 hour to these data. In converting times from the Astronomical Data page on the inside back cover, it should be remembered that daylight saving time is based on a meridian 15° east of the normal standard meridian for a particular place.

NOS, in partnership with other agencies and institutions, has established a series of Physical Oceanographic Real Time Systems (PORTS®) in selected areas. These PORTS® sites provide constantly updated information on tide and tidal current conditions, water temperature, and weather conditions. This information is updated every six minutes. PORTS® sites are currently in operation at several major harbors with future sites to be added. The information is accessible through a computer data connection or by a voice response system at the following sites:

PORTS® SITES	VOICE ACCESS	INTERNET ACCESS
CAPE COD	Not Available	www.tidesandcurrents.noaa.gov
CHARLESTON HARBOR	855-216-2137	"
CHERRY POINT	888-817-7794	"
CHESAPEAKE BAY	866-CH-PORTS (866-247-6787)	"
CORPUS CHRISTI	866-728-1897	"
CUYAHOGA	800-376-1192	"
DELAWARE RIVER & BAY	866-30-PORTS (866-307-6787)	"
HOUSTON/GALVESTON	866-HG-PORTS (866-447-6787)	"
HUMBOLDT BAY	855-876-5015	"
JACKSONVILLE	855-901-1549	"
LAKE CHARLES	888-817-7692	"
LOS ANGELES/ LONG BEACH	Not Available	"
LOWER COLUMBIA RIVER	888-53-PORTS (888-537-6787)	"

IMPORTANT NOTICES

PORTS® SITES	VOICE ACCESS	INTERNET ACCESS
LOWER MISSISSIPPI RIVER	888-817-7767	www.tidesandcurrents.noaa.gov
MATAGORDA BAY	888-524-9765	"
MIAMI	888-270-6145	"
MORGAN CITY	888-312-4113	"
MOBILE BAY	877-84-PORTS (877-847-6787)	"
NARRAGANSETT BAY	866-75-PORTS (866-757-6787)	"
NEW HAVEN	888-80-PORTS (888-807-6787)	"
NEW LONDON	855-626-0509	"
NEW YORK/NEW JERSEY	866-21-PORTS (866-217-6787)	"
PASCAGOULA	888-257-1857	"
PORT EVERGLADES	866-213-5269	"
PORT FOURCHON	855-687-2084	"
PORT OF ANCHORAGE	866-AK-PORTS (866-257-6787)	"
SABINE NECHES	888-257-1859	"
SAN FRANCISCO BAY	866-SB-PORTS (866-727-6787)	"
SAVANNAH	855-907-3136	"
SOO LOCKS	301-713-9596	"
TACOMA	888-60-PORTS (888-607-6787)	"
TAMPA BAY	866-TB-PORTS (866-827-6787)	"
TOLEDO	888-547-9131	"

PUBLISHED CAUTIONARY NOTICES

Published in Local Notice to Mariners and United States Coast Pilot Notices

NOAA is discontinuing the printed Tide Tables and Tidal Current Tables publications

Due to the availability of electronic predictions products, NOAA is ending the production of the printed Tide Tables and Tidal Current Tables publications. This, the final printed edition, will provide tide and tidal current predictions for the calendar year 2020.

NOAA and its predecessor agencies have produced and distributed predictions of high and low tides at ports along the U.S. coastline since 1867, and times/speeds of tidal currents since 1920. These predictions are currently produced in the form of six (6) annual publications, which are distributed through licensed commercial publishers.

NOAA is discontinuing the production of these annual publications due to: (a) Recent changes by the U.S. Coast Guard in the interpretation of the requirements for predictions, no longer requiring these publications in paper format. (b) The availability of online and electronic services providing tide and tidal current predictions which meet the U.S. Coast Guard requirements for navigation, and support other activities along the U.S. coast.

Tide and Tidal Current predictions are available through NOAA's Center for Operational Oceanographic Products and Services (CO-OPS) online services:

IMPORTANT NOTICES

- NOAA Tide Predictions: https://tidesandcurrents.noaa.gov/tide_predictions.html

- NOAA Current Predictions: https://tidesandcurrents.noaa.gov/noaacurrents/Regions

These online services provide predictions which equal or exceed the accuracy and availability of the predictions at domestic locations provided through printed publications, and provide additional capabilities allowing the predictions to better meet a variety of different user needs. These online services will provide predictions for locations for the U.S. coasts, and areas in which NOAA has some responsibility or authority. International predictions, previously provided by agencies in other countries for use in the printed publications, will not be available from the online services. Predictions for countries outside the U.S. may be obtained through the Oceanographic / Hydrographic agency in that country.

Contact NOAA's Center for Operational Oceanographic Products and Services (CO-OPS) with questions or for further information.

E-mail: Tide.Predictions@noaa.gov

Phone: 301-713-2815

(Issued: October 1, 2019)

DAILY TIDE PREDICTIONS UPDATED FOR CUBA

In 2016, the NOAA/National Ocean Services', Center for Operational Oceanographic Products and Services (CO-OPS) started an exchange of daily tide predictions with Servicio Hidrografico y Geodesico de La Republica de Cuba. As a result of this exchange of information, the Tide Tables – East Coast of North and South America will now include daily tide predictions for four reference stations in Cuba, beginning with the 2017 Tide Tables.

Havana; Moa, Holguin; Santiago de Cuba; Bahia de Cienfuegos

Tide predictions at these stations will be updated annually. As the exchange of tide prediction information between NOAA and authorities in Cuba matures, it is expected that subordinate stations along the coast of Cuba will be updated and there may be some changes in the stations at which daily predictions are provided. Mariners should expect changes to the tide predictions provided in Cuba for several years. It is anticipated that most of these changes will be to the subordinate stations provided.

For additional information, please contact CO-OPS via e-mail at Tide.Predictions@noaa.gov or (301) 713-2815.

(Issued: October1, 2016)

OBSERVED TIDAL CONDITIONS DIFFER FROM TIDAL PREDICTIONS IN THE HUDSON RIVER

The observed tides along the Hudson River have been reported to differ significantly from the published tide predictions; particularly in the northern section of the river from Newburgh to Albany, New York. Based on limited reports and comparisons to USGS stream gauges, it appears that high tides are occurring approximately 1 hour earlier than predicted.

NOAA has no information on what may be causing the difference between predictions and observations. This could be the result of natural changes (shoaling, erosion, etc) or artificial changes (dredging, construction, etc) in the Hudson River. Based on preliminary evidence, this does not appear to be a temporary condition and may indicate a long term change in the tidal conditions of the Hudson River.

IMPORTANT NOTICES

NOAA does not have any water level stations operating along the length of the Hudson River, with the nearest operating station being located at The Battery, New York. Without observational data in the area, the extent of the difference between predictions and observations cannot be confirmed; neither can the areas affected by this change. Resources are not available for the installation and operation of water level stations along the Hudson River.

Mariners operating in this area are urged to use caution.

(Issued: May 24, 2010)

TIDAL CURRENT PREDICTIONS INSIDE U.S. ESTUARIES

At present there are several U.S. estuaries with operational Physical Oceanographic Real Time Systems (PORTS) installed. PORTS systems are presently being installed in several additional estuaries. Over the next ten years there are projected to be twenty or more additional systems installed. In the past, the tidal current reference station has always been located at the entrance to each estuary. All tidal current secondary stations both inside and outside (along the coast) have been referred to the reference station at the entrance to the estuary. This will no longer be the case in estuaries with an operational PORTS system.

Estuaries with an operational PORTS system will have at least two reference stations. One will be the historic station at the entrance to the estuary. All secondary stations along the coast will continue to be referred to this station. The second tidal current reference station will be the primary PORTS station within the estuary. All secondary locations within the estuary itself will be referred to this location. Depending on the circulation dynamics of the estuary, daily tidal current predictions may be provided for one or more additional stations within the estuary.

(Issued October 1, 1999)

ARANSAS PASS – CORPUS CHRISTI BAY, TX

The Aransas-Corpus Christi Pilots have reported that published tidal current predictions for Aransas Pass deviate from observations by as much as two (2) hours. The published predictions must be used with extreme caution. The Pilots should be consulted for critical transits. Tidal Current predictions of the National Ocean Service (NOS) are derived from analysis of observed data at tidal harmonic frequencies which in turn are based on predictable astronomic positions of the moon and sun. The problem in many areas of the Gulf of Mexico, including the south Texas coast, is that localized meteorological conditions can significantly effect and alter the times of maximum flood and ebb currents. Real-time observation and reporting systems, such as the Physical Oceanographic Real Time System (PORTS) installed in the Galveston-Houston area, are the only means of providing accurate tidal current data for areas such as this.

(Issued July 17, 1997)

BISCAYNE BAY/PORT OF MIAMI, FL

The Biscayne Bay Pilots report that recent dredging and construction by the US Corps of Engineers (COE) supporting Miami port expansion has significantly effected the currents in Miami Harbor. Both flood and ebb currents should be expected to be stronger than indicated in official published predictions. The actual times for maximum and slack currents should be expected to deviate from the published predictions. Funding to support a survey to obtain new data for more accurate tidal current predictions is not available at this time. Installation of a Physical Oceanographic Real Time System (PORTS), like the one in operation in Tampa Bay, would be the best solution for long term marine safety.

(Issued July 17, 1997)

IMPORTANT NOTICES

CHARLESTON HARBOR, SC

The US Army Corps of Engineers (CEO) is planning dredging and construction projects for Charleston Harbor in 1996-1997. Such projects in the past in other areas have resulted in dramatic changes in the observed tidal currents of those areas. Once dredging and/or construction operations commence, the Tidal Current predictions for this region should be considered questionable and potentially dangerous to rely upon. Tide predictions will also be affected but to a lesser degree. Funding for a real time system to monitor the Tidal Currents and a resurvey of the area after COE operations are complete is presently not available. Therefore, once COE operations begin and until such time as a real-time system is installed or a resurvey of the area conducted, the National Oceanic and Atmospheric Administration, National Ocean Service will be unable to provide accurate Tidal Current predictions necessary for marine safety and navigation in this area.

(Issued June 5, 1996)

CHESAPEAKE & DELAWARE CANAL AND BALTIMORE HARBOR CONNECTING CHANNELS

The US Army Corps of Engineers (COE) is planning a project involving the Chesapeake & Delaware Canal (C&D) and the channels in the upper Chesapeake Bay connecting the canal to Baltimore, MD in 1996-1997. Such projects in the past in other areas have resulted in dramatic changes in the observed tidal currents of those areas. Once the project begins, the Tidal Current predictions for the C&D Canal and the channels connecting the canal to Baltimore should be considered questionable and potentially dangerous to rely upon. Tide predictions will be affected but to a lesser degree. Funding for a real-time system to monitor the Tidal Currents and a resurvey of these areas after COE operations are complete is presently not available. Therefore, once COE operations begin and until such time as a real-time system is installed or a resurvey of the area conducted, the National Oceanic and Atmospheric Administration, National Ocean Service will be unable to provide accurate Tidal Current predictions necessary for marine safety and navigation in this area.

(Issued June 5, 1996)

ST. AUGUSTINE, FL – ATLANTIC INTRACOASTAL WATERWAY

The US Coast Guard (USCG) has reported a problem involving the Tidal Currents in the Atlantic Intracoastal Waterway (AICW) in the St. Augustine, FL area. The specific location is the Bridge of Lions over the waterway. Numerous accidents have occurred at this site which are related to the currents in the waterway. There is no National Ocean Service (NOS) Tidal Current Station at or near the Bridge of Lions. Thus the NOS cannot, at this time, make Tidal Current predictions for this location. The USCG states that the cause of the accidents is loss of maneuverability (control) as a vessel passes under the bridge. The loss of maneuverability results in the vessel striking the bridge supports. The USCG states in part:

> "The affect of a 'fair' tide on a navigating vessel is to reduce the vessel's ability to maneuver. When a vessel is proceeding with a current (fair tide), less water flows across the vessel's rudders. This condition has the affect of reducing the vessel's maneuverability for a given speed over ground (all other things being equal).

The Bridge of Lions is a difficult bridge to navigate, even under ideal conditions. This circa 1926 Bascule bridge has a horizontal clearance of only 76' verses the 90' horizontal clearance of most of the other bridges on this section of the AICW."

In addition, according to the US Coast Pilot, Vol 4, Chapter 12, Tidal Currents in excess of 2 knots often run at right angles to the bridge opening. The Coast Pilot advises mariners to transit the bridge at minimal Tidal Current conditions. Funding for real-time monitoring of the Tidal Currents or a survey to obtain Tidal Current observations upon which to base Tidal Current predictions for this location is not presently available. A consortium of local, state, and federal officials in conjunction with the private sector and commercial shipping interests are presently studying various options to provide accurate Tidal Current predictions necessary for marine safety and navigation at this location.

(Issued June 5, 1996)

IMPORTANT NOTICES

WILMINGTON AND CAPE FEAR RIVER, NC

The US Army Corps of Engineers (COE) is due to begin dredging operations in the Wilmington and Cape Fear River area in 1997. The plans call for the deepening of the channel approaching Wilmington and extending up the Cape Fear River. Such actions in the past in other areas have resulted in dramatic changes in the observed tidal currents of those areas. Once dredging operations commence, the Tidal Current predictions for this region should be considered questionable at best and potentially dangerous to rely upon. Tide predictions will also be affected but to a lesser degree. Funding for a real-time system to monitor the Tidal Currents during the project and a resurvey of the area after COE operations are complete is presently not available. Therefore, once COE operations begin and until such time as a real-time system is installed or a resurvey of the area conducted, the National Oceanic and Atmospheric Administration, National Ocean Service will be unable to provide accurate Tidal Current predictions necessary for marine safety and navigation in this area.

(Issued June 5, 1996)

HAMPTON ROADS, VA

Tidal currents in Hampton Roads and Elizabeth River have been significantly altered by dredging and construction of a new bridge/tunnel. Recent dredging by the U.S. Army Corps of Engineers has deepened the channels by 10 feet to a depth of 50 feet. Pilots and officials at the Norfolk Naval Base report hazardous conditions including significantly higher than predicted maximum current velocities, and significant deviation in the predicted times of maximum current. Mariners should exercise EXTREME CAUTION and DISCRETION in the use of published NOS tidal current predictions for this area. Funding for a Quality Assurance study and a full scale resurvey of the area is presently not available.

(Issued March 24, 1992)

CHINCOTEAGUE CHANNEL, VA

United States Coast Guard (USCG) Personnel at the Chincoteague Coast Guard Station, VA report that the times of high and low water computed from differences in Table 2 of the East Coast Tide Tables are frequently off by as much as an hour. The channel is subject to shoaling and is frequently dredged. Exercise caution in using Table 2 Tide differences for this area.

(Issued May 17, 1991)

INTRODUCTION

Tide tables for the use of mariners have been published by the National Ocean Service (formerly the Coast and Geodetic Survey) since 1853. For a number of years these tables appeared as appendixes to the annual reports of the Superintendent of the Survey, and consisted of detailed instructions enabling the mariner to make his own prediction of tides as the occasion arose.

The first tables to give predictions for each day were those for the year 1867. They gave the times and heights of high waters only and were published in two separate parts, one for the Atlantic coast and the other for the Pacific coast of the United States. Together they contained daily predictions for 19 stations and tidal differences for 124 stations. A few years later predictions for the low waters were also included, and for the year 1896 the tables were extended to include the entire maritime world, with full predictions for 70 ports and tidal differences for about 3,000 stations.

The tidal tables are now issued in four volumes, as follows: *Europe and West Coast of Africa (including the Mediterranean Sea); East Coast of North and South America (including Greenland); West Coast of North and South America (including the Hawaiian Islands); Central and Western Pacific Ocean and Indian Ocean.* Together, they contain daily predictions for more than 250 reference ports and differences and other constants for more than 6,500 stations.

This edition of the Tide Tables, *East Coast of North and South America*, contains full daily predictions for more than 70 reference ports and differences and other constants for more than 2,500 stations in North America, South America, and Greenland. It also contains a table for obtaining the approximate height of the tide at any time, a table of local mean time of sunrise and sunset for every 5th day of the year for different latitudes, a table for the reduction of local mean time to standard time, a table of moonrise and moonset for 8 places, a table of the Greenwich mean time of the Moons' phases, apogee, perigee, greatest north and south and zero declination, and the time of the solar equinoxes and solstices, and a glossary of terms.

Up to and including the tide tables for the year 1884, all the tide predictions were computed by means of auxiliary tables and curves constructed from the results of tide observations at the different ports. From 1885 to 1911, inclusively, the predictions were generally made by means of the Ferrel Tide-predicting machine. From 1912 to 1965, inclusively, they were made by means of the Coast and Geodetic Survey tide-predicting machine No. 2. Since 1966, predictions have been made by electronic computer.

In the preparation of these tables all available observations were used. In some cases, however, the observations were insufficient for obtaining final results. As further information becomes available it will be included in subsequent editions. All persons using these tables are invited to send information or suggestions for increasing their usefulness to the National Ocean Service, Oceanographic Division, 1305 East-West Highway, N/OPS3, Silver Spring, Maryland 20910, U.S.A.

The information presented in *Table 4 - Local mean time of sunrise and sunset* and in *Table 6 - Moonrise and Moonset* is computed by the National Ocean Service using the Interactive Computer Ephemeris Program provided by the United States Naval Observatory.

In accordance with cooperative arrangements between the National Ocean Service and the authorities listed below, predictions for the following stations appear in this issue:

Canadian Hydrographic Service.—Harrington Harbour, Quebec, Halifax, St. John, Pictou, and Argentia.

Directoria de Hidrografia e Navegacao, Brazil.—Recife, Rio de Janeiro, and Santos.

Servicio Hidrografico, Argentina.—Buenos Aires, Puerto Ingeniero White, Comodoro Rivadiva, and Punta Loyola.

TABLE 1.— DAILY TIDE PREDICTIONS

EXPLANATION OF TABLE

This table contains the predicted times and heights of the high and low waters for each day of the year at a number of places which are designated as *reference stations*. By using tidal differences from Table 2, one can calculate the approximate times and heights of the tide at many other places which are called *subordinate stations*. Instructions on the use of the tidal differences are found in the explanation of Table 2.

High water is the maximum height reached by each rising tide, and low water is the minimum height reached by each falling tide. High and low waters can be selected from the predictions by the comparison of consecutive heights. Because of diurnal inequality at certain places, however, there may be a difference of only a few tenths of a foot between one high water and low water of a day, but a marked difference in height between the other high water and low water. Therefore, in using the Tide Tables it is essential to note carefully the heights as well as the times of the tides.

Time.— The kind of time used for the predictions at each reference station is indicated by the time meridian at the bottom of each page. Daylight-saving time is not used in this publication. If daylight-saving time is required, add one (1) hour to the predicted time.

Datum.— The datum from which the predicted heights are recorded is the same as that used for the nautical charts of the locality. The datum for the Atlantic coast of the United States is mean lower low water (MLLW). For foreign coasts a datum approximating to mean low water springs, Indian spring low water, or the lowest possible low water is generally used. The depression of the datum below mean sea level (MSL) for each of the reference stations of this volume is given on the preceding page.

Depth of water.— The nautical charts published by the United States and other maritime nations show the depth of the water as referred to a low water datum corresponding to that from which the predicted tidal heights are recorded. To find the actual depth of water at any time, the height of the tide should be added to the charted depth. If the height of the tide is negative—that is, if there is a minus sign (—) before the tabular height—the height should be subtracted from the charted depth. For any time between high and low water, the height of the tide may be estimated from the heights of the preceding and the following tides, or Table 3 may be used. The reference stations in Table 1 contain the heights in centimeters as well as in feet.

Variation in sea level.— Changes in winds and barometric conditions cause variations in sea level from day to day. In general, with onshore winds or a low barometer the heights of both the high and low waters will be higher than predicted, while with offshore winds or a high barometer they will be lower. There are also seasonal variations in sea level, but these variations have been included in the predictions for each station. At ocean stations the seasonal variation in sea level is usually less than half a foot.

At stations on tidal rivers the average seasonal variation in river level due to freshets and droughts may be considerably more than a foot. The predictions for these stations include an allowance for this seasonal variation representing average freshet and drought conditions. Unusual freshets or droughts, however, will cause the tides to be higher or lower, respectively, than predicted.

Number of tides.— There are usually two high and two low waters in a day. Tides follow the Moon more closely than they do the Sun, and the lunar or tidal day is about 50 minutes longer than the solar day. This causes the tide to occur later each day, and a tide that has occurred near the end of one calendar day will be followed by a corresponding tide that may skip the next day and occur in the early morning of the third day. Thus, on certain days of each month only a single high or a single low water occurs. At some stations, during portions of each month, the tide becomes diurnal—that is, only one high and one low water will occur during the period of a lunar day.

Relation of tide to current.— In using these tables of tide predictions bear in mind that they give the times and heights of high and low waters and not the times of turning of the current or slack water. For stations on the outer coast there is usually a small difference between the time of high or low water and the beginning of ebb or flood current, but for places in narrow channels, landlocked harbors, or on tidal rivers, the time of slack water may differ by several hours from the time of high or low water stand. The relation of the times of high and low water to the turning of the current depends upon a number of factors, so no simple or general rule can be given. For the predicted time of slack water, and other

TABLE 1.—DAILY TIDE PREDICTIONS

current data, reference should be made to the Tidal Current Tables prepared by the National Ocean Service, for the Atlantic and the Pacific coast of North America and Asia.

Typical tide curves.— The variations in the tide from day to day and from place to place are illustrated on the opposite page by the tide curves for representative ports along the Atlantic and Gulf coasts of the United States. Note that the range of tide for stations along the Atlantic coast varies from place to place but that the type is uniformly semidiurnal with the principal variations following the changes in the Moon's distance and phase. In the Gulf of Mexico, however, the type of tide differs considerably and the range of tide is uniformly small. At certain ports such as Pensacola there is usually only one high and one low water a day while at other ports such as Galveston the inequality is such that the tide is semidiurnal around the times the Moon is on the Equator but becomes diurnal around the times of maximum north or south declination of the Moon. In the Gulf of Mexico, consequently, the principal variations in the tide are due to the changing declination of the Moon. Key West, at the entrance to the Gulf of Mexico, has a type of tide which is a mixture of semidiurnal and diurnal types. Here the tide is semidiurnal but there is considerable inequality in the heights of high and low waters. By reference to the curves it will be seen that where the inequality is large there are times when there is only a few tenths of a foot difference between high water and low water.

TYPICAL TIDE CURVES FOR UNITED STATES PORTS

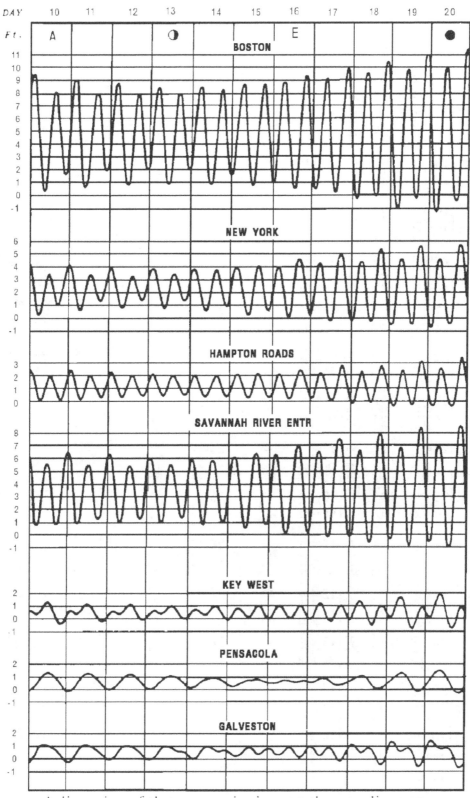

A discussion of these curves is given on the preceding page.

Lunar data:
A – Moon in apogee
☾ – last quarter
E – Moon on Equater
● – new Moon

StationId: 8410140
Source: NOAA/NOS/CO-OPS
Station Type: Primary
Time Zone: LST_LDT
Datum: MLLW

NOAA Tide Predictions

Eastport, ME, 2021

Times and Heights of High and Low Waters

January

Day	Time (h m)	Height (ft)	Height (cm)
1 F	06:12	1.2	37
	12:11	19.6	597
	18:40	-0.4	-12
2 Sa	00:40	18.2	555
	06:54	1.1	34
	12:54	19.6	597
	19:23	-0.4	-12
3 Su	01:23	18.4	561
	07:39	1.0	30
	13:39	19.5	594
	20:08	-0.3	-9
4 M	02:09	18.5	564
	08:28	0.9	27
	14:28	19.3	588
	20:56	-0.1	-3
5 Tu	02:59	18.6	567
	09:20	0.9	27
	15:21	18.9	576
	21:47	0.2	6
6 W	03:52	18.8	573
	10:16	0.9	27
	16:18	18.5	564
	22:43	0.5	15
7 Th	04:50	18.9	576
	11:17	0.8	24
	17:19	18.2	555
	23:42	0.7	21
8 F	05:50	19.2	585
	12:19	0.5	15
	18:22	18.1	552
9 Sa	00:43	0.8	24
	06:50	19.5	594
	13:22	0.0	0
	19:24	18.2	555
10 Su	01:44	0.7	21
	07:50	20.0	610
	14:22	-0.6	-18
	20:25	18.5	564
11 M	02:43	0.4	12
	08:47	20.4	622
	15:20	-1.1	-34
	21:22	18.8	573
12 Tu	03:39	0.1	3
	09:42	20.7	631
	16:14	-1.5	-46
	22:15	19.0	579
13 W	04:32	-0.1	-3
	10:34	20.8	634
	17:05	-1.6	-49
	23:06	19.1	582
14 Th	05:23	-0.1	-3
	11:23	20.6	628
	17:53	-1.4	-43
	23:55	19.0	579
15 F	06:11	0.1	3
	12:12	20.2	616
	18:40	-1.0	-30
16 Sa	00:42	18.7	570
	06:58	0.5	15
	12:59	19.6	597
	19:26	-0.4	-12
17 Su	01:29	18.3	558
	07:45	1.0	30
	13:47	18.9	576
	20:11	0.3	9
18 M	02:15	17.9	546
	08:32	1.5	46
	14:34	18.1	552
	20:57	1.1	34
19 Tu	03:02	17.5	533
	09:21	2.1	64
	15:24	17.3	527
	21:44	1.8	55
20 W	03:51	17.2	524
	10:11	2.5	76
	16:16	16.5	503
	22:33	2.5	76
21 Th	04:43	16.9	515
	11:05	2.8	85
	17:10	16.0	488
	23:25	3.0	91
22 F	05:36	16.8	512
	12:00	2.9	88
	18:07	15.7	479
23 Sa	00:19	3.2	98
	06:30	16.9	515
	12:55	2.6	79
	19:03	15.8	482
24 Su	01:13	3.2	98
	07:23	17.2	524
	13:49	2.2	67
	19:56	16.1	491
25 M	02:06	2.9	88
	08:13	17.7	539
	14:40	1.6	49
	20:45	16.6	506
26 Tu	02:55	2.4	73
	09:00	18.3	558
	15:27	0.8	24
	21:31	17.1	521
27 W	03:41	1.8	55
	09:44	18.9	576
	16:11	0.1	3
	22:13	17.7	539
28 Th	04:25	1.2	37
	10:27	19.5	594
	16:53	-0.5	-15
	22:54	18.3	558
29 F	05:07	0.6	18
	11:08	20.0	610
	17:35	-1.0	-30
	23:35	18.8	573
30 Sa	05:50	0.1	3
	11:50	20.4	622
	18:17	-1.3	-40
31 Su	00:17	19.3	588
	06:34	-0.3	-9
	12:34	20.5	625
	19:00	-1.4	-43

February

Day	Time (h m)	Height (ft)	Height (cm)
1 M	01:00	19.6	597
	07:19	-0.5	-15
	13:19	20.3	619
	19:45	-1.2	-37
2 Tu	01:46	19.8	604
	08:07	-0.5	-15
	14:08	19.9	607
	20:33	-0.8	-24
3 W	02:35	19.7	600
	08:59	-0.3	-9
	15:00	19.3	588
	21:24	-0.2	-6
4 Th	03:28	19.5	594
	09:55	0.1	3
	15:56	18.5	564
	22:19	0.6	18
5 F	04:25	19.2	585
	10:55	0.5	15
	16:58	17.8	543
	23:20	1.2	37
6 Sa	05:27	18.9	576
	12:00	0.7	21
	18:04	17.3	527
7 Su	00:24	1.6	49
	06:32	18.8	573
	13:05	0.6	18
	19:10	17.3	527
8 M	01:29	1.5	46
	07:35	19.0	579
	14:09	0.2	6
	20:14	17.6	536
9 Tu	02:31	1.2	37
	08:36	19.4	591
	15:09	-0.3	-9
	21:12	18.0	549
10 W	03:29	0.7	21
	09:32	19.8	604
	15:40	-0.7	-21
	22:04	18.5	564
11 Th	04:21	0.3	9
	10:23	20.0	610
	16:51	-1.0	-30
	22:52	18.8	573
12 F	05:08	0.0	0
	11:09	20.1	613
	17:35	-1.0	-30
	23:36	18.9	576
13 Sa	05:53	0.0	0
	11:53	19.9	607
	18:18	-0.7	-21
14 Su	00:18	18.8	573
	06:35	0.2	6
	12:36	19.4	591
	18:58	-0.2	-6
15 M	00:59	18.7	570
	07:17	0.6	18
	13:18	18.8	573
	19:38	0.4	12
16 Tu	01:40	18.4	561
	07:59	1.0	30
	14:00	18.1	552
	20:19	1.1	34
17 W	02:22	17.9	546
	08:42	1.5	46
	14:45	17.3	527
	21:01	1.9	58
18 Th	03:07	17.5	533
	09:28	2.1	64
	15:32	16.5	503
	21:47	2.6	79
19 F	03:54	17.0	518
	10:18	2.6	79
	16:23	15.9	485
	22:37	3.2	98
20 Sa	04:47	16.6	506
	11:12	2.9	88
	17:19	15.4	469
	23:32	3.6	110
21 Su	05:43	16.4	500
	12:09	2.9	88
	18:18	15.3	466
22 M	00:30	3.6	110
	06:40	16.6	506
	13:07	2.6	79
	19:15	15.7	479
23 Tu	01:27	3.3	101
	07:35	17.2	524
	14:02	1.9	58
	20:09	16.3	497
24 W	02:21	2.6	79
	08:27	18.0	549
	14:53	1.0	30
	20:58	17.2	524
25 Th	03:11	1.6	49
	09:15	18.9	576
	15:41	0.0	0
	21:43	18.1	552
26 F	03:57	0.6	18
	10:00	19.8	604
	16:25	-0.9	-27
	22:26	19.1	582
27 Sa	04:42	-0.3	-9
	10:44	20.6	628
	17:09	-1.6	-49
	23:09	19.9	607
28 Su	05:27	-1.1	-34
	11:27	21.0	640
	17:52	-1.9	-58
	23:52	20.5	625

March

Day	Time (h m)	Height (ft)	Height (cm)
1 M	06:12	-1.6	-49
	12:12	21.1	643
	18:36	-2.0	-61
2 Tu	00:36	20.9	637
	06:59	-1.8	-55
	12:59	20.9	637
	19:22	-1.7	-52
3 W	01:23	20.9	637
	07:47	-1.6	-49
	13:48	20.3	619
	20:10	-1.0	-30
4 Th	02:12	20.5	625
	08:39	-1.1	-34
	14:41	19.4	591
	21:02	-0.1	-3
5 F	03:06	19.9	607
	09:36	-0.4	-12
	15:38	18.3	558
	21:59	0.9	27
6 Sa	04:04	19.1	582
	10:37	0.4	12
	16:41	17.4	530
	23:02	1.7	52
7 Su	05:09	18.4	561
	11:43	0.9	27
	17:49	16.9	515
8 M	00:10	2.2	67
	06:17	18.1	552
	12:51	1.1	34
	18:59	16.8	512
9 Tu	01:17	2.1	64
	07:25	18.2	555
	13:57	0.8	24
	20:04	17.2	524
10 W	02:21	1.6	49
	08:26	18.6	567
	14:56	0.3	9
	21:01	17.7	539
11 Th	03:17	1.0	30
	09:21	19.1	582
	15:47	-0.1	-3
	21:50	18.3	558
12 F	04:07	0.4	12
	10:09	19.4	591
	16:32	-0.4	-12
	22:34	18.8	573
13 Sa	04:51	0.1	3
	10:52	19.5	594
	17:13	-0.4	-12
	23:13	19.0	579
14 Su	06:31	-0.1	-3
	12:32	19.4	591
	18:51	-0.2	-6
15 M	00:51	19.1	582
	07:10	0.0	0
	13:11	19.1	582
	19:29	0.2	6
16 Tu	01:28	18.9	576
	07:48	0.3	9
	13:49	18.6	567
	20:06	0.7	21
17 W	02:06	18.7	570
	08:27	0.6	18
	14:29	18.0	549
	20:44	1.3	40
18 Th	02:45	18.2	555
	09:07	1.1	34
	15:10	17.3	527
	21:24	2.0	61
19 F	03:27	17.7	539
	09:50	1.7	52
	15:54	16.6	506
	22:07	2.7	82
20 Sa	04:12	17.2	524
	10:37	2.2	67
	16:40	16.0	488
	22:56	3.3	101
21 Su	05:02	16.7	509
	11:29	2.7	82
	17:36	15.5	472
	23:50	3.7	113
22 M	05:58	16.4	500
	12:26	2.8	85
	18:35	15.4	469
23 Tu	00:49	3.7	113
	06:57	16.6	506
	13:25	2.6	79
	19:48	15.8	482
24 W	01:48	3.3	101
	07:56	17.1	521
	14:23	1.9	58
	20:30	16.5	503
25 Th	02:45	2.4	73
	08:51	18.0	549
	15:17	0.9	27
	21:22	17.6	536
26 F	03:38	1.2	37
	09:42	19.1	582
	16:07	-0.1	-3
	22:10	18.8	573
27 Sa	04:28	0.0	0
	10:30	20.1	613
	16:54	-1.1	-34
	22:55	20.0	610
28 Su	05:15	-1.2	-37
	11:17	20.9	637
	17:40	-1.8	-55
	23:40	20.9	637
29 M	06:02	-2.1	-64
	12:03	21.3	649
	18:25	-2.2	-67
30 Tu	00:25	21.6	658
	06:50	-2.6	-79
	13:11	21.4	652
	19:12	-2.1	-64
31 W	01:12	21.8	664
	07:38	-2.7	-82
	13:39	21.0	640
	20:00	-1.6	-49

StationId: 8410140
Source: NOAA/NOS/CO-OPS
Station Type: Primary
Time Zone: LST_LDT
Datum: MLLW

NOAA Tide Predictions

Eastport, ME,2021

Times and Heights of High and Low Waters

April

Day	Time	ft	cm	Day	Time	ft	cm
1 Th	02:00	21.6	658	16 F	02:13	18.4	561
	08:28	-2.3	-70		08:37	0.9	27
	14:30	20.3	619		14:40	17.2	524
	20:50	-0.8	-24		20:52	2.3	70
2 F	02:52	20.9	637	17 Sa	02:53	17.9	546
	09:22	-1.5	-46		09:18	1.4	43
	15:24	19.3	588		15:22	16.7	509
	21:44	0.2	6		21:35	2.8	85
3 Sa	03:47	20.0	610	18 Su	03:37	17.4	530
	10:19	-0.6	-18		10:04	1.9	58
	16:23	18.2	555		16:09	16.3	497
	22:43	1.2	37		22:22	3.3	101
4 Su	04:47	19.0	579	19 M	04:25	17.0	518
	11:20	0.4	12		10:54	2.2	67
	17:27	17.3	527		17:00	16.0	488
	23:47	2.0	61		23:15	3.5	107
5 M	05:54	18.1	552	20 Tu	05:20	16.8	512
	12:27	1.1	34		11:49	2.3	70
	18:36	16.8	512		17:56	16.0	488
6 Tu	00:56	2.4	73	21 W	00:12	3.4	104
	07:03	17.7	539		06:18	16.9	515
	13:34	1.3	40		12:46	2.1	64
	19:45	16.8	512		18:54	16.4	500
7 W	02:03	2.3	70	22 Th	01:11	2.9	88
	08:11	17.8	543		07:17	17.4	530
	14:38	1.2	37		13:44	1.6	49
	20:48	17.2	524		19:51	17.2	524
8 Th	03:05	1.7	52	23 F	02:09	1.9	58
	09:11	18.1	552		08:14	18.2	555
	15:35	0.8	24		14:39	0.7	21
	21:42	17.8	543		20:45	18.4	561
9 F	04:00	1.1	34	24 Sa	03:05	0.7	21
	10:03	18.5	564		09:09	19.2	585
	16:25	0.5	15		15:32	-0.2	-6
	22:28	18.4	561		21:35	19.6	597
10 Sa	04:47	0.5	15	25 Su	03:58	-0.6	-18
	10:49	18.8	573		10:00	20.1	613
	17:07	0.3	9		16:22	-1.0	-30
	23:09	18.8	573		22:24	20.8	634
11 Su	05:28	0.2	6	26 M	04:49	-1.7	-52
	11:30	18.9	576		10:50	20.8	634
	17:46	0.3	9		17:11	-1.6	-49
	23:46	19.1	582		23:12	21.7	661
12 M	06:07	0.0	0	27 Tu	05:38	-2.6	-79
	12:08	18.8	573		11:40	21.2	646
	18:23	0.5	15		17:59	-1.9	-58
13 Tu	00:22	19.1	582	28 W	00:00	22.2	677
	06:44	0.0	0		06:28	-3.0	-91
	12:45	18.6	567		12:29	21.1	643
	18:59	0.8	24		18:49	-1.7	-52
14 W	00:58	19.0	579	29 Th	00:49	22.2	677
	07:21	0.2	6		07:19	-2.9	-88
	13:22	18.2	555		13:20	20.7	631
	19:35	1.2	37		19:39	-1.2	-37
15 Th	01:35	18.8	573	30 F	01:40	21.7	661
	07:58	0.5	15		08:11	-2.4	-73
	14:00	17.7	539		14:13	20.0	610
	20:13	1.8	55		20:32	-0.4	-12

May

Day	Time	ft	cm	Day	Time	ft	cm
1 Sa	02:33	20.9	637	16 Su	02:26	18.1	552
	09:05	-1.6	-49		08:53	1.1	34
	15:09	19.1	582		14:56	16.9	515
	21:28	0.5	15		21:09	2.7	82
2 Su	03:30	19.9	607	17 M	03:09	17.8	543
	10:02	-0.6	-18		09:37	1.4	43
	16:08	18.2	555		15:41	16.7	509
	22:27	1.4	43		21:55	2.9	88
3 M	04:31	18.9	576	18 Tu	03:56	17.6	536
	11:03	0.4	12		10:25	1.5	46
	17:12	17.4	530		16:30	16.7	509
	23:31	2.1	64		22:45	2.9	88
4 Tu	05:36	18.1	552	19 W	04:48	17.5	533
	12:07	1.1	34		11:17	1.6	49
	18:18	17.1	521		17:23	16.9	515
					23:40	2.7	82
5 W	00:36	2.4	73	20 Th	05:44	17.6	536
	06:43	17.6	536		12:11	1.4	43
	13:11	1.4	43		18:19	17.4	530
	19:22	17.1	521				
6 Th	01:41	2.2	67	21 F	00:38	2.2	67
	07:48	17.5	533		06:42	17.9	546
	14:11	1.5	46		13:07	1.0	30
	20:21	17.5	533		19:15	18.2	555
7 F	02:41	1.8	55	22 Sa	01:36	1.3	40
	08:46	17.7	539		07:40	18.5	564
	15:05	1.3	40		14:03	0.5	15
	21:13	17.9	546		20:10	19.2	585
8 Sa	03:33	1.3	40	23 Su	02:34	0.2	6
	09:37	17.9	546		08:37	19.1	582
	15:54	1.2	37		14:58	-0.1	-3
	21:58	18.4	561		21:03	20.2	616
9 Su	04:20	0.8	24	24 M	03:30	-0.9	-27
	10:22	18.1	552		09:32	19.8	604
	16:37	1.1	34		15:52	-0.7	-21
	22:39	18.8	573		21:55	21.2	646
10 M	05:02	0.4	12	25 Tu	04:24	-1.9	-58
	11:03	18.2	555		10:25	20.3	619
	17:16	1.1	34		16:44	-1.1	-34
	23:17	19.0	579		22:46	21.8	664
11 Tu	05:40	0.2	6	26 W	05:16	-2.5	-76
	11:42	18.1	552		11:18	20.5	625
	17:54	1.2	37		17:36	-1.2	-37
	23:54	19.0	579		23:37	22.1	674
12 W	06:18	0.2	6	27 Th	06:09	-2.8	-85
	12:19	18.0	549		12:10	20.5	625
	18:31	1.5	46		18:28	-1.1	-34
13 Th	00:30	18.9	576	28 F	00:29	22.0	671
	06:55	0.3	9		07:01	-2.7	-82
	12:57	17.7	539		13:03	20.1	613
	19:08	1.8	55		19:21	-0.7	-21
14 F	01:07	18.7	570	29 Sa	01:22	21.5	655
	07:33	0.5	15		07:54	-2.2	-67
	13:35	17.5	533		13:57	19.6	597
	19:46	2.1	64		20:15	0.0	0
15 Sa	01:45	18.4	561	30 Su	02:16	20.7	631
	08:12	0.8	24		08:49	-1.4	-43
	14:14	17.2	524		14:53	18.9	576
	20:26	2.5	76		21:11	0.7	21
				31 M	03:13	19.8	604
					09:44	-0.5	-15
					15:51	18.3	558
					22:09	1.4	43

June

Day	Time	ft	cm	Day	Time	ft	cm
1 Tu	04:12	18.9	576	16 W	03:31	18.3	558
	10:41	0.3	9		09:59	0.7	21
	16:50	17.7	539		16:03	17.6	536
	23:08	1.9	58		22:20	2.0	61
2 W	05:13	18.1	552	17 Th	04:21	18.3	558
	11:40	1.0	30		10:48	0.8	24
	17:51	17.4	530		16:53	17.9	546
					23:13	1.7	52
3 Th	00:09	2.2	67	18 F	05:14	18.2	555
	06:15	17.5	533		11:40	0.7	21
	12:38	1.5	46		17:47	18.4	561
	18:50	17.4	530				
4 F	01:09	2.2	67	19 Sa	00:09	1.3	40
	07:15	17.2	524		06:11	18.3	558
	13:34	1.8	55		12:35	0.7	21
	19:45	17.6	536		18:42	19.0	579
5 Sa	02:06	2.0	61	20 Su	01:07	0.7	21
	08:11	17.1	521		07:10	18.5	564
	14:27	1.9	58		13:31	0.5	15
	20:36	17.9	546		19:39	19.7	600
6 Su	02:59	1.7	52	21 M	02:06	0.0	0
	09:03	17.2	524		08:09	18.8	573
	15:16	1.9	58		14:29	0.2	6
	21:22	18.2	555		20:35	20.4	622
7 M	03:47	1.3	40	22 Tu	03:05	-0.8	-24
	09:50	17.3	527		09:07	19.1	582
	16:02	1.9	58		15:26	-0.1	-3
	22:06	18.5	564		21:30	21.0	640
8 Tu	04:31	0.9	27	23 W	04:02	-1.5	-46
	10:34	17.4	530		10:04	19.5	594
	16:44	1.9	58		16:22	-0.3	-9
	22:46	18.7	570		22:25	21.4	652
9 W	05:12	0.6	18	24 Th	04:58	-2.0	-61
	11:15	17.5	533		10:59	19.7	600
	17:24	1.9	58		17:17	-0.5	-15
	23:25	18.8	573		23:19	21.6	658
10 Th	05:51	0.5	15	25 F	05:52	-2.2	-67
	11:54	17.5	533		11:53	19.7	600
	18:04	1.9	58		18:11	-0.5	-15
11 F	00:04	18.8	573	26 Sa	00:12	21.5	655
	06:30	0.5	15		06:45	-2.2	-67
	12:33	17.4	530		12:47	19.6	597
	18:43	2.0	61		19:05	-0.3	-9
12 Sa	00:42	18.7	570	27 Su	01:05	21.0	640
	07:09	0.5	15		07:38	-1.8	-55
	13:11	17.3	527		13:??	19.3	588
	19:23	2.1	64		19:58	0.1	3
13 Su	01:22	18.6	567	28 M	01:59	20.4	622
	07:49	0.6	18		08:30	-1.2	-37
	13:51	17.3	527		14:34	18.9	576
	20:03	2.2	67		20:51	0.6	18
14 M	02:02	18.5	564	29 Tu	02:53	19.7	600
	08:31	0.6	18		09:22	-0.5	-15
	14:33	17.3	527		15:27	18.4	561
	20:46	2.2	67		21:45	1.1	34
15 Tu	02:45	18.4	561	30 W	03:48	18.8	573
	09:14	0.7	21		10:14	0.3	9
	15:16	17.4	530		16:21	18.0	549
	21:31	2.2	67		22:39	1.6	49

StationId: 8410140
Source: NOAA/NOS/CO-OPS
Station Type: Primary
Time Zone: LST_LDT
Datum: MLLW

NOAA Tide Predictions

Eastport, ME,2021

Times and Heights of High and Low Waters

July

Day	Time (h m)	Height ft	Height cm	Day	Time (h m)	Height ft	Height cm
1 Th ☽	04:43	18.0	549	**16** F	03:56	18.9	576
	11:06	1.1	34		10:21	0.1	3
	17:15	17.7	539		16:25	18.9	576
	23:34	2.0	61		22:48	0.7	21
2 F	05:39	17.3	527	**17** Sa ◐	04:49	18.6	567
	11:59	1.7	52		11:12	0.4	12
	18:09	17.5	533		17:18	19.1	582
					23:44	0.6	18
3 Sa	00:30	2.3	70	**18** Su	05:45	18.4	561
	06:35	16.8	512		12:07	0.6	18
	12:52	2.2	67		18:14	19.4	591
	19:02	17.5	533				
4 Su	01:26	2.3	70	**19** M	00:43	0.4	12
	07:31	16.5	503		06:46	18.2	555
	13:44	2.5	76		13:06	0.8	24
	19:54	17.6	536		19:13	19.6	597
5 M	02:19	2.1	64	**20** Tu	01:44	0.1	3
	08:24	16.4	500		07:47	18.2	555
	14:35	2.7	82		14:06	0.8	24
	20:44	17.8	543		20:13	20.0	610
6 Tu	03:10	1.8	55	**21** W	02:46	-0.4	-12
	09:15	16.5	503		08:48	18.3	558
	15:25	2.6	79		15:07	0.7	21
	21:31	18.0	549		21:12	20.3	619
7 W	03:58	1.4	43	**22** Th	03:46	-0.9	-27
	10:02	16.8	512		09:48	18.6	567
	16:11	2.4	73		16:06	0.4	12
	22:15	18.3	558		22:09	20.7	631
8 Th	04:42	1.0	30	**23** F	04:43	-1.3	-40
	10:46	17.0	518		10:45	19.0	579
	16:55	2.2	67		17:03	0.0	0
	22:58	18.5	564		23:05	20.9	637
9 F	05:24	0.7	21	**24** Sa ○	05:37	-1.6	-49
	11:28	17.2	524		11:39	19.2	585
	17:37	2.0	61		17:57	-0.1	-3
	23:39	18.7	570		23:58	20.8	634
10 Sa ●	06:05	0.4	12	**25** Su	06:29	-1.6	-49
	12:08	17.4	530		12:30	19.2	585
	18:18	1.9	58		18:48	-0.1	-3
11 Su	00:19	18.9	576	**26** M	00:49	20.6	628
	06:45	0.2	6		07:19	-1.4	-43
	12:47	17.6	536		13:21	19.1	582
	18:59	1.7	52		19:38	0.1	3
12 M	00:59	19.0	579	**27** Tu	01:39	20.1	613
	07:26	0.1	3		08:07	-0.9	-27
	13:27	17.8	543		14:10	18.9	576
	19:40	1.5	46		20:28	0.4	12
13 Tu	01:39	19.1	582	**28** W	02:29	19.4	591
	08:07	0.0	0		08:54	-0.2	-6
	14:08	18.1	552		14:58	18.6	567
	20:23	1.3	40		21:16	0.9	27
14 W	02:22	19.1	582	**29** Th	03:18	18.6	567
	08:49	-0.1	-3		09:40	0.5	15
	14:51	18.4	561		15:45	18.2	555
	21:08	1.1	34		22:05	1.4	43
15 Th	03:08	19.1	582	**30** F	04:08	17.8	543
	09:34	0.0	0		10:27	1.3	40
	15:37	18.7	570		16:34	17.8	543
	21:56	0.9	27		22:55	1.9	58
				31 Sa ◐	04:59	17.0	518
					11:16	2.1	64
					17:25	17.4	530
					23:47	2.3	70

August

Day	Time (h m)	Height ft	Height cm	Day	Time (h m)	Height ft	Height cm
1 Su	05:52	16.4	500	**16** M	05:25	18.1	552
	12:07	2.7	82		11:45	1.0	30
	18:17	17.2	524		17:52	19.3	588
2 M	00:41	2.5	76	**17** Tu	00:24	0.4	12
	06:48	16.0	488		06:27	17.7	539
	13:00	3.1	94		12:47	1.4	43
	19:11	17.1	521		18:54	19.2	585
3 Tu	01:36	2.5	76	**18** W	01:28	0.4	12
	07:44	15.8	482		07:32	17.5	533
	13:54	3.3	101		13:51	1.5	46
	20:04	17.2	524		19:58	19.2	585
4 W	02:30	2.3	70	**19** Th	02:32	0.2	6
	08:38	16.0	488		08:36	17.7	539
	14:47	3.1	94		14:55	1.2	37
	20:55	17.5	533		21:00	19.5	594
5 Th	03:22	1.9	58	**20** F	03:33	-0.3	-9
	09:28	16.3	497		09:37	18.1	552
	15:38	2.8	85		15:55	0.8	24
	21:44	17.9	546		21:59	19.9	607
6 F	04:10	1.3	40	**21** Sa	04:31	-0.7	-21
	10:15	16.8	512		10:33	18.6	567
	16:25	2.3	70		16:51	0.3	9
	22:29	18.4	561		22:53	20.2	616
7 Sa	04:55	0.7	21	**22** Su ○	05:23	-1.0	-30
	10:59	17.3	527		11:24	19.0	579
	17:10	1.8	55		17:42	-0.1	-3
	23:12	18.9	576		23:44	20.3	619
8 Su ●	05:38	0.2	6	**23** M	06:11	-1.1	-34
	11:40	17.8	543		12:12	19.2	585
	17:52	1.2	37		18:30	-0.2	-6
	23:53	19.3	588				
9 M	06:19	-0.3	-9	**24** Tu	00:31	20.1	613
	12:20	18.3	558		06:56	-0.9	-27
	18:34	0.8	24		12:57	19.2	585
					19:16	-0.1	-3
10 Tu	00:34	19.7	600	**25** W	01:16	19.7	600
	06:59	-0.6	-18		07:40	-0.4	-12
	13:00	18.8	573		13:41	19.1	582
	19:16	0.3	9		20:00	0.2	6
11 W	01:15	19.8	604	**26** Th	02:01	19.1	582
	07:41	-0.8	-24		08:22	0.2	6
	13:41	19.2	585		14:24	18.7	570
	19:59	0.0	0		20:44	0.7	21
12 Th	01:59	19.9	607	**27** F	02:45	18.3	558
	08:24	-0.8	-24		09:04	1.0	30
	14:24	19.5	594		15:07	18.3	558
	20:45	-0.2	-6		21:29	1.2	37
13 F	02:45	19.7	600	**28** Sa	03:31	17.5	533
	09:08	-0.6	-18		09:48	1.8	55
	15:10	19.7	600		15:52	17.8	543
	21:34	-0.2	-6		22:15	1.8	55
14 Sa	03:34	19.3	588	**29** Su	04:19	16.8	512
	09:56	-0.1	-3		10:34	2.5	76
	16:00	19.7	600		16:40	17.3	527
	22:26	-0.1	-3		23:04	2.3	70
15 Su ◐	04:27	18.7	570	**30** M ◐	05:10	16.1	491
	10:48	0.4	12		11:23	3.2	98
	16:53	19.5	594		17:32	16.9	515
	23:23	0.2	6		23:57	2.7	82
				31 Tu	06:05	15.6	475
					12:17	3.6	110
					18:27	16.6	506

September

Day	Time (h m)	Height ft	Height cm	Day	Time (h m)	Height ft	Height cm
1 W	00:53	2.8	85	**16** Th	01:15	0.8	24
	07:03	15.5	472		07:22	17.2	524
	13:14	3.7	113		13:41	1.9	58
	19:24	16.7	509		19:48	18.6	567
2 Th	01:50	2.6	79	**17** F	02:20	0.6	18
	07:59	15.7	479		08:27	17.5	533
	14:10	3.5	107		14:45	1.5	46
	20:19	17.1	521		20:51	18.9	576
3 F	02:45	2.1	64	**18** Sa	03:21	0.2	6
	08:53	16.2	494		09:27	18.0	549
	15:04	2.9	88		15:45	0.9	27
	21:10	17.7	539		21:49	19.3	588
4 Sa	03:36	1.4	43	**19** Su	04:16	-0.3	-9
	09:41	16.9	515		10:20	18.6	567
	15:53	2.1	64		16:38	0.3	9
	21:58	18.5	564		22:40	19.7	600
5 Su	04:22	0.6	18	**20** M ○	05:05	-0.5	-15
	10:26	17.8	543		11:07	19.1	582
	16:39	1.2	37		17:26	-0.1	-3
	22:42	19.2	585		23:27	19.8	604
6 M	05:06	-0.2	-6	**21** Tu	05:49	-0.6	-18
	11:08	18.6	567		11:50	19.4	591
	17:23	0.4	12		18:10	-0.2	-6
	23:25	19.9	607				
7 Tu ●	05:48	-0.8	-24	**22** W	00:10	19.6	597
	11:49	19.4	591		06:30	-0.3	-9
	18:07	-0.4	-12		12:30	19.4	591
					18:51	-0.2	-6
8 W	00:07	20.3	619	**23** Th	00:51	19.2	585
	06:30	-1.2	-37		07:10	0.2	6
	12:30	20.0	610		13:10	19.2	585
	18:50	-0.9	-27		19:32	0.1	3
9 Th	00:50	20.5	625	**24** F	01:32	18.7	570
	07:13	-1.3	-40		07:49	0.8	24
	13:13	20.5	625		13:49	18.9	576
	19:35	-1.3	-40		20:12	0.6	18
10 F	01:35	20.4	622	**25** Sa	02:13	18.0	549
	07:57	-1.2	-37		08:29	1.5	46
	13:57	20.6	628		14:30	18.4	561
	20:22	-1.3	-40		20:54	1.1	34
11 Sa	02:22	20.1	613	**26** Su	02:56	17.3	527
	08:44	-0.7	-21		09:10	2.2	67
	14:45	20.5	625		15:13	17.8	543
	21:12	-1.0	-30		21:37	1.7	52
12 Su	03:13	19.4	591	**27** M	03:41	16.6	506
	09:34	-0.1	-3		09:54	2.9	88
	15:36	20.1	613		15:59	17.2	524
	22:06	-0.5	-15		22:24	2.3	70
13 M ◐	04:08	18.6	567	**28** Tu	04:30	16.0	488
	10:29	0.7	21		10:43	3.5	107
	16:33	19.5	594		16:49	16.7	509
	23:05	0.1	3		23:16	2.7	82
14 Tu	05:08	17.8	543	**29** W ◐	05:24	15.6	475
	11:29	1.4	43		11:37	3.9	119
	17:35	19.0	579		17:45	16.4	500
15 W	00:08	0.6	18	**30** Th	00:12	2.9	88
	06:14	17.3	527		06:22	15.5	472
	12:34	1.9	58		12:35	3.9	119
	18:41	18.6	567		18:43	16.5	503

StationId: 8410140
Source: NOAA/NOS/CO-OPS
Station Type: Primary
Time Zone: LST_LDT
Datum: MLLW

NOAA Tide Predictions

Eastport, ME, 2021

Times and Heights of High and Low Waters

October

Day	Time (h m)	Height (ft)	Height (cm)
1 F	01:10	2.7	82
	07:20	15.8	482
	13:32	3.5	107
	19:40	16.9	515
2 Sa	02:05	2.2	67
	08:14	16.4	500
	14:28	2.8	85
	20:34	17.7	539
3 Su	02:58	1.4	43
	09:04	17.4	530
	15:19	1.7	52
	21:23	18.6	567
4 M	03:46	0.4	12
	09:51	18.5	564
	16:07	0.6	18
	22:10	19.5	594
5 Tu	04:32	-0.4	-12
	10:34	19.6	597
	16:54	-0.5	-15
	22:55	20.3	619
6 W ●	05:17	-1.1	-34
	11:17	20.5	625
	17:39	-1.4	-43
	23:40	20.8	634
7 Th	06:01	-1.5	-46
	12:01	21.2	646
	18:25	-2.0	-61
8 F	00:25	20.9	637
	06:45	-1.6	-49
	12:45	21.6	658
	19:12	-2.3	-70
9 Sa	01:12	20.7	631
	07:32	-1.3	-40
	13:32	21.5	655
	20:01	-2.1	-64
10 Su	02:02	20.2	616
	08:22	-0.7	-21
	14:22	21.1	643
	20:53	-1.6	-49
11 M	02:55	19.4	591
	09:14	0.1	3
	15:16	20.3	619
	21:49	-0.8	-24
12 Tu	03:52	18.5	564
	10:12	1.0	30
	16:16	19.4	591
	22:49	0.0	0
13 W ◗	04:55	17.7	539
	11:15	1.8	55
	17:20	18.7	570
	23:54	0.7	21
14 Th	06:02	17.2	524
	12:22	2.1	64
	18:29	18.2	555
15 F	01:01	1.0	30
	07:11	17.2	524
	13:29	2.1	64
	19:37	18.2	555
16 Sa	02:05	0.9	27
	08:15	17.6	536
	14:33	1.6	49
	20:39	18.5	564
17 Su	03:04	0.6	18
	09:12	18.2	555
	15:31	1.0	30
	21:35	18.8	573
18 M	03:57	0.2	6
	10:01	18.8	573
	16:21	0.4	12
	22:23	19.1	582
19 Tu	04:43	0.1	3
	10:45	19.2	585
	17:06	0.0	0
	23:07	19.1	582
20 W ○	05:24	0.1	3
	11:25	19.4	591
	17:47	-0.2	-6
	23:47	19.0	579
21 Th	06:03	0.4	12
	12:03	19.4	591
	18:26	-0.1	-3
22 F	00:26	18.6	567
	06:41	0.8	24
	12:40	19.3	588
	19:04	0.2	6
23 Sa	01:05	18.2	555
	07:18	1.4	43
	13:18	18.9	576
	19:43	0.6	18
24 Su	01:44	17.7	539
	07:57	1.9	58
	13:57	18.4	561
	20:23	1.1	34
25 M	02:25	17.1	521
	08:37	2.5	76
	14:38	17.9	546
	21:05	1.6	49
26 Tu	03:08	16.6	506
	09:21	3.1	94
	15:23	17.3	527
	21:50	2.1	64
27 W	03:55	16.1	491
	10:08	3.5	107
	16:12	16.9	515
	22:40	2.5	76
28 Th ◖	04:47	15.8	482
	11:00	3.8	116
	17:05	16.6	506
	23:33	2.6	79
29 F	05:42	15.8	482
	11:56	3.7	113
	18:02	16.7	509
30 Sa	00:29	2.4	73
	06:39	16.2	494
	12:54	3.3	101
	19:11	17.1	521
31 Su	01:25	1.9	58
	07:34	17.0	518
	13:50	2.4	73
	19:55	17.8	543

November

Day	Time (h m)	Height (ft)	Height (cm)
1 M	02:18	1.2	37
	08:25	18.0	549
	14:44	1.3	40
	20:48	18.7	570
2 Tu	03:09	0.3	9
	09:14	19.2	585
	15:35	0.0	0
	21:38	19.6	597
3 W	03:58	-0.5	-15
	10:01	20.4	622
	16:25	-1.2	-37
	22:26	20.3	619
4 Th ●	04:45	-1.1	-34
	10:47	21.4	652
	17:13	-2.1	-64
	23:14	20.8	634
5 F	05:33	-1.5	-46
	11:33	22.0	671
	18:01	-2.7	-82
6 Sa	00:02	20.9	637
	06:21	-1.5	-46
	12:21	22.2	677
	18:51	-2.8	-85
7 Su	00:52	20.7	631
	06:10	-1.2	-37
	12:11	22.0	671
	18:42	-2.5	-76
8 M	00:44	20.1	613
	07:02	-0.5	-15
	13:03	21.3	649
	19:36	-1.8	-55
9 Tu	01:38	19.3	588
	07:57	0.3	9
	13:59	20.4	622
	20:33	-0.9	-27
10 W	02:37	18.5	564
	08:56	1.1	34
	15:00	19.4	591
	21:33	-0.1	-3
11 Th ◗	03:40	17.8	543
	09:59	1.8	55
	16:04	18.6	567
	22:36	0.7	21
12 F	04:46	17.4	530
	11:05	2.1	64
	17:12	18.0	549
	23:40	1.1	34
13 Sa	05:52	17.4	530
	12:11	2.0	61
	18:18	17.9	546
14 Su	00:42	1.1	34
	06:54	17.8	543
	13:13	1.7	52
	19:19	17.9	546
15 M	01:39	1.1	34
	07:48	18.2	555
	14:09	1.2	37
	20:13	18.1	552
16 Tu	02:30	0.9	27
	08:36	18.7	570
	14:59	0.7	21
	21:01	18.3	558
17 W	03:16	0.9	27
	09:19	19.1	582
	15:43	0.3	9
	21:44	18.3	558
18 Th	03:58	0.9	27
	09:59	19.3	588
	16:24	0.1	3
	22:24	18.2	555
19 F ○	04:36	1.1	34
	10:37	19.3	588
	17:02	0.1	3
	23:03	18.0	549
20 Sa	05:14	1.4	43
	11:14	19.1	582
	17:39	0.3	9
	23:40	17.8	543
21 Su	05:52	1.8	55
	11:51	18.8	573
	18:17	0.6	18
22 M	00:19	17.4	530
	06:30	2.2	67
	12:30	18.5	564
	18:57	0.9	27
23 Tu	00:59	17.1	521
	07:10	2.5	76
	13:10	18.1	552
	19:38	1.3	40
24 W	01:40	16.7	509
	07:52	2.9	88
	13:53	17.7	539
	20:21	1.6	49
25 Th	02:25	16.5	503
	08:38	3.2	98
	14:39	17.4	530
	21:07	1.8	55
26 F	03:13	16.4	500
	09:27	3.3	101
	15:29	17.2	524
	21:57	1.9	58
27 Sa	04:04	16.5	503
	10:20	3.1	94
	16:23	17.2	524
	22:50	1.9	58
28 Su	04:58	16.9	515
	11:16	2.7	82
	17:20	17.4	530
	23:44	1.5	46
29 M	05:53	17.6	536
	12:13	1.9	58
	18:17	17.9	546
30 Tu	00:39	1.0	30
	06:47	18.6	567
	13:09	0.9	27
	19:12	18.5	564

December

Day	Time (h m)	Height (ft)	Height (cm)
1 W	01:33	0.4	12
	07:39	19.7	600
	14:04	-0.3	-9
	20:07	19.3	588
2 Th	02:26	-0.2	-6
	08:30	20.8	634
	14:58	-1.4	-43
	20:59	19.9	607
3 F	03:18	-0.8	-24
	09:20	21.7	661
	15:50	-2.3	-70
	21:51	20.4	622
4 Sa ●	04:09	-1.2	-37
	10:10	22.2	677
	16:41	-2.8	-85
	22:42	20.5	625
5 Su	05:00	-1.2	-37
	11:01	22.3	680
	17:33	-2.9	-88
	23:34	20.4	622
6 M	05:52	-1.0	-30
	11:53	22.0	671
	18:26	-2.6	-79
7 Tu	00:27	20.0	610
	06:46	-0.6	-18
	12:47	21.4	652
	19:20	-1.9	-58
8 W	01:22	19.4	591
	07:41	0.1	3
	13:43	20.5	625
	20:15	-1.1	-34
9 Th	02:20	18.7	570
	08:38	0.8	24
	14:41	19.5	594
	21:12	-0.2	-6
10 F	03:19	18.1	552
	09:38	1.4	43
	15:42	18.6	567
	22:11	0.6	18
11 Sa ◗	04:20	17.7	539
	10:40	1.9	58
	16:46	17.8	543
	23:11	1.2	37
12 Su	05:22	17.6	536
	11:43	2.0	61
	17:49	17.4	530
13 M	00:10	1.6	49
	06:21	17.7	539
	12:43	1.9	58
	18:49	17.2	524
14 Tu	01:06	1.8	55
	07:16	17.9	546
	13:40	1.6	49
	19:44	17.2	524
15 W	01:58	1.8	55
	08:05	18.2	555
	14:31	1.2	37
	20:34	17.3	527
16 Th	02:46	1.8	55
	08:51	18.6	567
	15:17	0.8	24
	21:19	17.4	530
17 F	03:30	1.8	55
	09:33	18.8	573
	15:59	0.6	18
	22:01	17.5	533
18 Sa	04:11	1.7	52
	10:12	18.9	576
	16:38	0.4	12
	22:40	17.5	533
19 Su ○	04:50	1.8	55
	10:51	18.9	576
	17:17	0.4	12
	23:19	17.5	533
20 M	05:29	1.9	58
	11:29	18.8	573
	17:55	0.4	12
	23:57	17.4	530
21 Tu	06:07	2.0	61
	12:07	18.7	570
	18:34	0.6	18
22 W	00:36	17.3	527
	06:47	2.1	64
	12:47	18.5	564
	19:13	0.7	21
23 Th	01:15	17.2	524
	07:28	2.2	67
	13:27	18.3	558
	19:54	0.8	24
24 F	01:57	17.2	524
	08:10	2.3	70
	14:10	18.1	552
	20:38	1.0	30
25 Sa	02:41	17.3	527
	08:56	2.3	70
	14:57	18.0	549
	21:24	1.1	34
26 Su	03:28	17.5	533
	09:47	2.1	64
	15:48	17.8	543
	22:13	1.2	37
27 M	04:20	17.8	543
	10:41	1.8	55
	16:43	17.7	539
	23:07	1.2	37
28 Tu	05:14	18.3	558
	11:39	1.3	40
	17:41	17.9	546
29 W	00:03	1.0	30
	06:11	19.0	579
	12:38	0.6	18
	18:41	18.2	555
30 Th	01:00	0.7	21
	07:07	19.8	604
	13:37	-0.2	-6
	19:39	18.8	573
31 F	01:58	0.3	9
	08:03	20.6	628
	14:35	-1.1	-34
	20:36	18.8	573

StationId: 8413320
Source: NOAA/NOS/CO-OPS
Station Type: Primary
Time Zone: LST_LDT
Datum: MLLW

NOAA Tide Predictions

Bar Harbor, ME, 2021

Times and Heights of High and Low Waters

January

Day	Time	ft	cm
1 F	05:48	1.0	30
	11:56	11.6	354
	18:23	-0.3	-9
2 Sa	00:31	10.3	314
	06:29	0.9	27
	12:38	11.6	354
	19:04	-0.3	-9
3 Su	01:14	10.5	320
	07:15	0.8	24
	13:23	11.5	351
	19:49	-0.3	-9
4 M	02:00	10.6	323
	08:04	0.8	24
	14:13	11.3	344
	20:37	-0.2	-6
5 Tu	02:50	10.7	326
	08:59	0.7	21
	15:07	11.0	335
	21:28	0.0	0
6 W ◑	03:44	10.9	332
	09:59	0.6	18
	16:07	10.6	323
	22:24	0.2	6
7 Th	04:42	11.1	338
	11:03	0.4	12
	17:12	10.4	317
	23:24	0.3	9
8 F	05:42	11.3	344
	12:09	0.1	3
	18:18	10.3	314
9 Sa	00:26	0.4	12
	06:44	11.6	354
	13:13	-0.3	-9
	19:23	10.4	317
10 Su	01:28	0.4	12
	07:43	12.0	366
	14:14	-0.7	-21
	20:25	10.6	323
11 M	02:27	0.2	6
	08:40	12.3	375
	15:11	-1.1	-34
	21:22	10.8	329
12 Tu	03:23	0.1	3
	09:35	12.5	381
	16:05	-1.3	-40
	22:15	11.0	335
13 W ●	04:16	0.0	0
	10:26	12.6	384
	16:55	-1.3	-40
	23:05	11.1	338
14 Th	05:07	0.0	0
	11:16	12.4	378
	17:44	-1.1	-34
	23:53	11.0	335
15 F	05:57	0.2	6
	12:05	12.1	369
	18:31	-0.8	-24
16 Sa	00:40	10.8	329
	06:45	0.4	12
	12:52	11.7	357
	19:17	-0.4	-12
17 Su	01:27	10.6	323
	07:33	0.7	21
	13:40	11.1	338
	20:03	0.1	3
18 M	02:13	10.3	314
	08:22	1.0	30
	14:28	10.5	320
	20:48	0.6	18
19 Tu	03:00	10.1	308
	09:13	1.3	40
	15:18	9.9	302
	21:35	1.1	34
20 W ◐	03:49	9.9	302
	10:06	1.6	49
	16:12	9.4	287
	22:24	1.5	46
21 Th	04:40	9.7	296
	11:02	1.7	52
	17:08	9.0	274
	23:16	1.8	55
22 F	05:32	9.7	296
	11:59	1.6	49
	18:07	8.8	268
23 Sa	00:10	2.0	61
	06:25	9.8	299
	12:54	1.4	43
	19:03	8.8	268
24 Su	01:03	2.0	61
	07:17	10.0	305
	13:47	1.1	34
	19:56	9.0	274
25 M	01:54	1.8	55
	08:05	10.3	314
	14:34	0.7	21
	20:43	9.3	283
26 Tu	02:40	1.6	49
	08:50	10.7	326
	15:19	0.3	9
	21:27	9.6	293
27 W	03:23	1.2	37
	09:33	11.2	341
	16:00	-0.1	-3
	22:07	10.0	305
28 Th ○	04:05	0.9	27
	10:14	11.6	354
	16:40	-0.4	-12
	22:47	10.4	317
29 F	04:46	0.6	18
	10:54	11.9	363
	17:20	-0.7	-21
	23:27	10.7	326
30 Sa	05:27	0.3	9
	11:36	12.1	369
	18:00	-0.9	-27
31 Su	00:08	11.0	335
	06:11	0.0	0
	12:20	12.1	369
	18:42	-0.9	-27

February

Day	Time	ft	cm
1 M	00:50	11.3	344
	06:57	-0.1	-3
	13:06	12.0	366
	19:26	-0.8	-24
2 Tu	01:36	11.4	347
	07:47	-0.2	-6
	13:55	11.6	354
	20:13	-0.5	-15
3 W	02:25	11.5	351
	08:41	-0.1	-3
	14:49	11.1	338
	21:04	-0.1	-3
4 Th ◑	03:19	11.4	347
	09:40	0.0	0
	15:49	10.6	323
	22:01	0.3	9
5 F	04:17	11.3	344
	10:45	0.1	3
	16:55	10.1	308
	23:04	0.7	21
6 Sa	05:21	11.2	341
	11:53	0.1	3
	18:05	9.9	302
7 Su	00:10	0.9	27
	06:27	11.2	341
	13:01	-0.1	-3
	19:13	9.9	302
8 M	01:17	0.8	24
	07:32	11.4	347
	14:04	-0.3	-9
	20:16	10.1	308
9 Tu	02:19	0.6	18
	08:32	11.7	357
	15:02	-0.6	-18
	21:13	10.4	317
10 W	03:16	0.4	12
	09:27	11.9	363
	15:54	-0.8	-24
	22:04	10.7	326
11 Th ●	04:07	0.1	3
	10:17	12.1	369
	16:42	-0.9	-27
	22:50	10.9	332
12 F	04:55	0.0	0
	11:03	12.0	366
	17:26	-0.8	-24
	23:34	10.9	332
13 Sa	05:40	0.1	3
	11:47	11.8	360
	18:08	-0.5	-15
14 Su	00:15	10.9	332
	06:23	0.2	6
	12:29	11.4	347
	18:48	-0.2	-6
15 M	00:55	10.8	329
	07:05	0.4	12
	13:11	11.0	335
	19:27	0.3	9
16 Tu	01:34	10.6	323
	07:47	0.7	21
	13:53	10.4	317
	20:06	0.8	24
17 W	02:15	10.3	314
	08:31	1.0	30
	14:37	9.8	299
	20:47	1.2	37
18 Th	02:57	10.0	305
	09:18	1.3	40
	15:25	9.3	283
	21:32	1.7	52
19 F ◐	03:44	9.8	299
	10:09	1.5	46
	16:17	8.9	271
	22:22	2.1	64
20 Sa	04:36	9.6	293
	11:05	1.7	52
	17:15	8.6	262
	23:17	2.3	70
21 Su	05:32	9.5	290
	12:04	1.6	49
	18:16	8.5	259
22 M	00:16	2.3	70
	06:30	9.7	296
	13:02	1.4	43
	19:14	8.8	268
23 Tu	01:12	2.0	61
	07:25	10.1	308
	13:56	0.9	27
	20:06	9.2	280
24 W	02:05	1.6	49
	08:16	10.6	323
	14:44	0.4	12
	20:53	9.7	296
25 Th	02:52	1.1	34
	09:03	11.2	341
	15:28	-0.2	-6
	21:36	10.3	314
26 F	03:37	0.5	15
	09:47	11.8	360
	16:10	-0.7	-21
	22:18	10.9	332
27 Sa ○	04:21	-0.1	-3
	10:31	12.2	372
	16:52	-1.0	-30
	22:59	11.5	351
28 Su	05:06	-0.6	-18
	11:15	12.5	381
	17:34	-1.2	-37
	23:42	11.9	363

March

Day	Time	ft	cm
1 M	05:51	-0.9	-27
	12:01	12.5	381
	18:17	-1.2	-37
2 Tu	00:26	12.2	372
	06:39	-1.0	-30
	12:48	12.2	372
	19:02	-1.0	-30
3 W	01:12	12.2	372
	07:30	-1.0	-30
	13:39	11.7	357
	19:51	-0.6	-18
4 Th	02:02	12.1	369
	08:24	-0.7	-21
	14:34	11.1	338
	20:44	0.0	0
5 F	02:57	11.8	360
	09:24	-0.4	-12
	15:35	10.5	320
	21:43	0.6	18
6 Sa ◑	03:57	11.3	344
	10:29	0.0	0
	16:43	9.9	302
	22:49	1.0	30
7 Su	05:05	11.0	335
	11:39	0.2	6
	17:54	9.7	296
8 M	00:00	1.2	37
	06:15	10.9	332
	12:49	0.2	6
	19:04	9.7	296
9 Tu	01:09	1.1	34
	07:22	11.0	335
	13:53	0.0	0
	20:06	10.0	305
10 W	02:11	0.8	24
	08:23	11.2	341
	14:49	-0.2	-6
	21:01	10.4	317
11 Th	03:06	0.5	15
	09:16	11.4	347
	15:39	-0.4	-12
	21:48	10.7	326
12 F	03:55	0.2	6
	10:04	11.6	354
	16:23	-0.4	-12
	22:31	10.9	332
13 Sa ●	04:39	0.0	0
	10:47	11.6	354
	17:04	-0.3	-9
	23:10	11.0	335
14 Su	06:20	0.0	0
	12:27	11.4	347
	18:41	-0.1	-3
15 M	00:46	11.0	335
	06:59	0.1	3
	13:05	11.1	338
	19:17	0.2	6
16 Tu	01:22	11.0	335
	07:36	0.2	6
	13:42	10.7	326
	19:52	0.6	18
17 W	01:57	10.8	329
	08:14	0.5	15
	14:21	10.3	314
	20:27	1.0	30
18 Th	02:33	10.5	320
	08:53	0.8	24
	15:01	9.8	299
	21:05	1.5	46
19 F ◐	03:12	10.2	311
	09:35	1.1	34
	15:44	9.4	287
	21:47	1.9	58
20 Sa	03:56	9.9	302
	10:22	1.3	40
	16:36	9.0	274
	22:34	2.2	67
21 Su ◐	04:46	9.7	296
	11:16	1.5	46
	17:29	8.7	265
	23:29	2.4	73
22 M	05:42	9.6	293
	12:15	1.6	49
	18:29	8.6	262
23 Tu	00:29	2.4	73
	06:43	9.7	296
	13:15	1.4	43
	19:29	8.9	271
24 W	01:30	2.1	64
	07:43	10.0	305
	14:12	1.0	30
	20:25	9.4	287
25 Th	02:27	1.5	46
	08:39	10.6	323
	15:02	0.4	12
	21:15	10.1	308
26 F	03:19	0.8	24
	09:30	11.3	344
	15:52	-0.2	-6
	22:01	10.8	329
27 Sa	04:08	0.0	0
	10:19	11.9	363
	16:37	-0.7	-21
	22:46	11.6	354
28 Su ○	04:56	-0.7	-21
	11:06	12.3	375
	17:21	-1.1	-34
	23:30	12.3	375
29 M	05:43	-1.3	-40
	11:53	12.6	384
	18:06	-1.3	-40
30 Tu	00:14	12.7	387
	06:31	-1.6	-49
	12:41	12.5	381
	18:52	-1.2	-37
31 W	01:01	12.9	393
	07:21	-1.7	-52
	13:31	12.2	372
	19:40	-0.8	-24

StationId: 8413320
Source: NOAA/NOS/CO-OPS
Station Type: Primary
Time Zone: LST_LDT
Datum: MLLW

NOAA Tide Predictions

Bar Harbor, ME, 2021

Times and Heights of High and Low Waters

April

Day	Time (h m)	Height (ft)	Height (cm)
1 Th	01:49	12.8	390
	08:13	-1.5	-46
	14:24	11.7	357
	20:31	-0.3	-9
2 F	02:41	12.5	381
	09:09	-1.1	-34
	15:21	11.1	338
	21:27	0.3	9
3 Sa	03:38	11.9	363
	10:09	-0.6	-18
	16:23	10.5	320
	22:29	0.9	27
4 Su ◑	04:41	11.3	344
	11:15	0.0	0
	17:31	10.0	305
	23:38	1.3	40
5 M	05:51	10.9	332
	12:24	0.3	9
	18:42	9.8	299
6 Tu	00:49	1.4	43
	07:02	10.7	326
	13:32	0.4	12
	19:49	9.9	302
7 W	01:57	1.2	37
	08:09	10.7	326
	14:34	0.4	12
	20:49	10.2	311
8 Th	02:57	0.9	27
	09:08	10.9	332
	15:29	0.2	6
	21:41	10.5	320
9 F	03:50	0.5	15
	09:59	11.0	335
	16:16	0.1	3
	22:25	10.8	329
10 Sa	04:37	0.2	6
	10:45	11.1	338
	16:58	0.2	6
	23:05	11.0	335
11 Su	05:19	0.1	3
	11:26	11.1	338
	17:36	0.3	9
	23:42	11.2	341
12 M ●	05:57	0.0	0
	12:04	10.9	332
	18:11	0.5	15
13 Tu	00:16	11.2	341
	06:34	0.1	3
	12:40	10.7	326
	18:45	0.8	24
14 W	00:49	11.1	338
	07:09	0.2	6
	13:16	10.4	317
	19:19	1.1	34
15 Th	01:23	10.9	332
	07:45	0.4	12
	13:53	10.1	308
	19:54	1.4	43
16 F	01:58	10.7	326
	08:22	0.6	18
	14:31	9.8	299
	20:31	1.7	52
17 Sa	02:36	10.5	320
	09:02	0.9	27
	15:13	9.5	290
	21:12	2.0	61
18 Su	03:19	10.2	311
	09:46	1.1	34
	15:59	9.2	280
	21:58	2.2	67
19 M	04:07	10.0	305
	10:37	1.3	40
	16:51	9.0	274
	22:51	2.3	70
20 Tu ◐	05:01	9.9	302
	11:32	1.3	40
	17:48	9.1	277
	23:50	2.2	67
21 W	06:01	10.0	305
	12:31	1.1	34
	18:47	9.4	287
22 Th	00:51	1.9	58
	07:03	10.2	311
	13:29	0.8	24
	19:43	9.9	302
23 F	01:51	1.3	40
	08:02	10.7	326
	14:23	0.3	9
	20:36	10.7	326
24 Sa	02:47	0.5	15
	08:57	11.3	344
	15:14	-0.2	-6
	21:26	11.5	351
25 Su	03:40	-0.3	-9
	09:50	11.8	360
	16:03	-0.6	-18
	22:14	12.3	375
26 M	04:31	-1.1	-34
	10:41	12.2	372
	16:51	-0.9	-27
	23:01	12.9	393
27 Tu ○	05:21	-1.7	-52
	11:32	12.4	378
	17:39	-1.0	-30
	23:48	13.3	405
28 W	06:12	-2.0	-61
	12:23	12.3	375
	18:28	-0.8	-24
29 Th	00:38	13.4	408
	07:04	-1.9	-58
	13:15	12.1	369
	19:20	-0.5	-15
30 F	01:29	13.1	399
	07:58	-1.7	-52
	14:10	11.6	354
	20:14	0.0	0

May

Day	Time (h m)	Height (ft)	Height (cm)
1 Sa	02:24	12.6	384
	08:54	-1.2	-37
	15:08	11.1	338
	21:13	0.6	18
2 Su	03:22	12.0	366
	09:55	-0.6	-18
	16:10	10.6	323
	22:16	1.0	30
3 M ◑	04:26	11.4	347
	10:59	0.0	0
	17:16	10.2	311
	23:23	1.4	43
4 Tu	05:34	10.9	332
	12:04	0.4	12
	18:22	10.1	308
5 W	00:31	1.4	43
	06:42	10.6	323
	13:08	0.6	18
	19:25	10.2	311
6 Th	01:36	1.3	40
	07:46	10.5	320
	14:06	0.7	21
	20:22	10.4	317
7 F	02:35	1.0	30
	08:44	10.5	320
	14:59	0.7	21
	21:12	10.6	323
8 Sa	03:26	0.7	21
	09:34	10.5	320
	15:45	0.7	21
	21:55	10.9	332
9 Su	04:13	0.4	12
	10:20	10.5	320
	16:27	0.8	24
	22:35	11.1	338
10 M	04:54	0.2	6
	11:01	10.5	320
	17:05	0.9	27
	23:11	11.2	341
11 Tu ●	05:33	0.2	6
	11:39	10.4	317
	17:41	1.1	34
	23:45	11.2	341
12 W	06:09	0.2	6
	12:16	10.3	314
	18:15	1.3	40
13 Th	00:19	11.2	341
	06:44	0.3	9
	12:52	10.2	311
	18:50	1.5	46
14 F	00:54	11.0	335
	07:20	0.4	12
	13:29	10.0	305
	19:25	1.7	52
15 Sa	01:30	10.9	332
	07:57	0.6	18
	14:07	9.8	299
	20:03	1.9	58
16 Su	02:08	10.7	326
	08:36	0.7	21
	14:48	9.6	293
	20:44	2.1	64
17 M	02:50	10.6	323
	09:19	0.8	24
	15:32	9.5	290
	21:30	2.1	64
18 Tu	03:37	10.4	317
	10:07	0.9	27
	16:21	9.5	290
	22:21	2.1	64
19 W ◐	04:30	10.4	317
	10:58	0.9	27
	17:14	9.7	296
	23:18	1.9	58
20 Th	05:27	10.4	317
	11:53	0.8	24
	18:09	10.1	308
21 F	00:18	1.5	46
	06:27	10.5	320
	12:48	0.5	15
	19:05	10.6	323
22 Sa	01:19	0.9	27
	07:28	10.8	329
	13:44	0.2	6
	20:00	11.3	344
23 Su	02:17	0.2	6
	08:27	11.1	338
	14:38	-0.1	-3
	20:53	12.1	369
24 M	03:14	-0.6	-18
	09:24	11.5	351
	15:31	-0.3	-9
	21:44	12.7	387
25 Tu	04:08	-1.3	-40
	10:18	11.8	360
	16:23	-0.5	-15
	22:35	13.2	402
26 W ○	05:01	-1.7	-52
	11:12	12.0	366
	17:15	-0.5	-15
	23:26	13.5	411
27 Th	05:55	-1.9	-58
	12:06	12.0	366
	18:08	-0.4	-12
28 F	00:18	13.4	408
	06:48	-1.8	-55
	13:00	11.8	360
	19:03	-0.1	-3
29 Sa	01:12	13.1	399
	07:43	-1.5	-46
	13:56	11.5	351
	19:59	0.3	9
30 Su	02:08	12.6	384
	08:39	-1.0	-30
	14:53	11.1	338
	20:58	0.7	21
31 M	03:06	12.0	366
	09:37	-0.5	-15
	15:53	10.8	329
	21:59	1.1	34

June

Day	Time (h m)	Height (ft)	Height (cm)
1 Tu	04:07	11.4	347
	10:37	0.0	0
	16:53	10.5	320
	23:02	1.3	40
2 W ◐	05:10	10.8	329
	11:36	0.5	15
	17:54	10.4	317
3 Th	00:05	1.4	43
	06:13	10.4	317
	12:34	0.8	24
	18:52	10.4	317
4 F	01:06	1.3	40
	07:14	10.1	308
	13:29	1.0	30
	19:46	10.5	320
5 Sa	02:03	1.2	37
	08:11	10.0	305
	14:21	1.2	37
	20:35	10.6	323
6 Su	02:55	0.9	27
	09:03	10.0	305
	15:08	1.3	40
	21:20	10.8	329
7 M	03:43	0.7	21
	09:50	10.0	305
	15:51	1.4	43
	22:01	11.0	335
8 Tu	04:26	0.5	15
	10:33	10.0	305
	16:32	1.5	46
	22:39	11.1	338
9 W	05:06	0.4	12
	11:13	10.0	305
	17:10	1.6	49
	23:16	11.2	341
10 Th ●	05:44	0.3	9
	11:52	10.0	305
	17:47	1.6	49
	23:52	11.2	341
11 F	06:21	0.3	9
	12:29	10.0	305
	18:24	1.7	52
12 Sa	00:29	11.2	341
	06:57	0.4	12
	13:06	9.9	302
	19:01	1.8	55
13 Su	01:06	11.1	338
	07:35	0.4	12
	13:45	9.9	302
	19:40	1.8	55
14 M	01:45	11.1	338
	08:14	0.5	15
	14:25	9.9	302
	20:22	1.8	55
15 Tu	02:27	11.0	335
	08:56	0.5	15
	15:08	10.0	305
	21:07	1.7	52
16 W	03:13	10.9	332
	09:40	0.5	15
	15:54	10.2	311
	21:57	1.6	49
17 Th ○	04:04	10.8	329
	10:28	0.4	12
	16:44	10.4	317
	22:52	1.4	43
18 F ◐	04:59	10.7	326
	11:20	0.4	12
	17:37	10.8	329
	23:50	1.0	30
19 Sa	05:58	10.7	326
	12:14	0.4	12
	18:32	11.3	344
20 Su	00:51	0.5	15
	07:00	10.7	326
	13:11	0.3	9
	19:28	11.8	360
21 M	01:52	0.0	0
	08:01	10.8	329
	14:08	0.2	6
	20:25	12.3	375
22 Tu	02:52	-0.6	-18
	09:02	11.1	338
	15:05	0.1	3
	21:20	12.8	390
23 W	03:50	-1.1	-34
	10:00	11.3	344
	16:02	0.0	0
	22:15	13.1	399
24 Th ○	04:45	-1.5	-46
	10:56	11.5	351
	16:57	-0.1	-3
	23:09	13.2	402
25 F	05:40	-1.6	-49
	11:51	11.5	351
	17:53	0.0	0
26 Sa	00:03	13.2	402
	06:34	-1.5	-46
	12:46	11.5	351
	18:48	0.1	3
27 Su	00:57	12.9	393
	07:28	-1.2	-37
	13:40	11.3	344
	19:43	0.4	12
28 M	01:51	12.5	381
	08:21	-0.8	-24
	14:34	11.1	338
	20:39	0.7	21
29 Tu	02:46	11.9	363
	09:14	-0.4	-12
	15:28	10.9	332
	21:36	1.0	30
30 W	03:42	11.3	344
	10:07	0.1	3
	16:22	10.7	326
	22:33	1.2	37

StationId: 8413320
Source: NOAA/NOS/CO-OPS
Station Type: Primary
Time Zone: LST_LDT
Datum: MLLW

NOAA Tide Predictions

Bar Harbor, ME,2021

Times and Heights of High and Low Waters

July

	Time	Height ft	cm		Time	Height ft	cm
1 Th ☽	04:39 11:00 17:17 23:31	10.7 0.6 10.5 1.4	326 18 320 43	**16** F	03:41 10:01 16:16 22:29	11.1 0.1 11.1 0.7	338 3 338 21
2 F	05:37 11:53 18:10	10.2 1.1 10.4	311 34 317	**17** Sa ☽	04:36 10:52 17:08 23:28	10.9 0.3 11.4 0.5	332 9 347 15
3 Sa	00:29 06:35 12:46 19:02	1.4 9.8 1.4 10.4	43 299 43 317	**18** Su	05:35 11:47 18:05	10.6 0.4 11.6	323 12 354
4 Su	01:25 07:32 13:37 19:52	1.4 9.5 1.7 10.4	43 290 52 317	**19** M	00:30 06:38 12:46 19:04	0.3 10.5 0.6 11.8	9 320 18 360
5 M	02:18 08:26 14:27 20:40	1.2 9.4 1.8 10.6	37 287 55 323	**20** Tu	01:33 07:43 13:47 20:04	-0.1 10.4 0.6 12.1	-3 317 18 369
6 Tu	03:08 09:16 15:14 21:25	1.0 9.5 1.8 10.7	30 290 55 326	**21** W	02:36 08:47 14:49 21:04	-0.4 10.6 0.5 12.4	-12 323 15 378
7 W	03:54 10:02 15:59 22:07	0.8 9.6 1.8 10.9	24 293 55 332	**22** Th	03:36 09:47 15:48 22:02	-0.8 10.8 0.4 12.7	-24 329 12 387
8 Th	04:37 10:45 16:40 22:48	0.6 9.7 1.8 11.1	18 296 55 338	**23** F	04:33 10:44 16:45 22:57	-1.1 11.1 0.2 12.8	-34 338 6 390
9 F	05:17 11:25 17:20 23:27	0.4 9.8 1.7 11.2	12 299 52 341	**24** Sa ○	05:27 11:38 17:40 23:50	-1.2 11.2 0.1 12.8	-37 341 3 390
10 Sa ●	05:56 12:04 17:59	0.3 10.0 1.6	9 305 49	**25** Su	06:19 12:29 18:33	-1.1 11.3 0.2	-34 344 6
11 Su	00:05 06:33 12:41 18:37	11.3 0.2 10.1 1.5	344 6 308 46	**26** M	00:42 07:09 13:19 19:25	12.6 -0.9 11.3 0.3	384 -27 344 9
12 M	00:44 07:11 13:20 19:17	11.4 0.1 10.3 1.4	347 3 314 43	**27** Tu	01:32 07:58 14:08 20:15	12.2 -0.6 11.2 0.5	372 -18 341 15
13 Tu	01:24 07:50 14:00 20:00	11.5 0.1 10.5 1.2	351 3 320 37	**28** W	02:22 08:45 14:56 21:06	11.7 -0.1 11.0 0.8	357 -3 335 24
14 W	02:06 08:31 14:42 20:45	11.4 0.0 10.7 1.1	347 0 326 34	**29** Th	03:12 09:32 15:44 21:58	11.1 0.4 10.7 1.1	338 12 326 34
15 Th	02:52 09:14 15:27 21:35	11.3 0.0 10.9 0.9	344 0 332 27	**30** F	04:03 10:19 16:33 22:51	10.5 0.9 10.5 1.3	320 27 320 40
				31 Sa ☽	04:56 11:08 17:23 23:45	9.9 1.4 10.3 1.5	302 43 314 46

August

	Time	Height ft	cm		Time	Height ft	cm
1 Su	05:52 11:59 18:14	9.4 1.8 10.1	287 55 308	**16** M	05:18 11:26 17:43	10.4 0.7 11.6	317 21 354
2 M	00:41 06:49 12:52 19:07	1.6 9.1 2.1 10.1	49 277 64 308	**17** Tu	00:14 06:24 12:29 18:47	0.2 10.2 0.9 11.6	6 311 27 354
3 Tu	01:36 07:45 13:45 19:59	1.5 9.0 2.2 10.2	46 274 67 311	**18** W	01:20 07:32 13:36 19:52	0.1 10.1 1.0 11.7	3 308 30 357
4 W	02:29 08:39 14:37 20:49	1.3 9.1 2.1 10.4	40 277 64 317	**19** Th	02:26 08:38 14:40 20:55	-0.1 10.3 0.8 11.9	-3 314 24 363
5 Th	03:19 09:28 15:25 21:35	1.1 9.3 2.0 10.7	34 283 61 326	**20** F	03:26 09:38 15:41 21:53	-0.4 10.6 0.6 12.2	-12 323 18 372
6 F	04:05 10:13 16:10 22:19	0.8 9.6 1.7 11.0	24 293 52 335	**21** Sa	04:22 10:33 16:36 22:47	-0.7 10.9 0.3 12.3	-21 332 9 375
7 Sa	04:47 10:54 16:52 23:00	0.5 9.9 1.4 11.3	15 302 43 344	**22** Su ○	05:14 11:23 17:28 23:37	-0.8 11.2 0.1 12.4	-24 341 3 378
8 Su ●	05:26 11:34 17:32 23:40	0.2 10.2 1.2 11.6	6 311 37 354	**23** M	06:01 12:10 18:17	-0.8 11.3 0.1	-24 344 3
9 M	06:05 12:12 18:12	-0.1 10.6 0.9	-3 323 27	**24** Tu	00:25 06:46 12:54 19:03	12.2 -0.5 11.3 0.2	372 -15 344 6
10 Tu	00:20 06:43 12:51 18:54	11.8 -0.3 10.9 0.6	360 -9 332 18	**25** W	01:10 07:29 13:37 19:49	11.8 -0.2 11.2 0.4	360 -6 341 12
11 W	01:01 07:23 13:31 19:37	11.9 -0.4 11.2 0.4	363 -12 341 12	**26** Th	01:55 08:11 14:19 20:34	11.3 0.3 11.0 0.7	344 9 335 21
12 Th	01:45 08:04 14:14 20:24	11.8 -0.3 11.4 0.2	360 -9 347 6	**27** F	02:40 08:53 15:02 21:20	10.8 0.8 10.8 1.0	329 24 329 30
13 F	02:31 08:48 15:00 21:15	11.6 -0.2 11.6 0.2	354 -6 354 6	**28** Sa	03:26 09:36 15:49 22:08	10.2 1.3 10.4 1.3	311 40 317 40
14 Sa	03:22 09:36 15:49 22:09	11.3 0.0 11.7 0.1	344 0 357 3	**29** Su	04:14 10:21 16:33 22:59	9.6 1.8 10.1 1.5	293 55 308 46
15 Su ☽	04:17 10:28 16:44 23:09	10.8 0.4 11.7 0.2	329 12 357 6	**30** M ☽	05:07 11:11 17:28 23:54	9.2 2.2 9.9 1.7	280 67 302 52
				31 Tu	06:04 12:05 18:19	8.9 2.4 9.8	271 73 299

September

	Time	Height ft	cm		Time	Height ft	cm
1 W	00:51 07:03 13:02 19:16	1.7 8.8 2.4 9.9	52 268 73 302	**16** Th	01:11 07:25 13:30 19:45	0.2 10.0 1.2 11.3	6 305 37 344
2 Th	01:48 07:59 13:58 20:10	1.6 8.9 2.3 10.1	49 271 70 308	**17** F	02:16 08:30 14:35 20:48	0.1 10.2 0.9 11.5	3 311 27 351
3 F	02:40 08:51 14:50 21:01	1.2 9.2 1.9 10.6	37 280 58 323	**18** Sa	03:15 09:27 15:33 21:45	-0.2 10.6 0.5 11.7	-6 323 15 357
4 Sa	03:28 09:37 15:37 21:47	0.8 9.7 1.5 11.0	24 296 46 335	**19** Su	04:08 10:19 16:26 22:35	-0.3 11.0 0.2 11.9	-9 335 6 363
5 Su	04:12 10:20 16:21 22:30	0.4 10.2 1.0 11.5	12 311 30 351	**20** M ○	04:56 11:04 17:14 23:22	-0.4 11.2 0.0 11.8	-12 341 0 360
6 M	04:53 11:00 17:03 23:12	-0.1 10.7 0.5 11.9	-3 326 15 363	**21** Tu	05:39 11:47 17:58	-0.3 11.4 0.0	-9 347 0
7 Tu ●	05:32 11:40 17:46 23:54	-0.4 11.3 0.1 12.1	-12 344 3 369	**22** W	00:05 06:20 12:26 18:40	11.7 -0.1 11.4 0.0	357 -3 347 0
8 W	06:12 12:20 18:29	-0.6 11.7 -0.3	-18 357 -9	**23** Th	00:46 06:58 13:04 19:21	11.3 0.3 11.3 0.2	344 9 344 6
9 Th	00:38 06:53 13:02 19:15	12.2 -0.7 12.1 -0.5	372 -21 369 -15	**24** F	01:27 07:36 13:42 20:01	10.9 0.7 11.1 0.5	332 21 338 15
10 F	01:23 07:36 13:46 20:03	12.1 -0.5 12.2 -0.6	369 -15 372 -18	**25** Sa	02:08 08:14 14:20 20:42	10.4 1.2 10.8 0.8	317 37 329 24
11 Sa	02:12 08:23 14:34 20:55	11.7 -0.3 12.2 -0.5	357 -9 372 -15	**26** Su	02:50 08:54 15:01 21:26	9.9 1.7 10.4 1.2	302 52 317 37
12 Su	03:05 09:13 15:26 21:52	11.3 0.2 12.0 -0.3	344 6 366 -9	**27** M	03:35 09:37 15:44 22:14	9.5 2.1 10.1 1.5	290 64 308 46
13 M ☽	04:03 10:10 16:24 22:55	10.7 0.6 11.7 0.0	326 18 357 0	**28** Tu	04:25 10:26 16:36 23:08	9.1 2.4 9.8 1.7	277 73 299 52
14 Tu	05:07 11:12 17:28	10.3 1.0 11.4	314 30 347	**29** W ☽	05:20 11:21 17:33	8.8 2.6 9.7	268 79 296
15 W	00:02 06:16 12:21 18:36	0.2 10.0 1.2 11.3	6 305 37 344	**30** Th	00:05 06:19 12:19 18:32	1.8 8.8 2.6 9.7	55 268 79 296

StationId: 8413320
Source: NOAA/NOS/CO-OPS
Station Type: Primary
Time Zone: LST_LDT
Datum: MLLW

NOAA Tide Predictions

Bar Harbor, ME, 2021

Times and Heights of High and Low Waters

October

Day	Time	ft	cm	Day	Time	ft	cm
1 F	01:03	1.6	49	**16** Sa	02:01	0.2	6
	07:17	9.0	274		08:17	10.4	317
	13:18	2.3	70		14:25	0.9	27
	19:29	10.0	305		20:36	11.1	338
2 Sa	01:58	1.2	37	**17** Su	02:58	0.1	3
	08:10	9.4	287		09:11	10.8	329
	14:12	1.8	55		15:22	0.5	15
	20:23	10.5	320		21:31	11.3	344
3 Su	02:47	0.8	24	**18** M	03:48	0.0	0
	08:58	10.0	305		09:59	11.1	338
	15:02	1.2	37		16:11	0.2	6
	21:12	11.0	335		22:20	11.3	344
4 M	03:33	0.2	6	**19** Tu	04:33	0.0	0
	09:42	10.7	326		10:42	11.3	344
	15:49	0.5	15		16:56	0.0	0
	21:58	11.6	354		23:04	11.3	344
5 Tu	04:16	-0.2	-6	**20** W ○	05:14	0.2	6
	10:24	11.4	347		11:21	11.4	347
	16:34	-0.2	-6		17:38	-0.1	-3
	22:43	12.0	366		23:44	11.1	338
6 W ●	04:58	-0.6	-18	**21** Th	05:51	0.5	15
	11:06	12.1	369		11:57	11.4	347
	17:19	-0.7	-21		18:16	0.0	0
	23:29	12.3	375				
7 Th	05:40	-0.8	-24	**22** F	00:23	10.8	329
	11:49	12.6	384		06:28	0.8	24
	18:05	-1.2	-37		12:32	11.3	344
					18:54	0.2	6
8 F	00:15	12.3	375	**23** Sa	01:01	10.5	320
	06:24	-0.8	-24		07:03	1.2	37
	12:33	12.9	393		13:08	11.1	338
	18:53	-1.3	-40		19:31	0.4	12
9 Sa	01:03	12.1	369	**24** Su	01:39	10.1	308
	07:11	-0.6	-18		07:39	1.5	46
	13:20	12.9	393		13:44	10.8	329
	19:44	-1.3	-40		20:10	0.7	21
10 Su	01:54	11.7	357	**25** M	02:18	9.8	299
	08:00	-0.2	-6		08:17	1.9	58
	14:11	12.7	387		14:23	10.5	320
	20:38	-1.0	-30		20:51	1.0	30
11 M	02:50	11.2	341	**26** Tu	03:01	9.4	287
	08:55	0.3	9		08:59	2.2	67
	15:06	12.2	372		15:06	10.2	311
	21:37	-0.6	-18		21:36	1.3	40
12 Tu	03:50	10.7	326	**27** W	03:48	9.1	277
	09:55	0.8	24		09:46	2.4	73
	16:08	11.7	357		15:55	9.9	302
	22:42	-0.1	-3		22:26	1.5	46
13 W ◑	04:56	10.2	311	**28** Th ◐	04:40	8.9	271
	11:02	1.2	37		10:39	2.5	76
	17:16	11.3	344		16:49	9.8	299
	23:50	0.2	6		23:21	1.5	46
14 Th	06:06	10.0	305	**29** F	05:36	9.0	274
	12:13	1.3	40		11:37	2.5	76
	18:26	11.0	335		17:47	9.8	299
15 F	00:58	0.3	9	**30** Sa	00:17	1.4	43
	07:15	10.1	308		06:33	9.2	280
	13:22	1.2	37		12:36	2.1	64
	19:35	11.0	335		18:46	10.0	305
				31 Su	01:12	1.1	34
					07:27	9.7	296
					13:34	1.6	49
					19:43	10.4	317

November

Day	Time	ft	cm	Day	Time	ft	cm
1 M	02:03	0.6	18	**16** Tu	02:22	0.5	15
	08:17	10.4	317		08:34	11.1	338
	14:27	0.9	27		14:52	0.2	6
	20:36	10.9	332		20:59	10.7	326
2 Tu	02:52	0.2	6	**17** W	03:06	0.6	18
	09:04	11.2	341		09:16	11.3	344
	15:18	0.1	3		15:36	0.0	0
	21:27	11.4	347		21:43	10.6	323
3 W	03:39	-0.3	-9	**18** Th	03:47	0.7	21
	09:50	12.0	366		09:54	11.3	344
	16:07	-0.7	-21		16:16	0.0	0
	22:16	11.9	363		22:23	10.5	320
4 Th ●	04:25	-0.6	-18	**19** F ○	04:24	0.9	27
	10:35	12.7	387		10:30	11.3	344
	16:55	-1.3	-40		16:54	0.0	0
	23:05	12.1	369		23:01	10.3	314
5 F	05:11	-0.8	-24	**20** Sa	05:00	1.2	37
	11:21	13.2	402		11:05	11.2	341
	17:44	-1.7	-52		17:30	0.2	6
	23:54	12.2	372		23:37	10.1	308
6 Sa	05:59	-0.7	-21	**21** Su	05:35	1.4	43
	12:09	13.4	408		11:40	11.1	338
	18:34	-1.8	-55		18:06	0.4	12
7 Su	00:45	12.0	366	**22** M	00:14	9.9	302
	05:49	-0.5	-15		06:11	1.7	52
	11:59	13.3	405		12:16	10.9	332
	18:27	-1.7	-52		18:43	0.6	18
8 M	00:39	11.7	357	**23** Tu	00:52	9.7	296
	06:42	-0.1	-3		06:49	1.9	58
	12:52	12.9	393		12:54	10.6	323
	19:23	-1.3	-40		19:22	0.8	24
9 Tu	01:36	11.2	341	**24** W	01:32	9.5	290
	07:39	0.4	12		07:29	2.1	64
	13:50	12.3	375		13:35	10.4	317
	20:23	-0.8	-24		20:04	1.0	30
10 W	02:37	10.7	326	**25** Th	02:16	9.3	283
	08:42	0.8	24		08:13	2.2	67
	14:53	11.7	357		14:21	10.2	311
	21:26	-0.3	-9		20:50	1.1	34
11 Th ◐	03:42	10.4	317	**26** F	03:03	9.3	283
	09:49	1.2	37		09:03	2.2	67
	16:01	11.2	341		15:11	10.1	308
	22:32	0.1	3		21:40	1.1	34
12 F	04:50	10.2	311	**27** Sa ◐	03:55	9.4	287
	10:59	1.3	40		09:58	2.1	64
	17:10	10.8	329		16:06	10.0	305
	23:37	0.4	12		22:32	1.0	30
13 Sa	05:55	10.3	314	**28** Su	04:49	9.7	296
	12:06	1.1	34		10:56	1.8	55
	18:16	10.7	326		17:05	10.1	308
					23:26	0.8	24
14 Su	00:38	0.4	12	**29** M	05:43	10.2	311
	06:54	10.5	320		11:56	1.2	37
	13:08	0.8	24		18:04	10.3	314
	19:17	10.6	323				
15 M	01:33	0.5	15	**30** Tu	00:20	0.5	15
	07:47	10.8	329		06:36	10.9	332
	14:03	0.5	15		12:53	0.5	15
	20:11	10.7	326		19:02	10.7	326

December

Day	Time	ft	cm	Day	Time	ft	cm
1 W	01:13	0.2	6	**16** Th	02:37	1.1	34
	07:28	11.6	354		08:47	10.9	332
	13:49	-0.3	-9		15:12	0.3	9
	19:58	11.1	338		21:19	10.0	305
2 Th	02:05	-0.2	-6	**17** F	03:19	1.2	37
	08:18	12.4	378		09:27	11.1	338
	14:42	-1.0	-30		15:53	0.2	6
	20:52	11.5	351		22:01	10.0	305
3 F	02:56	-0.4	-12	**18** Sa	03:59	1.3	40
	09:08	13.0	396		10:05	11.1	338
	15:34	-1.6	-49		16:32	0.1	3
	21:44	11.8	360		22:39	10.0	305
4 Sa ●	03:47	-0.6	-18	**19** Su ○	04:36	1.4	43
	09:59	13.4	408		10:41	11.1	338
	16:26	-2.0	-61		17:09	0.2	6
	22:37	11.9	363		23:16	9.9	302
5 Su	04:39	-0.6	-18	**20** M	05:12	1.4	43
	10:50	13.5	411		11:17	11.1	338
	17:19	-2.0	-61		17:45	0.2	6
	23:30	11.8	360		23:52	9.9	302
6 M	05:32	-0.4	-12	**21** Tu	05:48	1.5	46
	11:42	13.4	408		11:53	11.0	335
	18:13	-1.8	-55		18:21	0.3	9
7 Tu	00:24	11.6	354	**22** W	00:29	9.8	299
	06:27	-0.1	-3		06:25	1.6	49
	12:37	13.0	396		12:31	10.9	332
	19:08	-1.4	-43		18:58	0.4	12
8 W	01:21	11.3	344	**23** Th	01:07	9.8	299
	07:25	0.2	6		07:04	1.7	52
	13:35	12.4	378		13:10	10.8	329
	20:06	-0.9	-27		19:37	0.5	15
9 Th	02:19	10.9	332	**24** F	01:47	9.8	299
	08:26	0.6	18		07:46	1.7	52
	14:35	11.7	357		13:52	10.6	323
	21:05	-0.4	-12		20:18	0.5	15
10 F	03:21	10.6	323	**25** Sa	02:30	9.8	299
	09:29	0.9	27		08:32	1.6	49
	15:39	11.1	338		14:39	10.5	320
	22:06	0.1	3		21:03	0.6	18
11 Sa ◐	04:23	10.4	317	**26** Su	03:17	10.0	305
	10:35	1.1	34		09:24	1.5	46
	16:44	10.6	323		15:31	10.3	314
	23:07	0.5	15		21:52	0.6	18
12 Su	05:24	10.4	317	**27** M ◐	04:08	10.3	314
	11:40	1.1	34		10:21	1.2	37
	17:48	10.2	311		16:28	10.2	311
					22:45	0.6	18
13 M	00:05	0.8	24	**28** Tu	05:03	10.7	326
	06:22	10.4	317		11:21	0.8	24
	12:41	1.0	30		17:29	10.2	311
	18:49	10.0	305		23:41	0.5	15
14 Tu	01:00	1.0	30	**29** W	05:59	11.1	338
	07:15	10.6	323		12:23	0.3	9
	13:36	0.7	21		18:32	10.3	314
	19:45	9.9	302				
15 W	01:51	1.1	34	**30** Th	00:39	0.4	12
	08:03	10.8	329		06:56	11.7	357
	14:26	0.5	15		13:23	-0.4	-12
	20:34	9.9	302		19:33	9.9	302
				31 F	01:37	0.1	3
					07:53	12.3	375
					14:22	-1.0	-30
					20:32	10.8	329

StationId: 8418150
Source: NOAA/NOS/CO-OPS
Station Type: Primary
Time Zone: LST_LDT
Datum: MLLW

NOAA Tide Predictions

Portland, ME,2021

Times and Heights of High and Low Waters

January

Day	Time	ft	cm
1 F	00:18	8.7	265
	06:04	0.8	24
	12:17	10.1	308
	18:42	-0.4	-12
2 Sa	00:57	8.8	268
	06:46	0.7	21
	12:59	10.1	308
	19:23	-0.5	-15
3 Su	01:39	8.9	271
	07:32	0.6	18
	13:44	10.0	305
	20:08	-0.4	-12
4 M	02:24	9.0	274
	08:22	0.6	18
	14:34	9.8	299
	20:56	-0.3	-9
5 Tu	03:14	9.2	280
	09:18	0.5	15
	15:29	9.5	290
	21:47	-0.2	-6
6 W ☾	04:07	9.4	287
	10:17	0.4	12
	16:29	9.2	280
	22:42	0.0	0
7 Th	05:03	9.7	296
	11:20	0.3	9
	17:33	9.0	274
	23:40	0.2	6
8 F	06:02	9.9	302
	12:26	0.0	0
	18:40	8.9	271
9 Sa	00:41	0.3	9
	07:04	10.2	311
	13:32	-0.4	-12
	19:47	8.9	271
10 Su	01:43	0.3	9
	08:03	10.5	320
	14:33	-0.8	-24
	20:48	9.1	277
11 M	02:42	0.2	6
	09:00	10.8	329
	15:30	-1.1	-34
	21:45	9.3	283
12 Tu	03:37	0.0	0
	09:54	10.9	332
	16:24	-1.3	-40
	22:39	9.4	287
13 W ●	04:30	0.0	0
	10:47	11.0	335
	17:15	-1.3	-40
	23:30	9.4	287
14 Th	05:21	0.0	0
	11:37	10.9	332
	18:03	-1.1	-34
15 F	00:18	9.4	287
	06:10	0.1	3
	12:25	10.6	323
	18:49	-0.9	-27
16 Sa	01:04	9.3	283
	06:58	0.3	9
	13:12	10.2	311
	19:34	-0.5	-15
17 Su	01:50	9.1	277
	07:47	0.6	18
	13:59	9.6	293
	20:19	0.0	0
18 M	02:37	8.9	271
	08:37	0.9	27
	14:48	9.1	277
	21:05	0.5	15
19 Tu	03:24	8.7	265
	09:29	1.1	34
	15:40	8.5	259
	21:51	0.9	27
20 W ☽	04:12	8.6	262
	10:23	1.3	40
	16:34	8.1	247
	22:39	1.3	40
21 Th	05:02	8.5	259
	11:20	1.4	43
	17:31	7.7	235
	23:30	1.6	49
22 F	05:54	8.5	259
	12:19	1.4	43
	18:30	7.5	229
23 Sa	00:24	1.8	55
	06:47	8.5	259
	13:18	1.2	37
	19:29	7.5	229
24 Su	01:20	1.8	55
	07:40	8.7	265
	14:11	1.0	30
	20:22	7.7	235
25 M	02:10	1.7	52
	08:28	9.0	274
	14:58	0.6	18
	21:10	7.9	241
26 Tu	02:56	1.4	43
	09:13	9.4	287
	15:40	0.2	6
	21:53	8.2	250
27 W	03:38	1.1	34
	09:55	9.7	296
	16:21	-0.1	-3
	22:34	8.5	259
28 Th ○	04:20	0.7	21
	10:36	10.1	308
	17:00	-0.5	-15
	23:14	8.8	268
29 F	05:01	0.4	12
	11:17	10.4	317
	17:39	-0.7	-21
	23:53	9.1	277
30 Sa	05:44	0.1	3
	11:58	10.5	320
	18:19	-0.9	-27
31 Su	00:33	9.4	287
	06:28	-0.1	-3
	12:41	10.5	320
	19:00	-1.0	-30

February

Day	Time	ft	cm
1 M	01:14	9.7	296
	07:14	-0.3	-9
	13:27	10.4	317
	19:44	-0.9	-27
2 Tu	01:59	9.8	299
	08:04	-0.3	-9
	14:16	10.0	305
	20:31	-0.6	-18
3 W	02:47	9.9	302
	08:59	-0.2	-6
	15:11	9.6	293
	21:22	-0.3	-9
4 Th ◑	03:41	9.9	302
	09:58	-0.1	-3
	16:12	9.1	277
	22:17	0.1	3
5 F	04:38	9.9	302
	11:01	0.0	0
	17:17	8.7	265
	23:18	0.5	15
6 Sa	05:40	9.8	299
	12:10	0.0	0
	18:28	8.5	259
7 Su	00:24	0.7	21
	06:47	9.8	299
	13:20	-0.1	-3
	19:38	8.5	259
8 M	01:32	0.8	24
	07:53	10.0	305
	14:25	-0.4	-12
	20:41	8.7	265
9 Tu	02:34	0.6	18
	08:53	10.2	311
	15:23	-0.6	-18
	21:37	8.9	271
10 W	03:30	0.3	9
	09:47	10.4	317
	16:14	-0.8	-24
	22:28	9.2	280
11 Th ●	04:22	0.1	3
	10:38	10.5	320
	17:02	-0.9	-27
	23:15	9.3	283
12 F	05:10	0.0	0
	11:25	10.4	317
	17:46	-0.8	-24
	23:58	9.4	287
13 Sa	05:55	0.0	0
	12:08	10.2	311
	18:26	-0.6	-18
14 Su	00:39	9.4	287
	06:37	0.1	3
	12:50	9.9	302
	19:04	-0.3	-9
15 M	01:17	9.3	283
	07:19	0.3	9
	13:31	9.4	287
	19:42	0.1	3
16 Tu	01:56	9.1	277
	08:02	0.5	15
	14:13	8.9	271
	20:20	0.6	18
17 W	02:36	8.9	271
	08:47	0.8	24
	14:59	8.4	256
	21:01	1.0	30
18 Th	03:19	8.7	265
	09:35	1.1	34
	15:48	8.0	244
	21:46	1.5	46
19 F ◑	04:05	8.5	259
	10:27	1.3	40
	16:42	7.6	232
	22:35	1.8	55
20 Sa	04:56	8.4	256
	11:23	1.5	46
	17:40	7.3	223
	23:29	2.0	61
21 Su	05:52	8.3	253
	12:25	1.4	43
	18:43	7.3	223
22 M	00:29	2.1	64
	06:52	8.5	259
	13:26	1.2	37
	19:42	7.5	229
23 Tu	01:28	1.9	58
	07:49	8.8	268
	14:19	0.8	24
	20:33	7.8	238
24 W	02:21	1.4	43
	08:39	9.3	283
	15:06	0.3	9
	21:19	8.3	253
25 Th	03:08	0.9	27
	09:25	9.8	299
	15:48	-0.2	-6
	22:02	8.8	268
26 F	03:53	0.4	12
	10:10	10.2	311
	16:30	-0.7	-21
	22:43	9.3	283
27 Sa ○	04:38	-0.2	-6
	10:54	10.6	323
	17:11	-1.0	-30
	23:24	9.9	302
28 Su	05:23	-0.6	-18
	11:38	10.8	329
	17:52	-1.2	-37

March

Day	Time	ft	cm
1 M	00:05	10.3	314
	06:09	-1.0	-30
	12:23	10.8	329
	18:35	-1.2	-37
2 Tu	00:48	10.6	323
	06:57	-1.1	-34
	13:10	10.6	323
	19:19	-1.1	-34
3 W	01:33	10.6	323
	07:47	-1.1	-34
	14:01	10.1	308
	20:07	-0.7	-21
4 Th	02:22	10.5	320
	08:42	-0.8	-24
	14:57	9.6	293
	21:00	-0.1	-3
5 F	03:17	10.3	314
	09:41	-0.5	-15
	15:59	9.0	274
	21:58	0.4	12
6 Sa ☾	04:18	9.9	302
	10:46	-0.1	-3
	17:06	8.6	262
	23:02	0.9	27
7 Su	05:24	9.6	293
	11:57	0.1	3
	18:18	8.3	253
8 M	00:13	1.1	34
	06:36	9.5	290
	13:10	0.2	6
	19:29	8.4	256
9 Tu	01:25	1.1	34
	07:44	9.6	293
	14:15	0.0	0
	20:31	8.6	262
10 W	02:28	0.8	24
	08:45	9.8	299
	15:11	-0.2	-6
	21:25	8.9	271
11 Th	03:23	0.5	15
	09:38	10.0	305
	16:00	-0.4	-12
	22:13	9.2	280
12 F	04:12	0.2	6
	10:26	10.0	305
	16:43	-0.4	-12
	22:55	9.4	287
13 Sa ●	04:56	0.0	0
	11:09	10.0	305
	17:23	-0.3	-9
	23:34	9.5	290
14 Su	06:37	0.0	0
	12:49	9.8	299
	18:58	-0.1	-3
15 M	01:10	9.6	293
	07:15	0.0	0
	13:27	9.6	293
	19:32	0.2	6
16 Tu	01:44	9.5	290
	07:53	0.1	3
	14:04	9.2	280
	20:06	0.5	15
17 W	02:17	9.4	287
	08:30	0.3	9
	14:42	8.8	268
	20:41	0.9	27
18 Th	02:53	9.2	280
	09:10	0.6	18
	15:23	8.4	256
	21:19	1.3	40
19 F	03:31	8.9	271
	09:53	0.8	24
	16:09	8.0	244
	22:02	1.7	52
20 Sa	04:16	8.7	265
	10:41	1.1	34
	16:59	7.7	235
	22:50	2.0	61
21 Su ☽	05:06	8.5	259
	11:34	1.3	40
	17:55	7.4	226
	23:43	2.1	64
22 M	06:02	8.4	256
	12:33	1.4	43
	18:56	7.4	226
23 Tu	00:43	2.1	64
	07:04	8.5	259
	13:36	1.3	40
	19:57	7.6	232
24 W	01:45	1.9	58
	08:06	8.8	268
	14:34	0.9	27
	20:52	8.1	247
25 Th	02:44	1.4	43
	09:02	9.3	283
	15:25	0.3	9
	21:41	8.7	265
26 F	03:37	0.7	21
	09:53	9.8	299
	16:11	-0.2	-6
	22:25	9.4	287
27 Sa	04:25	0.0	0
	10:41	10.3	314
	16:55	-0.7	-21
	23:09	10.1	308
28 Su ○	05:13	-0.7	-21
	11:28	10.7	326
	17:39	-1.1	-34
	23:52	10.7	326
29 M	06:01	-1.3	-40
	12:16	10.9	332
	18:23	-1.2	-37
30 Tu	00:36	11.1	338
	06:49	-1.6	-49
	13:04	10.8	329
	19:09	-1.2	-37
31 W	01:22	11.3	344
	07:39	-1.7	-52
	13:54	10.6	323
	19:56	-0.9	-27

StationId: 8418150
Source: NOAA/NOS/CO-OPS
Station Type: Primary
Time Zone: LST_LDT
Datum: MLLW

NOAA Tide Predictions

Portland, ME,2021

Times and Heights of High and Low Waters

April

Day	Time	Height ft	Height cm	Day	Time	Height ft	Height cm
1 Th	02:09	11.3	344	**16** F	02:17	9.4	287
	08:30	-1.5	-46		08:39	0.4	12
	14:47	10.1	308		14:56	8.4	256
	20:46	-0.4	-12		20:45	1.5	46
2 F	03:01	10.9	332	**17** Sa	02:55	9.1	277
	09:26	-1.1	-34		09:20	0.7	21
	15:44	9.6	293		15:38	8.1	247
	21:42	0.2	6		21:27	1.8	55
3 Sa	03:58	10.5	320	**18** Su	03:38	8.9	271
	10:27	-0.6	-18		10:06	0.9	27
	16:48	9.1	277		16:26	7.8	238
	22:43	0.7	21		22:15	2.0	61
4 Su	05:02	10.0	305	**19** M	04:27	8.7	265
	11:33	-0.1	-3		10:57	1.1	34
	17:56	8.7	265		17:19	7.7	235
	23:50	1.1	34		23:07	2.1	64
5 M	06:11	9.6	293	**20** Tu	05:22	8.7	265
	12:43	0.2	6		11:52	1.1	34
	19:06	8.5	259		18:15	7.8	238
6 Tu	01:03	1.3	40	**21** W	00:05	2.0	61
	07:23	9.3	283		06:21	8.7	265
	13:54	0.4	12		12:50	1.0	30
	20:14	8.6	262		19:13	8.1	247
7 W	02:15	1.2	37	**22** Th	01:07	1.7	52
	08:31	9.3	283		07:23	9.0	274
	14:58	0.3	9		13:48	0.7	21
	21:14	8.8	268		20:09	8.6	262
8 Th	03:17	0.9	27	**23** F	02:08	1.2	37
	09:30	9.5	290		08:23	9.4	287
	15:51	0.2	6		14:42	0.3	9
	22:05	9.1	277		21:00	9.3	283
9 F	04:10	0.6	18	**24** Sa	03:05	0.4	12
	10:21	9.6	293		09:19	9.8	299
	16:37	0.1	3		15:33	-0.2	-6
	22:49	9.4	287		21:48	10.0	305
10 Sa	04:56	0.3	9	**25** Su	03:58	-0.4	-12
	11:07	9.6	293		10:12	10.2	311
	17:17	0.2	6		16:20	-0.6	-18
	23:29	9.6	293		22:35	10.8	329
11 Su	05:38	0.1	3	**26** M	04:49	-1.1	-34
	11:49	9.5	290		11:03	10.6	323
	17:54	0.3	9		17:07	-0.9	-27
					23:21	11.3	344
12 M	00:05	9.7	296	**27** Tu	05:39	-1.6	-49
	06:17	0.0	0		11:54	10.7	326
	12:28	9.4	287		17:55	-1.0	-30
	18:28	0.5	15				
13 Tu	00:39	9.8	299	**28** W	00:09	11.7	357
	06:53	0.0	0		06:30	-1.9	-58
	13:04	9.2	280		12:46	10.7	326
	19:00	0.7	21		18:45	-0.8	-24
14 W	01:11	9.7	296	**29** Th	00:58	11.8	360
	07:27	0.1	3		07:22	-1.9	-58
	13:40	9.0	274		13:39	10.4	317
	19:33	1.0	30		19:35	-0.5	-15
15 Th	01:43	9.6	293	**30** F	01:49	11.6	354
	08:02	0.2	6		08:15	-1.7	-52
	14:17	8.7	265		14:33	10.0	305
	20:07	1.3	40		20:28	-0.1	-3

May

Day	Time	Height ft	Height cm	Day	Time	Height ft	Height cm
1 Sa	02:43	11.1	338	**16** Su	02:27	9.4	287
	09:12	-1.2	-37		08:55	0.5	15
	15:32	9.6	293		15:14	8.2	250
	21:26	0.4	12		21:00	1.8	55
2 Su	03:42	10.6	323	**17** M	03:10	9.3	283
	10:13	-0.6	-18		09:39	0.7	21
	16:36	9.2	280		15:59	8.1	247
	22:29	0.9	27		21:47	1.9	58
3 M	04:47	10.0	305	**18** Tu	03:57	9.1	277
	11:17	-0.1	-3		10:27	0.7	21
	17:41	8.9	271		16:49	8.1	247
	23:37	1.2	37		22:39	1.9	58
4 Tu	05:54	9.5	290	**19** W	04:50	9.1	277
	12:23	0.3	9		11:18	0.7	21
	18:47	8.8	268		17:40	8.3	253
					23:35	1.7	52
5 W	00:47	1.4	43	**20** Th	05:47	9.1	277
	07:02	9.2	280		12:11	0.6	18
	13:29	0.5	15		18:34	8.7	265
	19:50	8.9	271				
6 Th	01:55	1.3	40	**21** F	00:34	1.4	43
	08:07	9.1	277		06:46	9.2	280
	14:29	0.6	18		13:06	0.5	15
	20:47	9.1	277		19:28	9.2	280
7 F	02:56	1.0	30	**22** Sa	01:36	0.9	27
	09:06	9.1	277		07:48	9.4	287
	15:20	0.6	18		14:02	0.2	6
	21:36	9.3	283		20:22	9.9	302
8 Sa	03:48	0.7	21	**23** Su	02:36	0.2	6
	09:57	9.1	277		08:48	9.7	296
	16:05	0.7	21		14:56	-0.1	-3
	22:19	9.6	293		21:14	10.6	323
9 Su	04:34	0.5	15	**24** M	03:33	-0.6	-18
	10:43	9.1	277		09:45	10.0	305
	16:45	0.8	24		15:48	-0.4	-12
	22:57	9.7	296		22:04	11.2	341
10 M	05:15	0.3	9	**25** Tu	04:27	-1.2	-37
	11:25	9.0	274		10:40	10.2	311
	17:22	0.9	27		16:39	-0.5	-15
	23:34	9.8	299		22:54	11.6	354
11 Tu	05:53	0.1	3	**26** W	05:20	-1.6	-49
	12:04	8.9	271		11:35	10.3	314
	17:56	1.1	34		17:31	-0.5	-15
					23:46	11.8	360
12 W	00:08	9.8	299	**27** Th	06:13	-1.9	-58
	06:29	0.1	3		12:30	10.3	314
	12:42	8.8	268		18:23	-0.4	-12
	18:30	1.2	37				
13 Th	00:41	9.8	299	**28** F	00:38	11.8	360
	07:04	0.2	6		07:07	-1.8	-55
	13:19	8.7	265		13:25	10.1	308
	19:04	1.4	43		19:17	-0.2	-6
14 F	01:15	9.7	296	**29** Sa	01:32	11.6	354
	07:39	0.3	9		08:07	-1.5	-46
	13:55	8.5	259		14:20	9.9	302
	19:40	1.5	46		20:12	0.2	6
15 Sa	01:50	9.5	290	**30** Su	02:27	11.1	338
	08:16	0.4	12		08:57	-1.1	-34
	14:33	8.3	253		15:18	9.6	293
	20:18	1.7	52		21:10	0.6	18
				31 M	03:26	10.6	323
					09:56	-0.6	-18
					16:18	9.3	283
					22:12	0.9	27

June

Day	Time	Height ft	Height cm	Day	Time	Height ft	Height cm
1 Tu	04:28	10.0	305	**16** W	03:34	9.5	290
	10:56	-0.1	-3		10:01	0.3	9
	17:19	9.1	277		16:20	8.7	265
	23:17	1.2	37		22:15	1.4	43
2 W	05:31	9.5	290	**17** Th	04:25	9.4	287
	11:55	0.3	9		10:48	0.3	9
	18:18	9.0	274		17:09	9.0	274
					23:10	1.2	37
3 Th	00:22	1.3	40	**18** F	05:19	9.4	287
	06:33	9.1	277		11:38	0.3	9
	12:53	0.7	21		18:00	9.4	287
	19:15	9.1	277				
4 F	01:26	1.3	40	**19** Sa	00:08	0.9	27
	07:34	8.8	268		06:17	9.3	283
	13:49	0.9	27		12:31	0.2	6
	20:09	9.2	280		18:53	9.8	299
5 Sa	02:26	1.2	37	**20** Su	01:09	0.5	15
	08:33	8.6	262		07:19	9.3	283
	14:41	1.1	34		13:28	0.2	6
	20:58	9.3	283		19:49	10.3	314
6 Su	03:19	0.9	27	**21** M	02:11	0.0	0
	09:25	8.5	259		08:22	9.4	287
	15:27	1.2	37		14:25	0.1	3
	21:42	9.5	290		20:45	10.8	329
7 M	04:06	0.7	21	**22** Tu	03:11	-0.6	-18
	10:13	8.5	259		09:24	9.5	290
	16:09	1.3	40		15:22	0.0	0
	22:23	9.6	293		21:40	11.2	341
8 Tu	04:48	0.5	15	**23** W	04:08	-1.1	-34
	10:57	8.5	259		10:22	9.7	296
	16:48	1.4	43		16:17	-0.1	-3
	23:01	9.7	296		22:34	11.5	351
9 W	05:28	0.3	9	**24** Th	05:04	-1.4	-43
	11:39	8.5	259		11:19	9.8	299
	17:25	1.5	46		17:12	-0.1	-3
	23:39	9.8	299		23:29	11.6	354
10 Th	06:05	0.3	9	**25** F	05:59	-1.5	-46
	12:19	8.5	259		12:16	9.9	302
	18:02	1.5	46		18:07	-0.1	-3
11 F	00:15	9.8	299	**26** Sa	00:24	11.6	354
	06:42	0.2	6		06:53	-1.5	-46
	12:57	8.5	259		13:10	9.8	299
	18:38	1.5	46		19:01	0.0	0
12 Sa	00:51	9.8	299	**27** Su	01:18	11.4	347
	07:18	0.2	6		07:46	-1.3	-40
	13:35	8.5	259		14:04	9.7	296
	19:16	1.6	49		19:56	0.2	6
13 Su	01:28	9.7	296	**28** M	02:11	11.0	335
	07:55	0.3	9		08:39	-0.9	-27
	14:12	8.4	256		14:58	9.6	293
	19:55	1.6	49		20:51	0.5	15
14 M	02:06	9.7	296	**29** Tu	03:06	10.5	320
	08:34	0.3	9		09:32	-0.5	-15
	14:52	8.4	256		15:53	9.4	287
	20:37	1.6	49		21:49	0.8	24
15 Tu	02:48	9.6	293	**30** W	04:03	9.9	302
	09:15	0.3	9		10:26	0.0	0
	15:34	8.5	259		16:47	9.3	283
	21:24	1.5	46		22:49	1.1	34

StationId: 8418150
Source: NOAA/NOS/CO-OPS
Station Type: Primary
Time Zone: LST_LDT
Datum: MLLW

NOAA Tide Predictions

Portland, ME,2021

Times and Heights of High and Low Waters

July

Day	Time	ft	cm	Day	Time	ft	cm
1 Th ☽	05:00	9.3	283	**16** F	04:03	9.7	296
	11:18	0.5	15		10:20	0.0	0
	17:41	9.2	280		16:39	9.6	293
	23:48	1.3	40		22:48	0.6	18
2 F	05:57	8.8	268	**17** Sa ☽	04:57	9.4	287
	12:10	0.9	27		11:10	0.1	3
	18:33	9.1	277		17:30	9.9	302
					23:45	0.4	12
3 Sa	00:48	1.3	40	**18** Su	05:56	9.2	280
	06:55	8.4	256		12:03	0.3	9
	13:02	1.3	40		18:25	10.2	311
	19:24	9.1	277				
4 Su	01:47	1.3	40	**19** M	00:47	0.2	6
	07:53	8.2	250		06:58	9.0	274
	13:54	1.5	46		13:01	0.4	12
	20:15	9.2	280		19:23	10.4	317
5 M	02:43	1.2	37	**20** Tu	01:51	-0.1	-3
	08:49	8.1	247		08:05	9.0	274
	14:45	1.7	52		14:10	0.5	15
	21:03	9.3	283		20:24	10.7	326
6 Tu	03:33	0.9	27	**21** W	02:55	-0.4	-12
	09:40	8.1	247		09:09	9.1	277
	15:31	1.7	52		15:04	0.4	12
	21:47	9.4	287		21:24	10.9	332
7 W	04:18	0.7	21	**22** Th	03:56	-0.7	-21
	10:27	8.2	250		10:10	9.3	283
	16:14	1.7	52		16:02	0.3	9
	22:30	9.5	290		22:21	11.1	338
8 Th	05:00	0.5	15	**23** F	04:52	-1.0	-30
	11:11	8.3	253		11:07	9.4	287
	16:55	1.6	49		16:59	0.1	3
	23:10	9.7	296		23:17	11.3	344
9 F	05:39	0.4	12	**24** Sa ○	05:47	-1.1	-34
	11:53	8.4	256		12:02	9.6	293
	17:34	1.5	46		17:54	0.1	3
	23:50	9.8	299				
10 Sa ●	06:17	0.2	6	**25** Su	00:11	11.2	341
	12:32	8.5	259		06:39	-1.1	-34
	18:13	1.4	43		12:54	9.7	296
					18:47	0.1	3
11 Su	00:29	9.9	302	**26** M	01:03	11.1	338
	06:54	0.1	3		07:28	-1.0	-30
	13:10	8.6	262		13:44	9.7	293
	18:53	1.3	40		19:38	0.2	6
12 M	01:07	10.0	305	**27** Tu	01:53	10.7	326
	07:31	0.0	0		08:15	-0.6	-18
	13:48	8.7	265		14:32	9.6	293
	19:33	1.2	37		20:29	0.4	12
13 Tu	01:46	10.0	305	**28** W	02:42	10.2	311
	08:10	-0.1	-3		09:02	-0.2	-6
	14:26	8.9	271		15:20	9.5	290
	20:16	1.0	30		21:21	0.7	21
14 W	02:27	10.0	305	**29** Th	03:33	9.6	293
	08:50	-0.1	-3		09:48	0.2	6
	15:07	9.1	277		16:08	9.3	283
	21:02	0.9	27		22:14	0.9	27
15 Th	03:13	9.9	302	**30** F	04:25	9.1	277
	09:34	-0.1	-3		10:35	0.7	21
	15:51	9.4	287		16:56	9.2	280
	21:53	0.8	24		23:08	1.2	37
				31 Sa ☽	05:18	8.5	259
					11:23	1.2	37
					17:45	9.0	274

August

Day	Time	ft	cm	Day	Time	ft	cm
1 Su	00:03	1.4	43	**16** M	05:40	9.1	277
	06:13	8.1	247		11:42	0.5	15
	12:12	1.6	49		18:03	10.2	311
	18:35	8.9	271				
2 M	01:01	1.4	43	**17** Tu	00:30	0.1	3
	07:10	7.8	238		06:46	8.8	268
	13:05	1.9	58		12:43	0.7	21
	19:28	8.9	271		19:06	10.2	311
3 Tu	02:00	1.4	43	**18** W	01:38	0.1	3
	08:09	7.7	235		07:55	8.7	265
	14:00	2.0	61		13:49	0.8	24
	20:21	8.9	271		20:12	10.3	314
4 W	02:55	1.2	37	**19** Th	02:46	-0.1	-3
	09:04	7.8	238		09:01	8.8	268
	14:53	2.0	61		14:55	0.7	21
	21:12	9.1	277		21:16	10.5	320
5 Th	03:44	1.0	30	**20** F	03:47	-0.4	-12
	09:54	8.0	244		10:01	9.1	277
	15:41	1.8	55		15:55	0.5	15
	21:58	9.4	287		22:14	10.7	326
6 F	04:28	0.7	21	**21** Sa	04:42	-0.6	-18
	10:39	8.2	250		10:56	9.3	283
	16:24	1.5	46		16:50	0.3	9
	22:42	9.7	296		23:08	10.8	329
7 Sa	05:09	0.4	12	**22** Su ○	05:33	-0.7	-21
	11:22	8.4	256		11:47	9.6	293
	17:06	1.3	40		17:42	0.1	3
	23:23	9.9	302		23:59	10.8	329
8 Su ●	05:48	0.1	3	**23** M	06:21	-0.7	-21
	12:02	8.7	265		12:34	9.7	296
	17:47	1.0	30		18:32	0.0	0
9 M	00:03	10.2	311	**24** Tu	00:47	10.6	323
	06:25	-0.1	-3		07:05	-0.5	-15
	12:40	9.0	274		13:18	9.8	299
	18:28	0.7	21		19:18	0.1	3
10 Tu	00:43	10.3	314	**25** W	01:32	10.3	314
	07:03	-0.3	-9		07:46	-0.2	-6
	13:18	9.3	283		14:00	9.7	296
	19:10	0.5	15		20:03	0.3	9
11 W	01:24	10.4	317	**26** Th	02:16	9.8	299
	07:42	-0.5	-15		08:27	0.2	6
	13:56	9.6	293		14:41	9.5	290
	19:54	0.2	6		20:49	0.5	15
12 Th	02:07	10.3	314	**27** F	03:01	9.3	283
	08:22	-0.5	-15		09:07	0.6	18
	14:37	9.9	302		15:23	9.3	283
	20:41	0.1	3		21:35	0.8	24
13 F	02:53	10.1	308	**28** Sa	03:48	8.8	268
	09:06	-0.3	-9		09:50	1.1	34
	15:22	10.0	305		16:07	9.1	277
	21:32	0.0	0		22:25	1.1	34
14 Sa	03:44	9.8	299	**29** Su	04:38	8.3	253
	09:54	-0.1	-3		10:35	1.6	49
	16:11	10.2	311		16:55	8.9	271
	22:28	0.0	0		23:17	1.4	43
15 Su ☽	04:40	9.4	287	**30** M ☽	05:31	7.9	241
	10:46	0.2	6		11:24	1.9	58
	17:05	10.2	311		17:45	8.7	265
	23:27	0.1	3				
				31 Tu	00:12	1.5	46
					06:28	7.7	235
					12:17	2.2	67
					18:40	8.6	262

September

Day	Time	ft	cm	Day	Time	ft	cm
1 W	01:12	1.6	49	**16** Th	01:29	0.2	6
	07:27	7.6	232		07:49	8.7	265
	13:15	2.2	67		13:44	1.1	34
	19:38	8.7	265		20:06	10.0	305
2 Th	02:12	1.5	46	**17** F	02:37	0.1	3
	08:26	7.7	235		08:54	8.9	271
	14:13	2.1	64		14:51	0.9	27
	20:34	8.9	271		21:10	10.1	308
3 F	03:05	1.2	37	**18** Sa	03:37	-0.1	-3
	09:18	7.9	241		09:51	9.2	280
	15:06	1.8	55		15:50	0.5	15
	21:24	9.3	283		22:06	10.3	314
4 Sa	03:51	0.8	24	**19** Su	04:29	-0.3	-9
	10:03	8.3	253		10:43	9.5	290
	15:53	1.4	43		16:42	0.2	6
	22:10	9.7	296		22:57	10.4	317
5 Su	04:33	0.4	12	**20** M ○	05:15	-0.3	-9
	10:45	8.7	265		11:28	9.7	296
	16:36	0.9	27		17:30	0.1	3
	22:53	10.1	308		23:44	10.3	314
6 M	05:12	0.0	0	**21** Tu	05:58	-0.2	-6
	11:25	9.2	280		12:10	9.8	299
	17:19	0.4	12		18:15	0.0	0
	23:35	10.4	317				
7 Tu ●	05:51	-0.4	-12	**22** W	00:28	10.1	308
	12:04	9.7	296		06:37	0.0	0
	18:02	0.0	0		12:49	9.9	302
					18:57	0.0	0
8 W	00:17	10.6	323	**23** Th	01:09	9.8	299
	06:31	-0.6	-18		07:14	0.3	9
	12:44	10.1	308		13:26	9.8	299
	18:47	-0.4	-12		19:37	0.2	6
9 Th	01:01	10.6	323	**24** F	01:49	9.4	287
	07:11	-0.7	-21		07:50	0.6	18
	13:24	10.4	317		14:02	9.6	293
	19:33	-0.6	-18		20:17	0.4	12
10 F	01:46	10.5	320	**25** Sa	02:30	9.0	274
	07:54	-0.6	-18		08:27	1.1	34
	14:07	10.6	323		14:40	9.4	287
	20:21	-0.7	-21		20:58	0.7	21
11 Sa	02:34	10.2	311	**26** Su	03:12	8.6	262
	08:40	-0.4	-12		09:07	1.5	46
	14:52	10.6	323		15:20	9.1	277
	21:13	-0.6	-18		21:43	1.0	30
12 Su	03:27	9.8	299	**27** M	04:00	8.2	250
	09:31	0.0	0		09:51	1.8	55
	15:47	10.5	320		16:06	8.8	268
	22:10	-0.4	-12		22:10	1.3	40
13 M ☽	04:26	9.3	283	**28** Tu	04:51	7.8	238
	10:26	0.4	12		10:40	2.1	64
	16:45	10.3	314		16:58	8.6	262
	23:12	-0.1	-3		23:26	1.5	46
14 Tu	05:30	8.9	271	**29** W ☽	05:47	7.6	232
	11:27	0.8	24		11:34	2.3	70
	17:48	10.1	308		17:54	8.5	259
15 W	00:19	0.1	3	**30** Th	00:24	1.6	49
	06:39	8.7	265		06:45	7.6	232
	12:34	1.0	30		12:32	2.3	70
	18:57	9.9	302		18:53	8.6	262

StationId: 8418150
Source: NOAA/NOS/CO-OPS
Station Type: Primary
Time Zone: LST_LDT
Datum: MLLW

NOAA Tide Predictions

Portland, ME, 2021

Times and Heights of High and Low Waters

October

Day	Time	ft	cm
1 F	01:24	1.5	46
	07:44	7.7	235
	13:32	2.1	64
	19:52	8.8	268
2 Sa	02:20	1.2	37
	08:37	8.1	247
	14:29	1.7	52
	20:46	9.2	280
3 Su	03:09	0.7	21
	09:24	8.6	262
	15:19	1.1	34
	21:35	9.7	296
4 M	03:52	0.3	9
	10:06	9.3	283
	16:06	0.4	12
	22:21	10.1	308
5 Tu	04:34	-0.2	-6
	10:47	9.9	302
	16:51	-0.2	-6
	23:06	10.4	317
6 W ●	05:15	-0.5	-15
	11:28	10.5	320
	17:37	-0.8	-24
	23:51	10.6	323
7 Th	05:58	-0.7	-21
	12:11	10.9	332
	18:24	-1.2	-37
8 F	00:38	10.7	326
	06:42	-0.8	-24
	12:54	11.2	341
	19:12	-1.3	-40
9 Sa	01:26	10.5	320
	07:28	-0.6	-18
	13:41	11.3	344
	20:02	-1.3	-40
10 Su	02:17	10.2	311
	08:17	-0.3	-9
	14:31	11.1	338
	20:56	-1.0	-30
11 M	03:13	9.7	296
	09:11	0.2	6
	15:26	10.7	326
	21:55	-0.6	-18
12 Tu	04:15	9.3	283
	10:11	0.6	18
	16:29	10.3	314
	23:00	-0.2	-6
13 W ☽	05:22	8.9	271
	11:16	1.0	30
	17:37	9.9	302
14 Th	00:08	0.1	3
	06:31	8.8	268
	12:26	1.2	37
	18:47	9.7	296
15 F	01:18	0.3	9
	07:39	8.8	268
	13:38	1.1	34
	19:56	9.7	296
16 Sa	02:23	0.2	6
	08:41	9.1	277
	14:44	0.9	27
	20:59	9.8	299
17 Su	03:20	0.1	3
	09:35	9.4	287
	15:40	0.5	15
	21:53	9.8	299
18 M	04:09	0.1	3
	10:22	9.7	296
	16:30	0.2	6
	22:42	9.8	299
19 Tu	04:52	0.1	3
	11:04	9.9	302
	17:15	0.0	0
	23:26	9.7	296
20 W ○	05:31	0.3	9
	11:43	10.0	305
	17:56	-0.1	-3
21 Th	00:08	9.6	293
	06:08	0.5	15
	12:19	9.9	302
	18:35	0.0	0
22 F	00:47	9.3	283
	06:43	0.8	24
	12:54	9.8	299
	19:11	0.1	3
23 Sa	01:25	9.0	274
	07:17	1.1	34
	13:28	9.7	296
	19:48	0.3	9
24 Su	02:03	8.7	265
	07:53	1.4	43
	14:03	9.4	287
	20:26	0.6	18
25 M	02:43	8.4	256
	08:31	1.7	52
	14:42	9.1	277
	21:08	0.9	27
26 Tu	03:26	8.1	247
	09:14	2.0	61
	15:26	8.9	271
	21:55	1.1	34
27 W	04:16	7.8	238
	10:02	2.2	67
	16:16	8.7	265
	22:46	1.3	40
28 Th ☾	05:09	7.7	235
	10:55	2.3	70
	17:11	8.6	262
	23:40	1.4	43
29 F	06:04	7.7	235
	11:52	2.2	67
	18:09	8.6	262
30 Sa	00:36	1.3	40
	06:59	8.0	244
	12:51	2.0	61
	19:08	8.8	268
31 Su	01:31	1.0	30
	07:52	8.4	256
	13:50	1.5	46
	20:05	9.1	277

November

Day	Time	ft	cm
1 M	02:23	0.6	18
	08:41	9.1	277
	14:45	0.8	24
	20:59	9.5	290
2 Tu	03:11	0.2	6
	09:27	9.8	299
	15:40	0.0	0
	21:49	10.0	305
3 W	03:56	-0.3	-9
	10:11	10.5	320
	16:24	-0.7	-21
	22:38	10.3	314
4 Th ●	04:41	-0.6	-18
	10:55	11.1	338
	17:13	-1.3	-40
	23:27	10.5	320
5 F	05:28	-0.7	-21
	11:41	11.5	351
	18:02	-1.7	-52
6 Sa	00:17	10.5	320
	06:16	-0.7	-21
	12:29	11.7	357
	18:53	-1.8	-55
7 Su	01:09	10.4	317
	06:05	-0.5	-15
	12:19	11.6	354
	18:45	-1.7	-52
8 M	01:02	10.1	308
	06:58	-0.2	-6
	13:12	11.3	344
	19:40	-1.3	-40
9 Tu	01:59	9.7	296
	07:54	0.2	6
	14:10	10.8	329
	20:40	-0.8	-24
10 W	03:02	9.3	283
	08:56	0.7	21
	15:14	10.3	314
	21:45	-0.3	-9
11 Th ☽	04:08	9.0	274
	10:03	1.0	30
	16:22	9.8	299
	22:51	0.1	3
12 F	05:15	8.9	271
	11:13	1.1	34
	17:31	9.5	290
	23:57	0.3	9
13 Sa	06:19	9.0	274
	12:23	1.1	34
	18:38	9.3	283
14 Su	00:59	0.4	12
	07:18	9.2	280
	13:28	0.8	24
	19:39	9.3	283
15 M	01:54	0.5	15
	08:10	9.5	290
	14:24	0.5	15
	20:34	9.2	280
16 Tu	02:42	0.5	15
	08:56	9.7	296
	15:12	0.3	9
	21:22	9.2	280
17 W	03:25	0.6	18
	09:37	9.8	299
	15:56	0.1	3
	22:06	9.1	277
18 Th	04:03	0.8	24
	10:15	9.9	302
	16:36	0.0	0
	22:47	9.0	274
19 F ○	04:40	0.9	27
	10:51	9.9	302
	17:13	0.0	0
	23:26	8.9	271
20 Sa	05:15	1.1	34
	11:26	9.8	299
	17:49	0.1	3
21 Su	00:03	8.7	265
	05:50	1.3	40
	12:00	9.6	293
	18:25	0.2	6
22 M	00:40	8.5	259
	06:25	1.5	46
	12:36	9.5	290
	19:01	0.4	12
23 Tu	01:18	8.3	253
	07:03	1.7	52
	13:14	9.3	283
	19:41	0.6	18
24 W	01:59	8.1	247
	07:44	1.8	55
	13:55	9.1	277
	20:24	0.8	24
25 Th	02:44	7.9	241
	08:30	2.0	61
	14:42	8.9	271
	21:11	0.9	27
26 F	03:32	7.9	241
	09:21	2.0	61
	15:33	8.8	268
	22:00	0.9	27
27 Sa ☾	04:23	8.1	247
	10:16	1.9	58
	16:28	8.8	268
	22:51	0.9	27
28 Su	05:14	8.4	256
	11:13	1.6	49
	17:26	8.8	268
	23:44	0.7	21
29 M	06:06	8.9	271
	12:13	1.1	34
	18:25	9.0	274
30 Tu	00:38	0.5	15
	06:58	9.5	290
	13:12	0.4	12
	19:24	9.3	283

December

Day	Time	ft	cm
1 W	01:31	0.2	6
	07:49	10.2	311
	14:08	-0.3	-9
	20:20	9.6	293
2 Th	02:22	-0.2	-6
	08:38	10.8	329
	15:00	-1.0	-30
	21:13	9.9	302
3 F	03:12	-0.4	-12
	09:27	11.4	347
	15:52	-1.6	-49
	22:06	10.1	308
4 Sa ●	04:03	-0.6	-18
	10:18	11.7	357
	16:44	-1.9	-58
	23:00	10.2	311
5 Su	04:54	-0.6	-18
	11:09	11.8	360
	17:37	-2.0	-61
	23:54	10.1	308
6 M	05:47	-0.5	-15
	12:02	11.7	357
	18:31	-1.8	-55
7 Tu	00:48	10.0	305
	06:41	-0.3	-9
	12:57	11.4	347
	19:26	-1.4	-43
8 W	01:44	9.7	296
	07:38	0.1	3
	13:55	10.8	329
	20:23	-1.0	-30
9 Th	02:44	9.4	287
	08:39	0.5	15
	14:56	10.3	314
	21:24	-0.4	-12
10 F	03:46	9.2	280
	09:44	0.8	24
	16:01	9.7	296
	22:25	0.0	0
11 Sa ☽	04:48	9.1	277
	10:51	1.0	30
	17:05	9.2	280
	23:25	0.4	12
12 Su	05:48	9.1	277
	11:58	1.0	30
	18:10	8.8	268
13 M	00:24	0.7	21
	06:45	9.2	280
	13:02	0.9	27
	19:12	8.6	262
14 Tu	01:20	0.9	27
	07:38	9.3	283
	14:00	0.7	21
	20:08	8.5	259
15 W	02:10	1.0	30
	08:25	9.4	287
	14:49	0.4	12
	20:58	8.5	259
16 Th	02:55	1.1	34
	09:08	9.6	293
	15:34	0.2	6
	21:43	8.5	259
17 F	03:36	1.2	37
	09:48	9.6	293
	16:15	0.1	3
	22:25	8.5	259
18 Sa	04:14	1.2	37
	10:26	9.7	296
	16:53	0.1	3
	23:05	8.5	259
19 Su ○	04:51	1.3	40
	11:03	9.7	296
	17:29	0.1	3
	23:43	8.5	259
20 M	05:27	1.3	40
	11:39	9.6	293
	18:05	0.1	3
21 Tu	00:20	8.4	256
	06:03	1.3	40
	12:15	9.6	293
	18:40	0.2	6
22 W	00:56	8.3	253
	06:40	1.4	43
	12:52	9.5	290
	19:17	0.2	6
23 Th	01:33	8.3	253
	07:19	1.4	43
	13:30	9.4	287
	19:56	0.3	9
24 F	02:13	8.3	253
	08:03	1.4	43
	14:13	9.2	280
	20:38	0.4	12
25 Sa	02:56	8.4	256
	08:51	1.4	43
	15:01	9.1	277
	21:23	0.4	12
26 Su	03:43	8.6	262
	09:43	1.3	40
	15:53	8.9	271
	22:12	0.5	15
27 M ☾	04:32	8.9	271
	10:40	1.0	30
	16:50	8.8	268
	23:03	0.5	15
28 Tu	05:24	9.3	283
	11:39	0.7	21
	17:50	8.8	268
	23:58	0.4	12
29 W	06:19	9.7	296
	12:41	0.2	6
	18:54	8.9	271
30 Th	00:56	0.3	9
	07:16	10.3	314
	13:43	-0.4	-12
	19:56	9.1	277
31 F	01:54	0.1	3
	08:12	10.8	329
	14:41	-1.0	-30
	20:54	9.2	280

31

StationId: 8443970
Source: NOAA/NOS/CO-OPS
Station Type: Primary
Time Zone: LST_LDT
Datum: MLLW

NOAA Tide Predictions

Boston, MA, 2021

Times and Heights of High and Low Waters

January

Day	Time (h m)	ft	cm	Day	Time (h m)	ft	cm
1 F	00:29	8.9	271	**16** Sa	01:14	9.4	287
	06:22	0.8	24		07:09	0.3	9
	12:31	10.4	317		13:23	10.4	317
	18:58	-0.4	-12		19:43	-0.4	-12
2 Sa	01:11	9.0	274	**17** Su	02:00	9.3	283
	07:05	0.7	21		07:57	0.6	18
	13:15	10.4	317		14:10	9.9	302
	19:41	-0.4	-12		20:28	0.1	3
3 Su	01:53	9.1	277	**18** M	02:45	9.1	277
	07:52	0.7	21		08:46	0.9	27
	14:00	10.3	314		14:58	9.3	283
	20:26	-0.4	-12		21:14	0.5	15
4 M	02:39	9.3	283	**19** Tu	03:32	8.9	271
	08:42	0.6	18		09:38	1.2	37
	14:50	10.1	308		15:49	8.8	268
	21:14	-0.3	-9		22:01	1.0	30
5 Tu	03:28	9.5	290	**20** W	04:20	8.8	268
	09:37	0.5	15		10:31	1.4	43
	15:44	9.8	299		16:42	8.4	256
	22:06	-0.1	-3		22:50	1.4	43
6 W	04:20	9.7	296	**21** Th	05:09	8.7	265
	10:35	0.4	12		11:26	1.5	46
	16:42	9.5	290		17:37	8.0	244
	23:00	0.1	3		23:40	1.7	52
7 Th	05:16	9.9	302	**22** F	06:00	8.7	265
	11:36	0.3	9		12:22	1.5	46
	17:44	9.3	283		18:33	7.8	238
	23:57	0.2	6				
8 F	06:13	10.2	311	**23** Sa	00:32	1.8	55
	12:38	0.0	0		06:52	8.8	268
	18:47	9.1	277		13:18	1.4	43
					19:31	7.8	238
9 Sa	00:55	0.3	9	**24** Su	01:24	1.8	55
	07:12	10.5	320		07:45	9.0	274
	13:40	-0.3	-9		14:12	1.1	34
	19:52	9.1	277		20:25	7.9	241
10 Su	01:54	0.3	9	**25** M	02:15	1.7	52
	08:11	10.7	326		08:34	9.3	283
	14:41	-0.6	-18		15:01	0.7	21
	20:54	9.2	280		21:14	8.1	247
11 M	02:52	0.2	6	**26** Tu	03:03	1.4	43
	09:08	11.0	335		09:20	9.6	293
	15:38	-1.0	-30		15:46	0.3	9
	21:52	9.4	287		21:59	8.4	256
12 Tu	03:47	0.1	3	**27** W	03:49	1.1	34
	10:02	11.1	338		10:00	10.0	305
	16:31	-1.2	-37		16:29	-0.1	-3
	22:46	9.5	290		22:41	8.7	265
13 W	04:40	0.0	0	**28** Th	04:32	0.7	21
	10:54	11.2	341		10:45	10.3	314
	17:22	-1.2	-37		17:10	-0.4	-12
●	23:38	9.5	290	○	23:22	9.0	274
14 Th	05:31	0.0	0	**29** F	05:16	0.4	12
	11:45	11.0	335		11:27	10.6	323
	18:11	-1.1	-34		17:52	-0.7	-21
15 F	00:27	9.5	290	**30** Sa	00:03	9.3	283
	06:20	0.1	3		06:00	0.1	3
	12:35	10.7	326		12:11	10.7	326
	18:58	-0.8	-24		18:34	-0.9	-27
				31 Su	00:45	9.6	293
					06:45	-0.1	-3
					12:55	10.7	326
					19:17	-1.0	-30

February

Day	Time (h m)	ft	cm	Day	Time (h m)	ft	cm
1 M	01:28	9.9	302	**16** Tu	02:07	9.3	283
	07:32	-0.3	-9		08:14	0.6	18
	13:42	10.6	323		14:25	9.2	280
	20:01	-0.9	-27		20:34	0.6	18
2 Tu	02:13	10.1	308	**17** W	02:47	9.1	277
	08:22	-0.3	-9		09:00	0.9	27
	14:31	10.3	314		15:10	8.7	265
	20:49	-0.6	-18		21:17	1.1	34
3 W	03:01	10.2	311	**18** Th	03:31	8.9	271
	09:16	-0.2	-6		09:48	1.1	34
	15:25	9.8	299		15:59	8.3	253
	21:40	-0.3	-9		22:04	1.5	46
4 Th	03:53	10.2	311	**19** F	04:18	8.8	268
	10:14	-0.1	-3		10:41	1.4	43
	16:23	9.4	287		16:52	7.9	241
◔	22:35	0.1	3	◑	22:54	1.8	55
5 F	04:50	10.1	308	**20** Sa	05:09	8.6	262
	11:16	0.0	0		11:36	1.5	46
	17:26	8.9	271		17:48	7.6	232
	23:34	0.5	15		23:46	2.0	61
6 Sa	05:50	10.1	308	**21** Su	06:03	8.6	262
	12:20	0.1	3		12:32	1.5	46
	18:33	8.7	265		18:47	7.6	232
7 Su	00:35	0.7	21	**22** M	00:41	2.0	61
	06:54	10.1	308		07:00	8.8	268
	13:25	0.0	0		13:30	1.3	40
	19:41	8.6	262		19:45	7.7	235
8 M	01:38	0.7	21	**23** Tu	01:37	1.9	58
	07:58	10.2	311		07:55	9.1	277
	14:29	-0.2	-6		14:24	0.9	27
	20:47	8.8	268		20:38	8.0	244
9 Tu	02:40	0.6	18	**24** W	02:30	1.5	46
	08:59	10.4	317		08:47	9.5	290
	15:28	-0.5	-15		15:13	0.4	12
	21:44	9.0	274		21:26	8.5	259
10 W	03:36	0.4	12	**25** Th	03:19	1.0	30
	09:55	10.6	323		09:34	10.0	305
	16:26	-0.7	-21		15:58	-0.1	-3
	22:36	9.2	280		22:09	9.0	274
11 Th	04:28	0.2	6	**26** F	04:06	0.4	12
	10:45	10.6	323		10:19	10.5	320
	17:08	-0.7	-21		16:41	-0.6	-18
●	23:23	9.4	287		22:51	9.5	290
12 F	05:17	0.1	3	**27** Sa	04:52	-0.2	-6
	11:33	10.6	323		11:03	10.9	332
	17:52	-0.7	-21		17:24	-1.0	-30
				○	23:34	10.1	308
13 Sa	00:07	9.5	290	**28** Su	05:38	-0.7	-21
	06:03	0.1	3		11:49	11.0	335
	12:17	10.4	317		18:07	-1.2	-37
	18:34	-0.5	-15				
14 Su	00:48	9.5	290				
	06:47	0.1	3				
	13:00	10.1	308				
	19:14	-0.2	-6				
15 M	01:28	9.4	287				
	07:30	0.3	9				
	13:42	9.7	296				
	19:54	0.2	6				

March

Day	Time (h m)	ft	cm	Day	Time (h m)	ft	cm
1 M	00:17	10.5	320	**16** Tu	01:54	9.7	296
	06:25	-1.0	-30		08:03	0.2	6
	12:36	11.0	335		14:15	9.5	290
	18:51	-1.2	-37		20:20	0.6	18
2 Tu	01:01	10.8	329	**17** W	02:30	9.6	293
	07:13	-1.1	-34		08:43	0.4	12
	13:24	10.8	329		14:55	9.2	280
	19:36	-1.0	-30		20:58	0.9	27
3 W	01:47	10.9	332	**18** Th	03:08	9.4	287
	08:03	-1.1	-34		09:25	0.7	21
	14:14	10.4	317		15:37	8.7	265
	20:25	-0.7	-21		21:38	1.3	40
4 Th	02:36	10.8	329	**19** F	03:48	9.2	280
	08:57	-0.8	-24		10:10	1.0	30
	15:08	9.9	302		16:22	8.3	253
	21:17	-0.1	-3		22:23	1.7	52
5 F	03:30	10.6	323	**20** Sa	04:34	9.0	274
	09:56	-0.4	-12		11:00	1.3	40
	16:08	9.3	283		17:13	8.0	244
	22:14	0.4	12		23:24	2.0	61
6 Sa	04:29	10.2	311	**21** Su	05:24	8.8	268
	10:58	0.0	0		11:54	1.5	46
	17:13	8.8	268		18:08	7.7	235
◑	23:15	0.8	24	◐			
7 Su	05:33	9.9	302	**22** M	00:06	2.2	67
	12:04	0.2	6		06:19	8.7	265
	18:22	8.5	259		12:50	1.5	46
					19:05	7.7	235
8 M	00:20	1.1	34	**23** Tu	01:02	2.2	67
	06:41	9.8	299		07:17	8.8	268
	13:12	0.3	9		13:47	1.3	40
	19:33	8.5	259		20:03	7.9	241
9 Tu	01:26	1.1	34	**24** W	01:59	1.9	58
	07:49	9.8	299		08:15	9.1	277
	14:18	0.2	6		14:43	1.0	30
	20:39	8.7	265		20:59	8.3	253
10 W	02:30	1.0	30	**25** Th	02:56	1.4	43
	08:52	9.9	302		09:11	9.6	293
	15:16	0.0	0		15:35	0.5	15
	21:34	9.0	274		21:49	8.9	271
11 Th	03:27	0.6	18	**26** F	03:49	0.8	24
	09:46	10.1	308		10:02	10.1	308
	16:05	-0.1	-3		16:23	-0.1	-3
	22:21	9.3	283		22:34	9.6	293
12 F	04:16	0.4	12	**27** Sa	04:39	0.0	0
	10:33	10.2	311		10:51	10.6	323
	16:48	-0.2	-6		17:09	-0.6	-18
	23:03	9.5	290		23:18	10.3	314
13 Sa	05:01	0.2	6	**28** Su	05:27	-0.7	-21
	11:17	10.2	311		11:38	11.0	335
	17:28	-0.1	-3		17:53	-1.0	-30
●	23:42	9.7	296	○			
14 Su	06:43	0.0	0	**29** M	00:02	10.9	332
	12:57	10.0	305		06:15	-1.2	-37
	19:06	0.0	0		12:26	11.2	341
					18:39	-1.2	-37
15 M	01:18	9.7	296	**30** Tu	00:48	11.4	347
	07:23	0.1	3		07:04	-1.6	-49
	13:36	9.8	299		13:15	11.1	338
	19:43	0.3	9		19:25	-1.1	-34
				31 W	01:34	11.6	354
					07:54	-1.7	-52
					14:06	10.9	332
					20:13	-0.9	-27

StationId: 8443970
Source: NOAA/NOS/CO-OPS
Station Type: Primary
Time Zone: LST_LDT
Datum: MLLW

NOAA Tide Predictions

Boston, MA, 2021

Times and Heights of High and Low Waters

April

Day	Time	Height ft	Height cm
1 Th	02:23	11.6	354
	08:45	-1.5	-46
	14:58	10.4	317
	21:03	-0.4	-12
2 F	03:14	11.3	344
	09:40	-1.0	-30
	15:54	9.9	302
	21:57	0.2	6
3 Sa	04:09	10.8	329
	10:38	-0.5	-15
	16:55	9.3	283
	22:56	0.8	24
4 Su ☽	05:11	10.3	314
	11:42	0.0	0
	18:02	8.9	271
5 M	00:00	1.2	37
	06:18	9.8	299
	12:48	0.4	12
	19:11	8.7	265
6 Tu	01:06	1.4	43
	07:28	9.6	293
	13:55	0.6	18
	20:20	8.7	265
7 W	02:14	1.4	43
	08:37	9.5	290
	15:00	0.6	18
	21:23	9.0	274
8 Th	03:18	1.2	37
	09:39	9.6	293
	15:55	0.5	15
	22:15	9.3	283
9 F	04:13	0.8	24
	10:31	9.7	296
	16:42	0.4	12
	22:58	9.6	293
10 Sa	05:00	0.5	15
	11:15	9.8	299
	17:22	0.4	12
	23:36	9.8	299
11 Su	05:42	0.3	9
	11:56	9.8	299
	17:59	0.5	15
12 M ●	00:12	9.9	302
	06:21	0.1	3
	12:34	9.7	296
	18:35	0.6	18
13 Tu	00:46	10.0	305
	06:59	0.1	3
	13:12	9.5	290
	19:11	0.8	24
14 W	01:21	9.9	302
	07:37	0.2	6
	13:50	9.3	283
	19:48	1.0	30
15 Th	01:56	9.8	299
	08:16	0.4	12
	14:29	9.0	274
	20:26	1.3	40
16 F	02:34	9.7	296
	08:56	0.6	18
	15:09	8.7	265
	21:05	1.6	49
17 Sa	03:14	9.5	290
	09:39	0.9	27
	15:53	8.4	256
	21:49	1.9	58
18 Su	03:57	9.2	280
	10:26	1.1	34
	16:41	8.2	250
	22:37	2.1	64
19 M	04:47	9.1	277
	11:18	1.3	40
	17:33	8.0	244
	23:31	2.2	67
20 Tu ☽	05:41	9.0	274
	12:12	1.3	40
	18:28	8.1	247
21 W	00:27	2.1	64
	06:38	9.1	277
	13:08	1.2	37
	19:24	8.4	256
22 Th	01:25	1.8	55
	07:36	9.3	283
	14:03	0.9	27
	20:18	8.9	271
23 F	02:23	1.3	40
	08:34	9.7	296
	14:56	0.4	12
	21:10	9.6	293
24 Sa	03:19	0.5	15
	09:30	10.2	311
	15:47	0.0	0
	21:58	10.3	314
25 Su	04:12	-0.3	-9
	10:22	10.6	323
	16:36	-0.5	-15
	22:45	11.1	338
26 M	05:03	-1.0	-30
	11:13	10.9	332
	17:23	-0.8	-24
	23:32	11.6	354
27 Tu ○	05:53	-1.6	-49
	12:04	11.0	335
	18:11	-0.9	-27
28 W	00:20	12.0	366
	06:44	-1.8	-55
	12:56	11.0	335
	19:00	-0.8	-24
29 Th	01:10	12.1	369
	07:35	-1.8	-55
	13:49	10.7	326
	19:51	-0.5	-15
30 F	02:01	11.9	363
	08:28	-1.5	-46
	14:44	10.3	314
	20:43	0.0	0

May

Day	Time	Height ft	Height cm
1 Sa	02:55	11.5	351
	09:23	-1.0	-30
	15:41	9.9	302
	21:39	0.5	15
2 Su	03:52	10.9	332
	10:22	-0.4	-12
	16:42	9.4	287
	22:39	1.0	30
3 M ☽	04:55	10.3	314
	11:24	0.1	3
	17:48	9.1	277
	23:43	1.4	43
4 Tu	06:01	9.8	299
	12:28	0.6	18
	18:53	9.0	274
5 W	00:49	1.6	49
	07:09	9.5	290
	13:30	0.8	24
	19:57	9.1	277
6 Th	01:55	1.5	46
	08:14	9.3	283
	14:30	1.0	30
	20:54	9.3	283
7 F	02:57	1.3	40
	09:14	9.3	283
	15:24	1.0	30
	21:44	9.5	290
8 Sa	03:51	1.0	30
	10:06	9.3	283
	16:09	1.0	30
	22:26	9.7	296
9 Su	04:37	0.7	21
	10:50	9.4	287
	16:50	1.0	30
	23:04	9.9	302
10 M	05:18	0.5	15
	11:31	9.3	283
	17:27	1.1	34
	23:39	10.0	305
11 Tu ●	05:57	0.3	9
	12:09	9.3	283
	18:04	1.2	37
12 W	00:14	10.1	308
	06:34	0.3	9
	12:38	9.2	280
	18:41	1.3	40
13 Th	00:50	10.1	308
	07:12	0.3	9
	13:26	9.1	277
	19:19	1.4	43
14 F	01:27	10.0	305
	07:51	0.4	12
	14:05	8.9	271
	19:57	1.6	49
15 Sa	02:06	9.9	302
	08:31	0.6	18
	14:46	8.7	265
	20:38	1.8	55
16 Su	02:46	9.7	296
	09:13	0.7	21
	15:28	8.6	262
	21:21	2.0	61
17 M	03:29	9.6	293
	09:58	0.9	27
	16:14	8.5	259
	22:09	2.1	64
18 Tu	04:17	9.5	290
	10:47	1.0	30
	17:03	8.5	259
	23:01	2.0	61
19 W ☽	05:09	9.4	287
	11:39	1.0	30
	17:55	8.7	265
	23:57	1.8	55
20 Th	06:05	9.4	287
	12:32	0.8	24
	18:47	9.1	277
21 F	00:54	1.5	46
	07:02	9.6	293
	13:25	0.6	18
	19:40	9.6	293
22 Sa	01:52	0.9	27
	08:01	9.8	299
	14:19	0.4	12
	20:33	10.2	311
23 Su	02:50	0.2	6
	08:59	10.1	308
	15:12	0.1	3
	21:25	10.9	332
24 M	03:46	-0.5	-15
	09:56	10.3	314
	16:04	-0.2	-6
	22:15	11.5	351
25 Tu	04:40	-1.1	-34
	10:50	10.6	323
	16:56	-0.4	-12
	23:05	12.0	366
26 W ○	05:33	-1.5	-46
	11:44	10.6	323
	17:47	-0.5	-15
	23:56	12.2	372
27 Th	06:25	-1.7	-52
	12:38	10.6	323
	18:38	-0.4	-12
28 F	00:49	12.1	369
	07:18	-1.7	-52
	13:34	10.4	317
	19:31	-0.1	-3
29 Sa	01:43	11.9	363
	08:12	-1.4	-43
	14:29	10.2	311
	20:25	0.2	6
30 Su	02:38	11.4	347
	09:06	-0.9	-27
	15:26	9.9	302
	21:21	0.7	21
31 M	03:36	10.9	332
	10:03	-0.3	-9
	16:25	9.6	293
	22:20	1.1	34

June

Day	Time	Height ft	Height cm
1 Tu	04:36	10.3	314
	11:01	0.2	6
	17:25	9.4	287
	23:22	1.4	43
2 W ◐	05:38	9.8	299
	12:00	0.6	18
	18:25	9.3	283
3 Th	00:25	1.5	46
	06:40	9.4	287
	12:56	1.0	30
	19:21	9.3	283
4 F	01:26	1.5	46
	07:41	9.1	277
	13:51	1.3	40
	20:15	9.4	287
5 Sa	02:26	1.4	43
	08:39	8.9	271
	14:42	1.4	43
	21:04	9.5	290
6 Su	03:20	1.2	37
	09:33	8.9	271
	15:30	1.5	46
	21:49	9.7	296
7 M	04:08	0.9	27
	10:20	8.9	271
	16:13	1.5	46
	22:29	9.9	302
8 Tu	04:50	0.7	21
	11:02	8.9	271
	16:53	1.5	46
	23:07	10.0	305
9 W	05:30	0.6	18
	11:43	8.9	271
	17:33	1.5	46
	23:45	10.1	308
10 Th ●	06:10	0.5	15
	12:23	8.9	271
	18:12	1.6	49
11 F	00:23	10.1	308
	06:49	0.4	12
	13:03	8.8	268
	18:52	1.6	49
12 Sa	01:02	10.1	308
	07:28	0.4	12
	13:43	8.8	268
	19:32	1.6	49
13 Su	01:42	10.1	308
	08:08	0.4	12
	14:24	8.8	268
	20:14	1.7	52
14 M	02:23	10.0	305
	08:50	0.5	15
	15:05	8.8	268
	20:58	1.7	52
15 Tu	03:06	9.9	302
	09:33	0.5	15
	15:48	8.9	271
	21:44	1.7	52
16 W	03:52	9.9	302
	10:19	0.5	15
	16:34	9.1	277
	22:36	1.5	46
17 Th	04:42	9.8	299
	11:08	0.5	15
	17:23	9.3	283
	23:30	1.3	40
18 F ◐	05:37	9.7	296
	11:59	0.5	15
	18:14	9.7	296
19 Sa	00:27	1.0	30
	06:34	9.7	296
	12:52	0.5	15
	19:06	10.2	311
20 Su	01:25	0.5	15
	07:33	9.7	296
	13:46	0.4	12
	20:00	10.7	326
21 M	02:25	0.1	3
	08:33	9.7	296
	14:42	0.3	9
	20:55	11.1	338
22 Tu	03:24	-0.5	-15
	09:33	9.9	302
	15:36	0.1	3
	21:50	11.6	354
23 W	04:20	-0.9	-27
	10:31	10.0	305
	16:33	0.0	0
	22:44	11.9	363
24 Th ○	05:15	-1.3	-40
	11:27	10.1	308
	17:26	-0.1	-3
	23:38	12.0	366
25 F	06:09	-1.4	-43
	12:23	10.2	311
	18:20	0.0	0
26 Sa	00:33	11.9	363
	07:03	-1.3	-40
	13:19	10.1	308
	19:14	0.1	3
27 Su	01:28	11.6	354
	07:55	-1.1	-34
	14:13	10.0	305
	20:08	0.3	9
28 M	02:22	11.2	341
	08:47	-0.7	-21
	15:07	9.9	302
	21:02	0.6	18
29 Tu	03:16	10.7	326
	09:39	-0.2	-6
	16:00	9.7	296
	21:57	1.0	30
30 W	04:11	10.2	311
	10:31	0.3	9
	16:54	9.5	290
	22:54	1.2	37

StationId: 8443970
Source: NOAA/NOS/CO-OPS
Station Type: Primary
Time Zone: LST_LDT
Datum: MLLW

NOAA Tide Predictions

Boston, MA, 2021

Times and Heights of High and Low Waters

July

Day	Time (h m)	ft	cm	Day	Time (h m)	ft	cm
1 Th ☽	05:08	9.6	293	16 F	04:19	10.0	305
	11:24	0.8	24		10:39	0.2	6
	17:47	9.4	287		16:53	10.0	305
	23:53	1.4	43		23:07	0.7	21
2 F	06:05	9.1	277	17 Sa ☽	05:13	9.8	299
	12:16	1.2	37		11:30	0.3	9
	18:38	9.4	287		17:44	10.3	314
3 Sa	00:50	1.5	46	18 Su	00:04	0.5	15
	07:02	8.8	268		06:10	9.6	293
	13:07	1.5	46		12:24	0.4	12
	19:29	9.3	283		18:38	10.5	320
4 Su	01:46	1.5	46	19 M	01:03	0.3	9
	07:58	8.5	259		07:11	9.4	287
	13:57	1.8	55		13:20	0.6	18
	20:19	9.4	287		19:34	10.8	329
5 M	02:41	1.4	43	20 Tu	02:04	0.0	0
	08:53	8.4	256		08:13	9.3	283
	14:47	1.9	58		14:18	0.6	18
	21:07	9.5	290		20:33	11.0	335
6 Tu	03:33	1.2	37	21 W	03:05	-0.3	-9
	09:45	8.4	256		09:17	9.4	287
	15:35	1.9	58		15:18	0.5	15
	21:53	9.7	296		21:33	11.3	344
7 W	04:20	1.0	30	22 Th	04:05	-0.6	-18
	10:32	8.5	259		10:17	9.6	293
	16:20	1.8	55		16:15	0.4	12
	22:36	9.9	302		22:30	11.4	347
8 Th	05:02	0.8	24	23 F	05:01	-0.8	-24
	11:15	8.6	262		11:14	9.7	296
	17:03	1.7	52		17:11	0.2	6
	23:17	10.0	305		23:25	11.5	351
9 F	05:43	0.6	18	24 Sa ○	05:55	-1.0	-30
	11:57	8.7	265		12:09	9.9	302
	17:45	1.6	49		18:05	0.2	6
	23:57	10.1	308				
10 Sa ●	06:24	0.4	12	25 Su	00:19	11.5	351
	12:38	8.8	268		06:46	-0.9	-27
	18:26	1.5	46		13:02	10.0	305
					18:57	0.2	6
11 Su	00:38	10.2	311	26 M	01:12	11.3	344
	07:04	0.3	9		07:35	-0.8	-24
	13:18	8.9	271		13:53	10.0	305
	19:08	1.3	40		19:49	0.3	9
12 M	01:19	10.3	314	27 Tu	02:03	10.9	332
	07:44	0.1	3		08:23	-0.4	-12
	13:58	9.1	277		14:41	9.9	302
	19:51	1.2	37		20:39	0.5	15
13 Tu	02:00	10.3	314	28 W	02:53	10.5	320
	08:24	0.1	3		09:10	0.0	0
	14:39	9.3	283		15:28	9.8	299
	20:35	1.1	34		21:29	0.8	24
14 W	02:44	10.3	314	29 Th	03:43	9.9	302
	09:07	0.1	3		09:56	0.5	15
	15:20	9.5	290		16:14	9.6	293
	21:22	1.0	30		22:21	1.1	34
15 Th	03:29	10.2	311	30 F	04:33	9.4	287
	09:51	0.1	3		10:44	1.0	30
	16:05	9.7	296		17:02	9.4	287
	22:12	0.8	24		23:15	1.3	40
				31 Sa ☽	05:26	8.9	271
					11:32	1.5	46
					17:51	9.3	283

August

Day	Time (h m)	ft	cm	Day	Time (h m)	ft	cm
1 Su	00:09	1.5	46	16 M	05:53	9.4	287
	06:20	8.5	259		12:01	0.7	21
	12:22	1.8	55		18:15	10.6	323
	18:41	9.2	280				
2 M	01:04	1.6	49	17 Tu	00:45	0.2	6
	07:16	8.2	250		06:55	9.1	277
	13:13	2.1	64		13:00	0.9	27
	19:33	9.2	280		19:16	10.6	323
3 Tu	01:59	1.6	49	18 W	01:48	0.2	6
	08:12	8.1	247		08:01	9.0	274
	14:05	2.2	67		14:02	1.0	30
	20:25	9.3	283		20:19	10.6	323
4 W	02:54	1.5	46	19 Th	02:51	0.0	0
	09:08	8.1	247		09:07	9.1	277
	14:57	2.1	64		15:04	0.9	27
	21:17	9.4	287		21:22	10.8	329
5 Th	03:45	1.2	37	20 F	03:53	-0.2	-6
	09:59	8.3	253		10:08	9.4	287
	15:47	1.9	58		16:04	0.7	21
	22:04	9.7	296		22:21	11.0	335
6 F	04:31	0.9	27	21 Sa	04:48	-0.4	-12
	10:45	8.5	259		11:04	9.6	293
	16:33	1.7	52		16:59	0.4	12
	22:48	10.0	305		23:15	11.0	335
7 Sa	05:14	0.6	18	22 Su ○	05:39	-0.5	-15
	11:27	8.8	268		11:55	9.9	302
	17:17	1.4	43		17:51	0.2	6
	23:31	10.2	311				
8 Su ●	05:55	0.3	9	23 M	00:06	11.0	335
	12:08	9.1	277		06:27	-0.5	-15
	18:00	1.1	34		12:42	10.0	305
					18:40	0.2	6
9 M	00:12	10.4	317	24 Tu	00:55	10.8	329
	06:35	0.0	0		07:12	-0.3	-9
	12:48	9.4	287		13:27	10.0	305
	18:43	0.8	24		19:28	0.2	6
10 Tu	00:54	10.6	323	25 W	01:42	10.5	320
	07:16	-0.2	-6		07:55	0.0	0
	13:28	9.7	296		14:09	10.0	305
	19:27	0.5	15		20:13	0.4	12
11 W	01:37	10.7	326	26 Th	02:27	10.1	308
	07:57	-0.3	-9		08:36	0.4	12
	14:09	10.0	305		14:51	9.9	302
	20:12	0.3	9		20:59	0.6	18
12 Th	02:22	10.6	323	27 F	03:11	9.7	296
	08:39	-0.3	-9		09:19	0.8	24
	14:51	10.2	311		15:32	9.7	296
	21:00	0.2	6		21:46	0.9	27
13 F	03:08	10.4	317	28 Sa	03:58	9.2	280
	09:24	-0.2	-6		10:02	1.3	40
	15:36	10.4	317		16:16	9.5	290
	21:50	0.1	3		22:35	1.2	37
14 Sa	03:58	10.1	308	29 Su	04:47	8.7	265
	10:12	0.1	3		10:49	1.8	55
	16:24	10.5	320		17:04	9.2	280
	22:45	0.1	3		23:27	1.5	46
15 Su ☽	04:53	9.7	296	30 M ☽	05:40	8.3	253
	11:04	0.4	12		11:39	2.1	64
	17:18	10.6	323		17:55	9.1	277
	23:44	0.2	6				
				31 Tu	00:21	1.7	52
					06:35	8.0	244
					12:31	2.3	70
					18:48	9.0	274

September

Day	Time (h m)	ft	cm	Day	Time (h m)	ft	cm
1 W	01:17	1.7	52	16 Th	01:35	0.4	12
	07:32	7.9	241		07:54	8.9	271
	13:25	2.4	73		13:50	1.2	37
	19:44	9.1	277		20:10	10.3	314
2 Th	02:13	1.6	49	17 F	02:40	0.3	9
	08:29	8.0	244		09:00	9.1	277
	14:20	2.3	70		14:55	1.1	34
	20:39	9.3	283		21:15	10.4	317
3 F	03:07	1.4	43	18 Sa	03:40	0.2	6
	09:23	8.3	253		09:59	9.4	287
	15:13	2.0	61		15:55	0.8	24
	21:31	9.6	293		22:13	10.5	320
4 Sa	03:56	1.0	30	19 Su	04:33	0.0	0
	10:10	8.7	265		10:50	9.8	299
	16:03	1.5	46		16:48	0.5	15
	22:17	10.0	305		23:05	10.6	323
5 Su	04:40	0.5	15	20 M ○	05:20	-0.1	-3
	10:53	9.1	277		11:36	10.0	305
	16:49	1.0	30		17:36	0.3	9
	23:01	10.4	317		23:51	10.5	320
6 M	05:22	0.1	3	21 Tu	06:03	0.0	0
	11:33	9.6	293		12:17	10.1	308
	17:33	0.5	15		18:22	0.1	3
	23:44	10.7	326				
7 Tu ●	06:03	-0.2	-6	22 W	00:36	10.4	317
	12:13	10.1	308		06:44	0.2	6
	18:18	0.1	3		12:57	10.2	311
					19:05	0.2	6
8 W	00:28	10.9	332	23 Th	01:18	10.1	308
	06:45	-0.5	-15		07:23	0.5	15
	12:55	10.5	320		13:35	10.1	308
	19:03	-0.3	-9		19:47	0.3	9
9 Th	01:13	10.9	332	24 F	01:59	9.8	299
	07:27	-0.5	-15		08:02	0.8	24
	13:37	10.8	329		14:13	10.0	305
	19:50	-0.6	-18		20:29	0.5	15
10 F	02:00	10.8	329	25 Sa	02:41	9.4	287
	08:11	-0.5	-15		08:42	1.2	37
	14:21	11.0	335		14:52	9.8	299
	20:38	-0.6	-18		21:12	0.8	24
11 Sa	02:48	10.5	320	26 Su	03:24	8.9	271
	08:58	-0.2	-6		09:24	1.6	49
	15:08	11.1	338		15:34	9.5	290
	21:30	-0.5	-15		21:57	1.1	34
12 Su	03:40	10.1	308	27 M	04:11	8.5	259
	09:48	0.2	6		10:09	2.0	61
	16:00	10.9	332		16:20	9.2	280
	22:26	-0.2	-6		22:47	1.5	46
13 M ☽	04:37	9.6	293	28 Tu	05:02	8.2	250
	10:43	0.6	18		10:59	2.3	70
	16:56	10.7	326		17:11	9.0	274
	23:26	0.0	0		23:41	1.7	52
14 Tu	05:40	9.2	280	29 W ☽	05:57	8.0	244
	11:43	1.0	30		11:52	2.5	76
	17:58	10.5	320		18:06	8.9	271
15 W	00:30	0.3	9	30 Th	00:37	1.7	52
	06:46	9.0	274		06:54	7.9	241
	12:46	1.2	37		12:48	2.5	76
	19:03	10.3	314		19:03	9.0	274

StationId: 8443970
Source: NOAA/NOS/CO-OPS
Station Type: Primary
Time Zone: LST_LDT
Datum: MLLW

NOAA Tide Predictions

Boston, MA, 2021

Times and Heights of High and Low Waters

October

Day	Time (h m)	Height (ft)	Height (cm)
1 F	01:32	1.6	49
	07:50	8.1	247
	13:44	2.3	70
	19:59	9.2	280
2 Sa	02:26	1.3	40
	08:43	8.5	259
	14:39	1.9	58
	20:54	9.5	290
3 Su	03:16	0.9	27
	09:31	9.0	274
	15:31	1.3	40
	21:44	10.0	305
4 M	04:03	0.4	12
	10:15	9.6	293
	16:19	0.6	18
	22:30	10.4	317
5 Tu ○	04:47	0.0	0
	10:57	10.3	314
	17:06	-0.1	-3
	23:16	10.8	329
6 W ●	05:30	-0.4	-12
	11:39	10.9	332
	17:52	-0.7	-21
7 Th	00:02	10.9	332
	06:13	-0.6	-18
	12:22	11.3	344
	18:39	-1.1	-34
8 F	00:49	11.0	335
	06:58	-0.6	-18
	13:07	11.6	354
	19:28	-1.3	-40
9 Sa	01:39	10.8	329
	07:45	-0.5	-15
	13:54	11.7	357
	20:18	-1.2	-37
10 Su	02:30	10.5	320
	08:34	-0.2	-6
	14:45	11.5	351
	21:11	-0.9	-27
11 M	03:24	10.0	305
	09:27	0.3	9
	15:39	11.2	341
	22:08	-0.5	-15
12 Tu	04:24	9.6	293
	10:25	0.8	24
	16:39	10.7	326
	23:10	0.0	0
13 W ◑	05:29	9.2	280
	11:28	1.2	37
	17:44	10.3	314
14 Th	00:15	0.3	9
	06:37	9.0	274
	12:34	1.4	43
	18:52	10.0	305
15 F	01:20	0.5	15
	07:45	9.1	277
	13:40	1.4	43
	20:01	9.9	302
16 Sa	02:24	0.5	15
	08:48	9.3	283
	14:45	1.1	34
	21:05	9.9	302
17 Su	03:23	0.5	15
	09:44	9.6	293
	15:44	0.8	24
	22:01	10.0	305
18 M	04:13	0.4	12
	10:31	9.9	302
	16:35	0.5	15
	22:50	10.0	305
19 Tu	04:57	0.4	12
	11:12	10.1	308
	17:20	0.3	9
	23:33	10.0	305
20 W ○	05:37	0.5	15
	11:50	10.2	311
	18:01	0.1	3
21 Th	00:14	9.8	299
	06:15	0.7	21
	12:26	10.2	311
	18:41	0.1	3
22 F	00:54	9.6	293
	06:52	0.9	27
	13:02	10.2	311
	19:21	0.2	6
23 Sa	01:33	9.3	283
	07:30	1.2	37
	13:39	10.0	305
	20:01	0.4	12
24 Su	02:14	9.0	274
	08:09	1.5	46
	14:18	9.8	299
	20:42	0.7	21
25 M	02:55	8.7	265
	08:50	1.8	55
	14:59	9.6	293
	21:25	1.0	30
26 Tu	03:40	8.4	256
	09:34	2.1	64
	15:43	9.3	283
	22:13	1.3	40
27 W	04:29	8.2	250
	10:23	2.4	73
	16:33	9.1	277
	23:04	1.5	46
28 Th ◐	05:21	8.0	244
	11:16	2.5	76
	17:27	9.0	274
	23:58	1.5	46
29 F	06:16	8.1	247
	12:12	2.4	73
	18:23	9.0	274
30 Sa	00:51	1.4	43
	07:09	8.4	256
	13:08	2.1	64
	19:19	9.2	280
31 Su	01:44	1.1	34
	08:01	8.8	268
	14:03	1.6	49
	20:15	9.5	290

November

Day	Time (h m)	Height (ft)	Height (cm)
1 M	02:35	0.8	24
	08:50	9.4	287
	14:58	0.9	27
	21:08	9.9	302
2 Tu	03:24	0.3	9
	09:37	10.2	311
	15:50	0.1	3
	21:59	10.3	314
3 W	04:11	-0.1	-3
	10:22	10.9	332
	16:39	-0.6	-18
	22:48	10.6	323
4 Th ●	04:58	-0.4	-12
	11:07	11.5	351
	17:28	-1.2	-37
	23:37	10.8	329
5 F	05:44	-0.6	-18
	11:53	11.9	363
	18:18	-1.6	-49
6 Sa	00:27	10.8	329
	06:32	-0.6	-18
	12:41	12.1	369
	19:08	-1.7	-52
7 Su	01:20	10.6	323
	06:22	-0.5	-15
	12:32	12.0	366
	19:00	-1.6	-49
8 M	01:14	10.3	314
	07:14	-0.1	-3
	13:25	11.7	357
	19:54	-1.2	-37
9 Tu	02:10	9.9	302
	08:09	0.3	9
	14:21	11.2	341
	20:52	-0.7	-21
10 W	03:10	9.6	293
	09:08	0.8	24
	15:23	10.7	326
	21:53	-0.2	-6
11 Th ◑	04:15	9.3	283
	10:12	1.2	37
	16:29	10.1	308
	22:56	0.2	6
12 F	05:21	9.2	280
	11:18	1.3	40
	17:37	9.8	299
	23:59	0.5	15
13 Sa	06:26	9.2	280
	12:24	1.3	40
	18:43	9.5	290
14 Su	01:00	0.7	21
	07:26	9.4	287
	13:28	1.1	34
	19:46	9.4	287
15 M	01:56	0.8	24
	08:19	9.7	296
	14:27	0.8	24
	20:42	9.4	287
16 Tu	02:45	0.8	24
	09:05	9.9	302
	15:17	0.5	15
	21:30	9.4	287
17 W	03:29	0.9	27
	09:45	10.1	308
	16:00	0.3	9
	22:12	9.3	283
18 Th	04:08	0.9	27
	10:22	10.1	308
	16:40	0.2	6
	22:52	9.2	280
19 F ○	04:46	1.1	34
	10:57	10.1	308
	17:19	0.2	6
	23:31	9.1	277
20 Sa	05:24	1.2	37
	11:34	10.1	308
	17:57	0.2	6
21 Su	00:10	8.9	271
	06:02	1.4	43
	12:11	10.0	305
	18:36	0.4	12
22 M	00:50	8.8	268
	06:41	1.6	49
	12:50	9.8	299
	19:16	0.5	15
23 Tu	01:31	8.6	262
	07:22	1.8	55
	13:30	9.6	293
	19:58	0.7	21
24 W	02:13	8.4	256
	08:05	1.9	58
	14:13	9.4	287
	20:42	0.9	27
25 Th	02:58	8.3	253
	08:51	2.1	64
	15:00	9.2	280
	21:30	1.0	30
26 F	03:47	8.2	250
	09:42	2.1	64
	15:51	9.1	277
	22:20	1.1	34
27 Sa ◐	04:37	8.4	256
	10:37	2.0	61
	16:45	9.1	277
	23:11	1.0	30
28 Su	05:28	8.7	265
	11:33	1.7	52
	17:41	9.1	277
29 M	00:02	0.8	24
	06:19	9.2	280
	12:29	1.2	37
	18:38	9.3	283
30 Tu	00:54	0.6	18
	07:10	9.8	299
	13:26	0.5	15
	19:34	9.6	293

December

Day	Time (h m)	Height (ft)	Height (cm)
1 W	01:47	0.3	9
	08:00	10.5	320
	14:21	-0.2	-6
	20:30	9.9	302
2 Th	02:38	-0.1	-3
	08:50	11.2	341
	15:15	-0.9	-27
	21:23	10.2	311
3 F	03:29	-0.4	-12
	09:39	11.7	357
	16:07	-1.5	-46
	22:16	10.3	314
4 Sa ●	04:19	-0.6	-18
	10:29	12.1	369
	16:58	-1.8	-55
	23:09	10.4	317
5 Su	05:10	-0.6	-18
	11:20	12.2	372
	17:51	-1.9	-58
6 M	00:03	10.3	314
	06:02	-0.5	-15
	12:14	12.0	366
	18:44	-1.7	-52
7 Tu	00:59	10.1	308
	06:56	-0.2	-6
	13:09	11.7	357
	19:38	-1.4	-43
8 W	01:55	9.9	302
	07:51	0.1	3
	14:05	11.2	341
	20:33	-0.9	-27
9 Th	02:53	9.6	293
	08:50	0.6	18
	15:05	10.5	320
	21:31	-0.3	-9
10 F	03:54	9.4	287
	09:51	0.9	27
	16:08	9.9	302
	22:30	0.6	18
11 Sa ◑	04:55	9.3	283
	10:56	1.1	34
	17:12	9.4	287
	23:29	0.6	18
12 Su	05:55	9.3	283
	12:00	1.2	37
	18:15	9.0	274
13 M	00:26	0.9	27
	06:51	9.3	283
	13:02	1.1	34
	19:17	8.8	268
14 Tu	01:20	1.1	34
	07:45	9.4	287
	14:01	0.9	27
	20:14	8.7	265
15 W	02:11	1.2	37
	08:32	9.6	293
	14:52	0.7	21
	21:05	8.7	265
16 Th	02:57	1.3	40
	09:15	9.7	296
	15:37	0.5	15
	21:49	8.7	265
17 F	03:39	1.3	40
	09:54	9.9	302
	16:18	0.3	9
	22:30	8.7	265
18 Sa	04:19	1.3	40
	10:32	9.9	302
	16:57	0.2	6
	23:10	8.7	265
19 Su ○	04:58	1.3	40
	11:10	9.9	302
	17:35	0.2	6
	23:49	8.6	262
20 M	05:37	1.3	40
	11:48	9.9	302
	18:14	0.2	6
21 Tu	00:28	8.6	262
	06:17	1.4	43
	12:27	9.9	302
	18:53	0.2	6
22 W	01:08	8.6	262
	06:56	1.4	43
	13:07	9.8	299
	19:33	0.3	9
23 Th	01:47	8.5	259
	07:39	1.5	46
	13:48	9.6	293
	20:14	0.4	12
24 F	02:28	8.6	262
	08:24	1.5	46
	14:32	9.5	290
	20:57	0.5	15
25 Sa	03:12	8.6	262
	09:12	1.5	46
	15:19	9.3	283
	21:44	0.5	15
26 Su	03:59	8.8	268
	10:05	1.3	40
	16:11	9.2	280
	22:33	0.5	15
27 M ◐	04:48	9.2	280
	11:00	1.1	34
	17:06	9.1	277
	23:25	0.5	15
28 Tu	05:39	9.6	293
	11:58	0.7	21
	18:04	9.1	277
29 W	00:18	0.4	12
	06:33	10.0	305
	12:57	0.2	6
	19:04	9.2	280
30 Th	01:13	0.3	9
	07:28	10.6	323
	13:49	-0.4	-12
	20:05	9.4	287
31 F	02:10	0.1	3
	08:23	11.1	338
	14:53	-0.9	-27
	21:02	9.4	287

StationId: 8449130
Source: NOAA/NOS/CO-OPS
Station Type: Primary
Time Zone: LST_LDT
Datum: MLLW

NOAA Tide Predictions

Nantucket Island, MA,2021

Times and Heights of High and Low Waters

January

Day	Time	Height (ft)	Height (cm)		Day	Time	Height (ft)	Height (cm)
1 F	01:37	2.6	79		**16** Sa	02:27	2.9	88
	06:50	0.5	15			07:48	0.2	6
	13:31	3.6	110			14:30	3.6	110
	19:45	-0.1	-3			20:33	-0.1	-3
2 Sa	02:20	2.7	82		**17** Su	03:13	2.9	88
	07:36	0.4	12			08:41	0.3	9
	14:17	3.6	110			15:18	3.3	101
	20:28	-0.1	-3			21:19	0.0	0
3 Su	03:05	2.8	85		**18** M	03:58	2.9	88
	08:26	0.4	12			09:35	0.4	12
	15:06	3.5	107			16:07	3.1	94
	21:13	-0.1	-3			22:05	0.2	6
4 M	03:51	2.9	88		**19** Tu	04:43	3.0	91
	09:21	0.3	9			10:31	0.5	15
	15:58	3.4	104			16:57	2.8	85
	22:00	-0.1	-3			22:52	0.4	12
5 Tu	04:40	3.1	94		**20** W	05:28	3.0	91
	10:20	0.2	6			11:29	0.5	15
	16:53	3.3	101			17:49	2.6	79
	22:50	0.0	0			◑ 23:39	0.5	15
6 W	05:32	3.3	101		**21** Th	06:14	3.0	91
	11:22	0.2	6			12:27	0.5	15
	17:52	3.1	94			18:44	2.5	76
	◐ 23:42	0.0	0					
7 Th	06:25	3.5	107		**22** F	00:27	0.6	18
	12:26	0.0	0			07:02	3.1	94
	18:54	2.9	88			13:25	0.5	15
						19:39	2.4	73
8 F	00:37	0.1	3		**23** Sa	01:16	0.7	21
	07:20	3.7	113			07:50	3.2	98
	13:30	-0.1	-3			14:18	0.4	12
	19:58	2.8	85			20:34	2.3	70
9 Sa	01:32	0.1	3		**24** Su	02:03	0.7	21
	08:17	3.8	116			08:37	3.2	98
	14:32	-0.2	-6			15:07	0.3	9
	21:02	2.7	82			21:25	2.3	70
10 Su	02:28	0.1	3		**25** M	02:49	0.7	21
	09:14	4.0	122			09:25	3.3	101
	15:31	-0.4	-12			15:52	0.2	6
	22:04	2.7	82			22:13	2.3	70
11 M	03:24	0.1	3		**26** Tu	03:33	0.6	18
	10:10	4.1	125			10:11	3.4	104
	16:27	-0.4	-12			16:34	0.1	3
	23:03	2.7	82			22:58	2.4	73
12 Tu	04:18	0.1	3		**27** W	04:16	0.6	18
	11:06	4.1	125			10:56	3.5	107
	17:20	-0.5	-15			17:15	0.0	0
	23:59	2.8	85			23:41	2.5	76
13 W	05:11	0.1	3		**28** Th	04:59	0.4	12
	11:59	4.0	122			11:40	3.6	110
	● 18:11	-0.4	-12			○ 17:55	-0.1	-3
14 Th	00:51	2.8	85		**29** F	00:24	2.6	79
	06:04	0.1	3			05:43	0.3	9
	12:51	3.9	119			12:25	3.7	113
	18:59	-0.4	-12			18:35	-0.2	-6
15 F	01:40	2.9	88		**30** Sa	01:06	2.7	82
	06:56	0.2	6			06:30	0.2	6
	13:41	3.8	116			13:11	3.7	113
	19:47	-0.2	-6			19:17	-0.2	-6
					31 Su	01:50	2.9	88
						07:19	0.1	3
						13:59	3.6	110
						20:00	-0.2	-6

February

Day	Time	Height (ft)	Height (cm)		Day	Time	Height (ft)	Height (cm)
1 M	02:35	3.1	94		**16** Tu	03:14	3.0	91
	08:10	0.0	0			09:05	0.2	6
	14:49	3.5	107			15:35	2.9	88
	20:45	-0.2	-6			21:24	0.3	9
2 Tu	03:23	3.2	98		**17** W	03:55	3.0	91
	09:06	-0.1	-3			09:56	0.3	9
	15:42	3.3	101			16:21	2.7	82
	21:32	-0.2	-6			22:07	0.5	15
3 W	04:13	3.4	104		**18** Th	04:38	3.0	91
	10:05	-0.1	-3			10:49	0.4	12
	16:38	3.1	94			17:10	2.5	76
	22:23	-0.1	-3			22:52	0.6	18
4 Th	05:06	3.5	107		**19** F	05:24	3.1	94
	11:07	-0.1	-3			11:43	0.4	12
	17:38	2.9	88			18:02	2.4	73
	◐ 23:17	0.0	0			◑ 23:40	0.7	21
5 F	06:02	3.6	110		**20** Sa	06:13	3.1	94
	12:11	-0.1	-3			12:39	0.4	12
	18:42	2.7	82			18:56	2.3	70
6 Sa	00:14	0.1	3		**21** Su	00:30	0.7	21
	07:01	3.7	113			07:04	3.1	94
	13:16	-0.1	-3			13:33	0.4	12
	19:48	2.6	79			19:50	2.3	70
7 Su	01:13	0.2	6		**22** M	01:21	0.7	21
	08:02	3.8	116			07:56	3.2	98
	14:19	-0.2	-6			14:25	0.3	9
	20:53	2.6	79			20:43	2.3	70
8 M	02:12	0.2	6		**23** Tu	02:10	0.7	21
	09:03	3.8	116			08:48	3.3	101
	15:11	-0.2	-6			15:13	0.2	6
	21:56	2.6	79			21:33	2.4	73
9 Tu	03:10	0.2	6		**24** W	02:59	0.6	18
	10:02	3.8	116			09:38	3.4	104
	16:14	-0.2	-6			15:57	0.1	3
	22:54	2.7	82			22:20	2.5	76
10 W	04:06	0.2	6		**25** Th	03:46	0.4	12
	10:58	3.8	116			10:27	3.5	107
	17:05	-0.2	-6			16:40	0.0	0
	23:45	2.8	85			23:06	2.6	79
11 Th	04:59	0.1	3		**26** F	04:34	0.2	6
	11:49	3.7	113			11:15	3.6	110
	● 17:52	-0.2	-6			17:22	-0.1	-3
						23:50	2.8	85
12 F	00:32	2.8	85		**27** Sa	05:22	0.0	0
	05:50	0.1	3			12:02	3.6	110
	12:37	3.6	110			○ 18:04	-0.2	-6
	18:36	-0.2	-6					
13 Sa	01:15	2.9	88		**28** Su	00:34	3.0	91
	06:39	0.1	3			06:11	-0.2	-6
	13:23	3.5	107			12:51	3.6	110
	19:19	-0.1	-3			18:46	-0.3	-9
14 Su	01:56	2.9	88					
	07:28	0.2	6					
	14:07	3.3	101					
	20:00	0.0	0					
15 M	02:35	3.0	91					
	08:16	0.2	6					
	14:50	3.1	94					
	20:42	0.2	6					

March

Day	Time	Height (ft)	Height (cm)		Day	Time	Height (ft)	Height (cm)
1 M	01:19	3.3	101		**16** Tu	02:56	3.1	94
	07:03	-0.3	-9			08:52	0.1	3
	13:41	3.5	107			15:24	2.9	88
	19:31	-0.3	-9			21:04	0.4	12
2 Tu	02:06	3.5	107		**17** W	03:33	3.1	94
	07:56	-0.4	-12			09:37	0.1	3
	14:34	3.4	104			16:06	2.7	82
	20:17	-0.2	-6			21:44	0.5	15
3 W	02:55	3.6	110		**18** Th	04:12	3.1	94
	08:52	-0.4	-12			10:23	0.2	6
	15:28	3.2	98			16:50	2.6	79
	21:06	-0.1	-3			22:25	0.6	18
4 Th	03:47	3.7	113		**19** F	04:55	3.1	94
	09:50	-0.4	-12			11:11	0.2	6
	16:26	3.0	91			17:37	2.5	76
	21:59	0.0	0			23:09	0.7	21
5 F	04:43	3.7	113		**20** Sa	05:41	3.1	94
	10:52	-0.3	-9			12:02	0.3	9
	17:27	2.8	85			18:27	2.4	73
	22:56	0.1	3			23:56	0.7	21
6 Sa	05:42	3.7	113		**21** Su	06:30	3.1	94
	11:56	-0.2	-6			12:54	0.3	9
	18:32	2.7	82			19:18	2.3	70
	● 23:56	0.2	6			◑		
7 Su	06:45	3.7	113		**22** M	00:47	0.8	24
	13:01	-0.1	-3			07:23	3.1	94
	19:38	2.6	79			13:48	0.3	9
						20:11	2.3	70
8 M	00:59	0.3	9		**23** Tu	01:40	0.7	21
	07:49	3.6	110			08:16	3.1	94
	14:05	-0.1	-3			14:40	0.3	9
	20:44	2.6	79			21:03	2.4	73
9 Tu	02:01	0.3	9		**24** W	02:34	0.6	18
	08:53	3.6	110			09:10	3.2	98
	15:04	-0.1	-3			15:30	0.2	6
	21:45	2.7	82			21:53	2.5	76
10 W	03:01	0.3	9		**25** Th	03:27	0.5	15
	09:54	3.5	107			10:04	3.3	101
	15:57	-0.1	-3			16:16	0.1	3
	22:40	2.8	85			22:42	2.7	82
11 Th	03:57	0.2	6		**26** F	04:19	0.2	6
	10:49	3.5	107			10:56	3.4	104
	16:45	0.0	0			17:01	0.0	0
	23:27	2.8	85			23:28	2.9	88
12 F	04:48	0.2	6		**27** Sa	05:11	0.0	0
	11:38	3.4	104			11:48	3.5	107
	17:28	0.0	0			17:46	-0.1	-3
13 Sa	00:09	2.9	88		**28** Su	00:15	3.2	98
	05:37	0.1	3			06:02	-0.3	-9
	12:23	3.3	101			12:40	3.5	107
	● 18:09	0.1	3			○ 18:30	-0.2	-6
14 Su	00:46	3.0	91		**29** M	01:01	3.4	104
	07:23	0.1	3			06:54	-0.5	-15
	14:04	3.1	94			13:32	3.5	107
	19:47	0.2	6			19:15	-0.2	-6
15 M	02:21	3.0	91		**30** Tu	01:49	3.7	113
	08:08	0.1	3			07:47	-0.6	-18
	14:44	3.0	91			14:25	3.4	104
	20:25	0.3	9			20:02	-0.2	-6
					31 W	02:38	3.9	119
						08:41	-0.7	-21
						15:19	3.2	98
						20:51	-0.2	-6

StationId: 8449130
Source: NOAA/NOS/CO-OPS
Station Type: Primary
Time Zone: LST_LDT
Datum: MLLW

NOAA Tide Predictions

Nantucket Island, MA, 2021

Times and Heights of High and Low Waters

April

Day	Time	ft	cm	Day	Time	ft	cm
1 Th	03:30	3.9	119	**16** F	03:36	3.2	98
	09:37	-0.6	-18		09:53	0.1	3
	16:16	3.1	94		16:24	2.5	76
	21:43	-0.1	-3		21:47	0.7	21
2 F	04:25	3.9	119	**17** Sa	04:18	3.2	98
	10:35	-0.5	-15		10:38	0.1	3
	17:15	2.9	88		17:09	2.5	76
	22:38	0.1	3		22:31	0.8	24
3 Sa	05:23	3.9	119	**18** Su	05:04	3.2	98
	11:36	-0.4	-12		11:25	0.2	6
	18:16	2.8	85		17:56	2.4	73
	23:38	0.2	6		23:18	0.8	24
4 Su ◐	06:25	3.7	113	**19** M	05:54	3.2	98
	12:39	-0.2	-6		12:15	0.2	6
	19:20	2.7	82		18:45	2.4	73
5 M	00:41	0.3	9	**20** Tu ◐	00:09	0.8	24
	07:29	3.6	110		06:45	3.2	98
	13:43	-0.1	-3		13:06	0.3	9
	20:26	2.7	82		19:36	2.5	76
6 Tu	01:46	0.4	12	**21** W	01:04	0.7	21
	08:35	3.5	107		07:39	3.2	98
	14:45	0.0	0		13:57	0.2	6
	21:29	2.8	85		20:26	2.6	79
7 W	02:51	0.4	12	**22** Th	02:01	0.6	18
	09:40	3.4	104		08:35	3.2	98
	15:42	0.1	3		14:47	0.2	6
	22:27	2.8	85		21:16	2.8	85
8 Th	03:51	0.3	9	**23** F	02:58	0.3	9
	10:40	3.3	101		09:31	3.3	101
	16:33	0.1	3		15:35	0.1	3
	23:18	2.9	88		22:04	3.0	91
9 F	04:47	0.3	9	**24** Sa	03:54	0.1	3
	11:34	3.2	98		10:26	3.3	101
	17:18	0.2	6		16:23	0.0	0
					22:53	3.3	101
10 Sa	00:01	3.0	91	**25** Su	04:49	-0.2	-6
	05:37	0.2	6		11:22	3.3	101
	12:22	3.1	94		17:10	-0.1	-3
	17:58	0.3	9		23:42	3.6	110
11 Su	00:38	3.1	94	**26** M	05:44	-0.4	-12
	06:23	0.1	3		12:18	3.3	101
	13:05	3.0	91		17:57	-0.1	-3
	18:36	0.3	9				
12 M ●	01:12	3.1	94	**27** Tu ○	00:31	3.9	119
	07:05	0.1	3		06:37	-0.6	-18
	13:44	2.9	88		13:13	3.3	101
	19:13	0.4	12		18:46	-0.2	-6
13 Tu	01:45	3.2	98	**28** W	01:22	4.1	125
	07:47	0.0	0		07:31	-0.8	-24
	14:22	2.8	85		14:09	3.2	98
	19:50	0.5	15		19:36	-0.1	-3
14 W	02:19	3.2	98	**29** Th	02:14	4.2	128
	08:28	0.0	0		08:26	-0.8	-24
	15:01	2.7	82		15:05	3.1	94
	20:28	0.6	18		20:28	-0.1	-3
15 Th	02:56	3.2	98	**30** F	03:09	4.2	128
	09:10	0.0	0		09:22	-0.7	-21
	15:42	2.6	79		16:02	3.0	91
	21:07	0.6	18		21:22	0.0	0

May

Day	Time	ft	cm	Day	Time	ft	cm
1 Sa	04:06	4.1	125	**16** Su	03:49	3.4	104
	10:19	-0.6	-18		10:08	0.1	3
	17:01	2.9	88		16:43	2.5	76
	22:19	0.2	6		21:58	0.8	24
2 Su	05:05	3.9	119	**17** M	04:34	3.3	101
	11:19	-0.4	-12		10:53	0.1	3
	18:02	2.9	88		17:29	2.5	76
	23:21	0.3	9		22:46	0.8	24
3 M ◐	06:07	3.7	113	**18** Tu	05:23	3.3	101
	12:19	-0.2	-6		11:40	0.2	6
	19:04	2.9	88		18:15	2.6	79
					23:38	0.7	21
4 Tu ◐	00:25	0.4	12	**19** W	06:14	3.3	101
	07:10	3.5	107		12:28	0.2	6
	13:20	0.0	0		19:03	2.7	82
	20:06	2.9	88				
5 W ◐	01:32	0.5	15	**20** Th	00:35	0.6	18
	08:15	3.3	101		07:07	3.2	98
	14:18	0.1	3		13:18	0.2	6
	21:05	3.0	91		19:52	2.9	88
6 Th	02:37	0.5	15	**21** F	01:34	0.5	15
	09:18	3.1	94		08:03	3.2	98
	15:12	0.2	6		14:07	0.1	3
	21:59	3.0	91		20:41	3.1	94
7 F	03:38	0.4	12	**22** Sa	02:34	0.2	6
	10:18	3.0	91		09:01	3.2	98
	16:00	0.3	9		14:57	0.1	3
	22:46	3.1	94		21:31	3.4	104
8 Sa	04:32	0.3	9	**23** Su	03:33	0.0	0
	11:12	2.9	88		10:00	3.1	94
	16:43	0.4	12		15:47	0.0	0
	23:27	3.2	98		22:21	3.7	113
9 Su	05:21	0.2	6	**24** M	04:30	-0.3	-9
	12:00	2.8	85		10:59	3.1	94
	17:24	0.5	15		16:37	0.0	0
					23:13	4.0	122
10 M	00:03	3.2	98	**25** Tu	05:26	-0.5	-15
	06:05	0.2	6		11:58	3.1	94
	12:43	2.7	82		17:28	0.0	0
	18:02	0.6	18				
11 Tu ●	00:36	3.3	101	**26** W ○	00:06	4.2	128
	06:46	0.1	3		06:21	-0.7	-21
	13:22	2.6	79		12:56	3.1	94
	18:39	0.6	18		18:20	0.0	0
12 W	01:11	3.3	101	**27** Th	00:59	4.3	131
	07:25	0.1	3		07:16	-0.7	-21
	14:00	2.6	79		13:53	3.1	94
	19:16	0.7	21		19:12	0.0	0
13 Th	01:47	3.4	104	**28** F	01:55	4.3	131
	08:05	0.1	3		08:10	-0.7	-21
	14:38	2.6	79		14:50	3.0	91
	19:54	0.7	21		20:07	0.0	0
14 F	02:25	3.4	104	**29** Sa	02:51	4.3	131
	08:45	0.1	3		09:06	-0.6	-18
	15:18	2.5	76		15:47	3.0	91
	20:33	0.8	24		21:03	0.1	3
15 Sa	03:06	3.4	104	**30** Su	03:48	4.1	125
	09:26	0.1	3		10:01	-0.5	-15
	16:00	2.5	76		16:44	3.0	91
	21:14	0.8	24		22:01	0.3	9
				31 M	04:46	3.9	119
					10:57	-0.3	-9
					17:42	3.0	91
					23:02	0.4	12

June

Day	Time	ft	cm	Day	Time	ft	cm
1 Tu	05:46	3.7	113	**16** W	04:57	3.4	104
	11:54	-0.1	-3		11:07	0.1	3
	18:40	3.0	91		17:46	2.9	88
					23:14	0.6	18
2 W ○	00:06	0.5	15	**17** Th	05:47	3.3	101
	06:46	3.4	104		11:54	0.1	3
	12:50	0.1	3		18:32	3.0	91
	19:36	3.1	94				
3 Th	01:12	0.5	15	**18** F ◐	00:11	0.5	15
	07:47	3.2	98		06:41	3.3	101
	13:44	0.3	9		12:42	0.1	3
	20:30	3.1	94		19:21	3.3	101
4 F	02:16	0.5	15	**19** Sa	01:12	0.3	9
	08:48	3.0	91		07:38	3.2	98
	14:34	0.4	12		13:33	0.1	3
	21:20	3.2	98		20:11	3.5	107
5 Sa	03:16	0.5	15	**20** Su	02:13	0.1	3
	09:46	2.8	85		08:38	3.1	94
	15:21	0.5	15		14:24	0.1	3
	22:05	3.3	101		21:03	3.8	116
6 Su	04:10	0.4	12	**21** M	03:14	-0.1	-3
	10:41	2.7	82		09:39	3.0	91
	16:05	0.6	18		15:17	0.1	3
	22:46	3.3	101		21:56	4.0	122
7 M	04:58	0.3	9	**22** Tu	04:13	-0.3	-9
	11:31	2.6	79		10:40	2.9	88
	16:47	0.7	21		16:11	0.1	3
	23:24	3.4	104		22:51	4.2	128
8 Tu	05:42	0.2	6	**23** W	05:10	-0.4	-12
	12:15	2.6	79		11:40	2.9	88
	17:27	0.8	24		17:04	0.1	3
					23:46	4.3	131
9 W	00:02	3.4	104	**24** Th ○	06:05	-0.5	-15
	06:22	0.2	6		12:40	3.0	91
	12:55	2.5	76		17:59	0.1	3
	18:06	0.8	24				
10 Th ●	00:39	3.5	107	**25** F	00:43	4.4	134
	07:02	0.2	6		07:00	-0.6	-18
	13:34	2.5	76		13:37	3.0	91
	18:45	0.8	24		18:53	0.1	3
11 F	01:19	3.5	107	**26** Sa	01:39	4.3	131
	07:40	0.1	3		07:53	-0.5	-15
	14:13	2.5	76		14:33	3.0	91
	19:24	0.8	24		19:48	0.1	3
12 Sa	01:59	3.5	107	**27** Su	02:35	4.2	128
	08:19	0.1	3		08:46	-0.4	-12
	14:53	2.5	76		15:28	3.1	94
	20:04	0.8	24		20:44	0.2	6
13 Su	02:41	3.5	107	**28** M	03:30	4.0	122
	08:59	0.1	3		09:38	-0.3	-9
	15:34	2.6	79		16:21	3.1	94
	20:46	0.8	24		21:42	0.3	9
14 M	03:24	3.5	107	**29** Tu	04:25	3.8	116
	09:40	0.1	3		10:31	-0.1	-3
	16:17	2.6	79		17:14	3.1	94
	21:31	0.7	21		22:41	0.4	12
15 Tu	04:09	3.5	107	**30** W	05:21	3.5	107
	10:23	0.1	3		11:22	0.1	3
	17:01	2.7	82		18:06	3.2	98
	22:20	0.7	21		23:42	0.5	15

StationId: 8449130
Source: NOAA/NOS/CO-OPS
Station Type: Primary
Time Zone: LST_LDT
Datum: MLLW

NOAA Tide Predictions

Nantucket Island, MA,2021

Times and Heights of High and Low Waters

July

Day	Time (h m)	ft	cm	Day	Time (h m)	ft	cm
1 Th ◐	06:16	3.3	101	16 F	05:27	3.4	104
	12:13	0.3	9		11:22	0.1	3
	18:57	3.2	98		18:03	3.4	104
					23:52	0.3	9
2 F	00:44	0.6	18	17 Sa ◑	06:22	3.2	98
	07:13	3.0	91		12:12	0.2	6
	13:04	0.4	12		18:53	3.6	110
	19:46	3.3	101				
3 Sa	01:46	0.6	18	18 Su	00:54	0.2	6
	08:10	2.8	85		07:20	3.1	94
	13:53	0.6	18		13:04	0.2	6
	20:34	3.3	101		19:45	3.8	116
4 Su	02:45	0.5	15	19 M	01:56	0.1	3
	09:07	2.7	82		08:21	3.0	91
	14:40	0.7	21		13:58	0.2	6
	21:19	3.3	101		20:41	4.0	122
5 M	03:39	0.5	15	20 Tu	02:57	-0.1	-3
	10:02	2.6	79		09:23	2.9	88
	15:26	0.8	24		14:54	0.2	6
	22:03	3.4	104		21:38	4.1	125
6 Tu	04:28	0.4	12	21 W	03:57	-0.2	-6
	10:53	2.5	76		10:26	2.9	88
	16:10	0.8	24		15:51	0.2	6
	22:46	3.4	104		22:36	4.2	128
7 W	05:13	0.4	12	22 Th	04:55	-0.3	-9
	11:39	2.5	76		11:27	2.9	88
	16:53	0.9	27		16:47	0.2	6
	23:28	3.5	107		23:34	4.3	131
8 Th	05:55	0.3	9	23 F	05:50	-0.3	-9
	12:22	2.5	76		12:25	2.9	88
	17:34	0.8	24		17:42	0.2	6
9 F	00:10	3.5	107	24 Sa ○	00:30	4.3	131
	06:34	0.3	9		06:43	-0.3	-9
	13:02	2.5	76		13:20	3.0	91
	18:14	0.8	24		18:37	0.2	6
10 Sa ●	00:52	3.6	110	25 Su	01:26	4.2	128
	07:13	0.2	6		07:34	-0.2	-6
	13:43	2.6	79		14:13	3.1	94
	18:55	0.8	24		19:32	0.2	6
11 Su	01:34	3.6	110	26 M	02:19	4.0	122
	07:51	0.2	6		08:23	-0.2	-6
	14:23	2.6	79		15:03	3.1	94
	19:37	0.7	21		20:26	0.3	9
12 M	02:17	3.6	110	27 Tu	03:11	3.9	119
	08:30	0.1	3		09:11	0.0	0
	15:04	2.7	82		15:52	3.2	98
	20:21	0.6	18		21:21	0.3	9
13 Tu	03:01	3.6	110	28 W	04:02	3.6	110
	09:10	0.1	3		09:58	0.1	3
	15:47	2.9	88		16:39	3.2	98
	21:08	0.6	18		22:16	0.4	12
14 W	03:47	3.6	110	29 Th	04:53	3.4	104
	09:52	0.1	3		10:45	0.3	9
	16:30	3.0	91		17:25	3.3	101
	21:59	0.5	15		23:13	0.5	15
15 Th	04:35	3.5	107	30 F	05:44	3.1	94
	10:36	0.1	3		11:33	0.5	15
	17:15	3.2	98		18:12	3.3	101
	22:54	0.4	12				
				31 Sa ◐	00:11	0.6	18
					06:36	2.9	88
					12:21	0.6	18
					18:58	3.3	101

August

Day	Time (h m)	ft	cm	Day	Time (h m)	ft	cm
1 Su	01:09	0.6	18	16 M	00:37	0.1	3
	07:30	2.7	82		07:08	3.0	91
	13:10	0.8	24		12:41	0.3	9
	19:45	3.3	101		19:25	3.9	119
2 M	02:06	0.6	18	17 Tu	01:40	0.0	0
	08:25	2.6	79		08:10	2.9	88
	13:59	0.9	27		13:39	0.4	12
	20:33	3.4	104		20:25	4.0	122
3 Tu	03:01	0.6	18	18 W	02:43	0.0	0
	09:19	2.5	76		09:14	2.9	88
	14:47	0.9	27		14:36	0.4	12
	21:21	3.4	104		21:26	4.1	125
4 W	03:52	0.5	15	19 Th	03:43	0.0	0
	10:10	2.5	76		10:16	2.9	88
	15:34	0.9	27		15:38	0.3	9
	22:09	3.5	107		22:26	4.1	125
5 Th	04:38	0.5	15	20 F	04:40	-0.1	-3
	10:58	2.5	76		11:16	2.9	88
	16:20	0.9	27		16:35	0.3	9
	22:56	3.5	107		23:25	4.1	125
6 F	05:21	0.4	12	21 Sa	05:34	-0.1	-3
	11:43	2.6	79		12:11	3.0	91
	17:03	0.8	24		17:31	0.3	9
	23:41	3.6	110				
7 Sa	06:01	0.3	9	22 Su ○	00:21	4.0	122
	12:26	2.6	79		06:23	0.0	0
	17:46	0.7	21		13:02	3.1	94
					18:24	0.2	6
8 Su ●	00:25	3.6	110	23 M	01:13	3.9	119
	06:40	0.3	9		07:10	0.0	0
	13:08	2.7	82		13:55	3.2	98
	18:29	0.6	18		19:17	0.2	6
9 M	01:09	3.7	113	24 Tu	02:03	3.8	116
	07:19	0.2	6		07:55	0.1	3
	13:49	2.9	88		14:34	3.3	101
	19:13	0.5	15		20:07	0.3	9
10 Tu	01:54	3.7	113	25 W	02:50	3.6	110
	07:58	0.2	6		08:39	0.2	6
	14:30	3.0	91		15:16	3.3	101
	19:59	0.4	12		20:58	0.3	9
11 W	02:39	3.7	113	26 Th	03:37	3.4	104
	08:38	0.1	3		09:22	0.4	12
	15:13	3.2	98		15:58	3.3	101
	20:48	0.3	9		21:49	0.4	12
12 Th	03:27	3.6	110	27 F	04:23	3.2	98
	09:21	0.1	3		10:06	0.5	15
	15:58	3.4	104		16:40	3.4	104
	21:41	0.2	6		22:41	0.4	12
13 F	04:17	3.5	107	28 Sa	05:11	3.0	91
	10:06	0.1	3		10:51	0.7	21
	16:45	3.6	110		17:24	3.3	101
	22:37	0.1	3		23:34	0.5	15
14 Sa	05:11	3.3	101	29 Su	06:00	2.8	85
	10:54	0.2	6		11:38	0.8	24
	17:35	3.7	113		18:10	3.3	101
	23:36	0.1	3				
15 Su ◐	06:08	3.1	94	30 M ◐	00:29	0.6	18
	11:45	0.3	9		06:52	2.7	82
	18:29	3.8	116		12:27	0.9	27
					18:59	3.3	101
				31 Tu	01:24	0.6	18
					07:44	2.6	79
					13:18	1.0	30
					19:50	3.3	101

September

Day	Time (h m)	ft	cm	Day	Time (h m)	ft	cm
1 W	02:19	0.6	18	16 Th	02:29	0.1	3
	08:37	2.6	79		09:06	2.9	88
	14:09	1.0	30		14:28	0.5	15
	20:41	3.4	104		21:17	3.9	119
2 Th	03:11	0.6	18	17 F	03:29	0.1	3
	09:29	2.6	79		10:07	3.0	91
	14:59	0.9	27		15:29	0.4	12
	21:33	3.4	104		22:19	3.8	116
3 F	03:58	0.5	15	18 Sa	04:24	0.1	3
	10:17	2.6	79		11:04	3.1	94
	15:47	0.8	24		16:27	0.4	12
	22:22	3.5	107		23:17	3.8	116
4 Sa	04:42	0.5	15	19 Su	05:14	0.1	3
	11:03	2.7	82		11:55	3.2	98
	16:33	0.7	21		17:22	0.3	9
	23:10	3.6	110				
5 Su	05:23	0.4	12	20 M ○	00:10	3.7	113
	11:47	2.8	85		06:00	0.2	6
	17:18	0.6	18		12:40	3.3	101
	23:56	3.6	110		18:13	0.2	6
6 M	06:03	0.3	9	21 Tu	01:00	3.6	110
	12:29	3.0	91		06:43	0.3	9
	18:04	0.4	12		13:22	3.3	101
					19:02	0.2	6
7 Tu ●	00:43	3.7	113	22 W	01:45	3.4	104
	06:42	0.2	6		07:24	0.4	12
	13:12	3.2	98		14:00	3.4	104
	18:51	0.2	6		19:49	0.2	6
8 W	01:30	3.7	113	23 Th	02:29	3.2	98
	07:23	0.1	3		08:04	0.5	15
	13:55	3.4	104		14:38	3.4	104
	19:40	0.1	3		20:35	0.2	6
9 Th	02:18	3.6	110	24 F	03:12	3.1	94
	08:05	0.1	3		08:45	0.6	18
	14:39	3.6	110		15:16	3.4	104
	20:31	-0.1	-3		21:21	0.3	9
10 F	03:09	3.5	107	25 Sa	03:55	2.9	88
	08:50	0.1	3		09:26	0.7	21
	15:27	3.8	116		15:56	3.4	104
	21:24	-0.1	-3		22:08	0.3	9
11 Sa	04:02	3.4	104	26 Su	04:40	2.8	85
	09:37	0.2	6		10:10	0.8	24
	16:17	3.9	119		16:40	3.4	104
	22:21	-0.1	-3		22:57	0.4	12
12 Su	04:57	3.2	98	27 M	05:27	2.7	82
	10:28	0.3	9		10:56	0.9	27
	17:11	4.0	122		17:26	3.3	101
	23:20	-0.1	-3		23:49	0.5	15
13 M ◑	05:56	3.1	94	28 Tu	06:16	2.6	79
	11:24	0.4	12		11:45	1.0	30
	18:09	4.0	122		18:17	3.3	101
14 Tu	00:22	0.0	0	29 W ◑	00:42	0.5	15
	06:58	3.0	91		07:07	2.6	79
	12:23	0.4	12		12:37	1.0	30
	19:10	4.0	122		19:09	3.3	101
15 W	01:26	0.0	0	30 Th	01:35	0.6	18
	08:02	2.9	88		07:59	2.6	79
	13:25	0.5	15		13:30	1.0	30
	20:13	3.9	119		20:02	3.3	101

StationId: 8449130
Source: NOAA/NOS/CO-OPS
Station Type: Primary
Time Zone: LST_LDT
Datum: MLLW

NOAA Tide Predictions

Nantucket Island, MA,2021

Times and Heights of High and Low Waters

October

Day	Time (h m)	Height (ft)	Height (cm)	Day	Time (h m)	Height (ft)	Height (cm)
1 F	02:27	0.6	18	16 Sa	03:10	0.2	6
	08:49	2.6	79		09:53	3.1	94
	14:23	0.9	27		15:22	0.4	12
	20:55	3.3	101		22:08	3.5	107
2 Sa	03:14	0.5	15	17 Su	04:02	0.2	6
	09:38	2.8	85		10:46	3.2	98
	15:14	0.8	24		16:20	0.4	12
	21:47	3.4	104		23:06	3.4	104
3 Su	03:59	0.4	12	18 M	04:50	0.3	9
	10:24	2.9	88		11:33	3.3	101
	16:04	0.6	18		17:13	0.3	9
	22:37	3.5	107		23:58	3.3	101
4 M	04:41	0.3	9	19 Tu	05:33	0.4	12
	11:08	3.1	94		12:14	3.4	104
	16:53	0.3	9		18:01	0.2	6
	23:27	3.5	107				
5 Tu	05:23	0.2	6	20 W ○	00:45	3.2	98
	11:51	3.4	104		06:13	0.5	15
	17:42	0.1	3		12:51	3.4	104
					18:46	0.2	6
6 W ●	00:16	3.5	107	21 Th	01:28	3.0	91
	06:05	0.2	6		06:52	0.6	18
	12:35	3.6	110		13:26	3.5	107
	18:31	-0.1	-3		19:29	0.1	3
7 Th	01:06	3.5	107	22 F	02:08	2.9	88
	06:49	0.1	3		07:30	0.7	21
	13:21	3.8	116		14:01	3.5	107
	19:22	-0.3	-9		20:12	0.2	6
8 F	01:58	3.4	104	23 Sa	02:48	2.8	85
	07:34	0.1	3		08:09	0.8	24
	14:09	4.0	122		14:38	3.5	107
	20:04	-0.4	-12		20:54	0.2	6
9 Sa	02:51	3.4	104	24 Su	03:28	2.8	85
	08:21	0.1	3		08:50	0.8	24
	14:59	4.1	125		15:18	3.4	104
	21:08	-0.4	-12		21:38	0.2	6
10 Su	03:46	3.2	98	25 M	04:11	2.7	82
	09:12	0.2	6		09:32	0.9	27
	15:53	4.1	125		16:02	3.4	104
	22:05	-0.3	-9		22:24	0.3	9
11 M	04:44	3.1	94	26 Tu	04:56	2.6	79
	10:06	0.3	9		10:17	1.0	30
	16:51	4.1	125		16:49	3.3	101
	23:04	-0.2	-6		23:11	0.4	12
12 Tu	05:45	3.0	91	27 W	05:43	2.6	79
	11:05	0.4	12		11:05	1.0	30
	17:52	4.0	122		17:38	3.3	101
13 W ◔	00:06	-0.1	-3	28 Th ◑	00:01	0.4	12
	06:47	3.0	91		06:33	2.6	79
	12:08	0.5	15		11:57	1.0	30
	18:56	3.9	119		18:30	3.3	101
14 Th	01:10	0.0	0	29 F	00:52	0.5	15
	07:51	3.0	91		07:22	2.6	79
	13:14	0.5	15		12:52	0.9	27
	20:01	3.8	116		19:24	3.2	98
15 F	02:12	0.1	3	30 Sa	01:41	0.5	15
	08:54	3.0	91		08:11	2.8	85
	14:19	0.5	15		13:47	0.8	24
	21:06	3.6	110		20:17	3.2	98
				31 Su	02:29	0.4	12
					08:59	2.9	88
					14:42	0.6	18
					21:11	3.3	101

November

Day	Time (h m)	Height (ft)	Height (cm)	Day	Time (h m)	Height (ft)	Height (cm)
1 M	03:15	0.3	9	16 Tu	03:20	0.4	12
	09:45	3.2	98		10:06	3.4	104
	15:36	0.4	12		16:01	0.3	9
	22:05	3.3	101		22:41	2.9	88
2 Tu	04:00	0.3	9	17 W	04:02	0.5	15
	10:30	3.4	104		10:45	3.5	107
	16:29	0.1	3		16:47	0.2	6
	22:58	3.3	101		23:27	2.8	85
3 W	04:45	0.2	6	18 Th	04:42	0.6	18
	11:16	3.7	113		11:20	3.5	107
	17:20	-0.2	-6		17:29	0.1	3
	23:51	3.3	101				
4 Th ●	05:31	0.1	3	19 F ○	00:08	2.7	82
	12:03	4.0	122		05:21	0.7	21
	18:12	-0.4	-12		11:55	3.5	107
					18:10	0.1	3
5 F	00:45	3.3	101	20 Sa	00:46	2.7	82
	06:17	0.1	3		05:59	0.7	21
	12:52	4.2	128		12:30	3.5	107
	19:04	-0.6	-18		18:49	0.1	3
6 Sa	01:39	3.2	98	21 Su	01:24	2.6	79
	07:06	0.0	0		06:38	0.8	24
	13:43	4.3	131		13:08	3.5	107
	19:57	-0.6	-18		19:29	0.1	3
7 Su	01:34	3.2	98	22 M	02:03	2.6	79
	06:57	0.1	3		07:17	0.8	24
	13:37	4.3	131		13:48	3.4	104
	19:52	-0.6	-18		20:10	0.2	6
8 M	02:31	3.1	94	23 Tu	02:44	2.6	79
	07:50	0.1	3		07:59	0.9	27
	14:34	4.3	131		14:31	3.4	104
	20:48	-0.5	-15		20:53	0.2	6
9 Tu	03:30	3.1	94	24 W	03:27	2.6	79
	08:47	0.3	9		08:42	0.9	27
	15:33	4.1	125		15:17	3.3	101
	21:47	-0.3	-9		21:37	0.3	9
10 W	04:30	3.0	91	25 Th	04:12	2.6	79
	09:48	0.4	12		09:30	0.9	27
	16:35	3.9	119		16:05	3.3	101
	22:47	-0.2	-6		22:23	0.3	9
11 Th ◐	05:32	3.0	91	26 F	04:59	2.6	79
	10:53	0.5	15		10:21	0.9	27
	17:39	3.7	113		16:55	3.2	98
	23:48	0.0	0		23:10	0.3	9
12 F	06:34	3.1	94	27 Sa ◑	05:46	2.7	82
	12:01	0.5	15		11:18	0.8	24
	18:44	3.5	107		17:48	3.2	98
					23:57	0.3	9
13 Sa	00:48	0.1	3	28 Su	06:33	2.9	88
	07:35	3.2	98		12:15	0.7	21
	13:08	0.5	15		18:42	3.1	94
	19:49	3.3	101				
14 Su	01:43	0.2	6	29 M	00:45	0.3	9
	08:31	3.3	101		07:20	3.1	94
	14:12	0.4	12		13:13	0.4	12
	20:52	3.2	98		19:38	3.1	94
15 M	02:34	0.3	9	30 Tu	01:33	0.2	6
	09:21	3.4	104		08:08	3.4	104
	15:10	0.3	9		14:10	0.2	6
	21:49	3.0	91		20:35	3.1	94

December

Day	Time (h m)	Height (ft)	Height (cm)	Day	Time (h m)	Height (ft)	Height (cm)
1 W	02:22	0.2	6	16 Th	03:30	0.6	18
	08:56	3.7	113		10:12	3.4	104
	15:06	-0.1	-3		16:28	0.2	6
	21:32	3.0	91		23:04	2.6	79
2 Th	03:11	0.1	3	17 F	04:12	0.7	21
	09:46	4.0	122		10:50	3.4	104
	16:01	-0.4	-12		17:09	0.1	3
	22:29	3.0	91		23:45	2.5	76
3 F	04:00	0.0	0	18 Sa	04:52	0.7	21
	10:37	4.2	128		11:27	3.5	107
	16:54	-0.6	-18		17:49	0.1	3
	23:25	3.0	91				
4 Sa ●	04:51	0.0	0	19 Su ○	00:22	2.5	76
	11:29	4.3	131		05:31	0.7	21
	17:48	-0.7	-21		12:05	3.5	107
					18:27	0.1	3
5 Su	00:21	3.0	91	20 M	00:59	2.5	76
	05:43	0.0	0		06:10	0.7	21
	12:24	4.4	134		12:44	3.5	107
	18:41	-0.7	-21		19:05	0.1	3
6 M	01:17	3.0	91	21 Tu	01:37	2.5	76
	06:36	0.0	0		06:49	0.7	21
	13:20	4.4	134		13:24	3.4	104
	19:35	-0.7	-21		19:44	0.1	3
7 Tu	02:14	3.0	91	22 W	02:16	2.5	76
	07:32	0.1	3		07:30	0.7	21
	14:17	4.2	128		14:06	3.4	104
	20:30	-0.5	-15		20:23	0.1	3
8 W	03:12	3.0	91	23 Th	02:57	2.6	79
	08:30	0.2	6		08:14	0.7	21
	15:16	4.0	122		14:50	3.4	104
	21:26	-0.4	-12		21:04	0.1	3
9 Th	04:10	3.1	94	24 F	03:40	2.6	79
	09:31	0.3	9		09:00	0.7	21
	16:16	3.8	116		15:36	3.3	101
	22:23	-0.2	-6		21:46	0.1	3
10 F	05:09	3.1	94	25 Sa	04:24	2.7	82
	10:36	0.4	12		09:51	0.6	18
	17:18	3.5	107		16:25	3.2	98
	23:20	0.0	0		22:30	0.2	6
11 Sa ◐	06:08	3.2	98	26 Su	05:09	2.9	88
	11:43	0.4	12		10:47	0.5	15
	18:21	3.2	98		17:17	3.1	94
					23:17	0.2	6
12 Su	00:16	0.2	6	27 M ◑	05:56	3.1	94
	07:05	3.2	98		11:46	0.4	12
	12:50	0.4	12		18:12	3.0	91
	19:24	3.0	91				
13 M	01:10	0.3	9	28 Tu	00:05	0.2	6
	07:58	3.3	101		06:45	3.3	101
	13:54	0.4	12		12:47	0.2	6
	20:27	2.8	85		19:10	2.9	88
14 Tu	02:00	0.4	12	29 W	00:56	0.2	6
	08:48	3.4	104		07:35	3.6	110
	14:52	0.3	9		13:47	0.0	0
	21:26	2.7	82		20:10	2.8	85
15 W	02:46	0.6	18	30 Th	01:49	0.1	3
	09:32	3.4	104		08:28	3.8	116
	15:43	0.2	6		14:45	-0.2	-6
	22:18	2.6	79		21:10	2.8	85
				31 F	02:42	0.1	3
					09:22	4.0	122
					15:42	-0.4	-12
					22:10	2.7	82

StationId: 8447930
Source: NOAA/NOS/CO-OPS
Station Type: Primary
Time Zone: LST_LDT
Datum: MLLW

NOAA Tide Predictions

Woods Hole, MA, 2021

Times and Heights of High and Low Waters

January

Day	Time (h m)	Height (ft)	Height (cm)
1 F	03:26	0.0	0
	09:35	2.3	70
	17:00	-0.1	-3
	21:55	1.5	46
2 Sa	04:21	0.1	3
	10:20	2.2	67
	17:49	-0.1	-3
	22:45	1.6	49
3 Su	05:21	0.1	3
	11:08	2.1	64
	18:39	-0.1	-3
	23:37	1.6	49
4 M	06:29	0.2	6
	11:59	2.0	61
	19:30	-0.1	-3
5 Tu	00:31	1.7	52
	07:42	0.1	3
	12:52	1.8	55
	20:20	-0.1	-3
6 W ☽	01:29	1.9	58
	08:55	0.1	3
	13:49	1.7	52
	21:09	-0.1	-3
7 Th	02:29	2.0	61
	10:05	0.0	0
	14:49	1.6	49
	21:57	-0.1	-3
8 F	03:31	2.2	67
	11:12	-0.2	-6
	15:50	1.5	46
	22:47	-0.2	-6
9 Sa	04:31	2.4	73
	12:17	-0.3	-9
	16:48	1.5	46
	23:41	-0.2	-6
10 Su	05:28	2.6	79
	13:16	-0.4	-12
	17:42	1.6	49
11 M	00:38	-0.2	-6
	06:20	2.7	82
	14:11	-0.5	-15
	18:33	1.7	52
12 Tu	01:36	-0.3	-9
	07:10	2.8	85
	15:01	-0.5	-15
	19:22	1.7	52
13 W ●	02:30	-0.3	-9
	07:58	2.7	82
	15:49	-0.5	-15
	20:11	1.7	52
14 Th	03:20	-0.2	-6
	08:46	2.6	79
	16:36	-0.4	-12
	21:00	1.7	52
15 F	04:07	-0.1	-3
	09:33	2.4	73
	17:22	-0.2	-6
	21:50	1.7	52
16 Sa	04:55	0.0	0
	10:21	2.2	67
	18:08	-0.1	-3
	22:40	1.6	49
17 Su	05:49	0.2	6
	11:08	1.9	58
	18:54	0.1	3
	23:31	1.6	49
18 M	07:04	0.3	9
	11:55	1.7	52
	19:36	0.3	9
19 Tu	00:22	1.5	46
	08:25	0.4	12
	12:42	1.4	43
	19:48	0.4	12
20 W ◑	01:14	1.5	46
	09:34	0.5	15
	13:31	1.2	37
	20:00	0.4	12
21 Th	02:10	1.5	46
	10:36	0.4	12
	14:23	1.1	34
	20:34	0.5	15
22 F	03:09	1.5	46
	11:30	0.4	12
	15:18	1.0	30
	21:15	0.4	12
23 Sa	04:08	1.6	49
	12:15	0.4	12
	16:12	1.0	30
	22:00	0.3	9
24 Su	05:01	1.7	52
	12:48	0.3	9
	17:02	1.1	34
	22:49	0.2	6
25 M	05:47	1.8	55
	13:16	0.2	6
	17:49	1.2	37
	23:41	0.1	3
26 Tu	06:28	2.0	61
	13:49	0.0	0
	18:32	1.4	43
27 W	00:36	0.0	0
	07:08	2.1	64
	14:26	-0.1	-3
	19:15	1.5	46
28 Th ○	01:31	-0.1	-3
	07:48	2.3	70
	15:05	-0.2	-6
	19:59	1.6	49
29 F	02:25	-0.2	-6
	08:29	2.3	70
	15:46	-0.3	-9
	20:44	1.7	52
30 Sa	03:19	-0.2	-6
	09:13	2.3	70
	16:29	-0.3	-9
	21:32	1.8	55
31 Su	04:14	-0.2	-6
	09:59	2.2	67
	17:14	-0.3	-9
	22:22	1.9	58

February

Day	Time (h m)	Height (ft)	Height (cm)
1 M	05:14	-0.2	-6
	10:47	2.1	64
	18:01	-0.2	-6
	23:14	2.0	61
2 Tu	06:21	-0.1	-3
	11:37	1.9	58
	18:53	-0.1	-3
3 W	00:08	2.0	61
	07:35	-0.1	-3
	12:30	1.7	52
	19:47	-0.1	-3
4 Th ◐	01:05	2.1	64
	08:50	-0.1	-3
	13:26	1.5	46
	20:44	-0.1	-3
5 F	02:06	2.1	64
	10:01	-0.1	-3
	14:25	1.4	43
	21:42	0.0	0
6 Sa	03:10	2.2	67
	11:07	-0.2	-6
	15:27	1.3	40
	22:42	-0.1	-3
7 Su	04:14	2.2	67
	12:10	-0.3	-9
	16:27	1.4	43
	23:46	-0.1	-3
8 M	05:13	2.3	70
	13:07	-0.3	-9
	17:23	1.5	46
9 Tu	00:48	-0.2	-6
	06:05	2.4	73
	13:58	-0.4	-12
	18:14	1.6	49
10 W	01:44	-0.2	-6
	06:53	2.4	73
	14:45	-0.4	-12
	19:02	1.7	52
11 Th ●	02:32	-0.2	-6
	07:38	2.4	73
	15:27	-0.3	-9
	19:49	1.8	55
12 F	03:15	-0.2	-6
	08:23	2.3	70
	16:06	-0.2	-6
	20:36	1.8	55
13 Sa	03:52	-0.1	-3
	09:07	2.2	67
	16:39	-0.1	-3
	21:23	1.9	58
14 Su	04:26	0.0	0
	09:51	2.0	61
	17:01	0.1	3
	22:10	1.8	55
15 M	05:03	0.1	3
	10:35	1.8	55
	17:12	0.2	6
	22:57	1.7	52
16 Tu	05:49	0.2	6
	11:20	1.6	49
	17:35	0.3	9
	23:45	1.6	49
17 W	06:50	0.4	12
	12:05	1.3	40
	18:08	0.4	12
18 Th	00:34	1.5	46
	08:14	0.4	12
	12:52	1.2	37
	18:52	0.5	15
19 F ○	01:26	1.4	43
	09:32	0.5	15
	13:42	1.0	30
	19:45	0.5	15
20 Sa	02:25	1.4	43
	10:30	0.4	12
	14:36	1.0	30
	20:40	0.5	15
21 Su	03:28	1.4	43
	11:16	0.4	12
	15:34	1.0	30
	21:35	0.4	12
22 M	04:28	1.5	46
	11:55	0.3	9
	16:29	1.1	34
	22:29	0.3	9
23 Tu	05:17	1.7	52
	12:33	0.2	6
	17:19	1.2	37
	23:25	0.1	3
24 W	06:00	1.9	58
	13:11	0.0	0
	18:05	1.5	46
25 Th	00:23	-0.1	-3
	06:41	2.1	64
	13:51	-0.1	-3
	18:50	1.7	52
26 F	01:20	-0.2	-6
	07:22	2.3	70
	14:32	-0.3	-9
	19:35	1.9	58
27 Sa ○	02:16	-0.4	-12
	08:05	2.3	70
	15:13	-0.4	-12
	20:21	2.1	64
28 Su	03:12	-0.5	-15
	08:50	2.3	70
	15:55	-0.4	-12
	21:09	2.2	67

March

Day	Time (h m)	Height (ft)	Height (cm)
1 M	04:08	-0.5	-15
	09:37	2.2	67
	16:39	-0.3	-9
	21:59	2.3	70
2 Tu	05:09	-0.4	-12
	10:26	2.0	61
	17:26	-0.2	-6
	22:52	2.4	73
3 W	06:15	-0.3	-9
	11:17	1.8	55
	18:20	-0.1	-3
	23:47	2.3	70
4 Th	07:28	-0.3	-9
	12:10	1.6	49
	19:21	0.0	0
5 F	00:44	2.2	67
	08:42	-0.2	-6
	13:06	1.4	43
	20:29	0.0	0
6 Sa ☽	01:46	2.1	64
	09:51	-0.2	-6
	14:05	1.3	40
	21:40	0.0	0
7 Su	02:51	2.1	64
	10:56	-0.2	-6
	15:07	1.3	40
	22:49	0.0	0
8 M	03:56	2.0	61
	11:56	-0.2	-6
	16:08	1.3	40
	23:55	-0.1	-3
9 Tu	04:56	2.1	64
	12:50	-0.3	-9
	17:05	1.5	46
10 W	00:54	-0.1	-3
	05:47	2.1	64
	13:39	-0.2	-6
	17:55	1.6	49
11 Th	01:45	-0.2	-6
	06:32	2.1	64
	14:18	-0.2	-6
	18:42	1.8	55
12 F	02:29	-0.2	-6
	07:14	2.1	64
	14:58	-0.1	-3
	19:27	1.9	58
13 Sa ●	03:07	-0.2	-6
	07:56	2.1	64
	15:25	0.0	0
	20:11	2.0	61
14 Su	04:37	-0.1	-3
	09:38	2.0	61
	16:34	0.1	3
	21:55	2.0	61
15 M	05:03	0.0	0
	10:20	1.8	55
	16:42	0.2	6
	22:39	2.0	61
16 Tu	05:33	0.0	0
	11:03	1.7	52
	17:05	0.2	6
	23:24	1.9	58
17 W	06:15	0.2	6
	11:47	1.5	46
	17:37	0.3	9
18 Th	00:09	1.8	55
	07:07	0.3	9
	12:32	1.3	40
	18:14	0.4	12
19 F	00:55	1.6	49
	08:10	0.4	12
	13:17	1.2	37
	19:03	0.5	15
20 Sa	01:43	1.5	46
	09:22	0.4	12
	14:05	1.1	34
	17:03	0.5	15
21 Su ◑	02:38	1.4	43
	10:25	0.4	12
	14:58	1.0	30
	17:47	0.5	15
	19:29	0.7	21
	21:13	0.6	18
22 M	03:40	1.4	43
	11:17	0.4	12
	15:57	1.0	30
	22:14	0.5	15
23 Tu	04:43	1.5	46
	12:02	0.3	9
	16:55	1.2	37
	23:12	0.3	9
24 W	05:38	1.7	52
	12:45	0.1	3
	17:49	1.4	43
25 Th	00:10	0.1	3
	06:26	1.9	58
	13:28	0.0	0
	18:38	1.7	52
26 F	01:10	-0.1	-3
	07:11	2.1	64
	14:10	-0.2	-6
	19:25	2.0	61
27 Sa	02:10	-0.3	-9
	07:55	2.2	67
	14:53	-0.3	-9
	20:11	2.3	70
28 Su ● ○	03:08	-0.5	-15
	08:40	2.3	70
	15:36	-0.3	-9
	20:58	2.5	76
29 M	04:05	-0.6	-18
	09:26	2.2	67
	16:20	-0.4	-12
	21:47	2.7	82
30 Tu	05:03	-0.6	-18
	10:15	2.1	64
	17:06	-0.3	-9
	22:38	2.7	82
31 W	06:03	-0.6	-18
	11:05	1.9	58
	17:56	-0.2	-6
	23:32	2.7	82

StationId: 8447930
Source: NOAA/NOS/CO-OPS
Station Type: Primary
Time Zone: LST_LDT
Datum: MLLW

NOAA Tide Predictions

Woods Hole, MA, 2021

Times and Heights of High and Low Waters

April

Day	Time	ft	cm	Day	Time	ft	cm
1 Th	07:09	-0.5	-15	**16** F	06:44	0.2	6
	11:57	1.8	55		12:01	1.3	40
	18:53	-0.1	-3		15:28	0.5	15
2 F	00:27	2.5	76	**17** Sa	00:20	1.8	55
	08:19	-0.4	-12		07:43	0.3	9
	12:51	1.6	49		12:47	1.2	37
	20:02	0.1	3		15:57	0.5	15
3 Sa	01:25	2.3	70	**18** Su	01:06	1.6	49
	09:29	-0.3	-9		08:46	0.4	12
	13:48	1.4	43		13:34	1.1	34
	21:22	0.1	3		16:35	0.5	15
4 Su ◐	02:26	2.1	64	**19** M	01:56	1.6	49
	10:36	-0.2	-6		09:44	0.3	9
	14:46	1.3	40		14:26	1.1	34
	22:39	0.1	3		17:20	0.6	18
					19:05	0.7	21
					20:51	0.6	18
5 M	03:29	2.0	61	**20** Tu ◐	02:53	1.6	49
	11:37	-0.2	-6		10:34	0.3	9
	15:48	1.3	40		15:23	1.2	37
	23:49	0.1	3		21:56	0.5	15
6 Tu	04:33	1.9	58	**21** W	03:54	1.6	49
	12:34	-0.1	-3		11:18	0.2	6
	16:49	1.4	43		16:22	1.4	43
					22:56	0.3	9
7 W	00:52	0.0	0	**22** Th	04:54	1.7	52
	05:32	1.8	55		12:00	0.1	3
	13:26	-0.1	-3		17:18	1.6	49
	17:45	1.6	49		23:56	0.1	3
8 Th	01:48	0.0	0	**23** F	05:48	1.9	58
	06:22	1.8	55		12:43	0.0	0
	14:12	0.0	0		18:10	2.0	61
	18:35	1.8	55				
9 F	02:38	0.0	0	**24** Sa	00:58	-0.1	-3
	07:06	1.8	55		06:38	2.0	61
	14:51	0.0	0		13:28	-0.1	-3
	19:20	2.0	61		19:00	2.4	73
10 Sa	03:20	-0.1	-3	**25** Su	02:00	-0.3	-9
	07:47	1.8	55		07:27	2.1	64
	15:18	0.1	3		14:13	-0.2	-6
	20:04	2.1	64		19:48	2.7	82
11 Su	03:56	0.0	0	**26** M	03:01	-0.5	-15
	08:28	1.8	55		08:14	2.1	64
	15:13	0.2	6		15:00	-0.3	-9
	20:46	2.2	67		20:37	2.9	88
12 M ●	04:23	0.0	0	**27** Tu ○	03:59	-0.6	-18
	09:09	1.8	55		09:03	2.1	64
	15:19	0.2	6		15:48	-0.3	-9
	21:28	2.2	67		21:27	3.0	91
13 Tu	04:44	0.0	0	**28** W	04:57	-0.7	-21
	09:50	1.7	52		09:53	2.0	61
	15:46	0.2	6		16:38	-0.2	-6
	22:10	2.2	67		22:19	3.0	91
14 W	05:13	0.1	3	**29** Th	05:56	-0.6	-18
	10:33	1.6	49		10:44	1.9	58
	16:20	0.3	9		17:32	-0.1	-3
	22:53	2.0	61		23:13	2.9	88
15 Th	05:54	0.1	3	**30** F	06:59	-0.5	-15
	11:17	1.4	43		11:38	1.7	52
	16:57	0.4	12		18:34	0.0	0
	23:36	1.9	58				

May

Day	Time	ft	cm	Day	Time	ft	cm
1 Sa	00:09	2.7	82	**16** Su	07:20	0.3	9
	08:05	-0.4	-12		12:19	1.3	40
	12:32	1.6	49		15:32	0.6	18
	19:50	0.2	6				
2 Su	01:06	2.4	73	**17** M	00:36	1.9	58
	09:11	-0.3	-9		08:16	0.3	9
	13:29	1.5	46		13:07	1.3	40
	21:14	0.2	6		16:12	0.6	18
3 M ◐	02:04	2.2	67	**18** Tu	01:23	1.8	55
	10:14	-0.2	-6		09:08	0.3	9
	14:27	1.5	46		13:58	1.3	40
	22:29	0.2	6		16:59	0.7	21
					18:31	0.8	24
					20:33	0.6	18
4 Tu	03:03	1.9	58	**19** W ◐	02:15	1.8	55
	11:12	-0.1	-3		09:55	0.2	6
	15:26	1.5	46		14:52	1.5	46
	23:36	0.2	6		21:40	0.5	15
5 W	04:03	1.8	55	**20** Th	03:13	1.8	55
	12:05	0.0	0		10:38	0.2	6
	16:26	1.6	49		15:50	1.7	52
					22:43	0.4	12
6 Th	00:38	0.2	6	**21** F	04:13	1.8	55
	04:59	1.7	52		11:20	0.1	3
	12:54	0.1	3		16:48	2.0	61
	17:22	1.7	52		23:45	0.2	6
7 F	01:35	0.2	6	**22** Sa	05:12	1.8	55
	05:50	1.6	49		12:03	0.0	0
	13:37	0.2	6		17:43	2.3	70
	18:12	1.9	58				
8 Sa	02:24	0.1	3	**23** Su	00:49	0.0	0
	06:35	1.6	49		06:07	1.9	58
	14:08	0.3	9		12:48	-0.1	-3
	18:57	2.1	64		18:36	2.7	82
9 Su	03:06	0.1	3	**24** M	01:53	-0.3	-9
	07:17	1.6	49		07:00	2.0	61
	13:34	0.4	12		13:37	-0.1	-3
	19:40	2.2	67		19:27	3.0	91
10 M	03:41	0.1	3	**25** Tu	02:55	-0.4	-12
	07:58	1.6	49		07:50	2.0	61
	13:50	0.3	9		14:29	-0.2	-6
	20:21	2.3	70		20:18	3.1	94
11 Tu ●	04:07	0.1	3	**26** W ○	03:53	-0.5	-15
	08:39	1.6	49		08:40	2.0	61
	14:25	0.3	9		15:23	-0.2	-6
	21:02	2.3	70		21:09	3.2	98
12 W	04:29	0.1	3	**27** Th	04:50	-0.6	-18
	09:21	1.6	49		09:31	2.0	61
	15:05	0.3	9		16:18	-0.1	-3
	21:44	2.3	70		22:01	3.1	94
13 Th	04:58	0.1	3	**28** F	05:46	-0.5	-15
	10:04	1.5	46		10:23	1.9	58
	15:48	0.4	12		17:16	0.0	0
	22:26	2.2	67		22:55	3.0	91
14 F	05:38	0.1	3	**29** Sa	06:45	-0.4	-12
	10:48	1.5	46		11:17	1.8	55
	16:33	0.4	12		18:20	0.1	3
	23:08	2.1	64		23:49	2.7	82
15 Sa	06:26	0.2	6	**30** Su	07:46	-0.3	-9
	11:33	1.4	43		12:12	1.7	52
	17:21	0.5	15		19:36	0.2	6
	23:51	1.9	58				
				31 M	00:44	2.5	76
					08:47	-0.2	-6
					13:07	1.7	52
					20:57	0.3	9

June

Day	Time	ft	cm	Day	Time	ft	cm
1 Tu	01:38	2.2	67	**16** W	00:56	2.0	61
	09:45	0.0	0		08:32	0.2	6
	14:03	1.6	49		13:31	1.7	52
	22:10	0.4	12		20:19	0.6	18
2 W ◐	02:32	1.9	58	**17** Th	01:46	2.0	61
	10:40	0.1	3		09:18	0.2	6
	15:01	1.7	52		14:24	1.8	55
	23:16	0.4	12		21:28	0.5	15
3 Th	03:26	1.7	52	**18** F ◐	02:41	1.9	58
	11:30	0.2	6		10:02	0.2	6
	15:58	1.7	52		15:21	2.0	61
					22:33	0.4	12
4 F	00:18	0.4	12	**19** Sa	03:40	1.8	55
	04:21	1.5	46		10:45	0.1	3
	12:15	0.4	12		16:20	2.3	70
	16:54	1.9	58		23:38	0.2	6
5 Sa	01:15	0.3	9	**20** Su	04:41	1.8	55
	05:13	1.4	43		11:30	0.1	3
	12:45	0.5	15		17:19	2.6	79
	17:46	2.0	61				
6 Su	02:05	0.3	9	**21** M	00:43	0.0	0
	06:01	1.4	43		05:40	1.8	55
	11:59	0.5	15		12:18	0.0	0
	18:32	2.1	64		18:15	2.8	85
7 M	02:48	0.3	9	**22** Tu	01:48	-0.2	-6
	06:46	1.5	46		06:35	1.9	58
	12:23	0.5	15		13:10	0.0	0
	19:16	2.3	70		19:08	3.1	94
8 Tu	03:22	0.3	9	**23** W	02:49	-0.3	-9
	07:29	1.5	46		07:28	1.9	58
	13:02	0.4	12		14:07	-0.1	-3
	19:58	2.3	70		20:00	3.2	98
9 W	03:48	0.2	6	**24** Th ○	03:45	-0.4	-12
	08:11	1.5	46		08:19	2.0	61
	13:47	0.4	12		15:07	-0.1	-3
	20:39	2.3	70		20:52	3.2	98
10 Th ●	04:11	0.2	6	**25** F	04:39	-0.4	-12
	08:53	1.6	49		09:10	2.0	61
	14:37	0.4	12		16:05	0.0	0
	21:20	2.3	70		21:43	3.1	94
11 F	04:42	0.2	6	**26** Sa	05:31	-0.4	-12
	09:36	1.6	49		10:02	2.0	61
	15:28	0.4	12		17:04	0.0	0
	22:01	2.3	70		22:35	2.9	88
12 Sa	05:21	0.2	6	**27** Su	06:24	-0.3	-9
	10:20	1.6	49		10:54	1.9	58
	16:18	0.4	12		18:06	0.2	6
	22:43	2.2	67		23:26	2.7	82
13 Su	06:06	0.2	6	**28** M	07:19	-0.1	-3
	11:05	1.5	46		11:48	1.9	58
	17:10	0.5	15		19:16	0.3	9
	23:25	2.2	67				
14 M	06:54	0.2	6	**29** Tu	00:17	2.4	73
	11:52	1.5	46		08:14	0.0	0
	18:07	0.6	18		12:42	1.9	58
					20:32	0.4	12
15 Tu	00:10	2.1	64	**30** W	01:08	2.1	64
	07:43	0.2	6		09:09	0.2	6
	12:40	1.6	49		13:35	1.8	55
	19:11	0.6	18		21:43	0.5	15

StationId: 8447930
Source: NOAA/NOS/CO-OPS
Station Type: Primary
Time Zone: LST_LDT
Datum: MLLW

NOAA Tide Predictions

Woods Hole, MA, 2021

Times and Heights of High and Low Waters

July

Day	Time	ft	cm	Day	Time	ft	cm
1 Th ◐	01:58	1.9	58	16 F	01:22	2.0	61
	10:01	0.3	9		08:42	0.2	6
	14:30	1.8	55		13:59	2.2	67
	22:50	0.5	15		21:20	0.4	12
2 F	02:48	1.6	49	17 Sa ◑	02:16	1.9	58
	10:46	0.5	15		09:30	0.3	9
	15:25	1.9	58		14:56	2.3	70
	23:52	0.5	15		22:28	0.3	9
3 Sa	03:41	1.4	43	18 Su	03:14	1.8	55
	11:09	0.6	18		10:18	0.2	6
	16:22	1.9	58		15:57	2.5	76
					23:35	0.2	6
4 Su	00:49	0.5	15	19 M	04:16	1.7	52
	04:34	1.3	40		11:07	0.2	6
	10:39	0.7	21		16:58	2.7	82
	17:17	2.0	61				
5 M	01:41	0.5	15	20 Tu	00:40	0.0	0
	05:26	1.3	40		05:16	1.7	52
	11:06	0.6	18		12:00	0.1	3
	18:08	2.1	64		17:57	2.8	85
6 Tu	02:23	0.5	15	21 W	01:42	-0.1	-3
	06:15	1.4	43		06:14	1.8	55
	11:45	0.6	18		12:57	0.1	3
	18:53	2.2	67		18:52	3.0	91
7 W	02:56	0.4	12	22 Th	02:40	-0.2	-6
	07:00	1.5	46		07:01	1.9	58
	12:32	0.5	15		14:00	0.0	0
	19:36	2.3	70		19:44	3.1	94
8 Th	03:21	0.4	12	23 F	03:33	-0.3	-9
	07:44	1.6	49		07:59	2.0	61
	13:24	0.4	12		15:02	0.0	0
	20:17	2.4	73		20:34	3.1	94
9 F	03:46	0.3	9	24 Sa ○	04:22	-0.3	-9
	08:26	1.6	49		08:49	2.1	64
	14:19	0.4	12		16:00	0.0	0
	20:57	2.4	73		21:23	3.0	91
10 Sa ●	04:19	0.2	6	25 Su	05:10	-0.2	-6
	09:09	1.7	52		09:39	2.1	64
	15:14	0.4	12		16:54	0.1	3
	21:37	2.4	73		22:11	2.8	85
11 Su	04:56	0.2	6	26 M	05:56	-0.1	-3
	09:53	1.7	52		10:30	2.1	64
	16:07	0.4	12		17:49	0.2	6
	22:18	2.4	73		22:59	2.6	79
12 M	05:37	0.1	3	27 Tu	06:43	0.1	3
	10:38	1.8	55		11:21	2.1	64
	17:00	0.4	12		18:49	0.3	9
	23:00	2.4	73		23:47	2.3	70
13 Tu	06:21	0.2	6	28 W	07:30	0.3	9
	11:25	1.8	55		12:12	2.1	64
	17:57	0.4	12		19:58	0.5	15
	23:45	2.3	70				
14 W	07:07	0.2	6	29 Th	00:35	2.0	61
	12:14	1.9	58		08:16	0.4	12
	19:00	0.5	15		13:03	2.0	61
					21:10	0.6	18
15 Th	00:32	2.2	67	30 F	01:23	1.8	55
	07:54	0.2	6		08:54	0.6	18
	13:05	2.0	61		13:55	2.0	61
	20:09	0.5	15		22:17	0.6	18
				31 Sa ◐	02:11	1.6	49
					08:51	0.7	21
					14:49	1.9	58
					23:19	0.6	18

August

Day	Time	ft	cm	Day	Time	ft	cm
1 Su	03:02	1.4	43	16 M	02:54	1.7	52
	09:14	0.8	24		10:01	0.3	9
	15:47	1.9	58		15:36	2.5	76
					23:31	0.1	3
2 M	00:17	0.6	18	17 Tu	03:55	1.6	49
	03:57	1.3	40		10:59	0.3	9
	09:51	0.8	24		16:41	2.6	79
	16:46	1.9	58				
3 Tu	01:07	0.6	18	18 W	00:33	0.0	0
	04:52	1.3	40		04:57	1.7	52
	10:34	0.7	21		12:00	0.2	6
	17:42	2.0	61		17:42	2.7	82
4 W	01:48	0.6	18	19 Th	01:32	0.0	0
	05:44	1.4	43		05:55	1.8	55
	11:22	0.6	18		13:04	0.2	6
	18:30	2.1	64		18:37	2.8	85
5 Th	02:18	0.5	15	20 F	02:26	-0.1	-3
	06:32	1.5	46		06:49	1.9	58
	12:14	0.5	15		14:07	0.1	3
	19:13	2.2	67		19:27	2.8	85
6 F	02:42	0.4	12	21 Sa	03:15	-0.1	-3
	07:17	1.6	49		07:39	2.1	64
	13:09	0.4	12		15:04	0.1	3
	19:52	2.3	70		20:14	2.8	85
7 Sa	03:10	0.3	9	22 Su ○	04:00	-0.1	-3
	08:00	1.8	55		08:28	2.2	67
	14:06	0.4	12		15:55	0.1	3
	20:31	2.4	73		20:59	2.7	82
8 Su ●	03:45	0.2	6	23 M	04:41	0.0	0
	08:42	1.9	58		09:15	2.3	70
	15:02	0.3	9		16:42	0.1	3
	21:10	2.5	76		21:44	2.6	79
9 M	04:23	0.1	3	24 Tu	05:19	0.1	3
	09:26	2.0	61		10:03	2.3	70
	15:56	0.2	6		17:29	0.2	6
	21:51	2.5	76		22:29	2.4	73
10 Tu	05:02	0.1	3	25 W	05:50	0.3	9
	10:11	2.1	64		10:51	2.3	70
	16:51	0.2	6		18:18	0.3	9
	22:34	2.4	73		23:15	2.1	64
11 W	05:44	0.1	3	26 Th	06:09	0.5	15
	10:59	2.2	67		11:39	2.2	67
	17:49	0.2	6		19:15	0.5	15
	23:21	2.3	70				
12 Th	06:29	0.2	6	27 F	00:01	1.9	58
	11:48	2.3	70		06:24	0.6	18
	18:52	0.3	9		12:28	2.1	64
					20:25	0.6	18
13 F	00:09	2.2	67	28 Sa	00:48	1.7	52
	07:17	0.2	6		06:51	0.7	21
	12:40	2.4	73		13:19	2.0	61
	20:02	0.3	9		21:37	0.7	21
14 Sa	01:01	2.0	61	29 Su	01:36	1.5	46
	08:09	0.3	9		07:30	0.8	24
	13:35	2.4	73		14:11	1.9	58
	21:15	0.3	9		22:40	0.7	21
15 Su ◑	01:55	1.8	55	30 M ◐	02:26	1.3	40
	09:04	0.3	9		08:21	0.9	27
	14:34	2.5	76		15:09	1.8	55
	22:25	0.2	6		23:36	0.7	21
				31 Tu	03:21	1.3	40
					09:17	0.8	24
					16:11	1.8	55

September

Day	Time	ft	cm	Day	Time	ft	cm
1 W	00:22	0.7	21	16 Th	00:20	0.0	0
	04:18	1.3	40		04:40	1.7	52
	10:13	0.8	24		12:12	0.2	6
	17:11	1.9	58		17:25	2.5	76
2 Th	00:56	0.6	18	17 F	01:15	0.0	0
	05:14	1.4	43		05:39	1.8	55
	11:06	0.7	21		13:15	0.2	6
	18:02	2.0	61		18:19	2.5	76
3 F	01:22	0.5	15	18 Sa	02:06	-0.1	-3
	06:04	1.5	46		06:32	2.0	61
	12:00	0.5	15		14:12	0.1	3
	18:44	2.1	64		19:06	2.5	76
4 Sa	01:51	0.4	12	19 Su	02:51	0.0	0
	06:50	1.7	52		07:20	2.2	67
	12:56	0.4	12		15:03	0.1	3
	19:23	2.3	70		19:50	2.5	76
5 Su	02:26	0.3	9	20 M ○	03:31	0.0	0
	07:33	1.9	58		08:06	2.3	70
	13:53	0.3	9		15:48	0.1	3
	20:02	2.4	73		20:33	2.4	73
6 M	03:04	0.2	6	21 Tu	04:04	0.2	6
	08:16	2.1	64		08:51	2.4	73
	14:50	0.1	3		16:29	0.1	3
	20:42	2.5	76		21:15	2.3	70
7 Tu ●	03:43	0.1	3	22 W	04:23	0.3	9
	08:59	2.3	70		09:35	2.4	73
	15:45	0.0	0		17:08	0.2	6
	21:24	2.5	76		21:58	2.1	64
8 W	04:24	0.0	0	23 Th	04:29	0.4	12
	09:45	2.5	76		10:21	2.4	73
	16:42	0.0	0		17:45	0.3	9
	22:09	2.4	73		22:42	1.9	58
9 Th	05:07	0.1	3	24 F	04:46	0.5	15
	10:33	2.6	79		11:06	2.3	70
	17:40	0.0	0		18:27	0.4	12
	22:57	2.3	70		23:28	1.7	52
10 F	05:52	0.1	3	25 Sa	05:14	0.6	18
	11:24	2.7	82		11:54	2.1	64
	18:45	0.0	0		19:25	0.5	15
	23:48	2.1	64				
11 Sa	06:43	0.2	6	26 Su	00:14	1.5	46
	12:18	2.6	79		05:47	0.7	21
	19:56	0.1	3		12:42	2.0	61
					20:41	0.6	18
12 Su	00:41	1.9	58	27 M	01:02	1.4	43
	07:41	0.3	9		04:07	0.7	21
	13:15	2.6	79		13:34	1.8	55
	21:09	0.1	3		21:50	0.6	18
13 M ◑	01:37	1.7	52	28 Tu	01:53	1.3	40
	08:47	0.4	12		04:43	0.8	24
	14:15	2.5	76		14:29	1.7	52
	22:18	0.1	3		22:44	0.6	18
14 Tu	02:36	1.6	49	29 W	02:47	1.2	37
	09:57	0.4	12		05:25	0.8	24
	15:19	2.5	76		15:29	1.7	52
	23:21	0.0	0		23:24	0.6	18
15 W	03:38	1.6	49	30 Th ◑	03:44	1.2	37
	11:06	0.3	9		09:54	0.8	24
	16:24	2.4	73		16:29	1.7	52
					23:54	0.5	15

StationId: 8447930
Source: NOAA/NOS/CO-OPS
Station Type: Primary
Time Zone: LST_LDT
Datum: MLLW

NOAA Tide Predictions

Woods Hole, MA, 2021

Times and Heights of High and Low Waters

October

	Time	Height ft	cm		Time	Height ft	cm
1 F	04:41 / 10:51 / 17:22	1.4 / 0.6 / 1.9	43 / 18 / 58	**16** Sa	00:53 / 05:21 / 13:13 / 17:55	-0.1 / 1.8 / 0.1 / 2.1	-3 / 55 / 3 / 64
2 Sa	00:26 / 05:34 / 11:46 / 18:07	0.4 / 1.6 / 0.5 / 2.0	12 / 49 / 15 / 61	**17** Su	01:40 / 06:13 / 14:07 / 18:41	0.0 / 2.0 / 0.1 / 2.1	0 / 61 / 3 / 64
3 Su	01:01 / 06:21 / 12:43 / 18:49	0.3 / 1.8 / 0.3 / 2.2	9 / 55 / 9 / 67	**18** M	02:22 / 07:00 / 14:56 / 19:23	0.1 / 2.2 / 0.1 / 2.1	3 / 67 / 3 / 64
4 M	01:40 / 07:06 / 13:40 / 19:31	0.1 / 2.1 / 0.1 / 2.3	3 / 64 / 3 / 70	**19** Tu	02:55 / 07:44 / 15:38 / 20:05	0.2 / 2.4 / 0.1 / 2.0	6 / 73 / 3 / 61
5 Tu	02:21 / 07:50 / 14:38 / 20:14	0.0 / 2.4 / -0.1 / 2.3	0 / 73 / -3 / 70	**20** W ○	03:05 / 08:27 / 16:16 / 20:46	0.3 / 2.4 / 0.1 / 1.9	9 / 73 / 3 / 58
6 W ●	03:03 / 08:34 / 15:36 / 20:58	0.0 / 2.7 / -0.2 / 2.3	0 / 82 / -6 / 70	**21** Th	03:01 / 09:09 / 16:48 / 21:28	0.3 / 2.5 / 0.2 / 1.8	9 / 76 / 6 / 55
7 Th	03:46 / 09:21 / 16:33 / 21:45	-0.1 / 2.8 / -0.3 / 2.2	-3 / 85 / -9 / 67	**22** F	03:22 / 09:52 / 17:17 / 22:12	0.4 / 2.4 / 0.2 / 1.7	12 / 73 / 6 / 52
8 F	04:32 / 10:11 / 17:33 / 22:35	0.0 / 2.9 / -0.3 / 2.1	0 / 88 / -9 / 64	**23** Sa	03:53 / 10:36 / 17:53 / 22:56	0.4 / 2.3 / 0.3 / 1.6	12 / 70 / 9 / 49
9 Sa	05:20 / 11:03 / 18:37 / 23:28	0.0 / 2.9 / -0.2 / 1.9	0 / 88 / -6 / 58	**24** Su	04:28 / 11:22 / 18:41 / 23:43	0.5 / 2.1 / 0.4 / 1.4	15 / 64 / 12 / 43
10 Su	06:15 / 11:59 / 19:47	0.1 / 2.8 / -0.1	3 / 85 / -3	**25** M	03:10 / 12:09 / 19:43	0.6 / 2.0 / 0.5	18 / 61 / 15
11 M	00:22 / 07:21 / 12:57 / 20:58	1.8 / 0.3 / 2.7 / -0.1	55 / 9 / 82 / -3	**26** Tu	00:31 / 03:38 / 12:57 / 20:51	1.3 / 0.6 / 1.8 / 0.5	40 / 18 / 55 / 15
12 Tu	01:19 / 08:39 / 13:57 / 22:04	1.6 / 0.3 / 2.5 / -0.1	49 / 9 / 76 / -3	**27** W ◐	01:21 / 04:14 / 13:48 / 21:46	1.2 / 0.7 / 1.7 / 0.5	37 / 21 / 52 / 15
13 W ◐	02:19 / 09:58 / 15:00 / 23:05	1.6 / 0.3 / 2.3 / -0.1	49 / 9 / 70 / -3	**28** Th ◐	02:13 / 04:56 / 14:42 / 22:27	1.2 / 0.7 / 1.7 / 0.4	37 / 21 / 52 / 12
14 Th	03:21 / 11:09 / 16:03	1.6 / 0.3 / 2.2	49 / 9 / 67	**29** F	03:09 / 09:34 / 15:38 / 23:03	1.2 / 0.7 / 1.7 / 0.4	37 / 21 / 52 / 12
15 F	00:01 / 04:23 / 12:14 / 17:03	-0.1 / 1.6 / 0.2 / 2.2	-3 / 49 / 6 / 67	**30** Sa	04:06 / 10:34 / 16:34 / 23:39	1.4 / 0.6 / 1.7 / 0.3	43 / 18 / 52 / 9
				31 Su	05:00 / 11:32 / 17:26	1.6 / 0.4 / 1.9	49 / 12 / 58

November

	Time	Height ft	cm		Time	Height ft	cm
1 M	00:17 / 05:51 / 12:29 / 18:14	0.1 / 2.0 / 0.2 / 2.0	3 / 61 / 6 / 61	**16** Tu	00:48 / 05:39 / 13:45 / 17:55	0.2 / 2.2 / 0.1 / 1.7	6 / 67 / 3 / 52
2 Tu	00:57 / 06:38 / 13:29 / 19:01	0.0 / 2.3 / 0.0 / 2.1	0 / 70 / 0 / 64	**17** W	00:57 / 06:22 / 14:26 / 18:37	0.3 / 2.3 / 0.1 / 1.6	9 / 70 / 3 / 49
3 W	01:40 / 07:25 / 14:29 / 19:47	-0.1 / 2.6 / -0.2 / 2.1	-3 / 79 / -6 / 64	**18** Th	00:36 / 07:04 / 15:01 / 19:18	0.3 / 2.4 / 0.1 / 1.6	9 / 73 / 3 / 49
4 Th	02:25 / 08:12 / 15:28 / 20:34	-0.1 / 2.9 / -0.4 / 2.1	-3 / 88 / -12 / 64	**19** F ○	01:02 / 07:45 / 15:30 / 20:00	0.3 / 2.4 / 0.1 / 1.6	9 / 73 / 3 / 49
5 F	03:13 / 09:01 / 16:26 / 21:23	-0.2 / 3.1 / -0.5 / 2.1	-6 / 94 / -15 / 64	**20** Sa	01:39 / 08:27 / 15:56 / 20:43	0.3 / 2.3 / 0.2 / 1.5	9 / 70 / 6 / 46
6 Sa	04:03 / 09:52 / 17:25 / 22:14	-0.2 / 3.1 / -0.5 / 2.0	-6 / 94 / -15 / 61	**21** Su	02:20 / 09:10 / 16:29 / 21:27	0.3 / 2.2 / 0.2 / 1.5	9 / 67 / 6 / 46
7 Su	03:56 / 09:45 / 17:28 / 22:08	-0.1 / 3.0 / -0.4 / 1.8	-3 / 91 / -12 / 55	**22** M	03:04 / 09:54 / 17:13 / 22:13	0.4 / 2.1 / 0.3 / 1.4	12 / 64 / 9 / 43
8 M	04:56 / 10:41 / 18:34 / 23:03	0.0 / 2.8 / -0.3 / 1.7	0 / 85 / -9 / 52	**23** Tu	03:51 / 10:39 / 18:05 / 23:00	0.4 / 2.0 / 0.3 / 1.3	12 / 61 / 9 / 40
9 Tu	06:07 / 11:39 / 19:40	0.1 / 2.6 / -0.3	3 / 79 / -9	**24** W	04:46 / 11:23 / 19:00 / 23:49	0.6 / 1.8 / 0.3 / 1.2	18 / 55 / 9 / 37
10 W	00:01 / 07:31 / 12:37 / 20:43	1.6 / 0.2 / 2.4 / -0.2	49 / 6 / 73 / -6	**25** Th	02:52 / 12:09 / 19:53	0.6 / 1.7 / 0.3	18 / 52 / 9
11 Th ◐	01:00 / 08:51 / 13:36 / 21:42	1.6 / 0.2 / 2.2 / -0.2	49 / 6 / 67 / -6	**26** F	00:39 / 03:34 / 05:14 / 07:05 / 12:57 / 20:38	1.2 / 0.7 / 0.8 / 0.7 / 1.7 / 0.3	37 / 21 / 24 / 21 / 52 / 9
12 F	02:01 / 10:01 / 14:35 / 22:36	1.6 / 0.2 / 2.0 / -0.1	49 / 6 / 61 / -3	**27** Sa ◐	01:32 / 08:14 / 13:50 / 21:18	1.3 / 0.6 / 1.6 / 0.2	40 / 18 / 49 / 6
13 Sa	03:02 / 11:04 / 15:32 / 23:26	1.7 / 0.2 / 1.8 / 0.0	52 / 6 / 55 / 0	**28** Su	02:28 / 09:17 / 14:47 / 21:57	1.5 / 0.5 / 1.6 / 0.1	46 / 15 / 49 / 3
14 Su	04:00 / 12:04 / 16:24	1.8 / 0.1 / 1.7	55 / 3 / 52	**29** M	03:25 / 10:17 / 15:45 / 22:37	1.7 / 0.3 / 1.7 / 0.0	52 / 9 / 52 / 0
15 M	00:11 / 04:52 / 12:57 / 17:11	0.1 / 2.0 / 0.1 / 1.7	3 / 61 / 3 / 52	**30** Tu	04:20 / 11:18 / 16:40 / 23:20	2.1 / 0.1 / 1.8 / -0.1	64 / 3 / 55 / -3

December

	Time	Height ft	cm		Time	Height ft	cm
1 W	05:12 / 12:20 / 17:32	2.4 / -0.2 / 1.8	73 / -6 / 55	**16** Th	06:01 / 14:11 / 18:09 / 23:47	2.1 / 0.1 / 1.4 / 0.3	64 / 3 / 43 / 9
2 Th	00:05 / 06:03 / 13:22 / 18:23	-0.2 / 2.7 / -0.4 / 1.9	-6 / 82 / -12 / 58	**17** F	06:43 / 14:44 / 18:52	2.2 / 0.1 / 1.4	67 / 3 / 43
3 F	00:55 / 06:53 / 14:22 / 19:12	-0.3 / 3.0 / -0.5 / 1.9	-9 / 91 / -15 / 58	**18** Sa	00:28 / 07:25 / 15:10 / 19:34	0.2 / 2.2 / 0.1 / 1.5	6 / 67 / 3 / 46
4 Sa	01:48 / 07:43 / 15:19 / 20:02	-0.3 / 3.1 / -0.6 / 1.9	-9 / 94 / -18 / 58	**19** Su ○	01:15 / 08:06 / 15:35 / 20:17	0.2 / 2.2 / 0.1 / 1.4	6 / 67 / 3 / 43
5 Su	02:43 / 08:35 / 16:15 / 20:54	-0.3 / 3.1 / -0.6 / 1.9	-9 / 94 / -18 / 58	**20** M	02:04 / 08:48 / 16:06 / 21:01	0.2 / 2.1 / 0.1 / 1.4	6 / 64 / 3 / 43
6 M	03:41 / 09:28 / 17:13 / 21:48	-0.3 / 3.0 / -0.5 / 1.8	-9 / 91 / -15 / 55	**21** Tu	02:53 / 09:29 / 16:45 / 21:45	0.2 / 2.1 / 0.1 / 1.4	6 / 64 / 3 / 43
7 Tu	04:43 / 10:23 / 18:14 / 22:43	-0.1 / 2.8 / -0.4 / 1.7	-3 / 85 / -12 / 52	**22** W	03:44 / 10:11 / 17:30 / 22:31	0.3 / 2.0 / 0.1 / 1.3	9 / 61 / 3 / 40
8 W	05:54 / 11:18 / 19:15 / 23:39	0.0 / 2.5 / -0.3 / 1.6	0 / 76 / -9 / 49	**23** Th	04:37 / 10:52 / 18:17 / 23:18	0.3 / 1.9 / 0.1 / 1.3	9 / 58 / 3 / 40
9 Th	07:15 / 12:12 / 20:15	0.1 / 2.2 / -0.2	3 / 67 / -6	**24** F	05:38 / 11:35 / 19:05	0.4 / 1.8 / 0.2	12 / 55 / 6
10 F	00:37 / 08:33 / 13:07 / 21:12	1.6 / 0.2 / 2.0 / -0.1	49 / 6 / 61 / -3	**25** Sa	00:07 / 06:45 / 12:21 / 19:52	1.4 / 0.5 / 1.7 / 0.1	43 / 15 / 52 / 3
11 Sa ◐	01:35 / 09:43 / 14:01 / 22:06	1.6 / 0.2 / 1.7 / 0.0	49 / 6 / 52 / 0	**26** Su	00:58 / 07:55 / 13:12 / 20:36	1.5 / 0.4 / 1.6 / 0.1	46 / 12 / 49 / 3
12 Su	02:34 / 10:48 / 14:56 / 22:55	1.6 / 0.2 / 1.5 / 0.1	49 / 6 / 46 / 3	**27** M ◑	01:53 / 09:02 / 14:09 / 21:19	1.6 / 0.3 / 1.5 / 0.1	49 / 9 / 46 / 3
13 M	03:33 / 11:48 / 15:49 / 23:39	1.7 / 0.2 / 1.4 / 0.2	52 / 6 / 43 / 6	**28** Tu	02:52 / 10:06 / 15:09 / 22:03	1.9 / 0.1 / 1.5 / 0.0	58 / 3 / 46 / 0
14 Tu	04:27 / 12:43 / 16:39	1.9 / 0.1 / 1.3	58 / 3 / 40	**29** W	03:51 / 11:10 / 16:10 / 22:50	2.1 / -0.1 / 1.5 / -0.1	64 / -3 / 46 / -3
15 W	00:06 / 05:16 / 13:30 / 17:26 / 23:19	0.3 / 2.0 / 0.1 / 1.3 / 0.3	9 / 61 / 3 / 40 / 9	**30** Th	04:49 / 12:15 / 17:07 / 23:41	2.4 / -0.2 / 1.6 / -0.2	73 / -6 / 49 / -6
				31 F	05:44 / 13:17 / 18:01	2.7 / -0.4 / 1.7	82 / -12 / 52

43

StationId: 8452660
Source: NOAA/NOS/CO-OPS
Station Type: Primary
Time Zone: LST_LDT
Datum: MLLW

NOAA Tide Predictions

Newport, RI, 2021

Times and Heights of High and Low Waters

January

Day	Time (h m)	Height (ft)	Height (cm)	Day	Time (h m)	Height (ft)	Height (cm)
1 F	02:04 / 08:57 / 15:00 / 21:28	-0.3 / 3.7 / -0.1 / 3.2	-9 / 113 / -3 / 98	16 Sa	02:58 / 10:02 / 15:38 / 22:26	-0.2 / 3.7 / -0.1 / 3.4	-6 / 113 / -3 / 104
2 Sa	02:46 / 09:42 / 15:34 / 22:16	-0.2 / 3.7 / -0.1 / 3.2	-6 / 113 / -3 / 98	17 Su	03:41 / 10:48 / 16:10 / 23:15	0.0 / 3.4 / 0.0 / 3.2	0 / 104 / 0 / 98
3 Su	03:30 / 10:31 / 16:11 / 23:07	-0.2 / 3.6 / -0.1 / 3.3	-6 / 110 / -3 / 101	18 M	04:25 / 11:34 / 16:47	0.2 / 3.1 / 0.1	6 / 94 / 3
4 M	04:18 / 11:24 / 16:54	0.0 / 3.4 / -0.1	0 / 104 / -3	19 Tu	00:03 / 05:15 / 12:20 / 17:29	3.1 / 0.4 / 2.8 / 0.3	94 / 12 / 85 / 9
5 Tu	00:01 / 05:15 / 12:19 / 17:45	3.4 / 0.1 / 3.3 / 0.0	104 / 3 / 101 / 0	20 W	00:50 / 06:18 / 13:05 / 18:18	2.9 / 0.6 / 2.5 / 0.3	88 / 18 / 76 / 9
6 W	00:56 / 06:26 / 13:15 / 18:46	3.5 / 0.2 / 3.2 / 0.0	107 / 6 / 98 / 0	21 Th	01:35 / 07:40 / 13:51 / 19:14	2.8 / 0.7 / 2.4 / 0.4	85 / 21 / 73 / 12
7 Th	01:53 / 07:58 / 14:15 / 19:52	3.6 / 0.3 / 3.1 / 0.0	110 / 9 / 94 / 0	22 F	02:24 / 08:57 / 14:44 / 20:14	2.8 / 0.6 / 2.3 / 0.4	85 / 18 / 70 / 12
8 F	02:55 / 09:26 / 15:21 / 20:56	3.8 / 0.1 / 3.1 / -0.1	116 / 3 / 94 / -3	23 Sa	03:20 / 09:55 / 15:44 / 21:11	2.8 / 0.5 / 2.3 / 0.3	85 / 15 / 70 / 9
9 Sa	04:00 / 10:32 / 16:27 / 21:56	3.9 / 0.0 / 3.1 / -0.2	119 / 0 / 94 / -6	24 Su	04:19 / 10:42 / 16:41 / 22:04	2.8 / 0.3 / 2.4 / 0.1	85 / 9 / 73 / 3
10 Su	05:03 / 11:27 / 17:28 / 22:51	4.1 / -0.1 / 3.3 / -0.3	125 / -3 / 101 / -9	25 M	05:09 / 13:00 / 17:30 / 22:51	3.0 / 0.2 / 2.6 / 0.0	91 / 6 / 79 / 0
11 M	05:59 / 12:19 / 18:23 / 23:43	4.3 / -0.2 / 3.5 / -0.4	131 / -6 / 107 / -12	26 Tu	05:53 / 12:07 / 18:14 / 23:37	3.2 / 0.0 / 2.9 / -0.2	98 / 0 / 88 / -6
12 Tu	06:52 / 13:09 / 19:14	4.4 / -0.3 / 3.7	134 / -9 / 113	27 W	06:33 / 12:48 / 18:56	3.5 / -0.1 / 3.1	107 / -3 / 94
13 W ●	00:34 / 07:41 / 13:55 / 20:03	-0.4 / 4.4 / -0.3 / 3.7	-12 / 134 / -9 / 113	28 Th ○	00:21 / 07:34 / 13:28 / 19:38	-0.4 / 3.7 / -0.3 / 3.3	-12 / 113 / -9 / 101
14 Th	01:26 / 08:29 / 14:33 / 20:51	-0.4 / 4.2 / -0.3 / 3.7	-12 / 128 / -9 / 113	29 F	01:06 / 07:55 / 14:04 / 20:21	-0.5 / 3.8 / -0.4 / 3.5	-15 / 116 / -12 / 107
15 F	02:14 / 09:16 / 15:06 / 21:38	-0.3 / 4.0 / -0.2 / 3.6	-9 / 122 / -6 / 110	30 Sa	01:51 / 08:39 / 14:38 / 21:07	-0.5 / 3.9 / -0.5 / 3.6	-15 / 119 / -15 / 110
				31 Su	02:36 / 09:24 / 15:12 / 21:54	-0.5 / 3.9 / -0.5 / 3.7	-15 / 119 / -15 / 113

February

Day	Time (h m)	Height (ft)	Height (cm)	Day	Time (h m)	Height (ft)	Height (cm)
1 M	03:21 / 10:12 / 15:47 / 22:45	-0.5 / 3.7 / -0.5 / 3.7	-15 / 113 / -15 / 113	16 Tu	03:57 / 10:54 / 16:04 / 23:17	0.0 / 3.0 / 0.0 / 3.1	0 / 91 / 0 / 94
2 Tu	04:08 / 11:04 / 16:27 / 23:38	-0.3 / 3.5 / -0.4 / 3.7	-9 / 107 / -12 / 113	17 W	04:38 / 11:36 / 16:41 / 23:58	0.2 / 2.7 / 0.1 / 2.9	6 / 82 / 3 / 88
3 W	05:02 / 11:59 / 17:14	-0.1 / 3.3 / -0.2	-3 / 101 / -6	18 Th	05:26 / 12:19 / 17:24	0.5 / 2.5 / 0.3	15 / 76 / 9
4 Th ◑	00:34 / 06:09 / 12:56 / 18:10	3.7 / 0.2 / 3.1 / -0.1	113 / 6 / 94 / -3	19 F ◐	00:40 / 06:28 / 13:03 / 18:16	2.8 / 0.6 / 2.3 / 0.4	85 / 18 / 70 / 12
5 F	01:32 / 07:51 / 13:57 / 19:19	3.7 / 0.3 / 2.9 / 0.1	113 / 9 / 88 / 3	20 Sa	01:24 / 07:55 / 13:53 / 19:19	2.6 / 0.7 / 2.2 / 0.5	79 / 21 / 67 / 15
6 Sa	02:35 / 09:33 / 15:04 / 20:36	3.6 / 0.2 / 2.9 / 0.1	110 / 6 / 88 / 3	21 Su	02:17 / 09:17 / 14:52 / 20:28	2.6 / 0.6 / 2.2 / 0.4	79 / 18 / 67 / 12
7 Su	03:45 / 10:38 / 16:13 / 21:50	3.7 / 0.1 / 3.0 / 0.0	113 / 3 / 91 / 0	22 M	03:22 / 10:14 / 15:58 / 21:33	2.7 / 0.5 / 2.4 / 0.3	82 / 15 / 73 / 9
8 M	04:51 / 11:31 / 17:16 / 22:51	3.8 / 0.0 / 3.2 / -0.1	116 / 0 / 98 / -3	23 Tu	04:28 / 10:59 / 16:55 / 22:28	2.9 / 0.3 / 2.6 / 0.0	88 / 9 / 79 / 0
9 Tu	05:49 / 12:18 / 18:10 / 23:43	3.9 / -0.1 / 3.4 / -0.2	119 / -3 / 104 / -6	24 W	05:21 / 11:40 / 17:44 / 23:17	3.2 / 0.0 / 3.0 / -0.2	98 / 0 / 91 / -6
10 W	06:40 / 13:00 / 18:59	4.1 / -0.2 / 3.6	125 / -6 / 110	25 Th	06:07 / 12:18 / 18:30	3.5 / -0.2 / 3.3	107 / -6 / 101
11 Th ●	00:32 / 07:27 / 13:35 / 19:45	-0.3 / 4.1 / -0.2 / 3.7	-9 / 125 / -6 / 113	26 F	00:04 / 06:50 / 12:55 / 19:14	-0.4 / 3.8 / -0.4 / 3.7	-12 / 116 / -12 / 113
12 F ◑	01:18 / 08:10 / 14:04 / 20:29	-0.3 / 4.0 / -0.2 / 3.7	-9 / 122 / -6 / 113	27 Sa ○	00:51 / 07:34 / 13:32 / 19:58	-0.6 / 4.0 / -0.6 / 3.9	-18 / 122 / -18 / 119
13 Sa	02:00 / 08:52 / 14:31 / 21:12	-0.3 / 3.8 / -0.2 / 3.6	-9 / 116 / -6 / 110	28 Su	01:38 / 08:18 / 14:08 / 20:44	-0.7 / 4.1 / -0.7 / 4.1	-21 / 125 / -21 / 125
14 Su	02:40 / 09:33 / 15:00 / 21:54	-0.3 / 3.6 / -0.2 / 3.5	-9 / 110 / -6 / 107				
15 M	03:18 / 10:13 / 15:31 / 22:35	-0.1 / 3.3 / -0.1 / 3.3	-3 / 101 / -3 / 101				

March

Day	Time (h m)	Height (ft)	Height (cm)	Day	Time (h m)	Height (ft)	Height (cm)
1 M	02:25 / 09:05 / 14:45 / 21:32	-0.7 / 4.0 / -0.7 / 4.2	-21 / 122 / -21 / 128	16 Tu	03:55 / 10:40 / 15:55 / 22:55	-0.1 / 3.2 / -0.1 / 3.4	-3 / 98 / -3 / 104
2 Tu	03:11 / 09:54 / 15:22 / 22:23	-0.6 / 3.8 / -0.6 / 4.1	-18 / 116 / -18 / 125	17 W	04:31 / 11:17 / 16:28 / 23:31	0.0 / 3.0 / 0.0 / 3.2	0 / 91 / 0 / 98
3 W	03:58 / 10:46 / 16:03 / 23:17	-0.4 / 3.6 / -0.5 / 4.0	-12 / 110 / -15 / 122	18 Th	05:08 / 11:57 / 17:04	0.2 / 2.7 / 0.1	6 / 82 / 3
4 Th	04:50 / 11:42 / 16:49	-0.1 / 3.4 / -0.2	-3 / 104 / -6	19 F	00:09 / 05:48 / 12:40 / 17:43	3.0 / 0.4 / 2.5 / 0.3	91 / 12 / 76 / 9
5 F	00:14 / 05:57 / 12:41 / 17:45	3.9 / 0.2 / 3.1 / 0.1	119 / 6 / 94 / 3	20 Sa	00:50 / 06:36 / 13:26 / 18:30	2.8 / 0.6 / 2.4 / 0.5	85 / 18 / 73 / 15
6 Sa ◑	01:14 / 08:03 / 13:42 / 18:58	3.7 / 0.4 / 3.0 / 0.3	113 / 12 / 91 / 9	21 Su ◐	01:37 / 07:46 / 14:16 / 19:31	2.7 / 0.8 / 2.4 / 0.6	82 / 24 / 73 / 18
7 Su	02:19 / 09:34 / 14:49 / 20:42	3.5 / 0.3 / 2.9 / 0.4	107 / 9 / 88 / 12	22 M	02:30 / 09:28 / 15:12 / 20:46	2.7 / 0.8 / 2.4 / 0.6	82 / 24 / 73 / 18
8 M	03:30 / 10:35 / 15:59 / 22:12	3.5 / 0.3 / 3.0 / 0.3	107 / 9 / 91 / 9	23 Tu	03:33 / 10:37 / 16:26 / 22:01	2.7 / 0.6 / 2.6 / 0.4	82 / 18 / 79 / 12
9 Tu	04:39 / 11:23 / 17:02 / 23:06	3.6 / 0.2 / 3.2 / 0.1	110 / 6 / 98 / 3	24 W	04:42 / 11:23 / 17:18 / 23:03	2.9 / 0.4 / 2.9 / 0.1	88 / 12 / 88 / 3
10 W	05:36 / 12:03 / 17:55 / 23:50	3.7 / 0.1 / 3.5 / 0.0	113 / 3 / 107 / 0	25 Th	05:44 / 12:01 / 18:13 / 23:55	3.2 / 0.1 / 3.3 / -0.2	98 / 3 / 101 / -6
11 Th	06:24 / 12:34 / 18:42	3.8 / 0.0 / 3.7	116 / 0 / 113	26 F	06:36 / 12:38 / 19:02	3.6 / -0.2 / 3.7	110 / -6 / 113
12 F	00:28 / 07:07 / 12:59 / 19:25	-0.1 / 3.8 / -0.1 / 3.8	-3 / 116 / -3 / 116	27 Sa	00:45 / 07:23 / 13:15 / 19:48	-0.4 / 3.9 / -0.4 / 4.1	-12 / 119 / -12 / 125
13 Sa ●	01:05 / 07:47 / 13:45 / 20:05	-0.2 / 3.8 / -0.1 / 3.8	-6 / 116 / -3 / 116	28 Su ○	01:34 / 08:10 / 14:02 / 20:35	-0.6 / 4.1 / -0.6 / 4.5	-18 / 125 / -18 / 137
14 Su	01:42 / 08:26 / 14:29 / 20:51	-0.2 / 3.7 / -0.2 / 3.8	-6 / 113 / -6 / 116	29 M	02:24 / 08:57 / 14:35 / 21:22	-0.8 / 4.2 / -0.7 / 4.6	-24 / 128 / -21 / 140
15 M	03:19 / 10:03 / 15:22 / 22:20	-0.2 / 3.5 / -0.2 / 3.6	-6 / 107 / -6 / 110	30 Tu	03:13 / 09:45 / 15:16 / 22:11	-0.8 / 4.1 / -0.7 / 4.7	-24 / 125 / -21 / 143
				31 W	04:01 / 10:36 / 15:58 / 23:02	-0.6 / 3.9 / -0.6 / 4.5	-18 / 119 / -18 / 137

StationId: 8452660
Source: NOAA/NOS/CO-OPS
Station Type: Primary
Time Zone: LST_LDT
Datum: MLLW

NOAA Tide Predictions

Newport, RI,2021

Times and Heights of High and Low Waters

April

Day	Time (h m)	Height (ft)	Height (cm)		Day	Time (h m)	Height (ft)	Height (cm)
1 Th	04:49	-0.4	-12		16 F	04:43	0.2	6
	11:30	3.7	113			11:26	2.8	85
	16:42	-0.4	-12			16:33	0.3	9
	23:58	4.3	131			23:30	3.2	98
2 F	05:42	-0.1	-3		17 Sa	05:19	0.4	12
	12:27	3.5	107			12:09	2.7	82
	17:30	0.0	0			17:11	0.4	12
3 Sa	00:57	4.0	122		18 Su	00:14	3.0	91
	06:53	0.3	9			06:01	0.6	18
	13:27	3.3	101			12:57	2.6	79
	18:28	0.3	9			17:56	0.6	18
4 Su ◑	01:59	3.7	113		19 M	01:04	2.9	88
	09:02	0.4	12			06:57	0.7	21
	14:29	3.2	98			13:47	2.6	79
	19:52	0.5	15			18:54	0.7	21
5 M	03:03	3.5	107		20 Tu ◑	01:58	2.9	88
	10:20	0.5	15			08:21	0.8	24
	15:34	3.1	94			14:41	2.7	82
	22:16	0.6	18			20:08	0.7	21
6 Tu	04:12	3.4	104		21 W	02:56	3.0	91
	11:16	0.4	12			09:41	0.6	18
	16:41	3.2	98			15:40	2.9	88
	23:21	0.4	12			21:27	0.5	15
7 W	05:19	3.4	104		22 Th	04:00	3.1	94
	11:58	0.3	9			10:33	0.4	12
	17:43	3.4	104			16:42	3.2	98
						22:36	0.2	6
8 Th	00:07	0.3	9		23 F	05:05	3.3	101
	06:14	3.5	107			11:14	0.1	3
	12:29	0.3	9			17:40	3.6	110
	18:35	3.6	110			23:33	-0.1	-3
9 F	00:42	0.2	6		24 Sa	06:04	3.6	110
	07:01	3.6	110			11:54	-0.2	-6
	12:51	0.2	6			18:33	4.1	125
	19:20	3.8	116					
10 Sa	01:13	0.1	3		25 Su	00:25	-0.3	-9
	07:42	3.6	110			06:56	3.9	119
	13:12	0.1	3			12:35	-0.4	-12
	20:00	3.9	119			19:23	4.5	137
11 Su	01:46	0.0	0		26 M	01:16	-0.5	-15
	08:21	3.6	110			07:46	4.1	125
	13:59	0.0	0			13:48	-0.6	-18
	20:38	3.9	119			20:12	4.8	146
12 M ●	02:21	-0.1	-3		27 Tu ○	02:08	-0.6	-18
	08:57	3.5	107			08:36	4.1	125
	14:11	-0.1	-3			14:03	-0.6	-18
	21:13	3.9	119			21:01	5.0	152
13 Tu	02:57	-0.1	-3		28 W	03:01	-0.6	-18
	09:33	3.4	104			09:27	4.1	125
	14:46	-0.1	-3			14:50	-0.6	-18
	21:46	3.7	113			21:52	4.9	149
14 W	03:33	0.0	0		29 Th	03:52	-0.5	-15
	10:09	3.2	98			10:19	4.0	122
	15:21	0.0	0			15:37	-0.4	-12
	22:19	3.6	110			22:45	4.7	143
15 Th	04:08	0.1	3		30 F	04:42	-0.3	-9
	10:46	3.0	91			11:14	3.8	116
	15:57	0.1	3			16:25	-0.2	-6
	22:53	3.4	104			23:41	4.4	134

May

Day	Time (h m)	Height (ft)	Height (cm)		Day	Time (h m)	Height (ft)	Height (cm)
1 Sa	05:36	0.0	0		16 Su	04:59	0.4	12
	12:12	3.6	110			11:45	2.9	88
	17:17	0.1	3			16:48	0.5	15
						23:49	3.2	98
2 Su	00:41	4.1	125		17 M	05:38	0.6	18
	06:52	0.3	9			12:33	2.8	85
	13:12	3.5	107			17:32	0.6	18
	18:18	0.5	15					
3 M ◑	01:42	3.8	116		18 Tu	00:40	3.2	98
	08:39	0.5	15			06:25	0.6	18
	14:13	3.4	104			13:23	2.9	88
	20:10	0.7	21			18:27	0.7	21
4 Tu	02:43	3.5	107		19 W ◐	01:33	3.2	98
	09:49	0.5	15			07:27	0.6	18
	15:14	3.4	104			14:15	3.0	91
	22:07	0.7	21			19:37	0.7	21
5 W	03:45	3.3	101		20 Th	02:28	3.2	98
	10:40	0.5	15			08:36	0.5	15
	16:17	3.4	104			15:10	3.3	101
	23:04	0.6	18			20:56	0.6	18
6 Th	04:48	3.3	101		21 F	03:27	3.3	101
	11:15	0.5	15			09:35	0.3	9
	17:17	3.5	107			16:09	3.6	110
	23:46	0.5	15			22:09	0.3	9
7 F	05:44	3.3	101		22 Sa	04:30	3.4	104
	11:39	0.4	12			10:25	0.1	3
	18:09	3.7	113			17:09	4.0	122
						23:11	0.1	3
8 Sa	00:19	0.4	12		23 Su	05:33	3.6	110
	06:31	3.3	101			11:13	-0.2	-6
	11:59	0.3	9			18:06	4.4	134
	18:53	3.8	116					
9 Su	00:49	0.3	9		24 M	00:06	-0.2	-6
	07:13	3.3	101			06:31	3.8	116
	12:26	0.2	6			11:59	-0.3	-9
	19:33	3.9	119			18:59	4.8	146
10 M	01:21	0.2	6		25 Tu	01:00	-0.4	-12
	07:52	3.3	101			07:25	3.9	119
	12:58	0.1	3			12:47	-0.5	-15
	20:09	3.9	119			19:51	5.0	152
11 Tu ●	01:57	0.1	3		26 W ○	01:54	-0.4	-12
	08:29	3.3	101			08:18	4.1	125
	13:35	0.1	3			13:36	-0.5	-15
	20:43	3.9	119			20:43	5.1	155
12 W	02:36	0.1	3		27 Th	02:50	-0.4	-12
	09:05	0.1	3			09:10	4.1	125
	14:13	0.1	3			14:28	-0.4	-12
	21:15	3.8	116			21:35	5.0	152
13 Th	03:14	0.1	3		28 F	03:44	-0.3	-9
	09:42	3.2	98			10:03	4.0	122
	15:21	0.2	6			15:21	-0.3	-9
	21:49	3.6	110			22:30	4.8	146
14 F	03:50	0.2	6		29 Sa	04:35	-0.1	-3
	10:20	3.1	94			10:58	3.9	119
	15:30	0.3	9			16:13	0.0	0
	22:24	3.5	107			23:25	4.4	134
15 Sa	04:25	0.3	9		30 Su	05:27	0.1	3
	11:00	2.9	88			11:55	3.8	116
	16:08	0.4	12			17:06	0.3	9
	23:04	3.3	101					
					31 M	00:22	4.1	125
						06:29	0.3	9
						12:53	3.7	113
						18:08	0.6	18

June

Day	Time (h m)	Height (ft)	Height (cm)		Day	Time (h m)	Height (ft)	Height (cm)
1 Tu	01:20	3.8	116		16 W	00:18	3.5	107
	07:48	0.5	15			05:59	0.4	12
	13:51	3.6	110			12:59	3.2	98
	19:48	0.8	24			18:07	0.6	18
2 W ◑	02:16	3.5	107		17 Th	01:10	3.4	104
	08:54	0.6	18			06:48	0.4	12
	14:48	3.5	107			13:50	3.4	104
	21:32	0.8	24			19:12	0.6	18
3 Th	03:11	3.3	101		18 F ◐	02:03	3.4	104
	09:39	0.6	18			07:45	0.3	9
	15:45	3.5	107			14:43	3.6	110
	22:30	0.8	24			20:29	0.6	18
4 F	04:07	3.1	94		19 Sa	03:00	3.4	104
	10:10	0.6	18			08:45	0.2	6
	16:42	3.5	107			15:40	3.9	119
	23:12	0.7	21			21:47	0.4	12
5 Sa	05:04	3.0	91		20 Su	04:02	3.4	104
	10:38	0.5	15			09:43	0.1	3
	17:36	3.6	110			16:41	4.2	128
	23:47	0.6	18			22:54	0.2	6
6 Su	05:55	3.0	91		21 M	05:07	3.5	107
	11:10	0.4	12			10:38	-0.1	-3
	18:22	3.7	113			17:43	4.5	137
						23:53	0.0	0
7 M	00:20	0.5	15		22 Tu	06:10	3.6	110
	06:41	3.1	94			11:31	-0.2	-6
	11:46	0.4	12			18:40	4.7	143
	19:03	3.8	116					
8 Tu	00:56	0.4	12		23 W	00:48	-0.1	-3
	07:21	3.1	94			07:07	3.8	116
	12:24	0.3	9			12:23	-0.3	-9
	19:39	3.8	116					
9 W	01:35	0.3	9		24 Th ○	01:45	-0.2	-6
	08:00	3.2	98			08:01	4.0	122
	13:04	0.2	6			13:17	-0.3	-9
	20:14	3.8	116			20:28	5.0	152
10 Th ●	02:16	0.2	6		25 F	02:42	-0.2	-6
	08:38	3.2	98			08:54	4.1	125
	13:45	0.2	6			14:12	-0.2	-6
	20:49	3.8	116			21:21	4.9	149
11 F	02:57	0.2	6		26 Sa	03:35	-0.1	-3
	09:16	3.2	98			09:47	4.1	125
	14:27	0.2	6			15:08	-0.1	-3
	21:24	3.7	113			22:13	4.7	143
12 Sa	03:35	0.2	6		27 Su	04:22	0.0	0
	09:55	3.2	98			10:40	4.0	122
	15:09	0.3	9			16:02	0.1	3
	22:02	3.6	110			23:06	4.4	134
13 Su	04:10	0.3	9		28 M	05:04	0.1	3
	10:37	3.1	94			11:34	3.9	119
	15:49	0.3	9			16:53	0.3	9
	22:43	3.6	110			23:59	4.1	125
14 M	04:43	0.4	12		29 Tu	05:46	0.3	9
	11:22	3.1	94			12:29	3.8	116
	16:30	0.4	12			17:47	0.5	15
	23:29	3.5	107					
15 Tu	05:18	0.4	12		30 W	00:51	3.7	113
	12:09	3.1	94			06:29	0.5	15
	17:15	0.5	15			13:23	3.7	113
						18:53	0.8	24

StationId: 8452660
Source: NOAA/NOS/CO-OPS
Station Type: Primary
Time Zone: LST_LDT
Datum: MLLW

July

Day	Time	ft	cm	Day	Time	ft	cm
1 Th ☽	01:42	3.4	104	16 F	00:49	3.6	110
	07:16	0.6	18		06:14	0.2	6
	14:15	3.6	110		13:26	3.8	116
	20:26	0.9	27		18:51	0.5	15
2 F	02:32	3.2	98	17 Sa ☾	01:42	3.5	107
	08:05	0.6	18		07:06	0.2	6
	15:06	3.5	107		14:20	3.9	119
	21:38	0.9	27		20:08	0.6	18
3 Sa	03:22	2.9	88	18 Su	02:39	3.4	104
	08:53	0.7	21		08:06	0.2	6
	15:59	3.4	104		15:17	4.1	125
	22:30	0.9	27		21:34	0.5	15
4 Su	04:17	2.8	85	19 M	03:40	3.3	101
	09:40	0.6	18		09:10	0.2	6
	16:54	3.4	104		16:19	4.2	128
	23:12	0.8	24		22:49	0.4	12
5 M	05:13	2.8	85	20 Tu	04:47	3.4	104
	10:26	0.6	18		10:13	0.1	3
	17:46	3.5	107		17:25	4.4	134
	23:52	0.6	18		23:50	0.2	6
6 Tu	06:05	2.8	85	21 W	05:53	3.5	107
	11:11	0.5	15		11:14	0.0	0
	18:31	3.5	107		18:26	4.6	140
7 W	00:32	0.5	15	22 Th	00:45	0.1	3
	06:50	3.0	91		06:52	3.7	113
	11:55	0.4	12		12:11	0.0	0
	19:10	3.6	110		19:22	4.7	143
8 Th	01:13	0.4	12	23 F	01:39	0.0	0
	07:31	3.1	94		07:47	3.9	119
	12:39	0.3	9		13:06	-0.1	-3
	19:47	3.7	113		20:15	4.8	146
9 F	01:56	0.3	9	24 Sa ○	02:31	0.0	0
	08:11	3.2	98		08:38	4.1	125
	13:23	0.3	9		14:02	-0.1	-3
	20:24	3.8	116		21:05	4.7	143
10 Sa ●	02:39	0.3	9	25 Su	03:17	0.0	0
	08:50	3.3	101		09:29	4.2	128
	14:07	0.2	6		14:57	0.0	0
	21:02	3.8	116		21:54	4.5	137
11 Su	03:17	0.2	6	26 M	03:55	0.0	0
	09:30	3.4	104		10:18	4.1	125
	14:51	0.2	6		15:47	0.1	3
	21:41	3.9	119		22:42	4.3	131
12 M	03:51	0.2	6	27 Tu	04:27	0.1	3
	10:13	3.4	104		11:08	4.0	122
	15:33	0.2	6		16:30	0.3	9
	22:23	3.8	116		23:30	4.0	122
13 Tu	04:22	0.2	6	28 W	04:59	0.2	6
	10:57	3.5	107		11:58	3.9	119
	16:15	0.3	9		17:18	0.5	15
	23:08	3.8	116				
14 W	04:54	0.2	6	29 Th	00:17	3.6	110
	11:45	3.5	107		05:34	0.4	12
	17:00	0.3	9		12:48	3.7	113
	23:57	3.7	113		18:07	0.7	21
15 Th	05:31	0.2	6	30 F	01:05	3.3	101
	12:35	3.7	113		06:13	0.5	15
	17:50	0.4	12		13:36	3.5	107
					19:09	0.9	27
				31 Sa ☾	01:51	3.0	91
					06:58	0.6	18
					14:23	3.4	104
					20:28	1.0	30

August

Day	Time	ft	cm	Day	Time	ft	cm
1 Su	02:38	2.8	85	16 M	02:23	3.4	104
	07:51	0.7	21		07:37	0.4	12
	15:11	3.3	101		14:59	4.1	125
	21:42	1.0	30		21:41	0.6	18
2 M	03:29	2.7	82	17 Tu	03:26	3.3	101
	08:48	0.8	24		08:49	0.4	12
	16:04	3.2	98		16:04	4.1	125
	22:39	0.9	27		22:58	0.5	15
3 Tu	04:27	2.7	82	18 W	04:34	3.3	101
	09:47	0.7	21		10:05	0.4	12
	17:02	3.2	98		17:13	4.2	128
	23:26	0.8	24		23:55	0.4	12
4 W	05:26	2.7	82	19 Th	05:40	3.5	107
	10:42	0.6	18		11:13	0.3	9
	17:56	3.3	101		18:15	4.4	134
5 Th	00:09	0.6	18	20 F	00:45	0.3	9
	06:17	2.9	88		06:40	3.8	116
	11:32	0.5	15		12:11	0.2	6
	18:40	3.5	107		19:10	4.5	137
6 F	00:50	0.5	15	21 Sa	01:29	0.2	6
	07:01	3.1	94		07:32	4.0	122
	12:19	0.3	9		13:04	0.1	3
	19:20	3.7	113		20:00	4.6	140
7 Sa	01:31	0.3	9	22 Su ○	02:10	0.1	3
	07:42	3.3	101		08:21	4.2	128
	13:04	0.2	6		13:55	0.0	0
	19:58	3.9	119		20:46	4.5	137
8 Su ●	02:11	0.2	6	23 M	02:44	0.1	3
	08:23	3.5	107		09:08	4.3	131
	13:49	0.1	3		14:43	0.1	3
	20:37	4.0	122		21:31	4.4	134
9 M	02:47	0.2	6	24 Tu	03:14	0.1	3
	09:04	3.7	113		09:53	4.2	128
	14:33	0.0	0		15:26	0.1	3
	21:18	4.1	125		22:14	4.1	125
10 Tu	03:20	0.0	0	25 W	03:44	0.1	3
	09:47	3.8	116		10:38	4.1	125
	15:18	0.0	0		16:07	0.3	9
	22:01	4.1	125		22:57	3.8	116
11 W	03:52	0.0	0	26 Th	04:16	0.2	6
	10:32	3.9	119		11:22	3.9	119
	16:01	0.1	3		16:47	0.5	15
	22:47	4.0	122		23:41	3.5	107
12 Th	04:25	-0.1	-3	27 F	04:49	0.3	9
	11:19	4.0	122		12:07	3.7	113
	16:46	0.1	3		17:28	0.7	21
	23:36	3.8	116				
13 F	05:02	0.0	0	28 Sa	00:26	3.2	98
	12:10	4.1	125		05:26	0.5	15
	17:35	0.3	9		12:51	3.5	107
					18:17	0.9	27
14 Sa	00:29	3.7	113	29 Su	01:11	3.0	91
	05:44	0.1	3		06:08	0.6	18
	13:04	4.1	125		13:35	3.3	101
	18:34	0.5	15		19:20	1.0	30
15 Su ◐	01:25	3.5	107	30 M ◐	01:57	2.8	85
	06:35	0.2	6		06:59	0.6	18
	13:59	4.1	125		14:20	3.1	94
	19:54	0.6	18		20:49	1.1	34
				31 Tu	02:46	2.7	82
					08:02	0.9	27
					15:10	3.0	91
					22:06	1.0	30

September

Day	Time	ft	cm	Day	Time	ft	cm
1 W	03:41	2.6	79	16 Th	04:22	3.4	104
	09:11	0.9	27		10:26	0.6	18
	16:10	3.1	94		17:01	4.0	122
	23:00	0.9	27		23:52	0.5	15
2 Th	04:43	2.7	82	17 F	05:28	3.6	110
	10:16	0.9	27		11:32	0.4	12
	17:13	3.2	98		18:03	4.1	125
	23:43	0.7	21				
3 F	05:40	3.0	91	18 Sa	00:33	0.4	12
	11:11	0.5	15		06:26	3.9	119
	18:04	3.4	104		12:21	0.3	9
					18:55	4.2	128
4 Sa	00:22	0.5	15	19 Su	01:07	0.3	9
	06:28	3.2	98		07:16	4.1	125
	11:59	0.3	9		13:04	0.2	6
	18:48	3.7	113		19:41	4.3	131
5 Su	00:58	0.3	9	20 M ○	01:34	0.2	6
	07:12	3.6	110		08:01	4.3	131
	12:44	0.1	3		13:44	0.2	6
	19:29	3.9	119		20:24	4.2	128
6 M	01:33	0.1	3	21 Tu	02:00	0.1	3
	07:54	3.9	119		08:44	4.3	131
	13:29	0.0	0		14:23	0.1	3
	20:10	4.1	125		21:05	4.1	125
7 Tu ●	02:07	-0.1	-3	22 W	02:30	0.1	3
	08:36	4.1	125		09:25	4.3	131
	14:15	-0.1	-3		15:02	0.2	6
	20:53	4.2	128		21:45	3.9	119
8 W	02:42	-0.2	-6	23 Th	03:02	0.1	3
	09:20	4.3	131		10:05	4.1	125
	15:01	-0.2	-6		15:40	0.3	9
	21:38	4.2	128		22:24	3.6	110
9 Th	03:18	-0.3	-9	24 F	03:36	0.2	6
	10:06	4.4	134		10:44	3.9	119
	15:47	-0.1	-3		16:17	0.4	12
	22:25	4.1	125		23:05	3.4	104
10 F	03:56	-0.2	-6	25 Sa	04:11	0.3	9
	10:55	4.5	137		11:23	3.6	110
	16:33	0.0	0		16:55	0.6	18
	23:17	3.9	119		23:47	3.1	94
11 Sa	04:36	-0.1	-3	26 Su	04:48	0.5	15
	11:47	4.4	134		12:04	3.4	104
	17:22	0.2	6		17:37	0.8	24
12 Su	00:12	3.7	113	27 M	00:32	2.9	88
	05:20	0.1	3		05:29	0.7	21
	12:43	4.3	131		12:47	3.2	98
	18:21	0.5	15		18:28	1.0	30
13 M ◐	01:10	3.5	107	28 Tu	01:20	2.7	82
	06:12	0.3	9		06:16	0.8	24
	13:34	4.2	128		13:34	3.0	91
	20:01	0.7	21		19:47	1.1	34
14 Tu	02:11	3.4	104	29 W ◐	02:09	2.7	82
	07:18	0.5	15		07:17	1.0	30
	14:45	4.0	122		14:24	3.0	91
	21:56	0.7	21		21:29	1.1	34
15 W	03:14	3.3	101	30 Th	03:02	2.7	82
	08:46	0.7	21		08:33	1.0	30
	15:52	4.0	122		15:21	3.0	91
	23:01	0.6	18		22:28	0.9	27

StationId: 8452660
Source: NOAA/NOS/CO-OPS
Station Type: Primary
Time Zone: LST_LDT
Datum: MLLW

NOAA Tide Predictions

Newport, RI, 2021

Times and Heights of High and Low Waters

October

Day	h m	ft	cm
1 F	04:00	2.8	85
	09:47	0.8	24
	16:23	3.1	94
	23:10	0.7	21
2 Sa	05:00	3.1	94
	10:48	0.6	18
	17:22	3.4	104
	23:45	0.4	12
3 Su	05:53	3.4	104
	11:37	0.3	9
	18:12	3.7	113
4 M	00:17	0.2	6
	06:40	3.8	116
	12:23	0.0	0
	18:58	4.0	122
5 Tu	00:51	-0.1	-3
	07:25	4.2	128
	13:09	-0.2	-6
	19:43	4.2	128
6 W ●	01:27	-0.3	-9
	08:09	4.5	137
	13:56	-0.3	-9
	20:29	4.3	131
7 Th	02:05	-0.4	-12
	08:55	4.8	146
	14:44	-0.4	-12
	21:16	4.2	128
8 F	02:46	-0.4	-12
	09:42	4.8	146
	15:33	-0.3	-9
	22:06	4.1	125
9 Sa	03:29	-0.3	-9
	10:33	4.8	146
	16:21	-0.1	-3
	22:59	3.9	119
10 Su	04:13	-0.2	-6
	11:27	4.6	140
	17:12	0.1	3
	23:56	3.7	113
11 M	05:01	0.1	3
	12:26	4.3	131
	18:14	0.4	12
12 Tu	00:57	3.5	107
	05:56	0.4	12
	13:28	4.1	125
	20:21	0.7	21
13 W ◐	01:59	3.4	104
	07:09	0.7	21
	14:32	3.9	119
	21:49	0.6	18
14 Th	03:02	3.4	104
	09:29	0.7	21
	15:37	3.8	116
	22:48	0.6	18
15 F	04:08	3.5	107
	10:50	0.6	18
	16:44	3.8	116
	23:34	0.5	15

Day	h m	ft	cm
16 Sa	05:12	3.7	113
	11:41	0.5	15
	17:43	3.8	116
17 Su	00:08	0.4	12
	06:08	3.9	119
	12:22	0.4	12
	18:34	3.9	119
18 M	00:32	0.3	9
	06:56	4.1	125
	12:56	0.3	9
	19:18	3.9	119
19 Tu	00:52	0.2	6
	07:39	4.2	128
	13:28	0.2	6
	19:59	3.9	119
20 W ○	01:18	0.1	3
	08:19	4.2	128
	14:02	0.2	6
	20:38	3.8	116
21 Th	01:49	0.1	3
	08:57	4.2	128
	14:38	0.2	6
	21:16	3.6	110
22 F	02:24	0.1	3
	09:33	4.0	122
	15:15	0.2	6
	21:54	3.4	104
23 Sa	03:01	0.2	6
	10:08	3.8	116
	15:52	0.3	9
	22:32	3.2	98
24 Su	03:39	0.3	9
	10:43	3.6	110
	16:29	0.5	15
	23:13	3.0	91
25 M	04:17	0.4	12
	11:22	3.3	101
	17:07	0.6	18
	23:57	2.8	85
26 Tu	04:57	0.6	18
	12:05	3.1	94
	17:51	0.8	24
27 W	00:46	2.7	82
	05:42	0.8	24
	12:54	3.0	91
	18:50	1.0	30
28 Th ◑	01:36	2.7	82
	06:38	0.9	27
	13:46	3.0	91
	20:25	1.0	30
29 F	02:27	2.7	82
	07:51	0.9	27
	14:40	3.0	91
	21:37	0.8	24
30 Sa	03:22	2.9	88
	09:11	0.8	24
	15:38	3.1	94
	22:21	0.6	18
31 Su	04:20	3.2	98
	10:19	0.5	15
	16:38	3.3	101
	22:57	0.3	9

November

Day	h m	ft	cm
1 M	05:16	3.6	110
	11:13	0.2	6
	17:36	3.5	107
	23:33	0.0	0
2 Tu	06:08	4.0	122
	12:02	-0.1	-3
	18:28	3.8	116
3 W	00:11	-0.3	-9
	06:57	4.4	134
	12:49	-0.3	-9
	19:18	4.0	122
4 Th ●	00:51	-0.5	-15
	07:45	4.8	146
	13:39	-0.4	-12
	20:07	4.1	125
5 F	01:34	-0.6	-18
	08:33	5.0	152
	14:29	-0.5	-15
	20:57	4.1	125
6 Sa	02:20	-0.6	-18
	09:23	5.0	152
	15:21	-0.4	-12
	21:49	4.1	125
7 Su	02:08	-0.5	-15
	09:15	4.9	149
	15:12	-0.2	-6
	21:43	3.9	119
8 M	02:57	-0.3	-9
	10:11	4.6	140
	16:04	0.0	0
	22:40	3.7	113
9 Tu	03:48	0.0	0
	11:10	4.3	131
	17:10	0.3	9
	23:41	3.6	110
10 W	04:46	0.4	12
	12:12	4.0	122
	19:03	0.5	15
11 Th ◐	00:43	3.5	107
	06:08	0.6	18
	13:14	3.8	116
	20:22	0.5	15
12 F	01:45	3.5	107
	08:34	0.7	21
	14:15	3.6	110
	21:19	0.5	15
13 Sa	02:48	3.5	107
	09:42	0.6	18
	15:17	3.5	107
	22:01	0.4	12
14 Su	03:50	3.6	110
	10:30	0.5	15
	16:16	3.4	104
	22:29	0.4	12
15 M	04:45	3.8	116
	11:08	0.4	12
	17:07	3.4	104
	22:49	0.3	9

Day	h m	ft	cm
16 Tu	05:33	3.9	119
	11:39	0.3	9
	17:52	3.4	104
	23:12	0.2	6
17 W	06:15	4.0	122
	12:09	0.2	6
	18:33	3.4	104
	23:41	0.1	3
18 Th	06:54	4.0	122
	12:41	0.2	6
	19:12	3.4	104
19 F ○	00:16	0.1	3
	07:30	3.9	119
	13:17	0.1	3
	19:49	3.3	101
20 Sa	00:54	0.1	3
	08:04	3.8	116
	13:55	0.1	3
	20:27	3.2	98
21 Su	01:34	0.1	3
	08:38	3.7	113
	14:33	0.2	6
	21:05	3.1	94
22 M	02:14	0.2	6
	09:13	3.5	107
	15:09	0.3	9
	21:44	2.9	88
23 Tu	02:53	0.3	9
	09:51	3.3	101
	15:46	0.4	12
	22:27	2.8	85
24 W	03:33	0.4	12
	10:34	3.1	94
	16:24	0.6	18
	23:14	2.7	82
25 Th	04:15	0.5	15
	11:21	3.0	91
	17:08	0.7	21
26 F ◑	00:04	2.7	82
	05:05	0.6	18
	12:12	3.0	91
	18:05	0.7	21
27 Sa	00:54	2.8	85
	06:10	0.7	21
	13:05	3.0	91
	19:13	0.6	18
28 Su	01:46	3.0	91
	07:29	0.6	18
	14:00	3.1	94
	20:12	0.4	12
29 M	02:42	3.3	101
	08:45	0.4	12
	15:00	3.2	98
	21:03	0.1	3
30 Tu	03:41	3.6	110
	09:48	0.2	6
	16:02	3.3	101
	21:49	-0.1	-3

December

Day	h m	ft	cm
1 W	04:38	4.1	125
	10:42	-0.1	-3
	17:01	3.5	107
	22:35	-0.4	-12
2 Th	05:32	4.5	137
	11:33	-0.4	-12
	17:56	3.7	113
	23:21	-0.6	-18
3 F	06:24	4.8	146
	12:24	-0.5	-15
	18:48	3.9	119
4 Sa ●	00:09	-0.7	-21
	07:15	4.9	149
	13:18	-0.5	-15
	19:40	4.0	122
5 Su	01:00	-0.7	-21
	08:07	4.9	149
	14:12	-0.5	-15
	20:33	4.0	122
6 M	01:53	-0.6	-18
	09:00	4.8	146
	15:04	-0.3	-9
	21:27	3.9	119
7 Tu	02:46	-0.4	-12
	09:55	4.5	137
	15:56	-0.1	-3
	22:24	3.8	116
8 W	03:39	-0.1	-3
	10:53	4.2	128
	16:51	0.1	3
	23:22	3.6	110
9 Th	04:36	0.2	6
	11:51	3.9	119
	18:06	0.3	9
10 F	00:22	3.5	107
	05:53	0.5	15
	12:48	3.6	110
	19:28	0.4	12
11 Sa ◐	01:20	3.4	104
	08:04	0.6	18
	13:45	3.3	101
	20:26	0.4	12
12 Su	02:19	3.4	104
	09:15	0.6	18
	14:42	3.1	94
	21:06	0.4	12
13 M	03:19	3.4	104
	10:06	0.5	15
	15:41	3.0	91
	21:34	0.4	12
14 Tu	04:16	3.5	107
	10:44	0.5	15
	16:36	2.9	88
	22:02	0.3	9
15 W	05:07	3.5	107
	11:17	0.4	12
	17:25	2.9	88
	22:35	0.2	6

Day	h m	ft	cm
16 Th	05:51	3.6	110
	11:48	0.2	6
	18:08	3.0	91
	23:11	0.1	3
17 F	06:30	3.6	110
	12:23	0.1	3
	18:47	3.0	91
	23:50	0.0	0
18 Sa	07:06	3.6	110
	13:01	0.1	3
	19:25	3.1	94
19 Su ○	00:31	0.0	0
	07:41	3.6	110
	13:40	0.0	0
	20:02	3.1	94
20 M	01:13	0.0	0
	08:15	3.5	107
	14:19	0.0	0
	20:40	3.0	91
21 Tu	01:55	0.0	0
	08:50	3.4	104
	14:54	0.1	3
	21:19	2.9	88
22 W	02:35	0.0	0
	09:27	3.3	101
	15:27	0.1	3
	22:00	2.9	88
23 Th	03:14	0.1	3
	10:08	3.2	98
	15:59	0.2	6
	22:45	2.8	85
24 F	03:55	0.2	6
	10:54	3.1	94
	16:35	0.2	6
	23:33	2.9	88
25 Sa	04:40	0.3	9
	11:43	3.1	94
	17:17	0.2	6
26 Su ◐	00:23	3.0	91
	05:37	0.4	12
	12:35	3.0	91
	18:09	0.2	6
27 M ◑	01:14	3.2	98
	06:49	0.4	12
	13:29	3.0	91
	19:09	0.1	3
28 Tu	02:09	3.4	104
	08:10	0.3	9
	14:28	3.0	91
	20:11	0.0	0
29 W	03:09	3.6	110
	09:24	0.1	3
	15:34	3.0	91
	21:10	-0.2	-6
30 Th	04:12	3.9	119
	10:26	-0.1	-3
	16:39	3.2	98
	22:06	-0.4	-12
31 F	05:12	4.3	131
	11:22	-0.3	-9
	17:38	3.5	107
	22:59	-0.5	-15

StationId: 8510560
Source: NOAA/NOS/CO-OPS
Station Type: Primary
Time Zone: LST_LDT
Datum: MLLW

Montauk, NY, 2021

Times and Heights of High and Low Waters

January

Day	Time (h m)	Height (ft)	Height (cm)	Day	Time (h m)	Height (ft)	Height (cm)
1 F	04:10	0.0	0	16 Sa	05:13	-0.2	-6
	10:21	2.3	70		11:05	2.2	67
	17:11	-0.3	-9		17:49	-0.3	-9
	22:52	1.6	49		23:33	1.9	58
2 Sa	05:00	0.0	0	17 Su	06:08	0.0	0
	11:03	2.2	67		11:53	2.0	61
	17:59	-0.3	-9		18:36	-0.1	-3
	23:38	1.7	52				
3 Su	05:57	0.1	3	18 M	00:23	1.9	58
	11:48	2.1	64		07:07	0.1	3
	18:49	-0.3	-9		12:40	1.8	55
					19:22	0.0	0
4 M	00:27	1.8	55	19 Tu	01:15	1.8	55
	06:59	0.1	3		08:06	0.2	6
	12:36	2.0	61		13:31	1.5	46
	19:39	-0.2	-6		20:09	0.1	3
5 Tu	01:18	1.9	58	20 W ◑	02:09	1.8	55
	08:03	0.0	0		09:05	0.2	6
	13:29	1.8	55		14:25	1.3	40
	20:29	-0.2	-6		20:54	0.3	9
6 W ◑	02:13	2.0	61	21 Th	03:07	1.8	55
	09:07	-0.1	-3		10:00	0.2	6
	14:28	1.7	52		15:23	1.2	37
	21:19	-0.2	-6		21:40	0.3	9
7 Th	03:13	2.2	67	22 F	04:06	1.8	55
	10:08	-0.2	-6		10:53	0.2	6
	15:32	1.6	49		16:22	1.2	37
	22:11	-0.2	-6		22:27	0.3	9
8 F	04:12	2.4	73	23 Sa	05:02	1.9	58
	11:08	-0.3	-9		11:42	0.2	6
	16:34	1.6	49		17:16	1.2	37
	23:04	-0.3	-9		23:15	0.3	9
9 Sa	05:10	2.5	76	24 Su	05:51	1.9	58
	12:06	-0.4	-12		12:28	0.1	3
	17:32	1.6	49		18:04	1.3	40
	23:58	-0.3	-9				
10 Su	06:04	2.7	82	25 M	00:04	0.2	6
	13:01	-0.5	-15		06:35	2.0	61
	18:25	1.7	52		13:11	0.0	0
					18:48	1.4	43
11 M	00:53	-0.4	-12	26 Tu	00:52	0.1	3
	06:56	2.8	85		07:17	2.1	64
	13:53	-0.6	-18		13:53	-0.2	-6
	19:17	1.7	52		19:31	1.5	46
12 Tu	01:47	-0.4	-12	27 W	01:38	0.0	0
	07:48	2.8	85		07:57	2.2	67
	14:42	-0.6	-18		14:35	-0.3	-9
	20:08	1.8	55		20:13	1.6	49
13 W ●	02:39	-0.5	-15	28 Th ○	02:23	-0.1	-3
	08:38	2.7	82		08:36	2.3	70
	15:30	-0.6	-18		15:16	-0.4	-12
	20:59	1.9	58		20:56	1.7	52
14 Th	03:30	-0.4	-12	29 F	03:08	-0.2	-6
	09:28	2.6	79		09:16	2.4	73
	16:16	-0.6	-18		15:58	-0.5	-15
	21:50	1.9	58		21:40	1.8	55
15 F	04:21	-0.3	-9	30 Sa	03:55	-0.3	-9
	10:17	2.4	73		09:58	2.4	73
	17:02	-0.4	-12		16:41	-0.5	-15
	22:42	1.9	58		22:24	1.9	58
				31 Su	04:45	-0.3	-9
					10:41	2.3	70
					17:25	-0.5	-15
					23:10	2.0	61

February

Day	Time (h m)	Height (ft)	Height (cm)	Day	Time (h m)	Height (ft)	Height (cm)
1 M	05:41	-0.3	-9	16 Tu	06:29	0.1	3
	11:25	2.2	67		12:07	1.7	52
	18:12	-0.4	-12		18:28	0.2	6
	23:57	2.1	64				
2 Tu	06:41	-0.2	-6	17 W	00:33	2.0	61
	12:13	2.0	61		07:24	0.2	6
	19:02	-0.3	-9		12:53	1.5	46
					19:12	0.3	9
3 W	00:48	2.2	67	18 Th	01:23	1.9	58
	07:44	-0.2	-6		08:20	0.3	9
	13:05	1.8	55		13:43	1.4	43
	19:55	-0.2	-6		20:00	0.4	12
4 Th ◑	01:43	2.3	70	19 F ◐	02:18	1.8	55
	08:47	-0.2	-6		09:16	0.3	9
	14:03	1.6	49		14:41	1.2	37
	20:50	-0.1	-3		20:52	0.5	15
5 F	02:45	2.3	70	20 Sa	03:21	1.8	55
	09:50	-0.2	-6		10:10	0.3	9
	15:08	1.5	46		15:43	1.2	37
	21:48	-0.1	-3		21:48	0.5	15
6 Sa	03:51	2.3	70	21 Su	04:25	1.8	55
	10:52	-0.3	-9		11:03	0.3	9
	16:15	1.4	43		16:43	1.3	40
	22:48	-0.1	-3		22:43	0.4	12
7 Su	04:55	2.4	73	22 M	05:21	1.9	58
	11:51	-0.3	-9		11:52	0.2	6
	17:18	1.5	46		17:36	1.4	43
	23:48	-0.2	-6		23:37	0.3	9
8 M	05:54	2.4	73	23 Tu	06:08	2.0	61
	12:47	-0.4	-12		12:39	0.1	3
	18:14	1.6	49		18:22	1.5	46
9 Tu	00:46	-0.2	-6	24 W	00:28	0.2	6
	06:47	2.5	76		06:50	2.2	67
	13:38	-0.4	-12		13:22	-0.1	-3
	19:05	1.7	52		19:04	1.7	52
10 W	01:40	-0.3	-9	25 Th	01:17	0.0	0
	07:37	2.5	76		07:29	2.3	70
	14:25	-0.5	-15		14:04	-0.3	-9
	19:54	1.9	58		19:46	1.9	58
11 Th ●	02:30	-0.4	-12	26 F	02:04	-0.2	-6
	08:23	2.5	76		08:09	2.4	73
	15:06	-0.5	-15		14:45	-0.4	-12
	20:42	2.0	61		20:27	2.1	64
12 F	03:17	-0.3	-9	27 Sa ○	02:51	-0.3	-9
	09:09	2.4	73		08:50	2.5	76
	15:50	-0.4	-12		15:26	-0.5	-15
	21:29	2.1	64		21:11	2.3	70
13 Sa	04:04	-0.3	-9	28 Su	03:39	-0.4	-12
	09:53	2.3	70		09:32	2.5	76
	16:30	-0.3	-9		16:08	-0.5	-15
	22:16	2.1	64		21:55	2.5	76
14 Su	04:50	-0.2	-6				
	10:38	2.1	64				
	17:09	-0.2	-6				
	23:02	2.1	64				
15 M	05:38	-0.1	-3				
	11:22	1.9	58				
	17:48	0.0	0				
	23:47	2.1	64				

March

Day	Time (h m)	Height (ft)	Height (cm)	Day	Time (h m)	Height (ft)	Height (cm)
1 M	04:30	-0.5	-15	16 Tu	06:09	0.0	0
	10:17	2.4	73		11:53	2.0	61
	16:51	-0.4	-12		18:01	0.2	6
	22:42	2.6	79				
2 Tu	05:24	-0.5	-15	17 W	00:11	2.3	70
	11:04	2.2	67		06:55	0.1	3
	17:38	-0.3	-9		12:36	1.8	55
	23:30	2.6	79		18:37	0.4	12
3 W	06:22	-0.4	-12	18 Th	00:54	2.2	67
	11:53	2.0	61		07:45	0.2	6
	18:29	-0.2	-6		13:21	1.7	52
					19:18	0.5	15
4 Th	00:22	2.6	79	19 F	01:40	2.1	64
	07:25	-0.3	-9		08:39	0.3	9
	12:46	1.8	55		14:09	1.5	46
	19:27	0.0	0		20:10	0.7	21
5 F	01:19	2.5	76	20 Sa	02:32	2.0	61
	08:29	-0.2	-6		09:35	0.4	12
	13:44	1.7	52		15:04	1.4	43
	20:29	0.1	3		21:12	0.7	21
6 Sa ◑	02:23	2.4	73	21 Su ◐	03:34	1.9	58
	09:32	-0.1	-3		10:31	0.4	12
	14:51	1.5	46		16:07	1.4	43
	21:34	0.1	3		22:15	0.7	21
7 Su	03:34	2.3	70	22 M	04:42	1.9	58
	10:35	-0.1	-3		11:25	0.4	12
	16:02	1.5	46		17:10	1.5	46
	22:39	0.1	3		23:15	0.6	18
8 M	04:44	2.3	70	23 Tu	05:43	2.0	61
	11:35	-0.1	-3		12:15	0.3	9
	17:08	1.6	49		18:05	1.6	49
	23:42	0.1	3				
9 Tu	05:45	2.3	70	24 W	00:11	0.5	15
	12:30	-0.1	-3		06:33	2.1	64
	18:05	1.8	55		13:02	0.2	6
					18:52	1.8	55
10 W	00:40	0.0	0	25 Th	01:04	0.3	9
	06:36	2.3	70		07:13	2.3	70
	13:19	-0.1	-3		13:47	0.0	0
	18:54	2.0	61		19:34	2.1	64
11 Th	01:33	-0.1	-3	26 F	01:55	0.0	0
	07:22	2.3	70		07:57	2.4	73
	14:02	-0.2	-6		14:29	-0.2	-6
	19:39	2.1	64		20:15	2.3	70
12 F	02:20	-0.1	-3	27 Sa	02:44	-0.2	-6
	08:04	2.3	70		08:38	2.5	76
	14:42	-0.2	-6		15:11	-0.3	-9
	20:23	2.2	67		20:57	2.6	79
13 Sa ●	03:03	-0.2	-6	28 Su ○	03:33	-0.4	-12
	08:46	2.3	70		09:21	2.5	76
	15:22	-0.1	-3		15:52	-0.4	-12
	21:05	2.3	70		21:41	2.9	88
14 Su	04:44	-0.1	-3	29 M	04:23	-0.5	-15
	10:28	2.2	67		10:07	2.5	76
	16:53	0.0	0		16:35	-0.4	-12
	22:47	2.4	73		22:27	3.0	91
15 M	05:26	-0.1	-3	30 Tu	05:14	-0.6	-18
	11:10	2.1	64		10:54	2.4	73
	17:27	0.1	3		17:19	-0.3	-9
	23:29	2.4	73		23:15	3.1	94
				31 W	06:07	-0.5	-15
					11:43	2.3	70
					18:08	-0.2	-6

StationId: 8510560
Source: NOAA/NOS/CO-OPS
Station Type: Primary
Time Zone: LST_LDT
Datum: MLLW

NOAA Tide Predictions

Montauk, NY,2021

Times and Heights of High and Low Waters

April

Day	Time	ft	cm	Day	Time	ft	cm
1 Th	00:06	3.1	94	**16** F	00:21	2.4	73
	07:05	-0.4	-12		07:13	0.3	9
	12:35	2.1	64		12:55	1.8	55
	19:03	0.0	0		18:38	0.7	21
2 F	01:01	2.9	88	**17** Sa	01:05	2.3	70
	08:06	-0.2	-6		08:06	0.4	12
	13:29	2.0	61		13:42	1.7	52
	20:05	0.2	6		19:34	0.8	24
3 Sa	01:59	2.7	82	**18** Su	01:53	2.1	64
	09:09	-0.1	-3		09:01	0.5	15
	14:29	1.8	55		14:35	1.6	49
	21:14	0.3	9		20:42	0.9	27
4 Su	03:05	2.5	76	**19** M	02:49	2.0	61
	10:13	0.1	3		09:56	0.5	15
	15:37	1.8	55		15:34	1.6	49
	22:23	0.3	9		21:47	0.8	24
5 M	04:17	2.3	70	**20** Tu	03:53	2.0	61
	11:15	0.1	3		10:48	0.4	12
	16:50	1.8	55		16:36	1.7	52
	23:31	0.3	9		22:47	0.7	21
6 Tu	05:28	2.2	67	**21** W	04:55	2.1	64
	12:13	0.2	6		11:37	0.3	9
	17:59	1.9	58		17:31	1.9	58
					23:44	0.6	18
7 W	00:34	0.3	9	**22** Th	05:49	2.2	67
	06:29	2.2	67		12:23	0.2	6
	13:06	0.1	3		18:18	2.1	64
	18:54	2.1	64				
8 Th	01:32	0.2	6	**23** F	00:39	0.3	9
	07:18	2.2	67		06:37	2.3	70
	13:52	0.1	3		13:08	0.1	3
	19:39	2.2	67		19:01	2.4	73
9 F	02:22	0.1	3	**24** Sa	01:32	0.1	3
	08:00	2.2	67		07:22	2.4	73
	14:33	0.1	3		13:52	0.0	0
	20:20	2.4	73		19:44	2.8	85
10 Sa	03:05	0.1	3	**25** Su	02:24	-0.2	-6
	08:40	2.2	67		08:07	2.5	76
	15:09	0.2	6		14:35	-0.2	-6
	20:59	2.5	76		20:28	3.1	94
11 Su	03:45	0.0	0	**26** M	03:15	-0.4	-12
	09:20	2.1	64		08:54	2.5	76
	15:43	0.2	6		15:19	-0.2	-6
	21:38	2.6	79		21:13	3.3	101
12 M	04:23	0.0	0	**27** Tu	04:06	-0.5	-15
	10:01	2.1	64		09:42	2.5	76
	16:15	0.3	9		16:05	-0.2	-6
	22:17	2.6	79		22:02	3.4	104
13 Tu	05:02	0.0	0	**28** W	04:57	-0.6	-18
	10:43	2.0	61		10:32	2.4	73
	16:47	0.4	12		16:53	-0.2	-6
	22:58	2.6	79		22:53	3.4	104
14 W	05:42	0.1	3	**29** Th	05:50	-0.5	-15
	11:26	2.0	61		11:24	2.3	70
	17:20	0.5	15		17:45	0.0	0
	23:39	2.5	76		23:47	3.3	101
15 Th	06:25	0.2	6	**30** F	06:47	-0.3	-9
	12:10	1.9	58		12:18	2.2	67
	17:56	0.6	18		18:43	0.1	3

May

Day	Time	ft	cm	Day	Time	ft	cm
1 Sa	00:43	3.1	94	**16** Su	00:38	2.4	73
	07:46	-0.2	-6		07:37	0.3	9
	13:14	2.1	64		13:20	1.8	55
	19:49	0.3	9		19:13	0.8	24
2 Su	01:42	2.8	85	**17** M	01:23	2.3	70
	08:48	0.0	0		08:30	0.4	12
	14:15	2.0	61		14:10	1.8	55
	20:59	0.4	12		20:17	0.9	27
3 M	02:45	2.5	76	**18** Tu	02:10	2.2	67
	09:50	0.1	3		09:22	0.4	12
	15:22	2.0	61		15:03	1.8	55
	22:09	0.5	15		21:21	0.8	24
4 Tu	03:53	2.3	70	**19** W	03:05	2.1	64
	10:48	0.2	6		10:11	0.3	9
	16:34	2.0	61		15:59	1.9	58
	23:17	0.5	15		22:22	0.7	21
5 W	05:00	2.1	64	**20** Th	04:05	2.1	64
	11:43	0.3	9		10:58	0.3	9
	17:40	2.1	64		16:52	2.1	64
					23:20	0.5	15
6 Th	00:20	0.5	15	**21** F	05:04	2.1	64
	06:00	2.1	64		11:44	0.2	6
	12:32	0.3	9		17:42	2.4	73
	18:33	2.3	70				
7 F	01:16	0.4	12	**22** Sa	00:16	0.3	9
	06:49	2.0	61		05:58	2.2	67
	13:17	0.3	9		12:29	0.1	3
	19:16	2.4	73		18:28	2.7	82
8 Sa	02:04	0.3	9	**23** Su	01:11	0.0	0
	07:32	2.0	61		06:49	2.2	67
	13:56	0.4	12		13:15	0.0	0
	19:54	2.5	76		19:14	3.0	91
9 Su	02:46	0.2	6	**24** M	02:05	-0.2	-6
	08:12	2.0	61		07:38	2.3	70
	14:31	0.4	12		14:02	-0.1	-3
	20:32	2.6	79		20:01	3.3	101
10 M	03:24	0.2	6	**25** Tu	02:58	-0.4	-12
	08:53	2.0	61		08:28	2.3	70
	15:05	0.4	12		14:51	-0.1	-3
	21:10	2.7	82		20:50	3.5	107
11 Tu	04:01	0.1	3	**26** W	03:49	-0.5	-15
	09:34	2.0	61		09:18	2.3	70
	15:39	0.5	15		15:41	-0.2	-6
	21:50	2.7	82		21:42	3.5	107
12 W	04:38	0.1	3	**27** Th	04:41	-0.5	-15
	10:17	2.0	61		10:11	2.3	70
	16:13	0.5	15		16:32	-0.1	-3
	22:30	2.7	82		22:35	3.4	104
13 Th	05:17	0.1	3	**28** F	05:33	-0.4	-12
	11:01	1.9	58		11:05	2.3	70
	16:50	0.6	18		17:28	0.0	0
	23:13	2.6	79		23:30	3.3	101
14 F	06:00	0.2	6	**29** Sa	06:28	-0.3	-9
	11:46	1.9	58		12:01	2.2	67
	17:30	0.7	21		18:27	0.1	3
	23:55	2.5	76				
15 Sa	06:47	0.3	9	**30** Su	00:26	3.0	91
	12:32	1.8	55		07:25	-0.1	-3
	18:16	0.8	24		12:58	2.2	67
					19:33	0.3	9
				31 M	01:23	2.7	82
					08:23	0.0	0
					13:58	2.2	67
					20:41	0.4	12

June

Day	Time	ft	cm	Day	Time	ft	cm
1 Tu	02:21	2.5	76	**16** W	01:39	2.3	70
	09:20	0.1	3		08:47	0.2	6
	15:01	2.1	64		14:31	2.0	61
	21:49	0.5	15		20:58	0.7	21
2 W	03:21	2.2	67	**17** Th	02:27	2.2	67
	10:15	0.2	6		09:34	0.2	6
	16:06	2.2	67		15:21	2.1	64
	22:55	0.5	15		21:58	0.6	18
3 Th	04:22	2.0	61	**18** F	03:23	2.1	64
	11:05	0.3	9		10:20	0.2	6
	17:08	2.3	70		16:14	2.4	73
	23:56	0.5	15		22:57	0.4	12
4 F	05:21	1.9	58	**19** Sa	04:24	2.0	61
	11:52	0.4	12		11:07	0.2	6
	18:01	2.4	73		17:07	2.6	79
					23:55	0.2	6
5 Sa	00:51	0.5	15	**20** Su	05:24	2.0	61
	06:14	1.8	55		11:55	0.1	3
	12:34	0.5	15		17:59	2.9	88
	18:46	2.5	76				
6 Su	01:39	0.4	12	**21** M	00:52	0.0	0
	07:00	1.8	55		06:20	2.0	61
	13:14	0.5	15		12:44	0.1	3
	19:26	2.6	79		18:50	3.1	94
7 M	02:21	0.3	9	**22** Tu	01:47	-0.2	-6
	07:43	1.8	55		07:14	2.1	64
	13:52	0.6	18		13:37	0.0	0
	20:05	2.6	79		19:41	3.3	101
8 Tu	02:59	0.3	9	**23** W	02:41	-0.3	-9
	08:25	1.8	55		08:06	2.1	64
	14:30	0.6	18		14:30	-0.1	-3
	20:45	2.7	82		20:33	3.4	104
9 W	03:36	0.2	6	**24** Th	03:33	-0.4	-12
	09:08	1.8	55		08:58	2.2	67
	15:08	0.5	15		15:24	-0.1	-3
	21:26	2.7	82		21:26	3.4	104
10 Th	04:14	0.2	6	**25** F	04:24	-0.4	-12
	09:52	1.9	58		09:52	2.3	70
	15:48	0.5	15		16:19	-0.1	-3
	22:08	2.6	79		22:20	3.3	101
11 F	04:54	0.1	3	**26** Sa	05:15	-0.4	-12
	10:37	1.9	58		10:47	2.3	70
	16:29	0.6	18		17:13	0.0	0
	22:50	2.6	79		23:14	3.1	94
12 Sa	05:36	0.1	3	**27** Su	06:06	-0.3	-9
	11:23	1.9	58		11:42	2.3	70
	17:12	0.6	18		18:11	0.1	3
	23:33	2.5	76				
13 Su	06:21	0.2	6	**28** M	00:07	2.9	88
	12:09	1.9	58		06:58	-0.1	-3
	18:00	0.7	21		12:38	2.3	70
					19:13	0.3	9
14 M	00:14	2.5	76	**29** Tu	00:59	2.6	79
	07:09	0.2	6		07:51	0.0	0
	12:56	1.9	58		13:34	2.3	70
	18:55	0.7	21		20:17	0.4	12
15 Tu	00:55	2.4	73	**30** W	01:51	2.4	73
	07:58	0.2	6		08:44	0.2	6
	13:42	1.9	58		14:31	2.3	70
	19:56	0.7	21		21:22	0.5	15

StationId: 8510560
Source: NOAA/NOS/CO-OPS
Station Type: Primary
Time Zone: LST_LDT
Datum: MLLW

NOAA Tide Predictions

Montauk, NY, 2021

Times and Heights of High and Low Waters

July

Day	Time (h m)	ft	cm	Day	Time (h m)	ft	cm
1 Th	02:45	2.1	64	16 F	01:59	2.2	67
	09:34	0.3	9		08:57	0.2	6
	15:29	2.3	70		14:45	2.4	73
	22:24	0.6	18		21:37	0.4	12
2 F	03:41	1.9	58	17 Sa	02:53	2.1	64
	10:22	0.4	12		09:46	0.2	6
	16:28	2.3	70		15:39	2.6	79
	23:23	0.6	18		22:37	0.3	9
3 Sa	04:39	1.7	52	18 Su	03:54	2.0	61
	11:07	0.6	18		10:36	0.2	6
	17:23	2.4	73		16:37	2.8	85
					23:37	0.2	6
4 Su	00:18	0.5	15	19 M	04:57	1.9	58
	05:36	1.6	49		11:29	0.2	6
	11:50	0.6	18		17:36	2.9	88
	18:13	2.4	73				
5 M	01:07	0.5	15	20 Tu	00:35	0.0	0
	06:27	1.6	49		05:58	1.9	58
	12:33	0.7	21		12:24	0.2	6
	18:58	2.5	76		18:33	3.1	94
6 Tu	01:50	0.4	12	21 W	01:31	-0.1	-3
	07:14	1.7	52		06:55	2.0	61
	13:16	0.7	21		13:21	0.1	3
	19:41	2.5	76		19:27	3.2	98
7 W	02:31	0.4	12	22 Th	02:25	-0.2	-6
	07:59	1.7	52		07:49	2.1	64
	14:00	0.6	18		14:17	0.0	0
	20:23	2.6	79		20:20	3.2	98
8 Th	03:09	0.3	9	23 F	03:16	-0.2	-6
	08:42	1.8	55		08:42	2.2	67
	14:43	0.6	18		15:12	0.0	0
	21:05	2.6	79		21:12	3.2	98
9 F	03:48	0.2	6	24 Sa	04:05	-0.3	-9
	09:26	1.9	58		09:34	2.3	70
	15:27	0.5	15		16:06	-0.1	-3
	21:46	2.6	79		22:03	3.1	94
10 Sa	04:28	0.1	3	25 Su	04:53	-0.2	-6
	10:12	1.9	58		10:28	2.4	73
	16:11	0.5	15		16:59	0.0	0
	22:28	2.6	79		22:53	3.0	91
11 Su	05:10	0.1	3	26 M	05:39	-0.2	-6
	10:57	2.0	61		11:21	2.5	76
	16:56	0.5	15		17:53	0.1	3
	23:08	2.6	79		23:43	2.8	85
12 M	05:52	0.1	3	27 Tu	06:26	0.0	0
	11:42	2.0	61		12:13	2.5	76
	17:44	0.5	15		18:49	0.3	9
	23:48	2.6	79				
13 Tu	06:37	0.1	3	28 W	00:31	2.5	76
	12:26	2.1	64		07:13	0.1	3
	18:36	0.5	15		13:04	2.5	76
					19:48	0.4	12
14 W	00:29	2.5	76	29 Th	01:19	2.3	70
	07:23	0.1	3		08:00	0.3	9
	13:11	2.2	67		13:55	2.4	73
	19:35	0.5	15		20:48	0.5	15
15 Th	01:11	2.4	73	30 F	02:09	2.0	61
	08:10	0.2	6		08:48	0.5	15
	13:56	2.3	70		14:48	2.4	73
	20:36	0.5	15		21:47	0.6	18
				31 Sa	03:01	1.8	55
					09:35	0.6	18
					15:44	2.3	70
					22:44	0.6	18

August

Day	Time (h m)	ft	cm	Day	Time (h m)	ft	cm
1 Su	03:59	1.7	52	16 M	03:32	1.9	58
	10:21	0.7	21		10:14	0.4	12
	16:42	2.3	70		16:15	2.8	85
	23:38	0.6	18		23:20	0.2	6
2 M	04:59	1.6	49	17 Tu	04:39	1.9	58
	11:09	0.8	24		11:13	0.4	12
	17:40	2.3	70		17:20	2.9	88
3 Tu	00:29	0.6	18	18 W	00:20	0.2	6
	05:56	1.6	49		05:44	1.9	58
	11:57	0.8	24		12:13	0.3	9
	18:32	2.4	73		18:22	3.0	91
4 W	01:16	0.6	18	19 Th	01:16	0.1	3
	06:47	1.7	52		06:43	2.1	64
	12:46	0.7	21		13:13	0.2	6
	19:19	2.5	76		19:17	3.0	91
5 Th	01:59	0.5	15	20 F	02:09	0.0	0
	07:33	1.8	55		07:37	2.2	67
	13:35	0.7	21		14:10	0.1	3
	20:02	2.5	76		20:08	3.0	91
6 F	02:39	0.4	12	21 Sa	02:58	0.0	0
	08:17	1.9	58		08:28	2.4	73
	14:22	0.6	18		15:03	0.1	3
	20:42	2.6	79		20:56	3.0	91
7 Sa	03:19	0.2	6	22 Su	03:43	-0.1	-3
	09:00	2.0	61		09:18	2.5	76
	15:07	0.5	15		15:54	0.1	3
	21:21	2.7	82		21:43	2.9	88
8 Su	03:59	0.1	3	23 M	04:26	0.0	0
	09:43	2.1	64		10:06	2.6	79
	15:43	0.4	12		16:43	0.1	3
	22:00	2.7	82		22:29	2.8	85
9 M	04:39	0.0	0	24 Tu	05:08	0.0	0
	10:26	2.3	70		10:55	2.7	82
	16:37	0.3	9		17:32	0.2	6
	22:39	2.7	82		23:15	2.6	79
10 Tu	05:19	0.0	0	25 W	05:48	0.2	6
	11:09	2.4	73		11:42	2.7	82
	17:25	0.3	9		18:22	0.3	9
	23:20	2.7	82				
11 W	06:01	0.0	0	26 Th	00:01	2.4	73
	11:52	2.5	76		06:29	0.3	9
	18:17	0.3	9		12:29	2.6	79
					19:14	0.4	12
12 Th	00:02	2.5	76	27 F	00:47	2.2	67
	06:45	0.1	3		07:11	0.5	15
	12:37	2.6	79		13:16	2.6	79
	19:14	0.3	9		20:10	0.6	18
13 F	00:47	2.4	73	28 Sa	01:34	2.0	61
	07:32	0.2	6		07:56	0.7	21
	13:23	2.7	82		14:51	2.5	76
	20:15	0.3	9		21:07	0.7	21
14 Sa	01:36	2.2	67	29 Su	02:25	1.8	55
	08:23	0.3	9		08:45	0.9	27
	14:14	2.7	82		15:00	2.4	73
	21:18	0.3	9		22:04	0.7	21
15 Su	02:30	2.1	64	30 M	03:22	1.7	52
	09:17	0.4	12		09:38	0.9	27
	15:12	2.8	85		16:02	2.3	70
	22:20	0.3	9		22:59	0.8	24
				31 Tu	04:25	1.7	52
					10:33	1.0	30
					17:07	2.3	70
					23:50	0.7	21

September

Day	Time (h m)	ft	cm	Day	Time (h m)	ft	cm
1 W	05:27	1.7	52	16 Th	00:04	0.3	9
	11:28	0.9	27		05:36	2.0	61
	18:05	2.3	70		12:08	0.4	12
					18:12	2.8	85
2 Th	00:39	0.7	21	17 F	00:59	0.2	6
	06:21	1.8	55		06:35	2.2	67
	12:21	0.8	24		13:08	0.3	9
	18:54	2.4	73		19:06	2.8	85
3 F	01:23	0.6	18	18 Sa	01:49	0.2	6
	07:08	1.9	58		07:27	2.4	73
	13:11	0.7	21		14:03	0.2	6
	19:35	2.5	76		19:53	2.8	85
4 Sa	02:05	0.4	12	19 Su	02:35	0.1	3
	07:51	2.1	64		08:14	2.6	79
	13:59	0.5	15		14:54	0.2	6
	20:13	2.6	79		20:37	2.8	85
5 Su	02:45	0.3	9	20 M	03:17	0.1	3
	08:31	2.3	70		08:59	2.7	82
	14:45	0.4	12		15:40	0.2	6
	20:50	2.7	82		21:20	2.7	82
6 M	03:24	0.1	3	21 Tu	03:56	0.1	3
	09:11	2.5	76		09:42	2.8	85
	15:31	0.2	6		16:25	0.2	6
	21:28	2.8	85		22:03	2.6	79
7 Tu	04:04	0.0	0	22 W	04:32	0.2	6
	09:52	2.6	79		10:25	2.8	85
	16:18	0.1	3		17:09	0.2	6
	22:09	2.8	85		22:46	2.5	76
8 W	04:43	0.0	0	23 Th	05:08	0.4	12
	10:34	2.8	85		11:09	2.8	85
	17:06	0.1	3		17:53	0.3	9
	22:51	2.7	82		23:30	2.3	70
9 Th	05:25	0.0	0	24 F	05:44	0.5	15
	11:18	2.9	88		11:53	2.7	82
	17:58	0.1	3		18:40	0.4	12
	23:37	2.6	79				
10 F	06:09	0.1	3	25 Sa	00:16	2.1	64
	12:05	3.0	91		06:21	0.7	21
	18:55	0.1	3		12:38	2.6	79
					19:32	0.6	18
11 Sa	00:25	2.4	73	26 Su	01:03	2.0	61
	06:58	0.3	9		07:03	0.9	27
	12:55	3.0	91		13:27	2.5	76
	19:56	0.2	6		20:27	0.7	21
12 Su	01:16	2.2	67	27 M	01:54	1.8	55
	07:54	0.4	12		07:56	1.0	30
	13:49	3.0	91		14:21	2.3	70
	20:59	0.2	6		21:25	0.7	21
13 M	02:13	2.1	64	28 Tu	02:50	1.7	52
	08:56	0.5	15		09:00	1.1	34
	14:51	2.9	88		15:23	2.2	67
	22:03	0.3	9		22:20	0.8	24
14 Tu	03:17	2.0	61	29 W	03:53	1.7	52
	10:00	0.5	15		10:03	1.0	30
	15:59	2.8	85		16:30	2.2	67
	23:04	0.3	9		23:12	0.7	21
15 W	04:28	1.9	58	30 Th	04:58	1.8	55
	11:05	0.5	15		11:01	1.0	30
	17:09	2.8	85		17:31	2.3	70

StationId: 8510560
Source: NOAA/NOS/CO-OPS
Station Type: Primary
Time Zone: LST_LDT
Datum: MLLW

NOAA Tide Predictions

Montauk, NY, 2021

Times and Heights of High and Low Waters

October

Day	Time (h m)	ft	cm	Day	Time (h m)	ft	cm
1 F	00:00	0.6	18	**16** Sa	00:36	0.2	6
	05:54	1.9	58		06:26	2.3	70
	11:55	0.8	24		13:01	0.3	9
	18:20	2.4	73		18:49	2.5	76
2 Sa	00:45	0.5	15	**17** Su	01:24	0.2	6
	06:40	2.1	64		07:14	2.5	76
	12:46	0.7	21		13:54	0.3	9
	19:01	2.5	76		19:33	2.4	73
3 Su	01:27	0.4	12	**18** M	02:07	0.2	6
	07:21	2.3	70		07:57	2.6	79
	13:35	0.5	15		14:41	0.2	6
	19:39	2.6	79		20:14	2.4	73
4 M	02:07	0.2	6	**19** Tu	02:46	0.2	6
	07:59	2.5	76		08:37	2.7	82
	14:23	0.3	9		15:24	0.2	6
	20:17	2.7	82		20:55	2.3	70
5 Tu	02:47	0.1	3	**20** W ○	03:22	0.3	9
	08:38	2.8	85		09:16	2.8	85
	15:10	0.1	3		16:05	0.2	6
	20:56	2.7	82		21:36	2.3	70
6 W ●	03:27	0.0	0	**21** Th	03:56	0.4	12
	09:19	3.0	91		09:56	2.8	85
	15:58	-0.1	-3		16:45	0.2	6
	21:39	2.7	82		22:18	2.2	67
7 Th	04:08	0.0	0	**22** F	04:29	0.5	15
	10:02	3.2	98		10:38	2.8	85
	16:48	-0.2	-6		17:26	0.2	6
	22:25	2.6	79		23:02	2.1	64
8 F	04:51	0.0	0	**23** Sa	05:03	0.6	18
	10:48	3.3	101		11:21	2.7	82
	17:40	-0.2	-6		18:10	0.3	9
	23:13	2.5	76		23:48	2.0	61
9 Sa	05:38	0.1	3	**24** Su	05:38	0.7	21
	11:38	3.3	101		12:06	2.5	76
	18:36	-0.1	-3		18:58	0.4	12
10 Su	00:04	2.3	70	**25** M	00:36	1.9	58
	06:30	0.2	6		06:20	0.8	24
	12:32	3.2	98		12:54	2.4	73
	19:37	0.0	0		19:51	0.5	15
11 M	00:59	2.2	67	**26** Tu	01:26	1.8	55
	07:32	0.4	12		07:17	0.9	27
	13:30	3.0	91		13:46	2.2	67
	20:40	0.2	6		20:48	0.6	18
12 Tu	01:59	2.0	61	**27** W	02:21	1.7	52
	08:40	0.5	15		08:26	1.0	30
	14:34	2.8	85		14:43	2.1	64
	21:44	0.2	6		21:43	0.6	18
13 W ◔	03:05	2.0	61	**28** Th ◑	03:22	1.7	52
	09:50	0.5	15		09:33	1.0	30
	15:44	2.7	82		15:45	2.1	64
	22:46	0.3	9		22:34	0.6	18
14 Th	04:18	2.0	61	**29** F	04:25	1.7	52
	10:57	0.5	15		10:32	0.9	27
	16:55	2.6	79		16:45	2.1	64
	23:43	0.3	9		23:20	0.5	15
15 F	05:28	2.1	64	**30** Sa	05:20	1.9	58
	12:01	0.4	12		11:27	0.7	21
	17:57	2.5	76		17:36	2.2	67
				31 Su	00:04	0.3	9
					06:06	2.1	64
					12:20	0.5	15
					18:20	2.3	70

November

Day	Time (h m)	ft	cm	Day	Time (h m)	ft	cm
1 M	00:46	0.2	6	**16** Tu	00:35	0.2	6
	06:47	2.4	73		06:35	2.5	76
	13:11	0.3	9		13:25	0.1	3
	19:02	2.3	70		18:49	1.9	58
2 Tu	01:28	0.1	3	**17** W	01:13	0.2	6
	07:26	2.7	82		07:13	2.6	79
	14:00	0.0	0		14:06	0.1	3
	19:44	2.4	73		19:30	1.9	58
3 W	02:10	-0.1	-3	**18** Th	01:49	0.3	9
	08:06	3.0	91		07:51	2.6	79
	14:50	-0.2	-6		14:44	0.0	0
	20:27	2.4	73		20:11	1.9	58
4 Th ●	02:53	-0.1	-3	**19** F ○	02:23	0.3	9
	08:49	3.2	98		08:31	2.6	79
	15:39	-0.4	-12		15:22	0.0	0
	21:12	2.4	73		20:53	1.9	58
5 F	03:37	-0.2	-6	**20** Sa	02:58	0.4	12
	09:35	3.3	101		09:12	2.6	79
	16:05	-0.5	-15		16:01	0.1	3
	22:01	2.4	73		21:37	1.8	55
6 Sa	04:23	-0.2	-6	**21** Su	03:33	0.4	12
	10:25	3.4	104		09:55	2.5	76
	17:22	-0.4	-12		16:43	0.1	3
	22:52	2.3	70		22:23	1.8	55
7 Su	04:14	-0.1	-3	**22** M	04:12	0.5	15
	10:18	3.3	101		10:41	2.4	73
	17:18	-0.3	-9		17:29	0.2	6
	22:46	2.2	67		23:11	1.7	52
8 M	05:11	0.0	0	**23** Tu	04:57	0.6	18
	11:15	3.1	94		11:27	2.2	67
	18:17	-0.2	-6		18:19	0.3	9
	23:43	2.1	64				
9 Tu	06:15	0.2	6	**24** W	00:01	1.6	49
	12:14	2.9	88		05:52	0.7	21
	19:19	0.0	0		12:14	2.1	64
					19:12	0.3	9
10 W	00:44	2.0	61	**25** Th	00:53	1.6	49
	07:26	0.3	9		06:52	0.7	21
	13:17	2.6	79		13:02	2.0	61
	20:21	0.0	0		20:04	0.3	9
11 Th ◔	01:51	2.0	61	**26** F	01:48	1.6	49
	08:37	0.3	9		08:02	0.7	21
	14:23	2.4	73		13:54	1.9	58
	21:21	0.1	3		20:53	0.3	9
12 F	03:02	2.0	61	**27** Sa ◑	02:44	1.7	52
	09:45	0.4	12		09:02	0.6	18
	15:30	2.2	67		14:50	1.9	58
	22:16	0.1	3		21:39	0.2	6
13 Sa	04:11	2.1	64	**28** Su	03:38	1.8	55
	10:49	0.3	9		09:59	0.5	15
	16:31	2.1	64		15:45	1.9	58
	23:07	0.1	3		22:23	0.1	3
14 Su	05:09	2.3	70	**29** M	04:26	2.1	64
	11:48	0.3	9		10:53	0.2	6
	17:24	2.0	61		16:37	1.9	58
	23:54	0.2	6		23:07	0.0	0
15 M	05:55	2.4	73	**30** Tu	05:10	2.4	73
	12:40	0.2	6		11:47	0.0	0
	18:08	2.0	61		17:26	2.0	61
					23:51	-0.1	-3

December

Day	Time (h m)	ft	cm	Day	Time (h m)	ft	cm
1 W	05:54	2.7	82	**16** Th	00:41	0.2	6
	12:39	-0.3	-9		06:50	2.3	70
	18:13	2.0	61		13:44	0.0	0
					19:06	1.5	46
2 Th	00:37	-0.2	-6	**17** F	01:19	0.2	6
	06:39	3.0	91		07:30	2.3	70
	13:31	-0.5	-15		14:22	-0.1	-3
	19:01	2.1	64		19:48	1.6	49
3 F	01:24	-0.3	-9	**18** Sa	01:57	0.2	6
	07:26	3.2	98		08:11	2.3	70
	14:22	-0.6	-18		14:59	-0.1	-3
	19:49	2.1	64		20:31	1.6	49
4 Sa ●	02:13	-0.4	-12	**19** Su ○	02:35	0.2	6
	08:15	3.3	101		08:53	2.3	70
	15:13	-0.7	-21		15:38	-0.1	-3
	20:40	2.1	64		21:15	1.6	49
5 Su	03:04	-0.4	-12	**20** M	03:14	0.2	6
	09:08	3.2	98		09:36	2.3	70
	16:05	-0.7	-21		16:18	-0.1	-3
	21:33	2.1	64		22:01	1.6	49
6 M	03:58	-0.4	-12	**21** Tu	03:56	0.2	6
	10:03	3.1	94		10:20	2.2	67
	16:59	-0.6	-18		17:01	-0.1	-3
	22:29	2.0	61		22:48	1.6	49
7 Tu	04:56	-0.3	-9	**22** W	04:41	0.3	9
	10:59	2.9	88		11:02	2.1	64
	17:55	-0.4	-12		17:47	-0.1	-3
	23:27	2.0	61		23:35	1.6	49
8 W	06:00	-0.1	-3	**23** Th	05:32	0.3	9
	11:56	2.6	79		11:43	2.0	61
	18:53	-0.3	-9		18:35	0.0	0
9 Th	00:27	2.0	61	**24** F	00:22	1.6	49
	07:08	0.0	0		06:30	0.4	12
	12:54	2.4	73		12:24	1.9	58
	19:52	-0.2	-6		19:23	0.0	0
10 F	01:29	1.9	58	**25** Sa	01:09	1.6	49
	08:18	0.1	3		07:32	0.4	12
	13:53	2.1	64		13:08	1.8	55
	20:49	-0.1	-3		20:11	0.0	0
11 Sa ◔	02:35	2.0	61	**26** Su	01:58	1.7	52
	09:25	0.2	6		08:32	0.3	9
	14:54	1.8	55		13:58	1.7	52
	21:42	0.0	0		20:57	0.0	0
12 Su	03:41	2.0	61	**27** M ◑	02:49	1.9	58
	10:28	0.2	6		09:31	0.2	6
	15:55	1.7	52		14:56	1.6	49
	22:32	0.1	3		21:43	-0.1	-3
13 M	04:40	2.1	64	**28** Tu	03:42	2.1	64
	11:27	0.1	3		10:28	0.0	0
	16:51	1.6	49		15:57	1.6	49
	23:18	0.1	3		22:30	-0.1	-3
14 Tu	05:28	2.2	67	**29** W	04:35	2.3	70
	12:19	0.1	3		11:25	-0.2	-6
	17:40	1.5	46		16:54	1.6	49
					23:19	-0.2	-6
15 W	00:01	0.2	6	**30** Th	05:26	2.6	79
	06:10	2.3	70		12:20	-0.4	-12
	13:04	0.0	0		17:48	1.7	52
	18:24	1.5	46				
				31 F	00:11	-0.3	-9
					06:17	2.8	85
					13:14	-0.6	-18
					18:39	1.8	55

StationId: 8461490
Source: NOAA/NOS/CO-OPS
Station Type: Primary
Time Zone: LST_LDT
Datum: MLLW

NOAA Tide Predictions

New London, CT, 2021

Times and Heights of High and Low Waters

January

Day	Time	ft	cm
1 F	04:33	0.1	3
	10:45	2.8	85
	17:27	-0.2	-6
	23:17	2.1	64
2 Sa	05:22	0.1	3
	11:27	2.7	82
	18:15	-0.2	-6
3 Su	00:05	2.2	67
	06:16	0.2	6
	12:13	2.6	79
	19:04	-0.2	-6
4 M	00:55	2.3	70
	07:15	0.2	6
	13:01	2.5	76
	19:53	-0.2	-6
5 Tu	01:48	2.4	73
	08:17	0.2	6
	13:54	2.4	73
	20:44	-0.2	-6
6 W ☽	02:44	2.5	76
	09:20	0.1	3
	14:54	2.2	67
	21:37	-0.1	-3
7 Th	03:45	2.6	79
	10:24	0.0	0
	16:01	2.1	64
	22:32	-0.1	-3
8 F	04:45	2.8	85
	11:26	-0.1	-3
	17:06	2.0	61
	23:28	-0.1	-3
9 Sa	05:41	3.0	91
	12:25	-0.3	-9
	18:03	2.1	64
10 Su	00:24	-0.2	-6
	06:33	3.1	94
	13:21	-0.4	-12
	18:57	2.1	64
11 M	01:20	-0.2	-6
	07:24	3.2	98
	14:15	-0.5	-15
	19:49	2.2	67
12 Tu	02:15	-0.3	-9
	08:15	3.2	98
	15:04	-0.5	-15
	20:39	2.2	67
13 W ●	03:06	-0.3	-9
	09:04	3.1	94
	15:51	-0.5	-15
	21:29	2.3	70
14 Th	03:55	-0.3	-9
	09:53	3.0	91
	16:38	-0.4	-12
	22:19	2.3	70
15 F	04:44	-0.2	-6
	10:41	2.8	85
	17:24	-0.3	-9
	23:10	2.3	70
16 Sa	05:36	0.0	0
	11:30	2.7	82
	18:12	-0.2	-6
17 Su	00:02	2.3	70
	06:30	0.1	3
	12:20	2.4	73
	19:00	0.0	0
18 M	00:55	2.3	70
	07:26	0.2	6
	13:10	2.2	67
	19:47	0.1	3
19 Tu	01:47	2.3	70
	08:23	0.3	9
	14:01	2.0	61
	20:33	0.2	6
20 W ◐	02:41	2.3	70
	09:20	0.3	9
	14:57	1.8	55
	21:21	0.3	9
21 Th	03:39	2.3	70
	10:18	0.3	9
	15:57	1.7	52
	22:10	0.4	12
22 F	04:36	2.3	70
	11:12	0.3	9
	16:56	1.7	52
	22:59	0.4	12
23 Sa	05:29	2.4	73
	12:02	0.2	6
	17:48	1.7	52
	23:48	0.4	12
24 Su	06:16	2.5	76
	12:49	0.1	3
	18:35	1.8	55
25 M	00:35	0.3	9
	07:01	2.6	79
	13:33	0.0	0
	19:19	1.9	58
26 Tu	01:21	0.2	6
	07:43	2.6	79
	14:01	-0.1	-3
	20:01	2.0	61
27 W	02:06	0.1	3
	08:24	2.7	82
	14:56	-0.3	-9
	20:42	2.1	64
28 Th ○	02:49	-0.1	-3
	09:04	2.8	85
	15:36	-0.3	-9
	21:22	2.2	67
29 F	03:31	-0.2	-6
	09:42	2.8	85
	16:16	-0.4	-12
	22:04	2.3	70
30 Sa	04:16	-0.2	-6
	10:21	2.8	85
	16:59	-0.4	-12
	22:47	2.4	73
31 Su	05:05	-0.2	-6
	11:03	2.7	82
	17:44	-0.4	-12
	23:35	2.4	73

February

Day	Time	ft	cm
1 M	05:59	-0.2	-6
	11:49	2.6	79
	18:32	-0.4	-12
2 Tu	00:26	2.5	76
	06:58	-0.1	-3
	12:39	2.4	73
	19:22	-0.3	-9
3 W	01:19	2.6	79
	07:55	-0.1	-3
	13:33	2.2	67
	20:15	-0.2	-6
4 Th ◐	02:15	2.7	82
	09:02	-0.1	-3
	14:33	2.0	61
	21:11	-0.1	-3
5 F	03:18	2.7	82
	10:06	-0.1	-3
	15:42	1.9	58
	22:11	-0.1	-3
6 Sa	04:25	2.7	82
	11:09	-0.1	-3
	16:51	1.9	58
	23:13	0.0	0
7 Su	05:27	2.8	85
	12:09	-0.2	-6
	17:52	2.0	61
8 M	00:13	-0.1	-3
	06:23	2.8	85
	13:06	-0.3	-9
	18:46	2.1	64
9 Tu	01:11	-0.2	-6
	07:15	2.9	88
	13:59	-0.3	-9
	19:37	2.2	67
10 W	02:06	-0.2	-6
	08:05	2.9	88
	14:48	-0.4	-12
	20:26	2.3	70
11 Th ●	02:56	-0.3	-9
	08:51	2.9	88
	15:32	-0.4	-12
	21:12	2.3	70
12 F	03:42	-0.3	-9
	09:35	2.8	85
	16:13	-0.3	-9
	21:57	2.4	73
13 Sa	04:26	-0.2	-6
	10:18	2.7	82
	16:54	-0.2	-6
	22:43	2.4	73
14 Su	05:12	-0.1	-3
	11:02	2.5	76
	17:35	-0.1	-3
	23:30	2.4	73
15 M	06:00	0.0	0
	11:48	2.3	70
	18:17	0.1	3
16 Tu	00:17	2.4	73
	06:51	0.1	3
	12:36	2.2	67
	18:59	0.2	6
17 W	01:06	2.4	73
	07:43	0.2	6
	13:25	2.0	61
	19:43	0.4	12
18 Th	01:56	2.3	70
	08:36	0.3	9
	14:18	1.8	55
	20:30	0.5	15
19 F ◐	02:51	2.3	70
	09:31	0.3	9
	15:16	1.7	52
	21:21	0.6	18
20 Sa	03:51	2.2	67
	10:26	0.3	9
	16:19	1.7	52
	22:17	0.6	18
21 Su	04:51	2.3	70
	11:19	0.3	9
	17:15	1.8	55
	23:11	0.5	15
22 M	05:45	2.4	73
	12:09	0.2	6
	18:04	1.9	58
23 Tu	00:03	0.4	12
	06:32	2.5	76
	12:57	0.1	3
	18:49	2.0	61
24 W	00:52	0.2	6
	07:15	2.6	79
	13:42	-0.1	-3
	19:31	2.1	64
25 Th	01:40	0.0	0
	07:56	2.8	85
	14:25	-0.2	-6
	20:12	2.3	70
26 F ●	02:27	-0.2	-6
	08:36	2.9	88
	15:06	-0.3	-9
	20:53	2.5	76
27 Sa ○	03:12	-0.3	-9
	09:16	2.9	88
	15:47	-0.4	-12
	21:35	2.6	79
28 Su	03:59	-0.4	-12
	09:57	2.9	88
	16:28	-0.5	-15
	22:19	2.8	85

March

Day	Time	ft	cm
1 M	04:49	-0.4	-12
	10:40	2.8	85
	17:13	-0.4	-12
	23:06	2.9	88
2 Tu	05:43	-0.4	-12
	11:28	2.6	79
	18:01	-0.3	-9
	23:58	2.9	88
3 W	06:41	-0.3	-9
	12:21	2.4	73
	18:54	-0.2	-6
4 Th	00:53	2.9	88
	07:42	-0.2	-6
	13:17	2.2	67
	19:50	0.0	0
5 F	01:51	2.9	88
	08:44	-0.1	-3
	14:18	2.1	64
	20:52	0.1	3
6 Sa ◐	02:56	2.8	85
	09:48	0.0	0
	15:28	2.0	61
	21:57	0.3	9
7 Su	04:08	2.7	82
	10:52	0.0	0
	16:40	2.0	61
	23:03	0.1	3
8 M	05:16	2.7	82
	11:52	0.0	0
	17:43	2.1	64
9 Tu	00:05	0.1	3
	06:14	2.7	82
	12:49	0.0	0
	18:36	2.2	67
10 W	01:03	0.0	0
	07:05	2.7	82
	13:40	-0.1	-3
	19:25	2.4	73
11 Th	01:56	-0.1	-3
	07:51	2.7	82
	14:27	-0.1	-3
	20:10	2.5	76
12 F	02:44	-0.1	-3
	08:34	2.7	82
	15:08	-0.1	-3
	20:52	2.6	79
13 Sa ●	03:27	-0.1	-3
	09:14	2.6	79
	15:45	-0.1	-3
	21:33	2.7	82
14 Su	05:08	-0.1	-3
	10:54	2.6	79
	17:21	0.0	0
	23:14	2.7	82
15 M	05:48	0.0	0
	11:36	2.5	76
	17:56	0.2	6
	23:56	2.7	82
16 Tu	06:31	0.0	0
	12:19	2.3	70
	18:33	0.3	9
17 W	00:40	2.6	79
	07:17	0.1	3
	13:06	2.2	67
	19:13	0.5	15
18 Th	01:26	2.6	79
	08:05	0.2	6
	13:55	2.1	64
	19:57	0.6	18
19 F ◐	02:14	2.5	76
	08:55	0.3	9
	14:45	2.0	61
	20:46	0.7	21
20 Sa	03:06	2.4	73
	09:48	0.4	12
	15:40	1.9	58
	21:40	0.8	24
21 Su ◐	04:05	2.3	70
	10:42	0.4	12
	16:41	1.9	58
	22:38	0.7	21
22 M	05:10	2.3	70
	11:37	0.4	12
	17:40	2.0	61
	23:37	0.7	21
23 Tu	06:08	2.4	73
	12:29	0.3	9
	18:31	2.1	64
24 W	00:31	0.5	15
	06:58	2.5	76
	13:18	0.2	6
	19:16	2.2	67
25 Th	01:24	0.3	9
	07:42	2.7	82
	14:05	0.1	3
	19:58	2.5	76
26 F	02:15	0.1	3
	08:24	2.8	85
	14:50	-0.1	-3
	20:40	2.7	82
27 Sa	03:05	-0.2	-6
	09:05	2.9	88
	15:33	-0.2	-6
	21:22	2.9	88
28 Su ○	03:54	-0.4	-12
	09:48	2.9	88
	16:15	-0.3	-9
	22:06	3.2	98
29 M	04:42	-0.5	-15
	10:32	2.9	88
	16:58	-0.3	-9
	22:51	3.3	101
30 Tu	05:33	-0.5	-15
	11:18	2.8	85
	17:44	-0.3	-9
	23:40	3.4	104
31 W	06:26	-0.5	-15
	12:09	2.6	79
	18:34	-0.1	-3

StationId: 8461490
Source: NOAA/NOS/CO-OPS
Station Type: Primary
Time Zone: LST_LDT
Datum: MLLW

NOAA Tide Predictions

New London, CT, 2021

Times and Heights of High and Low Waters

April

Day	Time	ft	cm	Day	Time	ft	cm
1 Th	00:33	3.3	101	16 F	00:50	2.7	82
	07:24	-0.3	-9		07:32	0.3	9
	13:05	2.5	76		13:29	2.2	67
	19:30	0.0	0		19:20	0.8	24
2 F	01:30	3.2	98	17 Sa	01:37	2.6	79
	08:24	-0.2	-6		08:21	0.3	9
	14:04	2.4	73		14:18	2.2	67
	20:31	0.2	6		20:12	0.9	27
3 Sa	02:32	3.0	91	18 Su	02:27	2.5	76
	09:25	0.0	0		09:11	0.4	12
	15:06	2.3	70		15:09	2.1	64
	21:36	0.3	9		21:07	0.9	27
4 Su ☽	03:38	2.8	85	19 M	03:21	2.5	76
	10:28	0.1	3		10:04	0.5	15
	16:15	2.2	67		16:04	2.1	64
	22:44	0.3	9		22:04	0.9	27
5 M	04:51	2.7	82	20 Tu ◑	04:23	2.5	76
	11:31	0.2	6		10:57	0.4	12
	17:23	2.3	70		17:02	2.2	67
	23:51	0.3	9		23:04	0.8	24
6 Tu	06:01	2.6	79	21 W	05:24	2.5	76
	12:30	0.2	6		11:49	0.4	12
	18:30	2.4	73		17:55	2.4	73
7 W	00:54	0.3	9	22 Th	00:01	0.6	18
	06:59	2.6	79		06:17	2.6	79
	13:25	0.2	6		12:39	0.3	9
	19:22	2.5	76		18:42	2.6	79
8 Th	01:51	0.2	6	23 F	00:56	0.4	12
	07:47	2.6	79		07:04	2.7	82
	14:15	0.2	6		13:26	0.2	6
	20:07	2.6	79		19:25	2.8	85
9 F	02:42	0.1	3	24 Sa	01:50	0.1	3
	08:30	2.6	79		07:49	2.8	85
	14:59	0.2	6		14:12	0.0	0
	20:49	2.8	85		20:08	3.1	94
10 Sa	03:28	0.1	3	25 Su	02:44	-0.1	-3
	09:11	2.6	79		08:34	2.9	88
	15:38	0.2	6		14:59	-0.1	-3
	21:29	2.9	88		20:52	3.4	104
11 Su	04:09	0.0	0	26 M	03:35	-0.3	-9
	09:50	2.5	76		09:20	2.9	88
	16:14	0.3	9		15:44	-0.1	-3
	22:07	2.9	88		21:38	3.6	110
12 M ●	04:48	0.0	0	27 Tu ○	04:26	-0.5	-15
	10:30	2.5	76		10:08	2.9	88
	16:47	0.3	9		16:31	-0.1	-3
	22:46	3.0	91		22:26	3.7	113
13 Tu	05:25	0.1	3	28 W	05:17	-0.5	-15
	11:11	2.4	73		10:58	2.8	85
	17:20	0.5	15		17:19	-0.1	-3
	23:25	2.9	88		23:17	3.7	113
14 W	06:04	0.1	3	29 Th	06:10	-0.4	-12
	11:54	2.4	73		11:52	2.7	82
	17:55	0.6	18		18:12	0.1	3
15 Th	00:06	2.9	88	30 F	00:12	3.6	110
	06:46	0.2	6		07:06	-0.3	-9
	12:40	2.3	70		12:49	2.6	79
	18:34	0.7	21		19:11	0.2	6

May

Day	Time	ft	cm	Day	Time	ft	cm
1 Sa	01:12	3.4	104	16 Su	01:07	2.8	85
	08:05	-0.1	-3		07:51	0.4	12
	13:50	2.5	76		13:52	2.3	70
	20:15	0.3	9		19:45	0.9	27
2 Su	02:14	3.1	94	17 M	01:54	2.7	82
	09:05	0.1	3		08:40	0.4	12
	14:52	2.5	76		14:40	2.3	70
	21:21	0.4	12		20:39	0.9	27
3 M ☽	03:18	2.9	88	18 Tu ☽	02:43	2.7	82
	10:05	0.2	6		09:30	0.4	12
	15:58	2.5	76		15:30	2.4	73
	22:28	0.5	15		21:36	0.9	27
4 Tu	04:26	2.7	82	19 W ◑	03:35	2.6	79
	11:05	0.3	9		10:20	0.4	12
	17:07	2.5	76		16:24	2.5	76
	23:34	0.5	15		22:35	0.8	24
5 W	05:34	2.6	79	20 Th	04:35	2.6	79
	12:02	0.4	12		11:11	0.4	12
	18:09	2.6	79		17:18	2.6	79
					23:34	0.6	18
6 Th	00:36	0.5	15	21 F	05:33	2.6	79
	06:32	2.5	76		12:00	0.3	9
	12:54	0.4	12		18:08	2.9	88
	18:59	2.8	85				
7 F	01:32	0.4	12	22 Sa	00:32	0.4	12
	07:20	2.5	76		06:26	2.7	82
	13:42	0.4	12		12:48	0.2	6
	19:43	2.9	88		18:54	3.2	98
8 Sa	02:23	0.3	9	23 Su	01:28	0.2	6
	08:03	2.4	73		07:16	2.7	82
	14:25	0.5	15		13:37	0.2	6
	20:23	3.0	91		19:39	3.5	107
9 Su	03:08	0.3	9	24 M	02:24	-0.1	-3
	08:44	2.4	73		08:05	2.7	82
	15:05	0.5	15		14:27	0.1	3
	21:02	3.1	94		20:26	3.7	113
10 M	03:49	0.2	6	25 Tu	03:18	-0.3	-9
	09:25	2.4	73		08:56	2.8	85
	15:41	0.6	18		15:17	0.0	0
	21:40	3.1	94		21:15	3.8	116
11 Tu ●	04:26	0.2	6	26 W ○	04:10	-0.4	-12
	10:06	2.4	73		09:47	2.8	85
	16:15	0.6	18		16:08	0.0	0
	22:19	3.1	94		22:06	3.9	119
12 W	05:02	0.1	3	27 Th	05:00	-0.4	-12
	10:48	2.4	73		10:48	2.8	85
	16:50	0.7	21		17:00	0.1	3
	22:58	3.1	94		22:59	3.8	116
13 Th	05:39	0.2	6	28 F	05:52	-0.3	-9
	11:31	2.4	73		11:34	2.7	82
	17:26	0.8	24		17:54	0.2	6
	23:38	3.0	91		23:54	3.6	110
14 F	06:19	0.2	6	29 Sa	06:47	-0.2	-6
	12:17	2.4	73		12:32	2.7	82
	18:06	0.8	24		18:54	0.3	9
15 Sa	00:21	2.9	88	30 Su	00:54	3.4	104
	07:03	0.3	9		07:44	0.0	0
	13:04	2.4	73		13:33	2.7	82
	18:52	0.9	27		19:57	0.4	12
				31 M	01:54	3.1	94
					08:41	0.1	3
					14:33	2.7	82
					21:02	0.5	15

June

Day	Time	ft	cm	Day	Time	ft	cm
1 Tu	02:53	2.9	88	16 W	02:09	2.8	85
	09:38	0.3	9		08:58	0.3	9
	15:34	2.7	82		14:58	2.6	79
	22:06	0.6	18		21:12	0.8	24
2 W ☽	03:54	2.7	82	17 Th	02:56	2.7	82
	10:33	0.4	12		09:45	0.3	9
	16:37	2.7	82		15:47	2.7	82
	23:10	0.6	18		22:11	0.7	21
3 Th	04:56	2.5	76	18 F ◑	03:51	2.6	79
	11:27	0.5	15		10:34	0.3	9
	17:37	2.8	85		16:41	2.9	88
					23:11	0.5	15
4 F	00:11	0.6	18	19 Sa	04:53	2.6	79
	05:55	2.4	73		11:24	0.3	9
	12:17	0.6	18		17:35	3.1	94
	18:28	2.9	88				
5 Sa	01:07	0.5	15	20 Su	00:11	0.4	12
	06:46	2.3	70		05:54	2.5	76
	13:03	0.6	18		12:15	0.3	9
	19:13	3.0	91		18:26	3.4	104
6 Su	01:57	0.5	15	21 M	01:09	0.2	6
	07:32	2.3	70		06:49	2.5	76
	13:46	0.7	21		13:08	0.2	6
	19:54	3.1	94		19:16	3.6	110
7 M	02:43	0.4	12	22 Tu	02:06	0.0	0
	08:16	2.3	70		07:43	2.6	79
	14:28	0.7	21		14:02	0.2	6
	20:34	3.1	94		20:06	3.7	113
8 Tu	03:24	0.3	9	23 W	03:01	-0.2	-6
	09:00	2.3	70		08:36	2.6	79
	15:08	0.8	24		14:57	0.2	6
	21:15	3.1	94		20:57	3.8	116
9 W	04:01	0.2	6	24 Th ○	03:54	-0.3	-9
	09:43	2.4	73		09:29	2.7	82
	15:46	0.8	24		15:52	0.1	3
	21:55	3.1	94		21:50	3.8	116
10 Th ●	04:37	0.2	6	25 F	04:44	-0.3	-9
	10:25	2.4	73		10:23	2.7	82
	16:24	0.8	24		16:45	0.1	3
	22:35	3.1	94		22:43	3.7	113
11 F	05:14	0.2	6	26 Sa	05:34	-0.2	-6
	11:08	2.4	73		11:17	2.8	85
	17:02	0.8	24		17:39	0.2	6
	23:16	3.0	91		23:38	3.5	107
12 Sa	05:54	0.2	6	27 Su	06:26	-0.1	-3
	11:52	2.4	73		12:13	2.8	85
	17:43	0.8	24		18:36	0.3	9
	23:57	3.0	91				
13 Su	06:37	0.3	9	28 M	00:33	3.3	101
	12:38	2.4	73		07:19	0.0	0
	18:29	0.8	24		13:10	2.8	85
					19:36	0.4	12
14 M	00:41	2.9	88	29 Tu	01:29	3.1	94
	07:23	0.3	9		08:12	0.2	6
	13:25	2.5	76		14:07	2.8	85
	19:20	0.8	24		20:37	0.5	15
15 Tu	01:25	2.9	88	30 W	02:23	2.8	85
	08:10	0.3	9		09:04	0.3	9
	14:11	2.5	76		15:03	2.8	85
	20:15	0.8	24		21:38	0.6	18

StationId: 8461490
Source: NOAA/NOS/CO-OPS
Station Type: Primary
Time Zone: LST_LDT
Datum: MLLW

NOAA Tide Predictions

New London, CT, 2021

Times and Heights of High and Low Waters

July

Day	Time (h m)	Height (ft)	Height (cm)
1 Th ◑	03:18	2.6	79
	09:55	0.5	15
	16:00	2.8	85
	22:39	0.7	21
2 F	04:15	2.4	73
	10:45	0.6	18
	16:57	2.9	88
	23:39	0.7	21
3 Sa	05:14	2.2	67
	11:34	0.7	21
	17:51	2.9	88
4 Su	00:34	0.6	18
	06:11	2.2	67
	12:21	0.8	24
	18:39	3.0	91
5 M	01:24	0.6	18
	07:01	2.2	67
	13:07	0.9	27
	19:24	3.0	91
6 Tu	02:11	0.5	15
	07:48	2.2	67
	13:53	0.9	27
	20:07	3.1	94
7 W	02:53	0.4	12
	08:33	2.3	70
	14:37	0.8	24
	20:50	3.1	94
8 Th	03:33	0.3	9
	09:17	2.4	73
	15:20	0.8	24
	21:33	3.1	94
9 F	04:11	0.3	9
	10:00	2.4	73
	16:00	0.7	21
	22:14	3.1	94
10 Sa ●	04:48	0.2	6
	10:42	2.5	76
	16:41	0.7	21
	22:53	3.1	94
11 Su	05:27	0.2	6
	11:25	2.5	76
	17:22	0.6	18
	23:33	3.1	94
12 M	06:09	0.2	6
	12:08	2.6	79
	18:07	0.6	18
13 Tu	00:13	3.0	91
	06:53	0.2	6
	12:54	2.6	79
	18:58	0.6	18
14 W	00:55	2.9	88
	07:38	0.2	6
	13:39	2.7	82
	19:54	0.6	18
15 Th	01:39	2.8	85
	08:25	0.2	6
	14:25	2.8	85
	20:51	0.6	18
16 F	02:27	2.7	82
	09:12	0.3	9
	15:14	3.0	91
	21:50	0.5	15
17 Sa ◐	03:20	2.6	79
	10:02	0.3	9
	16:08	3.1	94
	22:52	0.4	12
18 Su	04:23	2.5	76
	10:55	0.4	12
	17:06	3.2	98
	23:53	0.3	9
19 M	05:29	2.4	73
	11:51	0.4	12
	18:04	3.4	104
20 Tu	00:52	0.2	6
	06:31	2.4	73
	12:48	0.4	12
	18:59	3.5	107
21 W	01:49	0.0	0
	07:27	2.5	76
	13:46	0.3	9
	19:52	3.6	110
22 Th	02:45	-0.1	-3
	08:21	2.6	79
	14:44	0.2	6
	20:45	3.6	110
23 F	03:37	-0.1	-3
	09:14	2.7	82
	15:40	0.2	6
	21:37	3.6	110
24 Sa ○	04:26	-0.2	-6
	10:06	2.8	85
	16:32	0.2	6
	22:28	3.5	107
25 Su	05:14	-0.1	-3
	10:57	2.8	85
	17:23	0.2	6
	23:18	3.4	104
26 M	06:01	0.0	0
	11:50	2.9	88
	18:16	0.3	9
27 Tu	00:08	3.2	98
	06:49	0.1	3
	12:43	2.9	88
	19:12	0.4	12
28 W	00:59	3.0	91
	07:37	0.3	9
	13:53	2.9	88
	20:09	0.5	15
29 Th	01:50	2.7	82
	08:25	0.4	12
	14:27	2.9	88
	21:06	0.6	18
30 F	02:41	2.5	76
	09:12	0.6	18
	15:19	2.9	88
	22:03	0.7	21
31 Sa ◐	03:35	2.3	70
	10:00	0.8	24
	16:13	2.9	88
	23:00	0.7	21

August

Day	Time (h m)	Height (ft)	Height (cm)
1 Su	04:35	2.2	67
	10:49	0.9	27
	17:10	2.9	88
	23:55	0.7	21
2 M	05:35	2.1	64
	11:40	1.0	30
	18:05	2.9	88
3 Tu	00:46	0.6	18
	06:30	2.2	67
	12:31	1.0	30
	18:55	2.9	88
4 W	01:34	0.6	18
	07:19	2.2	67
	13:20	0.9	27
	19:41	3.0	91
5 Th	02:18	0.5	15
	08:05	2.3	70
	14:07	0.8	24
	20:26	3.0	91
6 F	03:01	0.4	12
	08:49	2.4	73
	14:53	0.7	21
	21:08	3.1	94
7 Sa	03:41	0.3	9
	09:31	2.5	76
	15:36	0.6	18
	21:49	3.1	94
8 Su ●	04:19	0.2	6
	10:12	2.6	79
	16:24	0.5	15
	22:27	3.2	98
9 M	04:58	0.1	3
	10:53	2.7	82
	17:01	0.4	12
	23:05	3.1	94
10 Tu	05:38	0.1	3
	11:35	2.8	85
	17:47	0.4	12
	23:44	3.1	94
11 W	06:20	0.1	3
	12:19	3.0	91
	18:38	0.4	12
12 Th	00:26	3.0	91
	07:04	0.2	6
	13:05	3.1	94
	19:34	0.4	12
13 F	01:13	2.8	85
	07:52	0.2	6
	13:53	3.1	94
	20:32	0.4	12
14 Sa	02:04	2.7	82
	08:42	0.3	9
	14:44	3.2	98
	21:32	0.4	12
15 Su ◐	03:00	2.5	76
	09:36	0.4	12
	15:41	3.3	101
	22:34	0.4	12
16 M	04:04	2.4	73
	10:34	0.5	15
	16:45	3.3	101
	23:36	0.3	9
17 Tu	05:14	2.4	73
	11:36	0.5	15
	17:49	3.3	101
18 W	00:36	0.3	9
	06:19	2.4	73
	12:37	0.5	15
	18:48	3.4	104
19 Th	01:34	0.2	6
	07:16	2.5	76
	13:38	0.4	12
	19:43	3.4	104
20 F	02:29	0.1	3
	08:09	2.7	82
	14:36	0.3	9
	20:34	3.4	104
21 Sa	03:20	0.0	0
	09:00	2.8	85
	15:30	0.2	6
	21:23	3.4	104
22 Su ○	04:07	0.0	0
	09:49	2.9	88
	16:19	0.2	6
	22:10	3.3	101
23 M	04:50	0.1	3
	10:36	3.0	91
	17:07	0.2	6
	22:55	3.2	98
24 Tu	05:32	0.1	3
	11:23	3.0	91
	17:55	0.3	9
	23:41	3.0	91
25 W	06:14	0.3	9
	12:11	3.1	94
	18:45	0.4	12
26 Th	00:28	2.8	85
	06:57	0.5	15
	12:59	3.0	91
	19:37	0.5	15
27 F	01:17	2.6	79
	07:41	0.6	18
	13:48	3.0	91
	20:30	0.6	18
28 Sa	02:08	2.5	76
	08:27	0.8	24
	14:37	2.9	88
	21:24	0.7	21
29 Su	03:01	2.3	70
	09:14	1.0	30
	15:30	2.9	88
	22:18	0.7	21
30 M ◐	03:58	2.2	67
	10:05	1.1	34
	16:29	2.8	85
	23:13	0.7	21
31 Tu	05:01	2.2	67
	11:01	1.1	34
	17:30	2.8	85

September

Day	Time (h m)	Height (ft)	Height (cm)
1 W	00:05	0.7	21
	05:59	2.2	67
	11:56	1.1	34
	18:25	2.8	85
2 Th	00:54	0.7	21
	06:50	2.3	70
	12:48	1.0	30
	19:14	2.9	88
3 F	01:41	0.6	18
	07:36	2.5	76
	13:37	0.8	24
	19:58	3.0	91
4 Sa	02:25	0.5	15
	08:18	2.6	79
	14:25	0.7	21
	20:39	3.1	94
5 Su	03:06	0.3	9
	09:00	2.7	82
	15:10	0.5	15
	21:18	3.2	98
6 M	03:46	0.2	6
	09:40	2.9	88
	15:55	0.3	9
	21:56	3.2	98
7 Tu ●	04:25	0.1	3
	10:19	3.1	94
	16:40	0.2	6
	22:35	3.2	98
8 W	05:04	0.1	3
	11:00	3.2	98
	17:27	0.2	6
	23:15	3.1	94
9 Th	05:46	0.1	3
	11:44	3.3	101
	18:19	0.2	6
10 F	00:01	2.9	88
	06:31	0.2	6
	12:32	3.4	104
	19:15	0.2	6
11 Sa	00:51	2.8	85
	07:22	0.3	9
	13:24	3.4	104
	20:14	0.2	6
12 Su	01:47	2.6	79
	08:17	0.4	12
	14:20	3.4	104
	21:14	0.3	9
13 M ◐	02:46	2.5	76
	09:16	0.5	15
	15:21	3.3	101
	22:16	0.3	9
14 Tu	03:53	2.4	73
	10:20	0.6	18
	16:29	3.2	98
	23:19	0.3	9
15 W	05:05	2.4	73
	11:26	0.6	18
	17:38	3.2	98
16 Th	00:20	0.3	9
	06:12	2.5	76
	12:30	0.5	15
	18:39	3.2	98
17 F	01:17	0.3	9
	07:08	2.6	79
	13:30	0.4	12
	19:33	3.2	98
18 Sa	02:10	0.2	6
	07:59	2.8	85
	14:27	0.4	12
	20:21	3.2	98
19 Su	02:59	0.2	6
	08:46	2.9	88
	15:18	0.3	9
	21:06	3.1	94
20 M ○	03:43	0.2	6
	09:31	3.1	94
	16:06	0.3	9
	21:49	3.1	94
21 Tu	04:23	0.2	6
	10:13	3.2	98
	16:50	0.3	9
	22:30	3.0	91
22 W	05:01	0.3	9
	10:55	3.2	98
	17:33	0.3	9
	23:13	2.8	85
23 Th	05:38	0.5	15
	11:37	3.2	98
	18:17	0.4	12
	23:58	2.7	82
24 F	06:15	0.6	18
	12:22	3.1	94
	19:04	0.5	15
25 Sa	00:46	2.5	76
	06:56	0.8	24
	13:08	3.0	91
	19:54	0.6	18
26 Su	01:37	2.4	73
	07:41	1.0	30
	13:58	2.9	88
	20:45	0.6	18
27 M	02:30	2.3	70
	08:31	1.1	34
	14:50	2.8	85
	21:37	0.7	21
28 Tu	03:25	2.3	70
	09:26	1.1	34
	15:48	2.7	82
	22:30	0.7	21
29 W ◐	04:26	2.2	67
	10:24	1.1	34
	16:52	2.7	82
	23:24	0.7	21
30 Th	05:27	2.3	70
	11:22	1.1	34
	17:51	2.7	82

StationId: 8461490
Source: NOAA/NOS/CO-OPS
Station Type: Primary
Time Zone: LST_LDT
Datum: MLLW

NOAA Tide Predictions

New London, CT,2021

Times and Heights of High and Low Waters

October

Day	Time	ft	cm	Day	Time	ft	cm
1 F	00:14	0.7	21	16 Sa	00:56	0.3	9
	06:20	2.4	73		06:58	2.8	85
	12:16	0.9	27		13:20	0.4	12
	18:41	2.8	85		19:17	2.9	88
2 Sa	01:01	0.6	18	17 Su	01:46	0.3	9
	07:05	2.6	79		07:45	2.9	88
	13:07	0.8	24		14:15	0.4	12
	19:24	2.9	88		20:02	2.9	88
3 Su	01:45	0.4	12	18 M	02:33	0.3	9
	07:46	2.8	85		08:29	3.1	94
	13:56	0.6	18		15:05	0.3	9
	20:04	3.0	91		20:45	2.8	85
4 M	02:28	0.3	9	19 Tu	03:15	0.3	9
	08:26	3.0	91		09:09	3.2	98
	14:45	0.4	12		15:50	0.2	6
	20:44	3.1	94		21:26	2.7	82
5 Tu	03:10	0.2	6	20 W ○	03:54	0.4	12
	09:06	3.2	98		09:48	3.2	98
	15:33	0.1	3		16:31	0.2	6
	21:24	3.1	94		22:06	2.7	82
6 W ●	03:50	0.1	3	21 Th	04:29	0.5	15
	09:46	3.4	104		10:27	3.2	98
	16:20	0.0	0		17:10	0.2	6
	22:06	3.1	94		22:48	2.6	79
7 Th	04:32	0.0	0	22 F	05:03	0.6	18
	10:28	3.6	110		11:07	3.2	98
	17:09	-0.1	-3		17:50	0.3	9
	22:50	3.0	91		23:31	2.5	76
8 F	05:15	0.1	3	23 Sa	05:38	0.7	21
	11:14	3.7	113		11:48	3.1	94
	18:00	-0.1	-3		18:33	0.4	12
	23:38	2.9	88				
9 Sa	06:02	0.2	6	24 Su	00:18	2.4	73
	12:04	3.7	113		06:16	0.8	24
	18:56	0.0	0		12:33	3.0	91
					19:19	0.4	12
10 Su	00:32	2.7	82	25 M	01:09	2.3	70
	06:56	0.3	9		07:01	1.0	30
	13:00	3.6	110		13:22	2.8	85
	19:55	0.1	3		20:08	0.5	15
11 M	01:32	2.6	79	26 Tu	02:01	2.3	70
	07:57	0.4	12		07:54	1.0	30
	14:00	3.4	104		14:14	2.7	82
	20:56	0.2	6		20:59	0.6	18
12 Tu	02:34	2.5	76	27 W	02:55	2.2	67
	09:01	0.5	15		08:50	1.1	34
	15:04	3.2	98		15:09	2.6	79
	21:58	0.3	9		21:51	0.6	18
13 W ◑	03:42	2.4	73	28 Th ◑	03:51	2.2	67
	10:09	0.6	18		09:48	1.1	34
	16:14	3.1	94		16:08	2.6	79
	23:00	0.3	9		22:43	0.6	18
14 Th	04:54	2.5	76	29 F	04:51	2.3	70
	11:16	0.6	18		10:46	1.0	30
	17:24	3.0	91		17:07	2.6	79
					23:33	0.5	15
15 F	00:00	0.3	9	30 Sa	05:45	2.4	73
	06:02	2.6	79		11:43	0.8	24
	12:21	0.5	15		18:00	2.7	82
	18:26	2.9	88				
				31 Su	00:20	0.4	12
					06:31	2.6	79
					12:37	0.6	18
					18:46	2.7	82

November

Day	Time	ft	cm	Day	Time	ft	cm
1 M	01:05	0.3	9	16 Tu	01:03	0.3	9
	07:13	2.9	88		07:07	3.0	91
	13:29	0.4	12		13:48	0.2	6
	19:28	2.8	85		19:21	2.4	73
2 Tu	01:49	0.2	6	17 W	01:45	0.4	12
	07:53	3.1	94		07:46	3.1	94
	14:21	0.1	3		14:32	0.2	6
	20:10	2.9	88		20:02	2.4	73
3 W	02:33	0.1	3	18 Th	02:24	0.4	12
	08:33	3.4	104		08:24	3.1	94
	15:12	-0.1	-3		15:11	0.1	3
	20:54	2.9	88		20:44	2.3	70
4 Th ●	03:17	0.0	0	19 F ○	03:00	0.5	15
	09:16	3.6	110		09:02	3.1	94
	16:02	-0.3	-9		15:48	0.1	3
	21:40	2.8	85		21:25	2.3	70
5 F	04:03	-0.1	-3	20 Sa	03:35	0.5	15
	10:01	3.8	116		09:41	3.0	91
	16:51	-0.4	-12		16:25	0.1	3
	22:27	2.8	85		22:08	2.3	70
6 Sa	04:49	-0.1	-3	21 Su	04:10	0.6	18
	10:50	3.8	116		10:22	2.9	88
	17:42	-0.3	-9		17:04	0.2	6
	23:19	2.7	82		22:54	2.3	70
7 Su	04:40	0.0	0	22 M	04:48	0.7	21
	10:42	3.7	113		11:06	2.8	85
	17:37	-0.2	-6		17:48	0.2	6
	23:15	2.6	79		23:42	2.2	67
8 M	05:36	0.2	6	23 Tu	05:31	0.8	24
	11:41	3.5	107		11:53	2.7	82
	18:36	-0.1	-3		18:35	0.3	9
9 Tu	00:16	2.5	76	24 W	00:33	2.2	67
	06:40	0.3	9		06:22	0.8	24
	12:43	3.3	101		12:41	2.6	79
	19:36	0.0	0		19:24	0.3	9
10 W	01:20	2.5	76	25 Th	01:24	2.1	64
	07:46	0.4	12		07:18	0.8	24
	13:47	3.1	94		13:30	2.5	76
	20:37	0.1	3		20:13	0.3	9
11 Th ◐	02:26	2.4	73	26 F	02:16	2.2	67
	08:54	0.5	15		08:14	0.8	24
	14:53	2.9	88		14:20	2.5	76
	21:37	0.2	6		21:02	0.3	9
12 F	03:37	2.5	76	27 Sa ◐	03:10	2.2	67
	10:02	0.5	15		09:12	0.7	21
	16:01	2.7	82		15:15	2.4	73
	22:35	0.2	6		21:51	0.3	9
13 Sa	04:44	2.6	79	28 Su	04:04	2.4	73
	11:06	0.4	12		10:12	0.6	18
	17:02	2.6	79		16:12	2.4	73
	23:29	0.3	9		22:39	0.2	6
14 Su	05:40	2.8	85	29 M	04:54	2.6	79
	12:05	0.4	12		11:09	0.4	12
	17:54	2.5	76		17:05	2.4	73
					23:25	0.1	3
15 M	00:18	0.3	9	30 Tu	05:38	2.9	88
	06:26	2.9	88		12:04	0.2	6
	12:59	0.3	9		17:53	2.5	76
	18:39	2.4	73				

December

Day	Time	ft	cm	Day	Time	ft	cm
1 W	00:12	0.0	0	16 Th	01:15	0.4	12
	06:21	3.2	98		07:21	2.8	85
	12:59	-0.1	-3		14:09	0.1	3
	18:40	2.5	76		19:40	2.0	61
2 Th	01:00	-0.1	-3	17 F	01:56	0.4	12
	07:06	3.4	104		08:02	2.9	88
	13:52	-0.3	-9		14:48	0.0	0
	19:28	2.5	76		20:22	2.1	64
3 F	01:50	-0.2	-6	18 Sa	02:35	0.4	12
	07:52	3.6	110		08:42	2.8	85
	14:44	-0.5	-15		15:24	0.0	0
	20:17	2.5	76		21:04	2.1	64
4 Sa ●	02:40	-0.2	-6	19 Su ○	03:12	0.4	12
	08:41	3.7	113		09:22	2.8	85
	15:34	-0.6	-18		16:01	-0.1	-3
	21:08	2.5	76		21:46	2.1	64
5 Su	03:30	-0.2	-6	20 M	03:48	0.4	12
	09:32	3.7	113		10:02	2.8	85
	16:25	-0.5	-15		16:38	0.0	0
	22:01	2.5	76		22:30	2.1	64
6 M	04:23	-0.2	-6	21 Tu	04:26	0.4	12
	10:26	3.5	107		10:44	2.7	82
	17:18	-0.4	-12		17:19	0.0	0
	22:57	2.5	76		23:15	2.1	64
7 Tu	05:20	-0.1	-3	22 W	05:08	0.4	12
	11:24	3.3	101		11:26	2.6	79
	18:15	-0.3	-9		18:03	0.0	0
	23:58	2.4	73				
8 W	06:23	0.1	3	23 Th	00:03	2.1	64
	12:24	3.1	94		05:56	0.5	15
	19:13	-0.2	-6		12:09	2.5	76
					18:50	0.0	0
9 Th	01:00	2.4	73	24 F	00:50	2.1	64
	07:28	0.2	6		06:49	0.5	15
	13:24	2.8	85		12:51	2.4	73
	20:10	-0.1	-3		19:36	0.1	3
10 F	02:03	2.4	73	25 Sa	01:38	2.1	64
	08:33	0.3	9		07:45	0.5	15
	14:24	2.6	79		13:35	2.3	70
	21:07	0.0	0		20:23	0.1	3
11 Sa ◐	03:09	2.4	73	26 Su	02:26	2.2	67
	09:40	0.3	9		08:43	0.4	12
	15:26	2.4	73		14:24	2.2	67
	22:03	0.1	3		21:10	0.1	3
12 Su	04:14	2.5	76	27 M ◐	03:19	2.4	73
	10:42	0.3	9		09:43	0.3	9
	16:29	2.2	67		15:23	2.2	67
	22:56	0.2	6		21:59	0.0	0
13 M	05:11	2.6	79	28 Tu	04:13	2.6	79
	11:43	0.3	9		10:44	0.1	3
	17:24	2.1	64		16:26	2.1	64
	23:45	0.3	9		22:50	0.0	0
14 Tu	05:59	2.7	82	29 W	05:05	2.8	85
	12:23	0.2	6		11:42	-0.1	-3
	18:13	2.0	61		17:24	2.1	64
					23:42	-0.1	-3
15 W	00:31	0.3	9	30 Th	05:55	3.1	94
	06:41	2.8	85		12:39	-0.3	-9
	13:26	0.1	3		18:16	2.2	67
	18:57	2.0	61				
				31 F	00:35	-0.2	-6
					06:44	3.3	101
					13:34	-0.5	-15
					18:59	2.2	67

StationId: 8467150
Source: NOAA/NOS/CO-OPS
Station Type: Primary
Time Zone: LST_LDT
Datum: MLLW

NOAA Tide Predictions

Bridgeport, CT, 2021

Times and Heights of High and Low Waters

January

Day	Time (h:m)	Height (ft)	Height (cm)
1 F	00:23	6.3	192
	06:25	0.2	6
	12:31	7.1	216
	19:01	-0.3	-9
2 Sa	01:06	6.4	195
	07:10	0.2	6
	13:16	7.0	213
	19:45	-0.3	-9
3 Su	01:51	6.5	198
	07:58	0.2	6
	14:03	6.9	210
	20:31	-0.3	-9
4 M	02:39	6.6	201
	08:51	0.2	6
	14:55	6.7	204
	21:21	-0.2	-6
5 Tu	03:30	6.7	204
	09:49	0.2	6
	15:50	6.5	198
	22:14	-0.1	-3
6 W ◑	04:25	6.8	207
	10:51	0.1	3
	16:50	6.3	192
	23:11	-0.1	-3
7 Th	05:24	6.9	210
	11:55	0.0	0
	17:53	6.2	189
8 F	00:10	0.0	0
	06:24	7.1	216
	12:58	-0.2	-6
	18:58	6.1	186
9 Sa	01:10	-0.1	-3
	07:25	7.3	223
	13:59	-0.4	-12
	19:59	6.2	189
10 Su	02:08	-0.1	-3
	08:23	7.5	229
	14:57	-0.6	-18
	20:57	6.4	195
11 M	03:05	-0.2	-6
	09:18	7.6	232
	15:52	-0.7	-21
	21:52	6.5	198
12 Tu	04:00	-0.3	-9
	10:10	7.6	232
	16:43	-0.8	-24
	22:43	6.6	201
13 W ●	04:52	-0.3	-9
	11:00	7.6	232
	17:32	-0.8	-24
	23:33	6.6	201
14 Th	05:42	-0.3	-9
	11:50	7.4	226
	18:19	-0.6	-18
15 F	00:21	6.6	201
	06:31	-0.2	-6
	12:38	7.1	216
	19:04	-0.5	-15
16 Sa	01:09	6.5	198
	07:20	0.0	0
	13:26	6.8	207
	19:49	-0.2	-6
17 Su	01:56	6.4	195
	08:09	0.2	6
	14:13	6.5	198
	20:34	0.0	0
18 M	02:43	6.3	192
	08:59	0.4	12
	15:02	6.2	189
	21:19	0.3	9
19 Tu	03:31	6.2	189
	09:51	0.6	18
	15:53	5.8	177
	22:07	0.5	15
20 W ◐	04:20	6.1	186
	10:46	0.7	21
	16:46	5.6	171
	22:56	0.7	21
21 Th	05:12	6.1	186
	11:41	0.7	21
	17:42	5.4	165
	23:48	0.9	27
22 F	06:05	6.0	183
	12:36	0.7	21
	18:39	5.4	165
23 Sa	00:41	0.9	27
	06:58	6.1	186
	13:29	0.5	15
	19:34	5.5	168
24 Su	01:33	0.8	24
	07:50	6.3	192
	14:20	0.3	9
	20:25	5.6	171
25 M	02:23	0.7	21
	08:38	6.5	198
	15:07	0.1	3
	21:11	5.8	177
26 Tu	03:10	0.5	15
	09:22	6.7	204
	15:51	-0.1	-3
	21:54	6.0	183
27 W	03:55	0.2	6
	10:05	6.9	210
	16:34	-0.3	-9
	22:35	6.2	189
28 Th ○	04:39	0.0	0
	10:47	7.1	216
	17:15	-0.5	-15
	23:16	6.4	195
29 F	05:22	-0.2	-6
	11:29	7.2	219
	17:56	-0.6	-18
	23:58	6.6	201
30 Sa	06:06	-0.3	-9
	12:12	7.3	223
	18:38	-0.7	-21
31 Su	00:41	6.8	207
	06:51	-0.4	-12
	12:57	7.2	219
	19:21	-0.7	-21

February

Day	Time (h:m)	Height (ft)	Height (cm)
1 M	01:26	7.0	213
	07:40	-0.4	-12
	13:45	7.1	216
	20:06	-0.6	-18
2 Tu	02:14	7.0	213
	08:33	-0.3	-9
	14:36	6.8	207
	20:55	-0.4	-12
3 W	03:05	7.1	216
	09:29	-0.2	-6
	15:30	6.5	198
	21:49	-0.2	-6
4 Th ◑	04:00	7.0	213
	10:31	-0.1	-3
	16:30	6.2	189
	22:47	0.0	0
5 F	05:00	6.9	210
	11:36	0.0	0
	17:35	6.0	183
	23:50	0.2	6
6 Sa	06:04	6.9	210
	12:41	0.0	0
	18:42	5.9	180
7 Su	00:54	0.2	6
	07:09	6.9	210
	13:45	-0.1	-3
	19:47	6.0	183
8 M	01:57	0.1	3
	08:11	7.0	213
	14:45	-0.3	-9
	20:47	6.2	189
9 Tu	02:56	0.0	0
	09:09	7.2	219
	15:39	-0.4	-12
	21:41	6.4	195
10 W	03:51	-0.2	-6
	10:01	7.3	223
	16:29	-0.5	-15
	22:30	6.6	201
11 Th ●	04:41	-0.3	-9
	10:48	7.3	223
	17:14	-0.5	-15
	23:16	6.7	204
12 F	05:28	-0.3	-9
	11:34	7.2	219
	17:57	-0.5	-15
	23:59	6.7	204
13 Sa	06:12	-0.2	-6
	12:17	7.0	213
	18:37	-0.3	-9
14 Su	00:41	6.7	204
	06:55	-0.1	-3
	13:00	6.8	207
	19:16	-0.1	-3
15 M	01:23	6.6	201
	07:38	0.0	0
	13:43	6.5	198
	19:55	0.1	3
16 Tu	02:04	6.5	198
	08:22	0.2	6
	14:27	6.2	189
	20:36	0.4	12
17 W	02:47	6.4	195
	09:09	0.4	12
	15:13	5.9	180
	21:19	0.6	18
18 Th	03:31	6.2	189
	09:58	0.6	18
	16:02	5.6	171
	22:07	0.9	27
19 F ◐	04:20	6.0	183
	10:51	0.8	24
	16:56	5.4	165
	23:00	1.1	34
20 Sa	05:13	5.9	180
	11:48	0.8	24
	17:53	5.3	162
	23:56	1.1	34
21 Su	06:11	5.9	180
	12:45	0.8	24
	18:51	5.4	165
22 M	00:53	1.0	30
	07:08	6.1	186
	13:40	0.6	18
	19:46	5.6	171
23 Tu	01:48	0.8	24
	08:03	6.3	192
	14:31	0.3	9
	20:36	5.9	180
24 W	02:40	0.5	15
	08:52	6.7	204
	15:19	0.0	0
	21:22	6.2	189
25 Th	03:28	0.1	3
	09:38	7.0	213
	16:04	-0.3	-9
	22:05	6.6	201
26 F	04:14	-0.2	-6
	10:22	7.3	223
	16:46	-0.5	-15
	22:48	6.9	210
27 Sa ○	05:00	-0.5	-15
	11:06	7.5	229
	17:29	-0.7	-21
	23:31	7.2	219
28 Su	05:45	-0.8	-24
	11:51	7.5	229
	18:11	-0.8	-24

March

Day	Time (h:m)	Height (ft)	Height (cm)
1 M	00:15	7.5	229
	06:33	-0.8	-24
	12:37	7.5	229
	18:55	-0.8	-24
2 Tu	01:01	7.6	232
	07:22	-0.8	-24
	13:26	7.3	223
	19:41	-0.6	-18
3 W	01:50	7.6	232
	08:15	-0.6	-18
	14:18	6.9	210
	20:32	-0.4	-12
4 Th	02:42	7.5	229
	09:11	-0.4	-12
	15:13	6.6	201
	21:27	0.0	0
5 F	03:38	7.2	219
	10:13	-0.1	-3
	16:14	6.2	189
	22:29	0.3	9
6 Sa ◑	04:41	6.9	210
	11:18	0.1	3
	17:20	6.0	183
	23:35	0.5	15
7 Su	05:48	6.7	204
	12:26	0.3	9
	18:29	5.9	180
8 M	00:43	0.5	15
	06:57	6.7	204
	13:31	0.2	6
	19:35	6.1	186
9 Tu	01:48	0.4	12
	08:02	6.8	207
	14:30	0.1	3
	20:35	6.3	192
10 W	02:47	0.2	6
	08:58	6.9	210
	15:23	-0.1	-3
	21:27	6.6	201
11 Th	03:40	0.0	0
	09:48	7.0	213
	16:10	-0.2	-6
	22:13	6.8	207
12 F	04:27	-0.2	-6
	10:33	7.1	216
	16:52	-0.2	-6
	22:55	6.9	210
13 Sa ●	05:10	-0.2	-6
	11:14	7.0	213
	17:30	-0.1	-3
	23:34	7.0	213
14 Su	06:51	-0.2	-6
	12:54	6.9	210
	19:07	0.0	0
15 M	01:11	7.0	213
	13:34	6.7	204
	19:43	0.2	6
16 Tu	01:49	6.9	210
	08:09	0.0	0
	14:14	6.5	198
	20:19	0.4	12
17 W	02:26	6.8	207
	08:48	0.2	6
	14:55	6.3	192
	20:57	0.6	18
18 Th	03:05	6.6	201
	09:30	0.4	12
	15:38	6.1	186
	21:38	0.9	27
19 F	03:47	6.4	195
	10:16	0.6	18
	16:24	5.8	177
	22:24	1.1	34
20 Sa	04:34	6.2	189
	11:06	0.8	24
	17:14	5.7	174
	23:17	1.3	40
21 Su ◐	05:26	6.0	183
	12:02	0.9	27
	18:10	5.6	171
22 M	00:15	1.3	40
	06:25	6.0	183
	13:10	0.9	27
	19:08	5.6	171
23 Tu	01:15	1.2	37
	07:26	6.1	186
	13:58	0.8	24
	20:06	5.8	177
24 W	02:13	0.9	27
	08:25	6.4	195
	14:53	0.5	15
	20:59	6.2	189
25 Th	03:08	0.5	15
	09:19	6.8	207
	15:43	0.2	6
	21:47	6.6	201
26 F	03:59	0.1	3
	10:08	7.1	216
	16:30	-0.1	-3
	22:33	7.1	216
27 Sa	04:49	-0.4	-12
	10:55	7.4	226
	17:14	-0.4	-12
	23:18	7.6	232
28 Su ○	05:37	-0.7	-21
	11:42	7.6	232
	17:59	-0.6	-18
29 M	00:03	7.9	241
	06:25	-1.0	-30
	12:29	7.7	235
	18:43	-0.7	-21
30 Tu	00:49	8.1	247
	07:13	-1.1	-34
	13:17	7.6	232
	19:30	-0.6	-18
31 W	01:37	8.2	250
	08:04	-1.0	-30
	14:08	7.4	226
	20:19	-0.4	-12

StationId: 8467150
Source: NOAA/NOS/CO-OPS
Station Type: Primary
Time Zone: LST_LDT
Datum: MLLW

NOAA Tide Predictions

Bridgeport, CT, 2021

Times and Heights of High and Low Waters

April

Day	Time	ft	cm	Day	Time	ft	cm
1 Th	02:27	8.0	244	16 F	02:30	6.8	207
	08:57	-0.7	-21		08:58	0.4	12
	15:01	7.1	216		15:08	6.3	192
	21:12	-0.1	-3		21:05	1.1	34
2 F	03:21	7.7	235	17 Sa	03:11	6.6	201
	09:54	-0.4	-12		09:41	0.6	18
	15:58	6.7	204		15:52	6.1	186
	22:10	0.2	6		21:51	1.3	40
3 Sa	04:20	7.3	223	18 Su	03:57	6.4	195
	10:56	0.0	0		10:29	0.8	24
	16:59	6.4	195		16:40	6.0	183
	23:14	0.5	15		22:42	1.4	43
4 Su ◐	05:24	7.0	213	19 M	04:48	6.3	192
	12:01	0.3	9		11:23	0.9	27
	18:06	6.2	189		17:33	5.9	180
					23:39	1.4	43
5 M	00:22	0.7	21	20 Tu ◐	05:45	6.3	192
	06:33	6.7	204		12:20	0.9	27
	13:07	0.5	15		18:29	6.0	183
	19:14	6.2	189				
6 Tu	01:31	0.7	21	21 W	00:40	1.2	37
	07:43	6.6	201		06:46	6.3	192
	14:11	0.5	15		13:17	0.8	24
	20:19	6.4	195		19:26	6.3	192
7 W	02:35	0.6	18	22 Th	01:39	0.9	27
	08:46	6.7	204		07:47	6.5	198
	15:09	0.4	12		14:12	0.6	18
	21:17	6.6	201		20:20	6.7	204
8 Th	03:33	0.4	12	23 F	02:37	0.5	15
	09:42	6.8	207		08:44	6.9	210
	15:59	0.3	9		15:04	0.3	9
	22:06	6.9	210		21:12	7.1	216
9 F	04:23	0.2	6	24 Sa	03:31	0.0	0
	10:30	6.9	210		09:32	7.2	219
	16:44	0.2	6		15:54	0.0	0
	22:49	7.1	216		22:00	7.7	235
10 Sa	05:08	0.0	0	25 Su	04:23	-0.4	-12
	11:12	6.9	210		10:28	7.4	226
	17:23	0.2	6		16:42	-0.3	-9
	23:29	7.2	219		22:48	8.1	247
11 Su	05:49	-0.1	-3	26 M	05:14	-0.8	-24
	11:52	6.9	210		11:17	7.6	232
	18:00	0.3	9		17:29	-0.4	-12
					23:35	8.4	256
12 M ●	00:05	7.2	219	27 Tu ○	06:04	-1.0	-30
	06:27	-0.1	-3		12:07	7.6	232
	12:30	6.8	207		18:17	-0.5	-15
	18:36	0.4	12				
13 Tu	00:41	7.2	219	28 W	00:24	8.5	259
	07:04	-0.1	-3		06:55	-1.1	-34
	13:08	6.7	204		12:58	7.5	229
	19:11	0.6	18		19:07	-0.3	-9
14 W	01:16	7.1	216	29 Th	01:14	8.4	256
	07:41	0.1	3		07:46	-0.9	-27
	13:47	6.6	201		13:51	7.4	226
	19:47	0.7	21		19:59	-0.1	-3
15 Th	01:52	7.0	213	30 F	02:07	8.2	250
	08:19	0.2	6		08:40	-0.6	-18
	14:27	6.4	195		14:46	7.1	216
	20:25	0.9	27		20:55	0.2	6

May

Day	Time	ft	cm	Day	Time	ft	cm
1 Sa	03:03	7.8	238	16 Su	02:44	6.8	207
	09:37	-0.2	-6		09:14	0.6	18
	15:43	6.9	210		15:26	6.3	192
	21:55	0.5	15		21:25	1.3	40
2 Su	04:03	7.4	226	17 M	03:29	6.7	204
	10:38	0.1	3		10:00	0.7	21
	16:44	6.7	204		16:11	6.3	192
	22:59	0.7	21		22:15	1.3	40
3 M ◐	05:07	7.0	213	18 Tu	04:18	6.6	201
	11:40	0.4	12		10:50	0.8	24
	17:48	6.5	198		17:10	6.3	192
					23:10	1.2	37
4 Tu	00:06	0.9	27	19 W ◐	05:13	6.6	201
	06:13	6.7	204		11:44	0.8	24
	12:43	0.6	18		17:54	6.5	198
	18:53	6.5	198				
5 W ◑	01:12	0.9	27	20 Th	00:09	1.1	34
	07:19	6.5	198		06:11	6.6	201
	13:43	0.7	21		12:38	0.7	21
	19:54	6.7	204		18:49	6.8	207
6 Th	02:14	0.7	21	21 F	01:08	0.8	24
	08:21	6.5	198		07:12	6.7	204
	14:37	0.7	21		13:33	0.5	15
	20:49	6.9	210		19:44	7.1	216
7 F	03:10	0.6	18	22 Sa	02:07	0.4	12
	09:16	6.6	201		08:11	6.8	207
	15:26	0.7	21		14:27	0.3	9
	21:38	7.1	216		20:38	7.6	232
8 Sa	04:00	0.4	12	23 Su	03:04	0.0	0
	10:04	6.6	201		09:08	7.1	216
	16:10	0.6	18		15:20	0.1	3
	22:20	7.2	219		21:30	8.0	244
9 Su	04:44	0.2	6	24 M	03:59	-0.4	-12
	10:47	6.7	204		10:02	7.2	219
	16:51	0.6	18		16:11	-0.1	-3
	22:59	7.3	223		22:21	8.4	256
10 M	05:24	0.1	3	25 Tu	04:53	-0.7	-21
	11:27	6.7	204		10:55	7.4	226
	17:29	0.7	21		17:03	-0.2	-6
	23:35	7.3	223		23:11	8.6	262
11 Tu ●	06:02	0.0	0	26 W ○	05:45	-0.9	-27
	12:05	6.7	204		11:47	7.4	226
	18:05	0.8	24		17:55	-0.2	-6
12 W ○	00:11	7.3	223	27 Th	00:03	8.6	262
	06:39	0.1	3		06:37	-0.9	-27
	12:40	6.6	201		12:40	7.4	226
	18:42	0.9	27		18:48	-0.1	-3
13 Th	00:47	7.2	219	28 F	00:56	8.4	256
	07:16	0.1	3		07:30	-0.7	-21
	13:22	6.6	201		13:34	7.3	223
	19:20	1.0	30		19:42	0.1	3
14 F	01:24	7.1	216	29 Sa	01:50	8.1	247
	07:53	0.3	9		08:24	-0.5	-15
	14:02	6.5	198		14:30	7.1	216
	19:58	1.1	34		20:39	0.3	9
15 Sa	02:02	6.9	210	30 Su	02:47	7.8	238
	08:32	0.4	12		09:19	-0.2	-6
	14:43	6.4	195		15:26	7.0	213
	20:40	1.2	37		21:38	0.6	18
				31 M	03:45	7.4	226
					10:16	0.2	6
					16:24	6.9	210
					22:40	0.8	24

June

Day	Time	ft	cm	Day	Time	ft	cm
1 Tu	04:45	7.0	213	16 W	03:54	6.9	210
	11:13	0.5	15		10:21	0.5	15
	17:24	6.8	207		16:32	6.8	207
	23:43	0.9	27		22:45	0.9	27
2 W ◑	05:46	6.6	201	17 Th	04:46	6.8	207
	12:10	0.7	21		11:11	0.5	15
	18:23	6.8	207		17:22	7.0	213
					23:42	0.8	24
3 Th	00:45	0.9	27	18 F ◐	05:42	6.7	204
	06:47	6.4	195		12:04	0.5	15
	13:06	0.8	24		18:16	7.2	219
	19:20	6.8	207				
4 F	01:44	0.9	27	19 Sa	00:42	0.6	18
	07:47	6.3	192		06:41	6.7	204
	13:58	0.9	27		12:59	0.5	15
	20:13	7.0	213		19:12	7.5	229
5 Sa	02:39	0.7	21	20 Su	01:42	0.3	9
	08:42	6.3	192		07:42	6.7	204
	14:47	1.0	30		13:55	0.4	12
	21:02	7.1	216		20:09	7.8	238
6 Su	03:29	0.6	18	21 M	02:41	0.0	0
	09:32	6.3	192		08:43	6.8	207
	15:33	1.0	30		14:51	0.3	9
	21:46	7.2	219		21:04	8.1	247
7 M	04:14	0.4	12	22 Tu	03:39	-0.3	-9
	10:17	6.4	195		09:41	7.0	213
	16:16	1.0	30		15:47	0.2	6
	22:27	7.3	223		21:59	8.3	253
8 Tu	04:56	0.3	9	23 W	04:35	-0.5	-15
	10:59	6.5	198		10:36	7.1	216
	16:57	1.0	30		16:43	0.1	3
	23:05	7.3	223		22:53	8.4	256
9 W	05:36	0.2	6	24 Th ○	05:29	-0.6	-18
	11:40	6.5	198		11:30	7.2	219
	17:37	1.0	30		17:38	0.0	0
	23:43	7.2	219		23:46	8.4	256
10 Th ●	06:14	0.2	6	25 F	06:22	-0.6	-18
	12:19	6.6	201		12:24	7.2	219
	18:16	1.0	30		18:32	0.1	3
11 F	00:21	7.2	219	26 Sa	00:40	8.3	253
	06:52	0.2	6		07:14	-0.5	-15
	12:58	6.6	201		13:18	7.2	219
	18:56	1.0	30		19:27	0.2	6
12 Sa	01:00	7.1	216	27 Su	01:34	8.0	244
	07:30	0.3	9		08:05	-0.3	-9
	13:38	6.5	198		14:11	7.2	219
	19:36	1.1	34		20:22	0.4	12
13 Su	01:40	7.1	216	28 M	02:28	7.7	235
	08:10	0.3	9		08:57	-0.1	-3
	14:19	6.6	201		15:05	7.1	216
	20:18	1.1	34		21:17	0.5	15
14 M	02:21	7.0	213	29 Tu	03:22	7.3	223
	08:51	0.4	12		09:48	0.2	6
	15:01	6.6	201		15:58	7.0	213
	21:03	1.1	34		22:14	0.7	21
15 Tu	03:06	7.0	213	30 W	04:17	6.9	210
	09:35	0.4	12		10:40	0.5	15
	15:45	6.7	204		16:51	7.0	213
	21:51	1.0	30		23:12	0.9	27

StationId: 8467150
Source: NOAA/NOS/CO-OPS
Station Type: Primary
Time Zone: LST_LDT
Datum: MLLW

NOAA Tide Predictions

Bridgeport, CT, 2021

Times and Heights of High and Low Waters

July

Day	Time (h:m)	Height (ft)	Height (cm)
1 Th ◑	05:12	6.6	201
	11:31	0.7	21
	17:44	6.9	210
2 F	00:10	1.0	30
	06:09	6.3	192
	12:22	1.0	30
	18:38	6.9	210
3 Sa	01:06	1.0	30
	07:06	6.1	186
	13:14	1.1	34
	19:30	6.9	210
4 Su	02:01	0.9	27
	08:02	6.0	183
	14:04	1.3	40
	20:21	6.9	210
5 M	02:52	0.8	24
	08:56	6.1	186
	14:54	1.3	40
	21:09	7.0	213
6 Tu	03:40	0.7	21
	09:45	6.2	189
	15:41	1.2	37
	21:54	7.1	216
7 W	04:25	0.5	15
	10:30	6.3	192
	16:26	1.2	37
	22:37	7.1	216
8 Th	05:07	0.4	12
	11:12	6.5	198
	17:10	1.1	34
	23:17	7.2	219
9 F	05:48	0.3	9
	11:53	6.6	201
	17:52	1.0	30
	23:57	7.2	219
10 Sa ●	06:27	0.3	9
	12:33	6.6	201
	18:33	0.9	27
11 Su	00:37	7.3	223
	07:06	0.2	6
	13:12	6.7	204
	19:14	0.8	24
12 M	01:18	7.3	223
	07:46	0.2	6
	13:53	6.8	207
	19:56	0.8	24
13 Tu	02:00	7.3	223
	08:26	0.2	6
	14:34	7.0	213
	20:41	0.7	21
14 W	02:44	7.2	219
	09:08	0.2	6
	15:18	7.1	216
	21:29	0.6	18
15 Th	03:31	7.1	216
	09:53	0.2	6
	16:04	7.3	223
	22:22	0.6	18
16 F	04:22	7.0	213
	10:42	0.3	9
	16:54	7.4	226
	23:19	0.6	18
17 Sa ◖	05:17	6.8	207
	11:34	0.4	12
	17:48	7.5	229
18 Su	00:19	0.5	15
	06:17	6.6	201
	12:31	0.5	15
	18:46	7.6	232
19 M	01:21	0.4	12
	07:20	6.6	201
	13:31	0.6	18
	19:46	7.8	238
20 Tu	02:23	0.2	6
	08:23	6.6	201
	14:31	0.5	15
	20:46	7.9	241
21 W	03:23	0.0	0
	09:24	6.7	204
	15:31	0.4	12
	21:44	8.1	247
22 Th	04:21	-0.2	-6
	10:22	6.9	210
	16:30	0.3	9
	22:40	8.1	247
23 F	05:15	-0.3	-9
	11:16	7.1	216
	17:25	0.2	6
	23:34	8.1	247
24 Sa ○	06:06	-0.4	-12
	12:09	7.2	219
	18:19	0.2	6
25 Su	00:26	8.0	244
	06:56	-0.3	-9
	12:59	7.3	223
	19:10	0.2	6
26 M	01:16	7.8	238
	07:43	-0.2	-6
	13:49	7.3	223
	20:01	0.3	9
27 Tu	02:06	7.5	229
	08:29	0.1	3
	14:39	7.3	223
	20:52	0.5	15
28 W	02:55	7.2	219
	09:15	0.3	9
	15:25	7.2	219
	21:43	0.7	21
29 Th	03:45	6.9	210
	10:00	0.6	18
	16:13	7.1	216
	22:35	0.9	27
30 F	04:35	6.5	198
	10:48	0.9	27
	17:01	6.9	210
	23:29	1.0	30
31 Sa ◑	05:28	6.2	189
	11:37	1.2	37
	17:51	6.8	207

August

Day	Time (h:m)	Height (ft)	Height (cm)
1 Su	00:23	1.1	34
	06:23	6.0	183
	12:28	1.4	43
	18:44	6.7	204
2 M	01:18	1.1	34
	07:21	5.9	180
	13:22	1.5	46
	19:38	6.7	204
3 Tu	02:12	1.1	34
	08:17	5.9	180
	14:20	1.5	46
	20:31	6.7	204
4 W	03:03	0.9	27
	09:10	6.1	186
	15:07	1.4	43
	21:21	6.9	210
5 Th	03:52	0.8	24
	09:58	6.3	192
	15:56	1.2	37
	22:08	7.0	213
6 F	04:37	0.6	18
	10:42	6.5	198
	16:42	1.0	30
	22:51	7.2	219
7 Sa	05:19	0.4	12
	11:23	6.7	204
	17:26	0.8	24
	23:32	7.4	226
8 Su ●	05:59	0.2	6
	12:03	6.9	210
	18:08	0.6	18
9 M	00:13	7.5	229
	06:39	0.1	3
	12:43	7.1	216
	18:50	0.5	15
10 Tu	00:54	7.6	232
	07:18	0.0	0
	13:24	7.3	223
	19:34	0.3	9
11 W	01:37	7.6	232
	07:59	0.0	0
	14:06	7.5	229
	20:19	0.3	9
12 Th	02:22	7.5	229
	08:41	0.0	0
	14:50	7.6	232
	21:08	0.3	9
13 F	03:10	7.3	223
	09:26	0.1	3
	15:37	7.7	235
	22:01	0.3	9
14 Sa	04:01	7.1	216
	10:16	0.3	9
	16:28	7.7	235
	22:58	0.4	12
15 Su ◖	04:57	6.8	207
	11:11	0.5	15
	17:24	7.7	235
16 M	00:00	0.5	15
	05:59	6.6	201
	12:11	0.7	21
	18:25	7.6	232
17 Tu	01:04	0.5	15
	07:04	6.5	198
	13:15	0.8	24
	19:30	7.6	232
18 W	02:09	0.4	12
	08:10	6.5	198
	14:20	0.8	24
	20:34	7.6	232
19 Th	03:10	0.3	9
	09:13	6.7	204
	15:22	0.6	18
	21:35	7.8	238
20 F	04:08	0.1	3
	10:11	7.0	213
	16:21	0.4	12
	22:30	7.9	241
21 Sa	05:00	0.0	0
	11:03	7.2	219
	17:15	0.3	9
	23:22	7.9	241
22 Su ○	05:49	-0.1	-3
	11:52	7.4	226
	18:05	0.2	6
23 M	00:10	7.8	238
	06:34	-0.1	-3
	12:38	7.5	229
	18:52	0.2	6
24 Tu	00:56	7.7	235
	07:16	0.1	3
	13:22	7.5	229
	19:38	0.3	9
25 W	01:41	7.4	226
	07:57	0.3	9
	14:05	7.4	226
	20:23	0.5	15
26 Th	02:26	7.1	216
	08:38	0.5	15
	14:48	7.3	223
	21:09	0.7	21
27 F	03:11	6.8	207
	09:19	0.9	27
	15:31	7.1	216
	21:56	0.9	27
28 Sa	03:58	6.5	198
	10:03	1.2	37
	16:16	6.9	210
	22:45	1.1	34
29 Su	04:48	6.2	189
	10:51	1.4	43
	17:04	6.7	204
	23:38	1.2	37
30 M ◑	05:42	6.0	183
	11:44	1.7	52
	17:57	6.6	201
31 Tu	00:34	1.3	40
	06:39	5.9	180
	12:40	1.7	52
	18:54	6.5	198

September

Day	Time (h:m)	Height (ft)	Height (cm)
1 W	01:30	1.3	40
	07:37	5.9	180
	13:38	1.7	52
	19:52	6.6	201
2 Th	02:24	1.2	37
	08:33	6.1	186
	14:33	1.5	46
	20:47	6.7	204
3 F	03:15	1.0	30
	09:23	6.4	195
	15:25	1.2	37
	21:36	7.0	213
4 Sa	04:02	0.7	21
	10:08	6.7	204
	16:13	0.9	27
	22:22	7.3	223
5 Su	04:46	0.4	12
	10:50	7.0	213
	23:04	7.5	229
6 M	05:27	0.2	6
	11:31	7.4	226
	17:42	0.3	9
	23:46	7.7	235
7 Tu ●	06:07	0.0	0
	12:11	7.7	235
	18:26	0.0	0
8 W	00:29	7.8	238
	06:47	-0.1	-3
	12:53	7.9	241
	19:11	-0.1	-3
9 Th	01:13	7.7	235
	07:29	-0.1	-3
	13:36	8.1	247
	19:58	-0.2	-6
10 F	02:00	7.6	232
	08:13	0.0	0
	14:22	8.1	247
	20:48	-0.1	-3
11 Sa	02:49	7.4	226
	09:01	0.2	6
	15:12	8.1	247
	21:42	0.1	3
12 Su	03:43	7.1	216
	09:54	0.4	12
	16:03	7.9	241
	22:41	0.3	9
13 M ◖	04:41	6.8	207
	10:53	0.7	21
	17:05	7.6	232
	23:44	0.5	15
14 Tu	05:45	6.5	198
	11:58	0.9	27
	18:11	7.4	226
15 W	00:51	0.6	18
	06:53	6.5	198
	13:06	1.0	30
	19:19	7.3	223
16 Th	01:56	0.6	18
	08:01	6.6	201
	14:13	0.9	27
	20:26	7.4	226
17 F	02:57	0.5	15
	09:03	6.8	207
	15:15	0.7	21
	21:26	7.5	229
18 Sa	03:53	0.3	9
	09:58	7.1	216
	16:11	0.5	15
	22:19	7.6	232
19 Su	04:42	0.2	6
	10:47	7.4	226
	17:02	0.3	9
	23:07	7.6	232
20 M ○	05:27	0.1	3
	11:32	7.6	232
	17:48	0.2	6
	23:51	7.6	232
21 Tu	06:08	0.2	6
	12:13	7.6	232
	18:32	0.2	6
22 W ●	00:33	7.4	226
	06:46	0.3	9
	12:52	7.6	232
	19:13	0.3	9
23 Th	01:14	7.2	219
	07:24	0.5	15
	13:31	7.5	229
	19:54	0.4	12
24 F	01:56	6.9	210
	08:01	0.8	24
	14:10	7.3	223
	20:35	0.6	18
25 Sa	02:39	6.7	204
	08:40	1.1	34
	14:50	7.1	216
	21:18	0.8	24
26 Su	03:23	6.4	195
	09:23	1.3	40
	15:33	6.9	210
	22:04	1.0	30
27 M	04:11	6.2	189
	10:10	1.6	49
	16:21	6.6	201
	22:55	1.2	37
28 Tu	05:03	6.0	183
	11:03	1.8	55
	17:13	6.5	198
	23:50	1.4	43
29 W ◖	05:58	5.9	180
	12:01	1.8	55
	18:11	6.4	195
30 Th	00:47	1.4	43
	06:56	6.0	183
	13:01	1.7	52
	19:12	6.4	195

StationId: 8467150
Source: NOAA/NOS/CO-OPS
Station Type: Primary
Time Zone: LST_LDT
Datum: MLLW

NOAA Tide Predictions

Bridgeport, CT, 2021

Times and Heights of High and Low Waters

October

Day	Time	ft	cm
1 F	01:44	1.2	37
	07:53	6.2	189
	13:58	1.5	46
	20:09	6.6	201
2 Sa	02:36	1.0	30
	08:45	6.5	198
	14:52	1.1	34
	21:01	6.9	210
3 Su	03:24	0.7	21
	09:32	6.9	210
	15:42	0.7	21
	21:49	7.3	223
4 M	04:09	0.3	9
	10:15	7.4	226
	16:29	0.2	6
	22:34	7.5	229
5 Tu	04:52	0.0	0
	10:57	7.8	238
	17:15	-0.1	-3
	23:18	7.7	235
6 W ●	05:34	-0.2	-6
	11:39	8.2	250
	18:01	-0.4	-12
7 Th	00:03	7.8	238
	06:16	-0.3	-9
	12:23	8.4	256
	18:48	-0.6	-18
8 F	00:50	7.7	235
	07:01	-0.2	-6
	13:09	8.5	259
	19:37	-0.5	-15
9 Sa	01:39	7.6	232
	07:48	-0.1	-3
	13:58	8.4	256
	20:28	-0.4	-12
10 Su	02:31	7.3	223
	08:39	0.2	6
	14:50	8.2	250
	21:24	-0.1	-3
11 M	03:27	7.0	213
	09:36	0.5	15
	15:48	7.8	238
	22:25	0.2	6
12 Tu	04:27	6.7	204
	10:39	0.8	24
	16:50	7.5	229
	23:29	0.5	15
13 W ◐	05:33	6.5	198
	11:48	1.0	30
	17:58	7.2	219
14 Th	00:36	0.6	18
	06:42	6.5	198
	12:57	1.0	30
	19:08	7.0	213
15 F	01:40	0.6	18
	07:49	6.7	204
	14:04	0.8	24
	20:14	7.1	216
16 Sa	02:39	0.5	15
	08:49	7.0	213
	15:04	0.6	18
	21:12	7.1	216
17 Su	03:32	0.4	12
	09:41	7.2	219
	15:58	0.4	12
	22:03	7.2	219
18 M	04:18	0.3	9
	10:27	7.5	229
	16:46	0.2	6
	22:48	7.2	219
19 Tu	05:00	0.3	9
	11:08	7.6	232
	17:29	0.1	3
	23:30	7.2	219
20 W ○	05:39	0.4	12
	11:46	7.6	232
	18:09	0.1	3
21 Th	00:10	7.0	213
	06:16	0.5	15
	12:22	7.6	232
	18:48	0.1	3
22 F	00:49	6.9	210
	06:52	0.7	21
	12:59	7.4	226
	19:26	0.3	9
23 Sa	01:29	6.7	204
	07:29	0.9	27
	13:36	7.2	219
	20:04	0.4	12
24 Su	02:10	6.5	198
	08:07	1.1	34
	14:15	7.0	213
	20:45	0.6	18
25 M	02:53	6.3	192
	08:49	1.3	40
	14:57	6.8	207
	21:28	0.9	27
26 Tu	03:38	6.1	186
	09:35	1.5	46
	15:43	6.6	201
	22:17	1.0	30
27 W	04:27	6.0	183
	10:27	1.6	49
	16:34	6.4	195
	23:10	1.1	34
28 Th ◑	05:20	5.9	180
	11:24	1.6	49
	17:31	6.3	192
29 F	00:06	1.2	37
	06:15	6.0	183
	12:24	1.5	46
	18:30	6.3	192
30 Sa	01:01	1.0	30
	07:11	6.3	192
	13:22	1.2	37
	19:28	6.5	198
31 Su	01:54	0.8	24
	08:04	6.6	201
	14:18	0.8	24
	20:24	6.8	207

November

Day	Time	ft	cm
1 M	02:43	0.5	15
	08:53	7.1	216
	15:10	0.4	12
	21:15	7.1	216
2 Tu	03:31	0.2	6
	09:40	7.6	232
	16:01	-0.1	-3
	22:04	7.3	223
3 W	04:16	-0.1	-3
	10:25	8.1	247
	16:50	-0.5	-15
	22:51	7.5	229
4 Th ●	05:02	-0.3	-9
	11:10	8.4	256
	17:38	-0.8	-24
	23:39	7.6	232
5 F	05:48	-0.4	-12
	11:57	8.6	262
	18:27	-0.9	-27
6 Sa	00:28	7.5	229
	06:36	-0.3	-9
	12:45	8.6	262
	19:18	-0.8	-24
7 Su	01:20	7.3	223
	06:27	-0.2	-6
	12:37	8.4	256
	19:11	-0.6	-18
8 M	01:14	7.1	216
	07:22	0.1	3
	13:32	8.1	247
	20:07	-0.3	-9
9 Tu	02:12	6.9	210
	08:21	0.4	12
	14:32	7.6	232
	21:08	0.0	0
10 W	03:13	6.7	204
	09:26	0.6	18
	15:35	7.2	219
	22:11	0.3	9
11 Th ◐	04:17	6.5	198
	10:34	0.8	24
	16:41	6.9	210
	23:14	0.4	12
12 F	05:24	6.5	198
	11:42	0.8	24
	17:48	6.7	204
13 Sa	00:16	0.5	15
	06:28	6.7	204
	12:47	0.7	21
	18:52	6.6	201
14 Su	01:12	0.5	15
	07:26	6.9	210
	13:46	0.5	15
	19:50	6.6	201
15 M	02:03	0.4	12
	08:17	7.1	216
	14:38	0.3	9
	20:40	6.7	204
16 Tu	02:49	0.4	12
	09:01	7.3	223
	15:25	0.1	3
	21:26	6.7	204
17 W	03:31	0.4	12
	09:41	7.4	226
	16:07	0.0	0
	22:07	6.7	204
18 Th	04:10	0.5	15
	10:19	7.4	226
	16:46	0.0	0
	22:47	6.6	201
19 F ○	04:48	0.6	18
	10:55	7.3	223
	17:24	0.0	0
	23:25	6.5	198
20 Sa	05:25	0.7	21
	11:31	7.2	219
	18:01	0.1	3
21 Su	00:04	6.4	195
	06:02	0.8	24
	12:08	7.0	213
	18:38	0.2	6
22 M	00:44	6.3	192
	06:41	1.0	30
	12:47	6.8	207
	19:18	0.4	12
23 Tu	01:26	6.2	189
	07:22	1.1	34
	13:29	6.7	204
	19:59	0.5	15
24 W	02:09	6.1	186
	08:06	1.2	37
	14:13	6.5	198
	20:44	0.6	18
25 Th	02:55	6.0	183
	08:56	1.3	40
	15:01	6.4	195
	21:33	0.7	21
26 F ◐	03:44	6.0	183
	09:50	1.2	37
	15:54	6.3	192
	22:25	0.7	21
27 Sa ◑	04:35	6.1	186
	10:47	1.1	34
	16:50	6.3	192
	23:18	0.6	18
28 Su	05:29	6.4	195
	11:46	0.9	27
	17:48	6.3	192
29 M	00:11	0.5	15
	06:23	6.7	204
	12:44	0.5	15
	18:46	6.5	198
30 Tu	01:03	0.2	6
	07:16	7.2	219
	13:40	0.1	3
	19:42	6.7	204

December

Day	Time	ft	cm
1 W	01:54	0.0	0
	08:06	7.6	232
	14:34	-0.4	-12
	20:36	6.9	210
2 Th	02:45	-0.2	-6
	08:56	8.1	247
	15:26	-0.8	-24
	21:27	7.1	216
3 F	03:35	-0.4	-12
	09:45	8.4	256
	16:18	-1.0	-30
	22:18	7.2	219
4 Sa ●	04:26	-0.5	-15
	10:35	8.5	259
	17:09	-1.1	-34
	23:10	7.2	219
5 Su	05:17	-0.5	-15
	11:27	8.4	256
	18:02	-1.0	-30
6 M	00:03	7.1	216
	06:11	-0.4	-12
	12:21	8.2	250
	18:55	-0.8	-24
7 Tu	00:58	6.9	210
	07:07	-0.2	-6
	13:17	7.8	238
	19:50	-0.6	-18
8 W	01:55	6.8	207
	08:06	0.1	3
	14:15	7.4	226
	20:47	-0.3	-9
9 Th	02:54	6.6	201
	09:08	0.3	9
	15:15	7.0	213
	21:46	0.0	0
10 F	03:54	6.5	198
	10:13	0.5	15
	16:17	6.6	201
	22:45	0.2	6
11 Sa ◐	04:56	6.5	198
	11:17	0.6	18
	17:20	6.3	192
	23:42	0.4	12
12 Su	05:56	6.6	201
	12:20	0.6	18
	18:22	6.1	186
13 M	00:37	0.5	15
	06:53	6.7	204
	13:18	0.4	12
	19:20	6.0	183
14 Tu	01:28	0.5	15
	07:45	6.8	207
	14:11	0.3	9
	20:12	6.1	186
15 W	02:16	0.5	15
	08:31	6.9	210
	14:59	0.1	3
	21:00	6.1	186
16 Th	03:01	0.5	15
	09:13	7.0	213
	15:42	0.0	0
	21:43	6.2	189
17 F	03:43	0.5	15
	09:53	7.0	213
	16:22	-0.1	-3
	22:24	6.2	189
18 Sa	04:23	0.5	15
	10:31	7.0	213
	17:00	-0.1	-3
	23:03	6.2	189
19 Su ○	05:02	0.5	15
	11:09	6.9	210
	17:38	-0.1	-3
	23:42	6.2	189
20 M	05:40	0.6	18
	11:47	6.8	207
	18:16	0.0	0
21 Tu	00:21	6.2	189
	06:19	0.6	18
	12:25	6.7	204
	18:54	0.0	0
22 W	01:00	6.1	186
	06:59	0.7	21
	13:05	6.6	201
	19:34	0.1	3
23 Th	01:41	6.1	186
	07:42	0.7	21
	13:48	6.5	198
	20:15	0.2	6
24 F	02:24	6.1	186
	08:28	0.7	21
	14:33	6.4	195
	20:59	0.2	6
25 Sa	03:09	6.2	189
	09:19	0.7	21
	15:21	6.3	192
	21:47	0.2	6
26 Su	03:58	6.3	192
	10:14	0.6	18
	16:15	6.2	189
	22:38	0.2	6
27 M ◑	04:50	6.5	198
	11:13	0.4	12
	17:12	6.2	189
	23:32	0.2	6
28 Tu	05:45	6.8	207
	12:13	0.2	6
	18:13	6.2	189
29 W	00:27	0.1	3
	06:41	7.1	216
	13:13	-0.1	-3
	19:13	6.3	192
30 Th	01:23	-0.1	-3
	07:38	7.5	229
	14:11	-0.5	-15
	20:12	6.4	195
31 F	02:19	-0.3	-9
	08:33	7.8	238
	15:07	-0.8	-24
	21:07	6.5	198

StationId: 8516945
Source: NOAA/NOS/CO-OPS
Station Type: Primary
Time Zone: LST_LDT
Datum: MLLW

Kings Point, NY, 2021

Times and Heights of High and Low Waters

January

Day	Time	ft	cm		Day	Time	ft	cm
1 F	00:07	7.0	213		16 Sa	01:34	7.3	223
	06:15	0.1	3			07:59	0.1	3
	12:10	7.9	241			13:44	7.5	229
	18:56	-0.4	-12			20:29	-0.3	-9
2 Sa	00:47	7.1	216		17 Su	02:21	7.1	216
	06:58	0.0	0			08:48	0.3	9
	12:55	7.9	241			14:31	7.1	216
	19:36	-0.4	-12			21:11	0.1	3
3 Su	01:31	7.2	219		18 M	03:07	7.0	213
	07:46	0.0	0			09:40	0.6	18
	13:43	7.8	238			15:20	6.7	204
	20:21	-0.4	-12			21:50	0.5	15
4 M	02:19	7.4	226		19 Tu	03:54	6.8	207
	08:38	0.1	3			10:37	0.8	24
	14:35	7.6	232			16:14	6.3	192
	21:10	-0.3	-9			22:27	0.8	24
5 Tu	03:11	7.5	229		20 W	04:44	6.7	204
	09:37	0.2	6			11:35	0.9	27
	15:31	7.3	223			17:15	6.0	183
	22:03	-0.1	-3		☽	23:05	1.0	30
6 W	04:07	7.6	232		21 Th	05:40	6.6	201
	10:45	0.2	6			12:32	0.9	27
	16:32	7.0	213			18:19	5.9	180
☽	23:03	0.0	0					
7 Th	05:09	7.7	235		22 F	00:06	1.2	37
	12:12	0.1	3			06:39	6.6	201
	17:43	6.8	207			13:27	0.8	24
						19:19	5.9	180
8 F	00:11	0.1	3		23 Sa	01:12	1.2	37
	06:18	7.8	238			07:34	6.6	201
	13:36	-0.2	-6			14:19	0.6	18
	19:07	6.7	204			20:13	6.1	186
9 Sa	01:31	0.1	3		24 Su	02:08	1.1	34
	07:31	8.0	244			08:24	6.8	207
	14:42	-0.5	-15			15:07	0.4	12
	20:21	6.9	210			21:01	6.3	192
10 Su	02:44	0.0	0		25 M	02:55	0.9	27
	08:37	8.2	250			09:06	7.0	213
	15:41	-0.8	-24			15:52	0.1	3
	21:22	7.1	216			21:42	6.5	198
11 M	03:46	-0.2	-6		26 Tu	03:35	0.7	21
	09:35	8.4	256			09:40	7.2	219
	16:35	-1.1	-34			16:32	-0.1	-3
	22:17	7.3	223			22:17	6.7	204
12 Tu	04:42	-0.4	-12		27 W	04:09	0.4	12
	10:29	8.4	256			10:07	7.5	229
	17:26	-1.2	-37			17:07	-0.3	-9
	23:08	7.4	226			22:46	6.9	210
13 W	05:34	-0.4	-12		28 Th	04:43	0.1	3
	11:20	8.4	256			10:38	7.8	238
	18:14	-1.1	-34			17:37	-0.5	-15
●	23:58	7.4	226		○	23:13	7.1	216
14 Th	06:23	-0.4	-12		29 F	05:21	-0.2	-6
	12:09	8.2	250			11:14	8.0	244
	19:01	-0.9	-27			18:06	-0.7	-21
						23:47	7.4	226
15 F	00:46	7.4	226		30 Sa	06:02	-0.4	-12
	07:11	-0.2	-6			11:56	8.1	247
	12:57	7.9	241			18:39	-0.8	-24
	19:45	-0.6	-18					
					31 Su	00:27	7.7	235
						06:46	-0.5	-15
						12:40	8.1	247
						19:16	-0.8	-24

February

Day	Time	ft	cm		Day	Time	ft	cm
1 M	01:11	7.9	241		16 Tu	02:11	7.2	219
	07:33	-0.5	-15			08:38	0.4	12
	13:28	8.0	244			14:30	6.7	204
	19:59	-0.7	-21			20:19	0.5	15
2 Tu	01:58	8.0	244		17 W	02:40	7.0	213
	08:24	-0.4	-12			09:03	0.6	18
	14:19	7.7	235			15:08	6.4	195
	20:46	-0.5	-15			20:54	0.8	24
3 W	02:48	8.0	244		18 Th	03:13	6.8	207
	09:22	-0.2	-6			09:42	0.8	24
	15:14	7.3	223			15:51	6.1	186
	21:38	-0.2	-6			21:38	1.0	30
4 Th	03:44	7.8	238		19 F	03:54	6.6	201
	10:35	0.0	0			10:36	1.0	30
	16:16	6.8	207			16:47	5.9	180
☽	22:40	0.2	6		☽	22:29	1.2	37
5 F	04:46	7.7	235		20 Sa	04:45	6.4	195
	12:11	0.1	3			12:21	1.1	34
	17:34	6.5	198			18:13	5.8	177
						23:28	1.4	43
6 Sa	00:05	0.4	12		21 Su	05:48	6.3	192
	06:04	7.5	229			13:30	1.0	30
	13:28	-0.1	-3			19:26	5.9	180
	19:08	6.5	198					
7 Su	01:37	0.4	12		22 M	00:35	1.3	40
	07:31	7.6	232			07:18	6.4	195
	14:33	-0.3	-9			14:27	0.8	24
	20:21	6.7	204			20:21	6.1	186
8 M	02:45	0.2	6		23 Tu	01:52	1.1	34
	08:40	7.8	238			08:21	6.8	207
	15:31	-0.6	-18			15:11	0.4	12
	21:20	7.0	213			21:05	6.5	198
9 Tu	03:44	-0.1	-3		24 W	02:56	0.7	21
	09:38	8.0	244			09:04	7.2	219
	16:24	-0.9	-27			15:58	0.1	3
	22:12	7.3	223			21:41	6.8	207
10 W	04:37	-0.4	-12		25 Th	03:43	0.3	9
	10:29	8.1	247			09:41	7.6	232
	17:12	-1.0	-30			16:35	-0.3	-9
	23:00	7.5	229			22:12	7.3	223
11 Th	05:26	-0.5	-15		26 F	04:25	-0.2	-6
	11:16	8.1	247			10:17	8.0	244
	17:57	-0.9	-27			17:08	-0.6	-18
●	23:45	7.6	232			22:45	7.7	235
12 F	06:12	-0.5	-15		27 Sa	05:06	-0.6	-18
	11:59	8.0	244			10:57	8.2	250
	18:39	-0.8	-24			17:40	-0.8	-24
					○	23:23	8.1	247
13 Sa	00:27	7.6	232		28 Su	05:49	-0.9	-27
	06:54	-0.4	-12			11:40	8.4	256
	12:41	7.8	238			18:15	-1.0	-30
	19:17	-0.5	-15					
14 Su	01:06	7.5	229					
	07:34	-0.1	-3					
	13:19	7.4	226					
	19:48	-0.1	-3					
15 M	01:41	7.4	226					
	08:10	0.1	3					
	13:55	7.1	216					
	20:02	0.2	6					

March

Day	Time	ft	cm		Day	Time	ft	cm
1 M	00:04	8.4	256		16 Tu	01:58	7.6	232
	06:33	-1.0	-30			08:33	0.0	0
	12:25	8.3	253			14:22	7.1	216
	18:54	-0.9	-27			20:08	0.4	12
2 Tu	00:48	8.6	262		17 W	02:18	7.5	229
	07:21	-1.0	-30			08:44	0.3	9
	13:13	8.1	247			14:49	6.9	210
	19:36	-0.7	-21			20:36	0.6	18
3 W	01:36	8.6	262		18 Th	02:46	7.3	223
	08:13	-0.7	-21			09:11	0.4	12
	14:05	7.7	235			15:21	6.6	201
	20:24	-0.4	-12			21:14	0.8	24
4 Th	02:27	8.4	256		19 F	03:22	7.1	216
	09:13	-0.4	-12			09:50	0.7	21
	15:01	7.3	223			16:01	6.4	195
	21:19	0.1	3			21:58	1.1	34
5 F	03:23	8.0	244		20 Sa	04:04	6.9	210
	10:36	0.0	0			10:38	0.9	27
	16:08	6.8	207			16:47	6.2	189
	22:31	0.5	15			22:49	1.3	40
6 Sa	04:31	7.6	232		21 Su	04:53	6.7	204
	12:04	0.1	3			11:34	1.1	34
	17:40	6.5	198			17:42	6.0	183
☽					☽	23:46	1.4	43
7 Su	00:17	0.7	21		22 M	05:50	6.5	198
	06:06	7.3	223			12:42	1.2	37
	13:16	0.1	3			18:51	6.0	183
	19:06	6.6	201					
8 M	01:34	0.6	18		23 Tu	00:49	1.4	43
	07:31	7.4	226			06:56	6.5	198
	14:18	-0.1	-3			14:22	1.0	30
	20:13	6.8	207			20:15	6.2	189
9 Tu	02:38	0.2	6		24 W	02:00	1.1	34
	08:37	7.6	232			08:12	6.8	207
	15:15	-0.4	-12			15:26	0.7	21
	21:10	7.2	219			21:13	6.7	204
10 W	03:34	-0.1	-3		25 Th	03:12	0.7	21
	09:31	7.8	238			09:18	7.3	223
	16:06	-0.6	-18			16:16	0.2	6
	21:59	7.5	229			21:56	7.2	219
11 Th	04:25	-0.4	-12		26 F	04:12	0.2	6
	10:19	8.0	244			10:08	7.7	235
	16:53	-0.7	-21			16:54	-0.2	-6
	22:44	7.8	238			22:35	7.8	238
12 F	05:11	-0.5	-15		27 Sa	05:03	-0.4	-12
	11:03	8.0	244			10:52	8.1	247
	17:35	-0.6	-18			17:31	-0.6	-18
	23:25	7.9	241			23:15	8.4	256
13 Sa	05:54	-0.5	-15		28 Su	05:49	-0.8	-24
	11:43	7.9	241			11:36	8.4	256
	18:13	-0.4	-12			18:09	-0.8	-24
●					○	23:56	8.8	268
14 Su	00:02	7.9	241		29 M	06:35	-1.2	-37
	07:33	-0.4	-12			12:22	8.5	259
	13:20	7.7	235			18:49	-0.9	-27
	19:44	-0.1	-3					
15 M	01:34	7.8	238		30 Tu	00:40	9.1	277
	08:08	-0.2	-6			07:22	-1.3	-40
	13:53	7.4	226			13:09	8.4	256
	20:02	0.2	6			19:31	-0.8	-24
					31 W	01:26	9.1	277
						08:11	-1.2	-37
						13:59	8.1	247
						20:16	-0.5	-15

StationId: 8516945
Source: NOAA/NOS/CO-OPS
Station Type: Primary
Time Zone: LST_LDT
Datum: MLLW

NOAA Tide Predictions

Kings Point, NY, 2021

Times and Heights of High and Low Waters

April

Day	Time	ft	cm	Day	Time	ft	cm
1 Th	02:15	8.9	271	16 F	02:07	7.5	229
	09:05	-0.8	-24		08:39	0.4	12
	14:53	7.8	238		14:48	6.8	207
	21:08	-0.1	-3		20:44	0.9	27
2 F	03:09	8.5	259	17 Sa	02:46	7.4	226
	10:12	-0.4	-12		09:18	0.6	18
	15:55	7.3	223		15:27	6.7	204
	22:10	0.4	12		21:28	1.1	34
3 Sa	04:10	8.0	244	18 Su	03:30	7.2	219
	11:34	0.0	0		10:04	0.8	24
	17:11	6.9	210		16:12	6.5	198
	23:47	0.8	24		22:18	1.3	40
4 Su ◐	05:29	7.5	229	19 M	04:19	7.0	213
	12:50	0.2	6		10:57	0.9	27
	18:39	6.8	207		17:03	6.5	198
					23:14	1.3	40
5 M	01:13	0.8	24	20 Tu ◐	05:14	6.9	210
	07:05	7.3	223		11:58	1.0	30
	13:57	0.2	6		18:02	6.5	198
	19:54	6.9	210				
6 Tu	02:21	0.6	18	21 W	00:16	1.3	40
	08:20	7.3	223		06:16	6.9	210
	14:58	0.1	3		13:05	0.9	27
	20:57	7.2	219		19:07	6.7	204
7 W	03:22	0.3	9	22 Th	01:23	1.0	30
	09:22	7.5	229		07:24	7.1	216
	15:52	-0.1	-3		14:14	0.7	21
	21:51	7.5	229		20:13	7.2	219
8 Th	04:17	0.0	0	23 F	02:35	0.6	18
	10:14	7.7	235		08:33	7.4	226
	16:42	-0.2	-6		15:15	0.3	9
	22:39	7.8	238		21:09	7.8	238
9 F	05:06	-0.3	-9	24 Sa	03:42	0.1	3
	11:01	7.8	238		09:33	7.8	238
	17:27	-0.3	-9		16:06	-0.1	-3
	23:21	8.0	244		21:58	8.4	256
10 Sa	05:51	-0.4	-12	25 Su	04:40	-0.5	-15
	11:43	7.8	238		10:26	8.1	247
	18:07	-0.2	-6		16:53	-0.4	-12
	23:59	8.1	247		22:44	8.9	271
11 Su	06:33	-0.4	-12	26 M	05:32	-1.0	-30
	12:22	7.7	235		11:15	8.3	253
	18:43	0.0	0		17:38	-0.6	-18
					23:30	9.3	283
12 M ●	00:33	8.1	247	27 Tu ○	06:22	-1.3	-40
	07:10	-0.3	-9		12:04	8.4	256
	12:57	7.5	229		18:24	-0.6	-18
	19:11	0.3	9				
13 Tu	01:00	7.9	241	28 W	00:17	9.5	290
	07:42	-0.2	-6		07:12	-1.3	-40
	13:29	7.3	223		12:55	8.3	253
	19:19	0.5	15		19:11	-0.5	-15
14 W	01:17	7.8	238	29 Th	01:06	9.4	287
	08:02	0.1	3		08:04	-1.1	-34
	13:54	7.1	216		13:48	8.1	247
	19:33	0.7	21		20:02	-0.2	-6
15 Th	01:37	7.7	235	30 F	01:59	9.0	274
	08:11	0.2	6		09:03	-0.8	-24
	14:17	7.0	213		14:47	7.8	238
	20:05	0.8	24		21:00	0.2	6

May

Day	Time	ft	cm	Day	Time	ft	cm
1 Sa	02:57	8.5	259	16 Su	02:18	7.5	229
	10:10	-0.4	-12		08:55	0.5	15
	15:54	7.4	226		15:00	6.9	210
	22:18	0.6	18		21:05	1.1	34
2 Su	04:05	8.0	244	17 M	03:03	7.5	229
	11:22	0.0	0		09:40	0.6	18
	17:09	7.2	219		15:44	6.9	210
	23:44	0.8	24		21:54	1.1	34
3 M ◐	05:28	7.5	229	18 Tu	03:53	7.4	226
	12:30	0.2	6		10:30	0.7	21
	18:24	7.1	216		16:34	6.9	210
					22:49	1.1	34
4 Tu	00:56	0.8	24	19 W	04:46	7.3	223
	06:49	7.3	223		11:26	0.7	21
	13:32	0.3	9		17:29	7.0	213
	19:32	7.2	219	◐	23:49	1.1	34
5 W	02:01	0.6	18	20 Th	05:45	7.2	219
	07:58	7.2	219		12:24	0.6	18
	14:30	0.3	9		18:28	7.3	223
	20:32	7.5	229				
6 Th	02:59	0.4	12	21 F	00:54	0.8	24
	08:57	7.3	223		06:49	7.3	223
	15:23	0.2	6		13:25	0.5	15
	21:24	7.7	235		19:30	7.7	235
7 F	03:53	0.1	3	22 Sa	02:05	0.5	15
	09:49	7.4	226		07:57	7.4	226
	16:11	0.2	6		14:25	0.3	9
	22:11	8.0	244		20:30	8.2	250
8 Sa	04:42	-0.1	-3	23 Su	03:16	0.0	0
	10:35	7.5	229		09:02	7.7	235
	16:56	0.3	9		15:23	0.1	3
	22:53	8.1	247		21:25	8.8	268
9 Su	05:27	-0.2	-6	24 M	04:21	-0.5	-15
	11:18	7.5	229		10:02	7.9	241
	17:36	0.4	12		16:19	-0.2	-6
	23:31	8.2	250		22:17	9.2	280
10 M	06:08	-0.3	-9	25 Tu	05:18	-0.9	-27
	11:57	7.4	226		10:57	8.1	247
	18:12	0.5	15		17:14	-0.3	-9
					23:07	9.4	287
11 Tu ●	00:03	8.1	247	26 W	06:12	-1.2	-37
	06:45	-0.2	-6		11:50	8.2	250
	12:34	7.3	223		18:07	-0.3	-9
	18:39	0.7	21	○	23:59	9.4	287
12 W	00:29	7.9	241	27 Th	07:06	-1.2	-37
	07:18	-0.1	-3		12:44	8.1	247
	13:06	7.2	219		19:01	-0.2	-6
	18:47	0.9	27				
13 Th	00:43	7.8	238	28 F	00:52	9.2	280
	07:39	0.1	3		08:00	-1.0	-30
	13:31	7.1	216		13:41	8.0	244
	19:06	0.9	27		19:59	0.0	0
14 F	01:05	7.7	235	29 Sa	01:48	8.9	271
	07:49	0.3	9		08:57	-0.7	-21
	13:51	7.0	213		14:42	7.8	238
	19:40	0.9	27		21:03	0.3	9
15 Sa	01:38	7.6	232	30 Su	02:50	8.4	256
	08:17	0.4	12		09:58	-0.3	-9
	14:21	7.0	213		15:47	7.6	232
	20:20	1.0	30		22:15	0.6	18
				31 M	03:59	7.9	241
					11:01	0.0	0
					16:53	7.4	226
					23:26	0.7	21

June

Day	Time	ft	cm	Day	Time	ft	cm
1 Tu	05:11	7.5	229	16 W	03:31	7.7	235
	12:02	0.2	6		10:06	0.3	9
	17:58	7.4	226		16:09	7.4	226
					22:27	0.8	24
2 W ◑	00:32	0.8	24	17 Th	04:23	7.6	232
	06:21	7.2	219		10:57	0.4	12
	13:00	0.4	12		17:01	7.6	232
	19:00	7.4	226		23:26	0.7	21
3 Th	01:33	0.7	21	18 F ◐	05:20	7.4	226
	07:25	7.1	216		11:51	0.4	12
	13:55	0.6	18		17:57	7.8	238
	19:58	7.5	229				
4 F	02:30	0.5	15	19 Sa	00:30	0.6	18
	08:24	7.0	213		06:21	7.3	223
	14:47	0.6	18		12:48	0.4	12
	20:50	7.7	235		18:56	8.1	247
5 Sa	03:23	0.4	12	20 Su	01:42	0.3	9
	09:17	7.0	213		07:29	7.3	223
	15:36	0.7	21		13:49	0.3	9
	21:38	7.9	241		19:58	8.4	256
6 Su	04:12	0.2	6	21 M	03:00	0.0	0
	10:06	7.1	216		08:39	7.4	226
	16:21	0.8	24		14:52	0.3	9
	22:21	7.9	241		20:59	8.8	268
7 M	04:58	0.0	0	22 Tu	04:10	-0.4	-12
	10:50	7.1	216		09:45	7.6	232
	17:03	0.9	27		15:59	0.1	3
	23:00	7.9	241		21:58	9.0	274
8 Tu	05:41	0.0	0	23 W	05:10	-0.7	-21
	11:31	7.2	219		10:45	7.8	238
	17:40	0.9	27		17:04	0.0	0
	23:34	7.9	241		22:54	9.2	280
9 W	06:19	0.0	0	24 Th ○	06:06	-0.9	-27
	12:10	7.2	219		11:42	7.9	241
	18:10	1.0	30		18:04	-0.1	-3
					23:50	9.1	277
10 Th ●	00:01	7.8	238	25 F	06:59	-1.0	-30
	06:54	0.1	3		12:38	7.9	241
	12:43	7.1	216		19:02	-0.1	-3
	18:24	1.0	30				
11 F	00:18	7.7	235	26 Sa	00:46	9.0	274
	07:21	0.2	6		07:52	-0.9	-27
	13:10	7.1	216		13:34	7.9	241
	18:47	1.0	30		19:59	0.0	0
12 Sa	00:42	7.7	235	27 Su	01:43	8.7	265
	07:36	0.3	9		08:44	-0.6	-18
	13:30	7.1	216		14:32	7.8	238
	19:21	0.9	27		20:57	0.2	6
13 Su	01:16	7.7	235	28 M	02:42	8.3	253
	08:01	0.3	9		09:37	-0.3	-9
	13:59	7.1	216		15:29	7.7	235
	20:01	0.9	27		21:58	0.5	15
14 M	01:57	7.7	235	29 Tu	03:42	7.9	241
	08:37	0.3	9		10:32	0.0	0
	14:37	7.2	219		16:26	7.6	232
	20:45	0.8	24		22:59	0.7	21
15 Tu	02:42	7.7	235	30 W	04:43	7.5	229
	09:19	0.3	9		11:26	0.4	12
	15:21	7.3	223		17:23	7.5	229
	21:34	0.8	24				

StationId: 8516945
Source: NOAA/NOS/CO-OPS
Station Type: Primary
Time Zone: LST_LDT
Datum: MLLW

NOAA Tide Predictions

Kings Point, NY, 2021

Times and Heights of High and Low Waters

July

Day	Time (h m)	ft	cm	Day	Time (h m)	ft	cm
1 Th ◑	00:00	0.8	24	**16** F	04:02	7.7	235
	05:44	7.1	216		10:30	0.2	6
	12:20	0.7	21		16:34	8.1	247
	18:20	7.5	229		23:06	0.4	12
2 F	00:59	0.8	24	**17** Sa ◑	04:58	7.5	229
	06:46	6.8	207		11:23	0.3	9
	13:13	0.9	27		17:29	8.2	250
	19:16	7.4	226				
3 Sa	01:55	0.8	24	**18** Su	00:12	0.4	12
	07:45	6.7	204		05:59	7.2	219
	14:05	1.1	34		12:21	0.5	15
	20:09	7.5	229		18:29	8.3	253
4 Su	02:49	0.7	21	**19** M	01:33	0.3	9
	08:41	6.6	201		07:10	7.1	216
	14:55	1.2	37		13:26	0.6	18
	21:00	7.5	229		19:36	8.4	256
5 M	03:39	0.5	15	**20** Tu	02:57	0.1	3
	09:33	6.7	204		08:29	7.1	216
	15:43	1.3	40		14:43	0.6	18
	21:47	7.6	232		20:46	8.5	259
6 Tu	04:27	0.4	12	**21** W	04:04	-0.2	-6
	10:20	6.9	210		09:42	7.3	223
	16:28	1.2	37		16:03	0.4	12
	22:29	7.6	232		21:53	8.7	265
7 W	05:11	0.3	9	**22** Th	05:03	-0.5	-15
	11:04	7.0	213		10:43	7.6	232
	17:09	1.2	37		17:09	0.2	6
	23:07	7.6	232		22:54	8.8	268
8 Th	05:52	0.2	6	**23** F	05:58	-0.7	-21
	11:43	7.1	216		11:38	7.8	238
	17:43	1.1	34		18:06	0.0	0
	23:37	7.7	235		23:50	8.8	268
9 F	06:28	0.2	6	**24** Sa ○	06:48	-0.8	-24
	12:18	7.1	216		12:31	7.9	241
	18:06	1.0	30		18:59	-0.1	-3
	23:58	7.7	235				
10 Sa ●	06:59	0.2	6	**25** Su	00:43	8.7	265
	12:44	7.1	216		07:37	-0.7	-21
	18:31	0.8	24		13:22	8.0	244
					19:50	0.0	0
11 Su	00:23	7.8	238	**26** M	01:35	8.5	259
	07:21	0.1	3		08:23	-0.5	-15
	13:06	7.2	219		14:12	8.0	244
	19:05	0.7	21		20:41	0.1	3
12 M	00:58	7.9	241	**27** Tu	02:26	8.2	250
	07:45	0.1	3		09:09	-0.2	-6
	13:36	7.4	226		15:01	7.9	241
	19:44	0.6	18		21:32	0.4	12
13 Tu	01:38	8.0	244	**28** W	03:16	7.8	238
	08:18	0.0	0		09:54	0.2	6
	14:14	7.6	232		15:49	7.7	235
	20:28	0.5	15		22:26	0.6	18
14 W	02:23	8.0	244	**29** Th	04:07	7.3	223
	08:58	0.0	0		10:38	0.6	18
	14:57	7.8	238		16:37	7.6	232
	21:16	0.4	12		23:21	0.8	24
15 Th	03:11	7.9	241	**30** F	05:01	6.9	210
	09:42	0.1	3		11:23	1.0	30
	15:44	8.0	244		17:27	7.4	226
	22:08	0.4	12				
				31 Sa ◑	00:18	1.0	30
					05:59	6.6	201
					12:12	1.4	43
					18:21	7.2	219

August

Day	Time (h m)	ft	cm	Day	Time (h m)	ft	cm
1 Su	01:14	1.1	34	**16** M	00:06	0.4	12
	07:01	6.4	195		05:45	7.1	216
	13:07	1.6	49		12:03	0.8	24
	19:19	7.1	216		18:10	8.1	247
2 M	02:09	1.0	30	**17** Tu	01:40	0.4	12
	08:02	6.4	195		07:07	6.9	210
	14:06	1.7	52		13:29	0.9	27
	20:17	7.1	216		19:29	8.1	247
3 Tu	03:02	0.9	27	**18** W	02:54	0.2	6
	08:57	6.5	198		08:35	7.0	213
	15:01	1.6	49		15:01	0.8	24
	21:10	7.2	219		20:53	8.2	250
4 W	03:52	0.8	24	**19** Th	03:57	-0.1	-3
	09:48	6.7	204		09:43	7.3	223
	15:51	1.5	46		16:09	0.5	15
	21:57	7.3	223		22:00	8.4	256
5 Th	04:39	0.6	18	**20** F	04:53	-0.3	-9
	10:33	6.9	210		10:40	7.7	235
	16:36	1.3	40		17:00	0.2	6
	22:38	7.5	229		22:56	8.5	259
6 F	05:21	0.4	12	**21** Sa	05:44	-0.5	-15
	11:12	7.1	216		11:31	8.0	244
	17:13	1.0	30		18:00	-0.1	-3
	23:10	7.6	232		23:47	8.6	262
7 Sa	05:58	0.3	9	**22** Su ○	06:31	-0.6	-18
	11:46	7.2	219		12:19	8.1	247
	17:43	0.8	24		18:48	-0.2	-6
	23:35	7.8	238				
8 Su ●	06:30	0.1	3	**23** M	00:34	8.5	259
	12:11	7.4	226		07:16	-0.5	-15
	18:13	0.5	15		13:03	8.2	250
					19:35	-0.1	-3
9 M	00:03	8.0	244	**24** Tu	01:19	8.3	253
	06:54	0.0	0		07:57	-0.2	-6
	12:36	7.7	235		13:46	8.2	250
	18:48	0.3	9		20:19	0.1	3
10 Tu	00:38	8.2	250	**25** W	02:02	8.0	244
	07:20	-0.2	-6		08:34	0.1	3
	13:09	7.9	241		14:25	8.0	244
	19:28	0.1	3		21:02	0.3	9
11 W	01:19	8.3	253	**26** Th	02:44	7.6	232
	07:54	-0.2	-6		09:03	0.5	15
	13:48	8.2	250		15:02	7.8	238
	20:11	0.0	0		21:45	0.6	18
12 Th	02:04	8.2	250	**27** F	03:26	7.2	219
	08:33	-0.2	-6		09:17	0.9	27
	14:32	8.4	256		15:36	7.6	232
	20:59	0.0	0		22:30	0.9	27
13 F	02:52	8.0	244	**28** Sa	04:10	6.9	210
	09:16	-0.1	-3		09:45	1.2	37
	15:19	8.5	259		16:10	7.3	223
	21:51	0.1	3		23:21	1.2	37
14 Sa	03:44	7.7	235	**29** Su	05:01	6.5	198
	10:05	0.2	6		10:26	1.5	46
	16:10	8.5	259		16:51	7.1	216
	22:50	0.3	9				
15 Su ◑	04:40	7.4	226	**30** M ◑	00:21	1.3	40
	10:59	0.5	15		06:04	6.3	192
	17:06	8.3	253		11:16	1.8	55
					17:43	6.8	207
				31 Tu	01:22	1.4	43
					07:15	6.2	189
					12:17	1.9	58
					19:07	6.7	204

September

Day	Time (h m)	ft	cm	Day	Time (h m)	ft	cm
1 W	02:20	1.3	40	**16** Th	02:44	0.2	6
	08:18	6.3	192		08:37	7.2	219
	13:41	1.9	58		15:03	0.7	21
	20:26	6.8	207		20:58	7.9	241
2 Th	03:13	1.1	34	**17** F	03:43	0.0	0
	09:11	6.6	201		09:37	7.6	232
	15:06	1.6	49		16:03	0.3	9
	21:20	7.1	216		21:58	8.2	250
3 F	04:01	0.9	27	**18** Sa	04:36	-0.3	-9
	09:57	6.9	210		10:30	7.9	241
	15:56	1.3	40		16:57	0.0	0
	22:02	7.4	226		22:49	8.3	253
4 Sa	04:44	0.6	18	**19** Su	05:25	-0.4	-12
	10:35	7.2	219		11:17	8.2	250
	16:37	0.9	27		17:46	-0.2	-6
	22:35	7.7	235		23:36	8.4	256
5 Su	05:20	0.3	9	**20** M ○	06:09	-0.4	-12
	11:06	7.5	229		12:00	8.4	256
	17:14	0.5	15		18:32	-0.3	-9
	23:05	8.0	244				
6 M	05:50	0.0	0	**21** Tu	00:18	8.3	253
	11:32	7.9	241		06:50	-0.2	-6
	17:50	0.1	3		12:39	8.4	256
	23:38	8.3	253		19:15	-0.2	-6
7 Tu ●	06:18	-0.2	-6	**22** W	00:59	8.0	244
	12:03	8.3	253		07:26	0.1	3
	18:29	-0.2	-6		13:17	8.3	253
					19:55	0.0	0
8 W	00:16	8.4	256	**23** Th	01:36	7.7	235
	06:49	-0.3	-9		07:53	0.5	15
	12:40	8.6	262		13:45	8.1	247
	19:10	-0.4	-12		20:30	0.3	9
9 Th	00:59	8.4	256	**24** F	02:12	7.4	226
	07:26	-0.4	-12		08:02	0.8	24
	13:21	8.9	271		14:10	7.9	241
	19:54	-0.4	-12		20:57	0.6	18
10 F	01:45	8.3	253	**25** Sa	02:46	7.1	216
	08:07	-0.3	-9		08:23	1.0	30
	14:06	8.9	271		14:36	7.6	232
	20:43	-0.3	-9		21:13	0.8	24
11 Sa	02:34	8.0	244	**26** Su	03:20	6.8	207
	08:53	0.0	0		08:59	1.3	40
	14:55	8.8	268		15:11	7.4	226
	21:37	-0.1	-3		21:45	1.1	34
12 Su	03:28	7.7	235	**27** M	04:00	6.6	201
	09:44	0.4	12		09:43	1.5	46
	15:49	8.6	262		15:53	7.1	216
	22:44	0.2	6		22:31	1.3	40
13 M ◑	04:28	7.3	223	**28** Tu	04:48	6.4	195
	10:44	0.8	24		10:34	1.7	52
	16:49	8.2	250		16:42	6.8	207
					23:30	1.5	46
14 Tu	00:18	0.4	12	**29** W ◑	05:53	6.2	189
	05:44	7.0	213		11:32	1.9	58
	12:12	1.0	30		17:39	6.7	204
	18:06	7.9	241				
15 W	01:38	0.4	12	**30** Th	01:18	1.5	46
	07:21	6.9	210		07:22	6.3	192
	13:52	1.0	30		12:38	1.8	55
	19:43	7.8	238		18:51	6.7	204

StationId: 8516945
Source: NOAA/NOS/CO-OPS
Station Type: Primary
Time Zone: LST_LDT
Datum: MLLW

NOAA Tide Predictions

Kings Point, NY,2021

Times and Heights of High and Low Waters

October

Day	Time	ft	cm	Day	Time	ft	cm
1 F	02:23	1.3	40	**16** Sa	03:23	0.0	0
	08:24	6.6	201		09:22	7.8	238
	13:55	1.6	49		15:48	0.1	3
	20:17	6.9	210		21:45	7.9	241
2 Sa	03:13	1.0	30	**17** Su	04:14	-0.2	-6
	09:11	6.9	210		10:12	8.1	247
	15:06	1.2	37		16:40	-0.2	-6
	21:11	7.3	223		22:33	8.0	244
3 Su	03:55	0.6	18	**18** M	05:01	-0.2	-6
	09:48	7.4	226		10:56	8.4	256
	15:58	0.7	21		17:28	-0.3	-9
	21:52	7.7	235		23:18	8.0	244
4 M	04:31	0.2	6	**19** Tu	05:43	-0.1	-3
	10:20	7.9	241		11:37	8.5	259
	16:42	0.2	6		18:12	-0.4	-12
	22:31	8.1	247		23:59	7.9	241
5 Tu	05:04	-0.1	-3	**20** W	06:22	0.1	3
	10:53	8.5	259		12:13	8.4	256
	17:25	-0.3	-9		18:53	-0.3	-9
	23:11	8.3	253	O			
6 ● W	05:39	-0.3	-9	**21** Th	00:37	7.7	235
	11:30	8.9	271		06:55	0.4	12
	18:08	-0.7	-21		12:43	8.2	250
	23:54	8.5	259		19:30	-0.1	-3
7 Th	06:17	-0.5	-15	**22** F	01:12	7.4	226
	12:11	9.2	280		07:13	0.7	21
	18:52	-0.8	-24		13:07	8.0	244
					20:01	0.2	6
8 F	00:39	8.4	256	**23** Sa	01:44	7.2	219
	06:59	-0.4	-12		07:20	0.9	27
	12:55	9.3	283		13:26	7.8	238
	19:39	-0.8	-24		20:15	0.4	12
9 Sa	01:27	8.3	253	**24** Su	02:11	7.0	213
	07:44	-0.3	-9		07:48	1.1	34
	13:43	9.2	280		13:55	7.6	232
	20:30	-0.6	-18		20:31	0.6	18
10 Su	02:19	7.9	241	**25** M	02:40	6.8	207
	08:33	0.1	3		08:26	1.2	37
	14:35	8.9	271		14:32	7.3	223
	21:30	-0.2	-6		21:06	0.8	24
11 M	03:17	7.6	232	**26** Tu	03:18	6.6	201
	09:30	0.5	15		09:11	1.4	43
	15:33	8.5	259		15:15	7.1	216
	22:51	0.1	3		21:51	1.0	30
12 Tu	04:26	7.2	219	**27** W	04:02	6.4	195
	10:47	0.9	27		10:01	1.5	46
	16:42	8.0	244		16:04	6.9	210
					22:44	1.2	37
13 ◑ W	00:15	0.3	9	**28** Th	04:54	6.4	195
	05:56	7.0	213		10:57	1.6	49
	12:33	1.0	30		16:58	6.8	207
	18:17	7.6	232	◐	23:45	1.2	37
14 Th	01:25	0.3	9	**29** F	05:54	6.4	195
	07:19	7.1	216		11:59	1.6	49
	13:48	0.8	24		17:59	6.8	207
	19:43	7.6	232				
15 F	02:27	0.2	6	**30** Sa	00:52	1.1	34
	08:26	7.4	226		07:02	6.6	201
	14:51	0.5	15		13:07	1.3	40
	20:49	7.7	235		19:06	6.9	210
				31 Su	01:57	0.8	24
					08:04	7.1	216
					14:16	0.9	27
					20:13	7.2	219

November

Day	Time	ft	cm	Day	Time	ft	cm
1 M	02:50	0.5	15	**16** Tu	03:33	0.0	0
	08:52	7.6	232		09:32	8.2	250
	15:19	0.4	12		16:06	-0.4	-12
	21:09	7.6	232		21:56	7.5	229
2 Tu	03:36	0.1	3	**17** W	04:16	0.1	3
	09:35	8.3	253		10:11	8.3	253
	16:12	-0.2	-6		16:49	-0.4	-12
	21:59	7.9	241		22:37	7.4	226
3 W	04:20	-0.2	-6	**18** Th	04:54	0.3	9
	10:18	8.8	268		10:47	8.2	250
	17:02	-0.7	-21		17:30	-0.4	-12
	22:46	8.2	250		23:16	7.3	223
4 ● Th	05:04	-0.4	-12	**19** F	05:27	0.5	15
	11:09	9.3	283		11:17	8.0	244
	17:50	-1.0	-30		18:06	-0.2	-6
	23:32	8.3	253	O	23:51	7.1	216
5 F	05:50	-0.5	-15	**20** Sa	05:44	0.8	24
	11:46	9.5	290		11:38	7.8	238
	18:39	-1.2	-37		18:37	0.0	0
6 Sa	00:21	8.2	250	**21** Su	00:22	7.0	213
	06:36	-0.5	-15		05:54	0.9	27
	12:34	9.5	290		11:56	7.6	232
	19:29	-1.1	-34		18:51	0.3	9
7 Su	01:12	8.1	247	**22** M	00:45	6.8	207
	06:26	-0.3	-9		06:23	0.9	27
	12:25	9.2	280		12:25	7.4	226
	19:25	-0.8	-24		19:06	0.4	12
8 M	01:08	7.8	238	**23** Tu	01:11	6.7	204
	07:21	0.0	0		07:02	1.0	30
	13:21	8.8	268		13:03	7.3	223
	20:31	-0.4	-12		19:40	0.5	15
9 Tu	02:12	7.4	226	**24** W	01:47	6.6	201
	07:44	0.4	12		07:45	1.1	34
	14:25	8.2	250		13:46	7.2	219
	21:46	-0.1	-3		20:23	0.6	18
10 W	03:29	7.2	219	**25** Th	02:29	6.5	198
	10:02	0.7	21		08:34	1.2	37
	15:44	7.7	235		14:34	7.1	216
	22:58	0.1	3		21:12	0.7	21
11 Th	04:49	7.1	216	**26** F	03:17	6.6	201
	11:23	0.7	21		09:27	1.2	37
	17:11	7.4	226		15:26	7.0	213
◐					22:05	0.7	21
12 F	00:03	0.1	3	**27** Sa	04:10	6.7	204
	06:01	7.2	219		10:26	1.1	34
	12:31	0.6	18		16:22	6.9	210
	18:25	7.3	223	◔	23:01	0.6	18
13 Sa	01:02	0.1	3	**28** Su	05:06	6.9	210
	07:04	7.5	229		11:29	0.9	27
	13:32	0.3	9		17:24	6.9	210
	19:28	7.4	226		23:59	0.5	15
14 Su	01:56	0.0	0	**29** M	06:05	7.3	223
	07:59	7.8	238		12:37	0.5	15
	14:28	0.0	0		18:28	7.0	213
	20:23	7.4	226				
15 M	02:47	0.0	0	**30** Tu	00:55	0.2	6
	08:48	8.1	247		07:03	7.8	238
	15:19	-0.3	-9		13:44	0.1	3
	21:12	7.5	229		19:32	7.3	223

December

Day	Time	ft	cm	Day	Time	ft	cm
1 W	01:50	0.0	0	**16** Th	03:48	0.4	12
	07:57	8.4	256		09:46	7.8	238
	14:47	-0.4	-12		16:25	-0.4	-12
	20:30	7.5	229		22:15	7.0	213
2 Th	02:44	-0.3	-9	**17** F	04:28	0.5	15
	08:48	8.9	271		10:24	7.7	235
	15:45	-0.9	-27		17:06	-0.4	-12
	21:24	7.8	238		22:55	6.9	210
3 F	03:38	-0.5	-15	**18** Sa	05:04	0.6	18
	09:38	9.2	280		10:57	7.6	232
	16:39	-1.2	-37		17:44	-0.3	-9
	22:16	7.9	241		23:31	6.9	210
4 ● Sa	04:30	-0.6	-18	**19** Su	05:29	0.6	18
	10:28	9.3	283		11:22	7.5	229
	17:32	-1.3	-40		18:16	-0.1	-3
	23:08	7.9	241	O			
5 Su	05:24	-0.6	-18	**20** M	00:03	6.8	207
	11:19	9.2	280		05:40	0.7	21
	18:26	-1.2	-37		11:39	7.4	226
					18:38	0.0	0
6 M	00:03	7.8	238	**21** Tu	00:26	6.7	204
	06:19	-0.4	-12		06:07	0.6	18
	12:14	9.0	274		12:06	7.4	226
	19:23	-1.0	-30		18:52	0.1	3
7 Tu	01:02	7.6	232	**22** W	00:48	6.7	204
	07:20	-0.2	-6		06:43	0.6	18
	13:14	8.5	259		12:42	7.3	223
	20:24	-0.7	-21		19:21	0.1	3
8 W	02:07	7.4	226	**23** Th	01:20	6.7	204
	08:32	0.1	3		07:25	0.6	18
	14:20	8.0	244		13:23	7.3	223
	21:28	-0.4	-12		19:59	0.1	3
9 Th	03:17	7.2	219	**24** F	02:00	6.8	207
	09:50	0.4	12		08:10	0.6	18
	15:34	7.6	232		14:09	7.2	219
	22:32	-0.2	-6		20:43	0.1	3
10 F	04:26	7.2	219	**25** Sa	02:45	6.9	210
	11:01	0.4	12		09:01	0.6	18
	16:48	7.2	219		14:58	7.1	216
	23:33	0.0	0		21:31	0.2	6
11 ◐ Sa	05:32	7.2	219	**26** Su	03:34	7.1	216
	12:06	0.4	12		09:56	0.6	18
	17:56	7.0	213		15:52	7.0	213
					22:22	0.2	6
12 Su	00:30	0.1	3	**27** M	04:27	7.3	223
	06:33	7.4	226		10:57	0.4	12
	13:06	0.2	6		16:50	6.9	210
	18:59	6.9	210	◔	23:17	0.2	6
13 M	01:24	0.0	0	**28** Tu	05:24	7.5	229
	07:28	7.5	229		12:03	0.2	6
	14:01	0.0	0		17:54	6.8	207
	19:55	6.8	207				
14 Tu	02:15	0.3	9	**29** W	00:15	0.1	3
	08:19	7.7	235		06:25	7.9	241
	14:53	-0.2	-6		12:37	-0.1	-3
	20:46	6.9	210		19:02	6.9	210
15 W	03:03	0.3	9	**30** Th	01:16	0.0	0
	09:04	7.8	238		07:26	8.2	250
	15:41	-0.3	-9		14:32	-0.5	-15
	21:32	6.9	210		20:09	7.1	216
				31 F	02:20	-0.2	-6
					08:26	8.6	262
					15:37	-0.9	-27
					21:12	7.2	219

StationId: 8518750
Source: NOAA/NOS/CO-OPS
Station Type: Primary
Time Zone: LST_LDT
Datum: MLLW

NOAA Tide Predictions

The Battery, NY, 2021

Times and Heights of High and Low Waters

January

Day	Time	ft	cm	Day	Time	ft	cm
1 F	03:19	-0.1	-3	**16** Sa	04:19	-0.2	-6
	09:08	5.0	152		10:31	4.9	149
	16:11	-0.3	-9		16:54	-0.4	-12
	21:58	3.9	119		23:08	4.2	128
2 Sa	03:59	0.0	0	**17** Su	05:05	0.1	3
	09:51	4.9	149		11:20	4.6	140
	16:51	-0.2	-6		17:37	-0.2	-6
	22:47	4.0	122		23:56	4.1	125
3 Su	04:43	0.1	3	**18** M	05:54	0.5	15
	10:41	4.8	146		12:07	4.3	131
	17:35	-0.2	-6		18:22	0.1	3
	23:39	4.1	125				
4 M	05:33	0.2	6	**19** Tu	00:43	4.0	122
	11:36	4.6	140		06:49	0.7	21
	18:25	-0.1	-3		12:54	4.0	122
					19:10	0.4	12
5 Tu	00:31	4.2	128	**20** W	01:28	4.0	122
	06:39	0.3	9		07:50	0.9	27
	12:32	4.5	137		13:41	3.7	113
	19:24	-0.1	-3		◐ 20:02	0.5	15
6 W	01:25	4.4	134	**21** Th	02:14	3.9	119
	07:55	0.4	12		08:52	0.9	27
	13:31	4.3	131		14:32	3.5	107
	◑ 20:26	-0.1	-3		20:54	0.6	18
7 Th	02:23	4.6	140	**22** F	03:04	3.9	119
	09:06	0.2	6		09:48	0.8	24
	14:34	4.1	125		15:29	3.4	104
	21:26	-0.2	-6		21:44	0.6	18
8 F	03:24	4.8	146	**23** Sa	03:57	4.0	122
	10:10	0.0	0		10:39	0.6	18
	15:44	4.0	122		16:29	3.4	104
	22:22	-0.3	-9		22:32	0.6	18
9 Sa	04:28	5.0	152	**24** Su	04:50	4.2	128
	11:08	-0.3	-9		11:27	0.4	12
	16:55	4.1	125		17:25	3.5	107
	23:17	-0.4	-12		23:19	0.4	12
10 Su	05:29	5.2	158	**25** M	05:39	4.4	134
	12:05	-0.5	-15		12:14	0.2	6
	17:58	4.2	128		18:13	3.7	113
11 M	00:11	-0.5	-15	**26** Tu	00:05	0.3	9
	06:24	5.4	165		06:22	4.6	140
	12:59	-0.7	-21		13:00	0.0	0
	18:54	4.3	131		18:56	3.8	116
12 Tu	01:05	-0.6	-18	**27** W	00:51	0.1	3
	07:16	5.5	168		07:01	4.8	146
	13:51	-0.8	-24		13:44	-0.2	-6
	19:45	4.4	134		19:35	4.0	122
13 W	01:57	-0.6	-18	**28** Th	01:37	-0.2	-6
	08:05	5.5	168		07:38	5.0	152
	14:40	-0.9	-27		14:26	-0.4	-12
	● 20:35	4.4	134		○ 20:13	4.2	128
14 Th	02:46	-0.5	-15	**29** F	02:21	-0.3	-9
	08:53	5.4	165		08:18	5.1	155
	15:26	-0.8	-24		15:07	-0.6	-18
	21:26	4.4	134		20:53	4.3	131
15 F	03:34	-0.4	-12	**30** Sa	03:05	-0.4	-12
	09:42	5.1	155		08:55	5.1	155
	16:11	-0.7	-21		15:47	-0.6	-18
	22:17	4.3	131		21:36	4.4	134
				31 Su	03:48	-0.4	-12
					09:39	5.1	155
					16:27	-0.6	-18
					22:23	4.5	137

February

Day	Time	ft	cm	Day	Time	ft	cm
1 M	04:34	-0.4	-12	**16** Tu	05:19	0.3	9
	10:28	4.9	149		11:30	4.2	128
	17:09	-0.5	-15		17:32	0.2	6
	23:14	4.6	140		23:55	4.2	128
2 Tu	05:24	-0.2	-6	**17** W	06:05	0.6	18
	11:22	4.7	143		12:14	4.0	122
	17:56	-0.4	-12		18:08	0.5	15
3 W	00:07	4.7	143	**18** Th	00:35	4.1	125
	06:25	0.0	0		06:59	0.9	27
	12:18	4.4	134		13:00	3.7	113
	18:51	-0.2	-6		18:51	0.8	24
4 Th	01:01	4.7	143	**19** F	01:16	4.0	122
	07:36	0.2	6		08:03	1.0	30
	13:17	4.2	128		13:48	3.5	107
	◑ 19:56	0.0	0		◐ 19:50	1.0	30
5 F	01:59	4.7	143	**20** Sa	02:00	3.9	119
	08:48	0.2	6		09:06	1.0	30
	14:21	3.9	119		14:41	3.3	101
	21:03	0.1	3		20:56	1.0	30
6 Sa	03:03	4.7	143	**21** Su	02:52	3.9	119
	09:54	0.1	3		10:03	0.9	27
	15:33	3.8	116		15:46	3.3	101
	22:05	0.0	0		21:54	0.9	27
7 Su	04:11	4.8	146	**22** M	03:56	4.0	122
	10:54	-0.1	-3		10:54	0.7	21
	16:46	3.9	119		16:49	3.5	107
	23:03	-0.1	-3		22:47	0.7	21
8 M	05:17	4.9	149	**23** Tu	04:59	4.3	131
	11:50	-0.3	-9		11:42	0.4	12
	17:50	4.1	125		17:42	3.7	113
	23:59	-0.2	-6		23:37	0.4	12
9 Tu	06:15	5.1	155	**24** W	05:51	4.6	140
	12:43	-0.5	-15		12:29	0.1	3
	18:45	4.3	131		18:27	4.0	122
10 W	00:52	-0.3	-9	**25** Th	00:26	0.1	3
	07:06	5.2	158		06:35	4.9	149
	13:33	-0.6	-18		13:00	-0.2	-6
	19:34	4.5	137		19:08	4.4	134
11 Th	01:42	-0.4	-12	**26** F	01:15	-0.2	-6
	07:52	5.3	162		07:16	5.1	155
	14:19	-0.7	-21		13:57	-0.5	-15
	● 20:19	4.6	140		19:47	4.7	143
12 F	02:30	-0.4	-12	**27** Sa	02:02	-0.5	-15
	08:36	5.2	158		07:56	5.3	162
	15:02	-0.7	-21		14:39	-0.7	-21
	21:04	4.6	140		○ 20:27	4.9	149
13 Sa	03:14	-0.3	-9	**28** Su	02:48	-0.7	-21
	09:19	5.1	155		08:38	5.4	165
	15:43	-0.6	-18		15:21	-0.8	-24
	21:48	4.5	137		21:11	5.1	155
14 Su	03:56	-0.2	-6				
	10:03	4.8	146				
	16:20	-0.4	-12				
	22:31	4.4	134				
15 M	04:38	0.1	3				
	10:46	4.5	137				
	16:57	-0.1	-3				
	23:14	4.3	131				

March

Day	Time	ft	cm	Day	Time	ft	cm
1 M	03:35	-0.7	-21	**16** Tu	05:11	0.1	3
	09:24	5.3	162		11:14	4.5	137
	16:02	-0.8	-24		17:18	0.1	3
	21:58	5.2	158		23:28	4.7	143
2 Tu	04:22	-0.6	-18	**17** W	05:49	0.3	9
	10:14	5.0	152		11:56	4.2	128
	16:44	-0.6	-18		17:47	0.4	12
	22:49	5.2	158				
3 W	05:13	-0.4	-12	**18** Th	00:03	4.5	137
	11:09	4.8	146		06:28	0.6	18
	17:30	-0.3	-9		12:39	4.0	122
	23:43	5.1	155		18:14	0.7	21
4 Th	06:11	-0.1	-3	**19** F	00:38	4.3	131
	12:07	4.5	137		07:12	0.8	24
	18:26	0.0	0		13:24	3.7	113
					18:42	1.0	30
5 F	00:40	5.0	152	**20** Sa	01:14	4.2	128
	07:19	0.1	3		08:11	1.0	30
	13:09	4.2	128		14:11	3.6	110
	19:33	0.3	9		19:26	1.2	37
6 Sa	01:40	4.9	149	**21** Su	01:57	4.1	125
	08:31	0.3	9		09:21	1.1	34
	14:14	4.0	122		15:03	3.5	107
	◑ 20:45	0.4	12		◐ 20:55	1.3	40
7 Su	02:46	4.7	143	**22** M	02:50	4.1	125
	09:38	0.2	6		10:24	1.0	30
	15:26	3.9	119		15:56	3.5	107
	21:51	0.4	12		22:15	1.2	37
8 M	03:57	4.7	143	**23** Tu	03:55	4.1	125
	10:38	0.1	3		11:18	0.8	24
	16:37	4.0	122		17:06	3.7	113
	22:50	0.3	9		23:15	0.9	27
9 Tu	05:05	4.8	146	**24** W	05:08	4.3	131
	11:32	0.0	0		12:07	0.5	15
	17:40	4.2	128		18:04	4.0	122
	23:46	0.1	3				
10 W	06:02	4.9	149	**25** Th	00:09	0.5	15
	12:23	-0.2	-6		06:11	4.6	140
	18:32	4.5	137		12:54	0.2	6
					18:53	4.4	134
11 Th	00:37	-0.1	-3	**26** F	01:01	0.2	6
	06:51	5.1	155		07:03	5.0	152
	13:10	-0.3	-9		13:40	-0.1	-3
	19:17	4.7	143		19:37	4.8	146
12 F	01:25	-0.2	-6	**27** Sa	01:52	-0.2	-6
	07:34	5.1	155		07:56	5.2	158
	13:53	-0.4	-12		14:25	-0.4	-12
	19:58	4.8	146		20:19	5.2	158
13 Sa	02:11	-0.2	-6	**28** Su	02:42	-0.5	-15
	08:14	5.1	155		08:33	5.4	165
	14:34	-0.4	-12		15:09	-0.7	-21
	● 20:37	4.9	149		○ 21:01	5.6	171
14 Su	03:53	-0.2	-6	**29** M	03:31	-0.7	-21
	09:18	5.0	152		09:18	5.4	165
	16:11	-0.3	-9		15:52	-0.7	-21
	22:15	4.9	149		21:45	5.8	177
15 M	04:33	-0.1	-3	**30** Tu	04:20	-0.8	-24
	10:33	4.8	146		10:06	5.3	162
	16:46	-0.1	-3		16:36	-0.7	-21
	22:52	4.8	146		22:33	5.8	177
				31 W	05:09	-0.7	-21
					11:00	5.1	155
					17:21	-0.5	-15
					23:26	5.7	174

StationId: 8518750
Source: NOAA/NOS/CO-OPS
Station Type: Primary
Time Zone: LST_LDT
Datum: MLLW

NOAA Tide Predictions

The Battery, NY,2021

Times and Heights of High and Low Waters

April

Day	Time	ft	cm	Day	Time	ft	cm
1 Th	06:01	-0.5	-15	16 F	06:01	0.5	15
	11:58	4.8	146		12:11	4.0	122
	18:10	-0.2	-6		17:38	0.9	27
					23:45	4.6	140
2 F	00:23	5.5	168	17 Sa	06:40	0.8	24
	06:58	-0.2	-6		12:55	3.8	116
	13:00	4.5	137		18:08	1.1	34
	19:07	0.2	6				
3 Sa	01:23	5.2	158	18 Su	00:24	4.5	137
	08:03	0.1	3		07:29	1.0	30
	14:03	4.3	131		13:41	3.7	113
	20:16	0.6	18		18:49	1.3	40
4 Su	02:25	5.0	152	19 M	01:12	4.4	134
	09:12	0.3	9		08:36	1.1	34
	15:08	4.2	128		14:30	3.7	113
	21:29	0.7	21		19:58	1.4	43
5 M	03:31	4.8	146	20 Tu	02:08	4.4	134
	10:18	0.4	12		09:43	1.0	30
	16:15	4.1	125		15:43	3.8	116
	22:36	0.7	21		21:36	1.3	40
6 Tu	04:39	4.7	143	21 W	03:10	4.4	134
	11:17	0.3	9		10:39	0.8	24
	17:22	4.3	131		16:22	4.0	122
	23:35	0.6	18		22:44	1.0	30
7 W	05:45	4.7	143	22 Th	04:19	4.5	137
	12:09	0.2	6		11:30	0.5	15
	18:21	4.5	137		17:22	4.3	131
					23:42	0.6	18
8 Th	00:29	0.4	12	23 F	05:27	4.7	143
	06:41	4.8	146		12:17	0.2	6
	12:56	0.1	3		18:16	4.8	146
	19:11	4.7	143				
9 F	01:18	0.2	6	24 Sa	00:36	0.2	6
	07:28	4.9	149		06:27	5.0	152
	13:41	0.0	0		13:04	-0.1	-3
	19:53	5.0	152		19:04	5.3	162
10 Sa	02:05	0.1	3	25 Su	01:29	-0.2	-6
	08:10	4.9	149		07:20	5.2	158
	14:22	-0.1	-3		13:51	-0.4	-12
	20:32	5.1	155		19:50	5.7	174
11 Su	02:48	0.0	0	26 M	02:21	-0.5	-15
	08:49	4.9	149		08:09	5.3	162
	15:01	0.0	0		14:38	-0.5	-15
	21:07	5.2	158		20:35	6.1	186
12 M	03:30	0.0	0	27 Tu	03:13	-0.7	-21
	09:27	4.8	146		08:58	5.3	162
	15:37	0.1	3		15:26	-0.6	-18
	21:41	5.2	158		21:22	6.2	189
13 Tu	04:09	0.0	0	28 W	04:04	-0.8	-24
	10:05	4.6	140		09:50	5.2	158
	16:11	0.2	6		16:13	-0.5	-15
	22:14	5.1	155		22:12	6.2	189
14 W	04:47	0.1	3	29 Th	04:55	-0.8	-24
	10:45	4.4	134		10:47	5.0	152
	16:43	0.4	12		17:02	-0.3	-9
	22:44	4.9	149		23:07	6.0	183
15 Th	05:24	0.3	9	30 F	05:47	-0.5	-15
	11:27	4.2	128		11:49	4.8	146
	17:11	0.6	18		17:53	0.0	0
	23:14	4.8	146				

May

Day	Time	ft	cm	Day	Time	ft	cm
1 Sa	00:07	5.7	174	16 Su	06:18	0.6	18
	06:43	-0.2	-6		12:31	3.9	119
	12:52	4.6	140		17:49	1.1	34
	18:51	0.4	12		23:53	4.7	143
2 Su	01:09	5.3	162	17 M	07:02	0.8	24
	07:44	0.1	3		13:16	3.9	119
	13:54	4.5	137		18:32	1.2	37
	19:58	0.7	21				
3 M	02:10	5.1	155	18 Tu	00:45	4.6	140
	08:50	0.3	9		07:58	0.9	27
	14:55	4.4	134		14:02	3.9	119
	21:09	0.9	27		19:34	1.3	40
4 Tu	03:11	4.8	146	19 W	01:40	4.6	140
	09:53	0.4	12		09:01	0.8	24
	15:56	4.4	134		14:51	4.1	125
	22:15	0.9	27		21:02	1.2	37
5 W	04:13	4.6	140	20 Th	02:39	4.6	140
	10:49	0.4	12		09:59	0.7	21
	16:57	4.5	137		15:43	4.4	134
	23:14	0.8	24		22:15	1.0	30
6 Th	05:14	4.6	140	21 F	03:41	4.6	140
	11:39	0.3	9		10:51	0.4	12
	17:53	4.7	143		16:42	4.7	143
					23:16	0.6	18
7 F	00:06	0.6	18	22 Sa	04:48	4.7	143
	06:09	4.6	140		11:41	0.1	3
	12:24	0.3	9		17:39	5.2	158
	18:42	4.9	149				
8 Sa	00:54	0.5	15	23 Su	00:13	0.2	6
	06:58	4.6	140		05:53	4.8	146
	13:06	0.2	6		12:30	-0.1	-3
	19:24	5.1	155		18:33	5.6	171
9 Su	01:40	0.4	12	24 M	01:08	-0.1	-3
	07:41	4.6	140		06:53	5.0	152
	13:46	0.3	9		13:20	-0.3	-9
	20:02	5.2	158		19:24	6.0	183
10 M	02:24	0.3	9	25 Tu	02:03	-0.5	-15
	08:22	4.6	140		07:48	5.0	152
	14:25	0.3	9		14:11	-0.4	-12
	20:36	5.3	162		20:13	6.3	192
11 Tu	03:06	0.2	6	26 W	02:56	-0.7	-21
	09:01	4.5	137		08:42	5.1	155
	15:03	0.4	12		15:02	-0.4	-12
	21:09	5.3	162		21:02	6.3	192
12 W	03:46	0.1	3	27 Th	03:49	-0.8	-24
	09:40	4.4	134		09:36	5.0	152
	15:54	0.5	15		15:54	-0.3	-9
	21:39	5.2	158		21:55	6.2	189
13 Th	04:25	0.2	6	28 F	04:40	-0.7	-21
	10:20	4.3	131		10:35	4.9	149
	16:13	0.6	18		16:45	-0.1	-3
	22:08	5.1	155		22:52	6.0	183
14 F	05:02	0.3	9	29 Sa	05:32	-0.5	-15
	11:03	4.1	125		11:37	4.8	146
	16:45	0.8	24		17:38	0.1	3
	22:36	4.9	149		23:52	5.7	174
15 Sa	05:40	0.5	15	30 Su	06:25	-0.3	-9
	11:47	4.0	122		12:39	4.7	143
	17:16	0.9	27		18:34	0.5	15
	23:10	4.8	146				
				31 M	00:52	5.4	165
					07:21	0.0	0
					13:37	4.6	140
					19:37	0.8	24

June

Day	Time	ft	cm	Day	Time	ft	cm
1 Tu	01:50	5.1	155	16 W	00:25	4.8	146
	08:21	0.3	9		07:25	0.6	18
	14:33	4.6	140		13:35	4.3	131
	20:43	1.0	30		19:20	1.1	34
2 W	02:45	4.8	146	17 Th	01:19	4.8	146
	09:20	0.4	12		08:20	0.5	15
	15:28	4.6	140		14:22	4.5	137
	21:48	1.0	30		20:37	1.0	30
3 Th	03:40	4.5	137	18 F	02:14	4.7	143
	10:14	0.5	15		09:19	0.5	15
	16:23	4.6	140		15:13	4.7	143
	22:46	1.0	30		21:50	0.9	27
4 F	04:36	4.4	134	19 Sa	03:13	4.6	140
	11:02	0.5	15		10:15	0.3	9
	17:16	4.7	143		16:09	5.0	152
	23:38	0.8	24		22:54	0.6	18
5 Sa	05:31	4.3	131	20 Su	04:18	4.6	140
	11:46	0.5	15		11:09	0.1	3
	18:06	4.9	149		17:08	5.4	165
					23:53	0.2	6
6 Su	00:26	0.7	21	21 M	05:27	4.6	140
	06:23	4.3	131		12:01	0.0	0
	12:28	0.5	15		18:07	5.7	174
	18:50	5.0	152				
7 M	01:12	0.6	18	22 Tu	00:50	-0.1	-3
	07:11	4.3	131		06:33	4.7	143
	13:09	0.5	15		12:55	-0.1	-3
	19:30	5.2	158		19:03	6.0	183
8 Tu	01:57	0.4	12	23 W	01:46	-0.4	-12
	07:54	4.3	131		07:33	4.8	146
	13:50	0.6	18		13:50	-0.2	-6
	20:06	5.2	158		19:56	6.2	189
9 W	02:40	0.3	9	24 Th	02:40	-0.6	-18
	08:36	4.3	131		08:29	4.9	149
	14:30	0.6	18		14:44	-0.2	-6
	20:39	5.2	158		20:48	6.2	189
10 Th	03:22	0.2	6	25 F	03:33	-0.7	-21
	09:17	4.3	131		09:24	4.9	149
	15:10	0.6	18		15:38	-0.2	-6
	21:11	5.2	158		21:41	6.1	186
11 F	04:02	0.2	6	26 Sa	04:24	-0.7	-21
	09:59	4.2	128		10:21	4.9	149
	15:49	0.7	21		16:30	-0.1	-3
	21:42	5.1	155		22:37	5.9	180
12 Sa	04:41	0.2	6	27 Su	05:13	-0.5	-15
	10:39	4.1	125		11:20	4.8	146
	16:25	0.7	21		17:21	0.1	3
	22:13	5.1	155		23:34	5.6	171
13 Su	05:20	0.3	9	28 M	06:02	-0.3	-9
	11:22	4.1	125		12:18	4.7	143
	17:01	0.8	24		18:14	0.4	12
	22:50	5.0	152				
14 M	05:58	0.4	12	29 Tu	00:30	5.3	162
	12:06	4.1	125		06:53	0.0	0
	17:38	0.9	27		13:13	4.7	143
	23:35	4.9	149		19:10	0.7	21
15 Tu	06:39	0.5	15	30 W	01:22	5.0	152
	12:50	4.1	125		07:45	0.2	6
	18:22	1.0	30		14:04	4.7	143
					20:11	1.0	30

StationId: 8518750
Source: NOAA/NOS/CO-OPS
Station Type: Primary
Time Zone: LST_LDT
Datum: MLLW

NOAA Tide Predictions

The Battery, NY, 2021

Times and Heights of High and Low Waters

July

Day	Time	ft	cm	Day	Time	ft	cm
1 Th ☽	02:13	4.7	143	**16** F	01:00	4.8	146
	08:39	0.5	15		07:43	0.3	9
	14:54	4.6	140		13:55	4.9	149
	21:14	1.1	34		20:17	0.8	24
2 F	03:03	4.4	134	**17** Sa ☽	01:55	4.7	143
	09:31	0.6	18		08:42	0.4	12
	15:43	4.6	140		14:46	5.1	155
	22:13	1.1	34		21:30	0.8	24
3 Sa	03:55	4.2	128	**18** Su	02:54	4.5	137
	10:20	0.7	21		09:44	0.3	9
	16:33	4.7	143		15:42	5.2	158
	23:07	1.0	30		22:36	0.6	18
4 Su	04:50	4.0	122	**19** M	03:59	4.4	134
	11:06	0.8	24		10:44	0.3	9
	17:24	4.7	143		16:44	5.4	165
	23:56	0.9	27		23:37	0.3	9
5 M	05:47	4.0	122	**20** Tu	05:11	4.4	134
	11:50	0.8	24		11:42	0.2	6
	18:12	4.9	149		17:48	5.6	171
6 Tu	00:43	0.7	21	**21** W	00:34	0.0	0
	06:40	4.0	122		06:21	4.5	137
	12:34	0.8	24		12:38	0.1	3
	18:56	5.0	152		18:49	5.8	177
7 W	01:28	0.6	18	**22** Th	01:30	-0.2	-6
	07:28	4.1	125		07:23	4.6	140
	13:17	0.7	21		13:35	0.0	0
	19:37	5.1	155		19:45	6.0	183
8 Th	02:13	0.4	12	**23** F	02:24	-0.4	-12
	08:11	4.2	128		08:19	4.8	146
	14:01	0.7	21		14:30	-0.1	-3
	20:13	5.2	158		20:37	6.0	183
9 F	02:56	0.3	9	**24** Sa ○	03:15	-0.5	-15
	08:52	4.2	128		09:11	4.9	149
	14:45	0.6	18		15:23	-0.1	-3
	20:48	5.2	158		21:28	5.9	180
10 Sa ●	03:38	0.2	6	**25** Su	04:04	-0.5	-15
	09:32	4.3	131		10:04	4.9	149
	15:27	0.6	18		16:13	0.0	0
	21:21	5.2	158		22:19	5.8	177
11 Su	04:18	0.1	3	**26** M	04:50	-0.4	-12
	10:11	4.3	131		10:57	4.9	149
	16:07	0.6	18		17:02	0.2	6
	21:56	5.2	158		23:10	5.5	168
12 M	04:56	0.1	3	**27** Tu	05:35	-0.3	-9
	10:52	4.3	131		11:49	4.9	149
	16:46	0.6	18		17:50	0.4	12
	22:34	5.2	158				
13 Tu	05:34	0.1	3	**28** W	00:00	5.2	158
	11:35	4.4	134		06:19	0.0	0
	17:27	0.6	18		12:40	4.8	146
	23:18	5.1	155		18:40	0.7	21
14 W	06:12	0.2	6	**29** Th	00:50	4.9	149
	12:20	4.5	137		07:03	0.3	9
	18:12	0.7	21		13:27	4.8	146
					19:34	1.0	30
15 Th	00:07	5.0	152	**30** F	01:38	4.6	140
	06:54	0.2	6		07:50	0.6	18
	13:07	4.7	143		14:13	4.7	143
	19:07	0.8	24		20:34	1.2	37
				31 Sa ☽	02:26	4.3	131
					08:41	0.9	27
					14:59	4.6	140
					21:35	1.3	40

August

Day	Time	ft	cm	Day	Time	ft	cm
1 Su	03:16	4.0	122	**16** M	02:43	4.4	134
	09:33	1.0	30		09:22	0.5	15
	15:46	4.6	140		15:23	5.3	162
	22:32	1.2	37		22:21	0.6	18
2 M	04:11	3.8	116	**17** Tu	03:52	4.3	131
	10:25	1.1	34		10:28	0.5	15
	16:37	4.6	140		16:29	5.4	165
	23:24	1.1	34		23:23	0.4	12
3 Tu	05:11	3.8	116	**18** W	05:05	4.3	131
	11:14	1.1	34		11:29	0.4	12
	17:31	4.7	143		17:38	5.5	168
4 W	00:12	0.9	27	**19** Th	00:20	0.2	6
	06:08	3.9	119		06:15	4.5	137
	12:01	1.0	30		12:27	0.3	9
	18:22	4.8	146		18:40	5.6	171
5 Th	00:58	0.7	21	**20** F	01:14	0.0	0
	07:00	4.0	122		07:15	4.7	143
	12:48	0.9	27		13:22	0.2	6
	19:08	5.0	152		19:35	5.8	177
6 F	01:44	0.5	15	**21** Sa	02:06	-0.2	-6
	07:44	4.2	128		08:07	4.9	149
	13:34	0.7	21		14:16	0.0	0
	19:48	5.2	158		20:25	5.8	177
7 Sa	02:27	0.3	9	**22** Su ○	02:54	-0.3	-9
	08:25	4.4	134		08:58	5.1	155
	14:20	0.6	18		15:06	0.0	0
	20:24	5.3	162		21:11	5.8	177
8 Su ●	03:09	0.2	6	**23** M	03:40	-0.4	-12
	09:03	4.5	137		09:41	5.2	158
	15:04	0.4	12		15:54	0.1	3
	20:59	5.4	165		21:56	5.6	171
9 M	03:49	0.0	0	**24** Tu	04:22	-0.3	-9
	09:40	4.7	143		10:27	5.1	155
	15:47	0.3	9		16:39	0.2	6
	21:35	5.4	165		22:41	5.4	165
10 Tu	04:28	-0.1	-3	**25** W	05:02	-0.1	-3
	10:19	4.8	146		11:13	5.1	155
	16:30	0.3	9		17:23	0.4	12
	22:14	5.4	165		23:27	5.0	152
11 W	05:06	-0.1	-3	**26** Th	05:41	0.2	6
	11:02	4.9	149		11:59	5.0	152
	17:13	0.3	9		18:08	0.7	21
	22:59	5.3	162				
12 Th	05:44	-0.1	-3	**27** F	00:14	4.7	143
	11:48	5.0	152		06:18	0.5	15
		0.4	12		12:44	4.8	146
	23:49	5.1	155		18:56	1.0	30
13 F	06:25	0.1	3	**28** Sa	01:02	4.4	134
	12:38	5.1	155		06:57	0.8	24
	18:54	0.5	15		13:27	4.7	143
					19:50	1.2	37
14 Sa	00:44	4.8	146	**29** Su	01:50	4.1	125
	07:13	0.3	9		07:41	1.1	34
	13:30	5.2	158		14:10	4.6	140
	20:01	0.7	21		20:52	1.4	43
15 Su ☽	01:42	4.6	140	**30** M ☽	02:41	3.9	119
	08:13	0.4	12		08:37	1.4	43
	14:24	5.3	162		14:56	4.5	137
	21:13	0.7	21		21:54	1.4	43
				31 Tu	03:35	3.8	116
					09:41	1.5	46
					15:47	4.5	137
					22:50	1.3	40

September

Day	Time	ft	cm	Day	Time	ft	cm
1 W	04:35	3.8	116	**16** Th	05:02	4.4	134
	10:39	1.4	43		11:19	0.6	18
	16:45	4.5	137		17:29	5.3	162
	23:40	1.1	34				
2 Th	05:35	3.9	119	**17** F	00:04	0.2	6
	11:31	1.2	37		06:08	4.6	140
	17:44	4.7	143		12:16	0.4	12
					18:30	5.4	165
3 F	00:27	0.8	24	**18** Sa	00:55	0.0	0
	06:28	4.1	125		07:03	4.9	149
	12:20	1.0	30		13:09	0.3	9
	18:35	4.9	149		19:22	5.5	168
4 Sa	01:11	0.6	18	**19** Su	01:44	-0.1	-3
	07:14	4.4	134		07:51	5.1	155
	13:07	0.7	21		14:00	0.2	6
	19:18	5.2	158		20:07	5.6	171
5 Su	01:54	0.3	9	**20** M ○	02:29	-0.2	-6
	07:53	4.6	140		08:35	5.3	162
	13:48	0.4	12		14:48	0.1	3
	19:56	5.4	165		20:49	5.5	168
6 M	02:36	0.1	3	**21** Tu	03:11	-0.2	-6
	08:31	4.9	149		09:16	5.3	162
	14:40	0.2	6		15:33	0.1	3
	20:33	5.5	168		21:30	5.4	165
7 Tu ●	03:17	-0.1	-3	**22** W	03:51	-0.1	-3
	09:08	5.2	158		09:55	5.3	162
	15:26	0.0	0		16:16	0.2	6
	21:11	5.6	171		22:11	5.1	155
8 W	03:57	-0.3	-9	**23** Th	04:28	0.1	3
	09:47	5.4	165		10:34	5.2	158
	16:11	-0.1	-3		16:57	0.4	12
	21:53	5.5	168		22:54	4.8	146
9 Th	04:36	-0.3	-9	**24** F	05:02	0.3	9
	10:27	5.5	168		11:14	5.1	155
	16:58	0.0	0		17:38	0.6	18
	22:39	5.3	162		23:39	4.5	137
10 F	05:16	-0.2	-6	**25** Sa	05:35	0.7	21
	11:18	5.6	171		11:54	4.9	149
	17:46	0.1	3		18:20	0.9	27
	23:33	5.0	152				
11 Sa	05:59	0.0	0	**26** Su	00:27	4.2	128
	12:11	5.5	168		06:06	1.0	30
	18:41	0.3	9		12:35	4.7	143
					19:08	1.1	34
12 Su	00:32	4.8	146	**27** M	01:17	4.0	122
	06:49	0.3	9		06:37	1.3	40
	13:08	5.5	168		13:17	4.5	137
	19:46	0.5	15		20:07	1.3	40
13 M ☽	01:35	4.5	137	**28** Tu	02:08	3.8	116
	07:53	0.6	18		07:23	1.5	46
	14:07	5.4	165		14:03	4.4	134
	20:58	0.6	18		21:12	1.4	43
14 Tu	02:41	4.3	131	**29** W ☽	03:02	3.7	113
	09:07	0.8	24		08:48	1.6	49
	15:11	5.3	162		14:55	4.4	134
	22:07	0.6	18		22:13	1.3	40
15 W	03:50	4.3	131	**30** Th	03:59	3.7	113
	10:17	0.8	24		10:02	1.5	46
	16:20	5.2	158		15:55	4.4	134
	23:08	0.4	12		23:05	1.1	34

StationId: 8518750
Source: NOAA/NOS/CO-OPS
Station Type: Primary
Time Zone: LST_LDT
Datum: MLLW

NOAA Tide Predictions

The Battery, NY,2021

Times and Heights of High and Low Waters

October

Day	Time	ft	cm
1 F	04:58	3.9	119
	11:00	1.3	40
	16:57	4.6	140
	23:52	0.8	24
2 Sa	05:51	4.2	128
	11:51	1.0	30
	17:54	4.8	146
3 Su	00:36	0.5	15
	06:38	4.5	137
	12:40	0.6	18
	18:42	5.1	155
4 M	01:18	0.2	6
	07:19	4.9	149
	13:28	0.3	9
	19:25	5.3	162
5 Tu	02:01	-0.1	-3
	07:58	5.3	162
	14:17	0.0	0
	20:06	5.5	168
6 W ●	02:43	-0.3	-9
	08:36	5.7	174
	15:05	-0.3	-9
	20:48	5.5	168
7 Th	03:25	-0.4	-12
	09:17	5.9	180
	15:53	-0.4	-12
	21:32	5.4	165
8 F	04:07	-0.4	-12
	10:02	6.0	183
	16:42	-0.4	-12
	22:22	5.2	158
9 Sa	04:51	-0.3	-9
	10:52	5.9	180
	17:33	-0.2	-6
	23:20	4.9	149
10 Su	05:38	0.0	0
	11:49	5.8	177
	18:28	0.0	0
11 M	00:24	4.6	140
	06:32	0.3	9
	12:51	5.5	168
	19:31	0.3	9
12 Tu	01:31	4.4	134
	07:38	0.7	21
	13:55	5.3	162
	20:41	0.5	15
13 W ◐	02:37	4.3	131
	08:53	0.8	24
	15:01	5.1	155
	21:49	0.5	15
14 Th	03:44	4.3	131
	10:04	0.8	24
	16:07	5.0	152
	22:50	0.3	9
15 F	04:51	4.4	134
	11:07	0.7	21
	17:13	5.0	152
	23:43	0.2	6
16 Sa	05:53	4.7	143
	12:02	0.5	15
	18:11	5.1	155
17 Su	00:32	0.0	0
	06:46	4.9	149
	12:53	0.3	9
	19:01	5.1	155
18 M	01:17	-0.1	-3
	07:31	5.2	158
	13:41	0.2	6
	19:45	5.2	158
19 Tu	01:59	-0.1	-3
	08:11	5.3	162
	14:27	0.1	3
	20:25	5.1	155
20 W ○	02:39	-0.1	-3
	08:48	5.4	165
	15:11	0.1	3
	21:04	5.0	152
21 Th	03:17	0.0	0
	09:23	5.4	165
	15:52	0.2	6
	21:43	4.8	146
22 F	03:53	0.2	6
	09:57	5.3	162
	16:32	0.3	9
	22:24	4.5	137
23 Sa	04:27	0.4	12
	10:31	5.1	155
	17:11	0.4	12
	23:08	4.2	128
24 Su	04:59	0.7	21
	11:05	4.9	149
	17:51	0.7	21
	23:56	4.0	122
25 M	05:28	0.9	27
	11:41	4.7	143
	18:33	0.9	27
26 Tu	00:46	3.8	116
	05:57	1.2	37
	12:23	4.5	137
	19:24	1.1	34
27 W	01:37	3.7	113
	06:36	1.4	43
	13:12	4.4	134
	20:27	1.2	37
28 Th ◐	02:28	3.6	110
	07:43	1.5	46
	14:06	4.3	131
	21:31	1.1	34
29 F	03:20	3.7	113
	09:19	1.5	46
	15:04	4.3	131
	22:25	0.9	27
30 Sa	04:14	3.9	119
	10:26	1.2	37
	16:05	4.4	134
	23:13	0.6	18
31 Su	05:07	4.2	128
	11:21	0.8	24
	17:06	4.6	140
	23:57	0.3	9

November

Day	Time	ft	cm
1 M	05:57	4.6	140
	12:13	0.4	12
	18:02	4.9	149
2 Tu	00:41	0.0	0
	06:43	5.1	155
	13:04	0.1	3
	18:52	5.1	155
3 W	01:25	-0.3	-9
	07:26	5.6	171
	13:55	-0.3	-9
	19:40	5.2	158
4 Th ●	02:10	-0.5	-15
	08:09	5.9	180
	14:46	-0.5	-15
	20:27	5.2	158
5 F	02:56	-0.6	-18
	08:53	6.1	186
	15:36	-0.7	-21
	21:15	5.1	155
6 Sa	03:43	-0.6	-18
	09:40	6.1	186
	16:27	-0.7	-21
	22:09	4.9	149
7 Su	03:32	-0.4	-12
	09:33	6.0	183
	16:19	-0.6	-18
	22:09	4.7	143
8 M	04:22	-0.2	-6
	10:33	5.7	174
	17:14	-0.3	-9
	23:16	4.5	137
9 Tu	05:18	0.2	6
	11:37	5.4	165
	18:14	0.0	0
10 W	00:22	4.4	134
	06:23	0.5	15
	12:42	5.2	158
	19:20	0.2	6
11 Th ◐	01:26	4.3	131
	07:36	0.7	21
	13:44	4.9	149
	20:25	0.2	6
12 F	02:28	4.3	131
	08:46	0.7	21
	14:46	4.8	146
	21:25	0.2	6
13 Sa	03:30	4.4	134
	09:48	0.6	18
	15:47	4.6	140
	22:17	0.1	3
14 Su	04:29	4.6	140
	10:43	0.5	15
	16:44	4.6	140
	23:03	0.0	0
15 M	05:20	4.8	146
	11:33	0.3	9
	17:35	4.6	140
	23:46	0.0	0
16 Tu	06:05	5.0	152
	12:20	0.2	6
	18:20	4.6	140
17 W	00:27	0.0	0
	06:45	5.2	158
	13:05	0.1	3
	19:01	4.6	140
18 Th	01:07	0.0	0
	07:21	5.2	158
	13:28	0.0	0
	19:41	4.5	137
19 F ○	01:46	0.1	3
	07:54	5.2	158
	14:29	0.0	0
	20:20	4.3	131
20 Sa	02:23	0.2	6
	08:27	5.1	155
	15:09	0.1	3
	21:01	4.2	128
21 Su	02:59	0.4	12
	08:58	5.0	152
	15:48	0.2	6
	21:43	4.0	122
22 M	03:32	0.5	15
	09:33	4.8	146
	16:26	0.4	12
	22:28	3.8	116
23 Tu	04:04	0.7	21
	10:03	4.6	140
	17:06	0.5	15
	23:16	3.7	113
24 W	04:35	0.9	27
	10:44	4.5	137
	17:49	0.7	21
25 Th	00:04	3.6	110
	05:13	1.0	30
	11:32	4.4	134
	18:41	0.8	24
26 F	00:50	3.6	110
	06:06	1.1	34
	12:25	4.3	131
	19:41	0.8	24
27 Sa ◐	01:37	3.7	113
	07:31	1.2	37
	13:20	4.3	131
	20:39	0.6	18
28 Su	02:27	3.9	119
	08:49	1.0	30
	14:18	4.3	131
	21:31	0.4	12
29 M	03:20	4.3	131
	09:52	0.6	18
	15:20	4.4	134
	22:18	0.1	3
30 Tu	04:15	4.7	143
	10:47	0.2	6
	16:23	4.5	137
	23:05	-0.2	-6

December

Day	Time	ft	cm
1 W	05:08	5.1	155
	11:41	-0.1	-3
	17:23	4.6	140
	23:53	-0.5	-15
2 Th	05:58	5.6	171
	12:35	-0.5	-15
	18:18	4.8	146
3 F	00:43	-0.6	-18
	06:46	5.9	180
	13:28	-0.8	-24
	19:10	4.8	146
4 Sa ●	01:33	-0.7	-21
	07:34	6.1	186
	14:21	-0.9	-27
	20:03	4.8	146
5 Su	02:25	-0.7	-21
	08:25	6.0	183
	15:13	-1.0	-30
	20:58	4.7	143
6 M	03:17	-0.6	-18
	09:20	5.9	180
	16:04	-0.9	-27
	21:59	4.6	140
7 Tu	04:09	-0.4	-12
	10:20	5.6	171
	16:57	-0.6	-18
	23:03	4.4	134
8 W	05:04	-0.1	-3
	11:22	5.3	162
	17:53	-0.4	-12
9 Th	00:06	4.3	131
	06:04	0.2	6
	12:22	5.0	152
	18:52	-0.1	-3
10 F	01:05	4.3	131
	07:11	0.5	15
	13:20	4.7	143
	19:53	0.0	0
11 Sa ◐	02:02	4.3	131
	08:20	0.6	18
	14:16	4.4	134
	20:51	0.1	3
12 Su	02:59	4.3	131
	09:22	0.6	18
	15:13	4.2	128
	21:43	0.1	3
13 M	03:55	4.4	134
	10:18	0.5	15
	16:10	4.1	125
	22:29	0.1	3
14 Tu	04:48	4.5	137
	11:08	0.4	12
	17:04	4.0	122
	23:13	0.1	3
15 W	05:35	4.7	143
	11:55	0.2	6
	17:53	4.0	122
	23:55	0.1	3
16 Th	06:17	4.8	146
	12:41	0.1	3
	18:38	4.0	122
17 F	00:36	0.1	3
	06:55	4.9	149
	13:24	0.0	0
	19:20	4.1	125
18 Sa	01:17	0.1	3
	07:30	4.9	149
	14:06	-0.1	-3
	20:00	4.0	122
19 Su ○	01:57	0.2	6
	08:04	4.9	149
	14:47	-0.1	-3
	20:40	4.0	122
20 M	02:36	0.2	6
	08:37	4.8	146
	15:26	-0.1	-3
	21:21	3.8	116
21 Tu	03:13	0.3	9
	09:09	4.7	143
	16:04	0.0	0
	22:02	3.7	113
22 W	03:47	0.4	12
	09:42	4.6	140
	16:41	0.1	3
	22:44	3.7	113
23 Th	04:21	0.5	15
	10:19	4.5	137
	17:19	0.2	6
	23:27	3.7	113
24 F	04:58	0.6	18
	11:04	4.4	134
	18:00	0.3	9
25 Sa	00:10	3.7	113
	05:45	0.7	21
	11:53	4.3	131
	18:49	0.3	9
26 Su	00:55	3.9	119
	06:52	0.8	24
	12:45	4.2	128
	19:47	0.3	9
27 M ◐	01:43	4.1	125
	08:14	0.7	21
	13:41	4.2	128
	20:46	0.2	6
28 Tu	02:37	4.4	134
	09:24	0.4	12
	14:43	4.1	125
	21:41	0.0	0
29 W	03:36	4.7	143
	10:25	0.1	3
	15:51	4.1	125
	22:35	-0.2	-6
30 Th	04:36	5.1	155
	11:22	-0.2	-6
	17:00	4.2	128
	23:28	-0.5	-15
31 F	05:35	5.4	165
	12:18	-0.6	-18
	18:02	4.4	134

StationId: 8519483
Source: NOAA/NOS/CO-OPS
Station Type: Primary
Time Zone: LST_LDT
Datum: MLLW

NOAA Tide Predictions

Bergen Point West Reach, NY, 2021

Times and Heights of High and Low Waters

January

Day	Time	ft	cm	Day	Time	ft	cm
1 F	03:30	-0.1	-6	**16** Sa	04:28	-0.2	-6
	09:04	5.5	168		10:29	5.3	162
	16:20	-0.4	-12		17:01	-0.5	-15
	21:50	4.4	134		23:02	4.6	140
2 Sa	04:11	-0.1	-3	**17** Su	05:09	0.1	3
	09:46	5.5	168		11:18	5.0	152
	16:59	-0.4	-12		17:39	-0.2	-6
	22:37	4.4	134		23:52	4.5	137
3 Su	04:52	0.0	0	**18** M	05:52	0.4	12
	10:34	5.3	162		12:06	4.7	143
	17:39	-0.3	-9		18:17	0.1	3
	23:31	4.5	137				
4 M	05:39	0.2	6	**19** Tu	00:38	4.4	134
	11:29	5.1	155		06:39	0.7	21
	18:24	-0.2	-6		12:52	4.3	131
					18:58	0.4	12
5 Tu	00:26	4.7	143	**20** W	01:22	4.3	131
	06:36	0.3	9		07:39	1.0	30
	12:28	5.0	152		13:38	4.1	125
	19:19	-0.1	-3		19:46	0.6	18
6 W	01:22	4.8	146	**21** Th	02:06	4.3	131
	07:51	0.4	12		08:47	1.0	30
	13:28	4.8	146		14:27	3.9	119
	20:24	0.0	0		20:43	0.7	21
7 Th	02:19	5.0	152	**22** F	02:52	4.3	131
	09:09	0.3	9		09:50	0.9	27
	14:30	4.6	140		15:21	3.7	113
	21:29	-0.1	-3		21:40	0.7	21
8 F	03:20	5.2	158	**23** Sa	03:45	4.4	134
	10:17	0.1	3		10:44	0.7	21
	15:38	4.5	137		16:21	3.7	113
	22:29	-0.3	-9		22:32	0.6	18
9 Sa	04:25	5.4	165	**24** Su	04:41	4.6	140
	11:18	-0.2	-6		11:34	0.5	15
	16:49	4.5	137		17:21	3.8	116
	23:25	-0.4	-12		23:21	0.4	12
10 Su	05:28	5.7	174	**25** M	05:36	4.8	146
	12:15	-0.5	-15		12:23	0.2	6
	17:55	4.7	143		18:13	4.0	122
11 M	00:21	-0.5	-15	**26** Tu	00:10	0.2	6
	06:26	5.9	180		06:22	5.1	155
	13:10	-0.7	-21		13:10	-0.1	-3
	18:52	4.8	146		18:58	4.3	131
12 Tu	01:16	-0.6	-18	**27** W	00:59	0.0	0
	07:18	6.1	186		07:03	5.3	162
	14:03	-0.9	-27		13:55	-0.3	-9
	19:44	4.9	149		19:37	4.5	137
13 W	02:08	-0.7	-21	**28** Th	01:46	-0.2	-6
	08:06	6.1	186		07:40	5.6	171
	14:53	-1.0	-30		14:39	-0.6	-18
	20:33	5.0	152		20:15	4.7	143
14 Th	02:58	-0.6	-18	**29** F	02:33	-0.4	-12
	08:53	5.9	180		08:16	5.7	174
	15:38	-0.9	-27		15:20	-0.7	-21
	21:22	4.9	149		20:52	4.8	146
15 F	03:44	-0.5	-15	**30** Sa	03:17	-0.5	-15
	09:40	5.7	174		08:54	5.7	174
	16:21	-0.8	-24		15:59	-0.8	-24
	22:11	4.8	146		21:33	4.9	149
				31 Su	04:00	-0.5	-15
					09:36	5.6	171
					16:37	-0.8	-24
					22:18	5.0	152

February

Day	Time	ft	cm	Day	Time	ft	cm
1 M	04:44	-0.4	-12	**16** Tu	05:17	0.3	9
	10:23	5.4	165		11:23	4.6	140
	17:16	-0.7	-21		17:27	0.1	3
	23:09	5.1	155		23:44	4.6	140
2 Tu	05:31	-0.3	-9	**17** W	05:53	0.6	18
	11:16	5.2	158		12:07	4.3	131
	17:59	-0.5	-15		17:56	0.4	12
3 W	00:04	5.1	155	**18** Th	00:23	4.5	137
	06:25	0.0	0		06:36	0.9	27
	12:14	4.9	149		12:51	4.0	122
	18:49	-0.2	-6		18:30	0.7	21
4 Th	00:59	5.1	155	**19** F	01:02	4.4	134
	07:34	0.2	6		07:40	1.1	34
	13:14	4.6	140		13:38	3.8	116
	19:53	0.0	0		19:19	0.9	27
5 F	01:57	5.1	155	**20** Sa	01:46	4.3	131
	08:52	0.3	9		08:59	1.1	34
	14:16	4.4	134		14:31	3.7	113
	21:05	0.1	3		20:35	1.0	30
6 Sa	02:59	5.2	158	**21** Su	02:38	4.4	134
	10:02	0.2	6		10:06	1.0	30
	15:25	4.3	131		15:33	3.6	110
	22:12	0.0	0		21:48	0.9	27
7 Su	04:07	5.2	158	**22** M	03:42	4.5	137
	11:04	-0.1	-3		11:01	0.7	21
	16:38	4.3	131		16:41	3.8	116
	23:12	-0.1	-3		22:48	0.7	21
8 M	05:15	5.4	165	**23** Tu	04:50	4.7	143
	12:01	-0.3	-9		11:51	0.4	12
	17:45	4.5	137		17:40	4.1	125
					23:43	0.4	12
9 Tu	00:09	-0.3	-9	**24** W	05:49	5.0	152
	06:15	5.6	171		12:39	0.0	0
	12:55	-0.5	-15		18:29	4.4	134
	18:42	4.7	143				
10 W	01:03	-0.4	-12	**25** Th	00:34	0.0	0
	07:07	5.7	174		06:36	5.4	165
	13:45	-0.7	-21		13:26	-0.3	-9
	19:32	4.9	149		19:11	4.8	146
11 Th	01:54	-0.5	-15	**26** F	01:25	-0.3	-9
	07:53	5.8	177		07:18	5.7	174
	14:32	-0.8	-24		14:10	-0.6	-18
	20:17	5.1	155		19:51	5.2	158
12 F	02:41	-0.5	-15	**27** Sa	02:14	-0.6	-18
	08:36	5.7	174		07:58	5.9	180
	15:14	-0.8	-24		14:52	-0.9	-27
	21:00	5.1	155		20:30	5.5	168
13 Sa	03:25	-0.4	-12	**28** Su	03:01	-0.8	-24
	09:17	5.5	168		08:39	5.9	180
	15:52	-0.7	-21		15:33	-1.0	-30
	21:42	5.0	152		21:11	5.6	171
14 Su	04:05	-0.3	-9				
	09:59	5.3	162				
	16:27	-0.5	-15				
	22:23	4.9	149				
15 M	04:42	0.0	0				
	10:41	4.9	149				
	16:58	-0.2	-6				
	23:04	4.7	143				

March

Day	Time	ft	cm	Day	Time	ft	cm
1 M	03:47	-0.8	-24	**16** Tu	05:15	0.0	0
	09:22	5.8	177		11:06	4.9	149
	16:13	-1.0	-30		17:20	0.1	3
	21:56	5.7	174		23:14	5.1	155
2 Tu	04:32	-0.7	-21	**17** W	05:48	0.3	9
	10:10	5.6	171		11:43	4.6	140
	16:53	-0.8	-24		17:46	0.3	9
	22:47	5.7	174		23:44	4.9	149
3 W	05:20	-0.5	-15	**18** Th	06:20	0.5	15
	11:04	5.3	162		12:23	4.3	131
	17:36	-0.5	-15		18:12	0.6	18
	23:42	5.6	171				
4 Th	06:14	-0.2	-6	**19** F	00:16	4.8	146
	12:03	4.9	149		06:54	0.8	24
	18:26	-0.1	-3		13:06	4.1	125
					18:42	0.8	24
5 F	00:40	5.5	168	**20** Sa	00:56	4.7	143
	07:20	0.2	6		07:40	1.1	34
	13:05	4.6	140		13:54	3.9	119
	19:31	0.2	6		19:24	1.1	34
6 Sa	01:40	5.3	162	**21** Su	01:45	4.6	140
	08:36	0.3	9		09:00	1.2	37
	14:09	4.4	134		14:47	3.8	116
	20:48	0.4	12		20:29	1.2	37
7 Su	02:44	5.2	158	**22** M	02:40	4.6	140
	09:47	0.3	9		10:22	1.2	37
	15:17	4.3	131		15:48	3.8	116
	21:59	0.4	12		22:03	1.2	37
8 M	03:53	5.1	155	**23** Tu	03:45	4.6	140
	10:49	0.1	3		11:24	0.9	27
	16:28	4.4	134		16:56	4.0	122
	23:01	0.3	9		23:16	0.9	27
9 Tu	05:02	5.2	158	**24** W	04:58	4.8	146
	11:44	-0.1	-3		12:16	0.5	15
	17:34	4.6	140		18:00	4.4	134
	23:57	0.1	3				
10 W	06:02	5.4	165	**25** Th	00:15	0.5	15
	12:35	-0.3	-9		06:07	5.1	155
	18:29	4.9	149		13:04	0.1	3
					18:54	4.8	146
11 Th	00:48	-0.1	-3	**26** F	01:09	0.1	3
	06:51	5.5	168		07:04	5.5	168
	13:21	-0.4	-12		13:51	-0.3	-9
	19:15	5.2	158		19:41	5.4	165
12 F	01:37	-0.2	-6	**27** Sa	02:02	-0.3	-9
	07:35	5.6	171		07:52	5.8	177
	14:05	-0.5	-15		14:37	-0.6	-18
	19:56	5.3	162		20:23	5.8	177
13 Sa	02:22	-0.3	-9	**28** Su	02:53	-0.6	-18
	08:14	5.6	171		08:36	6.0	183
	14:44	-0.5	-15		15:21	-0.8	-24
	20:34	5.4	165		21:05	6.2	189
14 Su	04:03	-0.3	-9	**29** M	03:43	-0.9	-27
	09:52	5.4	165		09:26	6.0	183
	16:20	-0.4	-12		16:05	-0.9	-27
	22:09	5.4	165		21:48	6.4	195
15 M	04:41	-0.2	-6	**30** Tu	04:32	-1.0	-30
	10:29	5.2	158		10:06	5.9	180
	16:52	-0.2	-6		16:48	-0.9	-27
	22:43	5.2	158		22:34	6.4	195
				31 W	05:20	-0.9	-27
					10:57	5.6	171
					17:32	-0.6	-18
					23:25	6.2	189

StationId: 8519483
Source: NOAA/NOS/CO-OPS
Station Type: Primary
Time Zone: LST_LDT
Datum: MLLW

NOAA Tide Predictions

Bergen Point West Reach, NY,2021

Times and Heights of High and Low Waters

April

Day	Time	ft	cm	Day	Time	ft	cm
1 Th	06:09	-0.6	-18	16 F	05:57	0.5	15
	11:54	5.3	162		11:47	4.4	134
	18:17	-0.3	-9		17:42	0.8	24
					23:27	5.1	155
2 F	00:23	6.0	183	17 Sa	06:31	0.8	24
	07:03	-0.2	-6		12:30	4.2	128
	12:56	5.0	152		18:13	1.0	30
	19:10	0.1	3				
3 Sa	01:25	5.7	174	18 Su	00:10	5.0	152
	08:07	0.2	6		07:11	1.0	30
	14:00	4.7	143		13:51	4.1	125
	20:15	0.6	18		18:54	1.2	37
4 Su	02:27	5.4	165	19 M	01:03	4.9	149
	09:19	0.4	12		08:12	1.2	37
	15:03	4.6	140		14:15	4.1	125
	21:34	0.8	24		19:51	1.4	43
5 M	03:31	5.2	158	20 Tu	02:02	4.9	149
	10:28	0.4	12		09:35	1.1	34
	16:08	4.5	137		15:12	4.2	128
	22:45	0.8	24		21:22	1.4	43
6 Tu	04:36	5.1	155	21 W	03:05	4.9	149
	11:28	0.3	9		10:42	0.9	27
	17:14	4.7	143		16:14	4.4	134
	23:46	0.6	18		22:44	1.1	34
7 W	05:41	5.1	155	22 Th	04:13	5.0	152
	12:20	0.2	6		11:36	0.5	15
	18:15	4.9	149		17:17	4.8	146
					23:47	0.7	21
8 Th	00:40	0.4	12	23 F	05:23	5.2	158
	06:39	5.2	158		12:26	0.2	6
	13:07	0.0	0		18:15	5.3	162
	19:07	5.2	158				
9 F	01:29	0.2	6	24 Sa	00:44	0.2	6
	07:28	5.3	162		06:27	5.5	168
	13:51	-0.1	-3		13:13	-0.2	-6
	19:51	5.4	165		19:07	5.9	180
10 Sa	02:15	0.1	3	25 Su	01:38	-0.2	-6
	08:10	5.4	165		07:22	5.8	177
	14:31	-0.1	-3		14:01	-0.5	-15
	20:29	5.6	171		19:54	6.3	192
11 Su	02:58	0.0	0	26 M	02:32	-0.6	-18
	08:49	5.4	165		08:12	5.9	180
	15:09	-0.1	-3		14:50	-0.6	-18
	21:04	5.7	174		20:40	6.7	204
12 M	03:39	0.0	0	27 Tu	03:25	-0.8	-24
	09:25	5.3	162		09:00	6.0	183
	15:44	0.0	0		15:38	-0.7	-21
	21:36	5.7	174		21:25	6.8	207
13 Tu	04:17	0.0	0	28 W	04:16	-0.9	-27
	10:00	5.1	155		09:50	5.8	177
	16:16	0.2	6		16:25	-0.6	-18
	22:04	5.6	171		22:14	6.8	207
14 W	04:52	0.1	3	29 Th	05:07	-0.9	-27
	10:35	4.9	149		10:43	5.6	171
	16:46	0.4	12		17:13	-0.4	-12
	22:29	5.4	165		23:07	6.5	198
15 Th	05:25	0.3	9	30 F	05:57	-0.6	-18
	11:10	4.6	140		11:44	5.3	162
	17:14	0.6	18		18:02	-0.1	-3
	22:55	5.3	162				

May

Day	Time	ft	cm	Day	Time	ft	cm
1 Sa	00:07	6.2	189	16 Su	06:17	0.6	18
	06:51	-0.3	-9		12:07	4.3	131
	12:49	5.1	155		17:57	1.0	30
	18:56	0.4	12		23:42	5.3	162
2 Su	01:11	5.8	177	17 M	06:56	0.8	24
	07:50	0.1	3		12:58	4.2	128
	13:52	4.9	149		18:38	1.2	37
	20:00	0.7	21				
3 M	02:13	5.5	168	18 Tu	00:36	5.2	158
	08:57	0.4	12		07:45	0.9	27
	14:53	4.8	146		13:51	4.3	131
	21:15	1.0	30		19:32	1.3	40
4 Tu	03:13	5.3	162	19 W	01:35	5.1	155
	10:02	0.5	15		08:51	0.9	27
	15:51	4.8	146		14:44	4.5	137
	22:25	1.0	30		20:51	1.3	40
5 W	04:12	5.1	155	20 Th	02:36	5.1	155
	10:59	0.4	12		09:58	0.7	21
	16:50	4.9	149		15:39	4.8	146
	23:25	0.8	24		22:14	1.1	34
6 Th	05:11	5.0	152	21 F	03:38	5.2	158
	11:49	0.3	9		10:55	0.4	12
	17:46	5.1	155		16:38	5.2	158
					23:21	0.7	21
7 F	00:17	0.7	21	22 Sa	04:44	5.2	158
	06:07	5.0	152		11:47	0.1	3
	12:33	0.3	9		17:37	5.7	174
	18:37	5.3	162				
8 Sa	01:04	0.5	15	23 Su	00:20	0.2	6
	06:57	5.1	155		05:52	5.4	165
	13:14	0.3	9		12:37	-0.1	-3
	19:21	5.6	171		18:34	6.2	189
9 Su	01:49	0.4	12	24 M	01:16	-0.2	-6
	07:41	5.1	155		06:54	5.5	168
	13:53	0.3	9		13:28	-0.3	-9
	19:59	5.7	174		19:27	6.6	201
10 M	02:32	0.3	9	25 Tu	02:12	-0.5	-15
	08:21	5.1	155		07:50	5.7	174
	14:31	0.3	9		14:21	-0.5	-15
	20:34	5.8	177		20:17	6.9	210
11 Tu	03:14	0.2	6	26 W	03:08	-0.7	-21
	08:59	5.0	152		08:42	5.7	174
	15:08	0.4	12		15:14	-0.5	-15
	21:05	5.8	177		21:06	7.0	213
12 W	03:53	0.2	6	27 Th	04:01	-0.8	-24
	09:35	4.9	149		09:35	5.6	171
	15:44	0.5	15		16:06	-0.4	-12
	21:32	5.7	174		21:57	6.8	207
13 Th	04:31	0.2	6	28 F	04:53	-0.8	-24
	10:10	4.7	143		10:31	5.5	168
	16:17	0.6	18		16:57	-0.2	-6
	21:56	5.6	171		22:52	6.5	198
14 F	05:07	0.3	9	29 Sa	05:43	-0.6	-18
	10:45	4.5	137		11:33	5.3	162
	16:50	0.8	24		17:48	0.1	3
	22:23	5.5	168		23:53	6.2	189
15 Sa	05:42	0.5	15	30 Su	06:35	-0.3	-9
	11:22	4.4	134		12:37	5.1	155
	17:22	0.9	27		18:41	0.4	12
	22:57	5.4	165				
				31 M	00:55	5.9	180
					07:29	0.0	0
					13:37	5.0	152
					19:41	0.8	24

June

Day	Time	ft	cm	Day	Time	ft	cm
1 Tu	01:53	5.5	168	16 W	00:17	5.4	165
	08:27	0.3	9		07:22	0.5	15
	14:33	5.0	152		13:28	4.7	143
	20:48	1.0	30		19:20	1.1	34
2 W	02:48	5.3	162	17 Th	01:15	5.3	162
	09:26	0.4	12		08:13	0.5	15
	15:26	5.0	152		14:18	4.9	149
	21:56	1.1	34		20:29	1.1	34
3 Th	03:40	5.0	152	18 F	02:13	5.2	158
	10:21	0.5	15		09:14	0.5	15
	16:17	5.1	155		15:10	5.2	158
	22:56	1.0	30		21:49	1.0	30
4 F	04:33	4.8	146	19 Sa	03:12	5.2	158
	11:09	0.5	15		10:16	0.3	9
	17:09	5.2	158		16:06	5.6	171
	23:47	0.9	27		22:58	0.7	21
5 Sa	05:27	4.7	143	20 Su	04:15	5.1	155
	11:53	0.5	15		11:12	0.1	3
	17:59	5.3	162		17:05	5.9	180
					23:59	0.3	9
6 Su	00:34	0.7	21	21 M	05:22	5.1	155
	06:20	4.7	143		12:07	0.0	0
	12:33	0.5	15		18:06	6.3	192
	18:45	5.5	168				
7 M	01:20	0.6	18	22 Tu	00:58	-0.1	-3
	07:09	4.7	143		06:30	5.2	158
	13:13	0.5	15		13:02	-0.2	-6
	19:26	5.7	174		19:04	6.6	201
8 Tu	02:04	0.4	12	23 W	01:55	-0.4	-12
	07:53	4.8	146		07:31	5.3	162
	13:53	0.6	18		13:58	-0.2	-6
	20:03	5.8	177		19:59	6.8	207
9 W	02:48	0.3	9	24 Th	02:52	-0.6	-18
	08:34	4.8	146		08:28	5.4	165
	14:34	0.6	18		14:55	-0.3	-9
	20:36	5.8	177		20:51	6.8	207
10 Th	03:30	0.3	9	25 F	03:46	-0.7	-21
	09:12	4.7	143		09:22	5.4	165
	15:15	0.6	18		15:49	-0.2	-6
	21:06	5.8	177		21:43	6.7	204
11 F	04:11	0.2	6	26 Sa	04:37	-0.7	-21
	09:49	4.6	140		10:18	5.4	165
	15:55	0.7	21		16:42	-0.1	-3
	21:34	5.7	174		22:37	6.4	195
12 Sa	04:50	0.2	6	27 Su	05:26	-0.6	-18
	10:26	4.5	137		11:16	5.3	162
	16:32	0.8	24		17:32	0.1	3
	22:03	5.6	171		23:34	6.1	186
13 Su	05:27	0.3	9	28 M	06:13	-0.4	-12
	11:04	4.4	134		12:16	5.2	158
	17:09	0.8	24		18:22	0.4	12
	22:40	5.5	168				
14 M	06:03	0.4	12	29 Tu	00:32	5.8	177
	11:48	4.4	134		07:00	-0.1	-3
	17:47	0.9	27		13:13	5.2	158
	23:24	5.4	165		19:15	0.7	21
15 Tu	06:40	0.5	15	30 W	01:26	5.5	168
	12:38	4.5	137		07:49	0.2	6
	18:29	1.0	30		14:04	5.1	155
					20:13	1.0	30

69

StationId: 8519483
Source: NOAA/NOS/CO-OPS
Station Type: Primary
Time Zone: LST_LDT
Datum: MLLW

NOAA Tide Predictions

Bergen Point West Reach, NY, 2021

Times and Heights of High and Low Waters

July

Day	Time (h m)	Height ft	Height cm	Day	Time (h m)	Height ft	Height cm
1 Th ◑	02:16	5.1	155	16 F	00:57	5.4	165
	08:40	0.5	15		07:42	0.3	9
	14:52	5.1	155		13:53	5.3	162
	21:17	1.2	37		20:13	0.9	27
2 F	03:04	4.9	149	17 Sa ◐	01:54	5.2	158
	09:33	0.7	21		08:38	0.3	9
	15:39	5.1	155		14:45	5.6	171
	22:18	1.2	37		21:28	0.8	24
3 Sa	03:53	4.6	140	18 Su	02:52	5.1	155
	10:22	0.8	24		09:42	0.3	9
	16:26	5.1	155		15:40	5.8	177
	23:13	1.1	34		22:40	0.7	21
4 Su	04:45	4.5	137	19 M	03:54	5.0	152
	11:08	0.8	24		10:46	0.3	9
	17:15	5.2	158		16:41	6.0	183
					23:43	0.4	12
5 M	00:02	1.0	30	20 Tu	05:03	4.9	149
	05:40	4.4	134		11:46	0.2	6
	11:51	0.8	24		17:46	6.1	186
	18:04	5.3	162				
6 Tu	00:49	0.8	24	21 W	00:43	0.1	3
	06:35	4.4	134		06:14	5.0	152
	12:34	0.8	24		12:44	0.1	3
	18:51	5.5	168		18:49	6.4	195
7 W	01:35	0.6	18	22 Th	01:40	-0.2	-6
	07:24	4.5	137		07:09	5.1	155
	13:19	0.7	21		13:43	0.0	0
	19:34	5.6	171		19:46	6.5	198
8 Th	02:21	0.4	12	23 F	02:36	-0.4	-12
	08:09	4.6	140		08:16	5.3	162
	14:04	0.7	21		14:40	-0.1	-3
	20:11	5.7	174		20:39	6.6	201
9 F	03:06	0.3	9	24 Sa ○	03:29	-0.6	-18
	08:50	4.7	143		09:09	5.4	165
	14:50	0.6	18		15:34	-0.1	-3
	20:45	5.8	177		21:29	6.5	198
10 Sa ●	03:49	0.2	6	25 Su	04:18	-0.6	-18
	09:28	4.7	143		10:00	5.4	165
	15:34	0.6	18		16:25	-0.1	-3
	21:17	5.8	177		22:19	6.3	192
11 Su	04:29	0.1	3	26 M	05:03	-0.5	-15
	10:05	4.7	143		10:53	5.4	165
	16:17	0.6	18		17:13	0.1	3
	21:49	5.8	177		23:09	6.0	183
12 M	05:07	0.1	3	27 Tu	05:46	-0.3	-9
	10:43	4.7	143		11:46	5.3	162
	16:57	0.6	18		17:58	0.4	12
	22:27	5.7	174				
13 Tu	05:43	0.1	3	28 W	00:01	5.7	174
	11:25	4.8	146		06:26	-0.1	-3
	17:37	0.6	18		12:38	5.3	162
	23:11	5.6	171		18:44	0.7	21
14 W	06:19	0.1	3	29 Th	00:52	5.3	162
	12:13	4.9	149		07:06	0.3	9
	18:20	0.7	21		13:26	5.2	158
					19:33	1.0	30
15 Th	00:01	5.5	168	30 F	01:40	5.0	152
	06:58	0.2	6		07:46	0.6	18
	13:03	5.1	155		14:11	5.1	155
	19:10	0.8	24		20:29	1.3	40
				31 Sa ◑	02:26	4.7	143
					08:32	0.9	27
					14:55	5.1	155
					21:33	1.4	43

August

Day	Time (h m)	Height ft	Height cm	Day	Time (h m)	Height ft	Height cm
1 Su	03:13	4.5	137	16 M	02:40	4.9	149
	09:23	1.1	34		09:19	0.5	15
	15:39	5.0	152		15:22	5.8	177
	22:33	1.3	40		22:26	0.7	21
2 M	04:04	4.3	131	17 Tu	03:44	4.8	146
	10:18	1.1	34		10:30	0.5	15
	16:26	5.0	152		16:25	5.8	177
	23:27	1.2	37		23:31	0.5	15
3 Tu	05:00	4.2	128	18 W	04:54	4.8	146
	11:10	1.1	34		11:35	0.4	12
	17:19	5.1	155		17:33	5.9	180
4 W	00:17	1.0	30	19 Th	00:29	0.2	6
	06:00	4.2	128		06:06	4.9	149
	12:00	1.0	30		12:34	0.3	9
	18:14	5.3	162		18:38	6.1	186
5 Th	01:05	0.8	24	20 F	01:25	0.0	0
	06:55	4.4	134		07:09	5.1	155
	12:48	0.9	27		13:31	0.1	3
	19:03	5.5	168		19:35	6.3	192
6 F	01:52	0.5	15	21 Sa	02:17	-0.3	-9
	07:43	4.6	140		08:04	5.4	165
	13:37	0.7	21		14:26	0.0	0
	19:46	5.7	174		20:25	6.3	192
7 Sa	02:37	0.3	9	22 Su ○	03:07	-0.4	-12
	08:25	4.8	146		08:53	5.6	171
	14:26	0.6	18		15:18	0.0	0
	20:24	5.8	177		21:12	6.3	192
8 Su ●	03:21	0.1	3	23 M	03:53	-0.4	-12
	09:03	5.0	152		09:39	5.6	171
	15:14	0.4	12		16:06	0.0	0
	20:59	5.9	180		21:56	6.1	186
9 M	04:02	-0.1	-3	24 Tu	04:35	-0.4	-12
	09:39	5.1	155		10:24	5.6	171
	15:59	0.3	9		16:50	0.1	3
	21:34	6.0	183		22:40	5.8	177
10 Tu	04:40	-0.2	-6	25 W	05:13	-0.2	-6
	10:17	5.2	158		11:09	5.5	168
	16:42	0.2	6		17:32	0.4	12
	22:12	5.9	180		23:26	5.5	168
11 W	05:18	-0.2	-6	26 Th	05:48	0.1	3
	10:58	5.4	165		11:54	5.4	165
	17:25	0.2	6		18:12	0.7	21
	22:56	5.8	177				
12 Th	05:54	-0.2	-6	27 F	00:12	5.1	155
	11:44	5.5	168		06:20	0.4	12
	18:09	0.3	9		12:38	5.2	158
	23:45	5.6	171		18:52	1.0	30
13 F	06:32	0.0	0	28 Sa	01:00	4.8	146
	12:36	5.6	171		06:52	0.8	24
	18:59	0.5	15		13:21	5.1	155
					19:38	1.3	40
14 Sa	00:41	5.4	165	29 Su	01:47	4.5	137
	07:16	0.1	3		07:26	1.1	34
	13:29	5.7	174		14:03	5.0	152
	19:59	0.7	21		20:38	1.5	46
15 Su ◐	01:39	5.1	155	30 M ◑	02:35	4.3	131
	08:10	0.4	12		08:11	1.3	40
	14:24	5.8	177		14:46	4.9	149
	21:13	0.8	24		21:48	1.5	46
				31 Tu	03:25	4.2	128
					09:18	1.4	43
					15:34	4.9	149
					22:50	1.4	43

September

Day	Time (h m)	Height ft	Height cm	Day	Time (h m)	Height ft	Height cm
1 W	04:22	4.1	125	16 Th	04:50	4.8	146
	10:28	1.4	43		11:27	0.6	18
	16:29	5.0	152		17:23	5.7	174
	23:44	1.2	37				
2 Th	05:23	4.2	128	17 F	00:14	0.2	6
	11:28	1.2	37		05:58	5.0	152
	17:31	5.1	155		12:25	0.4	12
					18:27	5.8	177
3 F	00:33	0.9	27	18 Sa	01:06	0.0	0
	06:22	4.4	134		06:58	5.3	162
	12:21	1.0	30		13:19	0.3	9
	18:28	5.4	165		19:21	6.0	183
4 Sa	01:19	0.6	18	19 Su	01:55	-0.1	-3
	07:12	4.7	143		07:48	5.5	168
	13:12	0.7	21		14:10	0.1	3
	19:16	5.7	174		20:08	6.1	186
5 Su	02:04	0.3	9	20 M ○	02:40	-0.2	-6
	07:55	5.1	155		08:33	5.7	174
	14:02	0.4	12		14:59	0.1	3
	19:57	5.9	180		20:50	6.0	183
6 M	02:48	0.0	0	21 Tu	03:23	-0.2	-6
	08:33	5.4	165		09:13	5.8	177
	14:51	0.2	6		15:44	0.1	3
	20:36	6.1	186		21:31	5.9	180
7 Tu ●	03:30	-0.2	-6	22 W	04:02	-0.1	-3
	09:10	5.7	174		09:52	5.8	177
	15:38	0.0	0		16:26	0.2	6
	21:14	6.1	186		22:10	5.6	171
8 W	04:10	-0.4	-12	23 Th	04:37	0.1	3
	09:49	5.9	180		10:29	5.7	174
	16:25	-0.1	-3		17:05	0.3	9
	21:54	6.1	186		22:50	5.3	162
9 Th	04:49	-0.4	-12	24 F	05:09	0.3	9
	10:30	6.0	183		11:05	5.5	168
	17:10	-0.1	-3		17:41	0.6	18
	22:39	5.9	180		23:32	4.9	149
10 F	05:28	-0.3	-9	25 Sa	05:38	0.6	18
	11:17	6.1	186		11:41	5.3	162
	17:57	0.0	0		18:17	0.9	27
	23:30	5.6	171				
11 Sa	06:09	-0.1	-3	26 Su	00:18	4.6	140
	12:10	6.0	183		06:05	0.9	27
	18:47	0.2	6		12:18	5.1	155
					18:55	1.1	34
12 Su	00:28	5.3	162	27 M	01:06	4.4	134
	06:54	0.2	6		06:35	1.1	34
	13:08	5.9	180		13:00	5.0	152
	19:48	0.5	15		19:43	1.4	43
13 M ◐	01:31	5.0	152	28 Tu	01:57	4.2	128
	07:51	0.5	15		07:15	1.4	43
	14:08	5.8	177		13:47	4.9	149
	21:00	0.7	21		20:55	1.5	46
14 Tu	02:35	4.8	146	29 W ◑	02:48	4.1	125
	09:05	0.7	21		08:15	1.6	49
	15:10	5.7	174		14:39	4.8	146
	22:14	0.7	21		22:09	1.4	43
15 W	03:41	4.7	143	30 Th	03:44	4.1	125
	10:21	0.8	24		09:44	1.6	49
	16:16	5.7	174		15:37	4.9	149
	23:18	0.5	15		23:07	1.2	37

StationId: 8519483
Source: NOAA/NOS/CO-OPS
Station Type: Primary
Time Zone: LST_LDT
Datum: MLLW

NOAA Tide Predictions

Bergen Point West Reach, NY,2021

Times and Heights of High and Low Waters

October

Day	Time (h m)	ft	cm
1 F	04:44	4.2	128
	10:56	1.3	40
	16:41	5.0	152
	23:57	0.9	27
2 Sa	05:43	4.5	137
	11:53	1.0	30
	17:45	5.3	162
3 Su	00:43	0.5	15
	06:35	4.9	149
	12:46	0.6	18
	18:40	5.6	171
4 M	01:27	0.1	3
	07:21	5.4	165
	13:37	0.2	6
	19:27	5.9	180
5 Tu	02:11	-0.2	-6
	08:02	5.9	180
	14:27	-0.1	-3
	20:10	6.0	183
6 W ●	02:55	-0.4	-12
	08:41	6.2	189
	15:17	-0.3	-9
	20:52	6.1	186
7 Th	03:38	-0.5	-15
	09:22	6.5	198
	16:06	-0.5	-15
	21:36	6.0	183
8 F	04:21	-0.5	-15
	10:05	6.5	198
	16:55	-0.5	-15
	22:23	5.8	177
9 Sa	05:05	-0.4	-12
	10:53	6.5	198
	17:44	-0.3	-9
	23:17	5.5	168
10 Su	05:49	-0.2	-6
	11:49	6.3	192
	18:36	0.0	0
11 M	00:20	5.2	158
	06:39	0.2	6
	12:52	6.0	183
	19:36	0.3	9
12 Tu	01:27	4.9	149
	07:39	0.6	18
	13:57	5.8	177
	20:46	0.5	15
13 W ◑	02:32	4.8	146
	08:55	0.8	24
	15:00	5.6	171
	21:57	0.5	15
14 Th	03:37	4.8	146
	10:11	0.9	27
	16:04	5.5	168
	23:00	0.4	12
15 F	04:41	4.8	146
	11:16	0.7	21
	17:08	5.5	168
	23:54	0.2	6
16 Sa	05:44	5.1	155
	12:12	0.5	15
	18:08	5.5	168
17 Su	00:42	0.0	0
	06:40	5.3	162
	13:03	0.3	9
	19:00	5.6	171
18 M	01:27	-0.1	-3
	07:27	5.6	171
	13:52	0.2	6
	19:46	5.6	171
19 Tu	02:09	-0.1	-3
	08:09	5.8	177
	14:37	0.1	3
	20:27	5.6	171
20 W ○	02:49	-0.1	-3
	08:46	5.9	180
	15:21	0.1	3
	21:05	5.5	168
21 Th	03:27	0.1	3
	09:20	5.9	180
	16:01	0.1	3
	21:42	5.3	162
22 F	04:01	0.2	6
	09:52	5.7	174
	16:39	0.3	9
	22:19	5.0	152
23 Sa	04:33	0.4	12
	10:21	5.5	168
	17:15	0.4	12
	22:57	4.7	143
24 Su	05:03	0.6	18
	10:48	5.3	162
	17:50	0.7	21
	23:38	4.4	134
25 M	05:31	0.9	27
	11:20	5.2	158
	18:25	0.9	27
26 Tu	00:26	4.2	128
	06:03	1.1	34
	12:01	5.0	152
	19:06	1.1	34
27 W	01:19	4.0	122
	06:41	1.3	40
	12:52	4.9	149
	20:03	1.3	40
28 Th ◐	02:12	4.0	122
	07:33	1.4	43
	13:50	4.8	146
	21:19	1.3	40
29 F	03:05	4.1	125
	08:56	1.5	46
	14:50	4.8	146
	22:24	1.0	30
30 Sa	04:00	4.3	131
	10:20	1.3	40
	15:53	4.9	149
	23:16	0.7	21
31 Su	04:58	4.6	140
	11:24	0.9	27
	16:57	5.1	155

November

Day	Time (h m)	ft	cm
1 M	00:03	0.3	9
	05:53	5.1	155
	12:19	0.5	15
	17:59	5.3	162
2 Tu	00:49	0.0	0
	06:44	5.6	171
	13:12	0.0	0
	18:54	5.6	171
3 W	01:34	-0.3	-9
	07:30	6.1	186
	14:05	-0.3	-9
	19:44	5.8	177
4 Th ●	02:21	-0.6	-18
	08:14	6.5	198
	14:58	-0.6	-18
	20:31	5.8	177
5 F	03:09	-0.7	-21
	08:58	6.7	204
	15:49	-0.8	-24
	21:19	5.8	177
6 Sa	03:57	-0.7	-21
	09:44	6.7	204
	16:40	-0.8	-24
	22:09	5.6	171
7 Su	03:45	-0.5	-15
	09:35	6.6	201
	16:31	-0.6	-18
	22:06	5.3	162
8 M	04:34	-0.3	-9
	10:34	6.3	192
	17:23	-0.4	-12
	23:12	5.0	152
9 Tu	05:26	0.1	3
	11:39	5.9	180
	18:21	-0.1	-3
10 W	00:19	4.8	146
	06:26	0.4	12
	12:44	5.7	174
	19:26	0.2	6
11 Th ◑	01:23	4.8	146
	07:39	0.7	21
	13:45	5.4	165
	20:33	0.3	9
12 F	02:23	4.8	146
	08:53	0.8	24
	14:45	5.2	158
	21:34	0.2	6
13 Sa	03:23	4.9	149
	09:58	0.7	21
	15:43	5.1	155
	22:26	0.1	3
14 Su	04:20	5.0	152
	10:53	0.5	15
	16:41	5.0	152
	23:13	0.0	0
15 M	05:14	5.2	158
	11:43	0.3	9
	17:33	5.0	152
	23:55	0.0	0
16 Tu	06:01	5.5	168
	12:29	0.2	6
	18:20	5.1	155
17 W	00:36	0.0	0
	06:42	5.6	171
	13:14	0.1	3
	19:02	5.1	155
18 Th	01:15	0.1	3
	07:19	5.7	174
	13:57	0.0	0
	19:41	5.0	152
19 F ○	01:53	0.1	3
	07:52	5.7	174
	14:38	0.0	0
	20:19	4.9	149
20 Sa	02:29	0.2	6
	08:23	5.6	171
	15:17	0.1	3
	20:55	4.7	143
21 Su	03:04	0.4	12
	08:50	5.5	168
	15:54	0.2	6
	21:31	4.4	134
22 M	03:37	0.5	15
	09:16	5.3	162
	16:29	0.3	9
	22:09	4.2	128
23 Tu	04:09	0.7	21
	09:46	5.1	155
	17:04	0.5	15
	22:51	4.0	122
24 W	04:42	0.8	24
	10:26	5.0	152
	17:41	0.7	21
	23:41	4.0	122
25 Th	05:20	1.0	30
	11:15	4.9	149
	18:25	0.8	24
26 F	00:33	4.0	122
	06:07	1.1	34
	12:13	4.8	146
	19:23	0.8	24
27 Sa ◐	01:24	4.1	125
	07:15	1.2	37
	13:12	4.8	146
	20:30	0.7	21
28 Su	02:17	4.4	134
	08:42	1.1	34
	14:12	4.8	146
	21:30	0.4	12
29 M	03:12	4.7	143
	09:53	0.7	21
	15:15	4.9	149
	22:22	0.1	3
30 Tu	04:10	5.2	158
	10:53	0.3	9
	16:20	5.0	152
	23:12	-0.2	-6

December

Day	Time (h m)	ft	cm
1 W	05:07	5.7	174
	11:49	-0.1	-3
	17:24	5.1	155
2 Th	00:01	-0.5	-15
	06:01	6.1	186
	12:45	-0.5	-15
	18:21	5.3	162
3 F	00:53	-0.7	-21
	06:51	6.5	198
	13:40	-0.8	-24
	19:14	5.4	165
4 Sa ●	01:45	-0.8	-24
	07:40	6.7	204
	14:34	-1.0	-30
	20:05	5.4	165
5 Su	02:38	-0.8	-24
	08:29	6.7	204
	15:26	-1.1	-34
	20:58	5.3	162
6 M	03:29	-0.7	-21
	09:22	6.5	198
	16:17	-1.0	-30
	21:56	5.1	155
7 Tu	04:20	-0.5	-15
	10:20	6.2	189
	17:08	-0.8	-24
	22:59	4.9	149
8 W	05:13	-0.2	-6
	11:23	5.8	177
	18:00	-0.5	-15
9 Th	00:04	4.8	146
	06:09	0.2	6
	12:25	5.5	168
	18:57	-0.2	-6
10 F	01:03	4.7	143
	07:14	0.5	15
	13:22	5.1	155
	19:58	0.0	0
11 Sa ◑	01:59	4.7	143
	08:25	0.7	21
	14:16	4.9	149
	20:57	0.1	3
12 Su	02:53	4.8	146
	09:31	0.7	21
	15:11	4.6	140
	21:51	0.2	6
13 M	03:47	4.8	146
	10:28	0.5	15
	16:06	4.5	137
	22:37	0.2	6
14 Tu	04:40	4.9	149
	11:18	0.4	12
	17:01	4.4	134
	23:20	0.1	3
15 W	05:30	5.1	155
	12:05	0.2	6
	17:52	4.5	137
16 Th	00:02	0.1	3
	06:14	5.2	158
	12:50	0.1	3
	18:38	4.5	137
17 F	00:42	0.1	3
	06:54	5.4	165
	13:33	0.0	0
	19:20	4.5	137
18 Sa	01:23	0.1	3
	07:29	5.4	165
	14:16	-0.1	-3
	19:59	4.5	137
19 Su ○	02:03	0.2	6
	08:01	5.4	165
	14:56	-0.1	-3
	20:36	4.4	134
20 M	02:42	0.2	6
	08:30	5.3	162
	15:34	-0.1	-3
	21:12	4.3	131
21 Tu	03:19	0.3	9
	08:57	5.2	158
	16:10	-0.1	-3
	21:47	4.2	128
22 W	03:54	0.3	9
	09:27	5.1	155
	16:45	0.0	0
	22:24	4.1	125
23 Th	04:29	0.4	12
	10:05	5.0	152
	17:18	0.1	3
	23:07	4.1	125
24 F	05:06	0.5	15
	10:50	4.9	149
	17:54	0.2	6
	23:55	4.1	125
25 Sa	05:49	0.7	21
	11:43	4.8	146
	18:37	0.3	9
26 Su	00:45	4.3	131
	06:46	0.8	24
	12:40	4.7	143
	19:33	0.3	9
27 M ◐	01:37	4.6	140
	08:05	0.8	24
	13:38	4.7	143
	20:40	0.2	6
28 Tu	02:32	4.9	149
	09:24	0.5	15
	14:40	4.6	140
	21:42	0.0	0
29 W	03:32	5.2	158
	10:30	0.2	6
	15:48	4.6	140
	22:40	-0.2	-6
30 Th	04:35	5.5	168
	11:30	-0.2	-6
	16:58	4.7	143
	23:36	-0.5	-15
31 F	05:37	5.9	180
	12:28	-0.6	-18
	18:03	4.9	149

Station Id: 8518995
Source: NOAA/NOS/CO-OPS
Station Type: Primary
Time Zone: LST_LDT
Datum: MLLW

ALBANY, HUDSON RIVER, NY, 2021

Times and Heights of High and Low Waters

January

Day	Time (h m)	Height ft	Height cm	Day	Time (h m)	Height ft	Height cm
1 F	00:41	0.0	0	**16** Sa	01:18	-0.1	-3
	05:43	4.4	134		06:38	4.6	140
	12:17	0.1	3		13:21	0.2	6
	17:12	5.5	168		18:50	5.1	155
2 Sa	01:23	0.0	0	**17** Su	02:03	0.0	0
	06:23	4.5	137		07:30	4.6	140
	13:03	0.1	3		14:09	0.4	12
	17:58	5.5	168		19:42	5.0	152
3 Su	02:07	0.0	0	**18** M	02:46	0.1	3
	07:08	4.6	140		08:21	4.6	140
	13:53	0.2	6		14:58	0.6	18
	18:50	5.4	165		20:34	4.8	146
4 M	02:52	0.0	0	**19** Tu	03:28	0.3	9
	07:58	4.7	143		09:12	4.6	140
	14:49	0.3	9		15:50	0.7	21
	19:48	5.3	162		21:26	4.7	143
5 Tu	03:40	0.0	0	**20** W	04:10	0.4	12
	08:52	4.9	149		10:01	4.7	143
	15:51	0.3	9		16:45	0.8	24
	20:54	5.1	155		22:19	4.5	137
6 W	04:32	0.0	0	**21** Th	04:53	0.5	15
	09:50	5.0	152		10:51	4.7	143
	16:58	0.4	12		17:42	0.8	24
	22:05	4.9	149		23:14	4.4	134
7 Th	05:26	0.1	3	**22** F	05:38	0.6	18
	10:49	5.1	155		11:41	4.8	146
	18:05	0.4	12		18:39	0.7	21
	23:16	4.8	146				
8 F	06:23	0.0	0	**23** Sa	00:09	4.3	131
	11:50	5.2	158		06:26	0.6	18
	19:10	0.2	6		12:30	4.9	149
					19:35	0.6	18
9 Sa	00:21	4.7	143	**24** Su	01:02	4.3	131
	07:21	0.0	0		07:17	0.6	18
	12:48	5.4	165		13:17	5.0	152
	20:12	0.1	3		20:28	0.4	12
10 Su	01:22	4.7	143	**25** M	01:52	4.3	131
	08:18	0.0	0		08:07	0.5	15
	13:44	5.5	168		14:01	5.2	158
	21:11	-0.1	-3		21:18	0.2	6
11 M	02:18	4.7	143	**26** Tu	02:38	4.4	134
	09:13	-0.1	-3		08:57	0.4	12
	14:37	5.6	171		14:40	5.3	162
	22:05	-0.3	-9		22:05	0.1	3
12 Tu	03:11	4.7	143	**27** W	03:21	4.4	134
	10:06	-0.2	-6		09:45	0.3	9
	15:27	5.6	171		15:16	5.4	165
	22:57	-0.3	-9		22:49	0.0	0
13 W ●	04:02	4.7	143	**28** Th ○	04:01	4.5	137
	10:57	-0.1	-3		10:33	0.2	6
	16:17	5.5	168		15:49	5.5	168
	23:46	-0.3	-9		23:33	-0.1	-3
14 Th	04:53	4.7	143	**29** F	04:39	4.6	140
	11:46	-0.1	-3		11:19	0.1	3
	17:07	5.4	165		16:24	5.5	168
15 F	00:33	-0.2	-6	**30** Sa	00:15	-0.1	-3
	05:45	4.6	140		05:17	4.7	143
	12:34	0.1	3		12:06	0.0	0
	17:58	5.2	158		17:04	5.6	171
				31 Su	00:57	-0.1	-3
					05:57	4.9	149
					12:54	0.0	0
					17:51	5.5	168

February

Day	Time (h m)	Height ft	Height cm	Day	Time (h m)	Height ft	Height cm
1 M	01:40	-0.1	-3	**16** Tu	02:01	0.4	12
	06:42	5.0	152		07:40	5.0	152
	13:45	0.1	3		14:26	0.7	21
	18:44	5.4	165		19:58	4.9	149
2 Tu	02:24	-0.1	-3	**17** W	02:36	0.6	18
	07:31	5.2	158		08:24	5.0	152
	14:40	0.2	6		15:15	0.9	27
	19:43	5.3	162		20:48	4.7	143
3 W	03:11	0.0	0	**18** Th	03:09	0.7	21
	08:25	5.3	162		09:08	5.0	152
	15:41	0.3	9		15:41	1.0	30
	20:48	5.1	155		21:41	4.6	140
4 Th	04:03	0.1	3	**19** F ◐	03:45	0.9	27
	09:23	5.3	162		09:53	5.0	152
	16:45	0.4	12		17:04	1.0	30
	21:56	4.9	149		22:36	4.4	134
5 F	04:59	0.2	6	**20** Sa	04:31	1.0	30
	10:24	5.3	162		10:43	5.0	152
	17:50	0.4	12		18:02	1.0	30
	23:03	4.7	143		23:33	4.3	131
6 Sa	05:59	0.3	9	**21** Su	05:28	1.1	34
	11:28	5.3	162		11:37	5.0	152
	18:54	0.3	9		19:00	0.9	27
7 Su	00:08	4.7	143	**22** M	00:29	4.3	131
	07:00	0.2	6		06:31	1.1	34
	12:31	5.4	165		12:31	5.1	155
	19:55	0.2	6		19:55	0.8	24
8 M	01:09	4.8	146	**23** Tu	01:21	4.5	137
	07:59	0.2	6		07:33	0.9	27
	13:30	5.5	168		13:22	5.2	158
	20:53	0.0	0		20:47	0.6	18
9 Tu	02:05	4.9	149	**24** W	02:09	4.6	140
	08:56	0.1	3		08:30	0.8	24
	14:25	5.5	168		14:08	5.4	165
	21:46	-0.1	-3		21:35	0.4	12
10 W	02:57	5.0	152	**25** Th	02:52	4.8	146
	09:49	0.0	0		09:24	0.5	15
	15:15	5.6	171		14:50	5.6	171
	22:35	-0.2	-6		22:20	0.3	9
11 Th	03:47	5.1	155	**26** F	03:32	5.1	155
	10:39	-0.1	-3		10:14	0.3	9
	16:03	5.6	171		15:30	5.7	174
	● 23:22	-0.2	-6		23:04	0.2	6
12 F	04:35	5.1	155	**27** Sa ○	04:10	5.3	162
	11:26	0.0	0		11:04	0.2	6
	16:49	5.5	168		16:10	5.8	177
					23:46	0.1	3
13 Sa	00:05	-0.1	-3	**28** Su	04:48	5.4	165
	05:22	5.1	155		11:52	0.1	3
	12:12	0.2	6		16:53	5.8	177
	17:35	5.4	165				
14 Su	00:46	0.1	3				
	06:08	5.0	152				
	12:56	0.3	9				
	18:22	5.2	158				
15 M	01:25	0.2	6				
	06:54	5.0	152				
	13:41	0.5	15				
	19:09	5.1	155				

March

Day	Time (h m)	Height ft	Height cm	Day	Time (h m)	Height ft	Height cm
1 M	00:28	0.1	3	**16** Tu	01:44	0.7	21
	05:29	5.6	171		07:15	5.6	171
	12:42	0.1	3		14:14	0.8	24
	17:41	5.7	174		19:38	5.3	162
2 Tu	01:11	0.2	6	**17** W	02:14	0.9	27
	06:13	5.7	174		07:51	5.6	171
	13:34	0.2	6		14:57	1.0	30
	18:36	5.6	171		20:23	5.1	155
3 W	01:56	0.3	9	**18** Th	02:40	1.1	34
	07:03	5.8	177		08:22	5.6	171
	14:29	0.3	9		15:42	1.1	34
	19:36	5.4	165		21:11	4.9	149
4 Th	02:45	0.4	12	**19** F	03:06	1.2	37
	07:58	5.8	177		08:40	5.6	171
	15:28	0.5	15		16:31	1.3	40
	20:41	5.2	158		22:03	4.8	146
5 F	03:38	0.5	15	**20** Sa	03:41	1.3	40
	08:59	5.7	174		09:08	5.6	171
	16:31	0.6	18		17:26	1.4	43
	21:46	5.1	155		22:58	4.7	143
6 Sa ◐	04:37	0.7	21	**21** Su ◐	04:29	1.4	43
	10:04	5.6	171		09:54	5.5	168
	17:34	0.6	18		18:24	1.4	43
	22:51	5.0	152		23:55	4.6	140
7 Su	05:39	0.7	21	**22** M	05:34	1.5	46
	11:11	5.6	171		10:54	5.4	165
	18:36	0.6	18		19:23	1.3	40
	23:55	5.0	152				
8 M	06:42	0.7	21	**23** Tu	00:52	4.7	143
	12:16	5.6	171		06:51	1.5	46
	19:36	0.5	15		12:27	5.4	165
					20:19	1.2	37
9 Tu	00:55	5.2	158	**24** W	01:46	4.9	149
	07:42	0.5	15		08:02	1.4	43
	13:17	5.6	171		13:39	5.5	168
	20:32	0.3	9		21:12	1.0	30
10 W	01:51	5.4	165	**25** Th	02:36	5.2	158
	08:38	0.4	12		09:05	1.2	37
	14:11	5.8	177		14:34	5.6	171
	21:23	0.2	6		22:01	0.8	24
11 Th	02:42	5.6	171	**26** F	03:20	5.5	168
	09:31	0.3	9		10:02	0.9	27
	15:00	5.8	177		15:23	5.8	177
	22:10	0.1	3		22:47	0.7	21
12 F	03:29	5.7	174	**27** Sa	04:01	5.8	177
	10:20	0.3	9		10:55	0.6	18
	15:45	5.8	177		16:08	6.0	183
	22:53	0.2	6		23:32	0.5	15
13 Sa ●	04:13	5.7	174	**28** Su ○	04:40	6.0	183
	11:06	0.3	9		11:47	0.5	15
	16:29	5.8	177		16:52	6.0	183
	23:33	0.3	9				
14 Su	05:55	5.7	174	**29** M	00:15	0.5	15
	12:49	0.5	15		05:19	6.3	192
	18:11	5.7	174		12:37	0.4	12
					17:38	6.0	183
15 M	01:10	0.5	15	**30** Tu	00:59	0.5	15
	06:36	5.7	174		06:00	6.4	195
	13:32	0.6	18		13:29	0.4	12
	18:54	5.5	168		18:28	5.9	180
				31 W	01:43	0.6	18
					06:46	6.4	195
					14:21	0.4	12
					19:25	5.7	174

StationId: 8518995
Source: NOAA/NOS/CO-OPS
Station Type: Primary
Time Zone: LST_LDT
Datum: MLLW

NOAA Tide Predictions

ALBANY, HUDSON RIVER, NY,2021

Times and Heights of High and Low Waters

April

Day	Time (h m)	ft	cm	Day	Time (h m)	ft	cm
1 Th	02:30	0.7	21	16 F	01:54	1.4	43
	07:37	6.4	195		07:10	6.2	189
	15:16	0.6	18		15:14	1.2	37
	20:26	5.5	168		20:39	5.1	155
2 F	03:21	0.9	27	17 Sa	02:24	1.5	46
	08:35	6.3	192		07:39	6.2	189
	16:14	0.7	21		16:01	1.4	43
	21:31	5.4	165		21:28	5.0	152
3 Sa	04:17	1.0	30	18 Su	03:04	1.6	49
	09:40	6.1	186		08:21	6.1	186
	17:15	0.8	24		16:52	1.5	46
	22:35	5.3	162		22:20	4.9	149
4 Su	05:18	1.1	34	19 M	03:55	1.7	52
	10:47	5.9	180		09:10	6.0	183
	18:15	0.9	27		17:47	1.5	46
	23:38	5.4	165		23:16	5.0	152
5 M	06:21	1.2	37	20 Tu	05:00	1.8	55
	11:55	5.8	177		10:07	5.8	177
	19:15	0.8	24		18:44	1.5	46
6 Tu	00:40	5.5	168	21 W	00:13	5.1	155
	07:23	1.1	34		06:20	1.8	55
	13:00	5.8	177		11:18	5.7	174
	20:12	0.7	21		19:40	1.4	43
7 W	01:39	5.7	174	22 Th	01:08	5.3	162
	08:23	0.9	27		07:35	1.6	49
	13:59	5.8	177		12:51	5.6	171
	21:05	0.6	18		20:33	1.2	37
8 Th	02:33	5.9	180	23 F	01:59	5.6	171
	09:19	0.8	24		08:41	1.4	43
	14:52	5.9	180		13:59	5.7	174
	21:54	0.5	15		21:24	1.0	30
9 F	03:22	6.1	186	24 Sa	02:46	6.0	183
	10:11	0.6	18		09:41	1.1	34
	15:40	6.0	183		14:54	5.9	180
	22:39	0.5	15		22:12	0.9	27
10 Sa	04:07	6.3	192	25 Su	03:29	6.3	192
	10:59	0.6	18		10:37	0.8	24
	16:23	6.0	183		15:44	6.0	183
	23:20	0.6	18		22:59	0.8	24
11 Su	04:49	6.3	192	26 M	04:10	6.6	201
	11:44	0.6	18		11:30	0.6	18
	17:05	5.9	180		16:32	6.0	183
	23:58	0.7	21		23:45	0.7	21
12 M	05:27	6.3	192	27 Tu	04:52	6.8	207
	12:27	0.7	21		12:22	0.5	15
	17:46	5.8	177		17:21	5.9	180
13 Tu	00:32	0.9	27	28 W	00:31	0.8	24
	06:03	6.3	192		05:35	6.8	207
	13:09	0.8	24		13:14	0.4	12
	18:27	5.6	171		18:14	5.8	177
14 W	01:03	1.1	34	29 Th	01:18	0.9	27
	06:42	6.2	189		06:22	6.7	204
	13:50	1.0	30		14:07	0.5	15
	19:09	5.4	165		19:12	5.6	171
15 Th	01:30	1.3	40	30 F	02:08	1.0	30
	06:57	6.1	186		07:15	6.6	201
	14:31	1.1	34		15:02	0.6	18
	19:53	5.2	158		20:14	5.5	168

May

Day	Time (h m)	ft	cm	Day	Time (h m)	ft	cm
1 Sa	03:01	1.1	34	16 Su	02:01	1.4	43
	08:17	6.3	192		07:08	6.3	192
	15:58	0.7	21		15:34	1.1	34
	21:17	5.4	165		20:55	4.9	149
2 Su	03:58	1.2	37	17 M	02:44	1.5	46
	09:23	6.1	186		07:53	6.2	189
	16:55	0.8	24		16:21	1.1	34
	22:20	5.4	165		21:44	5.0	152
3 M	04:59	1.3	40	18 Tu	03:37	1.5	46
	10:30	5.9	180		08:44	6.1	186
	17:52	0.8	24		17:12	1.2	37
	23:21	5.5	168		22:36	5.1	155
4 Tu	06:01	1.3	40	19 W	04:41	1.6	49
	11:35	5.8	177		09:41	5.9	180
	18:49	0.8	24		18:05	1.1	34
					23:32	5.2	158
5 W	00:21	5.7	174	20 Th	05:57	1.6	49
	07:02	1.2	37		10:47	5.7	174
	12:37	5.7	174		18:59	1.1	34
	19:43	0.8	24				
6 Th	01:17	5.9	180	21 F	00:27	5.4	165
	08:00	1.1	34		07:11	1.5	46
	13:34	5.8	177		12:10	5.5	168
	20:33	0.7	21		19:53	1.0	30
7 F	02:10	6.1	186	22 Sa	01:21	5.7	174
	08:56	0.9	27		08:18	1.3	40
	14:27	5.8	177		13:26	5.5	168
	21:21	0.6	18		20:46	0.8	24
8 Sa	02:58	6.3	192	23 Su	02:11	6.1	186
	09:48	0.8	24		09:20	1.0	30
	15:14	5.8	177		14:28	5.5	168
	22:04	0.6	18		21:37	0.7	21
9 Su	03:42	6.5	198	24 M	02:59	6.4	195
	10:36	0.7	21		10:19	0.7	21
	15:59	5.8	177		15:22	5.5	168
	22:44	0.7	21		22:28	0.6	18
10 M	04:22	6.5	198	25 Tu	03:44	6.6	201
	11:21	0.6	18		11:14	0.4	12
	16:41	5.7	174		16:14	5.5	168
	23:21	0.9	27		23:17	0.6	18
11 Tu	04:58	6.5	198	26 W	04:28	6.7	204
	12:05	0.7	21		12:07	0.3	9
	17:22	5.5	168		17:06	5.5	168
	23:55	1.0	30				
12 W	05:31	6.4	195	27 Th	00:07	0.6	18
	12:47	0.7	21		05:15	6.7	204
	18:03	5.4	165		12:59	0.2	6
					18:00	5.3	162
13 Th	00:26	1.2	37	28 F	00:57	0.7	21
	05:57	6.3	192		06:04	6.5	198
	13:28	0.8	24		13:51	0.2	6
	18:45	5.2	158		18:57	5.2	158
14 F	00:55	1.3	40	29 Sa	01:48	0.8	24
	06:11	6.3	192		07:00	6.3	192
	14:09	0.9	27		14:44	0.3	9
	19:27	5.0	152		19:58	5.2	158
15 Sa	01:25	1.4	43	30 Su	02:42	0.9	27
	06:32	6.3	192		08:01	6.0	183
	14:51	1.0	30		15:37	0.4	12
	20:10	5.0	152		21:00	5.2	158
				31 M	03:38	1.0	30
					09:05	5.8	177
					16:30	0.5	15
					22:00	5.2	158

June

Day	Time (h m)	ft	cm	Day	Time (h m)	ft	cm
1 Tu	04:36	1.1	34	16 W	03:28	1.0	30
	10:08	5.6	171		08:25	5.8	177
	17:24	0.5	15		16:38	0.5	15
	22:58	5.3	162		21:57	5.0	152
2 W	05:36	1.1	34	17 Th	04:29	1.1	34
	11:09	5.5	168		09:21	5.5	168
	18:16	0.5	15		17:27	0.5	15
	23:55	5.5	168		22:50	5.2	158
3 Th	06:35	1.1	34	18 F	05:39	1.1	34
	12:07	5.4	165		10:26	5.3	162
	19:07	0.5	15		18:20	0.5	15
					23:47	5.3	162
4 F	00:49	5.6	171	19 Sa	06:51	1.0	30
	07:33	1.0	30		11:44	5.1	155
	13:03	5.3	162		19:15	0.5	15
	19:55	0.5	15				
5 Sa	01:41	5.8	177	20 Su	00:44	5.6	171
	08:29	0.8	24		07:58	0.8	24
	13:56	5.2	158		13:00	4.9	149
	20:42	0.5	15		20:11	0.4	12
6 Su	02:29	6.0	183	21 M	01:39	5.8	177
	09:22	0.7	21		09:02	0.6	18
	14:46	5.2	158		14:06	4.9	149
	21:25	0.6	18		21:06	0.4	12
7 M	03:13	6.1	186	22 Tu	02:32	6.0	183
	10:11	0.5	15		10:02	0.3	9
	15:33	5.2	158		15:04	4.9	149
	22:06	0.6	18		22:01	0.3	9
8 Tu	03:53	6.2	189	23 W	03:22	6.1	186
	10:58	0.4	12		10:58	0.0	0
	16:17	5.1	155		15:59	4.9	149
	22:45	0.7	21		22:55	0.2	6
9 W	04:29	6.2	189	24 Th	04:11	6.2	189
	11:42	0.3	9		11:51	-0.2	-6
	17:00	5.0	152		16:52	4.9	149
	23:22	0.8	24		23:47	0.2	6
10 Th	05:01	6.1	186	25 F	05:01	6.1	186
	12:24	0.3	9		12:43	-0.2	-6
	17:41	4.8	146		17:46	4.8	146
	23:57	0.9	27				
11 F	05:27	6.0	183	26 Sa	00:39	0.3	9
	13:06	0.3	9		05:52	6.0	183
	18:22	4.7	143		13:33	-0.2	-6
					18:41	4.8	146
12 Sa	00:33	0.9	27	27 Su	01:31	0.3	9
	05:43	6.0	183		06:46	5.7	174
	13:47	0.4	12		14:22	-0.2	-6
	19:02	4.7	143		19:39	4.8	146
13 Su	01:10	0.9	27	28 M	02:23	0.4	12
	06:09	6.0	183		07:44	5.5	168
	14:28	0.4	12		15:11	-0.1	-3
	19:43	4.7	143		20:36	4.8	146
14 M	01:50	0.9	27	29 Tu	03:16	0.6	18
	06:47	6.0	183		08:43	5.3	162
	15:09	0.5	15		16:00	0.0	0
	20:25	4.7	143		21:33	4.8	146
15 Tu	02:36	1.0	30	30 W	04:11	0.7	21
	07:33	5.9	180		09:41	5.1	155
	15:52	0.5	15		16:48	0.1	3
	21:09	4.8	146		22:28	4.9	149

StationId: 8518995
Source: NOAA/NOS/CO-OPS
Station Type: Primary
Time Zone: LST_LDT
Datum: MLLW

NOAA Tide Predictions

ALBANY, HUDSON RIVER, NY,2021

Times and Heights of High and Low Waters

July

Day	Time	ft	cm	Day	Time	ft	cm
1 Th ◐	05:07	0.8	24	16 F	04:19	0.5	15
	10:37	4.9	149		09:07	5.1	155
	17:36	0.2	6		16:52	-0.1	-3
	23:21	5.0	152		22:14	5.1	155
2 F	06:04	0.8	24	17 Sa ◖	05:25	0.5	15
	11:33	4.7	143		10:12	4.8	146
	18:24	0.2	6		17:44	0.0	0
					23:11	5.2	158
3 Sa	00:14	5.1	155	18 Su	06:34	0.5	15
	07:02	0.7	21		11:28	4.5	137
	12:29	4.6	140		18:41	0.0	0
	19:11	0.3	9				
4 Su	01:05	5.2	158	19 M	00:12	5.3	162
	07:59	0.6	18		07:41	0.4	12
	13:23	4.5	137		12:42	4.3	131
	19:57	0.4	12		19:42	0.1	3
5 M	01:54	5.4	165	20 Tu	01:13	5.4	165
	08:53	0.4	12		08:45	0.2	6
	14:16	4.4	134		13:49	4.3	131
	20:43	0.4	12		20:43	0.0	0
6 Tu	02:40	5.5	168	21 W	02:12	5.5	168
	09:44	0.2	6		09:45	-0.1	-3
	15:06	4.4	134		14:50	4.3	131
	21:28	0.4	12		21:42	-0.1	-3
7 W	03:22	5.5	168	22 Th	03:07	5.6	171
	10:32	0.0	0		10:41	-0.4	-12
	15:53	4.4	134		15:45	4.4	134
	22:11	0.4	12		22:38	-0.1	-3
8 Th	04:00	5.6	171	23 F	03:59	5.6	171
	11:17	-0.1	-3		11:34	-0.5	-15
	16:36	4.4	134		16:38	4.5	137
	22:53	0.4	12		23:31	-0.2	-6
9 F	04:34	5.6	171	24 Sa ○	04:50	5.6	171
	12:00	-0.2	-6		12:23	-0.6	-18
	17:18	4.3	131		17:30	4.5	137
	23:35	0.4	12				
10 Sa ●	05:03	5.6	171	25 Su	00:22	-0.2	-6
	12:42	-0.2	-6		05:40	5.5	168
	17:58	4.3	131		13:11	-0.6	-18
					18:22	4.5	137
11 Su	00:16	0.4	12	26 M	01:12	-0.1	-3
	05:27	5.6	171		06:31	5.3	162
	13:23	-0.2	-6		13:57	-0.6	-18
	18:37	4.3	131		19:15	4.5	137
12 M	00:58	0.3	9	27 Tu	02:02	0.0	0
	05:55	5.6	171		07:23	5.1	155
	14:03	-0.2	-6		14:41	-0.5	-15
	19:15	4.4	134		20:08	4.6	140
13 Tu	01:42	0.3	9	28 W	02:51	0.2	6
	06:34	5.5	168		08:16	4.9	149
	14:42	-0.2	-6		15:25	-0.3	-9
	19:53	4.6	140		21:00	4.6	140
14 W	02:29	0.3	9	29 Th	03:42	0.3	9
	07:20	5.5	168		09:07	4.7	143
	15:23	-0.2	-6		16:07	-0.2	-6
	20:35	4.7	143		21:51	4.6	140
15 Th	03:21	0.4	12	30 F	04:35	0.5	15
	08:11	5.3	162		10:02	4.5	137
	16:06	-0.2	-6		16:50	0.0	0
	21:22	4.9	149		22:41	4.7	143
				31 Sa ◐	05:30	0.6	18
					10:57	4.2	128
					17:33	0.2	6
					23:32	4.7	143

August

Day	Time	ft	cm	Day	Time	ft	cm
1 Su	06:27	0.6	18	16 M	06:19	0.2	6
	11:53	4.0	122		11:19	4.2	128
	18:18	0.3	9		18:18	-0.1	-3
					23:48	5.1	155
2 M	00:23	4.7	143	17 Tu	07:24	0.1	3
	07:25	0.5	15		12:30	4.1	125
	12:49	3.9	119		19:22	0.0	0
	19:07	0.4	12				
3 Tu	01:14	4.8	146	18 W	00:54	5.1	155
	08:21	0.3	9		08:28	0.0	0
	13:45	3.9	119		13:36	4.1	125
	19:58	0.4	12		20:25	-0.1	-3
4 W	02:03	4.9	149	19 Th	01:58	5.2	158
	09:14	0.1	3		09:27	-0.3	-9
	14:38	3.9	119		14:37	4.2	128
	20:49	0.4	12		21:26	-0.2	-6
5 Th	02:49	5.0	152	20 F	02:56	5.3	162
	10:04	-0.1	-3		10:22	-0.5	-15
	15:26	4.0	122		15:32	4.4	134
	21:39	0.3	9		22:22	-0.3	-9
6 F	03:31	5.1	155	21 Sa	03:49	5.3	162
	10:50	-0.3	-9		11:13	-0.7	-21
	16:11	4.1	125		16:24	4.6	140
	22:28	0.2	6		23:15	-0.4	-12
7 Sa	04:08	5.2	158	22 Su ○	04:38	5.3	162
	11:33	-0.4	-12		11:33	-0.8	-24
	16:52	4.2	128		12:00		
	23:15	0.1	3		17:13	4.7	143
8 Su ●	04:42	5.2	158	23 M	00:05	-0.4	-12
	12:15	-0.5	-15		05:25	5.3	162
	17:31	4.3	131		12:44	-0.7	-21
					18:00	4.7	143
9 M	00:00	0.0	0	24 Tu	00:53	-0.3	-9
	05:12	5.3	162		06:12	5.1	155
	12:55	-0.6	-18		13:26	-0.6	-18
	18:07	4.4	134		18:48	4.7	143
10 Tu	00:46	-0.1	-3	25 W	01:39	-0.1	-3
	05:45	5.3	162		06:59	5.0	152
	13:35	-0.6	-18		14:06	-0.5	-15
	18:43	4.6	140		19:35	4.7	143
11 W	01:32	-0.1	-3	26 Th	02:26	0.1	3
	06:23	5.3	162		07:47	4.7	143
	14:14	-0.6	-18		14:44	-0.3	-9
	19:21	4.7	143		20:22	4.7	143
12 Th	02:20	-0.1	-3	27 F	03:13	0.3	9
	07:09	5.2	158		08:36	4.5	137
	14:53	-0.5	-15		15:20	-0.1	-3
	20:03	4.9	149		21:08	4.7	143
13 F	03:12	0.0	0	28 Sa	04:02	0.4	12
	08:00	5.0	152		09:27	4.3	131
	15:36	-0.5	-15		15:55	0.1	3
	20:50	5.1	155		21:54	4.6	140
14 Sa	04:09	0.1	3	29 Su	04:55	0.6	18
	08:59	4.7	143		10:20	4.0	122
	16:23	-0.4	-12		16:30	0.3	9
	21:43	5.1	155		22:41	4.6	140
15 Su ◖	05:12	0.2	6	30 M ◖	05:50	0.6	18
	10:06	4.5	137		11:17	3.8	116
	17:17	-0.2	-6		17:12	0.5	15
	22:43	5.1	155		23:31	4.6	140
				31 Tu	06:48	0.6	18
					12:14	3.7	113
					18:07	0.6	18

September

Day	Time	ft	cm	Day	Time	ft	cm
1 W	00:25	4.6	140	16 Th	00:41	5.1	155
	07:45	0.5	15		08:08	0.0	0
	13:12	3.7	113		13:24	4.4	134
	19:09	0.6	18		20:10	0.0	0
2 Th	01:20	4.7	143	17 F	01:45	5.2	158
	08:40	0.3	9		09:06	-0.2	-6
	14:06	3.8	116		14:23	4.6	140
	20:12	0.6	18		21:10	-0.1	-3
3 F	02:12	4.8	146	18 Sa	02:43	5.3	162
	09:31	0.0	0		09:59	-0.4	-12
	14:56	4.0	122		15:17	4.8	146
	21:10	0.4	12		22:05	-0.3	-9
4 Sa	02:59	4.9	149	19 Su	03:35	5.4	165
	10:18	-0.2	-6		10:47	-0.6	-18
	15:41	4.2	128		16:06	5.0	152
	22:03	0.2	6		22:57	-0.3	-9
5 Su	03:40	5.1	155	20 M ○	04:22	5.4	165
	11:02	-0.3	-9		11:32	-0.6	-18
	16:22	4.4	134		16:52	5.1	155
	22:54	0.0	0		23:46	-0.3	-9
6 M	04:18	5.2	158	21 Tu	05:06	5.3	162
	11:44	-0.5	-15		12:14	-0.5	-15
	16:59	4.6	140		17:36	5.1	155
	23:42	-0.1	-3				
7 Tu ●	04:53	5.3	162	22 W	00:32	-0.2	-6
	12:25	-0.5	-15		05:50	5.2	158
	17:35	4.8	146		12:53	-0.4	-12
					18:19	5.1	155
8 W	00:30	-0.2	-6	23 Th	01:17	0.0	0
	05:30	5.3	162		06:33	5.0	152
	13:05	-0.6	-18		13:29	-0.2	-6
	18:11	5.0	152		19:00	5.1	155
9 Th	01:19	-0.2	-6	24 F	02:01	0.2	6
	06:11	5.2	158		07:18	4.7	143
	13:45	-0.5	-15		14:02	0.1	3
	18:49	5.2	158		19:40	5.0	152
10 F	02:08	-0.2	-6	25 Sa	02:45	0.4	12
	06:59	5.1	155		08:04	4.5	137
	14:26	-0.5	-15		14:31	0.3	9
	19:33	5.3	162		20:18	5.0	152
11 Sa	03:01	-0.1	-3	26 Su	03:31	0.6	18
	07:53	4.9	149		08:54	4.3	131
	15:10	-0.3	-9		14:57	0.4	12
	20:22	5.4	165		20:53	4.9	149
12 Su	03:58	0.0	0	27 M	04:20	0.7	21
	08:55	4.6	140		09:46	4.1	125
	16:00	-0.2	-6		15:27	0.6	18
	21:19	5.3	162		21:24	4.9	149
13 M ◖	05:00	0.2	6	28 Tu	05:13	0.8	24
	10:03	4.4	134		10:41	3.9	119
	16:57	0.0	0		16:10	0.7	21
	22:24	5.2	158		22:02	4.8	146
14 Tu	06:04	0.2	6	29 W ◐	06:09	0.8	24
	11:12	4.3	131		11:38	3.9	119
	18:01	0.1	3		17:09	0.9	27
	23:33	5.1	155		23:12	4.7	143
15 W	07:07	0.1	3	30 Th	07:06	0.7	21
	12:20	4.2	128		12:36	3.9	119
	19:06	0.1	3		18:24	0.9	27

StationId: 8518995
Source: NOAA/NOS/CO-OPS
Station Type: Primary
Time Zone: LST_LDT
Datum: MLLW

NOAA Tide Predictions

ALBANY, HUDSON RIVER, NY,2021

Times and Heights of High and Low Waters

October

Days 1–15

Day	Time	ft	cm
1 F	00:26	4.7	143
	08:01	0.6	18
	13:31	4.0	122
	19:36	0.8	24
2 Sa	01:28	4.8	146
	08:53	0.3	9
	14:21	4.3	131
	20:40	0.7	21
3 Su	02:21	5.0	152
	09:41	0.1	3
	15:06	4.6	140
	21:38	0.4	12
4 M	03:08	5.1	155
	10:26	-0.1	-3
	15:47	4.9	149
	22:32	0.2	6
5 Tu	03:50	5.3	162
	11:10	-0.2	-6
	16:25	5.2	158
	23:24	0.0	0
6 W ●	04:30	5.3	162
	11:52	-0.3	-9
	17:02	5.4	165
7 Th	00:14	-0.1	-3
	05:12	5.3	162
	12:34	-0.3	-9
	17:39	5.6	171
8 F	01:04	-0.1	-3
	05:57	5.2	158
	13:16	-0.3	-9
	18:20	5.7	174
9 Sa	01:56	-0.1	-3
	06:48	5.0	152
	14:01	-0.2	-6
	19:06	5.8	177
10 Su	02:49	0.0	0
	07:46	4.8	146
	14:49	0.0	0
	20:00	5.7	174
11 M	03:46	0.1	3
	08:50	4.7	143
	15:43	0.1	3
	21:03	5.5	168
12 Tu	04:45	0.2	6
	09:57	4.5	137
	16:43	0.3	9
	22:11	5.4	165
13 W ◐	05:46	0.2	6
	11:02	4.5	137
	17:46	0.3	9
	23:20	5.2	158
14 Th	06:47	0.2	6
	12:07	4.6	140
	18:50	0.3	9
15 F	00:27	5.2	158
	07:45	0.1	3
	13:08	4.7	143
	19:53	0.2	6

Days 16–31

Day	Time	ft	cm
16 Sa	01:29	5.3	162
	08:40	-0.1	-3
	14:05	5.0	152
	20:51	0.1	3
17 Su	02:25	5.3	162
	09:31	-0.2	-6
	14:58	5.2	158
	21:46	-0.1	-3
18 M	03:15	5.4	165
	10:18	-0.3	-9
	15:45	5.4	165
	22:37	-0.1	-3
19 Tu	04:01	5.4	165
	11:01	-0.3	-9
	16:29	5.5	168
	23:25	-0.1	-3
20 W ○	04:44	5.3	162
	11:41	-0.2	-6
	17:10	5.6	171
21 Th	00:10	0.0	0
	05:26	5.2	158
	12:18	0.0	0
	17:48	5.5	168
22 F	00:54	0.1	3
	06:09	5.0	152
	12:52	0.2	6
	18:24	5.4	165
23 Sa	01:37	0.3	9
	06:52	4.7	143
	13:22	0.4	12
	18:56	5.4	165
24 Su	02:19	0.5	15
	07:37	4.5	137
	13:48	0.5	15
	19:20	5.3	162
25 M	03:03	0.6	18
	08:24	4.3	131
	14:14	0.7	21
	19:38	5.3	162
26 Tu	03:48	0.7	21
	09:13	4.2	128
	14:50	0.7	21
	20:12	5.3	162
27 W	04:38	0.8	24
	10:05	4.1	125
	15:36	0.9	27
	20:58	5.2	158
28 Th ◑	05:30	0.8	24
	10:59	4.1	125
	16:34	1.0	30
	21:53	5.1	155
29 F	06:24	0.8	24
	11:55	4.2	128
	17:47	1.0	30
	23:04	5.0	152
30 Sa	07:18	0.7	21
	12:49	4.4	134
	19:03	1.0	30
31 Su	00:34	4.9	149
	08:11	0.5	15
	13:40	4.6	140
	20:12	0.8	24

November

Days 1–15

Day	Time	ft	cm
1 M	01:39	5.0	152
	09:00	0.3	9
	14:27	4.9	149
	21:13	0.6	18
2 Tu	02:32	5.1	155
	09:48	0.1	3
	15:10	5.3	162
	22:11	0.3	9
3 W	03:21	5.2	158
	10:34	0.0	0
	15:50	5.6	171
	23:05	0.1	3
4 Th ●	04:07	5.2	158
	11:19	-0.1	-3
	16:30	5.8	177
	23:57	0.0	0
5 F	04:53	5.2	158
	12:05	-0.1	-3
	17:11	6.0	183
6 Sa	00:49	-0.1	-3
	05:42	5.1	155
	12:51	0.0	0
	17:55	6.0	183
7 Su	01:42	-0.1	-3
	05:37	4.9	149
	12:40	0.0	0
	17:46	5.9	180
8 M	01:35	0.0	0
	06:37	4.8	146
	13:32	0.2	6
	18:45	5.7	174
9 Tu	02:31	0.1	3
	07:41	4.7	143
	14:28	0.3	9
	19:52	5.5	168
10 W	03:28	0.1	3
	08:45	4.6	140
	15:27	0.4	12
	21:00	5.4	165
11 Th ☽	04:25	0.2	6
	09:48	4.7	143
	16:29	0.4	12
	22:05	5.3	162
12 F	05:22	0.1	3
	10:49	4.8	146
	17:31	0.4	12
	23:08	5.2	158
13 Sa	06:17	0.1	3
	11:47	5.0	152
	18:32	0.3	9
14 Su	00:07	5.2	158
	07:09	0.0	0
	12:43	5.2	158
	19:29	0.2	6
15 M	01:01	5.2	158
	07:59	-0.1	-3
	13:34	5.4	165
	20:24	0.1	3

Days 16–30

Day	Time	ft	cm
16 Tu	01:51	5.3	162
	08:45	-0.2	-6
	14:21	5.6	171
	21:15	0.0	0
17 W	02:37	5.2	158
	09:27	-0.1	-3
	15:04	5.7	174
	22:03	0.0	0
18 Th	03:21	5.1	155
	10:07	0.0	0
	15:43	5.7	174
	22:48	0.0	0
19 F ○	04:04	5.0	152
	10:43	0.2	6
	16:19	5.6	171
	23:32	0.1	3
20 Sa	04:46	4.8	146
	11:17	0.3	9
	16:52	5.5	168
21 Su	00:14	0.2	6
	05:29	4.6	140
	11:49	0.5	15
	17:18	5.5	168
22 M	00:56	0.3	9
	06:12	4.4	134
	12:18	0.6	18
	17:35	5.4	165
23 Tu	01:37	0.4	12
	06:56	4.3	131
	12:51	0.6	18
	18:00	5.4	165
24 W	02:20	0.5	15
	07:41	4.2	128
	13:30	0.7	21
	18:41	5.4	165
25 Th	03:04	0.6	18
	08:28	4.2	128
	14:17	0.7	21
	19:29	5.4	165
26 F	03:52	0.6	18
	09:17	4.3	131
	15:13	0.8	24
	20:23	5.2	158
27 Sa ◑	04:42	0.6	18
	10:08	4.4	134
	16:21	0.9	27
	21:24	5.1	155
28 Su	05:33	0.5	15
	11:01	4.6	140
	17:35	0.9	27
	22:40	4.9	149
29 M	06:26	0.4	12
	11:54	4.8	146
	18:45	0.8	24
	23:57	4.9	149
30 Tu	07:18	0.3	9
	12:45	5.1	155
	19:50	0.5	15

December

Days 1–15

Day	Time	ft	cm
1 W	00:59	4.9	149
	08:10	0.2	6
	13:33	5.5	168
	20:50	0.3	9
2 Th	01:54	4.9	149
	09:00	0.0	0
	14:19	5.7	174
	21:47	0.1	3
3 F	02:46	4.9	149
	09:50	0.0	0
	15:03	5.9	180
	22:41	-0.1	-3
4 Sa ●	03:37	4.9	149
	10:41	-0.1	-3
	15:49	6.0	183
	23:34	-0.2	-6
5 Su	04:29	4.8	146
	11:31	0.0	0
	16:38	5.9	180
6 M	00:26	-0.2	-6
	05:24	4.7	143
	12:23	0.0	0
	17:33	5.7	174
7 Tu	01:19	-0.1	-3
	06:24	4.6	140
	13:16	0.1	3
	18:34	5.5	168
8 W	02:12	-0.1	-3
	07:25	4.6	140
	14:11	0.1	3
	19:39	5.4	165
9 Th	03:05	0.0	0
	08:27	4.6	140
	15:09	0.2	6
	20:43	5.2	158
10 F	03:58	0.0	0
	09:26	4.7	143
	16:08	0.3	9
	21:44	5.1	155
11 Sa ☽	04:51	0.0	0
	10:24	4.8	146
	17:08	0.3	9
	22:42	5.0	152
12 Su	05:43	0.0	0
	11:21	5.0	152
	18:07	0.3	9
	23:39	5.0	152
13 M	06:34	0.0	0
	12:15	5.1	155
	19:04	0.3	9
14 Tu	00:33	4.9	149
	07:22	0.0	0
	13:06	5.3	162
	19:59	0.2	6
15 W	01:24	4.9	149
	08:08	0.0	0
	13:53	5.4	165
	20:51	0.0	0

Days 16–31

Day	Time	ft	cm
16 Th	02:12	4.8	146
	08:51	0.1	3
	14:36	5.5	168
	21:39	0.0	0
17 F	02:58	4.8	146
	09:33	0.1	3
	15:16	5.5	168
	22:25	-0.1	-3
18 Sa	03:42	4.7	143
	10:11	0.2	6
	15:52	5.5	168
	23:09	-0.1	-3
19 Su ○	04:25	4.5	137
	10:48	0.3	9
	16:24	5.4	165
	23:51	0.0	0
20 M	05:06	4.4	134
	11:24	0.4	12
	16:51	5.4	165
21 Tu	00:31	0.1	3
	05:48	4.3	131
	12:00	0.4	12
	17:10	5.4	165
22 W	01:11	0.1	3
	06:28	4.3	131
	12:38	0.4	12
	17:39	5.4	165
23 Th	01:52	0.2	6
	07:08	4.3	131
	13:19	0.4	12
	18:20	5.4	165
24 F	02:32	0.2	6
	07:48	4.4	134
	14:06	0.5	15
	19:08	5.3	162
25 Sa	03:15	0.2	6
	08:30	4.5	137
	14:51	0.5	15
	20:01	5.2	158
26 Su	04:00	0.2	6
	09:17	4.7	143
	16:02	0.6	18
	20:59	5.0	152
27 M ◑	04:49	0.2	6
	10:10	4.8	146
	17:12	0.7	21
	22:08	4.8	146
28 Tu	05:42	0.2	6
	11:07	5.0	152
	18:23	0.6	18
	23:24	4.7	143
29 W	06:38	0.2	6
	12:04	5.2	158
	19:29	0.4	12
30 Th	00:33	4.6	140
	07:35	0.1	3
	13:14	5.4	165
	20:31	0.2	6
31 F	01:34	4.6	140
	08:32	0.0	0
	13:53	5.6	171
	21:31	0.1	3

StationId: 8531680
Source: NOAA/NOS/CO-OPS
Station Type: Primary
Time Zone: LST_LDT
Datum: MLLW

NOAA Tide Predictions

Sandy Hook, NJ, 2021

Times and Heights of High and Low Waters

January

Day	Time	ft	cm
1 F	02:51	-0.1	-3
	08:50	5.1	155
	15:41	-0.3	-9
	21:32	4.1	125
2 Sa	03:33	0.0	0
	09:34	5.1	155
	16:21	-0.2	-6
	22:21	4.1	125
3 Su	04:16	0.0	0
	10:23	5.0	152
	17:03	-0.2	-6
	23:13	4.2	128
4 M	05:05	0.2	6
	11:17	4.8	146
	17:50	-0.1	-3
5 Tu	00:07	4.4	134
	06:05	0.3	9
	12:13	4.7	143
	18:45	-0.1	-3
6 W	01:01	4.5	137
	07:17	0.4	12
	13:10	4.5	137
	19:48	-0.1	-3
7 Th	01:58	4.7	143
	08:31	0.3	9
	14:11	4.3	131
	20:50	-0.1	-3
8 F	02:57	5.0	152
	09:38	0.1	3
	15:16	4.2	128
	21:49	-0.3	-9
9 Sa	03:59	5.2	158
	10:39	-0.2	-6
	16:23	4.2	128
	22:45	-0.4	-12
10 Su	05:00	5.4	165
	11:36	-0.5	-15
	17:26	4.3	131
	23:40	-0.5	-15
11 M	05:56	5.6	171
	12:30	-0.6	-18
	18:23	4.5	137
12 Tu	00:34	-0.6	-18
	06:48	5.7	174
	13:23	-0.8	-24
	19:15	4.6	140
13 W	01:27	-0.6	-18
	07:37	5.7	174
	14:12	-0.8	-24
	20:05	4.6	140
14 Th	02:17	-0.5	-15
	08:25	5.6	171
	14:58	-0.8	-24
	20:54	4.5	137
15 F	03:04	-0.4	-12
	09:13	5.4	165
	15:42	-0.6	-18
	21:44	4.4	134
16 Sa	03:49	-0.2	-6
	10:00	5.1	155
	16:23	-0.4	-12
	22:33	4.3	131
17 Su	04:33	0.1	3
	10:48	4.8	146
	17:03	-0.2	-6
	23:22	4.2	128
18 M	05:18	0.4	12
	11:35	4.5	137
	17:44	0.1	3
19 Tu	00:08	4.1	125
	06:08	0.7	21
	12:21	4.2	128
	18:28	0.3	9
20 W	00:54	4.1	125
	07:07	0.9	27
	13:07	3.9	119
	19:17	0.5	15
21 Th	01:39	4.1	125
	08:11	0.9	27
	13:56	3.7	113
	20:11	0.6	18
22 F	02:26	4.1	125
	09:12	0.8	24
	14:50	3.5	107
	21:05	0.6	18
23 Sa	03:17	4.2	128
	10:06	0.7	21
	15:47	3.5	107
	21:56	0.5	15
24 Su	04:10	4.3	131
	10:55	0.5	15
	16:44	3.6	110
	22:45	0.4	12
25 M	05:02	4.5	137
	11:43	0.2	6
	17:36	3.8	116
	23:32	0.2	6
26 Tu	05:49	4.8	146
	12:29	0.0	0
	18:22	4.0	122
27 W	00:20	0.0	0
	06:32	5.0	152
	13:14	-0.2	-6
	19:05	4.2	128
28 Th	01:06	-0.2	-6
	07:13	5.2	158
	13:57	-0.4	-12
	19:46	4.3	131
29 F	01:52	-0.3	-9
	07:53	5.3	162
	14:38	-0.5	-15
	20:27	4.5	137
30 Sa	02:36	-0.4	-12
	08:35	5.4	165
	15:18	-0.6	-18
	21:11	4.6	140
31 Su	03:21	-0.5	-15
	09:19	5.3	162
	15:58	-0.6	-18
	21:59	4.7	143

February

Day	Time	ft	cm
1 M	04:06	-0.4	-12
	10:08	5.1	155
	16:39	-0.5	-15
	22:50	4.8	146
2 Tu	04:55	-0.2	-6
	11:00	4.9	149
	17:23	-0.4	-12
	23:43	4.8	146
3 W	05:51	0.0	0
	11:56	4.6	140
	18:14	-0.2	-6
4 Th	00:38	4.9	149
	06:59	0.2	6
	12:53	4.4	134
	19:17	0.0	0
5 F	01:35	4.9	149
	08:14	0.3	9
	13:55	4.1	125
	20:26	0.1	3
6 Sa	02:36	4.9	149
	09:23	0.2	6
	15:01	4.0	122
	21:32	0.1	3
7 Su	03:40	5.0	152
	10:21	0.0	0
	16:11	4.0	122
	22:32	-0.1	-3
8 M	04:45	5.1	155
	11:23	-0.2	-6
	17:16	4.2	128
	23:29	-0.2	-6
9 Tu	05:44	5.3	162
	12:16	-0.4	-12
	18:12	4.4	134
10 W	00:22	-0.3	-9
	06:35	5.4	165
	13:05	-0.6	-18
	19:02	4.6	140
11 Th	01:13	-0.4	-12
	07:22	5.5	168
	13:28	-0.6	-18
	19:48	4.7	143
12 F	02:00	-0.4	-12
	08:06	5.4	165
	14:34	-0.6	-18
	20:32	4.7	143
13 Sa	02:44	-0.3	-9
	08:49	5.3	162
	15:13	-0.5	-15
	21:15	4.7	143
14 Su	03:26	-0.2	-6
	09:31	5.0	152
	15:49	-0.4	-12
	21:58	4.6	140
15 M	04:05	0.0	0
	10:13	4.7	143
	16:23	-0.2	-6
	22:40	4.5	137
16 Tu	04:45	0.3	9
	10:57	4.4	134
	16:57	0.1	3
	23:21	4.4	134
17 W	05:26	0.6	18
	11:40	4.1	125
	17:31	0.4	12
18 Th	00:03	4.3	131
	06:15	0.8	24
	12:26	3.8	116
	18:11	0.7	21
19 F	00:45	4.2	128
	07:16	1.0	30
	13:14	3.6	110
	19:04	0.9	27
20 Sa	01:30	4.1	125
	08:25	1.0	30
	14:06	3.5	107
	20:11	0.9	27
21 Su	02:22	4.1	125
	09:27	0.9	27
	15:05	3.4	104
	21:16	0.9	27
22 M	03:21	4.2	128
	10:21	0.7	21
	16:07	3.6	110
	22:13	0.7	21
23 Tu	04:22	4.4	134
	11:11	0.4	12
	17:04	3.8	116
	23:05	0.4	12
24 W	05:17	4.7	143
	11:58	0.1	3
	17:54	4.2	128
	23:56	0.1	3
25 Th	06:06	5.1	155
	12:44	-0.2	-6
	18:39	4.5	137
26 F	00:45	-0.2	-6
	06:50	5.4	165
	13:28	-0.5	-15
	19:21	4.8	146
27 Sa	01:33	-0.5	-15
	07:33	5.6	171
	14:10	-0.7	-21
	20:04	5.1	155
28 Su	02:20	-0.7	-21
	08:16	5.6	171
	14:52	-0.8	-24
	20:48	5.3	162

March

Day	Time	ft	cm
1 M	03:06	-0.7	-21
	09:02	5.5	168
	15:33	-0.8	-24
	21:35	5.4	165
2 Tu	03:53	-0.6	-18
	09:51	5.3	162
	16:14	-0.6	-18
	22:26	5.4	165
3 W	04:43	-0.4	-12
	10:45	5.0	152
	16:59	-0.4	-12
	23:20	5.3	162
4 Th	05:38	-0.1	-3
	11:42	4.6	140
	17:50	-0.1	-3
5 F	00:16	5.2	158
	06:44	0.2	6
	12:41	4.3	131
	18:54	0.3	9
6 Sa	01:15	5.1	155
	07:57	0.3	9
	13:44	4.1	125
	20:08	0.5	15
7 Su	02:17	4.9	149
	09:08	0.3	9
	14:51	4.0	122
	21:19	0.4	12
8 M	03:24	4.9	149
	10:11	0.2	6
	16:00	4.1	125
	22:22	0.3	9
9 Tu	04:30	4.9	149
	11:06	0.0	0
	17:04	4.3	131
	23:18	0.1	3
10 W	05:28	5.1	155
	11:56	-0.1	-3
	17:58	4.6	140
11 Th	00:09	0.0	0
	06:19	5.2	158
	12:42	-0.3	-9
	18:45	4.8	146
12 F	00:57	-0.2	-6
	07:03	5.3	162
	13:25	-0.4	-12
	19:27	5.0	152
13 Sa	01:41	-0.2	-6
	07:43	5.3	162
	14:04	-0.4	-12
	20:06	5.0	152
14 Su	03:23	-0.2	-6
	09:22	5.2	158
	15:40	-0.3	-9
	21:44	5.0	152
15 M	04:02	-0.1	-3
	10:01	5.0	152
	16:13	-0.2	-6
	22:20	5.0	152
16 Tu	04:39	0.0	0
	10:40	4.7	143
	16:45	0.1	3
	22:57	4.8	146
17 W	05:16	0.3	9
	11:21	4.4	134
	17:15	0.3	9
	23:33	4.7	143
18 Th	05:53	0.5	15
	12:04	4.1	125
	17:46	0.6	18
19 F	00:10	4.5	137
	06:33	0.8	24
	12:49	3.8	116
	18:19	0.8	24
20 Sa	00:50	4.4	134
	07:24	1.0	30
	13:36	3.7	113
	19:04	1.1	34
21 Su	01:37	4.3	131
	08:34	1.1	34
	14:29	3.6	110
	20:15	1.2	37
22 M	02:31	4.3	131
	09:45	1.1	34
	15:26	3.6	110
	21:36	1.1	34
23 Tu	03:33	4.3	131
	10:44	0.9	27
	16:28	3.8	116
	22:41	0.9	27
24 W	04:39	4.5	137
	11:36	0.6	18
	17:28	4.1	125
	23:38	0.5	15
25 Th	05:41	4.8	146
	12:24	0.2	6
	18:21	4.5	137
26 F	00:30	0.1	3
	06:35	5.2	158
	13:10	-0.2	-6
	19:09	5.0	152
27 Sa	01:22	-0.2	-6
	07:23	5.5	168
	13:55	-0.5	-15
	19:54	5.4	165
28 Su	02:12	-0.6	-18
	08:09	5.7	174
	14:39	-0.7	-21
	20:38	5.8	177
29 M	03:02	-0.8	-24
	08:55	5.7	174
	15:23	-0.8	-24
	21:24	6.0	183
30 Tu	03:51	-0.8	-24
	09:43	5.5	168
	16:07	-0.7	-21
	22:12	6.0	183
31 W	04:40	-0.8	-24
	10:35	5.3	162
	16:51	-0.5	-15
	23:03	5.9	180

StationId: 8531680
Source: NOAA/NOS/CO-OPS
Station Type: Primary
Time Zone: LST_LDT
Datum: MLLW

Sandy Hook, NJ,2021

Times and Heights of High and Low Waters

April

Day	Time	ft	cm	Day	Time	ft	cm
1 Th	05:31	-0.5	-15	16 F	05:27	0.5	15
	11:31	5.0	152		11:33	4.1	125
	17:38	-0.2	-6		17:12	0.8	24
	23:59	5.7	174		23:23	4.8	146
2 F	06:26	-0.2	-6	17 Sa	06:04	0.7	21
	12:31	4.7	143		12:18	3.9	119
	18:32	0.2	6		17:46	1.0	30
3 Sa	00:58	5.4	165	18 Su	00:05	4.6	140
	07:29	0.2	6		06:48	0.9	27
	13:32	4.4	134		13:06	3.8	116
	19:37	0.6	18		18:28	1.2	37
4 Su ◑	01:58	5.2	158	19 M	00:55	4.5	137
	08:40	0.4	12		07:48	1.1	34
	14:34	4.3	131		13:58	3.8	116
	20:54	0.8	24		19:31	1.3	40
5 M	03:00	5.0	152	20 Tu ◐	01:52	4.5	137
	09:50	0.4	12		09:00	1.1	34
	15:39	4.2	128		14:53	3.9	119
	22:06	0.7	21		20:57	1.3	40
6 Tu	04:05	4.8	146	21 W	02:53	4.5	137
	10:51	0.3	9		10:04	0.9	27
	16:44	4.3	131		15:51	4.1	125
	23:08	0.6	18		22:10	1.0	30
7 W	05:08	4.8	146	22 Th	03:57	4.7	143
	11:43	0.2	6		10:58	0.5	15
	17:45	4.5	137		16:51	4.5	137
					23:10	0.6	18
8 Th	00:01	0.4	12	23 F	05:02	4.9	149
	06:05	4.9	149		11:46	0.2	6
	12:29	0.1	3		17:47	4.9	149
	18:37	4.8	146				
9 F	00:50	0.3	9	24 Sa	00:05	0.2	6
	06:54	5.0	152		06:01	5.2	158
	13:12	0.0	0		12:33	-0.2	-6
	19:21	5.0	152		18:38	5.5	168
10 Sa	01:35	0.1	3	25 Su	00:59	-0.2	-6
	07:37	5.1	155		06:55	5.4	165
	13:51	-0.1	-3		13:20	-0.4	-12
	20:00	5.2	158		19:27	5.9	180
11 Su	02:18	0.0	0	26 M	01:51	-0.5	-15
	08:17	5.1	155		07:45	5.5	168
	14:29	-0.1	-3		14:08	-0.6	-18
	20:36	5.3	162		20:14	6.3	192
12 M ●	02:59	0.0	0	27 Tu ○	02:44	-0.8	-24
	08:55	5.0	152		08:35	5.5	168
	15:04	0.0	0		14:55	-0.7	-21
	21:11	5.3	162		21:01	6.4	195
13 Tu	03:38	0.0	0	28 W	03:35	-0.8	-24
	09:33	4.8	146		09:26	5.4	165
	15:58	0.1	3		15:43	-0.6	-18
	21:44	5.2	158		21:50	6.4	195
14 W	04:15	0.1	3	29 Th	04:26	-0.8	-24
	10:11	4.6	140		10:20	5.2	158
	16:10	0.3	9		16:32	-0.4	-12
	22:16	5.1	155		22:44	6.2	189
15 Th	04:51	0.3	9	30 F	05:18	-0.5	-15
	10:51	4.3	131		11:18	4.9	149
	16:41	0.5	15		17:22	0.0	0
	22:49	4.9	149		23:41	5.9	180

May

Day	Time	ft	cm	Day	Time	ft	cm
1 Sa	06:12	-0.2	-6	16 Su	05:44	0.6	18
	12:19	4.7	143		11:53	4.0	122
	18:17	0.4	12		17:26	1.0	30
					23:36	4.8	146
2 Su	00:41	5.5	168	17 M	06:25	0.8	24
	07:12	0.1	3		12:42	3.9	119
	13:21	4.5	137		18:09	1.1	34
	19:22	0.7	21				
3 M ◑	01:41	5.2	158	18 Tu	00:28	4.8	146
	08:18	0.4	12		07:16	0.9	27
	14:21	4.4	134		13:32	4.0	122
	20:35	0.9	27		19:07	1.2	37
4 Tu	02:40	5.0	152	19 W ◐	01:24	4.7	143
	09:24	0.5	15		08:18	0.8	24
	15:20	4.4	134		14:24	4.2	128
	21:46	0.9	27		20:24	1.2	37
5 W	03:39	4.8	146	20 Th	02:22	4.8	146
	10:22	0.4	12		09:21	0.7	21
	16:20	4.5	137		15:18	4.5	137
	22:46	0.8	24		21:39	1.0	30
6 Th	04:37	4.7	143	21 F	03:22	4.8	146
	11:11	0.3	9		10:18	0.4	12
	17:16	4.7	143		16:16	4.8	146
	23:38	0.7	21		22:44	0.6	18
7 F	05:32	4.7	143	22 Sa	04:26	4.9	149
	11:55	0.3	9		11:09	0.1	3
	18:07	4.9	149		17:13	5.3	162
					23:41	0.2	6
8 Sa	00:25	0.5	15	23 Su	05:29	5.0	152
	06:22	4.7	143		11:59	-0.2	-6
	12:35	0.2	6		18:09	5.8	177
	18:50	5.2	158				
9 Su	01:10	0.4	12	24 M	00:37	-0.2	-6
	07:07	4.8	146		06:28	5.2	158
	13:14	0.2	6		12:49	-0.4	-12
	19:29	5.3	162		19:01	6.2	189
10 M	01:53	0.2	6	25 Tu	01:32	-0.5	-15
	07:48	4.7	143		07:24	5.3	162
	13:52	0.2	6		13:40	-0.5	-15
	20:05	5.4	165		19:51	6.5	198
11 Tu ●	02:34	0.2	6	26 W ○	02:27	-0.7	-21
	08:28	4.7	143		08:17	5.3	162
	14:45	0.3	9		14:31	-0.5	-15
	20:39	5.4	165		20:41	6.6	201
12 W	03:14	0.1	3	27 Th	03:20	-0.8	-24
	09:07	4.6	140		09:10	5.2	158
	15:05	0.4	12		15:24	-0.4	-12
	21:12	5.4	165		21:33	6.5	198
13 Th	03:53	0.2	6	28 F	04:12	-0.7	-21
	09:45	4.4	134		10:06	5.1	155
	15:41	0.5	15		16:15	-0.2	-6
	21:44	5.2	158		22:27	6.2	189
14 F	04:30	0.3	9	29 Sa	05:03	-0.5	-15
	10:26	4.2	128		11:04	4.9	149
	16:16	0.7	21		17:07	0.1	3
	22:16	5.1	155		23:24	5.9	180
15 Sa	05:07	0.4	12	30 Su	05:55	-0.3	-9
	11:08	4.1	125		12:05	4.8	146
	16:50	0.8	24		18:02	0.4	12
	22:52	5.0	152				
				31 M	00:22	5.5	168
					06:50	0.0	0
					13:03	4.7	143
					19:02	0.7	21

June

Day	Time	ft	cm	Day	Time	ft	cm
1 Tu	01:19	5.2	158	16 W	00:07	5.0	152
	07:48	0.3	9		06:48	0.5	15
	13:59	4.6	140		13:07	4.3	131
	20:09	1.0	30		18:50	1.0	30
2 W ◑	02:13	4.9	149	17 Th	01:01	4.9	149
	08:48	0.4	12		07:41	0.5	15
	14:54	4.6	140		13:57	4.6	140
	21:16	1.0	30		19:58	1.0	30
3 Th	03:06	4.7	143	18 F ◐	01:56	4.9	149
	09:43	0.5	15		08:40	0.4	12
	15:47	4.7	143		14:49	4.8	146
	22:16	1.0	30		21:13	0.9	27
4 F	03:59	4.5	137	19 Sa	02:54	4.8	146
	10:31	0.5	15		09:39	0.3	9
	16:39	4.8	146		15:45	5.2	158
	23:09	0.9	27		22:21	0.6	18
5 Sa	04:53	4.4	134	20 Su	03:56	4.8	146
	11:14	0.5	15		10:35	0.1	3
	17:29	4.9	149		16:43	5.5	168
	23:56	0.7	21		23:21	0.2	6
6 Su	05:45	4.4	134	21 M	05:02	4.8	146
	11:55	0.4	12		11:29	-0.1	-3
	18:14	5.1	155		17:42	5.9	180
7 M	00:41	0.5	15	22 Tu	00:19	-0.1	-3
	06:34	4.4	134		06:06	4.8	146
	12:35	0.4	12		12:23	-0.2	-6
	18:56	5.3	162		18:39	6.2	189
8 Tu	01:25	0.4	12	23 W	01:16	-0.3	-9
	07:19	4.4	134		07:06	4.9	149
	13:15	0.5	15		13:18	-0.3	-9
	19:34	5.4	165		19:33	6.4	195
9 W	02:09	0.3	9	24 Th ○	02:11	-0.5	-15
	08:02	4.4	134		08:02	5.0	152
	13:56	0.5	15		14:13	-0.3	-9
	20:10	5.4	165		20:25	6.4	195
10 Th ●	02:51	0.2	6	25 F	03:05	-0.6	-18
	08:42	4.4	134		08:56	5.1	155
	14:37	0.5	15		15:08	-0.3	-9
	20:45	5.4	165		21:17	6.3	192
11 F	03:31	0.2	6	26 Sa	03:56	-0.6	-18
	09:22	4.3	131		09:51	5.0	152
	15:17	0.6	18		16:00	-0.1	-3
	21:19	5.3	162		22:10	6.1	186
12 Sa	04:10	0.3	9	27 Su	04:45	-0.5	-15
	10:03	4.2	128		10:47	4.9	149
	15:56	0.7	21		16:51	0.1	3
	21:54	5.2	158		23:04	5.8	177
13 Su	04:48	0.3	9	28 M	05:33	-0.3	-9
	10:45	4.2	128		11:43	4.8	146
	16:34	0.7	21		17:42	0.4	12
	22:32	5.1	155		23:58	5.5	168
14 M	05:26	0.4	12	29 Tu	06:21	0.0	0
	11:30	4.1	125		12:38	4.8	146
	17:13	0.8	24		18:36	0.7	21
	23:17	5.0	152				
15 Tu	06:05	0.5	15	30 W	00:51	5.2	158
	12:18	4.2	128		07:11	0.2	6
	17:57	0.9	27		13:30	4.7	143
					19:34	1.0	30

StationId: 8531680
Source: NOAA/NOS/CO-OPS
Station Type: Primary
Time Zone: LST_LDT
Datum: MLLW

NOAA Tide Predictions

Sandy Hook, NJ,2021

Times and Heights of High and Low Waters

July

Day	Time (h m)	ft	cm	Day	Time (h m)	ft	cm
1 Th ◑	01:41	4.8	146	16 F	00:41	5.0	152
	08:02	0.4	12		07:07	0.3	9
	14:19	4.7	143		13:31	5.0	152
	20:37	1.1	34		19:39	0.8	24
2 F	02:30	4.6	140	17 Sa ◐	01:35	4.9	149
	08:54	0.6	18		08:03	0.3	9
	15:07	4.7	143		14:23	5.2	158
	21:39	1.1	34		20:52	0.8	24
3 Sa	03:20	4.3	131	18 Su	02:33	4.7	143
	09:44	0.7	21		09:06	0.3	9
	15:56	4.7	143		15:19	5.4	165
	22:34	1.1	34		22:02	0.6	18
4 Su	04:12	4.1	125	19 M	03:36	4.6	140
	10:31	0.7	21		10:09	0.3	9
	16:45	4.8	146		16:19	5.6	171
	23:24	0.9	27		23:06	0.3	9
5 M	05:07	4.1	125	20 Tu	04:43	4.5	137
	11:15	0.7	21		11:09	0.2	6
	17:34	5.0	152		17:22	5.8	177
6 Tu	00:11	0.7	21	21 W	00:05	0.1	3
	06:01	4.1	125		05:51	4.6	140
	11:59	0.7	21		12:07	0.0	0
	18:21	5.1	155		18:23	6.0	183
7 W	00:57	0.6	18	22 Th	01:01	-0.2	-6
	06:51	4.2	128		06:53	4.8	146
	12:43	0.7	21		13:04	-0.1	-3
	19:04	5.2	158		19:19	6.2	189
8 Th	01:42	0.4	12	23 F	01:56	-0.3	-9
	07:36	4.3	131		07:49	5.0	152
	13:28	0.6	18		13:59	-0.1	-3
	19:44	5.3	162		20:11	6.2	189
9 F	02:25	0.3	9	24 Sa ○	02:48	-0.5	-15
	08:18	4.3	131		08:42	5.1	155
	14:12	0.6	18		14:53	-0.1	-3
	20:22	5.4	165		21:01	6.2	189
10 Sa ●	03:08	0.2	6	25 Su	03:37	-0.5	-15
	08:59	4.4	134		09:33	5.1	155
	14:56	0.5	15		15:44	-0.1	-3
	20:58	5.4	165		21:51	6.0	183
11 Su	03:48	0.2	6	26 M	04:22	-0.4	-12
	09:39	4.4	134		10:24	5.1	155
	15:38	0.5	15		16:32	0.1	3
	21:36	5.4	165		22:40	5.7	174
12 M	04:26	0.1	3	27 Tu	05:05	-0.3	-9
	10:20	4.4	134		11:15	5.0	152
	16:19	0.5	15		17:11	0.3	9
	22:15	5.4	165		23:29	5.4	165
13 Tu	05:03	0.1	3	28 W	05:47	0.0	0
	11:04	4.5	137		12:05	4.9	149
	17:00	0.5	15		18:05	0.6	18
	22:59	5.3	162				
14 W	05:41	0.2	6	29 Th	00:17	5.1	155
	11:51	4.6	140		06:28	0.3	9
	17:44	0.6	18		12:53	4.8	146
	23:48	5.2	158		18:56	0.9	27
15 Th	06:21	0.2	6	30 F	01:05	4.7	143
	12:40	4.8	146		07:11	0.6	18
	18:35	0.7	21		13:38	4.8	146
					19:52	1.2	37
31 Sa ◑					01:52	4.4	134
					07:58	0.8	24
					14:23	4.7	143
					20:55	1.3	40

August

Day	Time (h m)	ft	cm	Day	Time (h m)	ft	cm
1 Su	02:41	4.1	125	16 M	02:20	4.6	140
	08:50	1.0	30		08:42	0.5	15
	15:09	4.7	143		14:59	5.5	168
	21:56	1.2	37		21:48	0.7	21
2 M	03:33	4.0	122	17 Tu	03:24	4.4	134
	09:44	1.1	34		09:53	0.6	18
	15:59	4.7	143		16:02	5.5	168
	22:50	1.1	34		22:53	0.5	15
3 Tu	04:29	3.9	119	18 W	04:33	4.4	134
	10:37	1.0	30		10:57	0.4	12
	16:51	4.8	146		17:08	5.6	171
	23:40	0.9	27		23:52	0.2	6
4 W	05:27	4.0	122	19 Th	05:41	4.6	140
	11:26	1.0	30		11:57	0.3	9
	17:44	4.9	149		18:10	5.8	177
5 Th	00:27	0.7	21	20 F	00:47	0.0	0
	06:21	4.1	125		06:42	4.8	146
	12:15	0.8	24		12:53	0.1	3
	18:33	5.1	155		19:06	5.9	180
6 F	01:13	0.5	15	21 Sa	01:38	-0.2	-6
	07:09	4.3	131		07:36	5.1	155
	13:02	0.7	21		13:47	0.0	0
	19:17	5.3	162		19:56	6.0	183
7 Sa	01:57	0.4	12	22 Su ○	02:27	-0.3	-9
	07:52	4.5	137		08:25	5.2	158
	13:49	0.5	15		14:37	0.0	0
	19:58	5.5	168		20:43	6.0	183
8 Su ●	02:39	0.2	6	23 M	03:12	-0.3	-9
	08:32	4.7	143		09:11	5.3	162
	14:34	0.4	12		15:25	0.0	0
	20:36	5.6	171		21:27	5.8	177
9 M	03:20	0.0	0	24 Tu	03:53	-0.3	-9
	09:12	4.8	146		09:56	5.3	162
	15:18	0.2	6		16:09	0.1	3
	21:15	5.6	171		22:11	5.6	171
10 Tu	03:59	-0.1	-3	25 W	04:32	-0.1	-3
	09:52	4.9	149		10:40	5.2	158
	15:55	0.2	6		16:52	0.4	12
	21:55	5.6	171		22:55	5.2	158
11 W	04:36	-0.1	-3	26 Th	05:08	0.1	3
	10:36	5.1	155		11:25	5.1	155
	16:45	0.2	6		17:34	0.6	18
	22:40	5.5	168		23:41	4.9	149
12 Th	05:14	-0.1	-3	27 F	05:43	0.4	12
	11:23	5.2	158		12:09	5.0	152
	17:31	0.3	9		18:17	0.9	27
	23:29	5.3	162				
13 F	05:54	0.0	0	28 Sa	00:28	4.5	137
	12:13	5.3	162		06:19	0.7	21
	18:22	0.5	15		12:48	4.8	146
					19:07	1.2	37
14 Sa	00:23	5.0	152	29 Su	01:15	4.2	128
	06:39	0.2	6		06:59	1.0	30
	13:06	5.4	165		13:36	4.7	143
	19:23	0.6	18		20:06	1.3	40
15 Su ◐	01:20	4.8	146	30 M ◑	02:04	4.0	122
	07:34	0.4	12		07:50	1.3	40
	14:01	5.4	165		14:22	4.6	140
	20:35	0.7	21		21:12	1.4	43
31 Tu					02:57	3.9	119
					08:55	1.4	43
					15:12	4.6	140
					22:14	1.3	40

September

Day	Time (h m)	ft	cm	Day	Time (h m)	ft	cm
1 W	03:53	3.8	116	16 Th	04:25	4.4	134
	09:59	1.3	40		10:50	0.6	18
	16:07	4.6	140		16:55	5.4	165
	23:07	1.1	34		23:38	0.3	9
2 Th	04:53	3.9	119	17 F	05:31	4.7	143
	10:56	1.2	37		11:48	0.4	12
	17:05	4.8	146		17:56	5.5	168
	23:55	0.9	27				
3 F	05:49	4.2	128	18 Sa	00:29	0.1	3
	11:48	0.9	27		06:29	4.9	149
	18:00	5.0	152		12:41	0.3	9
					18:50	5.7	174
4 Sa	00:40	0.6	18	19 Su	01:16	-0.1	-3
	06:38	4.5	137		07:20	5.2	158
	12:36	0.6	18		13:31	0.1	3
	18:47	5.3	162		19:37	5.7	174
5 Su	01:24	0.3	9	20 M ○	02:00	-0.2	-6
	07:22	4.8	146		08:04	5.4	165
	13:24	0.4	12		14:19	0.1	3
	19:30	5.6	171		20:20	5.7	174
6 M	02:06	0.1	3	21 Tu	02:42	-0.2	-6
	08:03	5.1	155		08:45	5.5	168
	14:11	0.1	3		15:03	0.1	3
	20:11	5.7	174		21:01	5.6	171
7 Tu ●	02:47	-0.1	-3	22 W	03:20	-0.1	-3
	08:43	5.4	165		09:25	5.5	168
	14:57	0.0	0		15:45	0.2	6
	20:51	5.8	177		21:41	5.3	162
8 W	03:27	-0.3	-9	23 Th	03:56	0.0	0
	09:24	5.6	171		10:03	5.4	165
	15:43	-0.1	-3		16:25	0.3	9
	21:34	5.7	174		22:22	5.0	152
9 Th	04:07	-0.3	-9	24 F	04:29	0.3	9
	10:08	5.7	174		10:42	5.2	158
	16:29	-0.1	-3		17:04	0.5	15
	22:20	5.5	168		23:05	4.7	143
10 F	04:47	-0.2	-6	25 Sa	05:02	0.6	18
	10:55	5.7	174		11:21	5.0	152
	17:17	0.0	0		17:44	0.8	24
	23:11	5.2	158		23:51	4.3	131
11 Sa	05:29	0.0	0	26 Su	05:34	0.8	24
	11:48	5.7	174		12:02	4.8	146
	18:09	0.2	6		18:26	1.1	34
12 Su	00:08	4.9	149	27 M	00:40	4.1	125
	06:16	0.2	6		06:10	1.1	34
	12:44	5.6	171		12:46	4.7	143
	19:10	0.5	15		19:19	1.3	40
13 M ◐	01:09	4.7	143	28 Tu	01:30	3.9	119
	07:14	0.5	15		06:55	1.4	43
	13:45	5.5	168		13:34	4.6	140
	20:22	0.7	21		20:25	1.4	43
14 Tu	02:12	4.5	137	29 W ◑	02:23	3.8	116
	08:28	0.8	24		08:03	1.5	46
	14:45	5.4	165		14:26	4.5	137
	21:35	0.7	21		21:33	1.3	40
15 W	03:18	4.4	134	30 Th	03:18	3.8	116
	09:43	0.8	24		09:21	1.5	46
	15:49	5.4	165		15:23	4.5	137
	22:41	0.5	15		22:31	1.1	34

StationId: 8531680
Source: NOAA/NOS/CO-OPS
Station Type: Primary
Time Zone: LST_LDT
Datum: MLLW

NOAA Tide Predictions

Sandy Hook, NJ,2021

Times and Heights of High and Low Waters

October

Day	Time (h m)	Height ft	Height cm	Day	Time (h m)	Height ft	Height cm
1 F	04:16	4.0	122	**16** Sa	05:16	4.7	143
	10:25	1.3	40		11:35	0.5	15
	16:23	4.7	143		17:36	5.2	158
	23:20	0.8	24				
2 Sa	05:12	4.2	128	**17** Su	00:05	0.1	3
	11:19	0.9	27		06:11	5.0	152
	17:20	5.0	152		12:26	0.3	9
					18:28	5.3	162
3 Su	00:05	0.5	15	**18** M	00:49	-0.1	-3
	06:03	4.6	140		06:58	5.3	162
	12:10	0.6	18		13:13	0.2	6
	18:12	5.2	158		19:13	5.3	162
4 M	00:48	0.2	6	**19** Tu	01:29	-0.1	-3
	06:49	5.1	155		07:40	5.4	165
	12:58	0.2	6		13:58	0.1	3
	18:59	5.5	168		19:55	5.2	158
5 Tu	01:30	-0.1	-3	**20** W	02:08	-0.1	-3
	07:32	5.5	168		08:18	5.5	168
	13:47	-0.1	-3		14:40	0.1	3
	19:43	5.7	174	○	20:34	5.1	155
6 W	02:13	-0.3	-9	**21** Th	02:45	0.0	0
	08:14	5.9	180		08:54	5.5	168
	14:36	-0.3	-9		15:21	0.1	3
●	20:27	5.7	174		21:13	4.9	149
7 Th	02:55	-0.5	-15	**22** F	03:20	0.1	3
	08:57	6.1	186		09:08	5.4	165
	15:24	-0.4	-12		16:00	0.2	6
	21:13	5.6	171		21:53	4.7	143
8 F	03:38	-0.5	-15	**23** Sa	03:54	0.4	12
	09:42	6.2	189		10:03	5.2	158
	16:13	-0.4	-12		16:38	0.4	12
	22:02	5.4	165		22:34	4.4	134
9 Sa	04:22	-0.3	-9	**24** Su	04:27	0.6	18
	10:31	6.1	186		10:37	5.0	152
	17:03	-0.3	-9		17:16	0.6	18
	22:56	5.1	155		23:19	4.1	125
10 Su	05:08	-0.1	-3	**25** M	05:00	0.8	24
	11:26	5.9	180		11:15	4.8	146
	17:57	0.0	0		17:55	0.8	24
	23:57	4.8	146				
11 M	05:59	0.3	9	**26** Tu	00:07	3.9	119
	12:26	5.7	174		05:35	1.1	34
	18:57	0.3	9		11:58	4.6	140
					18:40	1.0	30
12 Tu	01:01	4.5	137	**27** W	00:58	3.7	113
	07:01	0.6	18		06:17	1.3	40
	13:28	5.5	168		12:49	4.5	137
	20:07	0.5	15		19:39	1.2	37
13 W	02:05	4.4	134	**28** Th	01:50	3.7	113
	08:17	0.8	24		07:16	1.4	43
	14:31	5.3	162		13:43	4.4	134
◑	21:19	0.5	15	◐	20:47	1.2	37
14 Th	03:09	4.4	134	**29** F	02:43	3.8	116
	09:33	0.8	24		08:28	1.4	43
	15:34	5.2	158		14:40	4.5	137
	22:23	0.4	12		21:48	1.0	30
15 F	04:14	4.5	137	**30** Sa	03:37	4.0	122
	10:39	0.7	21		09:50	1.2	37
	16:37	5.1	155		15:39	4.6	140
	23:17	0.2	6		22:39	0.7	21
				31 Su	04:32	4.3	131
					10:49	0.8	24
					16:38	4.8	146
					23:25	0.3	9

November

Day	Time (h m)	Height ft	Height cm	Day	Time (h m)	Height ft	Height cm
1 M	05:25	4.8	146	**16** Tu	05:31	5.1	155
	11:42	0.4	12		11:51	0.2	6
	17:35	5.0	152		17:46	4.7	143
					23:55	-0.1	-3
2 Tu	00:10	-0.1	-3	**17** W	06:12	5.3	162
	06:15	5.3	162		12:35	0.1	3
	12:33	0.0	0		18:29	4.7	143
	18:27	5.2	158				
3 W	00:54	-0.3	-9	**18** Th	00:34	0.0	0
	07:02	5.7	174		06:49	5.4	165
	13:25	-0.3	-9		13:17	0.0	0
	19:17	5.4	165		19:09	4.6	140
4 Th	01:39	-0.5	-15	**19** F	01:12	0.1	3
	07:47	6.1	186		07:25	5.4	165
	14:16	-0.6	-18		13:58	0.0	0
●	20:05	5.4	165	○	19:49	4.5	137
5 F	02:26	-0.6	-18	**20** Sa	01:49	0.2	6
	08:33	6.3	192		07:58	5.3	162
	15:07	-0.7	-21		14:37	0.1	3
	20:54	5.3	162		20:28	4.3	131
6 Sa	03:13	-0.6	-18	**21** Su	02:26	0.3	9
	09:20	6.4	195		08:32	5.1	155
	15:58	-0.7	-21		15:16	0.2	6
	21:46	5.1	155		21:09	4.1	125
7 Su	03:02	-0.5	-15	**22** M	03:01	0.5	15
	09:12	6.2	189		09:06	4.9	149
	15:50	-0.6	-18		15:53	0.3	9
	21:43	4.9	149		21:52	3.9	119
8 M	03:52	-0.2	-6	**23** Tu	03:37	0.6	18
	10:09	5.9	180		09:42	4.8	146
	16:44	-0.3	-9		16:31	0.5	15
	22:46	4.6	140		22:38	3.7	113
9 Tu	04:47	0.1	3	**24** W	04:13	0.8	24
	11:11	5.6	171		10:23	4.6	140
	17:42	0.0	0		17:11	0.7	21
	23:50	4.5	137		23:26	3.7	113
10 W	05:49	0.5	15	**25** Th	04:53	0.9	27
	12:13	5.3	162		11:12	4.5	137
	18:47	0.2	6		17:58	0.8	24
11 Th	00:52	4.4	134	**26** F	00:16	3.7	113
	07:01	0.7	21		05:44	1.1	34
	13:13	5.1	155		12:06	4.4	134
☽	19:55	0.3	9		18:56	0.8	24
12 F	01:53	4.4	134	**27** Sa	01:06	3.8	116
	08:15	0.8	24		06:54	1.1	34
	14:13	4.9	149		13:01	4.4	134
	20:57	0.2	6	◐	19:58	0.6	18
13 Sa	02:54	4.5	137	**28** Su	01:58	4.1	125
	09:20	0.7	21		08:12	0.9	27
	15:11	4.8	146		13:57	4.5	137
	21:49	0.1	3		20:54	0.4	12
14 Su	03:52	4.7	143	**29** M	02:51	4.4	134
	10:16	0.5	15		09:10	0.6	18
	16:07	4.7	143		14:57	4.5	137
	22:35	0.0	0		21:45	0.1	3
15 M	04:45	4.9	149	**30** Tu	03:47	4.8	146
	11:05	0.3	9		10:16	0.2	6
	16:59	4.7	143		15:58	4.7	143
	23:16	0.0	0		22:33	-0.2	-6

December

Day	Time (h m)	Height ft	Height cm	Day	Time (h m)	Height ft	Height cm
1 W	04:41	5.3	162	**16** Th	05:42	4.9	149
	11:10	-0.2	-6		12:10	0.1	3
	16:58	4.8	146		18:03	4.1	125
	23:21	-0.5	-15				
2 Th	05:34	5.8	177	**17** F	00:02	0.1	3
	12:04	-0.5	-15		06:22	5.0	152
	17:54	4.9	149		12:53	0.0	0
					18:47	4.2	128
3 F	00:11	-0.7	-21	**18** Sa	00:43	0.1	3
	06:24	6.1	186		06:59	5.1	155
	12:58	-0.8	-24		13:35	-0.1	-3
	18:47	5.0	152		19:27	4.1	125
4 Sa	01:02	-0.8	-24	**19** Su	01:23	0.1	3
	07:14	6.3	192		07:35	5.1	155
	13:52	-0.9	-27		14:16	-0.1	-3
●	19:39	5.0	152	○	20:07	4.1	125
5 Su	01:55	-0.8	-24	**20** M	02:03	0.2	6
	08:04	6.3	192		08:10	5.0	152
	14:44	-1.0	-30		14:55	-0.1	-3
	20:33	4.9	149		20:47	4.0	122
6 M	02:47	-0.7	-21	**21** Tu	02:42	0.2	6
	08:57	6.1	186		08:44	4.9	149
	15:36	-0.9	-27		15:33	0.0	0
	21:31	4.7	143		21:27	3.9	119
7 Tu	03:39	-0.4	-12	**22** W	03:20	0.3	9
	09:54	5.8	177		09:20	4.8	146
	16:28	-0.6	-18		16:09	0.1	3
	22:31	4.6	140		22:10	3.8	116
8 W	04:34	-0.2	-6	**23** Th	03:57	0.4	12
	10:54	5.5	168		10:00	4.6	140
	17:22	-0.4	-12		16:46	0.2	6
	23:33	4.4	134		22:54	3.8	116
9 Th	05:32	0.2	6	**24** F	04:35	0.5	15
	11:52	5.2	158		10:44	4.6	140
	18:20	-0.1	-3		17:24	0.3	9
					23:41	3.8	116
10 F	00:32	4.4	134	**25** Sa	05:21	0.6	18
	06:37	0.5	15		11:34	4.5	137
	12:49	4.9	149		18:10	0.3	9
	19:21	0.0	0				
11 Sa	01:28	4.4	134	**26** Su	00:29	4.0	122
	07:47	0.6	18		06:21	0.7	21
	13:43	4.6	140		12:27	4.4	134
☽	20:20	0.1	3		19:05	0.3	9
12 Su	02:23	4.4	134	**27** M	01:20	4.2	128
	08:53	0.6	18		07:35	0.7	21
	14:37	4.4	134		13:23	4.3	131
	21:12	0.1	3	◐	20:06	0.1	3
13 M	03:18	4.5	137	**28** Tu	02:14	4.5	137
	09:50	0.5	15		08:48	0.5	15
	15:32	4.2	128		14:23	4.3	131
	21:58	0.1	3		21:05	0.0	0
14 Tu	04:10	4.6	140	**29** W	03:12	4.9	149
	10:40	0.4	12		09:52	0.1	3
	16:26	4.1	125		15:28	4.3	131
	22:41	0.1	3		22:01	-0.3	-9
15 W	04:58	4.8	146	**30** Th	04:12	5.2	158
	11:26	0.2	6		10:51	-0.2	-6
	17:17	4.1	125		16:34	4.4	134
	23:21	0.1	3		22:56	-0.5	-15
				31 F	05:10	5.6	171
					11:47	-0.6	-18
					17:36	4.5	137
					23:50	-0.6	-18

StationId: 8534720
Source: NOAA/NOS/CO-OPS
Station Type: Primary
Time Zone: LST_LDT
Datum: MLLW

NOAA Tide Predictions

Atlantic City, NJ,2021

Times and Heights of High and Low Waters

January

	Time	Height ft	cm		Time	Height ft	cm
1 F	02:09 08:35 15:12 21:06	-0.1 4.7 -0.2 3.3	-3 143 -6 101	**16** Sa	03:18 09:35 16:04 22:06	-0.2 4.5 -0.4 3.5	-6 137 -12 107
2 Sa	02:54 09:16 15:54 21:51	-0.1 4.6 -0.2 3.3	-3 140 -6 101	**17** Su	04:06 10:19 16:48 22:52	0.0 4.2 -0.1 3.4	0 128 -3 104
3 Su	03:42 10:00 16:39 22:41	0.0 4.5 -0.2 3.4	0 137 -6 104	**18** M	04:56 11:03 17:31 23:40	0.3 3.9 0.1 3.3	9 119 3 101
4 M	04:36 10:49 17:27 23:36	0.1 4.3 -0.2 3.5	3 131 -6 107	**19** Tu	05:48 11:50 18:14	0.5 3.5 0.2	15 107 6
5 Tu	05:37 11:43 18:19	0.2 4.0 -0.2	6 122 -6	**20** W ◖	00:31 06:44 12:40 18:59	3.3 0.7 3.2 0.4	101 21 98 12
6 W ◗	00:37 06:44 12:45 19:15	3.7 0.2 3.8 -0.2	113 6 116 -6	**21** Th	01:24 07:45 13:36 19:46	3.3 0.8 3.0 0.5	101 24 91 15
7 Th	01:41 07:54 13:51 20:13	3.9 0.2 3.6 -0.3	119 6 110 -9	**22** F	02:18 08:46 14:34 20:35	3.4 0.7 2.8 0.5	104 21 85 15
8 F	02:44 09:04 15:00 21:12	4.2 0.0 3.5 -0.3	128 0 107 -9	**23** Sa	03:12 09:43 15:32 21:24	3.6 0.6 2.8 0.4	110 18 85 12
9 Sa	03:45 10:09 16:06 22:10	4.5 -0.2 3.5 -0.4	137 -6 107 -12	**24** Su	04:03 10:36 16:25 22:12	3.8 0.5 2.9 0.3	116 15 88 9
10 Su	04:43 11:09 17:06 23:06	4.8 -0.4 3.5 -0.5	146 -12 107 -15	**25** M	04:50 11:23 17:14 22:58	4.1 0.3 3.0 0.1	125 9 91 3
11 M	05:37 12:04 18:03	5.0 -0.6 3.6	152 -18 110	**26** Tu	05:34 12:06 17:59 23:43	4.3 0.1 3.1 -0.1	131 3 94 -3
12 Tu	00:00 06:29 12:57 18:55	-0.6 5.1 -0.7 3.6	-18 155 -21 110	**27** W	06:16 12:47 18:42	4.5 -0.1 3.3	137 -3 101
13 W ●	00:51 07:18 13:46 19:45	-0.6 5.1 -0.7 3.7	-18 155 -21 113	**28** Th ○	00:27 06:57 13:27 19:23	-0.2 4.7 -0.3 3.4	-6 143 -9 104
14 Th	01:41 08:05 14:34 20:33	-0.6 5.0 -0.7 3.6	-18 152 -21 110	**29** F	01:11 07:37 14:06 20:04	-0.4 4.8 -0.4 3.6	-12 146 -12 110
15 F	02:30 08:50 15:19 21:19	-0.4 4.8 -0.5 3.6	-12 146 -15 110	**30** Sa	01:56 08:17 14:47 20:47	-0.5 4.8 -0.5 3.7	-15 146 -15 113
				31 Su	02:42 08:59 15:28 21:31	-0.5 4.7 -0.6 3.8	-15 143 -18 116

February

	Time	Height ft	cm		Time	Height ft	cm
1 M	03:32 09:43 16:12 22:19	-0.4 4.5 -0.5 3.9	-12 137 -15 119	**16** Tu	04:21 10:24 16:40 22:49	0.2 3.8 0.1 3.6	6 116 3 110
2 Tu	04:25 10:31 16:58 23:12	-0.3 4.2 -0.4 4.0	-9 128 -12 122	**17** W	05:06 11:04 17:16 23:32	0.4 3.4 0.3 3.5	12 104 9 107
3 W	05:24 11:24 17:50	-0.1 3.9 -0.3	-3 119 -9	**18** Th	05:56 11:50 17:56	0.7 3.1 0.5	21 94 15
4 Th ◖	00:11 06:30 12:25 18:47	4.0 0.1 3.6 -0.2	122 3 110 -6	**19** F ◖	00:21 06:54 12:42 18:43	3.5 0.8 2.9 0.6	107 24 88 18
5 F	01:16 07:40 13:34 19:49	4.1 0.1 3.3 -0.1	125 3 101 -3	**20** Sa	01:17 07:57 13:45 19:37	3.5 0.9 2.7 0.7	107 27 82 21
6 Sa	02:24 08:51 14:48 20:54	4.2 0.1 3.2 -0.1	128 3 98 -3	**21** Su	02:19 09:01 14:51 20:36	3.6 0.8 2.7 0.6	110 24 82 18
7 Su	03:31 09:58 15:58 21:57	4.4 0.0 3.2 -0.2	134 0 98 -6	**22** M	03:19 09:58 15:51 21:34	3.7 0.6 2.8 0.5	113 18 85 15
8 M	04:32 10:59 17:01 22:56	4.6 -0.2 3.3 -0.3	140 -6 101 -9	**23** Tu	04:14 10:49 16:44 22:28	4.0 0.4 3.0 0.2	122 12 91 6
9 Tu	05:28 11:53 17:55 23:51	4.7 -0.4 3.5 -0.4	143 -12 107 -12	**24** W	05:03 11:34 17:32 23:18	4.3 0.1 3.3 0.0	131 3 101 0
10 W	06:18 12:43 18:44	4.8 -0.5 3.6	146 -15 110	**25** Th	05:49 12:16 18:16	4.6 -0.2 3.6	140 -6 110
11 Th ●	00:41 07:04 13:28 19:29	-0.5 4.9 -0.6 3.7	-15 149 -18 113	**26** F	00:06 06:32 12:57 18:59	-0.3 4.8 -0.4 3.9	-9 146 -12 119
12 F	01:28 07:47 14:10 20:12	-0.5 4.8 -0.5 3.8	-15 146 -15 116	**27** Sa ○	00:53 07:14 13:37 19:41	-0.5 4.9 -0.6 4.2	-15 149 -18 128
13 Sa	02:13 08:27 14:50 20:52	-0.4 4.6 -0.4 3.8	-12 140 -12 116	**28** Su	01:41 07:57 14:18 20:24	-0.7 4.9 -0.7 4.4	-21 149 -21 134
14 Su	02:56 09:06 15:27 21:31	-0.2 4.4 -0.3 3.8	-6 134 -9 116				
15 M	03:38 09:45 16:04 22:09	0.0 4.1 -0.1 3.7	0 125 -3 113				

March

	Time	Height ft	cm		Time	Height ft	cm
1 M	02:29 08:40 15:00 21:10	-0.7 4.8 -0.7 4.5	-21 146 -21 137	**16** Tu	04:11 10:13 16:20 22:30	0.0 4.0 0.1 4.1	0 122 3 125
2 Tu	03:20 09:26 15:44 21:58	-0.6 4.6 -0.6 4.6	-18 140 -18 140	**17** W	04:50 10:49 16:52 23:05	0.2 3.7 0.3 4.0	6 113 9 122
3 W	04:14 10:15 16:32 22:50	-0.5 4.2 -0.5 4.5	-15 128 -15 137	**18** Th	05:31 11:27 17:25 23:43	0.4 3.4 0.5 3.9	12 104 15 119
4 Th	05:13 11:09 17:24 23:49	-0.2 3.8 -0.2 4.4	-6 116 -6 134	**19** F	06:16 12:08 18:02	0.7 3.1 0.7	21 94 21
5 F	06:17 12:12 18:24	0.0 3.5 0.0	0 107 0	**20** Sa	00:27 07:08 12:58 18:48	3.8 0.8 2.9 0.8	116 24 88 24
6 Sa ◗	00:56 07:28 13:26 19:32	4.3 0.2 3.2 0.2	131 6 98 6	**21** Su ◖	01:20 08:10 13:59 19:46	3.7 0.9 2.8 0.9	113 27 85 27
7 Su	02:07 08:39 14:43 20:42	4.3 0.2 3.1 0.2	131 6 94 6	**22** M	02:24 09:15 15:09 20:52	3.7 0.9 2.8 0.8	113 27 85 24
8 M	03:17 09:46 15:53 21:48	4.3 0.2 3.2 0.2	131 6 98 6	**23** Tu	03:31 10:15 16:15 21:58	3.8 0.7 2.9 0.7	116 21 88 21
9 Tu	04:20 10:46 16:53 22:48	4.4 0.0 3.4 0.0	134 0 104 0	**24** W	04:33 11:08 17:11 22:58	4.0 0.5 3.2 0.4	122 15 98 12
10 W	05:15 11:37 17:44 23:41	4.5 -0.1 3.7 -0.1	137 -3 113 -3	**25** Th	05:27 11:56 18:01 23:53	4.3 0.2 3.6 0.0	131 6 110 0
11 Th	06:02 12:22 18:29	4.6 -0.2 3.9	140 -6 119	**26** F	06:17 12:40 18:47	4.6 -0.2 4.1	140 -6 125
12 F	00:28 06:45 13:03 19:09	-0.2 4.6 -0.3 4.0	-6 140 -9 122	**27** Sa	00:45 07:03 13:22 19:31	-0.3 4.8 -0.4 4.5	-9 146 -12 137
13 Sa ●	01:12 07:24 13:40 19:46	-0.2 4.6 -0.3 4.1	-6 140 -9 125	**28** Su ○	01:35 07:49 14:05 20:16	-0.6 4.9 -0.7 4.8	-18 149 -21 146
14 Su	01:53 09:01 15:15 21:21	-0.2 4.5 -0.2 4.1	-6 137 -6 125	**29** M	02:25 08:34 14:48 21:01	-0.8 4.9 -0.7 5.1	-24 149 -21 155
15 M	03:32 09:37 15:48 21:55	-0.1 4.3 -0.1 4.1	-3 131 -3 125	**30** Tu	03:16 09:21 15:32 21:48	-0.8 4.7 -0.7 5.2	-24 143 -21 158
				31 W	04:08 10:09 16:19 22:37	-0.7 4.5 -0.6 5.1	-21 137 -18 155

StationId: 8534720
Source: NOAA/NOS/CO-OPS
Station Type: Primary
Time Zone: LST_LDT
Datum: MLLW

NOAA Tide Predictions

Atlantic City, NJ, 2021

Times and Heights of High and Low Waters

April

Day	Time (h m)	Height (ft)	Height (cm)
1 Th	05:03	-0.5	-15
	11:01	4.1	125
	17:09	-0.3	-9
	23:31	5.0	152
2 F	06:02	-0.2	-6
	11:59	3.8	116
	18:05	0.0	0
3 Sa	00:31	4.7	143
	07:06	0.0	0
	13:05	3.5	107
	19:08	0.3	9
4 ◑ Su	01:38	4.5	137
	08:14	0.2	6
	14:20	3.3	101
	20:18	0.5	15
5 M	02:50	4.3	131
	09:23	0.3	9
	15:35	3.3	101
	21:30	0.5	15
6 Tu	04:00	4.3	131
	10:28	0.3	9
	16:42	3.5	107
	22:36	0.5	15
7 W	05:01	4.3	131
	11:23	0.2	6
	17:38	3.7	113
	23:35	0.3	9
8 Th	05:54	4.3	131
	12:11	0.1	3
	18:25	3.9	119
9 F	00:25	0.2	6
	06:39	4.4	134
	12:53	0.0	0
	19:05	4.1	125
10 Sa	01:11	0.1	3
	07:20	4.4	134
	13:31	0.0	0
	19:42	4.3	131
11 Su	01:52	0.0	0
	07:57	4.3	131
	14:05	0.0	0
	20:17	4.4	134
12 ● M	02:32	0.0	0
	08:34	4.2	128
	14:38	0.0	0
	20:50	4.5	137
13 Tu	03:10	0.0	0
	09:09	4.0	122
	15:09	0.1	3
	21:23	4.5	137
14 W	03:47	0.1	3
	09:45	3.8	116
	15:40	0.3	9
	21:55	4.4	134
15 Th	04:25	0.3	9
	10:21	3.6	110
	16:11	0.5	15
	22:29	4.3	131
16 F	05:04	0.5	15
	10:58	3.4	104
	16:45	0.6	18
	23:06	4.2	128
17 Sa	05:47	0.6	18
	11:38	3.1	94
	17:23	0.8	24
	23:48	4.1	125
18 Su	06:35	0.8	24
	12:26	3.0	91
	18:10	0.9	27
19 M	00:38	4.0	122
	07:31	0.9	27
	13:25	2.9	88
	19:08	1.0	30
20 ◐ Tu	01:38	3.9	119
	08:31	0.8	24
	14:32	3.0	91
	20:16	0.9	27
21 W	02:44	4.0	122
	09:30	0.7	21
	15:38	3.2	98
	21:25	0.7	21
22 Th	03:49	4.1	125
	10:24	0.4	12
	16:36	3.6	110
	22:29	0.5	15
23 F	04:48	4.3	131
	11:14	0.1	3
	17:28	4.0	122
	23:28	0.1	3
24 Sa	05:42	4.5	137
	12:01	-0.2	-6
	18:16	4.5	137
25 Su	00:24	-0.3	-9
	06:33	4.7	143
	12:47	-0.5	-15
	19:04	5.0	152
26 M	01:17	-0.6	-18
	07:23	4.7	143
	13:32	-0.6	-18
	19:51	5.3	162
27 ○ Tu	02:09	-0.8	-24
	08:13	4.7	143
	14:19	-0.7	-21
	20:39	5.6	171
28 W	03:02	-0.8	-24
	09:03	4.5	137
	15:07	-0.6	-18
	21:28	5.6	171
29 Th	03:55	-0.7	-21
	09:55	4.3	131
	15:57	-0.4	-12
	22:19	5.5	168
30 F	04:51	-0.5	-15
	10:50	4.0	122
	16:50	-0.2	-6
	23:15	5.2	158

May

Day	Time (h m)	Height (ft)	Height (cm)
1 Sa	05:50	-0.3	-9
	11:50	3.8	116
	17:49	0.1	3
2 Su	00:14	4.9	149
	06:52	0.0	0
	12:56	3.5	107
	18:53	0.4	12
3 ◑ M	01:19	4.6	140
	07:56	0.2	6
	14:07	3.4	104
	20:03	0.6	18
4 Tu	02:27	4.3	131
	09:00	0.3	9
	15:17	3.5	107
	21:12	0.7	21
5 W	03:32	4.2	128
	09:59	0.3	9
	16:19	3.6	110
	22:16	0.7	21
6 Th	04:31	4.1	125
	10:51	0.3	9
	17:12	3.9	119
	23:13	0.6	18
7 F	05:23	4.1	125
	11:36	0.3	9
	17:56	4.1	125
8 Sa	00:03	0.4	12
	06:08	4.0	122
	12:16	0.2	6
	18:36	4.3	131
9 Su	00:48	0.3	9
	06:49	4.0	122
	12:53	0.2	6
	19:12	4.4	134
10 M	01:30	0.2	6
	07:28	3.9	119
	13:28	0.2	6
	19:46	4.6	140
11 ● Tu	02:10	0.2	6
	08:06	3.9	119
	14:01	0.2	6
	20:20	4.6	140
12 W	02:48	0.2	6
	08:43	3.8	116
	14:33	0.3	9
	20:54	4.7	143
13 Th	03:26	0.2	6
	09:20	3.6	110
	15:06	0.4	12
	21:28	4.6	140
14 F	04:04	0.3	9
	09:58	3.4	104
	15:40	0.5	15
	22:03	4.5	137
15 Sa	04:43	0.4	12
	10:36	3.3	101
	16:16	0.6	18
	22:40	4.4	134
16 Su	05:25	0.6	18
	11:17	3.2	98
	16:57	0.8	24
	23:21	4.3	131
17 M	06:10	0.6	18
	12:04	3.1	94
	17:45	0.9	27
18 Tu	00:08	4.2	128
	07:00	0.7	21
	12:58	3.1	94
	18:42	0.9	27
19 ◑ W	01:03	4.1	125
	07:53	0.6	18
	14:00	3.3	101
	19:48	0.9	27
20 Th	02:04	4.1	125
	08:48	0.5	15
	15:00	3.5	107
	20:57	0.7	21
21 F	03:08	4.2	128
	09:41	0.3	9
	16:01	3.9	119
	22:03	0.5	15
22 Sa	04:10	4.2	128
	10:33	0.0	0
	16:55	4.4	134
	23:05	0.1	3
23 Su	05:09	4.3	131
	11:24	-0.2	-6
	17:48	4.9	149
24 M	00:04	-0.2	-6
	06:05	4.4	134
	12:14	-0.4	-12
	18:38	5.3	162
25 Tu	01:00	-0.5	-15
	07:00	4.4	134
	13:04	-0.6	-18
	19:29	5.6	171
26 ○ W	01:55	-0.7	-21
	07:53	4.4	134
	13:54	-0.6	-18
	20:20	5.8	177
27 Th	02:49	-0.7	-21
	08:47	4.3	131
	14:46	-0.5	-15
	21:11	5.7	174
28 F	03:43	-0.7	-21
	09:42	4.1	125
	15:39	-0.3	-9
	22:04	5.6	171
29 Sa	04:38	-0.5	-15
	10:38	4.0	122
	16:34	-0.1	-3
	22:59	5.3	162
30 Su	05:34	-0.3	-9
	11:37	3.8	116
	17:33	0.2	6
	23:56	4.9	149
31 M	06:32	-0.1	-3
	12:39	3.7	113
	18:35	0.5	15

June

Day	Time (h m)	Height (ft)	Height (cm)
1 Tu	00:55	4.6	140
	07:30	0.1	3
	13:44	3.6	110
	19:40	0.7	21
2 ◐ W	01:56	4.3	131
	08:27	0.3	9
	14:46	3.6	110
	20:45	0.8	24
3 Th	02:55	4.0	122
	09:20	0.4	12
	15:44	3.8	116
	21:47	0.8	24
4 F	03:52	3.9	119
	10:09	0.4	12
	16:35	3.9	119
	22:44	0.8	24
5 Sa	04:44	3.7	113
	10:54	0.4	12
	17:20	4.1	125
	23:36	0.6	18
6 Su	05:31	3.7	113
	11:35	0.4	12
	18:01	4.3	131
7 M	00:22	0.5	15
	06:16	3.6	110
	12:13	0.4	12
	18:39	4.5	137
8 Tu	01:05	0.4	12
	06:58	3.6	110
	12:50	0.4	12
	19:16	4.6	140
9 W	01:47	0.3	9
	07:39	3.6	110
	13:26	0.4	12
	19:53	4.7	143
10 ● Th	02:26	0.3	9
	08:19	3.5	107
	14:02	0.4	12
	20:29	4.8	146
11 F	03:05	0.3	9
	08:58	3.5	107
	14:39	0.4	12
	21:06	4.7	143
12 Sa	03:44	0.3	9
	09:37	3.4	104
	15:16	0.5	15
	21:42	4.7	143
13 Su	04:23	0.3	9
	10:17	3.3	101
	15:55	0.6	18
	22:20	4.6	140
14 M	05:03	0.4	12
	10:58	3.3	101
	16:39	0.6	18
	23:01	4.5	137
15 Tu	05:45	0.4	12
	11:44	3.3	101
	17:28	0.7	21
	23:45	4.4	134
16 W	06:30	0.4	12
	12:34	3.4	104
	18:24	0.7	21
17 ◑ Th	00:35	4.3	131
	07:18	0.3	9
	13:30	3.6	110
	19:27	0.7	21
18 F	01:32	4.2	128
	08:10	0.2	6
	14:30	3.9	119
	20:34	0.6	18
19 Sa	02:34	4.1	125
	09:03	0.1	3
	15:29	4.3	131
	21:41	0.4	12
20 Su	03:38	4.0	122
	09:58	0.0	0
	16:27	4.7	143
	22:46	0.2	6
21 M	04:42	4.0	122
	10:53	-0.2	-6
	17:24	5.1	155
	23:47	-0.1	-3
22 Tu	05:43	4.0	122
	11:48	-0.3	-9
	18:18	5.4	165
23 W	00:46	-0.3	-9
	06:42	4.1	125
	12:42	-0.4	-12
	19:12	5.6	171
24 ○ Th	01:41	-0.5	-15
	07:39	4.1	125
	13:36	-0.4	-12
	20:05	5.7	174
25 F	02:36	-0.6	-18
	08:34	4.1	125
	14:30	-0.4	-12
	20:57	5.7	174
26 Sa	03:29	-0.5	-15
	09:28	4.1	125
	15:24	-0.2	-6
	21:49	5.5	168
27 Su	04:21	-0.4	-12
	10:22	4.0	122
	16:19	0.0	0
	22:40	5.2	158
28 M	05:13	-0.3	-9
	11:17	3.9	119
	17:14	0.2	6
	23:32	4.9	149
29 Tu	06:04	-0.1	-3
	12:12	3.8	116
	18:11	0.5	15
30 W	00:24	4.5	137
	06:55	0.2	6
	13:09	3.8	116
	19:10	0.7	21

StationId: 8534720
Source: NOAA/NOS/CO-OPS
Station Type: Primary
Time Zone: LST_LDT
Datum: MLLW

NOAA Tide Predictions

Atlantic City, NJ,2021

Times and Heights of High and Low Waters

July

Day	Time	ft	cm	Day	Time	ft	cm
1 Th ☽	01:17	4.2	128	**16** F	00:12	4.4	134
	07:45	0.3	9		06:46	0.2	6
	14:05	3.8	116		13:02	4.1	125
	20:10	0.9	27		19:10	0.6	18
2 F	02:12	3.9	119	**17** Sa ☾	01:07	4.2	128
	08:34	0.5	15		07:37	0.2	6
	14:59	3.8	116		14:01	4.3	131
	21:11	1.0	30		20:16	0.6	18
3 Sa	03:06	3.6	110	**18** Su	02:09	4.0	122
	09:21	0.6	18		08:32	0.2	6
	15:50	3.9	119		15:03	4.6	140
	22:09	0.9	27		21:25	0.5	15
4 Su	04:01	3.5	107	**19** M	03:16	3.8	116
	10:07	0.6	18		09:31	0.1	3
	16:38	4.1	125		16:05	4.8	146
	23:03	0.9	27		22:32	0.3	9
5 M	04:53	3.4	104	**20** Tu	04:25	3.8	116
	10:51	0.6	18		10:31	0.0	0
	17:23	4.3	131		17:06	5.1	155
	23:53	0.7	21		23:35	0.1	3
6 Tu	05:42	3.4	104	**21** W	05:30	3.8	116
	11:33	0.6	18		11:31	-0.1	-3
	18:06	4.5	137		18:04	5.4	165
7 W	00:39	0.6	18	**22** Th	00:34	-0.1	-3
	06:29	3.4	104		06:31	3.9	119
	12:15	0.6	18		12:28	-0.2	-6
	18:47	4.6	140		18:59	5.5	168
8 Th	01:22	0.5	15	**23** F	01:29	-0.3	-9
	07:13	3.4	104		07:28	4.0	122
	12:56	0.5	15		13:24	-0.2	-6
	19:27	4.8	146		19:52	5.6	171
9 F	02:02	0.4	12	**24** Sa ○	02:21	-0.4	-12
	07:55	3.5	107		08:21	4.1	125
	13:36	0.4	12		14:17	-0.2	-6
	20:06	4.8	146		20:42	5.6	171
10 Sa ●	02:42	0.3	9	**25** Su	03:10	-0.4	-12
	08:36	3.5	107		09:12	4.2	128
	14:16	0.4	12		15:09	-0.1	-3
	20:45	4.9	149		21:30	5.4	165
11 Su	03:20	0.2	6	**26** M	03:58	-0.3	-9
	09:15	3.6	110		10:01	4.2	128
	14:57	0.4	12		16:00	0.0	0
	21:22	4.9	149		22:17	5.1	155
12 M	03:58	0.2	6	**27** Tu	04:44	-0.1	-3
	09:55	3.6	110		10:49	4.1	125
	15:39	0.4	12		16:51	0.3	9
	22:01	4.8	146		23:03	4.8	146
13 Tu	04:37	0.2	6	**28** W	05:29	0.1	3
	10:36	3.7	113		11:37	4.1	125
	16:24	0.4	12		17:42	0.5	15
	22:41	4.7	143		23:48	4.4	134
14 W	05:17	0.2	6	**29** Th	06:13	0.3	9
	11:20	3.8	116		12:25	4.0	122
	17:13	0.5	15		18:35	0.8	24
	23:24	4.6	140				
15 Th	05:59	0.2	6	**30** F	00:35	4.1	125
	12:09	3.9	119		06:57	0.5	15
	18:08	0.6	18		13:15	3.9	119
					19:31	1.0	30
				31 Sa ☾	01:25	3.7	113
					07:41	0.7	21
					14:06	3.9	119
					20:29	1.1	34

August

Day	Time	ft	cm	Day	Time	ft	cm
1 Su	02:19	3.5	107	**16** M	01:53	3.8	116
	08:28	0.9	27		08:09	0.4	12
	14:59	4.0	122		14:43	4.8	146
	21:29	1.1	34		21:13	0.6	18
2 M	03:17	3.3	101	**17** Tu	03:06	3.7	113
	09:17	0.9	27		09:13	0.4	12
	15:53	4.1	125		15:51	4.9	149
	22:28	1.1	34		22:22	0.5	15
3 Tu	04:15	3.2	98	**18** W	04:19	3.7	113
	10:06	0.9	27		10:19	0.3	9
	16:44	4.2	128		16:55	5.1	155
	23:21	1.0	30		23:25	0.3	9
4 W	05:10	3.3	101	**19** Th	05:25	3.8	116
	10:56	0.8	24		11:22	0.2	6
	17:33	4.4	134		17:54	5.2	158
5 Th	00:09	0.8	24	**20** F	00:22	0.1	3
	06:00	3.4	104		06:24	4.0	122
	11:43	0.7	21		12:20	0.1	3
	18:18	4.6	140		18:48	5.4	165
6 F	00:53	0.6	18	**21** Sa	01:14	-0.1	-3
	06:46	3.5	107		07:17	4.2	128
	12:28	0.6	18		13:14	0.0	0
	19:01	4.8	146		19:38	5.4	165
7 Sa	01:33	0.4	12	**22** Su ○	02:02	-0.1	-3
	07:29	3.6	110		08:05	4.3	131
	13:12	0.4	12		14:04	0.0	0
	19:41	5.0	152		20:24	5.4	165
8 Su ●	02:12	0.3	9	**23** M	02:46	-0.2	-6
	08:10	3.8	116		08:50	4.4	134
	13:55	0.3	9		14:52	0.0	0
	20:21	5.1	155		21:07	5.2	158
9 M	02:50	0.2	6	**24** Tu	03:28	-0.1	-3
	08:49	4.0	122		09:33	4.4	134
	14:38	0.2	6		15:39	0.1	3
	20:59	5.1	155		21:49	5.0	152
10 Tu	03:27	0.1	3	**25** W	04:09	0.1	3
	09:29	4.1	125		10:15	4.4	134
	15:22	0.2	6		16:24	0.3	9
	21:38	5.0	152		22:30	4.7	143
11 W	04:05	0.0	0	**26** Th	04:47	0.3	9
	10:11	4.3	131		10:56	4.3	131
	16:09	0.2	6		17:10	0.6	18
	22:19	4.9	149		23:11	4.3	131
12 Th	04:46	0.0	0	**27** F	05:26	0.5	15
	10:55	4.4	134		11:37	4.3	131
	16:59	0.3	9		17:58	0.8	24
	23:03	4.7	143		23:54	3.9	119
13 F	05:29	0.1	3	**28** Sa	06:04	0.8	24
	11:43	4.5	137		12:21	4.1	125
	17:55	0.4	12		18:49	1.1	34
	23:52	4.4	134				
14 Sa	06:16	0.2	6	**29** Su	00:40	3.6	110
	12:37	4.6	140		06:46	1.0	30
	18:56	0.5	15		13:10	4.1	125
					19:46	1.2	37
15 Su ☾	00:48	4.1	125	**30** M ☾	01:34	3.4	104
	07:09	0.3	9		07:32	1.1	34
	13:37	4.7	143		14:05	4.0	122
	20:03	0.6	18		20:48	1.3	40
				31 Tu	02:35	3.2	98
					08:26	1.2	37
					15:05	4.1	125
					21:49	1.3	40

September

Day	Time	ft	cm	Day	Time	ft	cm
1 W	03:39	3.2	98	**16** Th	04:18	3.7	113
	09:23	1.2	37		10:13	0.6	18
	16:04	4.2	128		16:45	4.9	149
	22:45	1.1	34		23:13	0.4	12
2 Th	04:38	3.3	101	**17** F	05:21	3.9	119
	10:20	1.1	34		11:16	0.4	12
	16:58	4.4	134		17:43	5.1	155
	23:34	0.9	27				
3 F	05:30	3.4	104	**18** Sa	00:06	0.2	6
	11:13	0.9	27		06:15	4.1	125
	17:46	4.6	140		12:12	0.3	9
					18:34	5.1	155
4 Sa	00:18	0.7	21	**19** Su	00:54	0.1	3
	06:17	3.7	113		07:02	4.4	134
	12:02	0.6	18		13:03	0.2	6
	18:30	4.9	149		19:19	5.1	155
5 Su	00:58	0.4	12	**20** M ○	01:37	0.0	0
	06:59	4.0	122		07:45	4.5	137
	12:48	0.4	12		13:49	0.1	3
	19:12	5.0	152		20:01	5.0	152
6 M	01:36	0.2	6	**21** Tu	02:17	0.0	0
	07:40	4.3	131		08:25	4.7	143
	13:33	0.2	6		14:33	0.1	3
	19:53	5.2	158		20:41	4.9	149
7 Tu ●	02:14	0.0	0	**22** W	02:54	0.1	3
	08:20	4.5	137		09:03	4.7	143
	14:19	0.0	0		15:16	0.2	6
	20:33	5.2	158		21:19	4.7	143
8 W	02:53	-0.1	-3	**23** Th	03:30	0.2	6
	09:01	4.8	146		09:39	4.7	143
	15:05	-0.1	-3		15:57	0.4	12
	21:14	5.1	155		21:57	4.4	134
9 Th	03:33	-0.1	-3	**24** F	04:04	0.4	12
	09:44	4.9	149		10:15	4.6	140
	15:54	0.0	0		16:39	0.6	18
	21:58	4.9	149		22:35	4.1	125
10 F	04:15	-0.1	-3	**25** Sa	04:38	0.7	21
	10:29	5.0	152		10:53	4.5	137
	16:46	0.1	3		17:23	0.8	24
	22:45	4.6	140		23:16	3.8	116
11 Sa	05:00	0.0	0	**26** Su	05:13	0.9	27
	11:19	5.0	152		11:33	4.3	131
	17:42	0.3	9		18:11	1.0	30
	23:37	4.3	131				
12 Su	05:50	0.2	6	**27** M	00:01	3.5	107
	12:15	5.0	152		05:52	1.1	34
	18:45	0.4	12		12:18	4.2	128
					19:05	1.2	37
13 M ☾	00:37	3.9	119	**28** Tu	00:53	3.2	98
	06:48	0.4	12		06:39	1.3	40
	13:19	4.9	149		13:13	4.1	125
	19:53	0.6	18		20:05	1.3	40
14 Tu	01:48	3.7	113	**29** W ☾	01:56	3.1	94
	07:54	0.6	18		07:37	1.3	40
	14:29	4.8	146		14:15	4.1	125
	21:04	0.6	18		21:07	1.3	40
15 W	03:05	3.6	110	**30** Th	03:04	3.1	94
	09:04	0.6	18		08:41	1.3	40
	15:40	4.8	146		15:19	4.1	125
	22:12	0.5	15		22:04	1.1	34

StationId: 8534720
Source: NOAA/NOS/CO-OPS
Station Type: Primary
Time Zone: LST_LDT
Datum: MLLW

NOAA Tide Predictions

Atlantic City, NJ, 2021

Times and Heights of High and Low Waters

October

Day	Time (h m)	Height (ft)	Height (cm)
1 F	04:05	3.3	101
	09:44	1.1	34
	16:17	4.3	131
	22:53	0.9	27
2 Sa	04:57	3.6	110
	10:42	0.9	27
	17:09	4.6	140
	23:37	0.6	18
3 Su	05:44	3.9	119
	11:34	0.6	18
	17:55	4.8	146
4 M	00:18	0.3	9
	06:27	4.3	131
	12:23	0.3	9
	18:39	5.0	152
5 Tu	00:58	0.0	0
	07:09	4.7	143
	13:11	0.0	0
	19:23	5.1	155
6 W ●	01:38	-0.2	-6
	07:51	5.0	152
	13:59	-0.2	-6
	20:06	5.0	152
7 Th	02:19	-0.3	-9
	08:34	5.3	162
	14:48	-0.3	-9
	20:51	4.9	149
8 F	03:01	-0.3	-9
	09:19	5.5	168
	15:39	-0.3	-9
	21:38	4.7	143
9 Sa	03:47	-0.2	-6
	10:07	5.5	168
	16:33	-0.2	-6
	22:29	4.4	134
10 Su	04:36	0.0	0
	10:59	5.3	162
	17:31	0.0	0
	23:25	4.1	125
11 M	05:31	0.2	6
	11:58	5.1	155
	18:34	0.3	9
12 Tu	00:31	3.8	116
	06:42	0.5	15
	13:04	4.9	149
	19:42	0.4	12
13 W ◑	01:45	3.6	110
	07:43	0.7	21
	14:16	4.7	143
	20:52	0.5	15
14 Th	03:02	3.6	110
	08:56	0.7	21
	15:26	4.7	143
	21:56	0.4	12
15 F	04:11	3.8	116
	10:05	0.7	21
	16:30	4.7	143
	22:54	0.3	9
16 Sa	05:10	4.0	122
	11:06	0.5	15
	17:25	4.7	143
	23:44	0.2	6
17 Su	05:59	4.3	131
	12:00	0.4	12
	18:13	4.7	143
18 M	00:27	0.1	3
	06:43	4.5	137
	12:50	0.2	6
	18:56	4.7	143
19 Tu	01:07	0.1	3
	07:22	4.6	140
	13:32	0.2	6
	19:36	4.6	140
20 W ○	01:44	0.1	3
	07:58	4.7	143
	14:13	0.2	6
	20:14	4.4	134
21 Th	02:18	0.2	6
	08:32	4.8	146
	14:53	0.2	6
	20:50	4.2	128
22 F	02:51	0.3	9
	09:06	4.8	146
	15:33	0.3	9
	21:27	4.0	122
23 Sa	03:24	0.5	15
	09:40	4.7	143
	16:12	0.5	15
	22:05	3.7	113
24 Su	03:56	0.7	21
	10:16	4.6	140
	16:54	0.7	21
	22:45	3.5	107
25 M	04:31	0.8	24
	10:54	4.4	134
	17:38	0.9	27
	23:28	3.3	101
26 Tu	05:10	1.0	30
	11:37	4.2	128
	18:28	1.0	30
27 W	00:19	3.1	94
	05:57	1.2	37
	12:28	4.1	125
	19:24	1.1	34
28 Th ◐	01:19	3.0	91
	06:54	1.2	37
	13:27	4.0	122
	20:22	1.0	30
29 F	02:25	3.1	94
	08:01	1.2	37
	14:30	4.0	122
	21:17	0.9	27
30 Sa	03:26	3.3	101
	09:08	1.0	30
	15:31	4.2	128
	22:07	0.7	21
31 Su	04:20	3.6	110
	10:09	0.8	24
	16:26	4.3	131
	22:53	0.4	12

November

Day	Time (h m)	Height (ft)	Height (cm)
1 M	05:08	4.1	125
	11:06	0.4	12
	17:18	4.5	137
	23:37	0.0	0
2 Tu	05:54	4.5	137
	11:59	0.1	3
	18:06	4.6	140
3 W	00:20	-0.2	-6
	06:39	5.0	152
	12:48	-0.3	-9
	18:54	4.7	143
4 Th ●	01:04	-0.4	-12
	07:24	5.4	165
	13:41	-0.5	-15
	19:42	4.7	143
5 F	01:49	-0.6	-18
	08:10	5.6	171
	14:33	-0.6	-18
	20:31	4.5	137
6 Sa	02:35	-0.5	-15
	08:58	5.7	174
	15:26	-0.6	-18
	21:22	4.4	134
7 Su	02:24	-0.4	-12
	08:49	5.6	171
	15:21	-0.4	-12
	21:17	4.1	125
8 M	03:17	-0.2	-6
	09:44	5.4	165
	16:19	-0.2	-6
	22:16	3.8	116
9 Tu	04:15	0.1	3
	10:43	5.1	155
	17:21	0.0	0
	23:22	3.6	110
10 W	05:20	0.4	12
	11:48	4.8	146
	18:26	0.2	6
11 Th ◑	00:35	3.5	107
	06:30	0.6	18
	12:56	4.5	137
	19:31	0.2	6
12 F	01:47	3.6	110
	07:42	0.6	18
	14:04	4.4	134
	20:31	0.2	6
13 Sa	02:52	3.7	113
	08:49	0.6	18
	15:05	4.3	131
	21:25	0.2	6
14 Su	03:48	4.0	122
	09:45	0.5	15
	15:59	4.2	128
	22:13	0.1	3
15 M	04:36	4.2	128
	10:42	0.4	12
	16:46	4.1	125
	22:56	0.1	3
16 Tu	05:17	4.4	134
	11:29	0.3	9
	17:29	4.0	122
	23:34	0.1	3
17 W	05:55	4.5	137
	12:13	0.2	6
	18:09	4.0	122
18 Th	00:10	0.1	3
	06:30	4.6	140
	12:53	0.1	3
	18:48	3.9	119
19 F ○	00:44	0.2	6
	07:04	4.7	143
	13:33	0.1	3
	19:25	3.7	113
20 Sa	01:18	0.2	6
	07:39	4.7	143
	14:13	0.2	6
	20:03	3.6	110
21 Su	01:51	0.3	9
	08:13	4.6	140
	14:50	0.3	9
	20:41	3.4	104
22 M	02:25	0.5	15
	08:49	4.5	137
	15:30	0.4	12
	21:21	3.2	98
23 Tu	03:01	0.6	18
	09:27	4.4	134
	16:12	0.5	15
	22:02	3.1	94
24 W	03:40	0.7	21
	10:10	4.2	128
	16:56	0.6	18
	22:49	3.0	91
25 Th	04:26	0.8	24
	10:52	4.1	125
	17:44	0.7	21
	23:43	2.9	88
26 F	05:21	0.9	27
	11:44	4.0	122
	18:35	0.6	18
27 Sa ◑	00:42	3.1	94
	06:25	0.9	27
	12:42	3.9	119
	19:27	0.5	15
28 Su	01:42	3.3	101
	07:32	0.8	24
	13:43	3.9	119
	20:18	0.3	9
29 M	02:39	3.7	113
	08:37	0.6	18
	14:43	4.0	122
	21:08	0.0	0
30 Tu	03:32	4.1	125
	09:39	0.2	6
	15:41	4.0	122
	21:57	-0.2	-6

December

Day	Time (h m)	Height (ft)	Height (cm)
1 W	04:22	4.6	140
	10:37	-0.1	-3
	16:36	4.1	125
	22:46	-0.5	-15
2 Th	05:12	5.1	155
	11:32	-0.4	-12
	17:30	4.2	128
	23:35	-0.7	-21
3 F	06:01	5.4	165
	12:26	-0.7	-21
	18:23	4.2	128
4 Sa ●	00:25	-0.8	-24
	06:51	5.6	171
	13:20	-0.8	-24
	19:16	4.1	125
5 Su	01:16	-0.8	-24
	07:42	5.7	174
	14:13	-0.8	-24
	20:09	4.0	122
6 M	02:08	-0.6	-18
	08:35	5.6	171
	15:08	-0.7	-21
	21:05	3.9	119
7 Tu	03:03	-0.4	-12
	09:30	5.3	162
	16:04	-0.5	-15
	22:04	3.7	113
8 W	04:02	-0.2	-6
	10:26	5.0	152
	17:02	-0.3	-9
	23:06	3.6	110
9 Th	05:04	0.1	3
	11:26	4.6	140
	18:01	-0.2	-6
10 F	00:12	3.5	107
	06:10	0.3	9
	12:28	4.3	131
	18:59	0.0	0
11 Sa ◑	01:18	3.5	107
	07:17	0.5	15
	13:30	4.0	122
	19:56	0.1	3
12 Su	02:20	3.6	110
	08:23	0.5	15
	14:30	3.7	113
	20:48	0.1	3
13 M	03:16	3.8	116
	09:24	0.5	15
	15:25	3.6	110
	21:36	0.1	3
14 Tu	04:04	4.0	122
	10:18	0.4	12
	16:15	3.5	107
	22:19	0.1	3
15 W	04:47	4.1	125
	11:07	0.3	9
	17:01	3.4	104
	22:59	0.1	3
16 Th	05:26	4.3	131
	11:52	0.2	6
	17:43	3.4	104
	23:38	0.1	3
17 F	06:04	4.4	134
	12:33	0.1	3
	18:24	3.4	104
18 Sa	00:14	0.1	3
	06:41	4.5	137
	13:13	0.0	0
	19:04	3.3	101
19 Su ○	00:51	0.1	3
	07:17	4.5	137
	13:52	0.0	0
	19:43	3.3	101
20 M	01:26	0.1	3
	07:53	4.5	137
	14:31	0.1	3
	20:22	3.2	98
21 Tu	02:03	0.2	6
	08:29	4.5	137
	15:08	0.1	3
	21:00	3.1	94
22 W	02:40	0.3	9
	09:06	4.4	134
	15:46	0.2	6
	21:40	3.0	91
23 Th	03:20	0.4	12
	09:43	4.2	128
	16:25	0.2	6
	22:22	3.0	91
24 F	04:05	0.4	12
	10:24	4.1	125
	17:07	0.2	6
	23:08	3.1	94
25 Sa	04:56	0.5	15
	11:09	3.9	119
	17:51	0.2	6
26 Su	00:01	3.2	98
	05:55	0.5	15
	12:01	3.8	116
	18:40	0.1	3
27 M ◑	00:59	3.4	104
	07:01	0.5	15
	13:00	3.7	113
	19:33	0.0	0
28 Tu	01:58	3.8	116
	08:09	0.3	9
	14:04	3.6	110
	20:27	-0.2	-6
29 W	02:58	4.2	128
	09:15	0.1	3
	15:09	3.6	110
	21:23	-0.3	-9
30 Th	03:55	4.6	140
	10:18	-0.2	-6
	16:12	3.6	110
	22:19	-0.5	-15
31 F	04:51	5.0	152
	11:17	-0.5	-15
	17:12	3.7	113
	23:12	-0.6	-18

StationId: 8557380
Source: NOAA/NOS/CO-OPS
Station Type: Primary
Time Zone: LST_LDT
Datum: MLLW

NOAA Tide Predictions

Lewes, DE, 2021

Times and Heights of High and Low Waters

January

Day	Time (h m)	Height (ft)	Height (cm)	Day	Time (h m)	Height (ft)	Height (cm)
1 F	03:20	-0.2	-6	16 Sa	04:18	-0.3	-9
	09:57	4.8	146		10:48	4.7	143
	16:16	-0.2	-6		17:05	-0.3	-9
	22:21	3.5	107		23:12	3.6	110
2 Sa	04:05	-0.2	-6	17 Su	05:05	-0.1	-3
	10:40	4.7	143		11:31	4.3	131
	16:58	-0.2	-6		17:48	-0.1	-3
	23:07	3.5	107		23:57	3.6	110
3 Su	04:53	-0.2	-6	18 M	05:53	0.2	6
	11:25	4.6	140		12:15	4.0	122
	17:44	-0.2	-6		18:31	0.1	3
	23:57	3.6	110				
4 M	05:46	-0.1	-3	19 Tu	00:44	3.5	107
	12:14	4.4	134		06:45	0.4	12
	18:32	-0.2	-6		13:00	3.7	113
					19:16	0.3	9
5 Tu	00:51	3.7	113	20 W	01:34	3.5	107
	06:44	0.0	0		07:41	0.6	18
	13:07	4.2	128		13:49	3.4	104
	19:24	-0.2	-6		20:02	0.4	12
6 W	01:49	3.9	119	21 Th	02:27	3.5	107
	07:49	0.1	3		08:43	0.7	21
	14:05	3.9	119		14:43	3.1	94
	20:19	-0.2	-6		20:51	0.5	15
7 Th	02:51	4.1	125	22 F	03:23	3.6	110
	08:57	0.1	3		09:46	0.7	21
	15:07	3.7	113		15:41	3.0	91
	21:16	-0.3	-9		21:41	0.5	15
8 F	03:55	4.4	134	23 Sa	04:19	3.8	116
	10:06	0.0	0		10:47	0.7	21
	16:13	3.6	110		16:39	2.9	88
	22:15	-0.3	-9		22:32	0.4	12
9 Sa	04:57	4.6	140	24 Su	05:13	4.0	122
	11:13	-0.1	-3		11:41	0.5	15
	17:18	3.5	107		17:34	3.0	91
	23:12	-0.4	-12		23:21	0.3	9
10 Su	05:56	4.9	149	25 M	06:02	4.2	128
	12:14	-0.3	-9		12:29	0.3	9
	18:20	3.6	110		18:24	3.1	94
11 M	00:08	-0.5	-15	26 Tu	00:08	0.1	3
	06:52	5.1	155		06:49	4.4	134
	13:10	-0.5	-15		13:12	0.1	3
	19:16	3.6	110		19:10	3.2	98
12 Tu	01:02	-0.6	-18	27 W	00:53	-0.1	-3
	07:44	5.2	158		06:49	4.6	140
	14:02	-0.6	-18		13:52	-0.1	-3
	20:08	3.7	113		19:53	3.4	104
13 W ●	01:53	-0.6	-18	28 Th ○	01:36	-0.3	-9
	08:33	5.2	158		08:15	4.8	146
	14:51	-0.6	-18		14:32	-0.2	-6
	20:57	3.7	113		20:36	3.6	110
14 Th	02:43	-0.6	-18	29 F	02:20	-0.4	-12
	09:20	5.1	155		08:56	4.9	149
	15:37	-0.5	-15		15:11	-0.4	-12
	21:43	3.7	113		21:18	3.7	113
15 F	03:31	-0.5	-15	30 Sa	03:04	-0.5	-15
	10:05	4.9	149		09:38	5.0	152
	16:22	-0.4	-12		15:51	-0.5	-15
	22:28	3.7	113		22:01	3.9	119
				31 Su	03:51	-0.6	-18
					10:21	4.9	149
					16:33	-0.5	-15
					22:47	4.0	122

February

Day	Time (h m)	Height (ft)	Height (cm)	Day	Time (h m)	Height (ft)	Height (cm)
1 M	04:39	-0.5	-15	16 Tu	05:20	0.1	3
	11:05	4.7	143		11:35	3.9	119
	17:17	-0.5	-15		17:42	0.1	3
	23:35	4.1	125		23:57	3.8	116
2 Tu	05:32	-0.4	-12	17 W	06:05	0.3	9
	11:53	4.4	134		12:16	3.6	110
	18:04	-0.4	-12		18:21	0.3	9
3 W	00:27	4.2	128	18 Th	00:42	3.8	116
	06:29	-0.2	-6		06:55	0.6	18
	12:45	4.0	122		13:01	3.3	101
	18:54	-0.3	-9		19:04	0.5	15
4 Th ◐	01:25	4.2	128	19 F ◐	01:31	3.7	113
	07:33	0.0	0		07:51	0.8	24
	13:43	3.7	113		13:52	3.1	94
	19:50	-0.2	-6		19:52	0.6	18
5 F	02:28	4.3	131	20 Sa	02:27	3.7	113
	08:42	0.1	3		08:54	0.8	24
	14:49	3.4	104		14:51	2.9	88
	20:51	-0.1	-3		20:47	0.7	21
6 Sa	03:35	4.4	134	21 Su	03:28	3.8	116
	09:54	0.1	3		09:59	0.8	24
	16:00	3.3	101		15:55	2.9	88
	21:55	-0.1	-3		21:46	0.6	18
7 Su	04:43	4.5	137	22 M	04:29	3.9	119
	11:04	0.1	3		11:00	0.7	21
	17:11	3.3	101		16:56	3.0	91
	22:59	-0.1	-3		22:43	0.4	12
8 M	05:46	4.7	143	23 Tu	05:27	4.2	128
	12:06	-0.1	-3		11:52	0.5	15
	18:14	3.4	104		17:52	3.2	98
	23:59	-0.2	-6		23:37	0.2	6
9 Tu	06:44	4.8	146	24 W	06:18	4.4	134
	13:00	-0.2	-6		12:38	0.2	6
	19:09	3.6	110		18:41	3.4	104
10 W	00:54	-0.4	-12	25 Th	00:27	-0.1	-3
	07:35	4.9	149		07:05	4.7	143
	13:49	-0.3	-9		13:21	-0.1	-3
	19:57	3.7	113		19:27	3.7	113
11 Th ●	01:44	-0.5	-15	26 F	01:15	-0.4	-12
	08:21	5.0	152		07:50	4.9	149
	14:33	-0.4	-12		14:02	-0.3	-9
	20:41	3.9	119		20:11	4.0	122
12 F	02:30	-0.5	-15	27 Sa ○	02:01	-0.6	-18
	09:03	4.9	149		08:33	5.0	152
	15:14	-0.4	-12		14:42	-0.5	-15
	21:21	3.9	119		20:54	4.3	131
13 Sa	03:14	-0.4	-12	28 Su	02:48	-0.7	-21
	09:42	4.7	143		09:16	5.0	152
	15:52	-0.3	-9		15:23	-0.6	-18
	22:00	3.9	119		21:39	4.5	137
14 Su	03:56	-0.3	-9				
	10:17	4.5	137				
	16:29	-0.2	-6				
	22:38	3.9	119				
15 M	04:38	-0.1	-3				
	10:57	4.2	128				
	17:06	0.0	0				
	23:17	3.9	119				

March

Day	Time (h m)	Height (ft)	Height (cm)	Day	Time (h m)	Height (ft)	Height (cm)
1 M	03:36	-0.8	-24	16 Tu	05:12	0.0	0
	10:00	4.9	149		11:25	4.1	125
	16:05	-0.6	-18		17:24	0.1	3
	22:25	4.7	143		23:40	4.3	131
2 Tu	04:26	-0.7	-21	17 W	05:51	0.2	6
	10:46	4.7	143		12:01	3.9	119
	16:49	-0.6	-18		17:58	0.3	9
	23:13	4.7	143				
3 W	05:19	-0.5	-15	18 Th	00:18	4.2	128
	11:35	4.3	131		06:33	0.4	12
	17:37	-0.4	-12		12:40	3.6	110
					18:35	0.5	15
4 Th	00:05	4.7	143	19 F	00:59	4.1	125
	06:16	-0.2	-6		07:18	0.6	18
	12:28	3.9	119		13:23	3.3	101
	18:28	-0.2	-6		19:16	0.6	18
5 F	01:03	4.6	140	20 Sa	01:46	4.0	122
	07:20	0.0	0		08:09	0.8	24
	13:28	3.6	110		14:12	3.1	94
	19:26	0.0	0		20:04	0.8	24
6 Sa ◐	02:08	4.5	137	21 Su ◐	02:39	3.9	119
	08:29	0.2	6		09:07	0.9	27
	14:38	3.4	104		15:10	3.0	91
	20:32	0.2	6		21:00	0.8	24
7 Su	03:19	4.4	134	22 M	03:41	3.9	119
	09:43	0.3	9		10:11	0.9	27
	15:54	3.3	101		16:14	3.0	91
	21:42	0.3	9		22:03	0.8	24
8 M	04:31	4.5	137	23 Tu	04:45	4.0	122
	10:53	0.3	9		11:14	0.8	24
	17:06	3.4	104		17:18	3.2	98
	22:51	0.2	6		23:07	0.6	18
9 Tu	05:36	4.6	140	24 W	05:47	4.2	128
	11:53	0.3	9		12:10	0.5	15
	18:07	3.6	110		18:17	3.4	104
	23:52	0.1	3				
10 W	06:32	4.7	143	25 Th	00:06	0.3	9
	12:45	0.0	0		06:42	4.5	137
	18:57	3.8	116		12:59	0.2	6
					19:09	3.8	116
11 Th	00:45	-0.1	-3	26 F	01:01	0.0	0
	07:21	4.7	143		07:33	4.7	143
	13:29	-0.1	-3		13:44	-0.1	-3
	19:41	4.0	122		19:57	4.2	128
12 F	01:32	-0.2	-6	27 Sa	01:52	-0.3	-9
	08:03	4.7	143		08:21	4.9	149
	14:09	-0.2	-6		14:27	-0.3	-9
	20:20	4.1	125		20:44	4.6	140
13 Sa ●	02:15	-0.3	-9	28 Su ○	02:42	-0.6	-18
	08:41	4.7	143		09:07	5.0	152
	14:45	-0.2	-6		15:10	-0.5	-15
	20:56	4.2	128		21:29	4.9	149
14 Su	03:55	-0.2	-6	29 M	03:32	-0.8	-24
	10:17	4.5	137		09:53	5.0	152
	16:19	-0.1	-3		15:53	-0.7	-21
	22:31	4.3	131		22:15	5.2	158
15 M	04:34	-0.2	-6	30 Tu	04:22	-0.8	-24
	10:51	4.3	131		10:39	4.8	146
	16:52	0.0	0		16:37	-0.6	-18
	23:05	4.3	131		23:03	5.3	162
				31 W	05:13	-0.7	-21
					11:28	4.5	137
					17:23	-0.5	-15
					23:53	5.3	162

StationId: 8557380
Source: NOAA/NOS/CO-OPS
Station Type: Primary
Time Zone: LST_LDT
Datum: MLLW

NOAA Tide Predictions

Lewes, DE, 2021

Times and Heights of High and Low Waters

April

Date	Day	Time	ft	cm
1	Th	06:07	-0.5	-15
		12:19	4.2	128
		18:13	-0.3	-9
2	F	00:46	5.1	155
		07:05	-0.2	-6
		13:15	3.9	119
		19:07	0.0	0
3	Sa	01:45	4.9	149
		08:08	0.1	3
		14:18	3.6	110
		20:08	0.3	9
4	Su	02:50	4.7	143
		09:17	0.3	9
		15:30	3.5	107
		21:18	0.5	15
5	M	04:02	4.5	137
		10:28	0.4	12
		16:45	3.5	107
		22:31	0.5	15
6	Tu	05:14	4.4	134
		11:34	0.4	12
		17:53	3.6	110
		23:40	0.4	12
7	W	06:18	4.4	134
		12:31	0.3	9
		18:50	3.8	116
8	Th	00:40	0.3	9
		07:12	4.5	137
		13:19	0.2	6
		19:37	4.0	122
9	F	01:31	0.2	6
		07:58	4.5	137
		14:00	0.1	3
		20:18	4.2	128
10	Sa	02:17	0.0	0
		08:38	4.4	134
		14:37	0.1	3
		20:54	4.4	134
11	Su	02:57	0.0	0
		09:15	4.4	134
		15:11	0.1	3
		21:28	4.5	137
12	M	03:36	0.0	0
		09:49	4.2	128
		15:43	0.1	3
		22:01	4.6	140
13	Tu	04:13	0.0	0
		10:23	4.1	125
		16:15	0.2	6
		22:34	4.6	140
14	W	04:50	0.1	3
		10:57	3.9	119
		16:47	0.3	9
		23:09	4.6	140
15	Th	05:27	0.2	6
		11:33	3.7	113
		17:21	0.4	12
		23:46	4.5	137
16	F	06:06	0.4	12
		12:12	3.5	107
		17:58	0.6	18
17	Sa	00:26	4.4	134
		06:49	0.6	18
		12:55	3.3	101
		18:39	0.7	21
18	Su	01:12	4.3	131
		07:37	0.7	21
		13:43	3.2	98
		19:28	0.8	24
19	M	02:04	4.2	128
		08:31	0.8	24
		14:39	3.2	98
		20:24	0.8	24
20	Tu	03:02	4.1	125
		09:30	0.8	24
		15:40	3.2	98
		21:28	0.8	24
21	W	04:04	4.2	128
		10:30	0.7	21
		16:43	3.4	104
		22:33	0.6	18
22	Th	05:05	4.3	131
		11:26	0.4	12
		17:42	3.8	116
		23:36	0.4	12
23	F	06:04	4.5	137
		12:17	0.2	6
		18:36	4.2	128
24	Sa	00:34	0.0	0
		06:58	4.6	140
		13:05	-0.1	-3
		19:27	4.7	143
25	Su	01:30	-0.3	-9
		07:50	4.7	143
		13:52	-0.4	-12
		20:16	5.1	155
26	M	02:23	-0.6	-18
		08:40	4.8	146
		14:37	-0.6	-18
		21:04	5.4	165
27	Tu	03:15	-0.7	-21
		09:30	4.7	143
		15:24	-0.6	-18
		21:53	5.6	171
28	W	04:07	-0.8	-24
		10:20	4.5	137
		16:11	-0.6	-18
		22:43	5.7	174
29	Th	05:00	-0.7	-21
		11:11	4.3	131
		17:00	-0.4	-12
		23:35	5.6	171
30	F	05:55	-0.5	-15
		12:06	4.1	125
		17:53	-0.2	-6

May

Date	Day	Time	ft	cm
1	Sa	00:29	5.3	162
		06:53	-0.2	-6
		13:04	3.8	116
		18:50	0.1	3
2	Su	01:28	5.0	152
		07:54	0.0	0
		14:07	3.7	113
		19:53	0.4	12
3	M	02:32	4.7	143
		08:59	0.3	9
		15:16	3.6	110
		21:02	0.6	18
4	Tu	03:39	4.5	137
		10:04	0.4	12
		16:25	3.6	110
		22:14	0.6	18
5	W	04:46	4.3	131
		11:05	0.4	12
		17:28	3.8	116
		23:21	0.6	18
6	Th	05:47	4.2	128
		11:58	0.4	12
		18:22	4.0	122
7	F	00:19	0.5	15
		06:42	4.2	128
		12:43	0.3	9
		19:08	4.2	128
8	Sa	01:10	0.4	12
		07:26	4.1	125
		13:23	0.3	9
		19:48	4.4	134
9	Su	01:56	0.3	9
		08:07	4.0	122
		14:00	0.2	6
		20:24	4.6	140
10	M	02:37	0.2	6
		08:44	4.0	122
		14:34	0.2	6
		20:58	4.7	143
11	Tu	03:15	0.2	6
		09:21	3.9	119
		15:07	0.3	9
		21:33	4.8	146
12	W	03:52	0.2	6
		09:57	3.8	116
		15:40	0.3	9
		22:07	4.8	146
13	Th	04:29	0.2	6
		10:33	3.7	113
		16:15	0.4	12
		22:43	4.7	143
14	F	05:07	0.3	9
		11:11	3.5	107
		16:51	0.5	15
		23:22	4.7	143
15	Sa	05:45	0.4	12
		11:50	3.4	104
		17:30	0.6	18
16	Su	00:02	4.6	140
		06:27	0.5	15
		12:33	3.4	104
		18:13	0.6	18
17	M	00:47	4.5	137
		07:13	0.5	15
		13:21	3.3	101
		19:02	0.7	21
18	Tu	01:36	4.4	134
		08:03	0.6	18
		14:14	3.4	104
		19:58	0.7	21
19	W	02:30	4.3	131
		08:56	0.5	15
		15:11	3.5	107
		20:59	0.7	21
20	Th	03:28	4.3	131
		09:51	0.4	12
		16:10	3.8	116
		22:04	0.5	15
21	F	04:27	4.3	131
		10:45	0.2	6
		17:09	4.1	125
		23:08	0.3	9
22	Sa	05:26	4.3	131
		11:37	0.0	0
		18:05	4.6	140
23	Su	00:10	0.1	3
		06:24	4.4	134
		12:28	-0.2	-6
		18:59	5.0	152
24	M	01:09	-0.2	-6
		07:20	4.4	134
		13:18	-0.4	-12
		19:51	5.4	165
25	Tu	02:05	-0.5	-15
		08:15	4.4	134
		14:08	-0.5	-15
		20:42	5.7	174
26	W	03:00	-0.6	-18
		09:09	4.3	131
		14:58	-0.6	-18
		21:34	5.8	177
27	Th	03:54	-0.7	-21
		10:03	4.2	128
		15:49	-0.5	-15
		22:26	5.8	177
28	F	04:47	-0.6	-18
		10:57	4.1	125
		16:41	-0.3	-9
		23:19	5.6	171
29	Sa	05:42	-0.4	-12
		11:52	4.0	122
		17:36	-0.1	-3
30	Su	00:14	5.3	162
		06:37	-0.2	-6
		12:49	3.9	119
		18:34	0.1	3
31	M	01:10	5.0	152
		07:35	0.0	0
		13:49	3.8	116
		19:35	0.4	12

June

Date	Day	Time	ft	cm
1	Tu	02:08	4.7	143
		08:33	0.2	6
		14:51	3.7	113
		20:40	0.6	18
2	W	03:08	4.4	134
		09:30	0.3	9
		15:52	3.8	116
		21:46	0.7	21
3	Th	04:08	4.1	125
		10:25	0.4	12
		16:50	3.9	119
		22:50	0.7	21
4	F	05:05	3.9	119
		11:14	0.4	12
		17:43	4.1	125
		23:49	0.7	21
5	Sa	05:58	3.8	116
		11:59	0.4	12
		18:30	4.2	128
6	Su	00:42	0.6	18
		06:46	3.7	113
		12:41	0.4	12
		19:12	4.4	134
7	M	01:30	0.5	15
		07:31	3.6	110
		13:19	0.4	12
		19:51	4.6	140
8	Tu	02:13	0.4	12
		08:12	3.6	110
		13:57	0.4	12
		20:29	4.7	143
9	W	02:53	0.3	9
		08:53	3.5	107
		14:33	0.4	12
		21:06	4.8	146
10	Th	03:32	0.3	9
		09:32	3.5	107
		15:10	0.4	12
		21:44	4.8	146
11	F	04:09	0.3	9
		10:11	3.5	107
		15:48	0.4	12
		22:23	4.8	146
12	Sa	04:47	0.3	9
		10:50	3.5	107
		23:02	4.8	146
13	Su	05:26	0.3	9
		11:31	3.5	107
		17:08	0.4	12
		23:43	4.7	143
14	M	06:06	0.3	9
		12:14	3.5	107
		17:53	0.5	15
15	Tu	00:26	4.7	143
		06:49	0.3	9
		13:00	3.5	107
		18:42	0.5	15
16	W	01:13	4.6	140
		07:35	0.3	9
		13:51	3.6	110
		19:37	0.5	15
17	Th	02:03	4.4	134
		08:24	0.2	6
		14:45	3.8	116
		20:36	0.5	15
18	F	02:57	4.3	131
		09:16	0.1	3
		15:41	4.1	125
		21:40	0.4	12
19	Sa	03:54	4.2	128
		10:09	0.0	0
		16:39	4.4	134
		22:46	0.3	9
20	Su	04:54	4.1	125
		11:02	-0.1	-3
		17:37	4.8	146
		23:50	0.1	3
21	M	05:55	4.0	122
		11:57	-0.2	-6
		18:34	5.1	155
22	Tu	00:51	-0.1	-3
		06:56	4.0	122
		19:30	5.4	165
23	W	01:50	-0.3	-9
		07:55	4.0	122
		13:45	-0.4	-12
		20:25	5.6	171
24	Th	02:46	-0.4	-12
		08:52	4.0	122
		14:38	-0.4	-12
		21:19	5.7	174
25	F	03:40	-0.5	-15
		09:48	4.0	122
		15:32	-0.4	-12
		22:12	5.7	174
26	Sa	04:33	-0.5	-15
		10:42	4.0	122
		16:25	-0.3	-9
		23:04	5.5	168
27	Su	05:25	-0.4	-12
		11:35	4.0	122
		23:55	5.2	158
28	M	06:16	-0.2	-6
		12:28	4.0	122
		18:14	0.1	3
29	Tu	00:47	4.9	149
		07:07	0.0	0
		13:21	3.9	119
		19:11	0.3	9
30	W	01:38	4.6	140
		07:58	0.1	3
		14:15	3.9	119
		20:09	0.6	18

StationId: 8557380
Source: NOAA/NOS/CO-OPS
Station Type: Primary
Time Zone: LST_LDT
Datum: MLLW

NOAA Tide Predictions

Lewes, DE,2021

Times and Heights of High and Low Waters

July

Day	Time (h m)	ft	cm	Day	Time (h m)	ft	cm
1 Th ◑	02:30	4.3	131	16 F	01:38	4.5	137
	08:48	0.3	9		07:53	0.0	0
	15:10	3.9	119		14:19	4.3	131
	21:10	0.7	21		20:18	0.4	12
2 F	03:22	3.9	119	17 Sa ◐	02:31	4.2	128
	09:37	0.4	12		08:44	0.0	0
	16:04	4.0	122		15:15	4.5	137
	22:12	0.8	24		21:22	0.4	12
3 Sa	04:16	3.7	113	18 Su	03:29	4.0	122
	10:25	0.5	15		09:38	0.0	0
	16:56	4.1	125		16:15	4.7	143
	23:12	0.8	24		22:28	0.3	9
4 Su	05:10	3.5	107	19 M	04:31	3.8	116
	11:11	0.5	15		10:34	0.0	0
	17:45	4.2	128		17:16	4.9	149
					23:34	0.2	6
5 M	00:09	0.8	24	20 Tu	05:36	3.8	116
	06:03	3.4	104		11:33	-0.1	-3
	11:56	0.6	18		18:17	5.2	158
	18:32	4.4	134				
6 Tu	01:00	0.7	21	21 W	00:38	0.1	3
	06:53	3.3	101		06:41	3.8	116
	12:39	0.5	15		12:32	-0.1	-3
	19:17	4.5	137		19:16	5.4	165
7 W	01:46	0.6	18	22 Th	01:37	-0.1	-3
	07:40	3.4	104		07:43	3.8	116
	13:22	0.5	15		13:29	-0.2	-6
	20:00	4.7	143		20:13	5.5	168
8 Th	02:28	0.5	15	23 F	02:33	-0.2	-6
	08:24	3.4	104		08:40	3.9	119
	14:03	0.4	12		14:25	-0.3	-9
	20:41	4.8	146		21:06	5.5	168
9 F	03:08	0.4	12	24 Sa ○	03:25	-0.3	-9
	09:06	3.5	107		09:33	4.0	122
	14:44	0.3	9		15:18	-0.3	-9
	21:22	4.9	149		21:57	5.5	168
10 Sa ●	03:46	0.3	9	25 Su	04:14	-0.3	-9
	09:47	3.5	107		10:24	4.1	125
	15:25	0.3	9		16:10	-0.2	-6
	22:02	4.9	149		22:46	5.3	162
11 Su	04:24	0.2	6	26 M	05:02	-0.2	-6
	10:28	3.6	110		11:14	4.2	128
	16:06	0.2	6		17:01	-0.1	-3
	22:42	4.9	149		23:32	5.1	155
12 M	05:02	0.2	6	27 Tu	05:47	-0.1	-3
	11:09	3.7	113		11:59	4.2	128
	16:49	0.2	6		17:51	0.1	3
	23:23	4.9	149				
13 Tu	05:41	0.1	3	28 W	00:17	4.8	146
	11:52	3.8	116		06:32	0.0	0
	17:35	0.2	6		12:46	4.1	125
					18:42	0.4	12
14 W	00:05	4.8	146	29 Th	01:02	4.5	137
	06:23	0.1	3		07:15	0.2	6
	12:38	3.9	119		13:33	4.1	125
	18:25	0.3	9		19:34	0.6	18
15 Th	00:50	4.7	143	30 F	01:48	4.1	125
	07:07	0.0	0		07:59	0.4	12
	13:27	4.1	125		14:21	4.1	125
	19:19	0.3	9		20:30	0.8	24
				31 Sa ◐	02:35	3.8	116
					08:45	0.6	18
					15:12	4.1	125
					21:29	0.9	27

August

Day	Time (h m)	ft	cm	Day	Time (h m)	ft	cm
1 Su	03:27	3.5	107	16 M	03:12	3.9	119
	09:32	0.7	21		09:13	0.2	6
	16:04	4.1	125		15:55	4.9	149
	22:30	1.0	30		22:16	0.5	15
2 M	04:22	3.3	101	17 Tu	04:18	3.7	113
	10:21	0.8	24		10:15	0.2	6
	16:58	4.2	128		17:01	5.0	152
	23:30	1.0	30		23:24	0.4	12
3 Tu	05:20	3.2	98	18 W	05:28	3.7	113
	11:12	0.8	24		11:19	0.2	6
	17:51	4.3	131		18:06	5.1	155
4 W	00:25	0.9	27	19 Th	00:28	0.3	9
	06:15	3.2	98		06:35	3.7	113
	12:02	0.7	21		12:21	0.1	3
	18:42	4.5	137		19:07	5.2	158
5 Th	01:14	0.7	21	20 F	01:26	0.1	3
	07:07	3.3	101		07:35	3.9	119
	12:50	0.6	18		13:20	0.0	0
	19:30	4.6	140		20:02	5.3	162
6 F	01:58	0.6	18	21 Sa	02:18	0.0	0
	07:54	3.5	107		08:28	4.1	125
	13:35	0.5	15		14:15	-0.1	-3
	20:15	4.8	146		20:53	5.3	162
7 Sa	02:38	0.4	12	22 Su ○	03:06	-0.1	-3
	08:38	3.6	110		09:17	4.3	131
	14:19	0.3	9		15:06	-0.1	-3
	20:57	5.0	152		21:40	5.3	162
8 Su ●	03:16	0.3	9	23 M	03:50	-0.1	-3
	09:20	3.8	116		10:02	4.4	134
	15:03	0.2	6		15:54	-0.1	-3
	21:38	5.1	155		22:23	5.1	155
9 M	03:54	0.1	3	24 Tu	04:32	-0.1	-3
	10:02	4.0	122		10:45	4.4	134
	15:46	0.1	3		16:40	0.0	0
	22:19	5.1	155		23:04	4.9	149
10 Tu	04:32	0.0	0	25 W	05:12	0.1	3
	10:44	4.1	125		11:26	4.4	134
	16:31	0.0	0		17:25	0.2	6
	23:00	5.0	152		23:44	4.6	140
11 W	05:12	-0.1	-3	26 Th	05:51	0.2	6
	11:27	4.3	131		12:07	4.4	134
	17:18	0.0	0		18:11	0.4	12
	23:43	4.9	149				
12 Th	05:53	-0.1	-3	27 F	00:24	4.3	131
	12:13	4.5	137		06:29	0.4	12
	18:09	0.1	3		12:48	4.3	131
					18:58	0.6	18
13 F	00:28	4.7	143	28 Sa	01:06	4.0	122
	06:37	-0.1	-3		07:09	0.6	18
	13:02	4.6	140		13:33	4.3	131
	19:03	0.2	6		19:49	0.9	27
14 Sa	01:17	4.4	134	29 Su	01:59	3.7	113
	07:24	0.0	0		07:52	0.8	24
	13:55	4.7	143		14:21	4.2	128
	20:03	0.3	9		20:45	1.0	30
15 Su ◐	02:11	4.1	125	30 M ◐	02:42	3.4	104
	08:16	0.1	3		08:40	0.9	27
	14:53	4.8	146		15:14	4.2	128
	21:07	0.4	12		21:45	1.1	34
				31 Tu	03:39	3.3	101
					09:33	1.0	30
					16:12	4.2	128
					22:47	1.1	34

September

Day	Time (h m)	ft	cm	Day	Time (h m)	ft	cm
1 W	04:40	3.2	98	16 Th	05:26	3.7	113
	10:29	1.0	30		11:12	0.4	12
	17:10	4.3	131		17:57	5.0	152
	23:45	1.0	30				
2 Th	05:39	3.3	101	17 F	00:17	0.4	12
	11:26	0.9	27		06:30	3.9	119
	18:06	4.5	137		12:16	0.3	9
					18:57	5.0	152
3 F	00:36	0.9	27	18 Sa	01:12	0.2	6
	06:34	3.5	107		07:25	4.1	125
	12:18	0.7	21		13:13	0.2	6
	18:57	4.7	143		19:49	5.1	155
4 Sa	01:21	0.7	21	19 Su	01:59	0.1	3
	07:22	3.7	113		08:14	4.3	131
	13:08	0.5	15		14:05	0.1	3
	19:44	4.9	149		20:35	5.1	155
5 Su	02:02	0.4	12	20 M ○	02:42	0.1	3
	08:08	4.0	122		08:57	4.5	137
	13:52	0.2	6		14:52	0.0	0
	20:28	5.0	152		21:17	5.0	152
6 M	02:41	0.2	6	21 Tu	03:21	0.0	0
	08:51	4.2	128		09:37	4.6	140
	14:40	0.0	0		15:36	0.1	3
	21:10	5.1	155		21:56	4.8	146
7 Tu ●	03:20	0.0	0	22 W	03:58	0.1	3
	09:33	4.5	137		10:14	4.7	143
	15:26	-0.1	-3		16:18	0.1	3
	21:52	5.1	155		22:34	4.6	140
8 W	03:59	-0.1	-3	23 Th	04:34	0.2	6
	10:17	4.8	146		10:51	4.7	143
	16:13	-0.2	-6		16:59	0.3	9
	22:35	5.0	152		23:11	4.3	131
9 Th	04:40	-0.2	-6	24 F	05:09	0.4	12
	11:01	4.9	149		11:28	4.7	143
	17:02	-0.2	-6		17:41	0.5	15
	23:20	4.8	146		23:49	4.1	125
10 F	05:22	-0.2	-6	25 Sa	05:44	0.5	15
	11:48	5.1	155		12:07	4.6	140
	17:54	-0.1	-3		18:25	0.7	21
11 Sa	00:07	4.6	140	26 Su	00:29	3.8	116
	06:08	-0.1	-3		06:22	0.7	21
	12:39	5.1	155		12:49	4.5	137
	18:49	0.1	3		19:12	0.9	27
12 Su	00:59	4.3	131	27 M	01:14	3.5	107
	06:58	0.1	3		07:04	0.9	27
	13:34	5.1	155		13:36	4.3	131
	19:50	0.3	9		20:04	1.0	30
13 M ◐	01:57	4.0	122	28 Tu	02:04	3.3	101
	07:54	0.3	9		07:52	1.0	30
	14:35	5.0	152		14:29	4.2	128
	20:56	0.5	15		21:02	1.1	34
14 Tu	03:02	3.7	113	29 W ◑	03:01	3.2	98
	08:56	0.4	12		08:48	1.1	34
	15:41	4.9	149		15:28	4.2	128
	22:07	0.5	15		22:03	1.1	34
15 W	04:14	3.6	110	30 Th	04:02	3.2	98
	10:04	0.5	15		09:49	1.1	34
	16:51	4.9	149		16:29	4.3	131
	23:15	0.5	15		23:01	1.0	30

StationId: 8557380
Source: NOAA/NOS/CO-OPS
Station Type: Primary
Time Zone: LST_LDT
Datum: MLLW

NOAA Tide Predictions

Lewes, DE, 2021

Times and Heights of High and Low Waters

October

Day	Time	ft	cm
1 F	05:03	3.4	104
	10:49	0.9	27
	17:27	4.4	134
	23:53	0.8	24
2 Sa	05:59	3.6	110
	11:46	0.7	21
	18:20	4.6	140
3 Su	00:39	0.6	18
	06:49	4.0	122
	12:39	0.4	12
	19:09	4.8	146
4 M	01:22	0.3	9
	07:35	4.3	131
	13:29	0.1	3
	19:55	5.0	152
5 Tu	02:03	0.0	0
	08:20	4.7	143
	14:18	-0.1	-3
	20:40	5.0	152
6 W ●	02:44	-0.2	-6
	09:05	5.0	152
	15:06	-0.3	-9
	21:25	5.0	152
7 Th	03:25	-0.3	-9
	09:50	5.3	162
	15:56	-0.4	-12
	22:11	4.9	149
8 F	04:09	-0.4	-12
	10:36	5.5	168
	16:46	-0.4	-12
	22:59	4.6	140
9 Sa	04:54	-0.3	-9
	11:25	5.5	168
	17:40	-0.2	-6
	23:49	4.4	134
10 Su	05:43	-0.1	-3
	12:18	5.4	165
	18:36	0.0	0
11 M	00:45	4.1	125
	06:36	0.1	3
	13:15	5.2	158
	19:38	0.2	6
12 Tu	01:47	3.8	116
	07:36	0.3	9
	14:19	5.0	152
	20:45	0.4	12
13 W ◑	02:56	3.7	113
	08:43	0.5	15
	15:28	4.8	146
	21:55	0.5	15
14 Th	04:09	3.7	113
	09:55	0.6	18
	16:38	4.8	146
	23:01	0.4	12
15 F	05:19	3.8	116
	11:05	0.5	15
	17:43	4.7	143
16 Sa	00:00	0.3	9
	06:19	4.0	122
	12:08	0.4	12
	18:40	4.7	143
17 Su	00:50	0.2	6
	07:10	4.3	131
	13:03	0.3	9
	19:29	4.7	143
18 M	01:34	0.1	3
	07:54	4.5	137
	13:52	0.2	6
	20:13	4.6	140
19 Tu	02:13	0.1	3
	08:34	4.6	140
	14:36	0.1	3
	20:52	4.5	137
20 W ○	02:49	0.1	3
	09:10	4.8	146
	15:17	0.1	3
	21:29	4.4	134
21 Th	03:23	0.2	6
	09:45	4.8	146
	15:57	0.2	6
	22:05	4.2	128
22 F	03:57	0.3	9
	10:19	4.8	146
	16:36	0.3	9
	22:41	4.0	122
23 Sa	04:30	0.4	12
	10:55	4.8	146
	17:15	0.4	12
	23:18	3.8	116
24 Su	05:05	0.5	15
	11:33	4.7	143
	17:56	0.6	18
	23:58	3.5	107
25 M	05:43	0.7	21
	12:14	4.5	137
	18:40	0.7	21
26 Tu	00:42	3.4	104
	06:25	0.8	24
	13:00	4.4	134
	19:28	0.9	27
27 W ◐	01:31	3.2	98
	07:13	1.0	30
	13:51	4.3	131
	20:21	0.9	27
28 Th ◑	02:26	3.2	98
	08:08	1.0	30
	14:47	4.2	128
	21:19	0.9	27
29 F	03:26	3.2	98
	09:13	1.0	30
	15:46	4.2	128
	22:15	0.8	24
30 Sa	04:26	3.4	104
	10:13	0.8	24
	16:44	4.3	131
	23:07	0.6	18
31 Su	05:22	3.7	113
	11:14	0.6	18
	17:40	4.4	134
	23:55	0.3	9

November

Day	Time	ft	cm
1 M	06:14	4.1	125
	12:11	0.3	9
	18:32	4.6	140
2 Tu	00:41	0.0	0
	07:04	4.6	140
	13:05	0.0	0
	19:22	4.6	140
3 W	01:25	-0.3	-9
	07:51	5.0	152
	13:57	-0.3	-9
	20:11	4.7	143
4 Th ●	02:10	-0.5	-15
	08:38	5.4	165
	14:48	-0.5	-15
	20:59	4.6	140
5 F	02:55	-0.6	-18
	09:26	5.6	171
	15:40	-0.6	-18
	21:49	4.5	137
6 Sa	03:42	-0.6	-18
	10:15	5.7	174
	16:32	-0.6	-18
	22:40	4.3	131
7 Su	03:30	-0.5	-15
	10:06	5.7	174
	16:26	-0.4	-12
	22:34	4.1	125
8 M	04:22	-0.3	-9
	11:01	5.5	168
	17:23	-0.2	-6
	23:32	3.9	119
9 Tu	05:18	0.0	0
	11:59	5.2	158
	18:24	0.0	0
10 W	00:35	3.7	113
	06:20	0.2	6
	13:02	4.9	149
	19:29	0.2	6
11 Th ◐	01:43	3.6	110
	07:29	0.4	12
	14:09	4.7	143
	20:35	0.3	9
12 F	02:54	3.7	113
	08:41	0.5	15
	15:16	4.5	137
	21:37	0.3	9
13 Sa	04:00	3.8	116
	09:50	0.5	15
	22:32	0.2	6
14 Su	04:57	4.0	122
	10:53	0.4	12
	17:14	4.2	128
	23:20	0.2	6
15 M	05:47	4.2	128
	11:48	0.3	9
	18:03	4.2	128
16 Tu	00:02	0.1	3
	06:30	4.4	134
	12:36	0.2	6
	18:46	4.1	125
17 W	00:41	0.1	3
	07:08	4.6	140
	13:19	0.2	6
	19:26	3.9	119
18 Th	01:16	0.1	3
	07:44	4.7	143
	13:59	0.1	3
	20:03	3.8	116
19 F ○	01:51	0.1	3
	08:18	4.8	146
	14:38	0.1	3
	20:39	3.7	113
20 Sa	02:25	0.2	6
	08:53	4.8	146
	15:15	0.2	6
	21:16	3.6	110
21 Su	02:59	0.3	9
	09:29	4.7	143
	15:53	0.3	9
	21:53	3.5	107
22 M	03:35	0.4	12
	10:07	4.6	140
	16:32	0.4	12
	22:33	3.3	101
23 Tu	04:13	0.5	15
	10:48	4.5	137
	17:13	0.5	15
	23:15	3.2	98
24 W	04:55	0.6	18
	11:31	4.4	134
	17:57	0.5	15
25 Th	00:02	3.2	98
	05:42	0.7	21
	12:18	4.3	131
	18:45	0.6	18
26 F ◐	00:53	3.2	98
	06:35	0.7	21
	13:10	4.2	128
	19:36	0.5	15
27 Sa ◑	01:49	3.3	101
	07:29	0.7	21
	14:05	4.1	125
	20:29	0.4	12
28 Su	02:48	3.5	107
	08:38	0.6	18
	15:02	4.1	125
	21:22	0.2	6
29 M	03:45	3.8	116
	09:42	0.4	12
	15:59	4.1	125
	22:13	0.0	0
30 Tu	04:41	4.3	131
	10:44	0.1	3
	16:56	4.1	125
	23:03	-0.3	-9

December

Day	Time	ft	cm
1 W	05:34	4.7	143
	11:42	-0.2	-6
	17:51	4.2	128
	23:52	-0.5	-15
2 Th	06:25	5.1	155
	12:38	-0.4	-12
	18:45	4.2	128
3 F	00:41	-0.7	-21
	07:16	5.5	168
	13:32	-0.6	-18
	19:39	4.2	128
4 Sa ●	01:30	-0.8	-24
	08:07	5.7	174
	14:25	-0.8	-24
	20:32	4.1	125
5 Su	02:21	-0.8	-24
	08:59	5.7	174
	15:18	-0.7	-21
	21:25	4.0	122
6 M	03:12	-0.7	-21
	09:51	5.6	171
	16:12	-0.6	-18
	22:20	3.9	119
7 Tu	04:06	-0.5	-15
	10:45	5.4	165
	17:07	-0.5	-15
	23:16	3.8	116
8 W	05:03	-0.3	-9
	11:42	5.1	155
	18:04	-0.3	-9
9 Th	00:16	3.7	113
	06:03	0.0	0
	12:40	4.7	143
	19:03	-0.1	-3
10 F	01:19	3.6	110
	07:08	0.2	6
	13:41	4.4	134
	20:02	0.0	0
11 Sa ◐	02:24	3.6	110
	08:16	0.4	12
	14:42	4.1	125
	21:00	0.1	3
12 Su	03:27	3.7	113
	09:24	0.5	15
	15:43	3.8	116
	21:54	0.2	6
13 M	04:24	3.9	119
	10:28	0.5	15
	16:39	3.7	113
	22:42	0.2	6
14 Tu	05:15	4.1	125
	11:25	0.4	12
	17:31	3.6	110
	23:26	0.1	3
15 W	06:00	4.2	128
	12:16	0.3	9
	18:18	3.5	107
16 Th	00:07	0.1	3
	06:41	4.4	134
	13:00	0.2	6
	19:00	3.4	104
17 F	00:45	0.1	3
	07:19	4.5	137
	13:41	0.1	3
	19:39	3.4	104
18 Sa	01:23	0.1	3
	07:56	4.6	140
	14:20	0.1	3
	20:17	3.4	104
19 Su ○	01:59	0.1	3
	08:33	4.6	140
	14:57	0.1	3
	20:55	3.3	101
20 M	02:35	0.1	3
	09:10	4.6	140
	15:33	0.1	3
	21:32	3.3	101
21 Tu	03:13	0.1	3
	09:47	4.6	140
	16:10	0.1	3
	22:11	3.3	101
22 W	03:51	0.1	3
	10:24	4.5	137
	16:48	0.1	3
	22:52	3.2	98
23 Th	04:32	0.2	6
	11:07	4.4	134
	17:28	0.2	6
	23:35	3.3	101
24 F	05:18	0.3	9
	11:50	4.3	131
	18:11	0.2	6
25 Sa	00:23	3.3	101
	06:08	0.3	9
	12:36	4.1	125
	18:57	0.1	3
26 Su	01:15	3.4	104
	07:05	0.4	12
	13:27	4.0	122
	19:47	0.1	3
27 M ◑	02:11	3.7	113
	08:08	0.4	12
	14:23	3.8	116
	20:39	-0.1	-3
28 Tu	03:10	4.0	122
	09:14	0.3	9
	15:23	3.7	113
	21:34	-0.2	-6
29 W	04:09	4.3	131
	10:20	0.1	3
	16:25	3.7	113
	22:29	-0.4	-12
30 Th	05:07	4.7	143
	11:23	-0.2	-6
	17:27	3.7	113
	23:24	-0.5	-15
31 F	06:04	5.0	152
	12:22	-0.4	-12
	18:26	3.7	113

StationId: 8551910
Source: NOAA/NOS/CO-OPS
Station Type: Primary
Time Zone: LST_LDT
Datum: MLLW

NOAA Tide Predictions

Reedy Point, DE, 2021

Times and Heights of High and Low Waters

January

Day	Time (h m)	ft	cm	Day	Time (h m)	ft	cm
1 F	00:14	4.6	140	**16** Sa	01:06	4.8	146
	06:41	-0.2	-6		07:41	-0.2	-6
	12:19	5.7	174		13:24	5.4	165
	19:39	-0.1	-3		20:23	-0.2	-6
2 Sa	00:52	4.6	140	**17** Su	01:53	4.8	146
	07:24	-0.2	-6		08:27	-0.1	-3
	13:00	5.7	174		14:11	5.3	162
	20:22	-0.1	-3		21:05	-0.1	-3
3 Su	01:35	4.7	143	**18** M	02:41	4.7	143
	08:10	-0.1	-3		09:13	0.1	3
	13:46	5.6	171		14:59	5.1	155
	21:06	-0.1	-3		21:46	0.0	0
4 M	02:22	4.8	146	**19** Tu	03:30	4.7	143
	09:03	-0.1	-3		10:02	0.2	6
	14:38	5.5	168		15:50	4.9	149
	21:53	-0.1	-3		22:28	0.1	3
5 Tu	03:16	4.9	149	**20** W ☽	04:20	4.8	146
	10:02	0.0	0		10:53	0.3	9
	15:36	5.3	162		16:43	4.8	146
	22:44	-0.2	-6		23:12	0.1	3
6 W ☽	04:15	5.0	152	**21** Th	05:12	4.8	146
	11:07	0.1	3		11:47	0.3	9
	16:40	5.1	155		17:37	4.6	140
	23:39	-0.2	-6		23:59	0.2	6
7 Th	05:18	5.1	155	**22** F	06:04	4.9	149
	12:14	0.1	3		12:43	0.3	9
	17:46	5.0	152		18:32	4.6	140
8 F	00:37	-0.2	-6	**23** Sa	00:48	0.1	3
	06:21	5.3	162		06:56	5.0	152
	13:21	0.0	0		13:29	0.2	6
	18:51	4.9	149		19:26	4.5	137
9 Sa	01:35	-0.3	-9	**24** Su	01:40	0.1	3
	07:22	5.5	168		07:47	5.1	155
	14:25	-0.1	-3		14:34	0.1	3
	19:52	4.8	146		20:16	4.6	140
10 Su	02:34	-0.3	-9	**25** M	02:31	0.0	0
	08:21	5.6	171		08:35	5.3	162
	15:26	-0.3	-9		15:27	0.0	0
	20:51	4.8	146		21:04	4.6	140
11 M	03:31	-0.4	-12	**26** Tu	03:21	-0.1	-3
	09:17	5.7	174		09:20	5.4	165
	16:23	-0.4	-12		16:16	-0.1	-3
	21:47	4.9	149		21:49	4.6	140
12 Tu	04:25	-0.4	-12	**27** W	04:09	-0.2	-6
	10:11	5.8	177		10:03	5.5	168
	17:16	-0.5	-15		17:03	-0.2	-6
	22:39	4.9	149		22:32	4.7	143
13 W ●	05:17	-0.5	-15	**28** Th ○	04:56	-0.3	-9
	11:01	5.8	177		10:44	5.6	171
	18:07	-0.5	-15		17:48	-0.3	-9
	23:30	4.9	149		23:12	4.8	146
14 Th	06:07	-0.4	-12	**29** F	05:41	-0.4	-12
	11:50	5.7	174		11:24	5.7	174
	18:54	-0.4	-12		18:32	-0.3	-9
					23:52	4.9	149
15 F	00:18	4.8	146	**30** Sa	06:27	-0.4	-12
	06:55	-0.3	-9		12:04	5.8	177
	12:37	5.6	171		19:15	-0.3	-9
	19:39	-0.3	-9				
				31 Su	00:32	5.0	152
					07:13	-0.4	-12
					12:47	5.8	177
					19:57	-0.3	-9

February

Day	Time (h m)	ft	cm	Day	Time (h m)	ft	cm
1 M	01:15	5.1	155	**16** Tu	02:02	5.1	155
	08:02	-0.3	-9		08:41	0.1	3
	13:33	5.7	174		14:24	5.1	155
	20:41	-0.3	-9		21:00	0.2	6
2 Tu	02:02	5.2	158	**17** W	02:44	5.0	152
	08:55	-0.2	-6		09:25	0.2	6
	14:24	5.5	168		15:09	4.9	149
	21:28	-0.3	-9		21:37	0.3	9
3 W	02:54	5.3	162	**18** Th	03:28	5.0	152
	09:53	-0.1	-3		10:12	0.3	9
	15:21	5.2	158		15:59	4.7	143
	22:18	-0.2	-6		22:17	0.3	9
4 Th	03:52	5.3	162	**19** F ◐	04:16	5.0	152
	10:55	0.0	0		11:05	0.4	12
	16:23	5.0	152		16:53	4.6	140
◐	23:14	-0.1	-3		23:04	0.4	12
5 F	04:55	5.3	162	**20** Sa	05:09	5.0	152
	12:01	0.1	3		12:01	0.5	15
	17:30	4.8	146		17:49	4.5	137
					23:57	0.4	12
6 Sa	00:14	0.0	0	**21** Su	06:05	5.0	152
	06:00	5.3	162		13:00	0.5	15
	13:06	0.1	3		18:45	4.5	137
	18:36	4.7	143				
7 Su	01:16	0.0	0	**22** M	00:54	0.4	12
	07:05	5.4	165		07:01	5.1	155
	14:10	0.0	0		13:58	0.4	12
	19:39	4.7	143		19:39	4.6	140
8 M	02:17	-0.1	-3	**23** Tu	01:52	0.3	9
	08:07	5.5	168		07:55	5.3	162
	15:10	-0.1	-3		14:53	0.3	9
	20:38	4.8	146		20:30	4.7	143
9 Tu	03:15	-0.2	-6	**24** W	02:49	0.1	3
	09:05	5.6	171		08:46	5.5	168
	16:06	-0.3	-9		15:45	0.1	3
	21:33	4.9	149		21:18	4.9	149
10 W	04:10	-0.3	-9	**25** Th	03:42	-0.1	-3
	09:58	5.7	174		09:33	5.7	174
	16:57	-0.3	-9		16:33	-0.1	-3
	22:24	5.0	152		22:03	5.0	152
11 Th ●	05:01	-0.4	-12	**26** F	04:33	-0.2	-6
	10:47	5.7	174		10:18	5.8	177
	17:44	-0.4	-12		17:19	-0.2	-6
	23:12	5.1	155		22:45	5.2	158
12 F	05:49	-0.3	-9	**27** Sa ○	05:23	-0.4	-12
	11:33	5.7	174		11:02	5.9	180
	18:28	-0.3	-9		18:04	-0.3	-9
	23:57	5.1	155		23:27	5.4	165
13 Sa	06:34	-0.3	-9	**28** Su	06:11	-0.5	-15
	12:16	5.6	171		11:46	6.0	183
	19:09	-0.2	-6		18:47	-0.3	-9
14 Su	00:40	5.1	155				
	07:17	-0.2	-6				
	12:58	5.4	165				
	19:47	-0.1	-3				
15 M	01:21	5.1	155				
	07:59	0.0	0				
	13:40	5.3	162				
	20:24	0.1	3				

March

Day	Time (h m)	ft	cm	Day	Time (h m)	ft	cm
1 M	00:10	5.6	171	**16** Tu	01:48	5.5	168
	07:01	-0.5	-15		08:32	0.1	3
	12:31	5.9	180		14:11	5.3	162
	19:31	-0.3	-9		20:43	0.3	9
2 Tu	00:54	5.7	174	**17** W	02:24	5.5	168
	07:52	-0.4	-12		09:12	0.2	6
	13:19	5.7	174		14:51	5.2	158
	20:16	-0.2	-6		21:14	0.5	15
3 W	01:42	5.8	177	**18** Th	02:59	5.5	168
	08:45	-0.2	-6		09:53	0.4	12
	14:11	5.5	168		15:32	5.0	152
	21:03	-0.1	-3		21:47	0.5	15
4 Th	02:34	5.7	174	**19** F	03:36	5.4	165
	09:42	-0.1	-3		10:37	0.5	15
	15:08	5.2	158		16:18	4.8	146
	21:56	0.0	0		22:24	0.6	18
5 F	03:32	5.6	171	**20** Sa	04:18	5.4	165
	10:43	0.1	3		11:26	0.6	18
	16:10	5.0	152		17:09	4.7	143
	22:53	0.2	6		23:11	0.7	21
6 Sa ◐	04:36	5.5	168	**21** Su ◐	05:09	5.3	162
	11:47	0.2	6		12:21	0.7	21
	17:17	4.8	146		18:05	4.6	140
	23:55	0.3	9				
7 Su	05:44	5.4	165	**22** M	00:08	0.7	21
	12:51	0.3	9		06:09	5.3	162
	18:23	4.8	146		13:20	0.7	21
					19:03	4.7	143
8 M	00:58	0.3	9	**23** Tu	01:11	0.7	21
	06:50	5.4	165		07:12	5.3	162
	13:53	0.2	6		14:19	0.6	18
	19:26	4.9	149		20:00	4.8	146
9 Tu	02:00	0.2	6	**24** W	02:15	0.5	15
	07:53	5.5	168		08:13	5.5	168
	14:51	0.1	3		15:16	0.5	15
	20:25	5.0	152		20:54	5.0	152
10 W	02:58	0.1	3	**25** Th	03:17	0.4	12
	08:50	5.6	171		09:09	5.6	171
	15:44	-0.1	-3		16:09	0.3	9
	21:18	5.2	158		21:44	5.3	162
11 Th	03:52	-0.1	-3	**26** F	04:15	0.1	3
	09:42	5.7	174		10:01	5.8	177
	16:33	-0.1	-3		16:59	0.1	3
	22:07	5.4	165		22:31	5.6	171
12 F	04:42	-0.1	-3	**27** Sa	05:10	-0.1	-3
	10:28	5.7	174		10:50	6.0	183
	17:17	-0.1	-3		17:47	-0.1	-3
	22:51	5.5	168		23:17	5.8	177
13 Sa ●	05:28	-0.2	-6	**28** Su ○	06:03	-0.3	-9
	11:12	5.7	174		11:38	6.1	186
	17:58	-0.1	-3		18:33	-0.2	-6
	23:33	5.5	168				
14 Su	07:11	-0.1	-3	**29** M	00:01	6.1	186
	12:52	5.6	171		06:55	-0.4	-12
	19:35	0.1	3		12:25	6.0	183
					19:18	-0.2	-6
15 M	01:12	5.5	168	**30** Tu	00:46	6.2	189
	07:52	0.0	0		07:47	-0.4	-12
	13:32	5.5	168		13:13	5.9	180
	20:10	0.2	6		20:04	-0.1	-3
				31 W	01:33	6.3	192
					08:39	-0.3	-9
					14:04	5.7	174
					20:51	0.0	0

StationId: 8551910
Source: NOAA/NOS/CO-OPS
Station Type: Primary
Time Zone: LST_LDT
Datum: MLLW

NOAA Tide Predictions

Reedy Point, DE,2021

Times and Heights of High and Low Waters

April

Day	Time	ft	cm
1 Th	02:22	6.3	192
	09:34	-0.2	-6
	14:57	5.5	168
	21:42	0.2	6
2 F	03:15	6.1	186
	10:30	0.0	0
	15:55	5.2	158
	22:36	0.3	9
3 Sa	04:14	5.9	180
	11:29	0.2	6
	16:58	5.1	155
	23:35	0.5	15
4 Su	05:19	5.7	174
	12:30	0.3	9
	18:04	5.0	152
5 M	00:37	0.6	18
	06:27	5.6	171
	13:31	0.4	12
	19:09	5.0	152
6 Tu	01:40	0.6	18
	07:33	5.5	168
	14:30	0.3	9
	20:10	5.2	158
7 W	02:41	0.5	15
	08:34	5.6	171
	15:25	0.2	6
	21:06	5.4	165
8 Th	03:38	0.3	9
	09:29	5.7	174
	16:15	0.1	3
	21:57	5.6	171
9 F	04:31	0.2	6
	10:19	5.7	174
	17:02	0.1	3
	22:44	5.8	177
10 Sa	05:20	0.1	3
	11:04	5.7	174
	17:44	0.1	3
	23:26	5.9	180
11 Su	06:05	0.1	3
	11:47	5.7	174
	18:23	0.2	6
12 M	00:06	5.9	180
	06:48	0.1	3
	12:27	5.6	171
	19:00	0.3	9
13 Tu	00:42	5.9	180
	07:29	0.2	6
	13:06	5.5	168
	19:33	0.5	15
14 W	01:16	5.9	180
	08:08	0.3	9
	13:44	5.3	162
	20:05	0.6	18
15 Th	01:48	5.9	180
	08:47	0.4	12
	14:21	5.2	158
	20:35	0.7	21
16 F	02:19	5.8	177
	09:27	0.5	15
	15:00	5.0	152
	21:06	0.8	24
17 Sa	02:52	5.8	177
	10:08	0.6	18
	15:42	4.9	149
	21:44	0.8	24
18 Su	03:31	5.7	174
	10:55	0.7	21
	16:29	4.9	149
	22:32	0.8	24
19 M	04:20	5.7	174
	11:47	0.8	24
	17:23	4.8	146
	23:29	0.9	27
20 Tu	05:19	5.6	171
	12:43	0.8	24
	18:22	4.9	149
21 W	00:34	0.8	24
	06:26	5.6	171
	13:41	0.7	21
	19:21	5.1	155
22 Th	01:42	0.7	21
	07:32	5.7	174
	14:37	0.5	15
	20:17	5.4	165
23 F	02:48	0.5	15
	08:32	5.8	177
	15:31	0.4	12
	21:09	5.7	174
24 Sa	03:49	0.3	9
	09:29	5.9	180
	16:23	0.2	6
	22:00	6.0	183
25 Su	04:48	0.1	3
	10:22	6.0	183
	17:13	0.0	0
	22:48	6.3	192
26 M	05:44	-0.1	-3
	11:13	6.0	183
	18:01	0.0	0
	23:36	6.6	201
27 Tu	06:38	-0.2	-6
	12:04	5.9	180
	18:50	0.0	0
28 W	00:24	6.7	204
	07:32	-0.3	-9
	12:55	5.8	177
	19:39	0.1	3
29 Th	01:12	6.7	204
	08:26	-0.2	-6
	13:48	5.6	171
	20:29	0.2	6
30 F	02:04	6.5	198
	09:20	-0.1	-3
	14:43	5.4	165
	21:22	0.4	12

May

Day	Time	ft	cm
1 Sa	02:59	6.3	192
	10:15	0.1	3
	15:42	5.3	162
	22:18	0.5	15
2 Su	03:58	6.0	183
	11:12	0.2	6
	16:44	5.2	158
	23:17	0.7	21
3 M	05:02	5.8	177
	12:09	0.3	9
	17:47	5.2	158
4 Tu	00:17	0.7	21
	06:07	5.7	174
	13:05	0.4	12
	18:49	5.3	162
5 W	01:17	0.7	21
	07:09	5.6	171
	14:00	0.3	9
	19:48	5.5	168
6 Th	02:16	0.6	18
	08:08	5.6	171
	14:52	0.3	9
	20:41	5.7	174
7 F	03:12	0.5	15
	09:01	5.6	171
	15:40	0.3	9
	21:31	5.9	180
8 Sa	04:05	0.4	12
	09:50	5.7	174
	16:25	0.3	9
	22:16	6.0	183
9 Su	04:54	0.3	9
	10:36	5.6	171
	17:07	0.3	9
	22:58	6.1	186
10 M	05:40	0.2	6
	11:19	5.6	171
	17:47	0.4	12
	23:37	6.2	189
11 Tu	06:24	0.2	6
	12:01	5.4	165
	18:24	0.5	15
12 W	00:13	6.1	186
	07:05	0.3	9
	12:40	5.3	162
	18:59	0.7	21
13 Th	00:46	6.1	186
	07:41	0.4	12
	13:18	5.2	158
	19:32	0.8	24
14 F	01:18	6.0	183
	08:26	0.5	15
	13:55	5.1	155
	20:04	0.8	24
15 Sa	01:48	6.0	183
	09:05	0.6	18
	14:32	5.0	152
	20:38	0.8	24
16 Su	02:20	6.0	183
	09:46	0.7	21
	15:11	4.9	149
	21:18	0.9	27
17 M	03:00	6.0	183
	10:30	0.7	21
	15:56	5.0	152
	22:06	0.9	27
18 Tu	03:48	5.9	180
	11:18	0.7	21
	16:48	5.0	152
	23:02	0.9	27
19 W	04:45	5.9	180
	12:09	0.6	18
	17:45	5.2	158
20 Th	00:06	0.9	27
	05:49	5.8	177
	13:03	0.6	18
	18:44	5.4	165
21 F	01:14	0.8	24
	06:55	5.8	177
	13:58	0.4	12
	19:41	5.7	174
22 Sa	02:22	0.6	18
	07:59	5.8	177
	14:57	0.3	9
	20:37	6.0	183
23 Su	03:26	0.4	12
	08:59	5.8	177
	15:47	0.2	6
	21:30	6.3	192
24 M	04:27	0.2	6
	09:55	5.8	177
	16:40	0.1	3
	22:22	6.6	201
25 Tu	05:26	0.0	0
	10:50	5.7	174
	17:33	0.1	3
	23:13	6.8	207
26 W	06:22	-0.1	-3
	11:44	5.7	174
	18:25	0.1	3
27 Th	00:03	6.8	207
	07:17	-0.1	-3
	12:38	5.6	171
	19:17	0.2	6
28 F	00:55	6.7	204
	08:45	-0.1	-3
	13:32	5.4	165
	20:10	0.3	9
29 Sa	01:47	6.6	201
	09:04	0.0	0
	14:27	5.3	162
	21:04	0.4	12
30 Su	02:42	6.3	192
	09:57	0.1	3
	15:25	5.3	162
	21:59	0.6	18
31 M	03:40	6.1	186
	10:49	0.2	6
	16:24	5.2	158
	22:55	0.7	21

June

Day	Time	ft	cm
1 Tu	04:39	5.9	180
	11:42	0.3	9
	17:24	5.3	162
	23:52	0.8	24
2 W	05:40	5.7	174
	12:33	0.3	9
	18:22	5.4	165
3 Th	00:49	0.8	24
	06:38	5.6	171
	13:24	0.4	12
	19:17	5.6	171
4 F	01:46	0.7	21
	07:34	5.5	168
	14:13	0.4	12
	20:10	5.8	177
5 Sa	02:41	0.7	21
	08:28	5.5	168
	15:00	0.4	12
	20:58	6.0	183
6 Su	03:34	0.5	15
	09:18	5.5	168
	15:45	0.4	12
	21:44	6.1	186
7 M	04:24	0.4	12
	10:05	5.4	165
	16:28	0.4	12
	22:27	6.2	189
8 Tu	05:12	0.3	9
	10:51	5.3	162
	17:10	0.5	15
	23:07	6.2	189
9 W	05:58	0.3	9
	11:34	5.2	158
	17:50	0.6	18
	23:45	6.2	189
10 Th	06:41	0.3	9
	12:15	5.1	155
	18:29	0.7	21
11 F	00:20	6.1	186
	07:24	0.4	12
	12:53	5.0	152
	19:06	0.7	21
12 Sa	00:52	6.1	186
	08:05	0.5	15
	13:30	5.0	152
	19:43	0.8	24
13 Su	01:24	6.1	186
	08:45	0.5	15
	14:07	5.0	152
	20:21	0.8	24
14 M	01:59	6.1	186
	09:25	0.5	15
	14:45	5.0	152
	21:02	0.8	24
15 Tu	02:39	6.1	186
	10:07	0.5	15
	15:28	5.1	155
	21:50	0.8	24
16 W	03:26	6.1	186
	10:51	0.5	15
	16:18	5.2	158
	22:45	0.8	24
17 Th	04:21	6.0	183
	11:38	0.4	12
	17:13	5.4	165
	23:47	0.8	24
18 F	05:22	5.9	180
	12:29	0.4	12
	18:11	5.7	174
19 Sa	00:54	0.8	24
	06:27	5.7	174
	13:23	0.3	9
	19:10	5.9	180
20 Su	02:02	0.7	21
	07:31	5.6	171
	14:19	0.3	9
	20:08	6.2	189
21 M	03:07	0.5	15
	08:34	5.5	168
	15:16	0.2	6
	21:05	6.4	195
22 Tu	04:10	0.3	9
	09:34	5.5	168
	16:13	0.2	6
	22:00	6.6	201
23 W	05:10	0.1	3
	10:31	5.5	168
	17:10	0.2	6
	22:54	6.7	204
24 Th	06:07	0.0	0
	11:27	5.4	165
	18:05	0.2	6
	23:47	6.7	204
25 F	07:01	0.0	0
	12:21	5.4	165
	18:59	0.2	6
26 Sa	00:39	6.6	201
	07:54	0.0	0
	13:15	5.4	165
	19:52	0.3	9
27 Su	01:31	6.5	198
	08:44	0.0	0
	14:09	5.3	162
	20:44	0.4	12
28 M	02:24	6.3	192
	09:33	0.1	3
	15:03	5.3	162
	21:36	0.6	18
29 Tu	03:17	6.0	183
		0.2	6
	15:57	5.3	162
	22:29	0.7	21
30 W	04:11	5.8	177
	11:08	0.3	9
	16:52	5.4	165
	23:22	0.8	24

StationId: 8551910
Source: NOAA/NOS/CO-OPS
Station Type: Primary
Time Zone: LST_LDT
Datum: MLLW

NOAA Tide Predictions

Reedy Point, DE,2021

Times and Heights of High and Low Waters

July

Day	Time	ft	cm	Day	Time	ft	cm
1 Th ☽	05:07	5.6	171	16 F	04:01	6.0	183
	11:55	0.4	12		11:09	0.3	9
	17:47	5.5	168		16:44	5.7	174
					23:34	0.8	24
2 F	00:16	0.9	27	17 Sa ◐	05:00	5.8	177
	06:02	5.5	168		11:59	0.3	9
	12:42	0.4	12		17:43	5.9	180
	18:40	5.6	171				
3 Sa	01:11	0.8	24	18 Su	00:39	0.8	24
	06:57	5.4	165		06:05	5.6	171
	13:29	0.5	15		12:54	0.3	9
	19:32	5.8	177		18:44	6.1	186
4 Su	02:06	0.8	24	19 M	01:46	0.7	21
	07:51	5.3	162		07:11	5.4	165
	14:16	0.5	15		13:53	0.3	9
	20:21	5.9	180		19:45	6.2	189
5 M	03:00	0.7	21	20 Tu	02:52	0.6	18
	08:43	5.3	162		08:16	5.3	162
	15:02	0.5	15		14:54	0.3	9
	21:09	6.0	183		20:46	6.4	195
6 Tu	03:52	0.6	18	21 W	03:55	0.4	12
	09:33	5.2	158		09:17	5.3	162
	15:49	0.6	18		15:55	0.3	9
	21:54	6.1	186		21:44	6.5	198
7 W	04:43	0.5	15	22 Th	04:55	0.3	9
	10:21	5.2	158		10:16	5.3	162
	16:35	0.6	18		16:53	0.3	9
	22:37	6.2	189		22:40	6.6	201
8 Th	05:30	0.4	12	23 F	05:51	0.1	3
	11:06	5.1	155		11:12	5.4	165
	17:19	0.6	18		17:49	0.2	6
	23:17	6.2	189		23:33	6.6	201
9 F	06:16	0.4	12	24 Sa ○	06:43	0.0	0
	11:48	5.1	155		12:05	5.4	165
	18:02	0.6	18		18:42	0.3	9
	23:55	6.2	189				
10 Sa ●	06:59	0.4	12	25 Su	00:24	6.5	198
	12:27	5.1	155		07:32	0.0	0
	18:44	0.6	18		12:56	5.4	165
					19:33	0.3	9
11 Su	00:30	6.2	189	26 M	01:14	6.4	195
	07:41	0.4	12		08:09	0.1	3
	13:05	5.1	155		13:46	5.5	168
	19:25	0.6	18		20:23	0.4	12
12 M	01:05	6.2	189	27 Tu	02:02	6.2	189
	08:21	0.4	12		09:04	0.2	6
	13:42	5.1	155		14:36	5.5	168
	20:07	0.6	18		21:11	0.6	18
13 Tu	01:42	6.2	189	28 W	02:50	6.0	183
	09:02	0.4	12		09:47	0.3	9
	14:21	5.2	158		15:25	5.5	168
	20:51	0.6	18		22:00	0.7	21
14 W	02:22	6.2	189	29 Th	03:39	5.8	177
	09:42	0.4	12		10:29	0.4	12
	15:03	5.4	165		16:14	5.5	168
	21:39	0.7	21		22:49	0.8	24
15 Th	03:09	6.1	186	30 F	04:30	5.6	171
	10:24	0.3	9		11:12	0.5	15
	15:51	5.6	171		17:05	5.5	168
	22:33	0.7	21		23:40	0.9	27
				31 Sa ◐	05:23	5.4	165
					11:55	0.6	18
					17:56	5.6	171

August

Day	Time	ft	cm	Day	Time	ft	cm
1 Su	00:34	1.0	30	16 M	00:28	0.8	24
	06:18	5.2	158		05:50	5.4	165
	12:41	0.7	21		12:34	0.5	15
	18:48	5.7	174		18:24	6.1	186
2 M	01:29	0.9	27	17 Tu	01:34	0.8	24
	07:13	5.1	155		06:57	5.2	158
	13:29	0.7	21		13:36	0.5	15
	19:40	5.8	177		19:29	6.2	189
3 Tu	02:24	0.9	27	18 W	02:39	0.7	21
	08:08	5.1	155		08:03	5.2	158
	14:19	0.7	21		14:39	0.5	15
	20:31	5.9	180		20:32	6.2	189
4 W	03:18	0.8	24	19 Th	03:40	0.5	15
	09:00	5.1	155		09:05	5.3	162
	15:10	0.7	21		15:41	0.4	12
	21:20	6.0	183		21:32	6.3	192
5 Th	04:11	0.6	18	20 F	04:38	0.3	9
	09:49	5.1	155		10:03	5.4	165
	16:01	0.6	18		16:39	0.3	9
	22:06	6.1	186		22:28	6.4	195
6 F	05:00	0.5	15	21 Sa	05:31	0.2	6
	10:36	5.2	158		10:57	5.5	168
	16:49	0.6	18		17:33	0.3	9
	22:48	6.2	189		23:19	6.4	195
7 Sa	05:47	0.4	12	22 Su ○	06:21	0.1	3
	11:19	5.2	158		11:48	5.6	171
	17:36	0.5	15		18:24	0.3	9
	23:29	6.3	192				
8 Su ●	06:31	0.3	9	23 M	00:07	6.4	195
	11:59	5.3	162		07:07	0.1	3
	18:22	0.5	15		12:35	5.7	174
					19:13	0.3	9
9 M	00:07	6.3	192	24 Tu	00:53	6.3	192
	07:13	0.3	9		07:50	0.2	6
	12:38	5.4	165		13:21	5.7	174
	19:06	0.4	12		19:59	0.4	12
10 Tu	00:45	6.3	192	25 W	01:37	6.1	186
	07:54	0.3	9		08:30	0.3	9
	13:16	5.5	168		14:05	5.7	174
	19:51	0.4	12		20:44	0.6	18
11 W	01:24	6.3	192	26 Th	02:21	5.9	180
	08:34	0.2	6		09:09	0.5	15
	13:55	5.7	174		14:48	5.7	174
	20:38	0.5	15		21:29	0.7	21
12 Th	02:06	6.3	192	27 F	03:06	5.7	174
	09:15	0.2	6		09:47	0.6	18
	14:38	5.8	177		15:32	5.7	174
	21:28	0.6	18		22:15	0.9	27
13 F	02:52	6.1	186	28 Sa	03:53	5.4	165
	09:57	0.3	9		10:25	0.7	21
	15:26	5.9	180		16:18	5.6	171
	22:23	0.6	18		23:04	1.0	30
14 Sa	03:45	5.9	180	29 Su	04:43	5.2	158
	10:44	0.3	9		11:05	0.8	24
	16:19	6.0	183		17:07	5.6	171
	23:24	0.7	21		23:55	1.1	34
15 Su ◐	04:44	5.6	171	30 M ◐	05:37	5.1	155
	11:36	0.4	12		11:50	0.9	27
	17:19	6.0	183		17:59	5.6	171
				31 Tu	00:50	1.1	34
					06:34	5.0	152
					12:41	0.9	27
					18:55	5.7	174

September

Day	Time	ft	cm	Day	Time	ft	cm
1 W	01:46	1.0	30	16 Th	02:23	0.6	18
	07:30	5.0	152		07:53	5.2	158
	13:36	0.9	27		14:27	0.6	18
	19:50	5.8	177		20:21	6.1	186
2 Th	02:42	0.9	27	17 F	03:23	0.5	15
	08:25	5.0	152		08:54	5.3	162
	14:32	0.8	24		15:27	0.4	12
	20:42	5.9	180		21:20	6.2	189
3 F	03:36	0.8	24	18 Sa	04:18	0.3	9
	09:16	5.1	155		09:50	5.5	168
	15:27	0.7	21		16:24	0.3	9
	21:31	6.1	186		22:13	6.3	192
4 Sa	04:26	0.6	18	19 Su	05:08	0.2	6
	10:03	5.3	162		10:41	5.7	174
	16:20	0.5	15		17:16	0.2	6
	22:17	6.2	189		23:02	6.3	192
5 Su	05:13	0.4	12	20 M ○	05:54	0.1	3
	10:47	5.4	165		11:28	5.8	177
	17:11	0.4	12		18:05	0.2	6
	23:00	6.3	192		23:47	6.3	192
6 M	05:58	0.3	9	21 Tu	06:37	0.1	3
	11:28	5.6	171		12:12	5.9	180
	17:59	0.3	9		18:51	0.3	9
	23:41	6.4	195				
7 Tu ●	06:41	0.2	6	22 W	00:30	6.1	186
	12:08	5.8	177		07:17	0.3	9
	18:47	0.3	9		12:53	5.9	180
					19:35	0.4	12
8 W	00:22	6.4	195	23 Th	01:11	5.9	180
	07:23	0.1	3		07:54	0.4	12
	12:48	6.0	183		13:32	5.9	180
	19:35	0.3	9		20:18	0.6	18
9 Th	01:04	6.3	192	24 F	01:52	5.7	174
	08:04	0.1	3		08:29	0.6	18
	13:30	6.1	186		14:11	5.8	177
	20:25	0.3	9		21:00	0.7	21
10 F	01:48	6.2	189	25 Sa	02:33	5.5	168
	08:47	0.2	6		09:03	0.7	21
	14:14	6.2	189		14:49	5.8	177
	21:17	0.4	12		21:43	0.9	27
11 Sa	02:37	5.9	180	26 Su	03:17	5.3	162
	09:32	0.3	9		09:37	0.8	24
	15:03	6.2	189		15:29	5.7	174
	22:13	0.6	18		22:28	1.0	30
12 Su	03:31	5.7	174	27 M	04:04	5.1	155
	10:22	0.4	12		10:15	0.9	27
	15:58	6.2	189		16:14	5.6	171
	23:14	0.7	21		23:18	1.1	34
13 M ◐	04:32	5.4	165	28 Tu	04:56	4.9	149
	11:18	0.5	15		11:00	1.0	30
	17:01	6.1	186		17:06	5.6	171
14 Tu	00:17	0.8	24	29 W ◐	00:12	1.1	34
	05:39	5.2	158		05:52	4.8	146
	12:19	0.6	18		11:55	1.0	30
	18:09	6.0	183		18:04	5.6	171
15 W	01:21	0.7	21	30 Th	01:08	1.0	30
	06:47	5.1	155		06:50	4.8	146
	13:23	0.6	18		12:54	0.9	27
	19:17	6.0	183		19:04	5.7	174

StationId: 8551910
Source: NOAA/NOS/CO-OPS
Station Type: Primary
Time Zone: LST_LDT
Datum: MLLW

NOAA Tide Predictions

Reedy Point, DE,2021

Times and Heights of High and Low Waters

October

Day	Time (h m)	Height (ft)	Height (cm)
1 F	02:04	0.9	27
	07:46	5.0	152
	13:55	0.8	24
	20:01	5.8	177
2 Sa	02:58	0.7	21
	08:39	5.2	158
	14:55	0.6	18
	20:53	6.0	183
3 Su	03:49	0.5	15
	09:27	5.4	165
	15:51	0.5	15
	21:42	6.1	186
4 M	04:37	0.3	9
	10:13	5.7	174
	16:45	0.3	9
	22:29	6.2	189
5 Tu	05:23	0.1	3
	10:56	5.9	180
	17:37	0.1	3
	23:13	6.3	192
6 W ●	06:07	0.0	0
	11:39	6.2	189
	18:28	0.0	0
	23:58	6.2	189
7 Th	06:51	0.0	0
	12:21	6.3	192
	19:19	0.0	0
8 F	00:43	6.1	186
	07:35	0.0	0
	13:05	6.4	195
	20:11	0.1	3
9 Sa	01:31	5.9	180
	08:21	0.1	3
	13:52	6.4	195
	21:05	0.2	6
10 Su	02:22	5.7	174
	09:10	0.2	6
	14:44	6.3	192
	22:02	0.4	12
11 M	03:19	5.4	165
	10:04	0.4	12
	15:42	6.2	189
	23:01	0.5	15
12 Tu	04:21	5.1	155
	11:03	0.5	15
	16:46	6.0	183
13 W ◐	00:02	0.6	18
	05:28	5.0	152
	12:05	0.6	18
	17:55	5.8	177
14 Th	01:04	0.5	15
	06:36	5.0	152
	13:09	0.6	18
	19:03	5.8	177
15 F	02:03	0.4	12
	07:40	5.2	158
	14:11	0.5	15
	20:06	5.9	180
16 Sa	03:00	0.3	9
	08:39	5.4	165
	15:10	0.4	12
	21:02	5.9	180
17 Su	03:52	0.1	3
	09:32	5.6	171
	16:05	0.2	6
	21:53	6.0	183
18 M	04:39	0.0	0
	10:21	5.8	177
	16:56	0.1	3
	22:40	6.0	183
19 Tu	05:24	0.0	0
	11:05	5.9	180
	17:44	0.1	3
	23:24	5.9	180
20 W ○	06:04	0.1	3
	11:47	6.0	183
	18:29	0.2	6
21 Th	00:05	5.7	174
	06:42	0.2	6
	12:25	6.0	183
	19:12	0.3	9
22 F	00:46	5.6	171
	07:18	0.4	12
	13:02	5.9	180
	19:53	0.4	12
23 Sa	01:25	5.4	165
	07:51	0.5	15
	13:36	5.8	177
	20:34	0.6	18
24 Su	02:04	5.2	158
	08:23	0.7	21
	14:11	5.7	174
	21:15	0.7	21
25 M	02:44	5.0	152
	08:55	0.7	21
	14:46	5.7	174
	21:58	0.8	24
26 Tu	03:27	4.8	146
	09:32	0.8	24
	15:26	5.6	171
	22:44	0.9	27
27 W	04:15	4.7	143
	10:18	0.8	24
	16:14	5.5	168
	23:35	0.9	27
28 Th ◑	05:09	4.7	143
	11:13	0.8	24
	17:12	5.5	168
29 F	00:29	0.8	24
	06:06	4.7	143
	12:15	0.8	24
	18:15	5.5	168
30 Sa	01:23	0.7	21
	07:04	4.9	149
	13:19	0.7	21
	19:16	5.6	171
31 Su	02:17	0.5	15
	07:58	5.1	155
	14:22	0.5	15
	20:13	5.7	174

November

Day	Time (h m)	Height (ft)	Height (cm)
1 M	03:09	0.3	9
	08:49	5.4	165
	15:22	0.3	9
	21:07	5.8	177
2 Tu	03:58	0.1	3
	09:38	5.8	177
	16:20	0.1	3
	21:57	5.9	180
3 W	04:47	-0.1	-3
	10:25	6.1	186
	17:15	-0.1	-3
	22:47	5.9	180
4 Th ●	05:34	-0.2	-6
	11:11	6.3	192
	18:09	-0.2	-6
	23:35	5.9	180
5 F	06:21	-0.2	-6
	11:57	6.5	198
	19:03	-0.2	-6
6 Sa	00:24	5.7	174
	07:09	-0.2	-6
	12:44	6.5	198
	19:57	-0.2	-6
7 Su	01:15	5.5	168
	06:59	-0.1	-3
	12:35	6.4	195
	19:52	-0.1	-3
8 M	01:08	5.3	162
	07:52	0.0	0
	13:29	6.2	189
	20:48	0.1	3
9 Tu	02:06	5.1	155
	08:48	0.2	6
	14:28	6.0	183
	21:45	0.2	6
10 W	03:08	4.9	149
	09:47	0.3	9
	15:32	5.8	177
	22:43	0.2	6
11 Th ◐	04:13	4.9	149
	10:48	0.4	12
	16:38	5.6	171
	23:40	0.2	6
12 F	05:18	4.9	149
	11:49	0.4	12
	17:43	5.5	168
13 Sa	00:36	0.1	3
	06:20	5.1	155
	12:45	0.3	9
	18:43	5.5	168
14 Su	01:30	0.0	0
	07:17	5.3	162
	13:47	0.2	6
	19:38	5.6	171
15 M	02:20	-0.1	-3
	08:08	5.5	168
	14:42	0.1	3
	20:28	5.6	171
16 Tu	03:06	-0.1	-3
	08:56	5.7	174
	15:33	0.0	0
	21:15	5.5	168
17 W	03:50	-0.1	-3
	09:39	5.8	177
	16:21	0.0	0
	21:59	5.4	165
18 Th	04:31	0.0	0
	10:20	5.8	177
	17:06	0.0	0
	22:41	5.3	162
19 F ○	05:09	0.1	3
	10:58	5.8	177
	17:49	0.1	3
	23:22	5.1	155
20 Sa	05:45	0.2	6
	11:34	5.7	174
	18:30	0.2	6
21 Su	00:01	5.0	152
	06:20	0.3	9
	12:08	5.7	174
	19:10	0.3	9
22 M	00:39	4.8	146
	06:53	0.4	12
	12:41	5.6	171
	19:51	0.4	12
23 Tu	01:16	4.7	143
	07:26	0.4	12
	13:14	5.6	171
	20:31	0.5	15
24 W	01:55	4.6	140
	08:03	0.5	15
	13:51	5.5	168
	21:14	0.5	15
25 Th	02:37	4.5	137
	08:47	0.5	15
	14:35	5.5	168
	22:00	0.5	15
26 F	03:26	4.5	137
	09:40	0.5	15
	15:29	5.4	165
	22:49	0.4	12
27 Sa ◑	04:21	4.6	140
	10:40	0.5	15
	16:29	5.4	165
	23:41	0.3	9
28 Su	05:19	4.8	146
	11:45	0.4	12
	17:33	5.4	165
29 M	00:34	0.2	6
	06:16	5.1	155
	12:52	0.3	9
	18:34	5.4	165
30 Tu	01:27	0.0	0
	07:11	5.4	165
	13:56	0.1	3
	19:33	5.4	165

December

Day	Time (h m)	Height (ft)	Height (cm)
1 W	02:20	-0.2	-6
	08:04	5.7	174
	14:57	-0.1	-3
	20:29	5.4	165
2 Th	03:13	-0.3	-9
	08:56	6.0	183
	15:56	-0.3	-9
	21:22	5.4	165
3 F	04:05	-0.4	-12
	09:46	6.2	189
	16:53	-0.4	-12
	22:14	5.4	165
4 Sa ●	04:56	-0.5	-15
	10:37	6.3	192
	17:48	-0.4	-12
	23:07	5.3	162
5 Su	05:49	-0.4	-12
	11:28	6.3	192
	18:42	-0.4	-12
6 M	00:00	5.1	155
	06:41	-0.4	-12
	12:20	6.2	189
	19:36	-0.4	-12
7 Tu	00:54	5.0	152
	07:35	-0.3	-9
	13:15	6.0	183
	20:30	-0.3	-9
8 W	01:51	4.9	149
	08:31	-0.1	-3
	14:12	5.8	177
	21:24	-0.2	-6
9 Th	02:50	4.8	146
	09:27	0.0	0
	15:12	5.5	168
	22:17	-0.1	-3
10 F	03:51	4.8	146
	10:25	0.1	3
	16:14	5.3	162
	23:10	-0.1	-3
11 Sa ◐	04:52	4.8	146
	11:24	0.2	6
	17:14	5.2	158
12 Su	00:02	-0.1	-3
	05:51	5.0	152
	12:22	0.2	6
	18:12	5.1	155
13 M	00:53	-0.1	-3
	06:46	5.1	155
	13:19	0.1	3
	19:07	5.1	155
14 Tu	01:42	-0.1	-3
	07:38	5.3	162
	14:14	0.0	0
	19:59	5.1	155
15 W	02:29	-0.1	-3
	08:26	5.5	168
	15:06	-0.1	-3
	20:47	5.0	152
16 Th	03:14	-0.1	-3
	09:11	5.6	171
	15:55	-0.1	-3
	21:34	5.0	152
17 F	03:57	-0.1	-3
	09:54	5.6	171
	16:41	-0.2	-6
	22:17	4.9	149
18 Sa	04:38	-0.1	-3
	10:33	5.6	171
	17:25	-0.1	-3
	22:59	4.8	146
19 Su ○	05:17	0.0	0
	11:11	5.5	168
	18:07	-0.1	-3
	23:38	4.7	143
20 M	05:55	0.0	0
	11:45	5.5	168
	18:48	0.0	0
21 Tu	00:15	4.6	140
	06:31	0.1	3
	12:18	5.5	168
	19:28	0.1	3
22 W	01:01	4.5	137
	07:07	0.1	3
	12:51	5.5	168
	20:07	0.1	3
23 Th	01:27	4.5	137
	07:45	0.1	3
	13:27	5.5	168
	20:46	0.1	3
24 F	02:05	4.5	137
	08:27	0.1	3
	14:09	5.4	165
	21:27	0.1	3
25 Sa	02:49	4.6	140
	09:16	0.1	3
	14:57	5.4	165
	22:11	0.1	3
26 Su	03:39	4.7	143
	10:13	0.2	6
	15:54	5.3	162
	23:00	0.0	0
27 M ◑	04:36	4.9	149
	11:18	0.2	6
	16:56	5.2	158
	23:52	-0.1	-3
28 Tu	05:36	5.1	155
	12:26	0.1	3
	18:01	5.1	155
29 W	00:49	-0.2	-6
	06:36	5.4	165
	13:33	0.0	0
	19:04	5.0	152
30 Th	01:47	-0.3	-9
	07:34	5.6	171
	14:38	-0.1	-3
	20:04	5.0	152
31 F	02:45	-0.4	-12
	08:31	5.8	177
	15:39	-0.3	-9
	21:04	4.8	146

StationId: 8545240
Source: NOAA/NOS/CO-OPS
Station Type: Primary
Time Zone: LST_LDT
Datum: MLLW

Philadelphia, PA, 2021

Times and Heights of High and Low Waters

January

Day	Time	ft	cm
1 F	02:54	5.0	152
	09:26	-0.3	-9
	15:02	6.1	186
	22:16	-0.3	-9
2 Sa	03:35	5.0	152
	10:12	-0.3	-9
	15:44	6.1	186
	23:01	-0.3	-9
3 Su	04:19	5.1	155
	11:00	-0.3	-9
	16:30	6.1	186
	23:46	-0.4	-12
4 M	05:07	5.2	158
	11:52	-0.3	-9
	17:22	5.9	180
5 Tu	00:35	-0.4	-12
	06:00	5.3	162
	12:49	-0.3	-9
	18:20	5.8	177
6 W	01:26	-0.4	-12
	06:57	5.4	165
	13:50	-0.2	-6
	19:22	5.6	171
7 Th	02:20	-0.4	-12
	07:57	5.6	171
	14:54	-0.2	-6
	20:24	5.4	165
8 F	03:17	-0.4	-12
	08:56	5.8	177
	15:57	-0.2	-6
	21:25	5.3	162
9 Sa	04:14	-0.4	-12
	09:55	6.0	183
	17:00	-0.3	-9
	22:25	5.2	158
10 Su	05:12	-0.4	-12
	10:51	6.2	189
	17:59	-0.4	-12
	23:21	5.2	158
11 M	06:07	-0.5	-15
	11:46	6.3	192
	18:55	-0.5	-15
12 Tu	00:16	5.2	158
	07:01	-0.5	-15
	12:39	6.3	192
	19:48	-0.5	-15
13 W ●	01:08	5.2	158
	07:52	-0.5	-15
	13:29	6.3	192
	20:38	-0.5	-15
14 Th	01:59	5.2	158
	08:42	-0.5	-15
	14:19	6.2	189
	21:26	-0.5	-15
15 F	02:49	5.2	158
	09:30	-0.4	-12
	15:07	6.0	183
	22:12	-0.5	-15
16 Sa	03:37	5.1	155
	10:17	-0.4	-12
	15:56	5.9	180
	22:56	-0.4	-12
17 Su	04:26	5.1	155
	11:04	-0.3	-9
	16:44	5.7	174
	23:39	-0.4	-12
18 M	05:15	5.1	155
	11:51	-0.3	-9
	17:34	5.5	168
19 Tu	00:22	-0.4	-12
	06:04	5.2	158
	12:40	-0.2	-6
	18:25	5.3	162
20 W	01:06	-0.3	-9
	06:55	5.2	158
	13:31	-0.2	-6
	19:18	5.1	155
21 Th	01:51	-0.3	-9
	07:46	5.3	162
	14:24	-0.1	-3
	20:11	5.0	152
22 F	02:39	-0.3	-9
	08:38	5.4	165
	15:20	-0.1	-3
	21:05	4.9	149
23 Sa	03:29	-0.3	-9
	09:30	5.5	168
	16:15	-0.2	-6
	21:58	4.9	149
24 Su	04:20	-0.3	-9
	10:20	5.6	171
	17:09	-0.2	-6
	22:49	4.9	149
25 M	05:11	-0.3	-9
	11:08	5.8	177
	18:01	-0.3	-9
	23:37	5.0	152
26 Tu	06:00	-0.4	-12
	11:54	5.9	180
	18:50	-0.3	-9
27 W	00:23	5.0	152
	06:48	-0.4	-12
	12:38	6.0	183
	19:37	-0.4	-12
28 Th ○	01:06	5.0	152
	07:36	-0.5	-15
	13:30	6.1	186
	20:23	-0.4	-12
29 F	01:48	5.1	155
	08:22	-0.5	-15
	14:02	6.1	186
	21:08	-0.4	-12
30 Sa	02:30	5.2	158
	09:09	-0.6	-18
	14:44	6.2	189
	21:52	-0.5	-15
31 Su	03:12	5.3	162
	09:57	-0.6	-18
	15:28	6.1	186
	22:36	-0.5	-15

February

Day	Time	ft	cm
1 M	03:56	5.5	168
	10:47	-0.6	-18
	16:15	6.0	183
	23:22	-0.5	-15
2 Tu	04:44	5.6	171
	11:39	-0.5	-15
	17:07	5.8	177
3 W	00:09	-0.5	-15
	05:37	5.7	174
	12:35	-0.4	-12
	18:04	5.6	171
4 Th ◑	01:00	-0.5	-15
	06:33	5.7	174
	13:35	-0.3	-9
	19:04	5.4	165
5 F	01:55	-0.4	-12
	07:33	5.8	177
	14:37	-0.2	-6
	20:06	5.2	158
6 Sa	02:53	-0.3	-9
	08:35	5.8	177
	15:41	-0.1	-3
	21:09	5.1	155
7 Su	03:53	-0.3	-9
	09:36	5.9	180
	16:42	-0.2	-6
	22:09	5.1	155
8 M	04:52	-0.3	-9
	10:35	6.0	183
	17:41	-0.3	-9
	23:07	5.2	158
9 Tu	05:49	-0.3	-9
	11:31	6.1	186
	18:36	-0.4	-12
10 W	00:01	5.3	162
	06:43	-0.4	-12
	12:24	6.1	186
	19:28	-0.4	-12
11 Th ●	00:52	5.4	165
	07:34	-0.4	-12
	13:13	6.1	186
	20:15	-0.4	-12
12 F	01:41	5.4	165
	08:22	-0.4	-12
	14:00	6.1	186
	21:00	-0.4	-12
13 Sa	02:27	5.5	168
	09:08	-0.4	-12
	14:45	6.0	183
	21:42	-0.3	-9
14 Su	03:11	5.5	168
	09:53	-0.3	-9
	15:30	5.9	180
	22:23	-0.2	-6
15 M	03:55	5.5	168
	10:37	-0.2	-6
	16:15	5.7	174
	23:02	-0.2	-6
16 Tu	04:39	5.5	168
	11:21	-0.2	-6
	17:01	5.5	168
	23:41	-0.1	-3
17 W	05:24	5.5	168
	12:07	-0.1	-3
	17:49	5.4	165
18 Th	00:21	-0.1	-3
	06:11	5.5	168
	12:54	0.0	0
	18:40	5.2	158
19 F ◑	01:03	0.0	0
	07:00	5.5	168
	13:46	0.1	3
	19:33	5.0	152
20 Sa	01:50	0.0	0
	07:52	5.6	171
	14:41	0.1	3
	20:27	5.0	152
21 Su	02:42	0.1	3
	08:46	5.6	171
	15:37	0.2	6
	21:21	5.0	152
22 M	03:38	0.1	3
	09:39	5.7	174
	16:33	0.1	3
	22:13	5.0	152
23 Tu	04:34	0.0	0
	10:31	5.9	180
	17:27	0.1	3
	23:04	5.2	158
24 W	05:28	-0.1	-3
	11:21	6.1	186
	18:19	0.0	0
	23:51	5.3	162
25 Th	06:21	-0.2	-6
	12:09	6.2	189
	19:07	-0.1	-3
26 F	00:37	5.5	168
	07:12	-0.3	-9
	12:54	6.4	195
	19:54	-0.2	-6
27 Sa ○	01:20	5.7	174
	08:02	-0.4	-12
	13:38	6.5	198
	20:40	-0.2	-6
28 Su	02:03	5.9	180
	08:51	-0.4	-12
	14:23	6.5	198
	21:25	-0.3	-9

March

Day	Time	ft	cm
1 M	02:47	6.1	186
	09:41	-0.4	-12
	15:10	6.4	195
	22:10	-0.3	-9
2 Tu	03:33	6.3	192
	10:33	-0.4	-12
	15:59	6.2	189
	22:57	-0.3	-9
3 W	04:22	6.3	192
	11:26	-0.3	-9
	16:52	6.0	183
	23:45	-0.2	-6
4 Th	05:14	6.3	192
	12:21	-0.1	-3
	17:48	5.7	174
5 F ◑	00:37	-0.1	-3
	06:12	6.3	192
	13:20	0.0	0
	18:49	5.5	168
6 Sa	01:33	0.1	3
	07:13	6.2	189
	14:21	0.1	3
	19:51	5.4	165
7 Su	02:32	0.2	6
	08:16	6.1	186
	15:22	0.2	6
	20:54	5.3	162
8 M	03:33	0.2	6
	09:19	6.1	186
	16:23	0.2	6
	21:55	5.4	165
9 Tu	04:33	0.2	6
	10:19	6.2	189
	17:20	0.1	3
	22:52	5.6	171
10 W	05:30	0.1	3
	11:15	6.2	189
	18:14	0.0	0
	23:45	5.8	177
11 Th	06:24	0.0	0
	12:07	6.3	192
	19:03	0.0	0
12 F	00:34	5.9	180
	07:14	0.0	0
	12:54	6.3	192
	19:48	0.0	0
13 Sa ●	01:19	6.1	186
	08:01	0.0	0
	13:39	6.3	192
	20:30	0.1	3
14 Su	03:02	6.1	186
	09:46	0.0	0
	15:22	6.2	189
	22:10	0.2	6
15 M	03:43	6.2	189
	10:29	0.1	3
	16:04	6.1	186
	22:48	0.3	9
16 Tu	04:24	6.2	189
	11:11	0.1	3
	16:47	6.0	183
	23:25	0.4	12
17 W	05:03	6.2	189
	11:53	0.2	6
	17:30	5.8	177
18 Th	00:00	0.4	12
	05:44	6.2	189
	12:36	0.3	9
	18:16	5.6	171
19 F	00:37	0.5	15
	06:27	6.1	186
	13:21	0.4	12
	19:04	5.5	168
20 Sa	01:18	0.5	15
	07:13	6.1	186
	14:10	0.5	15
	19:55	5.4	165
21 Su ◑	02:05	0.5	15
	08:05	6.1	186
	15:03	0.6	18
	20:48	5.3	162
22 M	02:59	0.6	18
	09:00	6.1	186
	15:59	0.6	18
	21:43	5.4	165
23 Tu	03:58	0.6	18
	09:57	6.2	189
	16:56	0.6	18
	22:37	5.5	168
24 W	04:59	0.5	15
	10:53	6.3	192
	17:52	0.5	15
	23:29	5.7	174
25 Th	05:58	0.4	12
	11:46	6.5	198
	18:45	0.4	12
26 F	00:18	6.0	183
	06:54	0.3	9
	12:37	6.7	204
	19:35	0.3	9
27 Sa	01:05	6.3	192
	07:48	0.1	3
	13:25	6.8	207
	20:23	0.2	6
28 Su ○	01:51	6.6	201
	08:41	0.0	0
	14:13	6.8	207
	21:10	0.2	6
29 M	02:36	6.9	210
	09:33	-0.1	-3
	15:01	6.8	207
	21:57	0.2	6
30 Tu	03:22	7.1	216
	10:25	-0.1	-3
	16:04	6.6	201
	22:44	0.2	6
31 W	04:10	7.1	216
	11:18	0.0	0
	16:41	6.4	195
	23:32	0.3	9

StationId: 8545240
Source: NOAA/NOS/CO-OPS
Station Type: Primary
Time Zone: LST_LDT
Datum: MLLW

NOAA Tide Predictions

Philadelphia, PA,2021

Times and Heights of High and Low Waters

April

Day	Time (h m)	Height (ft)	Height (cm)	Day	Time (h m)	Height (ft)	Height (cm)
1 Th	05:00 / 12:11 / 17:36	7.1 / 0.1 / 6.2	216 / 3 / 189	16 F	05:07 / 12:09 / 17:45	6.7 / 0.7 / 5.9	204 / 21 / 180
2 F	00:23 / 05:54 / 13:06 / 18:33	0.4 / 7.0 / 0.2 / 6.0	12 / 213 / 6 / 183	17 Sa	00:01 / 05:46 / 12:52 / 18:30	0.9 / 6.7 / 0.7 / 5.8	27 / 204 / 21 / 177
3 Sa	01:16 / 06:52 / 14:04 / 19:34	0.5 / 6.8 / 0.4 / 5.8	15 / 207 / 12 / 177	18 Su	00:41 / 06:28 / 13:39 / 19:19	0.9 / 6.6 / 0.8 / 5.7	27 / 201 / 24 / 174
4 Su ☽	02:13 / 07:54 / 15:02 / 20:36	0.6 / 6.6 / 0.5 / 5.8	18 / 201 / 15 / 177	19 M	01:28 / 07:18 / 14:30 / 20:11	1.0 / 6.6 / 0.9 / 5.7	30 / 201 / 27 / 174
5 M	03:12 / 08:57 / 16:01 / 21:38	0.7 / 6.5 / 0.5 / 5.8	21 / 198 / 15 / 177	20 Tu ☽	02:23 / 08:16 / 15:24 / 21:06	1.0 / 6.6 / 0.9 / 5.8	30 / 201 / 27 / 177
6 Tu	04:12 / 10:00 / 16:59 / 22:37	0.7 / 6.4 / 0.5 / 6.0	21 / 195 / 15 / 183	21 W	03:24 / 09:16 / 16:20 / 22:00	1.0 / 6.6 / 0.9 / 6.0	30 / 201 / 27 / 183
7 W	05:12 / 11:00 / 17:54 / 23:33	0.6 / 6.5 / 0.4 / 6.2	18 / 198 / 12 / 189	22 Th	04:27 / 10:15 / 17:15 / 22:54	0.9 / 6.7 / 0.8 / 6.3	27 / 204 / 24 / 192
8 Th	06:09 / 11:54 / 18:46	0.5 / 6.5 / 0.4	15 / 198 / 12	23 F	05:29 / 11:11 / 18:09 / 23:45	0.8 / 6.8 / 0.7 / 6.7	24 / 207 / 21 / 204
9 F	00:24 / 07:02 / 12:45 / 19:33	6.4 / 0.4 / 6.6 / 0.4	195 / 12 / 201 / 12	24 Sa	06:29 / 12:05 / 19:01	0.7 / 6.9 / 0.6	21 / 210 / 18
10 Sa	01:11 / 07:52 / 13:31 / 20:17	6.6 / 0.4 / 6.6 / 0.4	201 / 12 / 201 / 12	25 Su	00:34 / 07:26 / 12:57 / 19:51	7.1 / 0.5 / 7.0 / 0.5	216 / 15 / 213 / 15
11 Su	01:55 / 08:38 / 14:15 / 20:58	6.8 / 0.4 / 6.5 / 0.6	207 / 12 / 198 / 18	26 M	01:22 / 08:21 / 13:47 / 20:41	7.4 / 0.4 / 6.9 / 0.5	226 / 12 / 210 / 15
12 M ●	02:36 / 09:22 / 14:57 / 21:37	6.8 / 0.4 / 6.4 / 0.7	207 / 12 / 195 / 21	27 Tu ○	02:09 / 09:15 / 14:38 / 21:30	7.6 / 0.3 / 6.8 / 0.5	232 / 9 / 207 / 15
13 Tu	03:15 / 10:05 / 15:38 / 22:13	6.8 / 0.5 / 6.3 / 0.8	207 / 15 / 192 / 24	28 W	02:58 / 10:09 / 15:30 / 22:19	7.7 / 0.3 / 6.7 / 0.6	235 / 9 / 204 / 18
14 W	03:53 / 10:46 / 16:20 / 22:49	6.8 / 0.5 / 6.1 / 0.9	207 / 15 / 186 / 27	29 Th	03:47 / 11:02 / 16:23 / 23:10	7.7 / 0.3 / 6.5 / 0.7	235 / 9 / 198 / 21
15 Th	04:30 / 11:27 / 17:02 / 23:24	6.8 / 0.6 / 6.0 / 0.9	207 / 18 / 183 / 27	30 F	04:40 / 11:55 / 17:19	7.6 / 0.4 / 6.3	232 / 12 / 192

May

Day	Time (h m)	Height (ft)	Height (cm)	Day	Time (h m)	Height (ft)	Height (cm)
1 Sa	00:02 / 05:35 / 12:49 / 18:17	0.8 / 7.4 / 0.5 / 6.2	24 / 226 / 15 / 189	16 Su	05:11 / 12:28 / 18:00	7.0 / 0.9 / 5.8	213 / 27 / 177
2 Su	00:56 / 06:33 / 13:44 / 19:17	0.9 / 7.1 / 0.6 / 6.1	27 / 216 / 18 / 186	17 M	00:14 / 05:52 / 13:13 / 18:47	1.1 / 6.9 / 0.9 / 5.9	34 / 210 / 27 / 180
3 M ☽	01:52 / 07:34 / 14:40 / 20:18	0.9 / 6.9 / 0.6 / 6.1	27 / 210 / 18 / 186	18 Tu	01:02 / 06:40 / 14:00 / 19:37	1.1 / 6.9 / 0.9 / 6.0	34 / 210 / 27 / 183
4 Tu	02:50 / 08:36 / 15:35 / 21:17	1.0 / 6.7 / 0.7 / 6.2	30 / 204 / 21 / 189	19 W ☽	01:56 / 07:37 / 14:51 / 20:31	1.1 / 6.8 / 0.8 / 6.1	34 / 207 / 24 / 186
5 W	03:49 / 09:36 / 16:30 / 22:15	1.0 / 6.6 / 0.6 / 6.4	30 / 201 / 18 / 195	20 Th	02:56 / 08:39 / 15:45 / 21:26	1.1 / 6.8 / 0.8 / 6.4	34 / 207 / 24 / 195
6 Th	04:47 / 10:34 / 17:23 / 23:08	0.9 / 6.6 / 0.6 / 6.7	27 / 201 / 18 / 204	21 F	04:00 / 09:40 / 16:40 / 22:20	1.1 / 6.8 / 0.8 / 6.7	34 / 207 / 24 / 204
7 F	05:43 / 11:27 / 18:12 / 23:58	0.8 / 6.6 / 0.6 / 6.9	24 / 201 / 18 / 210	22 Sa	05:04 / 10:39 / 17:35 / 23:13	1.0 / 6.8 / 0.7 / 7.1	30 / 207 / 21 / 216
8 Sa	06:36 / 12:17 / 18:59	0.7 / 6.6 / 0.6	21 / 201 / 18	23 Su	06:06 / 11:35 / 18:28	0.8 / 6.8 / 0.6	24 / 207 / 18
9 Su	00:44 / 07:26 / 13:04 / 19:42	7.1 / 0.6 / 6.6 / 0.7	216 / 18 / 201 / 21	24 M	00:05 / 07:05 / 12:30 / 19:21	7.4 / 0.7 / 6.8 / 0.6	226 / 21 / 207 / 18
10 M	01:27 / 08:13 / 13:48 / 20:23	7.2 / 0.6 / 6.5 / 0.8	219 / 18 / 198 / 24	25 Tu	00:55 / 08:02 / 13:24 / 20:13	7.7 / 0.5 / 6.7 / 0.6	235 / 15 / 204 / 18
11 Tu ●	02:07 / 08:58 / 14:31 / 21:03	7.2 / 0.6 / 6.4 / 1.0	219 / 18 / 195 / 30	26 W ○	01:45 / 08:58 / 14:17 / 21:05	7.8 / 0.4 / 6.6 / 0.7	238 / 12 / 201 / 21
12 W	02:46 / 09:41 / 15:13 / 21:40	7.2 / 0.7 / 6.2 / 1.1	219 / 21 / 189 / 34	27 Th	02:36 / 09:52 / 15:10 / 21:56	7.9 / 0.4 / 6.5 / 0.7	241 / 12 / 198 / 21
13 Th	03:23 / 10:22 / 15:54 / 22:17	7.1 / 0.7 / 6.1 / 1.2	216 / 21 / 186 / 37	28 F	03:27 / 10:45 / 16:05 / 22:48	7.8 / 0.4 / 6.3 / 0.8	238 / 12 / 192 / 24
14 F	03:59 / 11:04 / 16:35 / 22:54	7.1 / 0.8 / 5.9 / 1.2	216 / 24 / 180 / 37	29 Sa	04:21 / 11:37 / 17:01 / 23:41	7.6 / 0.4 / 6.2 / 0.8	232 / 12 / 189 / 24
15 Sa	04:35 / 11:45 / 17:17 / 23:33	7.0 / 0.8 / 5.9 / 1.1	213 / 24 / 180 / 34	30 Su	05:16 / 12:29 / 17:58	7.4 / 0.5 / 6.2	226 / 15 / 189
				31 M	00:35 / 06:13 / 13:21 / 18:56	0.9 / 7.1 / 0.5 / 6.2	27 / 216 / 15 / 189

June

Day	Time (h m)	Height (ft)	Height (cm)	Day	Time (h m)	Height (ft)	Height (cm)
1 Tu	01:29 / 07:11 / 14:13 / 19:54	1.0 / 6.9 / 0.5 / 6.2	30 / 210 / 15 / 189	16 W	00:43 / 06:14 / 13:33 / 19:05	0.9 / 6.9 / 0.6 / 6.1	27 / 210 / 18 / 186
2 W ◑	02:25 / 08:09 / 15:04 / 20:50	1.0 / 6.7 / 0.5 / 6.4	30 / 204 / 15 / 195	17 Th	01:37 / 07:09 / 14:22 / 19:58	0.9 / 6.8 / 0.6 / 6.3	27 / 207 / 18 / 192
3 Th	03:21 / 09:07 / 15:55 / 21:45	1.0 / 6.5 / 0.5 / 6.5	30 / 198 / 15 / 198	18 F ◑	02:36 / 08:09 / 15:13 / 20:53	1.0 / 6.7 / 0.5 / 6.6	30 / 204 / 15 / 201
4 F	04:18 / 10:02 / 16:45 / 22:37	0.9 / 6.5 / 0.5 / 6.8	27 / 198 / 15 / 207	19 Sa	03:39 / 09:11 / 16:08 / 21:49	1.0 / 6.6 / 0.5 / 6.9	30 / 201 / 15 / 210
5 Sa	05:13 / 10:55 / 17:34 / 23:26	0.8 / 6.4 / 0.6 / 6.9	24 / 195 / 18 / 210	20 Su	04:43 / 10:11 / 17:03 / 22:45	0.9 / 6.5 / 0.5 / 7.2	27 / 198 / 15 / 219
6 Su	06:07 / 11:46 / 18:21	0.7 / 6.4 / 0.6	21 / 195 / 18	21 M	05:46 / 11:10 / 17:59 / 23:39	0.8 / 6.4 / 0.5 / 7.4	24 / 195 / 15 / 226
7 M	00:13 / 06:58 / 12:34 / 19:05	7.1 / 0.7 / 6.3 / 0.7	216 / 21 / 192 / 21	22 Tu	06:46 / 12:08 / 18:55	0.7 / 6.3 / 0.6	21 / 192 / 18
8 Tu	00:57 / 07:46 / 13:20 / 19:48	7.2 / 0.6 / 6.2 / 0.8	219 / 18 / 189 / 24	23 W	00:32 / 07:45 / 13:03 / 19:50	7.6 / 0.5 / 6.3 / 0.6	232 / 15 / 192 / 18
9 W	01:39 / 08:32 / 14:05 / 20:30	7.2 / 0.6 / 6.1 / 0.9	219 / 18 / 186 / 27	24 Th ○	01:25 / 08:40 / 13:58 / 20:43	7.7 / 0.4 / 6.2 / 0.6	235 / 12 / 189 / 18
10 Th ●	02:18 / 09:16 / 14:47 / 21:10	7.2 / 0.7 / 6.0 / 1.0	219 / 21 / 183 / 30	25 F	02:17 / 09:34 / 14:52 / 21:36	7.7 / 0.4 / 6.2 / 0.6	235 / 12 / 189 / 18
11 F	02:56 / 09:58 / 15:29 / 21:50	7.1 / 0.7 / 5.9 / 1.1	216 / 21 / 180 / 34	26 Sa	03:10 / 10:26 / 15:46 / 22:28	7.6 / 0.4 / 6.1 / 0.7	232 / 12 / 186 / 21
12 Sa	03:33 / 10:40 / 16:09 / 22:30	7.1 / 0.7 / 5.8 / 1.1	216 / 21 / 177 / 34	27 Su	04:02 / 11:16 / 16:40 / 23:20	7.4 / 0.4 / 6.1 / 0.7	226 / 12 / 186 / 21
13 Su	04:09 / 11:22 / 16:50 / 23:11	7.0 / 0.7 / 5.8 / 1.0	213 / 21 / 177 / 30	28 M	04:55 / 12:05 / 17:35	7.2 / 0.4 / 6.1	219 / 12 / 186
14 M	04:46 / 12:04 / 17:32 / 23:55	7.0 / 0.7 / 5.8 / 1.0	213 / 21 / 177 / 30	29 Tu	00:12 / 05:49 / 12:53 / 18:29	0.8 / 6.9 / 0.4 / 6.1	24 / 210 / 12 / 186
15 Tu	05:26 / 12:48 / 18:16	7.0 / 0.7 / 5.9	213 / 21 / 180	30 W	01:04 / 06:44 / 13:41 / 19:23	0.8 / 6.7 / 0.4 / 6.2	24 / 204 / 12 / 189

StationId: 8545240
Source: NOAA/NOS/CO-OPS
Station Type: Primary
Time Zone: LST_LDT
Datum: MLLW

NOAA Tide Predictions

Philadelphia, PA, 2021

Times and Heights of High and Low Waters

July

Day	Time	ft	cm	Day	Time	ft	cm
1 Th ☽	01:57	0.9	27	**16** F	01:21	0.8	24
	07:38	6.5	198		06:47	6.7	204
	14:28	0.4	12		13:54	0.4	12
	20:17	6.3	192		19:29	6.5	198
2 F	02:50	0.9	27	**17** Sa ☾	02:20	0.8	24
	08:33	6.3	192		07:46	6.5	198
	15:16	0.5	15		14:45	0.4	12
	21:09	6.5	198		20:25	6.7	204
3 Sa	03:45	0.9	27	**18** Su	03:22	0.9	27
	09:27	6.2	189		08:48	6.3	192
	16:04	0.5	15		15:40	0.4	12
	22:01	6.6	201		21:23	6.9	210
4 Su	04:40	0.8	24	**19** M	04:25	0.8	24
	10:21	6.1	186		09:50	6.1	186
	16:53	0.5	15		16:38	0.5	15
	22:51	6.8	207		22:21	7.1	216
5 M	05:34	0.7	21	**20** Tu	05:28	0.8	24
	11:13	6.0	183		10:51	6.0	183
	17:41	0.6	18		17:36	0.5	15
	23:39	6.9	210		23:19	7.3	223
6 Tu	06:26	0.6	18	**21** W	06:29	0.7	21
	12:03	6.0	183		11:50	6.0	183
	18:28	0.7	21		18:34	0.5	15
7 W	00:25	7.0	213	**22** Th	00:15	7.4	226
	07:16	0.6	18		07:27	0.5	15
	12:51	5.9	180		12:46	6.0	183
	19:14	0.7	21		19:30	0.5	15
8 Th	01:09	7.0	213	**23** F	01:09	7.4	226
	08:04	0.6	18		08:22	0.4	12
	13:37	5.9	180		13:41	6.1	186
	19:59	0.8	24		20:25	0.5	15
9 F	01:51	7.0	213	**24** Sa ○	02:01	7.4	226
	08:49	0.6	18		09:14	0.4	12
	14:21	5.8	177		14:34	6.1	186
	20:42	0.8	24		21:17	0.5	15
10 Sa ●	02:31	7.0	213	**25** Su	02:53	7.3	223
	09:33	0.6	18		10:04	0.3	9
	15:02	5.8	177		15:26	6.1	186
	21:25	0.8	24		22:08	0.6	18
11 Su	03:09	7.0	213	**26** M	03:43	7.2	219
	10:16	0.6	18		10:51	0.3	9
	15:43	5.8	177		16:17	6.1	186
	22:09	0.8	24		22:58	0.7	21
12 M	03:47	7.0	213	**27** Tu	04:33	7.0	213
	10:58	0.5	15		11:37	0.4	12
	16:23	5.8	177		17:07	6.2	189
	22:53	0.8	24		23:47	0.7	21
13 Tu	04:25	7.0	213	**28** W	05:22	6.8	207
	11:40	0.5	15		12:21	0.4	12
	17:04	5.9	180		17:57	6.2	189
	23:39	0.8	24				
14 W	05:07	6.9	210	**29** Th	00:36	0.8	24
	12:22	0.4	12		06:13	6.5	198
	17:48	6.1	186		13:04	0.4	12
					18:47	6.3	192
15 Th	00:28	0.8	24	**30** F	01:26	0.8	24
	05:54	6.8	207		07:04	6.3	192
	13:07	0.4	12		13:48	0.5	15
	18:36	6.3	192		19:38	6.3	192
				31 Sa ☽	02:17	0.9	27
					07:57	6.1	186
					14:33	0.5	15
					20:29	6.4	195

August

Day	Time	ft	cm	Day	Time	ft	cm
1 Su	03:10	0.9	27	**16** M	03:07	0.9	27
	08:51	5.9	180		08:31	6.1	186
	15:20	0.6	18		15:18	0.6	18
	21:21	6.5	198		21:01	6.9	210
2 M	04:04	0.9	27	**17** Tu	04:10	0.9	27
	09:46	5.8	177		09:34	5.9	180
	16:09	0.7	21		16:17	0.6	18
	22:12	6.6	201		22:03	7.0	213
3 Tu	04:59	0.8	24	**18** W	05:12	0.8	24
	10:39	5.8	177		10:36	5.9	180
	17:00	0.7	21		17:18	0.6	18
	23:03	6.7	204		23:03	7.1	216
4 W	05:52	0.7	21	**19** Th	06:12	0.7	21
	11:31	5.8	177		11:36	6.0	183
	17:50	0.7	21		18:17	0.6	18
	23:52	6.9	210				
5 Th	06:44	0.7	21	**20** F	00:00	7.2	219
	12:20	5.8	177		07:09	0.6	18
	18:40	0.7	21		12:32	6.1	186
					19:13	0.6	18
6 F	00:38	7.0	213	**21** Sa	00:55	7.3	223
	07:33	0.6	18		08:02	0.5	15
	13:07	5.8	177		13:25	6.2	189
	19:29	0.7	21		20:07	0.5	15
7 Sa	01:22	7.0	213	**22** Su ○	01:46	7.3	223
	08:20	0.6	18		08:52	0.4	12
	13:52	5.9	180		14:16	6.3	192
	20:16	0.7	21		20:58	0.6	18
8 Su ●	02:04	7.1	216	**23** M	02:35	7.2	219
	09:04	0.5	15		09:38	0.4	12
	14:34	6.0	183		15:04	6.4	195
	21:02	0.7	21		21:47	0.6	18
9 M	02:44	7.1	216	**24** Tu	03:21	7.1	216
	09:48	0.5	15		10:22	0.5	15
	15:15	6.0	183		15:51	6.4	195
	21:48	0.6	18		22:35	0.7	21
10 Tu	03:24	7.1	216	**25** W	04:08	6.9	210
	10:30	0.4	12		11:05	0.5	15
	15:55	6.2	189		16:37	6.5	198
	22:34	0.6	18		23:21	0.8	24
11 W	04:04	7.0	213	**26** Th	04:54	6.7	204
	11:13	0.4	12		11:45	0.6	18
	16:36	6.3	192		17:22	6.5	198
	23:23	0.6	18				
12 Th	04:48	6.9	210	**27** F	00:07	0.9	27
	11:56	0.4	12		05:41	6.4	195
	17:20	6.5	198		12:26	0.7	21
					18:08	6.5	198
13 F	00:13	0.7	21	**28** Sa	00:54	0.9	27
	05:36	6.8	207		06:30	6.2	189
	12:41	0.4	12		12:58	0.8	24
	18:09	6.7	204		18:56	6.5	198
14 Sa	01:07	0.7	21	**29** Su	01:42	1.0	30
	06:29	6.5	198		07:21	6.0	183
	13:29	0.4	12		13:49	0.8	24
	19:03	6.8	207		19:46	6.5	198
15 Su ☾	02:05	0.8	24	**30** M ☽	02:33	1.0	30
	07:28	6.3	192		08:15	5.8	177
	14:21	0.5	15		14:35	0.9	27
	20:01	6.9	210		20:38	6.5	198
				31 Tu	03:27	1.0	30
					09:10	5.7	174
					15:25	0.9	27
					21:32	6.6	201

September

Day	Time	ft	cm	Day	Time	ft	cm
1 W	04:22	1.0	30	**16** Th	04:54	0.9	27
	10:04	5.7	174		10:23	6.0	183
	16:19	0.9	27		17:01	0.8	24
	22:25	6.7	204		22:49	7.0	213
2 Th	05:17	1.0	30	**17** F	05:53	0.8	24
	10:57	5.8	177		11:22	6.2	189
	17:14	0.9	27		18:00	0.7	21
	23:17	6.8	207		23:46	7.1	216
3 F	06:09	0.9	27	**18** Sa	06:48	0.6	18
	11:48	5.9	180		12:18	6.4	195
	18:07	0.8	24		18:56	0.6	18
4 Sa	00:06	7.0	213	**19** Su	00:39	7.2	219
	07:00	0.7	21		07:39	0.5	15
	12:36	6.1	186		13:09	6.5	198
	18:59	0.7	21		19:49	0.6	18
5 Su	00:52	7.1	216	**20** M ○	01:28	7.2	219
	07:47	0.6	18		08:26	0.5	15
	13:20	6.2	189		13:56	6.7	204
	19:50	0.6	18		20:39	0.6	18
6 M	01:35	7.2	219	**21** Tu	02:14	7.1	216
	08:33	0.6	18		09:10	0.5	15
	14:03	6.4	195		14:41	6.8	207
	20:39	0.6	18		21:26	0.7	21
7 Tu ●	02:18	7.2	219	**22** W	02:59	7.0	213
	09:17	0.5	15		09:51	0.6	18
	14:45	6.6	201		15:24	6.8	207
	21:27	0.6	18		22:11	0.8	24
8 W	03:00	7.2	219	**23** Th	03:42	6.8	207
	10:01	0.5	15		10:31	0.8	24
	15:26	6.8	207		16:05	6.8	207
	22:16	0.6	18		22:55	0.9	27
9 Th	03:43	7.1	216	**24** F	04:26	6.5	198
	10:44	0.4	12		11:09	0.9	27
	16:09	6.9	210		16:47	6.8	207
	23:07	0.6	18		23:39	0.9	27
10 F	04:29	6.9	210	**25** Sa	05:10	6.3	192
	11:29	0.5	15		11:46	0.9	27
	16:54	7.0	213		17:30	6.7	204
	23:59	0.7	21				
11 Sa	05:18	6.7	204	**26** Su	00:23	1.0	30
	12:16	0.5	15		05:57	6.1	186
	17:45	7.1	216		12:24	1.0	30
					18:14	6.7	204
12 Su	00:54	0.8	24	**27** M	01:09	1.1	34
	06:14	6.4	195		06:46	5.9	180
	13:06	0.6	18		13:05	1.0	30
	18:40	7.1	216		19:02	6.6	201
13 M ☽	01:51	0.9	27	**28** Tu	01:58	1.1	34
	07:14	6.2	189		07:38	5.8	177
	14:01	0.7	21		13:51	1.0	30
	19:41	7.0	213		19:54	6.6	201
14 Tu	02:52	1.0	30	**29** W ☽	02:50	1.1	34
	08:17	6.0	183		08:32	5.7	174
	14:59	0.8	24		14:43	1.0	30
	20:44	7.0	213		20:49	6.6	201
15 W	03:53	1.0	30	**30** Th	03:44	1.1	34
	09:21	5.9	180		09:27	5.7	174
	16:00	0.8	24		15:39	1.0	30
	21:48	7.0	213		21:45	6.7	204

StationId: 8545240
Source: NOAA/NOS/CO-OPS
Station Type: Primary
Time Zone: LST_LDT
Datum: MLLW

NOAA Tide Predictions

Philadelphia, PA,2021

Times and Heights of High and Low Waters

October

Day	h m	ft	cm	Day	h m	ft	cm
1 F	04:39	1.1	34	16 Sa	05:29	0.6	18
	10:21	5.8	177		11:06	6.3	192
	16:38	1.0	30		17:41	0.7	21
	22:39	6.8	207		23:28	6.9	210
2 Sa	05:33	0.9	27	17 Su	06:22	0.5	15
	11:13	6.1	186		12:00	6.5	198
	17:35	0.9	27		18:37	0.6	18
	23:30	7.0	213				
3 Su	06:24	0.8	24	18 M	00:20	6.9	210
	12:01	6.3	192		07:11	0.4	12
	18:30	0.7	21		12:49	6.7	204
					19:29	0.5	15
4 M	00:18	7.1	216	19 Tu	01:07	6.9	210
	07:13	0.6	18		07:56	0.4	12
	12:47	6.6	201		13:34	6.9	210
	19:24	0.6	18		20:17	0.5	15
5 Tu	01:05	7.2	219	20 W	01:52	6.8	207
	07:45	0.5	15		08:39	0.5	15
	13:31	6.9	210		14:16	6.9	210
	20:16	0.5	15	○	21:03	0.5	15
6 W	01:50	7.2	219	21 Th	02:35	6.6	201
	08:45	0.5	15		09:19	0.6	18
	14:14	7.1	216		14:56	6.9	210
●	21:07	0.5	15		21:47	0.6	18
7 Th	02:35	7.1	216	22 F	03:17	6.4	195
	09:31	0.4	12		09:57	0.8	24
	14:58	7.3	223		15:36	6.9	210
	21:58	0.5	15		22:30	0.7	21
8 F	03:21	7.0	213	23 Sa	03:59	6.2	189
	10:17	0.4	12		10:34	0.9	27
	15:43	7.4	226		16:15	6.8	207
	22:51	0.5	15		23:12	0.8	24
9 Sa	04:09	6.8	207	24 Su	04:42	6.0	183
	11:04	0.5	15		11:10	0.9	27
	16:31	7.4	226		16:54	6.7	204
	23:44	0.6	18		23:55	0.9	27
10 Su	05:02	6.5	198	25 M	05:26	5.8	177
	11:53	0.6	18		11:47	0.9	27
	17:23	7.3	223		17:35	6.6	201
11 M	00:39	0.7	21	26 Tu	00:39	0.9	27
	05:59	6.2	189		06:13	5.7	174
	12:46	0.7	21		12:29	0.9	27
	18:21	7.2	219		18:20	6.5	198
12 Tu	01:36	0.8	24	27 W	01:25	1.0	30
	06:59	6.0	183		07:02	5.5	168
	13:42	0.8	24		13:12	0.9	27
	19:23	7.0	213		19:10	6.5	198
13 W	02:35	0.9	27	28 Th	02:14	1.0	30
	08:03	5.9	180		07:54	5.5	168
	14:42	0.8	24		14:04	0.9	27
◐	20:28	6.9	210	◑	20:05	6.5	198
14 Th	03:34	0.8	24	29 F	03:07	0.9	27
	09:06	5.9	180		08:49	5.6	171
	15:42	0.8	24		15:02	0.9	27
	21:31	6.8	207		21:02	6.5	198
15 F	04:33	0.7	21	30 Sa	04:00	0.8	24
	10:08	6.1	186		09:43	5.8	177
	16:43	0.8	24		16:03	0.8	24
	22:32	6.8	207		21:59	6.6	201
				31 Su	04:54	0.7	21
					10:35	6.0	183
					17:04	0.7	21
					22:53	6.7	204

November

Day	h m	ft	cm	Day	h m	ft	cm
1 M	05:46	0.5	15	16 Tu	05:39	0.1	3
	11:25	6.4	195		11:24	6.5	198
	18:03	0.6	18		18:05	0.2	6
	23:44	6.8	207		23:43	6.3	192
2 Tu	06:37	0.4	12	17 W	06:24	0.1	3
	12:13	6.7	204		12:08	6.7	204
	18:59	0.4	12		18:54	0.2	6
3 W	00:34	6.8	207	18 Th	00:28	6.2	189
	07:26	0.3	9		07:06	0.2	6
	13:00	7.0	213		12:50	6.7	204
	19:54	0.3	9		19:40	0.2	6
4 Th	01:22	6.8	207	19 F	01:11	6.0	183
	08:14	0.2	6		07:47	0.3	9
	13:46	7.3	223		13:30	6.7	204
●	20:48	0.2	6	○	20:24	0.3	9
5 F	02:11	6.7	204	20 Sa	01:54	5.9	180
	09:02	0.2	6		08:26	0.4	12
	14:32	7.4	226		14:09	6.6	201
	21:41	0.2	6		21:06	0.3	9
6 Sa	03:00	6.5	198	21 Su	02:35	5.7	174
	09:51	0.2	6		09:03	0.5	15
	15:20	7.4	226		14:47	6.5	198
	22:34	0.2	6		21:48	0.4	12
7 Su	02:51	6.3	192	22 M	03:17	5.5	168
	09:41	0.3	9		09:41	0.5	15
	15:11	7.3	223		15:24	6.4	195
	22:28	0.3	9		22:29	0.5	15
8 M	03:45	6.1	186	23 Tu	03:58	5.3	162
	10:33	0.3	9		10:18	0.5	15
	16:05	7.2	219		16:05	6.3	192
	23:22	0.4	12		23:11	0.5	15
9 Tu	04:43	5.9	180	24 W	04:41	5.2	158
	11:27	0.4	12		10:58	0.5	15
	17:04	6.9	210		16:44	6.3	192
					23:55	0.5	15
10 W	00:18	0.4	12	25 Th	05:27	5.2	158
	05:43	5.7	174		11:42	0.4	12
	12:24	0.5	15		17:30	6.2	189
	18:06	6.7	204				
11 Th	01:14	0.4	12	26 F	00:41	0.4	12
	06:46	5.7	174		06:16	5.2	158
	13:00	0.5	15		12:33	0.4	12
◐	19:08	6.5	198		18:23	6.2	189
12 F	02:10	0.4	12	27 Sa	01:30	0.4	12
	07:48	5.7	174		07:08	5.3	162
	14:22	0.5	15		13:30	0.4	12
	20:10	6.4	195	◐	19:20	6.1	186
13 Sa	03:06	0.3	9	28 Su	02:22	0.3	9
	08:47	5.9	180		08:02	5.5	168
	15:21	0.5	15		14:32	0.4	12
	21:09	6.4	195		20:19	6.1	186
14 Su	04:00	0.2	6	29 M	03:15	0.2	6
	09:44	6.1	186		08:56	5.8	177
	16:19	0.4	12		15:35	0.3	9
	22:04	6.4	195		21:16	6.1	186
15 M	04:51	0.1	3	30 Tu	04:09	0.1	3
	10:36	6.3	192		09:49	6.2	189
	17:14	0.3	9		16:37	0.2	6
	22:55	6.3	192		22:12	6.1	186

December

Day	h m	ft	cm	Day	h m	ft	cm
1 W	05:02	0.0	0	16 Th	05:50	-0.2	-6
	10:40	6.5	198		11:40	6.2	189
	17:36	0.1	3		18:28	-0.2	-6
	23:05	6.1	186				
2 Th	05:54	-0.1	-3	17 F	00:03	5.5	168
	11:30	6.8	207		06:34	-0.2	-6
	18:34	-0.1	-3		12:23	6.2	189
	23:57	6.1	186		19:15	-0.2	-6
3 F	06:46	-0.2	-6	18 Sa	00:47	5.4	165
	12:20	7.0	213		07:16	-0.1	-3
	19:30	-0.1	-3		13:05	6.2	189
					19:59	-0.2	-6
4 Sa	00:49	6.0	183	19 Su	01:30	5.3	162
	07:38	-0.2	-6		07:57	0.0	0
	13:10	7.1	216		13:44	6.2	189
●	20:24	-0.2	-6	○	20:42	-0.1	-3
5 Su	01:41	5.9	180	20 M	02:12	5.1	155
	08:29	-0.2	-6		08:37	0.0	0
	14:01	7.1	216		14:23	6.1	186
	21:17	-0.2	-6		21:24	-0.1	-3
6 M	02:34	5.7	174	21 Tu	02:52	5.0	152
	09:21	-0.2	-6		09:16	0.0	0
	14:54	6.9	210		15:00	6.0	183
	22:10	-0.2	-6		22:04	0.0	0
7 Tu	03:29	5.6	171	22 W	03:32	4.9	149
	10:14	-0.1	-3		09:55	0.0	0
	15:49	6.7	204		15:37	6.0	183
	23:03	-0.1	-3		22:45	0.0	0
8 W	04:25	5.5	168	23 Th	04:12	4.9	149
	11:08	-0.1	-3		10:36	-0.1	-3
	16:46	6.5	198		16:16	6.0	183
	23:56	-0.1	-3		23:27	-0.1	-3
9 Th	05:23	5.4	165	24 F	04:54	5.0	152
	12:03	0.0	0		11:20	-0.1	-3
	17:45	6.2	189		16:59	5.9	180
10 F	00:48	-0.1	-3	25 Sa	00:10	-0.2	-6
	06:23	5.4	165		05:39	5.1	155
	12:59	0.0	0		12:10	-0.1	-3
	18:44	6.0	183		17:48	5.8	177
11 Sa	01:41	-0.1	-3	26 Su	00:56	-0.2	-6
	07:22	5.4	165		06:28	5.2	158
	13:57	0.1	3		13:05	-0.1	-3
◐	19:43	5.8	177		18:44	5.7	174
12 Su	02:33	-0.2	-6	27 M	01:45	-0.3	-9
	08:19	5.6	171		07:22	5.4	165
	14:54	0.0	0		14:06	0.0	0
	20:40	5.7	174	◐	19:43	5.6	171
13 M	03:25	-0.2	-6	28 Tu	02:38	-0.3	-9
	09:14	5.8	177		08:18	5.6	171
	15:51	0.0	0		15:10	0.0	0
	21:34	5.7	174		20:44	5.5	168
14 Tu	04:15	-0.3	-9	29 W	03:34	-0.3	-9
	10:06	5.9	180		09:15	5.9	180
	16:46	-0.1	-3		16:14	-0.1	-3
	22:26	5.6	171		21:43	5.5	168
15 W	05:04	-0.3	-9	30 Th	04:31	-0.4	-12
	10:54	6.1	186		10:11	6.2	189
	17:39	-0.2	-6		17:16	-0.2	-6
	23:16	5.6	171		22:40	5.5	168
				31 F	05:27	-0.4	-12
					11:05	6.4	195
					18:15	-0.3	-9
					23:37	5.2	158

StationId: 8570282
Source: NOAA/NOS/CO-OPS
Station Type: Subordinate
Time Zone: LST_LDT
Datum: MLLW

NOAA Tide Predictions

Ocean City, MD,2021

Times and Heights of High and Low Waters

January

Day	Time	ft	cm	Day	Time	ft	cm
1 F	02:47	-0.2	-6	**16** Sa	03:41	-0.5	-15
	09:19	2.8	85		10:06	2.5	76
	15:42	0.0	0		16:31	-0.2	-6
	21:35	2.0	61		22:24	1.9	58
2 Sa	03:32	-0.2	-6	**17** Su	04:29	-0.3	-9
	10:03	2.7	82		10:50	2.4	73
	16:27	0.0	0		17:15	-0.1	-3
	22:21	2.0	61		23:10	1.9	58
3 Su	04:21	-0.1	-3	**18** M	05:19	0.0	0
	10:47	2.6	79		11:33	2.2	67
	17:14	0.0	0		17:58	0.1	3
	23:10	2.0	61		23:57	1.9	58
4 M	05:16	0.0	0	**19** Tu	06:11	0.2	6
	11:35	2.5	76		12:18	2.0	61
	18:03	0.0	0		18:40	0.2	6
5 Tu	00:03	2.1	64	**20** W ☽	00:48	1.9	58
	06:15	0.0	0		07:04	0.4	12
	12:26	2.4	73		13:06	1.8	55
	18:54	-0.1	-3		19:24	0.3	9
6 W ☾	01:02	2.1	64	**21** Th	01:42	1.9	58
	07:17	0.1	3		08:00	0.5	15
	13:23	2.2	67		13:58	1.7	52
	19:46	-0.1	-3		20:10	0.3	9
7 Th	02:04	2.3	70	**22** F	02:38	1.9	58
	08:23	0.1	3		08:57	0.6	18
	14:24	2.0	61		14:53	1.6	49
	20:40	-0.2	-6		20:58	0.3	9
8 F	03:08	2.4	73	**23** Sa	03:34	2.0	61
	09:30	0.0	0		09:55	0.6	18
	15:26	1.9	58		15:48	1.6	49
	21:37	-0.3	-9		21:48	0.3	9
9 Sa	04:09	2.6	79	**24** Su	04:26	2.2	67
	10:36	-0.1	-3		10:51	0.5	15
	16:27	1.9	58		16:39	1.6	49
	22:34	-0.5	-15		22:39	0.2	6
10 Su	05:08	2.7	82	**25** M	05:15	2.3	70
	11:39	-0.2	-6		11:41	0.4	12
	17:24	1.9	58		17:27	1.7	52
	23:31	-0.6	-18		23:28	0.0	0
11 M	06:03	2.8	85	**26** Tu	06:02	2.5	76
	12:36	-0.3	-9		12:27	0.2	6
	18:19	1.9	58		18:14	1.8	55
12 Tu	00:25	-0.7	-21	**27** W	00:15	-0.2	-6
	06:56	2.9	88		06:47	2.6	79
	13:28	-0.4	-12		13:11	0.0	0
	19:11	1.9	58		18:59	1.9	58
13 W ●	01:16	-0.8	-24	**28** Th ○	01:00	-0.3	-9
	07:47	2.9	88		07:31	2.7	82
	14:16	-0.4	-12		13:53	-0.1	-3
	20:02	2.0	61		19:44	2.0	61
14 Th	02:05	-0.7	-21	**29** F	01:45	-0.5	-15
	08:36	2.8	85		08:15	2.8	85
	15:02	-0.4	-12		14:34	-0.2	-6
	20:50	2.0	61		20:29	2.1	64
15 F	02:53	-0.6	-18	**30** Sa	02:30	-0.5	-15
	09:22	2.7	82		08:59	2.8	85
	15:47	-0.3	-9		15:17	-0.3	-9
	21:37	1.9	58		21:15	2.2	67
				31 Su	03:18	-0.5	-15
					09:42	2.8	85
					16:00	-0.3	-9
					22:01	2.2	67

February

Day	Time	ft	cm	Day	Time	ft	cm
1 M	04:08	-0.5	-15	**16** Tu	04:47	0.0	0
	10:27	2.6	79		10:56	2.1	64
	16:46	-0.3	-9		17:09	0.1	3
	22:50	2.3	70		23:17	2.1	64
2 Tu	05:02	-0.3	-9	**17** W	05:33	0.2	6
	11:13	2.4	73		11:37	1.9	58
	17:33	-0.3	-9		17:49	0.2	6
	23:42	2.3	70				
3 W	06:00	-0.2	-6	**18** Th	00:02	2.0	61
	12:04	2.2	67		06:23	0.4	12
	18:24	-0.3	-9		12:21	1.8	55
					18:32	0.4	12
4 Th ☽	00:39	2.3	70	**19** F ☽	00:52	2.0	61
	07:02	0.0	0		07:16	0.6	18
	12:59	2.0	61		13:11	1.6	49
	19:18	-0.2	-6		19:19	0.4	12
5 F	01:41	2.4	73	**20** Sa	01:48	2.0	61
	08:08	0.1	3		08:12	0.7	21
	14:01	1.8	55		14:07	1.6	49
	20:15	-0.2	-6		20:11	0.5	15
6 Sa	02:48	2.4	73	**21** Su	02:48	2.0	61
	09:17	0.1	3		09:11	0.7	21
	15:07	1.7	52		15:06	1.6	49
	21:16	-0.2	-6		21:06	0.4	12
7 Su	03:54	2.5	76	**22** M	03:47	2.2	67
	10:26	0.1	3		10:10	0.6	18
	16:12	1.7	52		16:03	1.6	49
	22:18	-0.3	-9		22:03	0.3	9
8 M	04:57	2.5	76	**23** Tu	04:42	2.3	70
	11:31	0.0	0		11:05	0.5	15
	17:12	1.7	52		16:56	1.8	55
	23:18	-0.4	-12		22:58	0.1	3
9 Tu	05:54	2.6	79	**24** W	05:32	2.5	76
	12:26	-0.2	-6		11:55	0.3	9
	18:07	1.8	55		17:45	1.9	58
					23:49	-0.2	-6
10 W	00:14	-0.5	-15	**25** Th	06:20	2.6	79
	06:45	2.7	82		12:41	0.0	0
	13:15	-0.3	-9		18:33	2.1	64
	18:57	1.9	58				
11 Th ●	01:05	-0.6	-18	**26** F	00:39	-0.4	-12
	07:33	2.7	82		07:05	2.8	85
	13:58	-0.3	-9		13:24	-0.2	-6
	19:44	2.0	61		19:19	2.3	70
12 F	01:51	-0.7	-21	**27** Sa ○	01:26	-0.6	-18
	08:17	2.6	79		07:50	2.8	85
	14:38	-0.3	-9		14:06	-0.4	-12
	20:29	2.1	64		20:06	2.4	73
13 Sa	02:36	-0.6	-18	**28** Su	02:14	-0.7	-21
	08:58	2.5	76		08:35	2.8	85
	15:16	-0.3	-9		14:48	-0.5	-15
	21:12	2.1	64		20:53	2.6	79
14 Su	03:19	-0.5	-15				
	09:38	2.4	73				
	15:53	-0.2	-6				
	21:53	2.1	64				
15 M	04:02	-0.3	-9				
	10:17	2.3	70				
	16:31	0.0	0				
	22:35	2.1	64				

March

Day	Time	ft	cm	Day	Time	ft	cm
1 M	03:03	-0.7	-21	**16** Tu	04:36	-0.1	-3
	09:20	2.8	85		10:45	2.2	67
	15:31	-0.5	-15		16:48	0.1	3
	21:41	2.7	82		23:01	2.4	73
2 Tu	03:54	-0.6	-18	**17** W	05:17	0.0	0
	10:06	2.6	79		11:23	2.1	64
	16:17	-0.5	-15		17:24	0.2	6
	22:30	2.7	82		23:41	2.3	70
3 W	04:49	-0.5	-15	**18** Th	06:01	0.2	6
	10:53	2.4	73		12:02	1.9	58
	17:05	-0.4	-12		18:03	0.4	12
	23:21	2.6	79				
4 Th	05:47	-0.2	-6	**19** F ☽	00:23	2.3	70
	11:44	2.1	64		06:47	0.5	15
	17:57	-0.3	-9		12:44	1.8	55
					18:47	0.5	15
5 F	00:18	2.6	79	**20** Sa	01:10	2.2	67
	06:49	0.0	0		07:38	0.6	18
	12:41	1.9	58		13:31	1.7	52
	18:54	-0.1	-3		19:36	0.6	18
6 Sa ☾	01:21	2.5	76	**21** Su ☾	02:04	2.1	64
	07:56	0.1	3		08:33	0.7	21
	13:45	1.7	52		14:26	1.6	49
	19:56	0.0	0		20:30	0.6	18
7 Su	02:31	2.4	73	**22** M	03:04	2.1	64
	09:05	0.2	6		09:31	0.8	24
	14:55	1.7	52		15:27	1.6	49
	21:01	0.0	0		21:29	0.6	18
8 M	03:42	2.4	73	**23** Tu	04:07	2.2	67
	10:16	0.2	6		10:30	0.7	21
	16:04	1.7	52		16:28	1.7	52
	22:07	-0.1	-3		22:29	0.4	12
9 Tu	04:47	2.4	73	**24** W	05:06	2.4	73
	11:19	0.1	3		11:27	0.5	15
	17:04	1.8	55		17:25	1.9	58
	23:09	-0.2	-6		23:28	0.2	6
10 W	05:43	2.5	76	**25** Th	05:59	2.5	76
	12:11	0.0	0		12:18	0.3	9
	17:56	1.9	58		18:16	2.1	64
11 Th	00:04	-0.3	-9	**26** F	00:24	-0.1	-3
	06:31	2.5	76		06:48	2.7	82
	12:52	-0.1	-3		13:06	0.0	0
	18:42	2.0	61		19:06	2.4	73
12 F	00:52	-0.4	-12	**27** Sa	01:17	-0.4	-12
	07:13	2.5	76		07:36	2.8	85
	13:31	-0.1	-3		13:50	-0.2	-6
	19:24	2.2	67		19:54	2.6	79
13 Sa ●	01:36	-0.4	-12	**28** Su ○	02:07	-0.6	-18
	07:53	2.5	76		08:23	2.8	85
	14:06	-0.2	-6		14:34	-0.4	-12
	20:04	2.3	70		20:42	2.8	85
14 Su	03:16	-0.4	-12	**29** M	02:58	-0.7	-21
	09:30	2.4	73		09:10	2.8	85
	15:40	-0.1	-3		15:18	-0.6	-18
	21:43	2.3	70		21:30	3.0	91
15 M	03:56	-0.3	-9	**30** Tu	03:48	-0.7	-21
	10:08	2.3	70		09:57	2.7	82
	16:14	0.0	0		16:03	-0.6	-18
	22:22	2.4	73		22:19	3.0	91
				31 W	04:41	-0.6	-18
					10:45	2.5	76
					16:50	-0.5	-15
					23:10	3.0	91

StationId: 8570282
Source: NOAA/NOS/CO-OPS
Station Type: Subordinate
Time Zone: LST_LDT
Datum: MLLW

NOAA Tide Predictions

Ocean City, MD, 2021

Times and Heights of High and Low Waters

April

Days 1–15

Day	Time	ft	cm	Day	Time	ft	cm
1 Th	05:36	-0.5	-15	**16** F	05:33	0.3	9
	11:35	2.3	70		11:32	1.9	58
	17:40	-0.3	-9		17:26	0.5	15
					23:52	2.4	73
2 F	00:03	2.9	88	**17** Sa	06:18	0.5	15
	06:34	-0.2	-6		12:14	1.8	55
	12:28	2.1	64		18:10	0.6	18
	18:35	-0.2	-6				
3 Sa	01:00	2.7	82	**18** Su	00:37	2.4	73
	07:37	0.0	0		07:08	0.7	21
	13:26	1.9	58		13:00	1.8	55
	19:35	0.0	0		19:00	0.7	21
4 Su	02:03	2.6	79	**19** M	01:28	2.3	70
	08:43	0.2	6		08:01	0.8	24
	14:31	1.8	55		13:53	1.7	52
	20:40	0.2	6		19:56	0.7	21
5 M	03:14	2.4	73	**20** Tu	02:26	2.3	70
	09:52	0.3	9		08:57	0.8	24
	15:44	1.7	52		14:54	1.8	55
	21:48	0.2	6		20:56	0.6	18
6 Tu	04:27	2.4	73	**21** W	03:28	2.3	70
	10:59	0.3	9		09:53	0.7	21
	16:54	1.8	55		15:56	1.9	58
	22:56	0.2	6		21:58	0.5	15
7 W	05:31	2.3	70	**22** Th	04:27	2.4	73
	11:57	0.3	9		10:47	0.5	15
	17:52	1.9	58		16:54	2.1	64
	23:58	0.1	3		22:59	0.3	9
8 Th	06:23	2.3	70	**23** F	05:23	2.5	76
	12:44	0.2	6		11:39	0.2	6
	18:39	2.1	64		17:47	2.4	73
					23:59	0.0	0
9 F	00:51	0.0	0	**24** Sa	06:15	2.6	79
	07:07	2.3	70		12:29	-0.1	-3
	13:23	0.1	3		18:38	2.7	82
	19:20	2.2	67				
10 Sa	01:37	-0.1	-3	**25** Su	00:55	-0.3	-9
	07:45	2.3	70		07:05	2.7	82
	13:57	0.1	3		13:16	-0.3	-9
	19:59	2.4	73		19:28	2.9	88
11 Su	02:17	-0.1	-3	**26** M	01:49	-0.5	-15
	08:23	2.3	70		07:54	2.7	82
	14:30	0.0	0		14:02	-0.5	-15
	20:37	2.5	76		20:18	3.1	94
12 M	02:56	-0.1	-3	**27** Tu	02:41	-0.7	-21
	09:00	2.3	70		08:44	2.6	79
	15:02	0.0	0		14:49	-0.6	-18
	21:14	2.5	76		21:09	3.3	101
13 Tu	03:34	-0.1	-3	**28** W	03:34	-0.7	-21
	09:37	2.2	67		09:34	2.5	76
	15:36	0.1	3		15:36	-0.6	-18
	21:52	2.6	79		22:00	3.3	101
14 W	04:12	0.0	0	**29** Th	04:27	-0.6	-18
	10:15	2.1	64		10:25	2.4	73
	16:10	0.2	6		16:26	-0.5	-15
	22:31	2.6	79		22:52	3.2	98
15 Th	04:51	0.2	6	**30** F	05:22	-0.4	-12
	10:53	2.0	61		11:17	2.2	67
	16:47	0.3	9		17:19	-0.3	-9
	23:10	2.5	76		23:46	3.0	91

May

Day	Time	ft	cm	Day	Time	ft	cm
1 Sa	06:21	-0.2	-6	**16** Su	05:54	0.5	15
	12:12	2.1	64		11:49	1.9	58
	18:16	-0.1	-3		17:42	0.6	18
2 Su	00:43	2.8	85	**17** M	00:11	2.5	76
	07:22	0.1	3		06:42	0.6	18
	13:11	1.9	58		12:35	1.8	55
	19:18	0.1	3		18:32	0.6	18
3 M	01:44	2.6	79	**18** Tu	00:59	2.5	76
	08:26	0.2	6		07:33	0.6	18
	14:16	1.8	55		13:26	1.8	55
	20:23	0.3	9		19:28	0.6	18
4 Tu	02:51	2.4	73	**19** W	01:53	2.4	73
	09:29	0.3	9		08:25	0.6	18
	15:27	1.9	58		14:24	1.9	58
	21:31	0.4	12		20:29	0.6	18
5 W	03:59	2.3	70	**20** Th	02:51	2.4	73
	10:28	0.4	12		09:18	0.5	15
	16:35	1.9	58		15:25	2.1	64
	22:37	0.4	12		21:31	0.5	15
6 Th	05:00	2.2	67	**21** F	03:50	2.4	73
	11:20	0.3	9		10:10	0.3	9
	17:29	2.1	64		16:24	2.3	70
	23:38	0.3	9		22:34	0.3	9
7 F	05:50	2.2	67	**22** Sa	04:47	2.4	73
	12:04	0.3	9		11:02	0.1	3
	18:14	2.2	67		17:20	2.6	79
					23:36	0.1	3
8 Sa	00:31	0.3	9	**23** Su	05:42	2.5	76
	06:33	2.2	67		11:53	-0.2	-6
	12:43	0.2	6		18:13	2.9	88
	18:53	2.4	73				
9 Su	01:16	0.2	6	**24** M	00:35	-0.2	-6
	07:11	2.1	64		06:35	2.5	76
	13:18	0.2	6		12:43	-0.4	-12
	19:30	2.5	76		19:05	3.1	94
10 M	01:56	0.1	3	**25** Tu	01:32	-0.4	-12
	07:28	2.1	64		07:28	2.4	73
	13:52	0.2	6		13:33	-0.5	-15
	20:08	2.6	79		19:57	3.3	101
11 Tu	02:34	0.1	3	**26** W	02:26	-0.5	-15
	08:28	2.1	64		08:21	2.4	73
	14:26	0.2	6		14:26	-0.6	-18
	20:46	2.7	82		20:49	3.3	101
12 W	03:11	0.1	3	**27** Th	03:20	-0.6	-18
	09:07	2.1	64		09:13	2.3	70
	15:02	0.2	6		15:14	-0.6	-18
	21:25	2.7	82		21:42	3.3	101
13 Th	03:49	0.2	6	**28** F	04:13	-0.5	-15
	09:47	2.0	61		10:07	2.2	67
	15:38	0.3	9		16:06	-0.5	-15
	22:04	2.7	82		22:35	3.2	98
14 F	04:28	0.3	9	**29** Sa	05:08	-0.3	-9
	10:26	2.0	61		11:00	2.2	67
	16:16	0.4	12		17:00	-0.3	-9
	22:45	2.6	79		23:29	3.0	91
15 Sa	05:10	0.4	12	**30** Su	06:04	-0.2	-6
	11:07	1.9	58		11:55	2.1	64
	16:57	0.5	15		17:57	-0.1	-3
	23:27	2.6	79				
				31 M	00:24	2.8	85
					07:02	0.0	0
					12:52	2.0	61
					18:58	0.1	3

June

Day	Time	ft	cm	Day	Time	ft	cm
1 Tu	01:20	2.6	79	**16** W	00:34	2.6	79
	07:59	0.2	6		07:05	0.4	12
	13:53	1.9	58		13:02	2.0	61
	20:01	0.3	9		19:06	0.5	15
2 W	02:19	2.3	70	**17** Th	01:23	2.5	76
	08:54	0.3	9		07:54	0.4	12
	14:57	1.9	58		13:57	2.1	64
	21:05	0.4	12		20:06	0.5	15
3 Th	03:20	2.2	67	**18** F	02:18	2.4	73
	09:46	0.3	9		08:44	0.3	9
	16:00	2.0	61		14:56	2.3	70
	22:08	0.5	15		21:08	0.4	12
4 F	04:17	2.1	64	**19** Sa	03:16	2.3	70
	10:33	0.4	12		09:35	0.1	3
	16:54	2.1	64		15:56	2.5	76
	23:08	0.5	15		22:12	0.3	9
5 Sa	05:07	2.0	61	**20** Su	04:15	2.3	70
	11:17	0.4	12		10:28	0.0	0
	17:39	2.3	70		16:54	2.7	82
					23:16	0.1	3
6 Su	00:02	0.5	15	**21** M	05:14	2.2	67
	05:53	2.0	61		11:22	-0.2	-6
	11:57	0.3	9		17:50	3.0	91
	18:20	2.4	73				
7 M	00:49	0.4	12	**22** Tu	00:18	-0.1	-3
	06:35	1.9	58		06:10	2.2	67
	12:36	0.3	9		12:16	-0.4	-12
	19:00	2.5	76		18:45	3.1	94
8 Tu	01:31	0.3	9	**23** W	01:17	-0.2	-6
	07:16	2.0	61		07:06	2.2	67
	13:15	0.3	9		13:10	-0.5	-15
	19:40	2.6	79		19:39	3.2	98
9 W	02:10	0.3	9	**24** Th	02:13	-0.4	-12
	07:57	2.0	61		08:00	2.2	67
	13:54	0.2	6		14:03	-0.6	-18
	20:20	2.7	82		20:33	3.3	101
10 Th	02:48	0.3	9	**25** F	03:06	-0.4	-12
	08:39	2.0	61		08:55	2.2	67
	14:32	0.2	6		14:56	-0.6	-18
	21:01	2.7	82		21:27	3.2	98
11 F	03:27	0.3	9	**26** Sa	03:58	-0.4	-12
	09:20	2.0	61		09:48	2.2	67
	15:12	0.2	6		15:48	-0.5	-15
	21:42	2.8	85		22:19	3.1	94
12 Sa	04:07	0.3	9	**27** Su	04:49	-0.3	-9
	10:02	2.0	61		10:41	2.2	67
	15:52	0.3	9		16:42	-0.3	-9
	22:24	2.7	82		23:10	2.9	88
13 Su	04:48	0.4	12	**28** M	05:41	-0.1	-3
	10:43	1.9	58		11:33	2.1	64
	16:34	0.3	9		17:37	-0.1	-3
	23:05	2.7	82				
14 M	05:32	0.4	12	**29** Tu	00:00	2.7	82
	11:26	1.9	58		06:32	0.0	0
	17:20	0.4	12		12:26	2.1	64
	23:48	2.6	79		18:34	0.1	3
15 Tu	06:17	0.4	12	**30** W	00:50	2.5	76
	12:12	2.0	61		07:23	0.1	3
	18:10	0.5	15		13:20	2.1	64
					19:32	0.3	9

StationId: 8570282
Source: NOAA/NOS/CO-OPS
Station Type: Subordinate
Time Zone: LST_LDT
Datum: MLLW

NOAA Tide Predictions

Ocean City, MD, 2021

Times and Heights of High and Low Waters

July

Day	Time	ft	cm	Day	Time	ft	cm
1 Th ◑	01:41	2.3	70	**16** F	00:57	2.5	76
	08:11	0.3	9		07:22	0.2	6
	14:17	2.1	64		13:32	2.4	73
	20:31	0.5	15		19:47	0.4	12
2 F	02:34	2.1	64	**17** Sa ◑	01:50	2.4	73
	08:57	0.4	12		08:12	0.1	3
	15:14	2.1	64		14:30	2.5	76
	21:30	0.6	18		20:50	0.4	12
3 Sa	03:28	1.9	58	**18** Su	02:48	2.2	67
	09:42	0.4	12		09:04	0.1	3
	16:09	2.2	67		15:31	2.6	79
	22:29	0.7	21		21:55	0.4	12
4 Su	04:21	1.8	55	**19** M	03:50	2.1	64
	10:27	0.5	15		10:00	0.0	0
	16:59	2.3	70		16:33	2.8	85
	23:26	0.7	21		23:01	0.3	9
5 M	05:11	1.8	55	**20** Tu	04:52	2.1	64
	11:12	0.5	15		10:58	-0.1	-3
	17:45	2.4	73		17:33	2.9	88
6 Tu	00:17	0.6	18	**21** W	00:05	0.1	3
	05:59	1.8	55		05:52	2.1	64
	11:57	0.4	12		11:56	-0.2	-6
	18:29	2.5	76		18:31	3.1	94
7 W	01:02	0.5	15	**22** Th	01:05	0.0	0
	06:44	1.9	58		06:49	2.1	64
	12:42	0.3	9		12:54	-0.4	-12
	19:13	2.6	79		19:26	3.1	94
8 Th	01:44	0.4	12	**23** F	02:00	-0.1	-3
	07:28	1.9	58		07:44	2.2	67
	13:25	0.3	9		13:49	-0.5	-15
	19:55	2.7	82		20:20	3.2	98
9 F	02:24	0.4	12	**24** Sa ○	02:51	-0.2	-6
	08:11	2.0	61		08:38	2.2	67
	14:07	0.2	6		14:42	-0.5	-15
	20:38	2.8	85		21:11	3.1	94
10 Sa ●	03:03	0.3	9	**25** Su	03:39	-0.2	-6
	08:54	2.0	61		09:29	2.2	67
	14:49	0.2	6		15:32	-0.4	-12
	21:20	2.8	85		22:00	3.0	91
11 Su	03:43	0.3	9	**26** M	04:25	-0.2	-6
	09:37	2.1	64		10:19	2.3	70
	15:31	0.1	3		16:22	-0.3	-9
	22:02	2.8	85		22:46	2.9	88
12 M	04:24	0.3	9	**27** Tu	05:10	-0.1	-3
	10:20	2.1	64		11:07	2.3	70
	16:15	0.2	6		17:13	-0.1	-3
	22:43	2.8	85		23:31	2.7	82
13 Tu	05:06	0.2	6	**28** W	05:54	0.1	3
	11:04	2.2	67		11:54	2.3	70
	17:01	0.2	6		18:05	0.2	6
	23:26	2.8	85				
14 W	05:49	0.2	6	**29** Th	00:15	2.4	73
	11:50	2.2	67		06:38	0.2	6
	17:52	0.3	9		12:42	2.2	67
					18:58	0.4	12
15 Th	00:10	2.7	82	**30** F	01:00	2.2	67
	06:35	0.2	6		07:22	0.4	12
	12:38	2.3	70		13:32	2.2	67
	18:48	0.4	12		19:52	0.6	18
				31 Sa ◑	01:48	2.0	61
					08:06	0.5	15
					14:25	2.2	67
					20:48	0.8	24

August

Day	Time	ft	cm	Day	Time	ft	cm
1 Su	02:40	1.9	58	**16** M	02:26	2.1	64
	08:51	0.6	18		08:40	0.2	6
	15:20	2.2	67		15:11	2.7	82
	21:46	0.9	27		21:42	0.5	15
2 M	03:35	1.8	55	**17** Tu	03:31	2.0	61
	09:39	0.7	21		09:40	0.2	6
	16:16	2.3	70		16:17	2.8	85
	22:44	0.9	27		22:50	0.4	12
3 Tu	04:31	1.8	55	**18** W	04:38	2.0	61
	10:30	0.7	21		10:42	0.1	3
	17:10	2.4	73		17:21	2.9	88
	23:39	0.8	24		23:56	0.3	9
4 W	05:24	1.8	55	**19** Th	05:41	2.0	61
	11:21	0.6	18		11:44	0.0	0
	17:59	2.5	76		18:21	3.0	91
5 Th	00:29	0.7	21	**20** F	00:55	0.2	6
	06:13	1.9	58		06:38	2.1	64
	12:11	0.5	15		12:44	-0.1	-3
	18:46	2.7	82		19:15	3.0	91
6 F	01:14	0.6	18	**21** Sa	01:46	0.1	3
	06:59	2.0	61		07:31	2.2	67
	12:58	0.3	9		13:38	-0.3	-9
	19:30	2.8	85		20:05	3.0	91
7 Sa	01:55	0.5	15	**22** Su ○	02:32	0.0	0
	07:44	2.1	64		08:21	2.3	70
	13:43	0.2	6		14:28	-0.3	-9
	20:13	2.9	88		20:52	3.0	91
8 Su ●	02:35	0.3	9	**23** M	03:14	-0.1	-3
	08:28	2.2	67		09:08	2.4	73
	14:49	0.1	3		15:16	-0.2	-6
	20:55	2.9	88		21:36	2.9	88
9 M	03:15	0.2	6	**24** Tu	03:54	0.0	0
	09:11	2.3	70		09:53	2.5	76
	15:11	0.0	0		16:01	-0.1	-3
	21:37	3.0	91		22:18	2.7	82
10 Tu	03:55	0.1	3	**25** W	04:33	0.1	3
	09:55	2.4	73		10:37	2.5	76
	15:56	0.0	0		16:47	0.1	3
	22:19	2.9	88		22:59	2.6	79
11 W	04:36	0.1	3	**26** Th	05:12	0.2	6
	10:40	2.5	76		11:20	2.5	76
	16:44	0.0	0		17:34	0.3	9
	23:02	2.8	85		23:39	2.4	73
12 Th	05:18	0.1	3	**27** F	05:51	0.4	12
	11:26	2.6	79		12:03	2.5	76
	17:36	0.1	3		18:22	0.5	15
	23:46	2.7	82				
13 F	06:03	0.1	3	**28** Sa	00:21	2.2	67
	12:15	2.6	79		06:32	0.6	18
	18:32	0.3	9		12:48	2.4	73
					19:13	0.8	24
14 Sa	00:34	2.5	76	**29** Su	01:06	2.0	61
	06:52	0.1	3		07:16	0.7	21
	13:08	2.7	82		13:38	2.3	70
	19:32	0.4	12		20:07	0.9	27
15 Su ◑	01:27	2.3	70	**30** M ◑	01:56	1.9	58
	07:44	0.2	6		08:04	0.8	24
	14:07	2.7	82		14:33	2.3	70
	20:36	0.5	15		21:03	1.0	30
				31 Tu	02:52	1.8	55
					08:55	0.9	27
					15:33	2.3	70
					22:01	1.1	34

September

Day	Time	ft	cm	Day	Time	ft	cm
1 W	03:53	1.8	55	**16** Th	04:31	2.0	61
	09:50	0.9	27		10:32	0.3	9
	16:32	2.4	73		17:12	2.8	85
	22:59	1.0	30		23:46	0.5	15
2 Th	04:50	1.9	58	**17** F	05:35	2.1	64
	10:46	0.8	24		11:37	0.2	6
	17:26	2.5	76		18:11	2.8	85
	23:52	0.9	27				
3 F	05:42	2.0	61	**18** Sa	00:40	0.3	9
	11:40	0.6	18		06:30	2.2	67
	18:15	2.7	82		12:35	0.1	3
					19:01	2.8	85
4 Sa	00:39	0.7	21	**19** Su	01:26	0.2	6
	06:30	2.1	64		07:18	2.4	73
	12:31	0.4	12		13:27	0.0	0
	19:00	2.8	85		19:46	2.8	85
5 Su	01:22	0.5	15	**20** M ○	02:07	0.1	3
	07:16	2.3	70		08:03	2.5	76
	13:19	0.2	6		14:14	-0.1	-3
	19:44	3.0	91		20:28	2.8	85
6 M	02:03	0.3	9	**21** Tu	02:44	0.1	3
	08:00	2.5	76		08:45	2.6	79
	14:06	0.0	0		14:58	0.0	0
	20:27	3.0	91		21:08	2.7	82
7 Tu	02:43	0.1	3	**22** W	03:19	0.1	3
	08:45	2.7	82		09:25	2.7	82
	14:52	-0.1	-3		15:40	0.1	3
	21:10	3.0	91		21:47	2.6	79
8 W	03:23	0.0	0	**23** Th	03:54	0.2	6
	09:30	2.8	85		10:05	2.7	82
	15:39	-0.1	-3		16:21	0.2	6
	21:53	3.0	91		22:26	2.4	73
9 Th	04:04	-0.1	-3	**24** F	04:30	0.3	9
	10:16	2.9	88		10:45	2.7	82
	16:28	-0.1	-3		17:04	0.4	12
	22:38	2.8	85		23:05	2.3	70
10 F	04:47	0.0	0	**25** Sa	05:07	0.5	15
	11:03	3.0	91		11:26	2.6	79
	17:21	0.0	0		17:48	0.6	18
	23:24	2.6	79		23:46	2.1	64
11 Sa	05:34	0.0	0	**26** Su	05:46	0.7	21
	11:53	3.0	91		12:10	2.6	79
	18:18	0.2	6		18:36	0.8	24
12 Su	00:14	2.4	73	**27** M	00:29	2.0	61
	06:24	0.1	3		06:30	0.8	24
	12:47	2.9	88		12:57	2.5	76
	19:19	0.4	12		19:28	1.0	30
13 M	01:08	2.2	67	**28** Tu ◑	01:17	1.9	58
	07:20	0.3	9		07:20	1.0	30
	13:50	2.9	88		13:50	2.4	73
	20:24	0.5	15		20:24	1.1	34
14 Tu	02:10	2.0	61	**29** W	02:13	1.8	55
	08:21	0.3	9		08:15	1.0	30
	14:55	2.8	85		14:50	2.4	73
	21:32	0.6	18		21:21	1.2	37
15 W	03:20	2.0	61	**30** Th	03:15	1.8	55
	09:26	0.4	12		09:13	1.0	30
	16:06	2.8	85		15:52	2.4	73
	22:41	0.6	18		22:18	1.1	34

StationId: 8570282
Source: NOAA/NOS/CO-OPS
Station Type: Subordinate
Time Zone: LST_LDT
Datum: MLLW

NOAA Tide Predictions

Ocean City, MD, 2021

Times and Heights of High and Low Waters

October

Day	Time (h m)	ft	cm
1 F	04:16	1.9	58
	10:12	0.9	27
	16:49	2.6	79
	23:11	0.9	27
2 Sa	05:10	2.1	64
	11:09	0.7	21
	17:40	2.7	82
3 Su	00:00	0.7	21
	06:00	2.3	70
	12:03	0.4	12
	18:27	2.8	85
4 M	00:44	0.4	12
	06:47	2.6	79
	12:54	0.2	6
	19:12	2.9	88
5 Tu	01:27	0.2	6
	07:32	2.8	85
	13:44	0.0	0
	19:56	3.0	91
6 W ●	02:08	0.0	0
	08:18	3.0	91
	14:33	-0.2	-6
	20:42	2.9	88
7 Th	02:50	-0.2	-6
	09:05	3.2	98
	15:22	-0.3	-9
	21:28	2.8	85
8 F	03:34	-0.2	-6
	09:53	3.3	101
	16:13	-0.2	-6
	22:15	2.7	82
9 Sa	04:19	-0.2	-6
	10:42	3.3	101
	17:07	-0.1	-3
	23:04	2.5	76
10 Su	05:08	-0.1	-3
	11:34	3.2	98
	18:04	0.1	3
	23:56	2.3	70
11 M	06:02	0.1	3
	12:30	3.1	94
	19:07	0.3	9
12 Tu	00:53	2.1	64
	07:02	0.3	9
	13:31	2.9	88
	20:13	0.5	15
13 W ◐	01:58	2.0	61
	08:07	0.4	12
	14:40	2.7	82
	21:21	0.5	15
14 Th	03:11	1.9	58
	09:14	0.4	12
	15:52	2.7	82
	22:27	0.5	15
15 F	04:24	2.0	61
	10:23	0.4	12
	16:58	2.6	79
	23:27	0.4	12
16 Sa	05:27	2.1	64
	11:28	0.3	9
	17:54	2.6	79
17 Su	00:17	0.3	9
	06:17	2.3	70
	12:25	0.2	6
	18:40	2.6	79
18 M	00:59	0.2	6
	07:01	2.5	76
	13:14	0.2	6
	19:21	2.6	79
19 Tu	01:36	0.2	6
	07:41	2.6	79
	13:58	0.1	3
	20:00	2.5	76
20 W ○	02:10	0.1	3
	08:19	2.7	82
	14:39	0.1	3
	20:38	2.4	73
21 Th	02:44	0.2	6
	08:57	2.8	85
	15:18	0.2	6
	21:16	2.3	70
22 F	03:17	0.2	6
	09:36	2.8	85
	15:57	0.3	9
	21:55	2.2	67
23 Sa	03:52	0.3	9
	10:15	2.8	85
	16:37	0.4	12
	22:34	2.1	64
24 Su	04:29	0.5	15
	10:55	2.7	82
	17:19	0.6	18
	23:15	2.0	61
25 M	05:08	0.6	18
	11:38	2.6	79
	18:05	0.8	24
	23:57	1.9	58
26 Tu	05:52	0.8	24
	12:23	2.5	76
	18:55	0.9	27
27 W	00:44	1.8	55
	06:42	0.9	27
	13:14	2.4	73
	19:48	1.0	30
28 Th ◑	01:37	1.8	55
	07:38	1.0	30
	14:10	2.4	73
	20:43	1.0	30
29 F	02:37	1.8	55
	08:37	0.9	27
	15:09	2.4	73
	21:37	0.9	27
30 Sa	03:39	2.0	61
	09:37	0.8	24
	16:07	2.5	76
	22:29	0.7	21
31 Su	04:36	2.2	67
	10:37	0.6	18
	17:01	2.6	79
	23:18	0.5	15

November

Day	Time (h m)	ft	cm
1 M	05:28	2.4	73
	11:35	0.4	12
	17:50	2.7	82
2 Tu	00:05	0.2	6
	06:17	2.7	82
	12:30	0.1	3
	18:39	2.7	82
3 W	00:50	-0.1	-3
	07:05	3.0	91
	13:23	-0.2	-6
	19:26	2.7	82
4 Th ●	01:35	-0.3	-9
	07:53	3.2	98
	14:15	-0.3	-9
	20:15	2.7	82
5 F	02:21	-0.4	-12
	08:42	3.4	104
	15:06	-0.4	-12
	21:04	2.6	79
6 Sa	03:07	-0.5	-15
	09:32	3.4	104
	15:59	-0.4	-12
	21:54	2.5	76
7 Su	02:56	-0.4	-12
	09:24	3.4	104
	15:53	-0.2	-6
	21:46	2.3	70
8 M	03:48	-0.3	-9
	10:18	3.2	98
	16:51	-0.1	-3
	22:41	2.2	67
9 Tu	04:44	-0.1	-3
	11:14	3.0	91
	17:52	0.1	3
	23:39	2.0	61
10 W	05:45	0.1	3
	12:15	2.8	85
	18:56	0.3	9
11 Th ◐	00:43	1.9	58
	06:51	0.3	9
	12:33	2.6	79
	20:00	0.3	9
12 F	01:55	1.9	58
	07:59	0.4	12
	14:28	2.5	76
	21:01	0.4	12
13 Sa	03:07	2.0	61
	09:07	0.4	12
	15:32	2.4	73
	21:56	0.3	9
14 Su	04:08	2.1	64
	10:12	0.4	12
	16:26	2.3	70
	22:43	0.2	6
15 M	04:57	2.3	70
	11:09	0.3	9
	17:11	2.2	67
	23:24	0.2	6
16 Tu	05:38	2.4	73
	11:58	0.2	6
	17:51	2.2	67
17 W	00:01	0.1	3
	06:16	2.6	79
	12:40	0.2	6
	18:30	2.2	67
18 Th	00:36	0.1	3
	06:53	2.7	82
	13:19	0.2	6
	19:09	2.1	64
19 F ○	01:10	0.1	3
	07:31	2.7	82
	13:57	0.2	6
	19:48	2.1	64
20 Sa	01:46	0.1	3
	08:10	2.7	82
	14:35	0.2	6
	20:27	2.0	61
21 Su	02:22	0.2	6
	08:50	2.7	82
	15:14	0.3	9
	21:07	2.0	61
22 M	03:00	0.3	9
	09:36	2.7	82
	15:55	0.5	15
	21:48	1.9	58
23 Tu	03:40	0.4	12
	10:13	2.6	79
	16:48	0.6	18
	22:30	1.8	55
24 W	04:23	0.5	15
	10:56	2.5	76
	17:26	0.7	21
	23:15	1.8	55
25 Th	05:11	0.6	18
	11:42	2.4	73
	18:15	0.7	21
26 F	00:05	1.8	55
	06:05	0.7	21
	12:33	2.4	73
	19:05	0.7	21
27 Sa ◑	01:02	1.8	55
	07:04	0.7	21
	13:27	2.4	73
	19:56	0.6	18
28 Su	02:01	2.0	61
	08:05	0.6	18
	14:24	2.3	70
	20:46	0.4	12
29 M	03:00	2.2	67
	09:07	0.5	15
	15:21	2.4	73
	21:37	0.2	6
30 Tu	03:56	2.5	76
	10:08	0.2	6
	16:15	2.4	73
	22:27	-0.1	-3

December

Day	Time (h m)	ft	cm
1 W	04:49	2.7	82
	11:07	0.0	0
	17:08	2.4	73
	23:17	-0.3	-9
2 Th	05:40	3.0	91
	12:04	-0.3	-9
	17:59	2.4	73
3 F	00:06	-0.5	-15
	06:31	3.2	98
	12:59	-0.4	-12
	18:51	2.4	73
4 Sa ●	00:56	-0.7	-21
	07:23	3.3	101
	13:52	-0.5	-15
	19:43	2.3	70
5 Su	01:46	-0.8	-24
	08:16	3.3	101
	14:45	-0.5	-15
	20:36	2.3	70
6 M	02:38	-0.7	-21
	09:09	3.3	101
	15:39	-0.4	-12
	21:30	2.2	67
7 Tu	03:31	-0.6	-18
	10:03	3.1	94
	16:35	-0.3	-9
	22:24	2.1	64
8 W	04:28	-0.4	-12
	10:57	2.9	88
	17:32	-0.1	-3
	23:21	2.0	61
9 Th	05:28	-0.2	-6
	11:53	2.7	82
	18:31	0.0	0
10 F	00:22	1.9	58
	06:31	0.1	3
	12:52	2.4	73
	19:28	0.1	3
11 Sa ◐	01:27	1.9	58
	07:36	0.2	6
	13:52	2.2	67
	20:22	0.1	3
12 Su	02:34	2.0	61
	08:41	0.3	9
	14:52	2.0	61
	21:13	0.2	6
13 M	03:35	2.1	64
	09:45	0.4	12
	15:47	1.9	58
	22:00	0.2	6
14 Tu	04:25	2.2	67
	10:45	0.4	12
	16:35	1.9	58
	22:43	0.1	3
15 W	05:09	2.3	70
	11:36	0.3	9
	17:19	1.8	55
	23:24	0.1	3
16 Th	05:49	2.4	73
	12:20	0.2	6
	18:00	1.8	55
17 F	00:03	0.1	3
	06:28	2.5	76
	12:59	0.2	6
	18:41	1.8	55
18 Sa	00:42	0.0	0
	07:08	2.6	79
	13:37	0.2	6
	19:22	1.9	58
19 Su ○	01:20	0.0	0
	07:49	2.6	79
	14:14	0.2	6
	20:03	1.9	58
20 M	01:58	0.0	0
	08:29	2.6	79
	14:52	0.2	6
	20:44	1.9	58
21 Tu	02:37	0.0	0
	09:10	2.6	79
	15:32	0.2	6
	21:25	1.8	55
22 W	03:18	0.1	3
	09:51	2.6	79
	16:13	0.3	9
	22:07	1.8	55
23 Th	04:00	0.2	6
	10:32	2.5	76
	16:57	0.3	9
	22:50	1.8	55
24 F	04:47	0.3	9
	11:14	2.4	73
	17:42	0.3	9
	23:37	1.9	58
25 Sa	05:39	0.3	9
	11:59	2.3	70
	18:28	0.3	9
26 Su	00:29	1.9	58
	06:36	0.4	12
	12:49	2.3	70
	19:16	0.2	6
27 M ◑	01:26	2.0	61
	07:37	0.4	12
	13:45	2.2	67
	20:07	0.1	3
28 Tu	02:26	2.2	67
	08:40	0.3	9
	14:44	2.1	64
	20:59	-0.1	-3
29 W	03:25	2.5	76
	09:44	0.1	3
	15:43	2.1	64
	21:53	-0.3	-9
30 Th	04:23	2.7	82
	10:47	-0.1	-3
	16:41	2.1	64
	22:48	-0.5	-15
31 F	05:19	2.9	88
	11:48	-0.3	-9
	17:37	2.1	64
	23:42	-0.6	-18

StationId: 8574680
Source: NOAA/NOS/CO-OPS
Station Type: Primary
Time Zone: LST_LDT
Datum: MLLW

Baltimore, Fort McHenry, Patapsco River, MD,2021

Times and Heights of High and Low Waters

January

Day	Time	Height (ft)	Height (cm)	Day	Time	Height (ft)	Height (cm)
1 F	03:04 / 07:50 / 13:41 / 20:27	0.0 / 0.6 / -0.3 / 1.3	0 / 18 / -9 / 40	16 Sa	03:42 / 08:39 / 14:50 / 21:26	-0.1 / 0.7 / -0.4 / 1.1	-3 / 21 / -12 / 34
2 Sa	03:42 / 08:36 / 14:30 / 21:11	-0.1 / 0.6 / -0.3 / 1.3	-3 / 18 / -9 / 40	17 Su	04:20 / 09:29 / 15:42 / 22:08	-0.1 / 0.7 / -0.3 / 1.0	-3 / 21 / -9 / 30
3 Su	04:21 / 09:25 / 15:23 / 21:57	-0.1 / 0.7 / -0.2 / 1.2	-3 / 21 / -6 / 37	18 M	04:56 / 10:22 / 16:36 / 22:48	-0.1 / 0.7 / -0.1 / 0.9	-3 / 21 / -3 / 27
4 M	05:00 / 10:19 / 16:24 / 22:44	-0.1 / 0.7 / -0.2 / 1.1	-3 / 21 / -6 / 34	19 Tu	05:30 / 11:18 / 17:36 / 23:27	-0.1 / 0.8 / 0.0 / 0.8	-3 / 24 / 0 / 24
5 Tu	05:40 / 11:17 / 17:34 / 23:33	-0.2 / 0.8 / -0.1 / 1.0	-6 / 24 / -3 / 30	20 W ☾	06:03 / 12:16 / 18:43	-0.2 / 0.8 / 0.1	-6 / 24 / 3
6 W ☽	06:21 / 12:19 / 18:53	-0.3 / 0.9 / 0.0	-9 / 27 / 0	21 Th	00:08 / 06:38 / 13:16 / 19:57	0.7 / -0.2 / 0.8 / 0.1	21 / -6 / 24 / 3
7 Th	00:25 / 07:04 / 13:23 / 20:15	0.9 / -0.3 / 1.1 / 0.0	27 / -9 / 34 / 0	22 F	00:52 / 07:17 / 14:14 / 21:09	0.6 / -0.3 / 0.9 / 0.2	18 / -9 / 27 / 6
8 F	01:19 / 07:49 / 14:27 / 21:33	0.8 / -0.4 / 1.2 / 0.0	24 / -12 / 37 / 0	23 Sa	01:41 / 07:59 / 15:08 / 22:12	0.6 / -0.3 / 1.0 / 0.1	18 / -9 / 30 / 3
9 Sa	02:15 / 08:38 / 15:29 / 22:44	0.7 / -0.5 / 1.3 / 0.0	21 / -15 / 40 / 0	24 Su	02:34 / 08:44 / 15:57 / 23:06	0.5 / -0.3 / 1.0 / 0.1	15 / -9 / 30 / 3
10 Su	03:14 / 09:29 / 16:28 / 23:46	0.6 / -0.5 / 1.4 / -0.1	18 / -15 / 43 / -3	25 M	03:28 / 09:32 / 16:41 / 23:52	0.5 / -0.3 / 1.1 / 0.0	15 / -9 / 34 / 0
11 M	04:13 / 10:23 / 17:24	0.6 / -0.5 / 1.4	18 / -15 / 43	26 Tu	04:21 / 10:22 / 17:23	0.5 / -0.3 / 1.1	15 / -9 / 34
12 Tu	00:41 / 05:11 / 11:18 / 18:18	-0.1 / 0.6 / -0.5 / 1.4	-3 / 18 / -15 / 43	27 W	00:34 / 05:19 / 11:11 / 18:04	0.0 / 0.5 / -0.4 / 1.2	0 / 15 / -12 / 37
13 W ●	01:31 / 06:06 / 12:13 / 19:09	-0.1 / 0.6 / -0.5 / 1.4	-3 / 18 / -15 / 43	28 Th ○	01:12 / 05:58 / 11:59 / 18:45	0.0 / 0.6 / -0.4 / 1.2	0 / 18 / -12 / 37
14 Th	02:17 / 06:58 / 13:07 / 19:57	-0.1 / 0.6 / -0.5 / 1.3	-3 / 18 / -15 / 40	29 F	01:49 / 06:42 / 12:47 / 19:27	-0.1 / 0.6 / -0.4 / 1.2	-3 / 18 / -12 / 37
15 F	03:00 / 07:49 / 13:59 / 20:43	-0.1 / 0.7 / -0.4 / 1.2	-3 / 21 / -12 / 37	30 Sa	02:26 / 07:27 / 13:36 / 20:08	-0.1 / 0.7 / -0.4 / 1.2	-3 / 21 / -12 / 37
				31 Su	03:02 / 08:15 / 14:28 / 20:51	-0.1 / 0.8 / -0.4 / 1.2	-3 / 24 / -12 / 37

February

Day	Time	Height (ft)	Height (cm)	Day	Time	Height (ft)	Height (cm)
1 M	03:38 / 09:05 / 15:24 / 21:35	-0.2 / 0.8 / -0.3 / 1.1	-6 / 24 / -9 / 34	16 Tu	03:52 / 09:47 / 16:12 / 22:05	-0.1 / 0.9 / 0.0 / 0.9	-3 / 27 / 0 / 27
2 Tu	04:15 / 09:59 / 16:26 / 22:20	-0.2 / 0.9 / -0.2 / 1.0	-6 / 27 / -6 / 30	17 W	04:21 / 10:36 / 17:07 / 22:41	-0.1 / 0.9 / 0.1 / 0.8	-3 / 27 / 3 / 24
3 W	04:54 / 10:57 / 17:38 / 23:08	-0.3 / 1.0 / -0.1 / 0.9	-9 / 30 / -3 / 27	18 Th	04:54 / 11:26 / 18:11 / 23:22	-0.1 / 1.0 / 0.2 / 0.7	-3 / 30 / 6 / 21
4 Th ☽	05:37 / 11:59 / 18:57	-0.3 / 1.1 / 0.0	-9 / 34 / 0	19 F ☾	05:31 / 12:19 / 19:20	-0.2 / 1.0 / 0.2	-6 / 30 / 6
5 F	00:01 / 06:24 / 13:03 / 20:16	0.8 / -0.4 / 1.2 / 0.0	24 / -12 / 37 / 0	20 Sa	00:09 / 06:16 / 13:14 / 20:29	0.7 / -0.2 / 1.0 / 0.2	21 / -6 / 30 / 6
6 Sa	00:58 / 07:17 / 14:10 / 21:30	0.7 / -0.4 / 1.2 / 0.0	21 / -12 / 37 / 0	21 Su	01:03 / 07:08 / 14:10 / 21:31	0.6 / -0.1 / 1.0 / 0.2	18 / -3 / 30 / 6
7 Su	02:00 / 08:16 / 15:15 / 22:35	0.6 / -0.4 / 1.3 / 0.0	18 / -12 / 40 / 0	22 M	02:01 / 08:05 / 15:06 / 22:23	0.6 / -0.1 / 1.1 / 0.2	18 / -3 / 34 / 6
8 M	03:03 / 09:19 / 16:18 / 23:30	0.6 / -0.4 / 1.3 / 0.0	18 / -12 / 40 / 0	23 Tu	03:00 / 09:05 / 15:59 / 23:08	0.6 / -0.1 / 1.1 / 0.1	18 / -3 / 34 / 3
9 Tu	04:04 / 10:21 / 17:17	0.6 / -0.4 / 1.3	18 / -12 / 40	24 W	03:54 / 10:02 / 16:48 / 23:49	0.7 / -0.2 / 1.2 / 0.1	21 / -6 / 37 / 3
10 W	00:20 / 05:01 / 11:20 / 18:09	0.0 / 0.7 / -0.4 / 1.3	0 / 21 / -12 / 40	25 Th	04:44 / 10:57 / 17:35	0.7 / -0.2 / 1.2	21 / -6 / 37
11 Th ●	01:04 / 05:53 / 12:14 / 18:57	0.0 / 0.7 / -0.4 / 1.2	0 / 21 / -12 / 37	26 F	00:28 / 05:32 / 11:50 / 18:19	0.1 / 0.8 / -0.3 / 1.3	3 / 24 / -9 / 40
12 F	01:45 / 06:41 / 13:04 / 19:39	0.0 / 0.8 / -0.4 / 1.2	0 / 24 / -12 / 37	27 Sa ○	01:04 / 06:18 / 12:41 / 19:02	0.0 / 0.9 / -0.3 / 1.3	0 / 27 / -9 / 40
13 Sa	02:22 / 07:28 / 13:51 / 20:18	0.0 / 0.8 / -0.3 / 1.1	0 / 24 / -9 / 34	28 Su	01:40 / 07:05 / 13:33 / 19:44	0.0 / 1.0 / -0.3 / 1.2	0 / 30 / -9 / 37
14 Su	02:55 / 08:14 / 14:37 / 20:54	0.0 / 0.9 / -0.3 / 1.1	0 / 27 / -9 / 34				
15 M	03:25 / 09:00 / 15:23 / 21:29	0.0 / 0.9 / -0.2 / 1.0	0 / 27 / -6 / 30				

March

Day	Time	Height (ft)	Height (cm)	Day	Time	Height (ft)	Height (cm)
1 M	02:15 / 07:54 / 14:28 / 20:27	-0.1 / 1.1 / -0.2 / 1.2	-3 / 34 / -6 / 37	16 Tu	03:25 / 09:30 / 16:10 / 21:52	0.1 / 1.2 / 0.1 / 1.0	3 / 37 / 3 / 30
2 Tu	02:51 / 08:45 / 15:27 / 21:11	-0.1 / 1.2 / -0.1 / 1.1	-3 / 37 / -3 / 34	17 W	03:50 / 10:11 / 16:57 / 22:27	0.1 / 1.3 / 0.2 / 1.0	3 / 40 / 6 / 30
3 W	03:29 / 09:39 / 16:32 / 21:58	-0.2 / 1.3 / 0.0 / 1.0	-6 / 40 / 0 / 30	18 Th	04:20 / 10:53 / 17:48 / 23:05	0.1 / 1.3 / 0.3 / 0.9	3 / 40 / 9 / 27
4 Th ☽	04:10 / 10:36 / 17:43 / 22:49	-0.2 / 1.4 / 0.0 / 0.9	-6 / 43 / 0 / 27	19 F	04:55 / 11:36 / 18:44 / 23:49	0.1 / 1.3 / 0.3 / 0.8	3 / 40 / 9 / 24
5 F	04:58 / 11:37 / 18:57 / 23:46	-0.2 / 1.4 / 0.1 / 0.8	-6 / 43 / 3 / 24	20 Sa	05:37 / 12:23 / 19:44	0.1 / 1.3 / 0.4	3 / 40 / 12
6 Sa ☽	05:54 / 12:42 / 20:09	-0.2 / 1.4 / 0.1	-6 / 43 / 3	21 Su ☾	00:40 / 06:28 / 13:15 / 20:44	0.8 / 0.1 / 1.2 / 0.4	24 / 3 / 37 / 12
7 Su	00:48 / 06:59 / 13:52 / 21:15	0.8 / -0.1 / 1.3 / 0.1	24 / -3 / 40 / 3	22 M	01:36 / 07:28 / 14:12 / 21:40	0.8 / 0.1 / 1.2 / 0.4	24 / 3 / 37 / 12
8 M	01:54 / 08:11 / 15:02 / 22:13	0.8 / -0.1 / 1.3 / 0.1	24 / -3 / 40 / 3	23 Tu	02:35 / 08:35 / 15:14 / 22:31	0.8 / 0.2 / 1.2 / 0.3	24 / 6 / 37 / 9
9 Tu	02:58 / 09:22 / 16:08 / 23:04	0.8 / -0.1 / 1.3 / 0.1	24 / -3 / 40 / 3	24 W	03:33 / 09:42 / 16:14 / 23:17	0.9 / 0.1 / 1.3 / 0.3	27 / 3 / 40 / 9
10 W	03:57 / 10:26 / 17:06 / 23:49	0.9 / -0.2 / 1.3 / 0.1	27 / -6 / 40 / 3	25 Th	04:26 / 10:46 / 17:09 / 23:58	1.0 / 0.1 / 1.3 / 0.3	30 / 3 / 40 / 9
11 Th	04:50 / 11:22 / 17:54	1.0 / -0.2 / 1.3	30 / -6 / 40	26 F	05:17 / 11:44 / 17:59	1.1 / 0.0 / 1.3	34 / 0 / 40
12 F	00:29 / 05:39 / 12:13 / 18:36	0.2 / 1.1 / -0.2 / 1.2	6 / 34 / -6 / 37	27 Sa	00:36 / 06:06 / 12:41 / 18:46	0.2 / 1.2 / 0.0 / 1.3	6 / 37 / 0 / 40
13 Sa ●	01:04 / 06:24 / 12:59 / 19:12	0.2 / 1.1 / -0.2 / 1.2	6 / 34 / -6 / 37	28 Su ○	01:13 / 06:55 / 13:36 / 19:31	0.2 / 1.4 / -0.1 / 1.3	6 / 43 / -3 / 40
14 Su	01:34 / 08:07 / 14:43 / 20:46	0.1 / 1.2 / -0.1 / 1.2	3 / 37 / -3 / 37	29 M	01:49 / 07:44 / 14:32 / 20:15	0.1 / 1.5 / 0.0 / 1.3	3 / 46 / 0 / 40
15 M	03:00 / 08:49 / 15:26 / 21:19	0.1 / 1.2 / 0.0 / 1.1	3 / 37 / 0 / 34	30 Tu	02:25 / 08:34 / 15:30 / 21:01	0.0 / 1.6 / 0.0 / 1.2	0 / 49 / 0 / 37
				31 W	03:04 / 09:25 / 16:31 / 21:48	0.0 / 1.7 / 0.1 / 1.1	0 / 52 / 3 / 34

StationId: 8574680
Source: NOAA/NOS/CO-OPS
Station Type: Primary
Time Zone: LST_LDT
Datum: MLLW

Times and Heights of High and Low Waters

April

Day	Time	ft	cm	Day	Time	ft	cm
1 Th	03:46	0.0	0	**16** F	03:30	0.3	9
	10:19	1.7	52		10:14	1.6	49
	17:35	0.1	3		17:33	0.4	12
	22:40	1.0	30		22:40	1.0	30
2 F	04:33	0.0	0	**17** Sa	04:10	0.3	9
	11:15	1.7	52		10:53	1.6	49
	18:41	0.2	6		18:20	0.4	12
	23:36	1.0	30		23:27	1.0	30
3 Sa	05:30	0.1	3	**18** Su	04:56	0.3	9
	12:15	1.6	49		11:38	1.5	46
	19:47	0.3	9		19:09	0.5	15
4 Su	00:37	1.0	30	**19** M	00:19	1.0	30
	06:37	0.1	3		05:52	0.4	12
	13:21	1.5	46		12:29	1.5	46
	20:50	0.3	9		20:00	0.5	15
5 M	01:43	1.0	30	**20** Tu	01:14	1.1	34
	07:54	0.2	6		06:58	0.4	12
	14:33	1.4	43		13:27	1.4	43
	21:49	0.3	9		20:51	0.5	15
6 Tu	02:48	1.1	34	**21** W	02:10	1.1	34
	09:12	0.2	6		08:10	0.4	12
	15:44	1.4	43		14:28	1.4	43
	22:41	0.3	9		21:38	0.4	12
7 W	03:50	1.1	34	**22** Th	03:05	1.2	37
	10:23	0.1	3		09:22	0.4	12
	16:48	1.4	43		15:29	1.4	43
	23:28	0.3	9		22:22	0.4	12
8 Th	04:46	1.2	37	**23** F	03:59	1.3	40
	11:25	0.1	3		10:30	0.3	9
	17:41	1.3	40		16:26	1.4	43
					23:03	0.4	12
9 F	00:09	0.3	9	**24** Sa	04:52	1.5	46
	05:37	1.3	40		11:33	0.3	9
	12:19	0.1	3		17:19	1.4	43
	18:24	1.3	40		23:42	0.3	9
10 Sa	00:44	0.3	9	**25** Su	05:43	1.7	52
	06:24	1.4	43		12:34	0.2	6
	13:08	0.1	3		18:09	1.4	43
	19:02	1.3	40				
11 Su	01:14	0.3	9	**26** M	00:20	0.2	6
	07:07	1.5	46		06:34	1.8	55
	13:53	0.2	6		13:34	0.2	6
	19:36	1.2	37		18:57	1.3	40
12 M	01:39	0.3	9	**27** Tu	00:58	0.1	3
	07:47	1.5	46		07:24	1.9	58
	14:37	0.2	6		14:33	0.2	6
	20:09	1.2	37		19:46	1.2	37
13 Tu	02:03	0.3	9	**28** W	01:39	0.1	3
	08:25	1.6	49		08:15	2.0	61
	15:21	0.3	9		15:32	0.2	6
	20:36	1.1	34		20:36	1.2	37
14 W	02:28	0.2	6	**29** Th	02:23	0.1	3
	09:02	1.6	49		09:06	2.0	61
	16:04	0.3	9		16:31	0.2	6
	21:19	1.1	34		21:29	1.1	34
15 Th	02:57	0.2	6	**30** F	03:12	0.1	3
	09:37	1.6	49		09:59	2.0	61
	16:48	0.4	12		17:29	0.3	9
	21:57	1.0	30		22:25	1.1	34

May

Day	Time	ft	cm	Day	Time	ft	cm
1 Sa	04:08	0.2	6	**16** Su	03:39	0.5	15
	10:55	1.9	58		10:21	1.7	52
	18:28	0.3	9		17:55	0.5	15
	23:25	1.1	34		23:08	1.1	34
2 Su	05:13	0.3	9	**17** M	04:30	0.5	15
	11:55	1.8	55		11:06	1.7	52
	19:25	0.4	12		18:38	0.5	15
					23:57	1.2	37
3 M	00:28	1.2	37	**18** Tu	05:28	0.5	15
	06:28	0.4	12		11:57	1.6	49
	13:00	1.6	49		19:21	0.5	15
	20:21	0.4	12				
4 Tu	01:32	1.2	37	**19** W	00:50	1.2	37
	07:49	0.4	12		06:36	0.6	18
	14:07	1.5	46		12:52	1.6	49
	21:13	0.4	12		20:05	0.5	15
5 W	02:36	1.3	40	**20** Th	01:44	1.3	40
	09:06	0.4	12		07:50	0.6	18
	15:12	1.4	43		13:50	1.5	46
	22:01	0.5	15		20:48	0.4	12
6 Th	03:36	1.4	43	**21** F	02:39	1.5	46
	10:15	0.4	12		09:05	0.5	15
	16:10	1.4	43		14:48	1.5	46
	22:44	0.4	12		21:29	0.4	12
7 F	04:31	1.5	46	**22** Sa	03:35	1.6	49
	11:15	0.4	12		10:05	0.5	15
	16:59	1.3	40		15:44	1.4	43
	23:20	0.4	12		22:10	0.3	9
8 Sa	05:21	1.6	49	**23** Su	04:30	1.8	55
	12:10	0.4	12		11:27	0.5	15
	17:41	1.3	40		16:38	1.3	40
	23:51	0.4	12		22:50	0.2	6
9 Su	06:06	1.7	52	**24** M	05:23	2.0	61
	13:01	0.4	12		12:32	0.4	12
	18:19	1.2	37		17:32	1.3	40
					23:32	0.2	6
10 M	00:18	0.4	12	**25** Tu	06:15	2.1	64
	06:48	1.7	52		13:33	0.4	12
	13:48	0.4	12		18:26	1.2	37
	18:56	1.2	37				
11 Tu	00:44	0.4	12	**26** W	00:16	0.1	3
	07:25	1.8	55		07:06	2.2	67
	14:33	0.4	12		14:20	0.3	9
	19:34	1.1	34		19:20	1.2	37
12 W	01:11	0.3	9	**27** Th	01:03	0.1	3
	08:00	1.8	55		07:57	2.2	67
	15:15	0.5	15		15:27	0.3	9
	20:12	1.1	34		20:16	1.2	37
13 Th	01:41	0.3	9	**28** F	01:55	0.2	6
	08:33	1.8	55		08:49	2.2	67
	15:56	0.5	15		16:21	0.3	9
	20:52	1.1	34		21:12	1.2	37
14 F	02:16	0.4	12	**29** Sa	02:51	0.2	6
	09:07	1.8	55		09:42	2.1	64
	16:36	0.5	15		17:13	0.4	12
	21:35	1.1	34		22:11	1.2	37
15 Sa	02:55	0.4	12	**30** Su	03:54	0.3	9
	09:42	1.8	55		10:37	1.9	58
	17:15	0.5	15			0.4	12
	22:20	1.1	34		23:10	1.3	40
				31 M	05:03	0.4	12
					11:34	1.8	55
					18:55	0.4	12

June

Day	Time	ft	cm	Day	Time	ft	cm
1 Tu	00:11	1.3	40	**16** W	05:13	0.6	18
	06:17	0.5	15		11:32	1.7	52
	12:33	1.7	52		18:42	0.4	12
	19:44	0.5	15				
2 W	01:13	1.4	43	**17** Th	00:25	1.4	43
	07:33	0.5	15		06:21	0.6	18
	13:31	1.5	46		12:22	1.6	49
	20:30	0.5	15		19:20	0.4	12
3 Th	02:15	1.5	46	**18** F	01:19	1.5	46
	08:47	0.6	18		07:36	0.7	21
	14:27	1.4	43		13:15	1.5	46
	21:12	0.5	15		20:00	0.4	12
4 F	03:14	1.6	49	**19** Sa	02:16	1.7	52
	09:57	0.6	18		08:56	0.7	21
	15:18	1.3	40		14:10	1.4	43
	21:49	0.4	12		20:40	0.3	9
5 Sa	04:10	1.7	52	**20** Su	03:13	1.8	55
	11:00	0.6	18		10:13	0.6	18
	16:06	1.3	40		15:06	1.3	40
	22:22	0.4	12		21:22	0.2	6
6 Su	05:00	1.7	52	**21** M	04:09	2.0	61
	11:59	0.6	18		11:25	0.6	18
	16:51	1.2	37		16:04	1.2	37
	22:53	0.4	12		22:07	0.2	6
7 M	05:45	1.8	55	**22** Tu	05:04	2.1	64
	12:52	0.6	18		12:31	0.5	15
	17:34	1.1	34		17:03	1.2	37
	23:23	0.4	12		22:56	0.2	6
8 Tu	06:25	1.9	58	**23** W	05:58	2.2	67
	13:40	0.6	18		13:30	0.4	12
	18:18	1.1	34		18:02	1.1	34
	23:55	0.4	12		23:48	0.2	6
9 W	07:01	1.9	58	**24** Th	06:51	2.3	70
	14:23	0.5	15		14:24	0.4	12
	19:02	1.1	34		19:01	1.1	34
10 Th	00:30	0.4	12	**25** F	00:43	0.2	6
	07:34	1.9	58		07:43	2.2	67
	15:03	0.5	15		15:14	0.4	12
	19:47	1.1	34		19:59	1.2	37
11 F	01:08	0.4	12	**26** Sa	01:42	0.2	6
	08:07	1.9	58		08:35	2.1	64
	15:40	0.5	15		16:02	0.4	12
	20:31	1.1	34		20:56	1.2	37
12 Sa	01:49	0.4	12	**27** Su	02:43	0.3	9
	08:41	1.9	58		09:27	2.0	61
	16:15	0.5	15		16:48	0.4	12
	21:15	1.1	34		21:52	1.3	40
13 Su	02:33	0.5	15	**28** M	03:45	0.4	12
	09:18	1.9	58		10:19	1.9	58
	16:51	0.5	15		17:33	0.4	12
	22:00	1.2	37		22:49	1.4	43
14 M	03:21	0.5	15	**29** Tu	04:50	0.5	15
	09:59	1.8	55		11:09	1.8	55
	17:27	0.5	15		18:16	0.5	15
	22:45	1.2	37		23:46	1.4	43
15 Tu	04:14	0.6	18	**30** W	05:58	0.6	18
	10:44	1.8	55		11:59	1.6	49
	18:04	0.5	15		18:57	0.5	15
	23:33	1.3	40				

StationId: 8574680
Source: NOAA/NOS/CO-OPS
Station Type: Primary
Time Zone: LST_LDT
Datum: MLLW

Baltimore, Fort McHenry, Patapsco River, MD, 2021

Times and Heights of High and Low Waters

July

Day	Time (h m)	Height (ft)	Height (cm)	Day	Time (h m)	Height (ft)	Height (cm)
1 Th ◐	00:45	1.5	46	16 F	00:00	1.6	49
	07:08	0.6	18		06:15	0.7	21
	12:47	1.5	46		11:54	1.6	49
	19:35	0.4	12		18:36	0.3	9
2 F	01:45	1.6	49	17 Sa ◐	00:56	1.7	52
	08:21	0.7	21		07:33	0.7	21
	13:34	1.4	43		12:44	1.5	46
	20:11	0.4	12		19:15	0.3	9
3 Sa	02:44	1.6	49	18 Su	01:53	1.8	55
	09:34	0.7	21		08:55	0.7	21
	14:22	1.3	40		13:39	1.3	40
	20:45	0.4	12		19:58	0.2	6
4 Su	03:40	1.7	52	19 M	02:52	2.0	61
	10:42	0.7	21		10:14	0.7	21
	15:10	1.2	37		14:38	1.2	37
	21:20	0.4	12		20:45	0.2	6
5 M	04:31	1.8	55	20 Tu	03:51	2.1	64
	11:43	0.7	21		11:24	0.6	18
	16:01	1.1	34		15:41	1.1	34
	21:57	0.4	12		21:39	0.2	6
6 Tu	05:16	1.9	58	21 W	04:49	2.2	67
	12:36	0.7	21		12:24	0.5	15
	16:53	1.1	34		16:45	1.1	34
	22:36	0.4	12		22:37	0.2	6
7 W	05:56	1.9	58	22 Th	05:45	2.2	67
	13:22	0.6	18		13:18	0.5	15
	17:45	1.1	34		17:48	1.2	37
	23:18	0.4	12		23:38	0.2	6
8 Th	06:33	1.9	58	23 F	06:39	2.2	67
	14:01	0.6	18		14:06	0.5	15
	18:36	1.1	34		18:47	1.2	37
9 F	00:03	0.4	12	24 Sa ○	00:39	0.3	9
	07:08	1.9	58		07:32	2.1	64
	14:38	0.5	15		14:51	0.5	15
	19:23	1.1	34		19:43	1.3	40
10 Sa ●	00:49	0.4	12	25 Su	01:40	0.3	9
	07:44	1.9	58		08:22	2.0	61
	15:12	0.5	15		15:34	0.5	15
	20:08	1.1	34		20:37	1.4	43
11 Su	01:35	0.5	15	26 M	02:38	0.4	12
	08:20	1.9	58		09:09	1.9	58
	15:45	0.5	15		16:14	0.5	15
	20:51	1.2	37		21:30	1.4	43
12 M	02:23	0.5	15	27 Tu	03:36	0.4	12
	08:59	1.9	58		09:54	1.8	55
	16:18	0.5	15		16:51	0.5	15
	21:35	1.3	40		22:22	1.5	46
13 Tu	03:12	0.5	15	28 W	04:33	0.5	15
	09:40	1.9	58		10:37	1.7	52
	16:52	0.4	12		17:27	0.5	15
	22:20	1.3	40		23:16	1.6	49
14 W	04:06	0.6	18	29 Th	05:34	0.6	18
	10:22	1.8	55		11:18	1.6	49
	17:25	0.4	12		17:59	0.4	12
	23:08	1.4	43				
15 Th	05:06	0.6	18	30 F	00:11	1.6	49
	11:07	1.7	52		06:40	0.7	21
	18:00	0.4	12		11:59	1.5	46
					18:31	0.4	12
				31 Sa ◐	01:07	1.7	52
					07:52	0.8	24
					12:42	1.3	40
					19:04	0.4	12

August

Day	Time (h m)	Height (ft)	Height (cm)	Day	Time (h m)	Height (ft)	Height (cm)
1 Su	02:04	1.7	52	16 M	01:32	2.0	61
	09:07	0.9	27		08:57	0.7	21
	13:28	1.2	37		13:18	1.3	40
	19:40	0.4	12		19:25	0.3	9
2 M	02:59	1.8	55	17 Tu	02:33	2.1	64
	10:18	0.8	24		10:10	0.7	21
	14:21	1.1	34		14:22	1.2	37
	20:22	0.4	12		20:23	0.3	9
3 Tu	03:50	1.8	55	18 W	03:35	2.1	64
	11:18	0.8	24		11:13	0.6	18
	15:19	1.1	34		15:30	1.2	37
	21:09	0.4	12		21:28	0.3	9
4 W	04:38	1.9	58	19 Th	04:37	2.1	64
	12:07	0.7	21		12:08	0.6	18
	16:20	1.1	34		16:37	1.2	37
	22:00	0.4	12		22:36	0.3	9
5 Th	05:21	1.9	58	20 F	05:36	2.1	64
	12:49	0.7	21		12:56	0.6	18
	17:17	1.1	34		17:39	1.3	40
	22:53	0.5	15		23:42	0.3	9
6 F	06:02	1.9	58	21 Sa	06:30	2.0	61
	13:26	0.6	18		13:40	0.5	15
	18:10	1.2	37		18:35	1.4	43
	23:46	0.5	15				
7 Sa	06:41	1.9	58	22 Su ○	00:43	0.4	12
	14:00	0.6	18		07:19	2.0	61
	18:57	1.2	37		14:21	0.5	15
					19:28	1.5	46
8 Su ●	00:37	0.5	15	23 M	01:39	0.4	12
	07:19	1.9	58		08:04	1.9	58
	14:33	0.5	15		14:58	0.5	15
	19:41	1.3	40		20:18	1.5	46
9 M	01:26	0.5	15	24 Tu	02:32	0.4	12
	07:58	1.9	58		08:45	1.8	55
	15:05	0.5	15		15:31	0.5	15
	20:24	1.4	43		21:06	1.6	49
10 Tu	02:16	0.5	15	25 W	03:24	0.5	15
	08:37	1.9	58		09:23	1.7	52
	15:37	0.5	15		16:01	0.5	15
	21:08	1.5	46		21:55	1.7	52
11 W	03:07	0.5	15	26 Th	04:17	0.6	18
	09:17	1.9	58		10:00	1.6	49
	16:09	0.4	12		16:29	0.5	15
	21:54	1.6	49		22:43	1.7	52
12 Th	04:03	0.6	18	27 F	05:13	0.7	21
	09:58	1.8	55		10:36	1.5	46
	16:41	0.4	12		16:56	0.4	12
	22:43	1.7	52		23:32	1.7	52
13 F	05:06	0.7	21	28 Sa	06:15	0.8	24
	10:42	1.7	52		11:14	1.4	43
	17:15	0.3	9		17:26	0.4	12
	23:36	1.8	55				
14 Sa	06:18	0.7	21	29 Su	00:22	1.8	55
	11:28	1.5	46		07:24	0.9	27
	17:53	0.3	9		11:56	1.3	40
					18:01	0.4	12
15 Su ◐	00:32	1.9	58	30 M ◐	01:13	1.8	55
	07:37	0.8	24		08:36	0.9	27
	12:20	1.4	43		12:45	1.2	37
	18:35	0.3	9		18:43	0.4	12
				31 Tu	02:06	1.8	55
					09:42	0.9	27
					13:43	1.1	34
					19:34	0.5	15

September

Day	Time (h m)	Height (ft)	Height (cm)	Day	Time (h m)	Height (ft)	Height (cm)
1 W	02:59	1.8	55	16 Th	03:22	2.0	61
	10:38	0.8	24		10:52	0.6	18
	14:47	1.1	34		15:27	1.2	37
	20:32	0.5	15		21:33	0.4	12
2 Th	03:51	1.8	55	17 F	04:26	2.0	61
	11:24	0.8	24		11:43	0.6	18
	15:50	1.2	37		16:32	1.3	40
	21:34	0.5	15		22:44	0.4	12
3 F	04:40	1.8	55	18 Sa	05:24	1.9	58
	12:04	0.7	21		12:27	0.6	18
	16:49	1.2	37		17:30	1.4	43
	22:35	0.5	15		23:48	0.4	12
4 Sa	05:26	1.8	55	19 Su	06:14	1.9	58
	12:40	0.6	18		13:07	0.5	15
	17:40	1.3	40		18:24	1.5	46
	23:32	0.5	15				
5 Su	06:08	1.9	58	20 M ○	00:44	0.4	12
	13:14	0.6	18		06:58	1.8	55
	18:27	1.4	43		13:43	0.5	15
					19:13	1.6	49
6 M	00:25	0.5	15	21 Tu	01:36	0.5	15
	06:49	1.9	58		07:37	1.8	55
	13:47	0.5	15		14:14	0.5	15
	19:12	1.5	46		19:59	1.7	52
7 Tu ●	01:17	0.5	15	22 W	02:26	0.5	15
	07:29	1.9	58		08:13	1.7	52
	14:18	0.5	15		14:41	0.4	12
	19:56	1.6	49		20:44	1.7	52
8 W	02:10	0.5	15	23 Th	03:15	0.6	18
	08:09	1.8	55		08:47	1.6	49
	14:49	0.4	12		15:06	0.4	12
	20:42	1.7	52		21:27	1.8	55
9 Th	03:05	0.5	15	24 F	04:05	0.7	21
	08:50	1.7	52		09:22	1.5	46
	15:21	0.3	9		15:30	0.4	12
	21:30	1.8	55		22:09	1.8	55
10 F	04:05	0.6	18	25 Sa	04:58	0.7	21
	09:32	1.6	49		09:57	1.4	43
	15:55	0.3	9		15:58	0.4	12
	22:20	1.9	58		22:52	1.8	55
11 Sa	05:11	0.7	21	26 Su	05:55	0.8	24
	10:18	1.5	46		10:36	1.3	40
	16:32	0.3	9		16:31	0.4	12
	23:13	2.0	61		23:35	1.8	55
12 Su	06:23	0.7	21	27 M	06:56	0.8	24
	11:08	1.4	43		11:21	1.2	37
	17:15	0.3	9		17:10	0.4	12
13 M ◐	00:10	2.1	64	28 Tu ◐	00:21	1.8	55
	07:38	0.7	21		07:57	0.8	24
	12:04	1.3	40		12:14	1.1	34
	18:05	0.3	9		17:58	0.5	15
14 Tu	01:11	2.1	64	29 W	01:11	1.7	52
	08:50	0.7	21		08:55	0.8	24
	13:08	1.2	37		13:14	1.1	34
	19:07	0.3	9		18:55	0.5	15
15 W	02:16	2.0	61	30 Th ◐	02:05	1.7	52
	09:55	0.7	21		09:46	0.8	24
	14:17	1.2	37		14:18	1.1	34
	20:18	0.4	12		20:01	0.6	18

StationId: 8574680
Source: NOAA/NOS/CO-OPS
Station Type: Primary
Time Zone: LST_LDT
Datum: MLLW

NOAA Tide Predictions

Baltimore, Fort McHenry, Patapsco River, MD, 2021

Times and Heights of High and Low Waters

October

Day	Time (h m)	ft	cm	Day	Time (h m)	ft	cm
1 F	03:00	1.7	52	**16** Sa	04:09	1.7	52
	10:31	0.7	21		11:10	0.5	15
	15:20	1.2	37		16:24	1.3	40
	21:10	0.6	18		22:47	0.4	12
2 Sa	03:54	1.7	52	**17** Su	05:02	1.7	52
	11:11	0.6	18		11:51	0.4	12
	16:17	1.3	40		17:20	1.4	43
	22:15	0.5	15		23:47	0.4	12
3 Su	04:44	1.7	52	**18** M	05:47	1.6	49
	11:48	0.6	18		12:28	0.4	12
	17:09	1.4	43		18:11	1.5	46
	23:15	0.5	15				
4 M	05:30	1.7	52	**19** Tu	00:42	0.4	12
	12:22	0.5	15		06:26	1.5	46
	17:57	1.5	46		12:59	0.3	9
					18:58	1.6	49
5 Tu	00:13	0.5	15	**20** W ○	01:33	0.4	12
	06:13	1.7	52		07:03	1.4	43
	12:55	0.4	12		13:25	0.3	9
	18:44	1.6	49		19:41	1.7	52
6 W ●	01:09	0.5	15	**21** Th	02:22	0.5	15
	06:55	1.7	52		07:37	1.4	43
	13:27	0.3	9		13:49	0.3	9
	19:31	1.8	55		20:21	1.7	52
7 Th	02:07	0.5	15	**22** F	03:10	0.5	15
	07:38	1.6	49		08:12	1.3	40
	14:00	0.2	6		14:13	0.2	6
	20:18	1.9	58		21:00	1.8	55
8 F	03:06	0.5	15	**23** Sa	03:58	0.6	18
	08:22	1.5	46		08:48	1.2	37
	14:35	0.2	6		14:41	0.2	6
	21:07	2.0	61		21:37	1.8	55
9 Sa	04:08	0.5	15	**24** Su	04:46	0.6	18
	09:08	1.4	43		09:26	1.1	34
	15:13	0.1	3		15:12	0.2	6
	21:58	2.1	64		22:14	1.7	52
10 Su	05:14	0.5	15	**25** M	05:35	0.6	18
	09:58	1.3	40		10:08	1.1	34
	15:57	0.1	3		15:49	0.3	9
	22:52	2.1	64		22:54	1.7	52
11 M	06:21	0.6	18	**26** Tu	06:25	0.6	18
	10:53	1.2	37		10:56	1.0	30
	16:48	0.2	6		16:33	0.3	9
	23:50	2.0	61		23:37	1.6	49
12 Tu	07:28	0.6	18	**27** W	07:15	0.6	18
	11:55	1.1	34		11:49	1.0	30
	17:49	0.3	9		17:25	0.4	12
13 W ◐	00:53	1.9	58	**28** Th ◑	00:25	1.6	49
	08:32	0.6	18		08:05	0.6	18
	13:03	1.1	34		12:47	1.0	30
	19:02	0.3	9		18:25	0.4	12
14 Th	02:00	1.9	58	**29** F	01:17	1.6	49
	09:30	0.5	15		08:52	0.5	15
	14:13	1.2	37		13:47	1.0	30
	20:22	0.4	12		19:33	0.4	12
15 F	03:07	1.8	55	**30** Sa	02:13	1.5	46
	10:23	0.5	15		09:35	0.5	15
	15:21	1.3	40		14:47	1.1	34
	21:39	0.4	12		20:44	0.4	12
				31 Su	03:07	1.5	46
					10:15	0.4	12
					15:44	1.2	37
					21:53	0.4	12

November

Day	Time (h m)	ft	cm	Day	Time (h m)	ft	cm
1 M	03:58	1.5	46	**16** Tu	04:08	1.2	37
	10:52	0.3	9		10:42	0.1	3
	16:38	1.3	40		16:57	1.4	43
	22:59	0.4	12		23:36	0.3	9
2 Tu	04:47	1.5	46	**17** W	04:48	1.1	34
	11:27	0.2	6		11:11	0.1	3
	17:29	1.5	46		17:42	1.5	46
3 W	00:03	0.4	12	**18** Th	00:29	0.3	9
	05:34	1.4	43		05:26	1.0	30
	12:02	0.1	3		11:37	0.0	0
	18:19	1.7	52		18:22	1.5	46
4 Th ●	01:04	0.3	9	**19** F ○	01:18	0.3	9
	06:20	1.3	40		06:03	1.0	30
	12:38	0.0	0		12:03	0.0	0
	19:08	1.8	55		18:59	1.6	49
5 F	02:05	0.3	9	**20** Sa	02:04	0.3	9
	07:07	1.2	37		06:42	0.9	27
	13:15	-0.1	-3		12:32	0.0	0
	19:57	1.9	58		19:34	1.6	49
6 Sa	03:06	0.3	9	**21** Su	02:48	0.3	9
	07:56	1.1	34		07:21	0.8	24
	13:57	-0.1	-3		13:05	0.0	0
	20:48	2.0	61		20:09	1.6	49
7 Su	03:07	0.3	9	**22** M	03:29	0.3	9
	07:47	1.1	34		08:08	0.8	24
	13:43	-0.1	-3		13:42	0.0	0
	20:40	2.0	61		20:44	1.5	46
8 M	04:07	0.3	9	**23** Tu	04:10	0.3	9
	08:42	1.0	30		08:47	0.8	24
	14:35	0.0	0		14:23	0.1	3
	21:35	1.9	58		21:22	1.5	46
9 Tu	05:07	0.3	9	**24** W	04:51	0.3	9
	09:42	1.0	30		09:34	0.8	24
	15:34	0.0	0		15:09	0.1	3
	22:33	1.8	55		22:04	1.4	43
10 W	06:06	0.3	9	**25** Th	05:33	0.3	9
	10:45	1.0	30		10:24	0.8	24
	16:43	0.1	3		16:01	0.1	3
	23:35	1.7	52		22:50	1.4	43
11 Th ◑	07:03	0.3	9	**26** F	06:16	0.3	9
	11:52	1.0	30		11:18	0.8	24
	18:00	0.2	6		17:00	0.2	6
					23:39	1.3	40
12 F	00:39	1.6	49	**27** Sa ◑	06:58	0.2	6
	07:57	0.3	9		12:15	0.9	27
	13:01	1.1	34		18:07	0.2	6
	19:19	0.2	6				
13 Sa	01:41	1.5	46	**28** Su	00:30	1.3	40
	08:46	0.3	9		07:39	0.1	3
	14:08	1.1	34		13:14	1.0	30
	20:33	0.3	9		19:20	0.2	6
14 Su	02:37	1.4	43	**29** M	01:22	1.2	37
	09:30	0.2	6		08:18	0.0	0
	15:11	1.2	37		14:12	1.1	34
	21:39	0.3	9		20:35	0.2	6
15 M	03:25	1.3	40	**30** Tu	02:14	1.2	37
	10:09	0.1	3		08:56	-0.1	-3
	16:07	1.3	40		15:09	1.3	40
	22:40	0.3	9		21:48	0.2	6

December

Day	Time (h m)	ft	cm	Day	Time (h m)	ft	cm
1 W	03:05	1.1	34	**16** Th	04:08	0.7	21
	09:35	-0.2	-6		10:23	-0.2	-6
	16:03	1.4	43		17:22	1.3	40
	22:57	0.2	6				
2 Th	03:57	1.0	30	**17** F	00:20	0.1	3
	10:15	-0.3	-9		04:52	0.7	21
	16:56	1.6	49		10:55	-0.2	-6
					18:02	1.3	40
3 F	00:02	0.1	3	**18** Sa	01:07	0.1	3
	04:49	0.9	27		05:35	0.6	18
	10:57	-0.3	-9		11:29	-0.3	-9
	17:48	1.7	52		18:38	1.3	40
4 Sa ●	01:03	0.1	3	**19** Su ○	01:49	0.1	3
	05:41	0.8	24		06:18	0.6	18
	11:43	-0.4	-12		12:06	-0.2	-6
	18:39	1.8	55		19:12	1.3	40
5 Su	02:00	0.1	3	**20** M	02:27	0.1	3
	06:36	0.8	24		07:01	0.6	18
	12:32	-0.4	-12		12:45	-0.2	-6
	19:32	1.8	55		19:46	1.3	40
6 M	02:55	0.0	0	**21** Tu	03:03	0.1	3
	07:31	0.8	24		07:43	0.6	18
	13:26	-0.3	-9		13:26	-0.2	-6
	20:25	1.7	52		20:21	1.3	40
7 Tu	03:49	0.0	0	**22** W	03:39	0.1	3
	08:28	0.8	24		08:26	0.6	18
	14:25	-0.3	-9		14:09	-0.2	-6
	21:20	1.6	49		20:58	1.2	37
8 W	04:42	0.0	0	**23** Th	04:14	0.0	0
	09:27	0.8	24		09:10	0.6	18
	15:29	-0.2	-6		14:55	-0.1	-3
	22:17	1.5	46		21:38	1.2	37
9 Th	05:35	0.1	3	**24** F	04:51	0.0	0
	10:29	0.8	24		09:57	0.6	18
	16:37	-0.1	-3		15:45	-0.1	-3
	23:14	1.3	40		22:21	1.2	37
10 F	06:26	0.0	0	**25** Sa	05:29	0.0	0
	11:33	0.9	27		10:48	0.7	21
	17:49	0.0	0		16:41	0.0	0
					23:06	1.1	34
11 Sa ◑	00:10	1.2	37	**26** Su	06:06	-0.1	-3
	07:16	0.0	0		11:44	0.8	24
	12:40	0.9	27		17:47	0.0	0
	19:04	0.0	0		23:53	1.0	30
12 Su	01:03	1.1	34	**27** M ◑	06:44	-0.2	-6
	08:01	0.0	0		12:42	0.9	27
	13:47	1.0	30		19:04	0.1	3
	20:16	0.1	3				
13 M	01:53	1.0	30	**28** Tu	00:43	0.9	27
	08:42	-0.1	-3		07:24	-0.3	-9
	14:50	1.1	34		13:42	1.0	30
	21:26	0.1	3		20:25	0.1	3
14 Tu	02:40	0.9	27	**29** W	01:35	0.8	24
	09:18	-0.1	-3		08:06	-0.4	-12
	15:48	1.1	34		14:42	1.2	37
	22:30	0.2	6		21:43	0.1	3
15 W	03:25	0.8	24	**30** Th	02:30	0.7	21
	09:51	-0.2	-6		08:50	-0.4	-12
	16:38	1.2	37		15:39	1.3	40
	23:28	0.2	6		22:53	0.0	0
				31 F	03:27	0.6	18
					09:39	-0.5	-15
					16:36	1.5	46

StationId: 8593005
Source: NOAA/NOS/CO-OPS
Station Type: Subordinate
Time Zone: LST_LDT
Datum: MLLW

NOAA Tide Predictions

WASHINGTON NAVY YARD,D.C., DC,2021

Times and Heights of High and Low Waters

January

Day	Time	ft	cm	Day	Time	ft	cm
1 F	04:13	-0.4	-12	16 Sa	05:00	-0.6	-18
	09:46	2.2	67		10:41	2.2	67
	16:05	-0.4	-12		17:12	-0.5	-15
	21:49	2.6	79		22:59	2.4	73
2 Sa	04:54	-0.4	-12	17 Su	05:43	-0.5	-15
	10:25	2.3	70		11:29	2.2	67
	16:52	-0.4	-12		18:00	-0.4	-12
	22:34	2.6	79		23:49	2.3	70
3 Su	05:35	-0.4	-12	18 M	06:23	-0.4	-12
	11:09	2.3	70		12:17	2.2	67
	17:40	-0.4	-12		18:46	-0.3	-9
	23:23	2.5	76				
4 M	06:16	-0.4	-12	19 Tu	00:39	2.2	67
	11:55	2.4	73		07:00	-0.3	-9
	18:30	-0.4	-12		13:03	2.2	67
					19:33	-0.2	-6
5 Tu	00:15	2.5	76	20 W	01:28	2.1	64
	06:59	-0.4	-12		07:37	-0.2	-6
	12:45	2.4	73		13:49	2.2	67
	19:24	-0.4	-12		20:23	-0.1	-3
6 W	01:10	2.4	73	21 Th	02:20	2.0	61
	07:47	-0.4	-12		08:18	-0.2	-6
	13:38	2.5	76		14:40	2.1	64
	20:26	-0.3	-9		21:18	0.0	0
7 Th	02:10	2.3	70	22 F	03:17	1.9	58
	08:42	-0.4	-12		09:04	-0.2	-6
	14:38	2.5	76		15:35	2.1	64
	21:36	-0.3	-9		22:15	0.0	0
8 F	03:16	2.2	67	23 Sa	04:13	1.9	58
	09:43	-0.4	-12		09:56	-0.2	-6
	15:43	2.5	76		16:28	2.2	67
	22:45	-0.3	-9		23:11	-0.1	-3
9 Sa	04:23	2.1	64	24 Su	05:06	1.9	58
	10:46	-0.4	-12		10:50	-0.2	-6
	16:46	2.6	79		17:17	2.2	67
	23:51	-0.4	-12				
10 Su	05:25	2.1	64	25 M	00:06	-0.1	-3
	11:50	-0.4	-12		05:55	1.9	58
	17:45	2.6	79		11:45	-0.2	-6
					18:03	2.3	70
11 M	00:53	-0.5	-15	26 Tu	00:56	-0.2	-6
	06:23	2.1	64		06:42	2.0	61
	12:51	-0.5	-15		12:14	-0.3	-9
	18:41	2.7	82		18:46	2.4	73
12 Tu	01:49	-0.6	-18	27 W	01:43	-0.4	-12
	07:19	2.2	67		07:25	2.0	61
	13:49	-0.6	-18		13:32	-0.4	-12
	19:35	2.7	82		19:28	2.4	73
13 W ●	02:40	-0.7	-21	28 Th ○	02:25	-0.4	-12
	08:11	2.2	67		08:05	2.1	64
	14:42	-0.6	-18		14:20	-0.5	-15
	20:27	2.6	79		20:10	2.5	76
14 Th	03:29	-0.7	-21	29 F	03:06	-0.5	-15
	09:02	2.2	67		08:43	2.2	67
	15:33	-0.6	-18		15:06	-0.6	-18
	21:17	2.5	76		20:51	2.5	76
15 F	04:15	-0.6	-18	30 Sa	03:47	-0.5	-15
	09:51	2.2	67		09:21	2.3	70
	16:23	-0.5	-15		15:52	-0.6	-18
	22:07	2.5	76		21:34	2.5	76
				31 Su	04:28	-0.6	-18
					10:02	2.4	73
					16:41	-0.6	-18
					22:21	2.5	76

February

Day	Time	ft	cm	Day	Time	ft	cm
1 M	05:10	-0.6	-18	16 Tu	05:41	-0.2	-6
	10:46	2.5	76		11:37	2.4	73
	17:30	-0.6	-18		18:13	-0.2	-6
	23:10	2.5	76				
2 Tu	05:53	-0.6	-18	17 W	00:06	2.3	70
	11:33	2.6	79		06:13	-0.2	-6
	18:20	-0.6	-18		12:17	2.4	73
					18:55	-0.1	-3
3 W	00:01	2.5	76	18 Th	00:51	2.2	67
	06:37	-0.5	-15		06:44	-0.1	-3
	12:23	2.6	79		12:57	2.4	73
	19:14	-0.5	-15		19:38	0.0	0
4 Th ◐	00:55	2.3	70	19 F ◑	01:37	2.1	64
	07:24	-0.5	-15		07:20	-0.1	-3
	13:16	2.6	79		13:40	2.3	70
	20:15	-0.4	-12		20:29	0.1	3
5 F	01:53	2.2	67	20 Sa	02:28	2.0	61
	08:19	-0.4	-12		08:04	0.0	0
	14:15	2.5	76		14:30	2.3	70
	21:23	-0.3	-9		21:27	0.2	6
6 Sa	02:59	2.1	64	21 Su	03:27	1.9	58
	09:23	-0.3	-9		08:59	0.1	3
	15:22	2.5	76		15:29	2.3	70
	22:31	-0.3	-9		22:26	0.2	6
7 Su	04:07	2.0	61	22 M	04:24	2.0	61
	10:31	-0.3	-9		10:02	0.1	3
	16:29	2.5	76		16:28	2.3	70
	23:36	-0.3	-9		23:23	0.1	3
8 M	05:12	2.1	64	23 Tu	05:17	2.0	61
	11:37	-0.3	-9		11:06	0.0	0
	17:31	2.5	76		17:21	2.4	73
9 Tu	00:36	-0.4	-12	24 W	00:17	0.0	0
	06:11	2.1	64		06:05	2.2	67
	12:40	-0.4	-12		12:09	-0.1	-3
	18:29	2.5	76		18:12	2.5	76
10 W	01:31	-0.5	-15	25 Th	01:07	-0.1	-3
	07:06	2.2	67		06:50	2.3	70
	13:38	-0.4	-12		13:07	-0.2	-6
	19:23	2.5	76		19:00	2.6	79
11 Th ●	02:20	-0.6	-18	26 F	01:52	-0.2	-6
	07:57	2.3	70		07:32	2.5	76
	14:29	-0.5	-15		13:23	-0.3	-9
	20:14	2.5	76		19:46	2.7	82
12 F	03:05	-0.6	-18	27 Sa ○	02:35	-0.3	-9
	08:44	2.4	73		08:13	2.6	79
	15:17	-0.5	-15		14:48	-0.5	-15
	21:02	2.5	76		20:31	2.7	82
13 Sa	03:48	-0.5	-15	28 Su	03:17	-0.4	-12
	09:29	2.4	73		08:54	2.8	85
	15:36	-0.5	-15		15:36	-0.5	-15
	21:48	2.5	76		21:17	2.8	85
14 Su	04:28	-0.4	-12				
	10:12	2.4	73				
	16:48	-0.4	-12				
	22:35	2.4	73				
15 M	05:06	-0.3	-9				
	10:55	2.4	73				
	17:32	-0.3	-9				
	23:21	2.3	70				

March

Day	Time	ft	cm	Day	Time	ft	cm
1 M	03:59	-0.4	-12	16 Tu	05:26	0.1	3
	09:37	2.9	88		11:19	2.8	85
	16:26	-0.5	-15		18:03	0.0	0
	22:04	2.7	82		23:51	2.6	79
2 Tu	04:44	-0.4	-12	17 W	05:58	0.2	6
	10:23	2.9	88		11:56	2.8	85
	17:17	-0.5	-15		18:43	0.1	3
	22:54	2.7	82				
3 W	05:29	-0.4	-12	18 Th	00:33	2.5	76
	11:12	2.9	88		06:28	0.2	6
	18:10	-0.4	-12		12:32	2.8	85
	23:46	2.6	79		19:21	0.2	6
4 Th	06:16	-0.3	-9	19 F	01:15	2.4	73
	12:03	2.9	88		07:00	0.3	9
	19:05	-0.2	-6		13:09	2.8	85
					20:00	0.4	12
5 F	00:41	2.5	76	20 Sa	01:57	2.4	73
	07:07	-0.2	-6		07:38	0.3	9
	12:57	2.8	85		13:48	2.7	82
	20:05	-0.1	-3		20:43	0.5	15
6 Sa ●	01:40	2.4	73	21 Su ◑	02:43	2.3	70
	08:04	0.0	0		08:23	0.4	12
	13:57	2.7	82		14:33	2.7	82
	21:10	0.0	0		21:36	0.5	15
7 Su	02:46	2.3	70	22 M	03:37	2.3	70
	09:11	0.1	3		09:17	0.5	15
	15:05	2.6	79		15:29	2.6	79
	22:15	0.0	0		22:36	0.5	15
8 M	03:56	2.3	70	23 Tu	04:38	2.3	70
	10:20	0.1	3		10:24	0.5	15
	16:15	2.6	79		16:36	2.6	79
	23:17	0.0	0		23:35	0.5	15
9 Tu	05:01	2.3	70	24 W	05:35	2.4	73
	11:26	0.1	3		11:33	0.4	12
	17:19	2.6	79		17:40	2.7	82
10 W	00:15	-0.1	-3	25 Th	00:31	0.4	12
	05:59	2.5	76		06:25	2.6	79
	12:28	0.0	0		12:39	0.3	9
	18:17	2.6	79		18:37	2.8	85
11 Th	01:08	-0.1	-3	26 F	01:24	0.3	9
	06:51	2.6	79		07:12	2.8	85
	13:23	-0.1	-3		13:40	0.1	3
	19:10	2.7	82		19:30	2.9	88
12 F	01:55	-0.2	-6	27 Sa	02:14	0.2	6
	07:39	2.7	82		07:57	3.0	91
	14:13	-0.2	-6		14:36	0.0	0
	19:59	2.7	82		20:20	3.0	91
13 Sa ●	02:37	-0.2	-6	28 Su ○	03:00	0.1	3
	08:23	2.8	85		08:42	3.2	98
	14:58	-0.2	-6		15:28	-0.2	-6
	20:43	2.7	82		21:08	3.0	91
14 Su	04:16	-0.1	-3	29 M	03:45	0.0	0
	10:03	2.8	85		09:26	3.3	101
	16:41	-0.2	-6		16:18	-0.2	-6
	22:26	2.7	82		21:56	3.0	91
15 M	04:53	0.0	0	30 Tu	04:30	0.0	0
	10:42	2.8	85		10:12	3.4	104
	17:23	-0.1	-3		17:10	-0.2	-6
	23:08	2.6	79		22:44	3.0	91
				31 W	05:17	0.0	0
					10:59	3.4	104
					18:04	-0.1	-3
					23:36	2.9	88

StationId: 8593005
Source: NOAA/NOS/CO-OPS
Station Type: Subordinate
Time Zone: LST_LDT
Datum: MLLW

NOAA Tide Predictions

WASHINGTON NAVY YARD,D.C., DC,2021

Times and Heights of High and Low Waters

April

Day	Time (h m)	Height (ft)	Height (cm)
1 Th	06:06	0.1	3
	11:50	3.4	104
	18:58	0.0	0
16 F	00:01	2.7	82
	05:51	0.6	18
	11:51	3.1	94
	18:53	0.6	18
2 F	00:31	2.8	85
	06:58	0.1	3
	12:44	3.3	101
	19:54	0.1	3
17 Sa	00:41	2.7	82
	06:27	0.7	21
	12:27	3.1	94
	19:30	0.6	18
3 Sa	01:29	2.7	82
	07:53	0.3	9
	13:41	3.1	94
	20:52	0.2	6
18 Su	01:22	2.6	79
	07:08	0.7	21
	13:08	3.1	94
	20:09	0.7	21
4 Su	02:30	2.7	82
	08:54	0.4	12
	14:42	3.0	91
	21:53	0.3	9
19 M	02:04	2.6	79
	07:54	0.8	24
	13:54	3.0	91
	20:54	0.8	24
5 M	03:36	2.6	79
	10:01	0.5	15
	15:51	2.9	88
	22:54	0.4	12
20 Tu	02:53	2.7	82
	08:49	0.8	24
	14:48	3.0	91
	21:49	0.8	24
6 Tu	04:44	2.7	82
	11:08	0.5	15
	17:02	2.8	85
	23:53	0.4	12
21 W	03:50	2.7	82
	09:54	0.8	24
	15:53	2.9	88
	22:48	0.8	24
7 W	05:47	2.8	85
	12:11	0.5	15
	18:05	2.8	85
22 Th	04:50	2.8	85
	11:04	0.7	21
	17:03	3.0	91
	23:45	0.7	21
8 Th	00:47	0.3	9
	06:41	2.9	88
	13:10	0.4	12
	19:01	2.8	85
23 F	05:45	3.0	91
	12:11	0.6	18
	18:05	3.0	91
9 F	01:38	0.3	9
	07:31	3.0	91
	14:04	0.3	9
	19:51	2.9	88
24 Sa	00:40	0.6	18
	06:35	3.2	98
	13:14	0.4	12
	19:00	3.1	94
10 Sa	02:24	0.3	9
	08:16	3.1	94
	14:52	0.2	6
	20:38	2.9	88
25 Su	01:34	0.5	15
	07:24	3.4	104
	14:13	0.2	6
	19:53	3.2	98
11 Su	03:05	0.3	9
	08:57	3.2	98
	15:36	0.2	6
	21:21	2.9	88
26 M	02:25	0.3	9
	08:12	3.6	110
	15:08	0.1	3
	20:44	3.2	98
12 M	03:42	0.3	9
	09:35	3.2	98
	16:17	0.2	6
	22:02	2.9	88
27 Tu	03:14	0.3	9
	09:00	3.7	113
	16:01	0.1	3
	21:34	3.2	98
13 Tu	04:16	0.4	12
	10:10	3.2	98
	16:57	0.3	9
	22:41	2.9	88
28 W	04:02	0.3	9
	09:48	3.7	113
	16:54	0.1	3
	22:25	3.1	94
14 W	04:47	0.5	15
	10:44	3.2	98
	17:37	0.4	12
	23:21	2.8	85
29 Th	04:53	0.3	9
	10:38	3.7	113
	17:49	0.2	6
	23:18	3.1	94
15 Th	05:18	0.6	18
	11:17	3.2	98
	18:15	0.5	15
30 F	05:47	0.4	12
	11:30	3.6	110
	18:44	0.2	6

May

Day	Time (h m)	Height (ft)	Height (cm)
1 Sa	00:16	3.0	91
	06:43	0.5	15
	12:27	3.5	107
	19:39	0.3	9
16 Su	00:11	2.8	85
	06:03	0.9	27
	11:55	3.3	101
	19:05	0.7	21
2 Su	01:17	2.9	88
	07:41	0.6	18
	13:26	3.3	101
	20:34	0.4	12
17 M	00:50	2.8	85
	06:47	0.9	27
	12:38	3.3	101
	19:42	0.7	21
3 M	02:18	2.9	88
	08:42	0.7	21
	14:28	3.1	94
	21:30	0.5	15
18 Tu	01:32	2.9	88
	07:35	0.9	27
	13:27	3.2	98
	20:23	0.8	24
4 Tu	03:21	2.9	88
	09:46	0.8	24
	15:35	3.0	91
	22:27	0.6	18
19 W	02:17	2.9	88
	08:28	0.9	27
	14:20	3.2	98
	21:10	0.8	24
5 W	04:25	3.0	91
	10:50	0.8	24
	16:43	2.9	88
	23:22	0.6	18
20 Th	03:10	3.0	91
	09:29	0.9	27
	15:22	3.1	94
	22:05	0.8	24
6 Th	05:25	3.1	94
	11:50	0.7	21
	17:44	2.9	88
21 F	04:09	3.1	94
	10:38	0.8	24
	16:30	3.1	94
	23:02	0.7	21
7 F	00:13	0.6	18
	06:17	3.2	98
	12:47	0.6	18
	18:37	3.0	91
22 Sa	05:08	3.3	101
	11:46	0.7	21
	17:34	3.1	94
	23:59	0.6	18
8 Sa	01:02	0.6	18
	07:05	3.3	101
	13:39	0.5	15
	19:26	3.0	91
23 Su	06:03	3.5	107
	12:51	0.5	15
	18:33	3.2	98
9 Su	01:47	0.6	18
	07:48	3.3	101
	14:27	0.5	15
	20:12	3.0	91
24 M	00:56	0.5	15
	06:55	3.6	110
	13:53	0.4	12
	19:28	3.2	98
10 M	02:28	0.6	18
	08:29	3.4	104
	15:11	0.4	12
	20:55	3.0	91
25 Tu	01:52	0.4	12
	07:46	3.8	116
	14:51	0.3	9
	20:21	3.2	98
11 Tu	03:06	0.6	18
	09:06	3.4	104
	15:53	0.5	15
	21:36	3.0	91
26 W	02:47	0.4	12
	08:37	3.8	116
	15:45	0.2	6
	21:14	3.2	98
12 W	03:40	0.6	18
	09:40	3.4	104
	16:32	0.5	15
	22:15	2.9	88
27 Th	03:40	0.4	12
	09:27	3.8	116
	16:39	0.2	6
	22:07	3.1	94
13 Th	04:13	0.7	21
	10:12	3.4	104
	17:12	0.6	18
	22:54	2.9	88
28 F	04:33	0.4	12
	10:18	3.7	113
	17:33	0.3	9
	23:01	3.1	94
14 F	04:46	0.8	24
	10:43	3.3	101
	17:50	0.6	18
	23:32	2.8	85
29 Sa	05:30	0.5	15
	11:12	3.6	110
	18:26	0.3	9
15 Sa	05:23	0.8	24
	11:17	3.3	101
	18:28	0.7	21
30 Su	00:00	3.0	91
	06:28	0.6	18
	12:10	3.4	104
	19:18	0.4	12
31 M	01:00	3.0	91
	07:26	0.7	21
	13:09	3.3	101
	20:10	0.5	15

June

Day	Time (h m)	Height (ft)	Height (cm)
1 Tu	01:59	3.0	91
	08:24	0.8	24
	14:10	3.1	94
	21:01	0.6	18
16 W	01:01	3.0	91
	07:20	0.8	24
	13:05	3.2	98
	19:55	0.6	18
2 W	02:57	3.0	91
	09:24	0.8	24
	15:12	3.0	91
	21:53	0.6	18
17 Th	01:47	3.1	94
	08:11	0.8	24
	13:58	3.2	98
	20:39	0.6	18
3 Th	03:57	3.1	94
	10:24	0.8	24
	16:15	2.9	88
	22:44	0.7	21
18 F	02:37	3.2	98
	09:09	0.8	24
	14:56	3.1	94
	21:30	0.6	18
4 F	04:54	3.1	94
	11:23	0.8	24
	17:15	2.9	88
	23:34	0.7	21
19 Sa	03:34	3.3	101
	10:17	0.7	21
	16:01	3.0	91
	22:27	0.6	18
5 Sa	05:46	3.2	98
	12:18	0.7	21
	18:08	2.9	88
20 Su	04:35	3.4	104
	11:26	0.7	21
	17:08	3.0	91
	23:26	0.5	15
6 Su	00:21	0.7	21
	06:34	3.3	101
	13:10	0.7	21
	18:58	2.9	88
21 M	05:35	3.5	107
	12:33	0.6	18
	18:09	3.0	91
7 M	01:06	0.7	21
	07:18	3.3	101
	14:00	0.6	18
	19:44	2.9	88
22 Tu	00:26	0.5	15
	06:31	3.6	110
	13:36	0.4	12
	19:07	3.0	91
8 Tu	01:49	0.7	21
	07:59	3.4	104
	14:45	0.5	15
	20:29	2.9	88
23 W	01:28	0.4	12
	07:25	3.7	113
	14:35	0.3	9
	20:03	3.0	91
9 W	02:30	0.7	21
	08:37	3.4	104
	15:27	0.5	15
	21:11	2.9	88
24 Th	02:28	0.4	12
	08:18	3.7	113
	15:30	0.2	6
	20:58	3.0	91
10 Th	03:08	0.7	21
	09:12	3.4	104
	16:07	0.5	15
	21:50	2.9	88
25 F	03:24	0.4	12
	09:11	3.7	113
	16:22	0.2	6
	21:51	3.0	91
11 F	03:45	0.7	21
	09:44	3.4	104
	16:46	0.6	18
	22:28	2.8	85
26 Sa	04:19	0.4	12
	10:03	3.6	110
	17:13	0.2	6
	22:44	3.0	91
12 Sa	04:23	0.8	24
	10:16	3.4	104
	17:24	0.6	18
	23:04	2.8	85
27 Su	05:15	0.5	15
	10:56	3.5	107
	18:03	0.3	9
	23:40	3.0	91
13 Su	05:03	0.8	24
	10:51	3.3	101
	18:02	0.6	18
	23:41	2.8	85
28 M	06:11	0.6	18
	11:51	3.3	101
	18:52	0.4	12
14 M	05:46	0.8	24
	11:31	3.3	101
	18:39	0.6	18
29 Tu	00:36	3.0	91
	07:06	0.6	18
	12:49	3.2	98
	19:39	0.4	12
15 Tu	00:20	2.9	88
	06:32	0.8	24
	12:16	3.3	101
	19:16	0.6	18
30 W	01:31	3.0	91
	08:00	0.7	21
	13:45	3.0	91
	20:25	0.5	15

StationId: 8593005
Source: NOAA/NOS/CO-OPS
Station Type: Subordinate
Time Zone: LST_LDT
Datum: MLLW

NOAA Tide Predictions

WASHINGTON NAVY YARD,D.C., DC,2021

Times and Heights of High and Low Waters

July

Day	Time	ft	cm	Day	Time	ft	cm
1 Th ◑	02:25	3.0	91	**16** F	01:19	3.2	98
	08:55	0.8	24		07:56	0.7	21
	14:42	2.9	88		13:37	3.1	94
	21:11	0.6	18		20:12	0.5	15
2 F	03:19	3.0	91	**17** Sa ◐	02:09	3.3	101
	09:52	0.8	24		08:54	0.7	21
	15:40	2.8	85		14:33	3.0	91
	21:59	0.7	21		21:01	0.5	15
3 Sa	04:15	3.1	94	**18** Su	03:05	3.3	101
	10:49	0.8	24		10:02	0.7	21
	16:40	2.7	82		15:37	2.9	88
	22:47	0.7	21		22:00	0.5	15
4 Su	05:09	3.1	94	**19** M	04:07	3.4	104
	11:45	0.8	24		11:12	0.7	21
	17:35	2.7	82		16:46	2.9	88
	23:34	0.7	21		23:04	0.5	15
5 M	05:59	3.2	98	**20** Tu	05:12	3.4	104
	12:38	0.8	24		12:19	0.6	18
	18:27	2.7	82		17:52	2.9	88
6 Tu	00:22	0.7	21	**21** W	00:09	0.5	15
	06:45	3.2	98		06:13	3.5	107
	13:30	0.7	21		13:22	0.5	15
	19:16	2.8	85		18:52	2.9	88
7 W	01:09	0.7	21	**22** Th	01:15	0.5	15
	07:28	3.3	101		07:10	3.6	110
	14:17	0.6	18		14:21	0.3	9
	20:02	2.8	85		19:50	3.0	91
8 Th	01:56	0.7	21	**23** F	02:16	0.4	12
	08:08	3.3	101		08:05	3.6	110
	15:00	0.5	15		15:13	0.2	6
	20:45	2.8	85		20:44	3.0	91
9 F	02:40	0.6	18	**24** Sa ○	03:13	0.4	12
	08:45	3.3	101		08:58	3.6	110
	15:40	0.5	15		16:02	0.2	6
	21:24	2.8	85		21:36	3.1	94
10 Sa ●	03:22	0.6	18	**25** Su	04:06	0.4	12
	09:19	3.3	101		09:49	3.5	107
	16:18	0.4	12		16:50	0.2	6
	22:01	2.9	88		22:25	3.1	94
11 Su	04:04	0.6	18	**26** M	04:58	0.4	12
	09:54	3.3	101		10:39	3.4	104
	16:56	0.5	15		17:36	0.3	9
	22:36	2.9	88		23:15	3.1	94
12 M	04:46	0.6	18	**27** Tu	05:51	0.5	15
	10:31	3.3	101		11:31	3.2	98
	17:34	0.5	15		18:20	0.4	12
	23:11	3.0	91				
13 Tu	05:31	0.6	18	**28** W	00:06	3.1	94
	11:11	3.3	101		06:42	0.6	18
	18:11	0.5	15		12:23	3.1	94
	23:50	3.0	91		19:03	0.5	15
14 W	06:17	0.6	18	**29** Th	00:56	3.1	94
	11:57	3.3	101		07:31	0.7	21
	18:50	0.5	15		13:15	3.0	91
					19:43	0.6	18
15 Th	00:32	3.1	94	**30** F	01:45	3.1	94
	07:05	0.6	18		08:21	0.8	24
	12:46	3.2	98		14:07	2.9	88
	19:29	0.5	15		20:23	0.7	21
				31 Sa ◑	02:34	3.0	91
					09:14	0.9	27
					15:01	2.7	82
					21:04	0.8	24

August

Day	Time	ft	cm	Day	Time	ft	cm
1 Su	03:26	3.0	91	**16** M	02:41	3.4	104
	10:11	1.0	30		09:51	0.8	24
	15:59	2.6	79		15:19	2.9	88
	21:51	0.8	24		21:42	0.6	18
2 M	04:23	3.0	91	**17** Tu	03:46	3.4	104
	11:08	1.0	30		11:01	0.8	24
	16:59	2.6	79		16:31	2.8	85
	22:43	0.8	24		22:53	0.7	21
3 Tu	05:18	3.1	94	**18** W	04:55	3.4	104
	12:03	0.9	27		12:06	0.7	21
	17:54	2.6	79		17:41	2.8	85
	23:37	0.8	24				
4 W	06:08	3.1	94	**19** Th	00:02	0.7	21
	12:55	0.8	24		06:00	3.4	104
	18:45	2.7	82		13:07	0.5	15
					18:42	2.9	88
5 Th	00:31	0.8	24	**20** F	01:07	0.6	18
	06:54	3.2	98		07:00	3.4	104
	13:44	0.7	21		14:03	0.4	12
	19:32	2.8	85		19:39	3.0	91
6 F	01:24	0.7	21	**21** Sa	02:07	0.5	15
	07:37	3.2	98		07:55	3.5	107
	14:28	0.6	18		14:54	0.3	9
	20:16	2.9	88		20:31	3.1	94
7 Sa	02:14	0.6	18	**22** Su ○	03:02	0.4	12
	08:17	3.3	101		08:46	3.5	107
	15:09	0.5	15		15:40	0.3	9
	20:55	2.9	88		21:19	3.2	98
8 Su ●	03:01	0.6	18	**23** M	03:52	0.4	12
	08:56	3.3	101		09:35	3.4	104
	15:47	0.4	12		16:23	0.3	9
	21:31	3.0	91		22:04	3.3	101
9 M	03:45	0.5	15	**24** Tu	04:40	0.4	12
	09:33	3.4	104		10:21	3.4	104
	16:25	0.4	12		17:04	0.4	12
	22:05	3.1	94		22:48	3.3	101
10 Tu	04:29	0.5	15	**25** W	05:27	0.5	15
	10:12	3.4	104		11:07	3.2	98
	17:03	0.4	12		17:44	0.5	15
	22:41	3.2	98		23:32	3.2	98
11 W	05:14	0.5	15	**26** Th	06:14	0.6	18
	10:53	3.4	104		11:54	3.1	94
	17:42	0.4	12		18:22	0.6	18
	23:21	3.3	101				
12 Th	06:01	0.5	15	**27** F	00:16	3.2	98
	11:38	3.3	101		07:00	0.8	24
	18:22	0.4	12		12:42	3.0	91
					18:57	0.7	21
13 F	00:05	3.4	104	**28** Sa	01:00	3.2	98
	06:51	0.6	18		07:45	0.9	27
	12:27	3.2	98		13:30	2.9	88
	19:04	0.4	12		19:31	0.8	24
14 Sa	00:53	3.4	104	**29** Su	01:45	3.1	94
	07:44	0.6	18		08:34	1.0	30
	13:19	3.1	94		14:20	2.7	82
	19:49	0.5	15		20:07	0.9	27
15 Su ◐	01:44	3.4	104	**30** M ◑	02:32	3.1	94
	08:43	0.7	21		09:27	1.1	34
	14:15	3.0	91		15:15	2.6	79
	20:40	0.6	18		20:52	0.9	27
				31 Tu	03:25	3.0	91
					10:25	1.1	34
					16:17	2.6	79
					21:49	1.0	30

September

Day	Time	ft	cm	Day	Time	ft	cm
1 W	04:27	3.0	91	**16** Th	04:43	3.3	101
	11:22	1.1	34		11:50	0.7	21
	17:18	2.6	79		17:31	2.9	88
	22:53	1.0	30		23:55	0.8	24
2 Th	05:26	3.1	94	**17** F	05:51	3.3	101
	12:15	1.0	30		12:48	0.6	18
	18:11	2.7	82		18:32	3.0	91
	23:55	0.9	27				
3 F	06:18	3.1	94	**18** Sa	00:58	0.7	21
	13:05	0.8	24		06:50	3.3	101
	18:59	2.8	85		13:41	0.5	15
					19:26	3.2	98
4 Sa	00:54	0.8	24	**19** Su	01:56	0.5	15
	07:05	3.2	98		07:44	3.4	104
	13:51	0.7	21		14:30	0.4	12
	19:41	3.0	91		20:14	3.3	101
5 Su	01:48	0.7	21	**20** M ○	02:47	0.4	12
	07:48	3.3	101		08:33	3.4	104
	14:34	0.6	18		15:14	0.4	12
	20:21	3.1	94		20:59	3.4	104
6 M	02:38	0.5	15	**21** Tu	03:35	0.4	12
	08:30	3.4	104		09:18	3.4	104
	15:13	0.5	15		15:54	0.4	12
	20:58	3.3	101		21:40	3.4	104
7 Tu ●	03:24	0.4	12	**22** W	04:19	0.5	15
	09:10	3.5	107		10:01	3.3	101
	15:52	0.4	12		16:31	0.5	15
	21:34	3.4	104		22:20	3.4	104
8 W	04:09	0.4	12	**23** Th	05:02	0.6	18
	09:51	3.5	107		10:43	3.2	98
	16:31	0.4	12		17:06	0.6	18
	22:12	3.5	107		22:58	3.4	104
9 Th	04:56	0.4	12	**24** F	05:46	0.7	21
	10:33	3.4	104		11:25	3.1	94
	17:12	0.4	12		17:39	0.7	21
	22:54	3.6	110		23:37	3.3	101
10 F	05:45	0.5	15	**25** Sa	06:29	0.8	24
	11:19	3.4	104		12:09	3.0	91
	17:55	0.4	12		18:11	0.8	24
	23:40	3.6	110				
11 Sa	06:38	0.6	18	**26** Su	00:16	3.3	101
	12:08	3.3	101		07:11	0.9	27
	18:41	0.5	15		12:54	2.8	85
					18:44	0.8	24
12 Su	00:30	3.6	110	**27** M	00:56	3.2	98
	07:34	0.7	21		07:55	1.0	30
	13:02	3.1	94		13:40	2.7	82
	19:30	0.6	18		19:22	0.9	27
13 M ◐	01:23	3.5	107	**28** Tu	01:39	3.1	94
	08:34	0.8	24		08:42	1.1	34
	14:01	3.0	91		14:31	2.6	79
	20:27	0.7	21		20:07	1.0	30
14 Tu	02:22	3.4	104	**29** W ◑	02:26	3.1	94
	09:40	0.8	24		09:36	1.1	34
	15:07	2.8	85		15:29	2.6	79
	21:34	0.8	24		21:04	1.1	34
15 W	03:29	3.3	101	**30** Th	03:25	3.0	91
	10:47	0.8	24		10:34	1.1	34
	16:22	2.8	85		16:32	2.6	79
	22:47	0.8	24		22:12	1.1	34

StationId: 8593005
Source: NOAA/NOS/CO-OPS
Station Type: Subordinate
Time Zone: LST_LDT
Datum: MLLW

NOAA Tide Predictions

WASHINGTON NAVY YARD,D.C., DC,2021

Times and Heights of High and Low Waters

October

Day	Time	ft	cm	Day	Time	ft	cm
1 F	04:34	3.0	91	**16** Sa	05:39	3.1	94
	11:29	1.0	30		12:23	0.5	15
	17:29	2.7	82		18:16	3.0	91
	23:20	1.0	30				
2 Sa	05:36	3.1	94	**17** Su	00:43	0.6	18
	12:20	0.9	27		06:36	3.1	94
	18:18	2.9	88		13:14	0.4	12
					19:07	3.2	98
3 Su	00:22	0.8	24	**18** M	01:39	0.4	12
	06:28	3.2	98		07:27	3.2	98
	13:08	0.7	21		14:02	0.4	12
	19:02	3.1	94		19:54	3.3	101
4 M	01:19	0.6	18	**19** Tu	02:29	0.3	9
	07:16	3.3	101		08:14	3.2	98
	13:54	0.6	18		14:44	0.3	9
	19:43	3.3	101		20:36	3.3	101
5 Tu	02:12	0.5	15	**20** W	03:15	0.3	9
	08:01	3.4	104		08:58	3.2	98
	14:37	0.4	12		15:23	0.3	9
	20:23	3.5	107	○	21:16	3.4	104
6 W	03:02	0.3	9	**21** Th	03:58	0.3	9
	08:45	3.4	104		09:39	3.1	94
	15:19	0.3	9		15:58	0.4	12
●	21:04	3.6	110		21:53	3.3	101
7 Th	03:50	0.3	9	**22** F	04:39	0.4	12
	09:28	3.4	104		10:19	3.0	91
	16:00	0.3	9		16:31	0.5	15
	21:46	3.7	113		22:28	3.3	101
8 F	04:39	0.3	9	**23** Sa	05:20	0.5	15
	10:13	3.4	104		10:59	2.9	88
	16:44	0.3	9		17:02	0.6	18
	22:30	3.7	113		23:03	3.2	98
9 Sa	05:31	0.4	12	**24** Su	06:01	0.7	21
	11:00	3.3	101		11:40	2.8	85
	17:31	0.3	9		17:33	0.7	21
	23:18	3.7	113		23:38	3.2	98
10 Su	06:26	0.4	12	**25** M	06:41	0.7	21
	11:52	3.1	94		12:22	2.7	82
	18:22	0.4	12		18:09	0.7	21
11 M	00:10	3.6	110	**26** Tu	00:15	3.1	94
	07:23	0.5	15		07:21	0.8	24
	12:49	3.0	91		13:05	2.6	79
	19:18	0.6	18		18:50	0.8	24
12 Tu	01:07	3.5	107	**27** W	00:56	3.1	94
	08:22	0.6	18		08:01	0.9	27
	13:51	2.9	88		13:49	2.6	79
	20:19	0.7	21		19:37	0.8	24
13 W ◑	02:08	3.3	101	**28** Th ◐	01:42	3.0	91
	09:24	0.7	21		08:47	0.9	27
	14:58	2.8	85		14:39	2.5	76
	21:27	0.8	24		20:31	0.8	24
14 Th	03:17	3.1	94	**29** F	02:36	2.9	88
	10:27	0.7	21		09:40	0.9	27
	16:10	2.8	85		15:36	2.6	79
	22:38	0.8	24		21:34	0.8	24
15 F	04:31	3.1	94	**30** Sa	03:40	2.9	88
	11:27	0.6	18		10:36	0.8	24
	17:18	2.9	88		16:36	2.7	82
	23:43	0.7	21		22:43	0.7	21
				31 Su	04:49	2.9	88
					11:30	0.7	21
					17:30	2.8	85
					23:48	0.6	18

November

Day	Time	ft	cm	Day	Time	ft	cm
1 M	05:49	3.0	91	**16** Tu	00:17	0.2	6
	12:21	0.5	15		06:05	2.8	85
	18:19	3.0	91		12:29	0.1	3
					18:29	3.0	91
2 Tu	00:48	0.4	12	**17** W	01:07	0.1	3
	06:41	3.0	91		06:51	2.8	85
	13:11	0.3	9		13:12	0.1	3
	19:05	3.2	98		19:11	3.0	91
3 W	01:46	0.2	6	**18** Th	01:53	0.1	3
	07:31	3.1	94		07:35	2.8	85
	14:00	0.2	6		13:51	0.1	3
	19:50	3.4	104		19:50	3.1	94
4 Th	02:40	0.1	3	**19** F	02:36	0.1	3
	08:19	3.2	98		08:17	2.7	82
	14:47	0.1	3		14:27	0.1	3
●	20:36	3.5	107	○	20:27	3.0	91
5 F	03:32	0.0	0	**20** Sa	03:17	0.1	3
	09:06	3.1	94		08:57	2.6	79
	15:33	0.0	0		15:01	0.2	6
	21:22	3.6	110		21:01	3.0	91
6 Sa	04:24	0.0	0	**21** Su	03:57	0.2	6
	09:54	3.1	94		09:36	2.5	76
	16:21	0.0	0		15:34	0.3	9
	22:10	3.6	110		21:35	3.0	91
7 Su	04:18	0.1	3	**22** M	04:36	0.3	9
	09:44	3.0	91		10:15	2.5	76
	16:13	0.1	3		16:09	0.3	9
	22:00	3.5	107		22:08	2.9	88
8 M	05:13	0.1	3	**23** Tu	05:14	0.3	9
	10:38	2.9	88		10:54	2.4	73
	17:10	0.2	6		16:47	0.3	9
	22:55	3.3	101		22:45	2.8	85
9 Tu	06:09	0.2	6	**24** W	05:51	0.3	9
	11:38	2.8	85		11:33	2.4	73
	18:09	0.3	9		17:30	0.4	12
	23:54	3.2	98		23:26	2.8	85
10 W	07:05	0.3	9	**25** Th	06:28	0.4	12
	12:40	2.7	82		12:13	2.4	73
	19:10	0.4	12		18:16	0.4	12
11 Th ◐	00:57	3.0	91	**26** F	00:12	2.7	82
	08:02	0.3	9		07:07	0.4	12
	13:44	2.6	79		12:56	2.4	73
	20:15	0.4	12		19:05	0.4	12
12 F	02:03	2.8	85	**27** Sa ◑	01:02	2.7	82
	09:01	0.3	9		07:51	0.3	9
	14:51	2.7	82		13:44	2.5	76
	21:21	0.4	12		20:02	0.3	9
13 Sa	03:14	2.7	82	**28** Su	01:59	2.6	79
	09:58	0.3	9		08:43	0.3	9
	15:56	2.7	82		14:40	2.5	76
	22:24	0.4	12		21:07	0.3	9
14 Su	04:18	2.7	82	**29** M	03:05	2.6	79
	10:51	0.3	9		09:38	0.2	6
	16:53	2.8	85		15:40	2.7	82
	23:22	0.3	9		22:14	0.2	6
15 M	05:15	2.7	82	**30** Tu	04:09	2.6	79
	11:42	0.2	6		10:33	0.1	3
	17:43	2.9	88		16:37	2.8	85
					23:19	0.1	3

December

Day	Time	ft	cm	Day	Time	ft	cm
1 W	05:07	2.6	79	**16** Th	00:41	-0.2	-6
	11:28	0.0	0		06:25	2.3	70
	17:29	3.0	91		12:37	-0.2	-6
					18:44	2.6	79
2 Th	00:22	-0.1	-3	**17** F	01:29	-0.2	-6
	06:01	2.7	82		07:11	2.3	70
	12:24	-0.2	-6		13:19	-0.2	-6
	18:21	3.1	94		19:25	2.7	82
3 F	01:21	-0.2	-6	**18** Sa	02:13	-0.3	-9
	06:54	2.7	82		07:55	2.3	70
	13:19	-0.3	-9		13:59	-0.2	-6
	19:11	3.2	98		20:03	2.7	82
4 Sa	02:17	-0.3	-9	**19** Su	02:54	-0.3	-9
	07:46	2.7	82		08:36	2.2	67
	14:12	-0.3	-9		14:37	-0.2	-6
●	20:02	3.3	101	○	20:38	2.6	79
5 Su	03:10	-0.4	-12	**20** M	03:33	-0.2	-6
	08:37	2.6	79		09:15	2.2	67
	15:05	-0.3	-9		15:15	-0.1	-3
	20:53	3.2	98		21:12	2.6	79
6 M	04:03	-0.4	-12	**21** Tu	04:11	-0.2	-6
	09:29	2.6	79		09:52	2.2	67
	16:01	-0.3	-9		15:53	-0.1	-3
	21:45	3.1	94		21:46	2.6	79
7 Tu	04:57	-0.3	-9	**22** W	04:48	-0.2	-6
	10:25	2.5	76		10:28	2.2	67
	16:59	-0.2	-6		16:33	-0.1	-3
	22:42	2.9	88		22:23	2.5	76
8 W	05:51	-0.3	-9	**23** Th	05:24	-0.2	-6
	11:24	2.5	76		11:03	2.2	67
	17:58	-0.2	-6		17:15	-0.1	-3
	23:42	2.8	85		23:04	2.5	76
9 Th	06:43	-0.2	-6	**24** F	05:58	-0.2	-6
	12:24	2.4	73		11:41	2.2	67
	18:56	-0.1	-3		17:59	-0.1	-3
					23:49	2.5	76
10 F	00:42	2.6	79	**25** Sa	06:34	-0.2	-6
	07:35	-0.1	-3		12:21	2.3	70
	13:23	2.4	73		18:44	-0.2	-6
	19:55	0.0	0				
11 Sa ◐	01:44	2.5	76	**26** Su	00:37	2.4	73
	08:28	-0.1	-3		07:14	-0.2	-6
	14:23	2.4	73		13:07	2.4	73
	20:56	0.0	0		19:35	-0.2	-6
12 Su	02:47	2.4	73	**27** M ◑	01:29	2.4	73
	09:21	-0.1	-3		07:59	-0.2	-6
	15:24	2.4	73		13:58	2.4	73
	21:57	0.0	0		20:35	-0.1	-3
13 M	03:49	2.3	70	**28** Tu	02:28	2.3	70
	10:13	-0.1	-3		08:53	-0.3	-9
	16:21	2.5	76		14:57	2.5	76
	22:54	0.0	0		21:44	-0.2	-6
14 Tu	04:46	2.3	70	**29** W	03:34	2.3	70
	11:03	-0.1	-3		09:51	-0.3	-9
	17:12	2.5	76		15:59	2.6	79
	23:49	-0.1	-3		22:54	-0.2	-6
15 W	05:37	2.3	70	**30** Th	04:37	2.2	67
	11:51	-0.1	-3		10:52	-0.4	-12
	17:59	2.6	79		16:59	2.7	82
				31 F	00:02	-0.3	-9
					05:36	2.3	70
					11:56	-0.4	-12
					17:56	2.8	85

StationId: 8638863
Source: NOAA/NOS/CO-OPS
Station Type: Primary
Time Zone: LST_LDT
Datum: MLLW

NOAA Tide Predictions

Chesapeake Bay Bridge Tunnel, VA,2021

Times and Heights of High and Low Waters

January

Day	Time	ft	cm	Day	Time	ft	cm
1 F	03:00	-0.2	-6	16 Sa	04:07	-0.3	-9
	09:30	2.8	85		10:29	2.7	82
	15:49	-0.2	-6		16:50	-0.2	-6
	21:51	2.1	64		22:53	2.2	67
2 Sa	03:45	-0.2	-6	17 Su	04:55	-0.1	-3
	10:11	2.7	82		11:10	2.5	76
	16:32	-0.2	-6		17:31	-0.1	-3
	22:36	2.2	67		23:38	2.2	67
3 Su	04:34	-0.1	-3	18 M	05:43	0.1	3
	10:55	2.7	82		11:51	2.3	70
	17:18	-0.2	-6		18:12	0.0	0
	23:26	2.2	67				
4 M	05:28	-0.1	-3	19 Tu	00:24	2.2	67
	11:43	2.5	76		06:35	0.2	6
	18:07	-0.2	-6		12:34	2.1	64
					18:53	0.1	3
5 Tu	00:20	2.3	70	20 W ◑	01:13	2.2	67
	06:28	0.0	0		07:30	0.3	9
	12:35	2.4	73		13:20	1.9	58
	18:59	-0.2	-6		19:37	0.1	3
6 W ◑	01:19	2.4	73	21 Th	02:05	2.2	67
	07:33	0.0	0		08:28	0.4	12
	13:32	2.3	70		14:11	1.8	55
	19:55	-0.3	-9		20:24	0.2	6
7 Th	02:23	2.5	76	22 F	03:00	2.2	67
	08:42	0.0	0		09:27	0.4	12
	14:36	2.1	64		15:07	1.7	52
	20:54	-0.3	-9		21:15	0.2	6
8 F	03:28	2.7	82	23 Sa	03:56	2.3	70
	09:52	0.0	0		10:23	0.4	12
	15:43	2.1	64		16:06	1.7	52
	21:54	-0.4	-12		22:06	0.1	3
9 Sa	04:33	2.8	85	24 Su	04:49	2.3	70
	10:58	-0.1	-3		11:14	0.3	9
	16:51	2.1	64		17:02	1.8	55
	22:53	-0.4	-12		22:56	0.1	3
10 Su	05:34	3.0	91	25 M	05:39	2.5	76
	11:58	-0.2	-6		12:00	0.2	6
	17:55	2.1	64		17:53	1.9	58
	23:51	-0.5	-15		23:44	0.0	0
11 M	06:32	3.1	94	26 Tu	06:25	2.6	79
	12:54	-0.3	-9		12:43	0.0	0
	18:53	2.2	67		18:40	2.0	61
12 Tu	00:46	-0.5	-15	27 W	00:30	-0.2	-6
	07:25	3.1	94		07:08	2.7	82
	13:47	-0.4	-12		13:24	-0.1	-3
	19:46	2.3	70		19:24	2.1	64
13 W ●	01:39	-0.5	-15	28 Th ○	01:15	-0.3	-9
	08:15	3.1	94		07:50	2.8	85
	14:36	-0.4	-12		14:04	-0.2	-6
	20:36	2.3	70		20:06	2.2	67
14 Th	02:30	-0.5	-15	29 F	02:00	-0.3	-9
	09:02	3.0	91		08:31	2.9	88
	15:22	-0.4	-12		14:45	-0.3	-9
	21:23	2.3	70		20:49	2.3	70
15 F	03:19	-0.4	-12	30 Sa	02:45	-0.4	-12
	09:47	2.9	88		09:11	2.9	88
	16:07	-0.3	-9		15:26	-0.4	-12
	22:08	2.3	70		21:33	2.4	73
				31 Su	03:32	-0.4	-12
					09:53	2.8	85
					16:08	-0.4	-12
					22:19	2.5	76

February

Day	Time	ft	cm	Day	Time	ft	cm
1 M	04:22	-0.3	-9	16 Tu	05:07	0.1	3
	10:37	2.7	82		11:12	2.3	70
	16:53	-0.4	-12		17:21	0.1	3
	23:07	2.6	79		23:37	2.4	73
2 Tu	05:15	-0.2	-6	17 W	05:51	0.2	6
	11:24	2.6	79		11:49	2.1	64
	17:41	-0.4	-12		17:58	0.2	6
3 W	00:00	2.6	79	18 Th	00:20	2.3	70
	06:14	-0.1	-3		06:38	0.4	12
	12:15	2.4	73		12:31	2.0	61
	18:32	-0.3	-9		18:40	0.2	6
4 Th ◐	00:57	2.6	79	19 F ◐	01:07	2.3	70
	07:18	0.0	0		07:30	0.5	15
	13:12	2.2	67		13:19	1.8	55
	19:29	-0.3	-9		19:28	0.3	9
5 F	02:01	2.6	79	20 Sa	02:00	2.2	67
	08:27	0.1	3		08:29	0.5	15
	14:16	2.0	61		14:14	1.8	55
	20:31	-0.2	-6		20:23	0.3	9
6 Sa	03:10	2.7	82	21 Su	03:00	2.2	67
	09:39	0.1	3		09:30	0.5	15
	15:29	2.0	61		15:16	1.8	55
	21:37	-0.2	-6		21:22	0.3	9
7 Su	04:21	2.7	82	22 M	04:02	2.3	70
	10:48	0.0	0		10:28	0.4	12
	16:43	2.0	61		16:19	1.8	55
	22:42	-0.2	-6		22:20	0.2	6
8 M	05:28	2.8	85	23 Tu	05:01	2.4	73
	11:50	-0.1	-3		11:21	0.3	9
	17:50	2.1	64		17:18	2.0	61
	23:44	-0.3	-9		23:15	0.1	3
9 Tu	06:26	2.9	88	24 W	05:54	2.6	79
	12:44	-0.2	-6		12:08	0.2	6
	18:47	2.2	67		18:09	2.2	67
10 W	00:40	-0.3	-9	25 Th	00:06	-0.1	-3
	07:18	2.9	88		06:41	2.8	85
	13:33	-0.2	-6		12:52	0.0	0
	19:36	2.3	70		18:57	2.4	73
11 Th ●	01:31	-0.4	-12	26 F	00:55	-0.3	-9
	08:04	2.9	88		07:25	2.9	88
	14:18	-0.2	-6		13:35	-0.2	-6
	20:21	2.4	73		19:42	2.6	79
12 F	02:18	-0.4	-12	27 Sa ○	01:42	-0.4	-12
	08:46	2.9	88		08:08	3.0	91
	14:58	-0.2	-6		14:16	-0.3	-9
	21:02	2.5	76		20:27	2.8	85
13 Sa	03:02	-0.3	-9	28 Su	02:30	-0.4	-12
	09:24	2.8	85		08:50	3.0	91
	14:55	-0.2	-6		14:59	-0.4	-12
	21:42	2.5	76		21:12	2.9	88
14 Su	03:45	-0.2	-6				
	10:00	2.6	79				
	16:12	-0.1	-3				
	22:20	2.5	76				
15 M	04:26	-0.1	-3				
	10:36	2.5	76				
	16:46	0.0	0				
	22:58	2.4	73				

March

Day	Time	ft	cm	Day	Time	ft	cm
1 M	03:19	-0.5	-15	16 Tu	04:58	0.0	0
	09:34	2.9	88		11:03	2.5	76
	15:42	-0.5	-15		17:03	0.1	3
	21:59	3.0	91		23:21	2.7	82
2 Tu	04:10	-0.4	-12	17 W	05:35	0.2	6
	10:19	2.8	85		11:37	2.4	73
	16:28	-0.4	-12		17:37	0.2	6
	22:48	3.0	91		23:57	2.6	79
3 W	05:03	-0.3	-9	18 Th	06:14	0.3	9
	11:07	2.6	79		12:13	2.2	67
	17:16	-0.3	-9		18:13	0.3	9
	23:40	3.0	91				
4 Th	06:01	-0.1	-3	19 F	00:36	2.5	76
	11:59	2.4	73		06:56	0.4	12
	18:09	-0.2	-6		12:53	2.1	64
					18:54	0.4	12
5 F	00:38	2.9	88	20 Sa	01:20	2.5	76
	07:04	0.1	3		07:44	0.5	15
	12:57	2.2	67		13:39	2.0	61
	19:09	-0.1	-3		19:43	0.5	15
6 Sa ◑	01:42	2.8	85	21 Su ◑	02:11	2.4	73
	08:14	0.2	6		08:39	0.6	18
	14:05	2.1	64		14:32	1.9	58
	20:17	0.0	0		20:40	0.5	15
7 Su	02:56	2.7	82	22 M	03:10	2.4	73
	09:27	0.2	6		09:40	0.6	18
	15:24	2.1	64		15:33	1.9	58
	21:28	0.1	3		21:42	0.5	15
8 M	04:13	2.7	82	23 Tu	04:15	2.4	73
	10:36	0.2	6		10:41	0.6	18
	16:40	2.1	64		16:39	2.0	61
	22:38	0.1	3		22:46	0.4	12
9 Tu	05:20	2.7	82	24 W	05:19	2.5	76
	11:37	0.2	6		11:38	0.4	12
	17:44	2.3	70		17:41	2.2	67
	23:40	0.0	0		23:46	0.2	6
10 W	06:17	2.8	85	25 Th	06:16	2.7	82
	12:28	0.1	3		12:29	0.2	6
	18:36	2.4	73		18:37	2.5	76
11 Th	00:33	-0.1	-3	26 F	00:41	0.0	0
	07:05	2.8	85		07:08	2.8	85
	13:13	0.0	0		13:16	0.0	0
	19:21	2.5	76		19:28	2.7	82
12 F	01:21	-0.1	-3	27 Sa	01:33	-0.2	-6
	07:46	2.8	85		07:55	3.0	91
	13:52	0.0	0		14:01	-0.2	-6
	20:01	2.6	79		20:16	3.0	91
13 Sa ●	02:03	-0.2	-6	28 Su ○	02:24	-0.3	-9
	08:23	2.8	85		08:42	3.0	91
	14:27	0.0	0		14:47	-0.3	-9
	20:38	2.7	82		21:03	3.2	98
14 Su	03:43	-0.1	-3	29 M	03:14	-0.4	-12
	09:58	2.7	82		09:27	3.0	91
	16:00	0.0	0		15:30	-0.4	-12
	22:12	2.7	82		21:50	3.4	104
15 M	04:21	-0.1	-3	30 Tu	04:05	-0.4	-12
	10:30	2.6	79		10:14	3.0	91
	16:32	0.0	0		16:16	-0.4	-12
	22:46	2.7	82		22:39	3.4	104
				31 W	04:57	-0.4	-12
					11:01	2.8	85
					17:04	-0.4	-12
					23:29	3.4	104

StationId: 8638863
Source: NOAA/NOS/CO-OPS
Station Type: Primary
Time Zone: LST_LDT
Datum: MLLW

NOAA Tide Predictions

Chesapeake Bay Bridge Tunnel, VA, 2021

Times and Heights of High and Low Waters

April

Day	Time	ft	cm	Day	Time	ft	cm
1 Th	05:51	-0.2	-6	16 F	05:43	0.3	9
	11:52	2.7	82		11:45	2.3	70
	17:55	-0.2	-6		17:38	0.4	12
2 F	00:22	3.2	98	17 Sa	00:02	2.7	82
	06:48	0.0	0		06:23	0.4	12
	12:47	2.5	76		12:24	2.2	67
	18:52	0.0	0		18:20	0.5	15
3 Sa	01:21	3.0	91	18 Su	00:44	2.6	79
	07:52	0.1	3		07:09	0.5	15
	13:48	2.3	70		13:09	2.1	64
	19:55	0.1	3		19:09	0.6	18
4 Su	02:27	2.8	85	19 M	01:34	2.5	76
	09:01	0.3	9		08:01	0.6	18
	14:59	2.2	67		14:01	2.1	64
	21:07	0.3	9		20:06	0.6	18
5 M	03:43	2.7	82	20 Tu	02:30	2.5	76
	10:12	0.4	12		08:59	0.6	18
	16:18	2.2	67		15:00	2.1	64
	22:22	0.3	9		21:09	0.5	15
6 Tu	04:59	2.7	82	21 W	03:32	2.5	76
	11:18	0.3	9		09:59	0.5	15
	17:30	2.3	70		16:04	2.2	67
	23:30	0.3	9		22:15	0.4	12
7 W	06:04	2.7	82	22 Th	04:36	2.6	79
	12:14	0.3	9		10:56	0.4	12
	18:29	2.5	76		17:06	2.5	76
					23:17	0.2	6
8 Th	00:30	0.2	6	23 F	05:36	2.7	82
	06:57	2.7	82		11:49	0.2	6
	13:01	0.2	6		18:04	2.7	82
	19:17	2.6	79				
9 F	01:20	0.1	3	24 Sa	00:16	0.0	0
	07:42	2.7	82		06:32	2.8	85
	13:42	0.2	6		12:39	0.0	0
	19:58	2.7	82		18:58	3.0	91
10 Sa	02:04	0.1	3	25 Su	01:12	-0.2	-6
	08:21	2.7	82		07:24	2.9	88
	14:18	0.1	3		13:27	-0.2	-6
	20:35	2.8	85		19:49	3.3	101
11 Su	02:44	0.0	0	26 M	02:05	-0.3	-9
	08:56	2.7	82		08:15	2.9	88
	14:51	0.1	3		14:15	-0.4	-12
	21:09	2.9	88		20:39	3.5	107
12 M	03:21	0.0	0	27 Tu	02:58	-0.4	-12
	09:28	2.6	79		09:05	2.9	88
	15:22	0.1	3		15:03	-0.4	-12
	21:41	2.9	88		21:29	3.6	110
13 Tu	03:56	0.1	3	28 W	03:50	-0.4	-12
	10:01	2.5	76		09:55	2.9	88
	15:53	0.2	6		15:52	-0.4	-12
	22:14	2.9	88		22:20	3.6	110
14 W	04:31	0.1	3	29 Th	04:43	-0.4	-12
	10:34	2.4	73		10:46	2.8	85
	16:26	0.2	6		16:44	-0.3	-9
	22:48	2.9	88		23:12	3.5	107
15 Th	05:06	0.2	6	30 F	05:38	-0.2	-6
	11:08	2.4	73		11:39	2.6	79
	17:00	0.3	9		17:38	-0.1	-3
	23:23	2.8	85				

May

Day	Time	ft	cm	Day	Time	ft	cm
1 Sa	00:07	3.3	101	16 Su	05:58	0.3	9
	06:36	0.0	0		12:02	2.2	67
	12:36	2.5	76		17:54	0.5	15
	18:38	0.0	0				
2 Su	01:06	3.1	94	17 M	00:18	2.6	79
	07:38	0.1	3		06:42	0.4	12
	13:39	2.4	73		12:46	2.2	67
	19:44	0.2	6		18:44	0.5	15
3 M	02:11	2.8	85	18 Tu	01:05	2.6	79
	08:43	0.3	9		07:32	0.4	12
	14:49	2.3	70		13:37	2.2	67
	20:56	0.3	9		19:40	0.5	15
4 Tu	03:22	2.7	82	19 W	01:58	2.5	76
	09:48	0.3	9		08:25	0.4	12
	16:01	2.4	73		14:33	2.3	70
	22:08	0.4	12		20:42	0.5	15
5 W	04:32	2.5	76	20 Th	02:56	2.5	76
	10:47	0.4	12		09:21	0.3	9
	17:06	2.5	76		15:34	2.4	73
	23:13	0.3	9		21:48	0.4	12
6 Th	05:34	2.5	76	21 F	03:57	2.5	76
	11:39	0.3	9		10:17	0.2	6
	18:01	2.6	79		16:35	2.7	82
					22:52	0.2	6
7 F	00:10	0.3	9	22 Sa	04:58	2.6	79
	06:25	2.5	76		11:11	0.0	0
	12:24	0.3	9		17:34	2.9	88
	18:47	2.7	82		23:53	0.0	0
8 Sa	00:59	0.2	6	23 Su	05:58	2.6	79
	07:09	2.5	76		12:04	-0.1	-3
	13:03	0.2	6		18:31	3.2	98
	19:27	2.8	85				
9 Su	01:42	0.2	6	24 M	00:52	-0.2	-6
	07:48	2.4	73		06:55	2.7	82
	13:38	0.2	6		12:56	-0.3	-9
	20:03	2.9	88		19:25	3.4	104
10 M	02:21	0.1	3	25 Tu	01:48	-0.3	-9
	08:24	2.4	73		07:51	2.7	82
	14:12	0.2	6		13:47	-0.4	-12
	20:37	3.0	91		20:18	3.6	110
11 Tu	02:57	0.1	3	26 W	02:42	-0.4	-12
	08:59	2.4	73		08:45	2.7	82
	14:45	0.2	6		14:44	-0.4	-12
	21:11	3.0	91		21:11	3.6	110
12 W	03:31	0.1	3	27 Th	03:36	-0.4	-12
	09:33	2.4	73		09:38	2.7	82
	15:19	0.2	6		15:33	-0.4	-12
	21:45	2.9	88		22:03	3.6	110
13 Th	04:06	0.2	6	28 F	04:30	-0.4	-12
	10:08	2.3	70		10:32	2.7	82
	15:54	0.3	9		16:27	-0.3	-9
	22:20	2.9	88		22:57	3.4	104
14 F	04:41	0.2	6	29 Sa	05:24	-0.2	-6
	10:44	2.3	70		11:27	2.6	79
	16:31	0.3	9		17:24	-0.1	-3
	22:56	2.8	85		23:52	3.2	98
15 Sa	05:18	0.3	9	30 Su	06:20	-0.1	-3
	11:22	2.2	67		12:24	2.5	76
	17:11	0.4	12		18:24	0.0	0
	23:35	2.7	82				
				31 M	00:49	3.0	91
					07:18	0.1	3
					13:24	2.4	73
					19:28	0.2	6

June

Day	Time	ft	cm	Day	Time	ft	cm
1 Tu	01:48	2.7	82	16 W	00:41	2.6	79
	08:16	0.2	6		07:05	0.2	6
	14:27	2.4	73		13:15	2.3	70
	20:35	0.3	9		19:19	0.4	12
2 W	02:50	2.5	76	17 Th	01:31	2.6	79
	09:13	0.3	9		07:55	0.2	6
	15:30	2.4	73		14:09	2.5	76
	21:42	0.4	12		20:20	0.3	9
3 Th	03:51	2.4	73	18 F	02:25	2.5	76
	10:06	0.3	9		08:47	0.1	3
	16:30	2.5	76		15:07	2.6	79
	22:45	0.4	12		21:25	0.3	9
4 F	04:49	2.3	70	19 Sa	03:24	2.4	73
	10:54	0.3	9		09:42	0.0	0
	17:23	2.6	79		16:08	2.8	85
	23:41	0.4	12		22:30	0.2	6
5 Sa	05:42	2.2	67	20 Su	04:26	2.4	73
	11:38	0.3	9		10:38	-0.1	-3
	18:09	2.7	82		17:08	3.0	91
					23:34	0.0	0
6 Su	00:30	0.3	9	21 M	05:30	2.4	73
	06:29	2.2	67		11:34	-0.2	-6
	12:18	0.3	9		18:08	3.2	98
	18:51	2.8	85				
7 M	01:13	0.3	9	22 Tu	00:35	-0.1	-3
	07:11	2.2	67		06:32	2.4	73
	12:56	0.3	9		12:31	-0.3	-9
	19:29	2.8	85		19:06	3.4	104
8 Tu	01:53	0.2	6	23 W	01:33	-0.2	-6
	07:51	2.2	67		07:32	2.5	76
	13:34	0.2	6		13:27	-0.3	-9
	20:06	2.9	88		20:02	3.5	107
9 W	02:30	0.2	6	24 Th	02:28	-0.3	-9
	08:30	2.2	67		08:30	2.6	79
	14:12	0.2	6		14:22	-0.3	-9
	20:43	2.9	88		20:56	3.5	107
10 Th	03:06	0.1	3	25 F	03:22	-0.3	-9
	09:07	2.2	67		09:25	2.6	79
	14:50	0.2	6		15:18	-0.3	-9
	21:20	2.9	88		21:50	3.4	104
11 F	03:41	0.1	3	26 Sa	04:15	-0.3	-9
	09:45	2.2	67		10:19	2.6	79
	15:28	0.2	6		16:13	-0.2	-6
	21:57	2.9	88		22:43	3.3	101
12 Sa	04:18	0.2	6	27 Su	05:07	-0.2	-6
	10:22	2.2	67		11:12	2.6	79
	16:08	0.3	9		17:09	-0.1	-3
	22:35	2.8	85		23:34	3.1	94
13 Su	04:56	0.2	6	28 M	05:58	-0.1	-3
	11:01	2.2	67		12:05	2.6	79
	16:50	0.3	9		18:06	0.0	0
	23:14	2.8	85				
14 M	05:36	0.2	6	29 Tu	00:26	2.9	88
	11:42	2.2	67		06:49	0.0	0
	17:34	0.3	9		12:59	2.5	76
	23:56	2.7	82		19:05	0.2	6
15 Tu	06:19	0.2	6	30 W	01:17	2.6	79
	12:26	2.3	70		07:39	0.1	3
	18:24	0.4	12		13:53	2.5	76
					20:05	0.3	9

StationId: 8638863
Source: NOAA/NOS/CO-OPS
Station Type: Primary
Time Zone: LST_LDT
Datum: MLLW

NOAA Tide Predictions

Chesapeake Bay Bridge Tunnel, VA, 2021

Times and Heights of High and Low Waters

July

Day	Time	ft	cm	Day	Time	ft	cm
1 Th ◐	02:08	2.4	73	**16** F	01:06	2.6	79
	08:27	0.2	6		07:25	0.0	0
	14:48	2.5	76		13:46	2.8	85
	21:07	0.4	12		20:02	0.3	9
2 F	03:01	2.2	67	**17** Sa ◗	01:59	2.5	76
	09:15	0.3	9		08:17	0.0	0
	15:42	2.5	76		14:43	2.9	88
	22:07	0.5	15		21:07	0.3	9
3 Sa	03:55	2.1	64	**18** Su	02:58	2.4	73
	10:01	0.4	12		09:13	0.0	0
	16:35	2.6	79		15:44	3.0	91
	23:03	0.5	15		22:13	0.2	6
4 Su	04:50	2.0	61	**19** M	04:03	2.3	70
	10:47	0.4	12		10:13	0.0	0
	17:24	2.6	79		16:48	3.1	94
	23:54	0.4	12		23:19	0.2	6
5 M	05:43	2.0	61	**20** Tu	05:11	2.3	70
	11:32	0.4	12		11:14	0.0	0
	18:10	2.7	82		17:52	3.2	98
6 Tu	00:40	0.4	12	**21** W	00:22	0.0	0
	06:32	2.0	61		06:18	2.4	73
	12:16	0.3	9		12:15	-0.1	-3
	18:54	2.8	85		18:53	3.3	101
7 W	01:22	0.3	9	**22** Th	01:21	-0.1	-3
	07:18	2.1	64		07:21	2.5	76
	13:00	0.3	9		13:14	-0.1	-3
	19:37	2.8	85		19:51	3.4	104
8 Th	02:01	0.3	9	**23** F	02:16	-0.1	-3
	08:00	2.2	67		08:19	2.6	79
	13:43	0.3	9		14:11	-0.2	-6
	20:17	2.9	88		20:46	3.4	104
9 F	02:39	0.2	6	**24** Sa ○	03:07	-0.2	-6
	08:41	2.2	67		09:13	2.7	82
	14:25	0.2	6		15:06	-0.2	-6
	20:57	2.9	88		21:37	3.3	101
10 Sa ●	03:16	0.2	6	**25** Su	03:56	-0.2	-6
	09:21	2.3	70		10:03	2.7	82
	15:06	0.2	6		15:59	-0.1	-3
	21:35	2.9	88		22:25	3.2	98
11 Su	03:53	0.1	3	**26** M	04:43	-0.1	-3
	10:00	2.4	73		10:51	2.8	85
	15:48	0.2	6		16:51	0.0	0
	22:14	2.9	88		23:11	3.1	94
12 M	04:32	0.1	3	**27** Tu	05:28	0.0	0
	10:40	2.4	73		11:38	2.8	85
	16:31	0.2	6		17:43	0.1	3
	22:53	2.9	88		23:55	2.8	85
13 Tu	05:11	0.1	3	**28** W	06:11	0.1	3
	11:21	2.5	76		12:25	2.7	82
	17:17	0.2	6		18:34	0.3	9
	23:34	2.8	85				
14 W	05:53	0.1	3	**29** Th	00:38	2.6	79
	12:06	2.6	79		06:53	0.2	6
	18:07	0.2	6		13:11	2.7	82
					19:27	0.4	12
15 Th	00:18	2.7	82	**30** F	01:23	2.4	73
	06:37	0.0	0		07:35	0.3	9
	12:54	2.7	82		13:58	2.7	82
	19:02	0.3	9		20:23	0.6	18
				31 Sa ◗	02:09	2.2	67
					08:19	0.5	15
					14:48	2.6	79
					21:20	0.6	18

August

Day	Time	ft	cm	Day	Time	ft	cm
1 Su	03:00	2.1	64	**16** M	02:41	2.4	73
	09:06	0.5	15		08:51	0.2	6
	15:40	2.6	79		15:27	3.1	94
	22:17	0.7	21		22:01	0.4	12
2 M	03:56	2.0	61	**17** Tu	03:50	2.3	70
	09:56	0.6	18		09:57	0.2	6
	16:35	2.6	79		16:35	3.2	98
	23:12	0.7	21		23:10	0.4	12
3 Tu	04:56	2.0	61	**18** W	05:04	2.4	73
	10:49	0.6	18		11:03	0.2	6
	17:29	2.7	82		17:44	3.2	98
4 W	00:02	0.6	18	**19** Th	00:13	0.3	9
	05:53	2.1	64		06:15	2.5	76
	11:40	0.5	15		12:08	0.2	6
	18:20	2.8	85		18:47	3.3	101
5 Th	00:47	0.5	15	**20** F	01:10	0.2	6
	06:44	2.2	67		07:16	2.6	79
	12:30	0.5	15		13:08	0.1	3
	19:07	2.9	88		19:43	3.3	101
6 F	01:28	0.4	12	**21** Sa	02:02	0.1	3
	07:30	2.3	70		08:10	2.8	85
	13:16	0.4	12		14:04	0.0	0
	19:50	2.9	88		20:34	3.3	101
7 Sa	02:08	0.3	9	**22** Su ○	02:49	0.0	0
	08:13	2.4	73		08:58	2.9	88
	14:01	0.3	9		14:55	0.0	0
	20:31	3.0	91		21:20	3.3	101
8 Su ●	02:46	0.2	6	**23** M	03:32	0.0	0
	08:54	2.6	79		09:43	3.0	91
	15:44	0.2	6		15:44	0.1	3
	21:11	3.1	94		22:02	3.2	98
9 M	03:24	0.1	3	**24** Tu	04:13	0.1	3
	09:34	2.7	82		10:25	3.0	91
	15:28	0.2	6		16:30	0.2	6
	21:50	3.1	94		22:42	3.0	91
10 Tu	04:03	0.1	3	**25** W	04:51	0.2	6
	10:15	2.8	85		11:06	3.0	91
	16:13	0.1	3		17:15	0.3	9
	22:30	3.0	91		23:20	2.8	85
11 W	04:43	0.0	0	**26** Th	05:28	0.3	9
	10:58	2.9	88		11:46	3.0	91
	17:01	0.2	6		18:00	0.4	12
	23:12	3.0	91		23:59	2.6	79
12 Th	05:24	0.0	0	**27** F	06:04	0.4	12
	11:43	3.0	91		12:26	2.9	88
	17:51	0.2	6		18:46	0.6	18
	23:56	2.8	85				
13 F	06:09	0.0	0	**28** Sa	00:39	2.5	76
	12:31	3.1	94		06:42	0.5	15
	18:46	0.3	9		12:53	2.8	85
					19:36	0.7	21
14 Sa	00:45	2.7	82	**29** Su	01:22	2.3	70
	06:57	0.1	3		07:25	0.7	21
	13:24	3.1	94		13:55	2.8	85
	19:47	0.4	12		20:29	0.8	24
15 Su ◐	01:39	2.5	76	**30** M ◐	02:11	2.2	67
	07:51	0.1	3		08:13	0.7	21
	14:22	3.1	94		14:47	2.7	82
	20:52	0.4	12		21:26	0.9	27
				31 Tu	03:08	2.1	64
					09:09	0.8	24
					15:45	2.7	82
					22:25	0.9	27

September

Day	Time	ft	cm	Day	Time	ft	cm
1 W	04:11	2.1	64	**16** Th	05:06	2.5	76
	10:08	0.8	24		11:01	0.4	12
	16:46	2.7	82		17:39	3.2	98
	23:19	0.8	24				
2 Th	05:14	2.2	67	**17** F	00:03	0.4	12
	11:06	0.7	21		06:13	2.7	82
	17:43	2.8	85		12:06	0.4	12
					18:40	3.2	98
3 F	00:08	0.7	21	**18** Sa	00:56	0.3	9
	06:09	2.3	70		07:09	2.8	85
	12:00	0.6	18		13:04	0.3	9
	18:34	2.9	88		19:31	3.2	98
4 Sa	00:52	0.5	15	**19** Su	01:42	0.2	6
	06:58	2.5	76		07:57	3.0	91
	12:50	0.5	15		13:55	0.2	6
	19:19	3.0	91		20:17	3.2	98
5 Su	01:32	0.4	12	**20** M ○	02:24	0.2	6
	07:42	2.7	82		08:40	3.1	94
	13:37	0.3	9		14:42	0.2	6
	20:02	3.1	94		20:57	3.2	98
6 M	02:12	0.2	6	**21** Tu	03:02	0.2	6
	08:25	2.9	88		09:19	3.2	98
	14:22	0.2	6		15:25	0.2	6
	20:43	3.2	98		21:35	3.1	94
7 Tu ●	02:51	0.1	3	**22** W	03:37	0.2	6
	09:07	3.1	94		09:56	3.2	98
	15:08	0.1	3		16:06	0.3	9
	21:24	3.2	98		22:10	2.9	88
8 W	03:31	0.0	0	**23** Th	04:11	0.3	9
	09:49	3.3	101		10:31	3.2	98
	15:55	0.1	3		16:46	0.4	12
	22:06	3.2	98		22:46	2.8	85
9 Th	04:12	0.0	0	**24** F	04:44	0.4	12
	10:33	3.4	104		11:07	3.2	98
	16:44	0.1	3		17:26	0.5	15
	22:49	3.1	94		23:22	2.6	79
10 F	04:56	0.0	0	**25** Sa	05:19	0.5	15
	11:20	3.4	104		11:44	3.1	94
	17:36	0.2	6		18:07	0.6	18
	23:36	2.9	88				
11 Sa	05:42	0.1	3	**26** Su	00:00	2.5	76
	12:10	3.4	104		05:56	0.6	18
	18:32	0.3	9		12:24	3.0	91
					18:51	0.8	24
12 Su	00:27	2.7	82	**27** M	00:42	2.3	70
	06:34	0.2	6		06:38	0.8	24
	13:04	3.4	104		13:09	2.8	85
	19:33	0.4	12		19:41	0.9	27
13 M ◐	01:25	2.6	79	**28** Tu	01:31	2.2	67
	07:32	0.3	9		07:28	0.9	27
	14:07	3.3	101		14:00	2.7	82
	20:41	0.5	15		20:37	0.9	27
14 Tu	02:31	2.5	76	**29** W ◑	02:27	2.2	67
	08:38	0.4	12		08:26	0.9	27
	15:15	3.2	98		14:58	2.7	82
	21:53	0.5	15		21:36	0.9	27
15 W	03:48	2.4	73	**30** Th	03:30	2.2	67
	09:45	0.5	15		09:29	0.9	27
	16:29	3.1	94		16:00	2.7	82
	23:01	0.5	15		22:34	0.8	24

StationId: 8638863
Source: NOAA/NOS/CO-OPS
Station Type: Primary
Time Zone: LST_LDT
Datum: MLLW

NOAA Tide Predictions

Chesapeake Bay Bridge Tunnel, VA, 2021

Times and Heights of High and Low Waters

October

Day	Time	ft	cm	Day	Time	ft	cm
1 F	04:34	2.3	70	**16** Sa	06:03	2.7	82
	10:32	0.8	24		12:00	0.4	12
	17:00	2.8	85		18:24	3.0	91
	23:25	0.7	21				
2 Sa	05:32	2.5	76	**17** Su	00:34	0.3	9
	11:29	0.7	21		06:54	2.9	88
	17:54	2.9	88		12:55	0.3	9
					19:12	3.0	91
3 Su	00:11	0.5	15	**18** M	01:16	0.2	6
	06:23	2.7	82		07:38	3.1	94
	12:22	0.5	15		13:42	0.3	9
	18:43	3.0	91		19:54	2.9	88
4 M	00:54	0.3	9	**19** Tu	01:54	0.2	6
	07:10	3.0	91		08:17	3.2	98
	13:12	0.3	9		14:25	0.3	9
	19:28	3.1	94		20:31	2.9	88
5 Tu	01:35	0.1	3	**20** W ○	02:28	0.2	6
	07:54	3.2	98		08:52	3.2	98
	14:00	0.1	3		15:05	0.3	9
	20:12	3.2	98		21:06	2.8	85
6 W ●	02:17	0.0	0	**21** Th	03:01	0.2	6
	08:39	3.5	107		09:26	3.2	98
	14:49	0.0	0		15:42	0.3	9
	20:57	3.2	98		21:40	2.7	82
7 Th	03:00	-0.1	-3	**22** F	03:33	0.3	9
	09:24	3.6	110		09:59	3.2	98
	15:38	0.0	0		16:19	0.4	12
	21:42	3.1	94		22:15	2.6	79
8 F	03:44	-0.2	-6	**23** Sa	04:06	0.4	12
	10:10	3.7	113		10:33	3.1	94
	16:28	0.0	0		16:55	0.4	12
	22:29	3.0	91		22:50	2.5	76
9 Sa	04:30	-0.1	-3	**24** Su	04:41	0.5	15
	10:59	3.7	113		11:10	3.0	91
	17:22	0.1	3		17:33	0.5	15
	23:19	2.9	88		23:29	2.3	70
10 Su	05:20	0.0	0	**25** M	05:19	0.6	18
	11:51	3.6	110		11:49	2.9	88
	18:19	0.2	6		18:15	0.6	18
11 M	00:14	2.7	82	**26** Tu	00:10	2.2	67
	06:16	0.2	6		06:02	0.7	21
	12:48	3.4	104		12:32	2.8	85
	19:21	0.4	12		19:01	0.7	21
12 Tu	01:15	2.5	76	**27** W	00:57	2.2	67
	07:18	0.4	12		06:51	0.8	24
	13:52	3.2	98		13:20	2.7	82
	20:30	0.5	15		19:54	0.8	24
13 W ◐	02:27	2.5	76	**28** Th ◐	01:51	2.1	64
	08:29	0.5	15		07:47	0.8	24
	15:04	3.1	94		14:15	2.6	79
	21:41	0.5	15		20:50	0.8	24
14 Th	03:47	2.5	76	**29** F	02:51	2.2	67
	09:45	0.5	15		08:51	0.8	24
	16:20	3.0	91		15:14	2.6	79
	22:48	0.5	15		21:47	0.7	21
15 F	05:02	2.6	79	**30** Sa	03:54	2.3	70
	10:58	0.5	15		09:56	0.7	21
	17:27	3.0	91		16:14	2.6	79
	23:45	0.4	12		22:39	0.5	15
				31 Su	04:53	2.5	76
					10:57	0.5	15
					17:11	2.7	82
					23:28	0.3	9

November

Day	Time	ft	cm	Day	Time	ft	cm
1 M	05:47	2.8	85	**16** Tu	06:13	2.9	88
	11:54	0.3	9		12:24	0.2	6
	18:04	2.8	85		18:26	2.5	76
2 Tu	00:14	0.1	3	**17** W	00:20	0.1	3
	06:37	3.1	94		06:50	3.0	91
	12:47	0.1	3		13:06	0.2	6
	18:54	2.9	88		19:03	2.4	73
3 W	01:00	-0.1	-3	**18** Th	00:54	0.1	3
	07:25	3.4	104		07:25	3.0	91
	13:39	-0.1	-3		13:43	0.2	6
	19:43	2.9	88		19:39	2.4	73
4 Th ●	01:45	-0.3	-9	**19** F ○	01:28	0.1	3
	08:13	3.6	110		07:59	3.0	91
	14:30	-0.2	-6		14:19	0.2	6
	20:32	2.9	88		20:14	2.3	70
5 F	02:32	-0.3	-9	**20** Sa	02:02	0.1	3
	09:01	3.7	113		08:32	3.0	91
	15:21	-0.2	-6		14:54	0.2	6
	21:21	2.9	88		20:49	2.3	70
6 Sa	03:20	-0.4	-12	**21** Su	02:37	0.2	6
	09:51	3.7	113		09:07	2.9	88
	16:14	-0.2	-6		15:29	0.3	9
	22:12	2.8	85		21:26	2.2	67
7 Su	03:10	-0.3	-9	**22** M	03:13	0.3	9
	09:42	3.7	113		09:43	2.8	85
	16:08	-0.1	-3		16:06	0.3	9
	22:05	2.7	82		22:04	2.1	64
8 M	04:03	-0.1	-3	**23** Tu	03:52	0.4	12
	10:36	3.5	107		10:22	2.7	82
	17:06	0.0	0		16:46	0.4	12
	23:03	2.6	79		22:45	2.1	64
9 Tu	05:02	0.0	0	**24** W	04:34	0.4	12
	11:34	3.3	101		11:03	2.6	79
	18:08	0.1	3		17:29	0.4	12
					23:29	2.0	61
10 W	00:06	2.4	73	**25** Th	05:21	0.5	15
	06:07	0.2	6		11:48	2.5	76
	12:38	3.0	91		18:17	0.4	12
	19:14	0.2	6				
11 Th ◐	01:18	2.4	73	**26** F	00:19	2.0	61
	07:19	0.4	12		06:15	0.5	15
	13:48	2.9	88		12:37	2.5	76
	20:21	0.3	9		19:08	0.4	12
12 F	02:34	2.4	73	**27** Sa	01:15	2.1	64
	08:34	0.4	12		07:16	0.5	15
	14:58	2.7	82		13:31	2.4	73
	21:22	0.3	9		20:01	0.3	9
13 Sa	03:43	2.5	76	**28** Su	02:14	2.2	67
	09:44	0.4	12		08:21	0.5	15
	16:02	2.6	79		14:29	2.4	73
	22:16	0.2	6		20:54	0.2	6
14 Su	04:42	2.7	82	**29** M	03:14	2.5	76
	10:45	0.4	12		09:25	0.3	9
	16:57	2.6	79		15:28	2.4	73
	23:02	0.2	6		21:46	0.0	0
15 M	05:31	2.8	85	**30** Tu	04:12	2.7	82
	11:38	0.3	9		10:26	0.1	3
	17:44	2.5	76		16:26	2.5	76
	23:43	0.1	3		22:37	-0.2	-6

December

Day	Time	ft	cm	Day	Time	ft	cm
1 W	05:07	3.0	91	**16** Th	06:22	2.7	82
	11:24	-0.1	-3		12:43	0.1	3
	17:23	2.5	76		18:35	2.0	61
	23:28	-0.4	-12				
2 Th	05:59	3.3	101	**17** F	00:23	0.0	0
	12:20	-0.2	-6		06:59	2.8	85
	18:17	2.6	79		13:21	0.1	3
					19:14	2.1	64
3 F	00:18	-0.5	-15	**18** Sa	01:00	0.0	0
	06:52	3.5	107		07:35	2.8	85
	13:14	-0.4	-12		13:57	0.0	0
	19:11	2.6	79		19:51	2.1	64
4 Sa ●	01:09	-0.6	-18	**19** Su ○	01:37	0.0	0
	07:43	3.6	110		08:11	2.8	85
	14:07	-0.4	-12		14:32	0.0	0
	20:05	2.6	79		20:28	2.1	64
5 Su	02:01	-0.6	-18	**20** M	02:15	0.0	0
	08:36	3.6	110		08:47	2.7	82
	15:00	-0.4	-12		15:07	0.0	0
	20:58	2.6	79		21:05	2.0	61
6 M	02:55	-0.5	-15	**21** Tu	02:52	0.0	0
	09:29	3.5	107		09:23	2.7	82
	15:49	-0.4	-12		15:43	0.1	3
	21:53	2.5	76		21:43	2.0	61
7 Tu	03:51	-0.4	-12	**22** W	03:31	0.1	3
	10:23	3.3	101		10:00	2.6	79
	16:51	-0.3	-9		16:21	0.1	3
	22:51	2.4	73		22:22	2.0	61
8 W	04:50	-0.2	-6	**23** Th	04:13	0.1	3
	11:19	3.0	91		10:39	2.5	76
	17:49	-0.1	-3		17:01	0.1	3
	23:52	2.3	70		23:05	2.0	61
9 Th	05:53	0.0	0	**24** F	04:58	0.2	6
	12:18	2.8	85		11:20	2.5	76
	18:49	0.0	0		17:44	0.1	3
					23:51	2.1	64
10 F	00:57	2.3	70	**25** Sa	05:49	0.2	6
	07:01	0.1	3		12:04	2.4	73
	13:19	2.6	79		18:30	0.0	0
	19:48	0.0	0				
11 Sa ◐	02:05	2.3	70	**26** Su	00:42	2.1	64
	08:11	0.2	6		06:47	0.2	6
	14:22	2.4	73		12:54	2.3	70
	20:44	0.1	3		19:20	0.0	0
12 Su	03:10	2.4	73	**27** M ◑	01:38	2.3	70
	09:19	0.3	9		07:50	0.2	6
	15:23	2.2	67		13:50	2.2	67
	21:36	0.1	3		20:13	-0.1	-3
13 M	04:08	2.5	76	**28** Tu	02:38	2.5	76
	10:20	0.3	9		08:56	0.1	3
	16:20	2.1	64		14:50	2.2	67
	22:23	0.1	3		21:08	-0.2	-6
14 Tu	04:59	2.6	79	**29** W	03:39	2.7	82
	11:14	0.2	6		10:02	0.0	0
	17:10	2.1	64		15:53	2.1	64
	23:05	0.0	0		22:05	-0.4	-12
15 W	05:43	2.6	79	**30** Th	04:40	2.9	88
	12:01	0.2	6		11:04	-0.2	-6
	17:54	2.0	61		16:57	2.2	67
	23:45	0.0	0		23:02	-0.5	-15
				31 F	05:39	3.1	94
					12:03	-0.3	-9
					17:58	2.2	67
					23:57	-0.5	-15

StationId: 8638610
Source: NOAA/NOS/CO-OPS
Station Type: Primary
Time Zone: LST_LDT
Datum: MLLW

NOAA Tide Predictions

Sewells Point, VA,2021

Times and Heights of High and Low Waters

January

Day	Time	Height (ft)	Height (cm)
1 F	04:00	-0.3	-9
	10:23	2.5	76
	16:51	-0.3	-9
	22:49	1.9	58
2 Sa	04:43	-0.3	-9
	11:04	2.5	76
	17:33	-0.3	-9
	23:34	2.0	61
3 Su	05:32	-0.3	-9
	11:50	2.4	73
	18:18	-0.3	-9
4 M	00:23	2.0	61
	06:27	-0.2	-6
	12:38	2.3	70
	19:07	-0.3	-9
5 Tu	01:14	2.1	64
	07:28	-0.1	-3
	13:28	2.2	67
	19:58	-0.3	-9
6 W ◗	02:08	2.1	64
	08:33	-0.1	-3
	14:23	2.0	61
	20:53	-0.3	-9
7 Th	03:10	2.2	67
	09:43	-0.1	-3
	15:26	1.9	58
	21:52	-0.3	-9
8 F	04:18	2.3	70
	10:52	-0.1	-3
	16:36	1.8	55
	22:53	-0.4	-12
9 Sa	05:25	2.4	73
	11:57	-0.2	-6
	17:42	1.8	55
	23:52	-0.5	-15
10 Su	06:26	2.6	79
	12:58	-0.3	-9
	18:44	1.9	58
11 M	00:51	-0.5	-15
	07:24	2.6	79
	13:56	-0.4	-12
	19:41	1.9	58
12 Tu	01:48	-0.6	-18
	08:19	2.7	82
	14:48	-0.5	-15
	20:36	2.0	61
13 W ●	02:42	-0.6	-18
	09:09	2.7	82
	15:35	-0.5	-15
	21:26	2.0	61
14 Th	03:31	-0.6	-18
	09:55	2.6	79
	16:19	-0.5	-15
	22:14	2.0	61
15 F	04:18	-0.5	-15
	10:39	2.5	76
	17:02	-0.4	-12
	23:01	2.0	61
16 Sa	05:05	-0.4	-12
	11:22	2.3	70
	17:44	-0.3	-9
	23:47	2.0	61
17 Su	05:54	-0.2	-6
	12:04	2.1	64
	18:26	-0.2	-6
18 M	00:33	1.9	58
	06:46	0.0	0
	12:46	2.0	61
	19:08	-0.1	-3
19 Tu	01:17	1.9	58
	07:38	0.1	3
	13:29	1.8	55
	19:49	-0.1	-3
20 W ◖	02:02	1.8	55
	08:33	0.2	6
	14:14	1.7	52
	20:32	0.0	0
21 Th	02:51	1.8	55
	09:31	0.2	6
	15:06	1.5	46
	21:19	0.0	0
22 F	03:48	1.8	55
	10:31	0.2	6
	16:07	1.5	46
	22:11	0.0	0
23 Sa	04:49	1.9	58
	11:27	0.2	6
	17:08	1.5	46
	23:03	0.0	0
24 Su	05:44	2.0	61
	12:18	0.1	3
	18:02	1.5	46
	23:54	-0.1	-3
25 M	06:33	2.1	64
	13:07	0.0	0
	18:51	1.6	49
26 Tu	00:44	-0.2	-6
	07:18	2.2	67
	13:52	-0.1	-3
	19:38	1.7	52
27 W	01:32	-0.3	-9
	08:02	2.3	70
	14:33	-0.2	-6
	20:22	1.8	55
28 Th ○	02:19	-0.4	-12
	08:43	2.4	73
	15:12	-0.3	-9
	21:04	1.9	58
29 F	03:03	-0.5	-15
	09:24	2.5	76
	15:49	-0.4	-12
	21:46	2.0	61
30 Sa	03:47	-0.5	-15
	10:04	2.5	76
	16:27	-0.5	-15
	22:29	2.1	64
31 Su	04:32	-0.5	-15
	10:47	2.5	76
	17:08	-0.5	-15
	23:14	2.2	67

February

Day	Time	Height (ft)	Height (cm)
1 M	05:21	-0.5	-15
	11:32	2.4	73
	17:51	-0.5	-15
2 Tu	00:02	2.3	70
	06:15	-0.4	-12
	12:19	2.3	70
	18:39	-0.5	-15
3 W	00:53	2.3	70
	07:15	-0.3	-9
	13:10	2.1	64
	19:30	-0.4	-12
4 Th ◐	01:47	2.3	70
	08:19	-0.2	-6
	14:04	1.9	58
	20:27	-0.3	-9
5 F	02:48	2.3	70
	09:28	-0.1	-3
	15:06	1.8	55
	21:29	-0.3	-9
6 Sa	03:59	2.3	70
	10:39	-0.1	-3
	16:19	1.7	52
	22:36	-0.3	-9
7 Su	05:14	2.3	70
	11:45	-0.1	-3
	17:31	1.7	52
	23:41	-0.3	-9
8 M	06:20	2.4	73
	12:47	-0.2	-6
	18:35	1.8	55
9 Tu	00:42	-0.4	-12
	07:18	2.5	76
	13:43	-0.2	-6
	19:33	1.9	58
10 W	01:40	-0.5	-15
	08:10	2.5	76
	14:32	-0.3	-9
	20:26	2.0	61
11 Th ●	02:33	-0.5	-15
	08:56	2.5	76
	15:16	-0.4	-12
	21:12	2.1	64
12 F	03:20	-0.5	-15
	09:37	2.5	76
	15:54	-0.4	-12
	21:55	2.2	67
13 Sa	04:03	-0.4	-12
	10:16	2.4	73
	16:31	-0.4	-12
	22:35	2.2	67
14 Su	04:44	-0.3	-9
	10:53	2.3	70
	17:06	-0.3	-9
	23:14	2.2	67
15 M	05:26	-0.2	-6
	11:31	2.2	67
	17:40	-0.2	-6
	23:53	2.1	64
16 Tu	06:09	0.0	0
	12:09	2.0	61
	18:16	-0.1	-3
17 W	00:32	2.1	64
	06:55	0.1	3
	12:49	1.9	58
	18:54	0.0	0
18 Th	01:12	2.0	61
	07:43	0.2	6
	13:31	1.7	52
	19:35	0.1	3
19 F ◐	01:55	2.0	61
	08:36	0.3	9
	14:17	1.6	49
	20:22	0.2	6
20 Sa	02:45	1.9	58
	09:36	0.4	12
	15:12	1.5	46
	21:17	0.2	6
21 Su	03:48	1.9	58
	10:39	0.4	12
	16:18	1.5	46
	22:19	0.2	6
22 M	04:56	2.0	61
	11:36	0.3	9
	17:22	1.6	49
	23:18	0.1	3
23 Tu	05:54	2.1	64
	12:27	0.2	6
	18:17	1.7	52
24 W	00:13	0.0	0
	06:45	2.3	70
	13:15	0.0	0
	19:06	1.9	58
25 Th	01:07	-0.2	-6
	07:33	2.4	73
	14:00	-0.1	-3
	19:53	2.1	64
26 F	01:58	-0.3	-9
	08:17	2.6	79
	14:41	-0.3	-9
	20:38	2.3	70
27 Sa ○	02:46	-0.5	-15
	09:01	2.7	82
	15:21	-0.4	-12
	21:22	2.4	73
28 Su	03:32	-0.5	-15
	09:44	2.7	82
	16:00	-0.5	-15
	22:06	2.6	79

March

Day	Time	Height (ft)	Height (cm)
1 M	04:19	-0.5	-15
	10:27	2.6	79
	16:41	-0.5	-15
	22:52	2.7	82
2 Tu	05:09	-0.5	-15
	11:13	2.5	76
	17:25	-0.4	-12
	23:41	2.7	82
3 W	06:03	-0.3	-9
	12:02	2.4	73
	18:14	-0.4	-12
4 Th	00:34	2.7	82
	07:03	-0.2	-6
	12:54	2.2	67
	19:08	-0.2	-6
5 F	01:29	2.6	79
	08:06	0.0	0
	13:49	2.0	61
	20:08	-0.1	-3
6 Sa ◗	02:31	2.5	76
	09:15	0.1	3
	14:52	1.9	58
	21:15	-0.1	-3
7 Su	03:45	2.4	73
	10:26	0.2	6
	16:08	1.9	58
	22:26	0.0	0
8 M	05:05	2.4	73
	11:32	0.2	6
	17:25	1.9	58
	23:34	-0.1	-3
9 Tu	06:12	2.4	73
	12:30	0.1	3
	18:28	2.1	64
10 W	00:35	-0.1	-3
	07:07	2.5	76
	13:23	0.0	0
	19:23	2.2	67
11 Th	01:32	-0.2	-6
	07:55	2.5	76
	14:09	-0.1	-3
	20:11	2.3	70
12 F	02:22	-0.2	-6
	08:37	2.5	76
	14:49	-0.1	-3
	20:53	2.4	73
13 Sa ●	03:05	-0.2	-6
	09:14	2.5	76
	15:24	-0.1	-3
	21:31	2.5	76
14 Su	04:45	-0.2	-6
	10:49	2.5	76
	16:57	-0.1	-3
	23:06	2.5	76
15 M	05:22	-0.1	-3
	11:24	2.4	73
	17:27	-0.1	-3
	23:40	2.5	76
16 Tu	05:58	0.0	0
	11:59	2.3	70
	17:58	0.0	0
17 W	00:14	2.4	73
	06:36	0.1	3
	12:36	2.2	67
	18:31	0.1	3
18 Th	00:51	2.4	73
	07:16	0.3	9
	13:15	2.1	64
	19:08	0.2	6
19 F	01:29	2.3	70
	08:00	0.4	12
	13:56	2.0	61
	19:50	0.3	9
20 Sa	02:11	2.2	67
	08:49	0.5	15
	14:40	1.9	58
	20:38	0.4	12
21 Su ◐	02:59	2.2	67
	09:45	0.6	18
	15:30	1.8	55
	21:34	0.4	12
22 M	03:56	2.1	64
	10:48	0.6	18
	16:32	1.8	55
	22:38	0.4	12
23 Tu	05:04	2.2	67
	11:50	0.5	15
	17:44	1.9	58
	23:44	0.3	9
24 W	06:11	2.3	70
	12:44	0.4	12
	18:40	2.0	61
25 Th	00:44	0.2	6
	07:08	2.4	73
	13:33	0.2	6
	19:33	2.3	70
26 F	01:41	0.0	0
	07:59	2.6	79
	14:20	0.0	0
	20:22	2.5	76
27 Sa	02:35	-0.2	-6
	08:47	2.7	82
	15:05	-0.1	-3
	21:10	2.7	82
28 Su ○	03:27	-0.3	-9
	09:35	2.8	85
	15:24	-0.3	-9
	21:56	2.9	88
29 M	04:16	-0.4	-12
	10:21	2.8	85
	16:31	-0.3	-9
	22:43	3.1	94
30 Tu	05:05	-0.4	-12
	11:07	2.8	85
	17:15	-0.3	-9
	23:31	3.1	94
31 W	05:56	-0.3	-9
	11:55	2.6	79
	18:01	-0.3	-9

StationId: 8638610
Source: NOAA/NOS/CO-OPS
Station Type: Primary
Time Zone: LST_LDT
Datum: MLLW

NOAA Tide Predictions

Sewells Point, VA,2021

Times and Heights of High and Low Waters

April

Day	Time (h m)	ft	cm	Day	Time (h m)	ft	cm
1 Th	00:22	3.1	94	16 F	00:16	2.6	79
	06:51	-0.2	-6		06:45	0.4	12
	12:46	2.5	76		12:47	2.2	67
	18:52	-0.2	-6		18:32	0.4	12
2 F	01:16	3.0	91	17 Sa	00:55	2.5	76
	07:51	0.0	0		07:27	0.5	15
	13:41	2.4	73		13:28	2.1	64
	19:51	0.0	0		19:15	0.5	15
3 Sa	02:15	2.8	85	18 Su	01:38	2.5	76
	08:54	0.2	6		08:14	0.6	18
	14:38	2.2	67		14:11	2.1	64
	20:55	0.1	3		20:06	0.5	15
4 Su	03:18	2.6	79	19 M	02:25	2.4	73
	10:01	0.3	9		09:06	0.6	18
	15:42	2.1	64		15:00	2.0	61
	22:05	0.2	6		21:02	0.6	18
5 M	04:32	2.5	76	20 Tu	03:18	2.4	73
	11:08	0.4	12		10:04	0.6	18
	17:00	2.1	64		15:56	2.1	64
	23:18	0.3	9		22:06	0.5	15
6 Tu	05:50	2.5	76	21 W	04:20	2.4	73
	12:11	0.4	12		11:03	0.5	15
	18:15	2.2	67		17:01	2.1	64
					23:14	0.4	12
7 W	00:25	0.2	6	22 Th	05:27	2.4	73
	06:54	2.5	76		11:59	0.4	12
	13:05	0.3	9		18:04	2.3	70
	19:14	2.3	70				
8 Th	01:24	0.2	6	23 F	00:17	0.3	9
	07:45	2.5	76		06:29	2.5	76
	13:53	0.2	6		12:50	0.3	9
	20:04	2.5	76		18:59	2.6	79
9 F	02:17	0.1	3	24 Sa	01:16	0.1	3
	08:29	2.5	76		07:24	2.6	79
	14:36	0.2	6		13:40	0.1	3
	20:48	2.6	79		19:51	2.8	85
10 Sa	03:04	0.1	3	25 Su	02:13	-0.1	-3
	09:10	2.5	76		08:16	2.7	82
	15:14	0.1	3		14:28	-0.1	-3
	21:27	2.7	82		20:41	3.1	94
11 Su	03:46	0.1	3	26 M	03:08	-0.2	-6
	09:46	2.5	76		09:08	2.8	85
	15:49	0.1	3		15:17	-0.2	-6
	22:02	2.7	82		21:31	3.2	98
12 M	04:24	0.1	3	27 Tu	04:00	-0.3	-9
	10:22	2.5	76		10:04	2.8	85
	16:21	0.1	3		16:04	-0.2	-6
	22:35	2.7	82		22:21	3.3	101
13 Tu	04:59	0.1	3	28 W	04:51	-0.3	-9
	10:56	2.4	73		10:48	2.7	82
	16:52	0.2	6		16:51	-0.2	-6
	23:07	2.7	82		23:12	3.3	101
14 W	05:33	0.2	6	29 Th	05:43	-0.2	-6
	11:31	2.4	73		11:39	2.6	79
	17:22	0.2	6		17:41	-0.2	-6
	23:41	2.7	82				
15 Th	06:07	0.3	9	30 F	00:05	3.2	98
	12:08	2.3	70		06:38	-0.1	-3
	17:55	0.3	9		12:32	2.5	76
					18:36	0.0	0

May

Day	Time (h m)	ft	cm	Day	Time (h m)	ft	cm
1 Sa	01:02	3.1	94	16 Su	00:29	2.6	79
	07:37	0.1	3		07:02	0.4	12
	13:29	2.4	73		13:04	2.2	67
	19:37	0.1	3		18:51	0.5	15
2 Su	02:01	2.9	88	17 M	01:12	2.5	76
	08:39	0.3	9		07:47	0.5	15
	14:28	2.3	70		13:49	2.1	64
	20:44	0.3	9		19:42	0.5	15
3 M	03:03	2.7	82	18 Tu	01:59	2.5	76
	09:41	0.4	12		08:36	0.5	15
	15:32	2.3	70		14:36	2.2	67
	21:54	0.4	12		20:39	0.5	15
4 Tu	04:10	2.5	76	19 W	02:49	2.5	76
	10:42	0.4	12		09:27	0.5	15
	16:44	2.3	70		15:28	2.2	67
	23:04	0.4	12		21:41	0.5	15
5 W	05:21	2.4	73	20 Th	03:45	2.4	73
	11:39	0.4	12		10:22	0.4	12
	17:54	2.4	73		16:27	2.4	73
					22:47	0.4	12
6 Th	00:08	0.4	12	21 F	04:48	2.4	73
	06:22	2.4	73		11:17	0.3	9
	12:30	0.4	12		17:29	2.5	76
	18:50	2.5	76		23:52	0.3	9
7 F	01:04	0.3	9	22 Sa	05:52	2.5	76
	07:12	2.4	73		12:11	0.2	6
	13:14	0.3	9		18:28	2.8	85
	19:36	2.6	79				
8 Sa	01:55	0.3	9	23 Su	00:53	0.1	3
	07:56	2.4	73		06:52	2.5	76
	13:55	0.3	9		13:03	0.0	0
	20:17	2.7	82		19:22	3.0	91
9 Su	02:41	0.2	6	24 M	01:52	-0.1	-3
	08:37	2.4	73		07:48	2.6	79
	14:34	0.3	9		13:55	-0.1	-3
	20:55	2.8	85		20:15	3.2	98
10 M	03:22	0.2	6	25 Tu	02:50	-0.2	-6
	09:16	2.4	73		08:43	2.6	79
	15:11	0.2	6		14:43	-0.2	-6
	21:31	2.8	85		21:09	3.3	101
11 Tu	04:00	0.2	6	26 W	03:45	-0.3	-9
	09:53	2.4	73		09:37	2.6	79
	15:46	0.2	6		15:41	-0.2	-6
	22:04	2.8	85		22:03	3.4	104
12 W	04:36	0.2	6	27 Th	04:37	-0.3	-9
	10:30	2.4	73		10:30	2.6	79
	16:20	0.3	9		16:32	-0.2	-6
	22:38	2.8	85		22:56	3.3	101
13 Th	05:10	0.2	6	28 F	05:29	-0.2	-6
	11:06	2.3	70		11:23	2.5	76
	16:53	0.3	9		17:25	-0.1	-3
	23:12	2.7	82		23:50	3.2	98
14 F	05:44	0.3	9	29 Sa	06:23	-0.1	-3
	11:43	2.3	70		12:18	2.5	76
	17:28	0.4	12		18:22	0.0	0
	23:49	2.7	82				
15 Sa	06:21	0.4	12	30 Su	00:47	3.0	91
	12:23	2.2	67		07:20	0.1	3
	18:06	0.4	12		13:16	2.4	73
					19:24	0.1	3
				31 M	01:44	2.8	85
					08:17	0.2	6
					14:15	2.4	73
					20:30	0.3	9

June

Day	Time (h m)	ft	cm	Day	Time (h m)	ft	cm
1 Tu	02:40	2.6	79	16 W	01:36	2.5	76
	09:13	0.3	9		08:07	0.3	9
	15:13	2.4	73		14:14	2.3	70
	21:35	0.4	12		20:21	0.4	12
2 W	03:37	2.4	73	17 Th	02:24	2.5	76
	10:07	0.3	9		08:55	0.2	6
	16:16	2.4	73		15:03	2.4	73
	22:40	0.4	12		21:21	0.4	12
3 Th	04:38	2.3	70	18 F	03:17	2.4	73
	10:58	0.4	12		09:46	0.2	6
	17:19	2.4	73		15:58	2.5	76
	23:42	0.4	12		22:26	0.3	9
4 F	05:39	2.2	67	19 Sa	04:16	2.4	73
	11:46	0.4	12		10:40	0.1	3
	18:14	2.5	76		16:59	2.7	82
					23:31	0.2	6
5 Sa	00:36	0.4	12	20 Su	05:21	2.3	70
	06:31	2.1	64		11:37	0.0	0
	12:30	0.3	9		18:01	2.8	85
	19:01	2.6	79				
6 Su	01:25	0.4	12	21 M	00:34	0.1	3
	07:18	2.1	64		06:24	2.3	70
	13:11	0.3	9		12:33	0.0	0
	19:42	2.6	79		18:59	3.0	91
7 M	02:11	0.3	9	22 Tu	01:35	0.0	0
	08:01	2.2	67		07:24	2.4	73
	13:52	0.3	9		13:29	-0.1	-3
	20:21	2.7	82		19:56	3.2	98
8 Tu	02:55	0.3	9	23 W	02:34	-0.1	-3
	08:43	2.2	67		08:22	2.4	73
	14:33	0.3	9		14:26	-0.2	-6
	20:59	2.7	82		20:53	3.2	98
9 W	03:35	0.2	6	24 Th	03:31	-0.2	-6
	09:25	2.2	67		09:20	2.4	73
	15:13	0.3	9		15:24	-0.2	-6
	21:36	2.7	82		21:49	3.2	98
10 Th	04:12	0.2	6	25 F	04:24	-0.2	-6
	10:04	2.2	67		10:15	2.5	76
	15:51	0.3	9		16:19	-0.2	-6
	22:13	2.7	82		22:43	3.2	98
11 F	04:48	0.2	6	26 Sa	05:14	-0.2	-6
	10:42	2.2	67		11:09	2.5	76
	16:29	0.3	9		17:12	-0.1	-3
	22:49	2.7	82		23:35	3.0	91
12 Sa	05:22	0.2	6	27 Su	06:04	-0.1	-3
	11:21	2.2	67		12:03	2.5	76
	17:07	0.3	9		18:07	0.0	0
	23:27	2.7	82				
13 Su	05:59	0.2	6	28 M	00:28	2.9	88
	12:01	2.2	67		06:55	0.0	0
	17:47	0.3	9		12:58	2.5	76
					19:06	0.1	3
14 M	00:07	2.6	79	29 Tu	01:20	2.7	82
	06:38	0.3	9		07:46	0.1	3
	12:43	2.2	67		13:52	2.4	73
	18:32	0.4	12		20:07	0.3	9
15 Tu	00:50	2.6	79	30 W	02:10	2.5	76
	07:21	0.3	9		08:35	0.2	6
	13:27	2.2	67		14:44	2.4	73
	19:24	0.4	12		21:08	0.4	12

StationId: 8638610
Source: NOAA/NOS/CO-OPS
Station Type: Primary
Time Zone: LST_LDT
Datum: MLLW

NOAA Tide Predictions

Sewells Point, VA, 2021

Times and Heights of High and Low Waters

July

Day	Time (h m)	Height ft	Height cm
1 Th ☽	02:59	2.3	70
	09:23	0.3	9
	15:36	2.4	73
	22:07	0.5	15
2 F	03:50	2.1	64
	10:09	0.3	9
	16:31	2.4	73
	23:06	0.5	15
3 Sa	04:46	2.0	61
	10:56	0.4	12
	17:27	2.4	73
4 Su	00:01	0.5	15
	05:45	2.0	61
	11:42	0.4	12
	18:18	2.5	76
5 M	00:51	0.5	15
	06:37	2.0	61
	12:27	0.4	12
	19:03	2.6	79
6 Tu	01:38	0.4	12
	07:25	2.0	61
	13:12	0.4	12
	19:46	2.6	79
7 W	02:24	0.3	9
	08:11	2.1	64
	13:57	0.3	9
	20:28	2.7	82
8 Th	03:07	0.3	9
	08:56	2.1	64
	14:43	0.3	9
	21:09	2.7	82
9 F	03:47	0.2	6
	09:38	2.2	67
	15:27	0.3	9
	21:49	2.7	82
10 Sa ●	04:23	0.2	6
	10:18	2.2	67
	16:08	0.2	6
	22:28	2.8	85
11 Su	04:59	0.2	6
	10:58	2.3	70
	16:49	0.2	6
	23:06	2.7	82
12 M	05:34	0.1	3
	11:38	2.3	70
	17:30	0.2	6
	23:46	2.7	82
13 Tu	06:12	0.1	3
	12:20	2.4	73
	18:16	0.3	9
14 W	00:28	2.7	82
	06:53	0.1	3
	13:04	2.5	76
	19:07	0.3	9
15 Th	01:14	2.6	79
	07:37	0.1	3
	13:51	2.6	79
	20:04	0.3	9
16 F	02:02	2.5	76
	08:24	0.1	3
	14:40	2.6	79
	21:04	0.3	9
17 Sa ◑	02:54	2.4	73
	09:15	0.1	3
	15:33	2.7	82
	22:08	0.3	9
18 Su	03:51	2.3	70
	10:11	0.1	3
	16:34	2.8	85
	23:15	0.3	9
19 M	04:56	2.3	70
	11:11	0.1	3
	17:40	2.9	88
20 Tu	00:20	0.2	6
	06:04	2.2	67
	12:12	0.1	3
	18:44	3.0	91
21 W	01:21	0.1	3
	07:08	2.3	70
	13:13	0.0	0
	19:44	3.1	94
22 Th	02:21	0.1	3
	08:09	2.4	73
	14:13	0.0	0
	20:42	3.2	98
23 F	03:17	0.0	0
	09:07	2.5	76
	15:13	-0.1	-3
	21:38	3.2	98
24 Sa ○	04:08	-0.1	-3
	10:02	2.6	79
	16:08	-0.1	-3
	22:29	3.1	94
25 Su	04:54	-0.1	-3
	10:54	2.6	79
	16:59	0.0	0
	23:17	3.0	91
26 M	05:39	0.0	0
	11:43	2.6	79
	17:50	0.1	3
27 Tu	00:03	2.8	85
	06:23	0.1	3
	12:32	2.6	79
	18:43	0.2	6
28 W	00:49	2.7	82
	07:07	0.2	6
	13:20	2.6	79
	19:37	0.4	12
29 Th	01:34	2.5	76
	07:50	0.3	9
	14:06	2.6	79
	20:32	0.5	15
30 F	02:18	2.3	70
	08:32	0.4	12
	14:50	2.5	76
	21:27	0.6	18
31 Sa ☽	03:04	2.2	67
	09:15	0.5	15
	15:37	2.5	76
	22:23	0.7	21

August

Day	Time (h m)	Height ft	Height cm
1 Su	03:55	2.1	64
	10:01	0.6	18
	16:30	2.5	76
	23:20	0.7	21
2 M	04:54	2.0	61
	10:52	0.6	18
	17:28	2.5	76
3 Tu	00:14	0.7	21
	05:56	2.0	61
	11:44	0.6	18
	18:23	2.6	79
4 W	01:03	0.6	18
	06:50	2.1	64
	12:36	0.6	18
	19:12	2.6	79
5 Th	01:50	0.5	15
	07:40	2.1	64
	13:26	0.5	15
	19:58	2.7	82
6 F	02:34	0.5	15
	08:26	2.3	70
	14:15	0.4	12
	20:42	2.8	85
7 Sa	03:16	0.4	12
	09:10	2.4	73
	15:03	0.3	9
	21:23	2.9	88
8 Su ●	03:54	0.3	9
	09:51	2.5	76
	15:43	0.3	9
	22:03	2.9	88
9 M	04:30	0.2	6
	10:31	2.6	79
	16:30	0.2	6
	22:43	2.9	88
10 Tu	05:05	0.1	3
	11:12	2.7	82
	17:14	0.2	6
	23:23	2.9	88
11 W	05:42	0.1	3
	11:54	2.8	85
	18:00	0.2	6
12 Th	00:06	2.9	88
	06:22	0.1	3
	12:39	2.9	88
	18:52	0.3	9
13 F	00:53	2.8	85
	07:07	0.1	3
	13:27	2.9	88
	19:49	0.4	12
14 Sa	01:42	2.6	79
	07:56	0.2	6
	14:18	3.0	91
	20:50	0.4	12
15 Su ◑	02:34	2.5	76
	08:26	0.2	6
	15:13	3.0	91
	21:55	0.5	15
16 M	03:32	2.4	73
	09:49	0.3	9
	16:16	3.0	91
	23:03	0.5	15
17 Tu	04:40	2.3	70
	10:55	0.3	9
	17:27	3.0	91
18 W	00:09	0.5	15
	05:54	2.3	70
	12:02	0.3	9
	18:36	3.1	94
19 Th	01:11	0.4	12
	07:01	2.4	73
	13:06	0.3	9
	19:38	3.1	94
20 F	02:08	0.3	9
	08:02	2.6	79
	14:07	0.2	6
	20:34	3.2	98
21 Sa	03:01	0.2	6
	08:58	2.7	82
	15:05	0.2	6
	21:25	3.2	98
22 Su ○	03:48	0.2	6
	09:49	2.8	85
	15:57	0.2	6
	22:11	3.1	94
23 M	04:30	0.1	3
	10:35	2.9	88
	16:45	0.2	6
	22:53	3.0	91
24 Tu	05:08	0.2	6
	11:18	2.9	88
	17:30	0.3	9
	23:34	2.9	88
25 W	05:45	0.3	9
	12:00	2.9	88
	18:15	0.4	12
26 Th	00:14	2.7	82
	06:22	0.4	12
	12:41	2.9	88
	19:02	0.6	18
27 F	00:56	2.6	79
	07:00	0.5	15
	13:22	2.8	85
	19:52	0.7	21
28 Sa	01:38	2.4	73
	07:39	0.6	18
	14:03	2.7	82
	20:42	0.8	24
29 Su	02:23	2.3	70
	08:22	0.7	21
	14:46	2.7	82
	21:36	0.9	27
30 M ☽	03:10	2.2	67
	09:09	0.8	24
	15:35	2.6	79
	22:34	0.9	27
31 Tu	04:06	2.1	64
	10:03	0.9	27
	16:33	2.6	79
	23:32	0.9	27

September

Day	Time (h m)	Height ft	Height cm
1 W	05:11	2.1	64
	11:03	0.9	27
	17:38	2.6	79
2 Th	00:25	0.9	27
	06:14	2.2	67
	12:02	0.8	24
	18:35	2.7	82
3 F	01:12	0.8	24
	07:07	2.3	70
	12:56	0.7	21
	19:25	2.8	85
4 Sa	01:56	0.6	18
	07:54	2.5	76
	13:48	0.6	18
	20:10	3.0	91
5 Su	02:38	0.5	15
	08:38	2.7	82
	14:38	0.5	15
	20:53	3.1	94
6 M	03:18	0.4	12
	09:21	2.9	88
	15:26	0.3	9
	21:35	3.1	94
7 Tu ●	03:56	0.3	9
	10:02	3.0	91
	16:12	0.3	9
	22:17	3.1	94
8 W	04:34	0.2	6
	10:44	3.2	98
	16:57	0.2	6
	22:59	3.1	94
9 Th	05:12	0.1	3
	11:27	3.3	101
	17:44	0.3	9
	23:44	3.0	91
10 F	05:53	0.2	6
	12:14	3.3	101
	18:36	0.3	9
11 Sa	00:32	2.9	88
	06:39	0.2	6
	13:04	3.3	101
	19:34	0.5	15
12 Su	01:24	2.7	82
	07:32	0.3	9
	13:59	3.3	101
	20:37	0.6	18
13 M ◑	02:19	2.6	79
	08:31	0.4	12
	15:07	3.2	98
	21:44	0.6	18
14 Tu	03:20	2.5	76
	09:36	0.5	15
	16:04	3.1	94
	22:53	0.7	21
15 W	04:32	2.4	73
	10:47	0.6	18
	17:20	3.1	94
	23:59	0.7	21
16 Th	05:51	2.5	76
	11:58	0.5	15
	18:31	3.1	94
17 F	00:57	0.6	18
	06:58	2.6	79
	13:02	0.5	15
	19:29	3.1	94
18 Sa	01:50	0.5	15
	07:55	2.8	85
	14:01	0.4	12
	20:20	3.1	94
19 Su	02:38	0.4	12
	08:46	3.0	91
	14:55	0.4	12
	21:06	3.1	94
20 M ○	03:21	0.3	9
	09:31	3.1	94
	15:44	0.4	12
	21:48	3.1	94
21 Tu	04:00	0.3	9
	10:12	3.1	94
	16:27	0.4	12
	22:26	3.0	91
22 W	04:35	0.3	9
	10:50	3.2	98
	17:08	0.5	15
	23:03	2.9	88
23 Th	05:08	0.4	12
	11:25	3.1	94
	17:47	0.6	18
	23:41	2.8	85
24 F	05:40	0.5	15
	12:01	3.1	94
	18:27	0.7	21
25 Sa	00:20	2.6	79
	06:13	0.6	18
	12:39	3.0	91
	19:11	0.8	24
26 Su	01:02	2.5	76
	06:51	0.8	24
	13:19	2.9	88
	19:59	0.9	27
27 M	01:46	2.4	73
	07:34	0.9	27
	14:02	2.8	85
	20:50	1.0	30
28 Tu	02:32	2.3	70
	08:23	1.0	30
	14:53	2.7	82
	21:46	1.0	30
29 W ☽	03:24	2.2	67
	09:20	1.0	30
	15:44	2.7	82
	22:45	1.0	30
30 Th	04:26	2.2	67
	10:23	1.0	30
	16:48	2.7	82
	23:41	1.0	30

StationId: 8638610
Source: NOAA/NOS/CO-OPS
Station Type: Primary
Time Zone: LST_LDT
Datum: MLLW

NOAA Tide Predictions

Sewells Point, VA, 2021

Times and Heights of High and Low Waters

October

Day	Time	ft	cm
1 F	05:34	2.3	70
	11:28	0.9	27
	17:52	2.8	85
2 Sa	00:30	0.8	24
	06:31	2.5	76
	12:27	0.8	24
	18:46	2.9	88
3 Su	01:14	0.7	21
	07:20	2.7	82
	13:21	0.6	18
	19:34	3.0	91
4 M	01:57	0.5	15
	08:05	2.9	88
	14:13	0.5	15
	20:20	3.1	94
5 Tu	02:39	0.3	9
	08:49	3.1	94
	15:04	0.3	9
	21:06	3.1	94
6 W ●	03:21	0.2	6
	09:33	3.3	101
	15:52	0.2	6
	21:51	3.1	94
7 Th	04:02	0.1	3
	10:18	3.5	107
	16:40	0.2	6
	22:36	3.1	94
8 F	04:44	0.1	3
	11:03	3.6	110
	17:29	0.2	6
	23:23	3.0	91
9 Sa	05:28	0.1	3
	11:52	3.5	107
	18:22	0.3	9
10 Su	00:14	2.8	85
	06:17	0.2	6
	12:46	3.5	107
	19:21	0.4	12
11 M	01:08	2.7	82
	07:13	0.4	12
	13:43	3.3	101
	20:25	0.6	18
12 Tu	02:07	2.6	79
	08:18	0.5	15
	14:45	3.2	98
	21:31	0.6	18
13 W ◐	03:11	2.5	76
	09:28	0.6	18
	15:53	3.0	91
	22:39	0.7	21
14 Th	04:26	2.5	76
	10:42	0.6	18
	17:09	2.9	88
	23:42	0.6	18
15 F	05:45	2.6	79
	11:53	0.6	18
	18:18	2.9	88
16 Sa	00:37	0.6	18
	06:49	2.7	82
	12:55	0.6	18
	19:13	2.9	88
17 Su	01:25	0.5	15
	07:42	2.9	88
	13:51	0.5	15
	20:00	2.9	88
18 M	02:10	0.4	12
	08:28	3.0	91
	14:42	0.4	12
	20:42	2.9	88
19 Tu	02:50	0.3	9
	09:09	3.1	94
	15:27	0.4	12
	21:22	2.8	85
20 W ○	03:27	0.3	9
	09:46	3.1	94
	16:08	0.4	12
	21:59	2.8	85
21 Th	04:01	0.3	9
	10:20	3.1	94
	16:45	0.4	12
	22:35	2.7	82
22 F	04:33	0.4	12
	10:54	3.1	94
	17:21	0.5	15
	23:12	2.6	79
23 Sa	05:05	0.5	15
	11:27	3.0	91
	17:57	0.6	18
	23:50	2.5	76
24 Su	05:37	0.6	18
	12:03	2.9	88
	18:37	0.7	21
25 M	00:30	2.4	73
	06:13	0.7	21
	12:42	2.8	85
	19:20	0.8	24
26 Tu	01:13	2.3	70
	06:56	0.8	24
	13:25	2.7	82
	20:09	0.8	24
27 W	02:00	2.2	67
	07:46	0.8	24
	14:12	2.7	82
	21:01	0.9	27
28 Th ◐	02:49	2.2	67
	08:43	0.9	27
	15:02	2.6	79
	21:55	0.9	27
29 F	03:45	2.2	67
	09:46	0.9	27
	16:00	2.6	79
	22:51	0.8	24
30 Sa	04:49	2.3	70
	10:53	0.8	24
	17:04	2.6	79
	23:42	0.6	18
31 Su	05:50	2.5	76
	11:56	0.7	21
	18:04	2.7	82

November

Day	Time	ft	cm
1 M	00:30	0.5	15
	06:43	2.7	82
	12:53	0.5	15
	18:57	2.8	85
2 Tu	01:15	0.3	9
	07:31	2.9	88
	13:48	0.3	9
	19:47	2.8	85
3 W	02:01	0.1	3
	08:18	3.2	98
	14:42	0.1	3
	20:37	2.9	88
4 Th ●	02:47	0.0	0
	09:06	3.4	104
	15:34	0.0	0
	21:26	2.9	88
5 F	03:34	-0.1	-3
	09:55	3.5	107
	16:24	-0.1	-3
	22:15	2.8	85
6 Sa	04:21	-0.2	-6
	10:44	3.5	107
	17:15	0.0	0
	23:05	2.7	82
7 Su	04:08	-0.1	-3
	10:35	3.5	107
	17:08	0.1	3
	22:58	2.6	79
8 M	05:00	0.0	0
	11:31	3.3	101
	18:07	0.2	6
	23:55	2.5	76
9 Tu	06:00	0.1	3
	12:30	3.1	94
	19:10	0.3	9
10 W	00:56	2.4	73
	07:07	0.3	9
	13:31	2.9	88
	20:13	0.4	12
11 Th ◑	02:01	2.4	73
	08:18	0.4	12
	14:35	2.7	82
	21:15	0.4	12
12 F	03:13	2.4	73
	09:30	0.5	15
	15:45	2.6	79
	22:14	0.4	12
13 Sa	04:28	2.4	73
	10:40	0.5	15
	16:51	2.5	76
	23:07	0.3	9
14 Su	05:30	2.6	79
	11:40	0.4	12
	17:46	2.5	76
	23:53	0.3	9
15 M	06:20	2.7	82
	12:34	0.4	12
	18:32	2.4	73
16 Tu	00:36	0.2	6
	07:04	2.8	85
	13:23	0.3	9
	19:14	2.4	73
17 W	01:16	0.2	6
	07:43	2.9	88
	14:07	0.3	9
	19:54	2.4	73
18 Th	01:54	0.2	6
	08:19	2.9	88
	14:47	0.2	6
	20:33	2.4	73
19 F ○	02:30	0.2	6
	08:54	2.9	88
	15:24	0.2	6
	21:11	2.3	70
20 Sa	03:04	0.2	6
	09:27	2.8	85
	15:59	0.2	6
	21:48	2.3	70
21 Su	03:38	0.2	6
	10:01	2.8	85
	16:33	0.3	9
	22:25	2.2	67
22 M	04:11	0.3	9
	10:37	2.7	82
	17:10	0.4	12
	23:04	2.1	64
23 Tu	04:48	0.3	9
	11:15	2.6	79
	17:50	0.4	12
	23:46	2.0	61
24 W	05:29	0.4	12
	11:56	2.5	76
	18:34	0.5	15
25 Th	00:31	2.0	61
	06:17	0.5	15
	12:41	2.5	76
	19:21	0.5	15
26 F	01:18	2.0	61
	07:13	0.5	15
	13:28	2.4	73
	20:09	0.4	12
27 Sa ◑	02:09	2.0	61
	08:54	0.5	15
	14:19	2.3	70
	21:01	0.3	9
28 Su	03:05	2.1	64
	09:19	0.5	15
	15:18	2.3	70
	21:54	0.2	6
29 M	04:07	2.3	70
	10:25	0.3	9
	16:21	2.3	70
	22:46	0.1	3
30 Tu	05:06	2.5	76
	11:27	0.2	6
	17:21	2.3	70
	23:37	-0.1	-3

December

Day	Time	ft	cm
1 W	06:00	2.8	85
	12:25	0.0	0
	18:17	2.4	73
2 Th	00:27	-0.2	-6
	06:52	3.0	91
	13:22	-0.2	-6
	19:11	2.4	73
3 F	01:19	-0.4	-12
	07:44	3.1	94
	14:18	-0.3	-9
	20:05	2.4	73
4 Sa ●	02:11	-0.4	-12
	08:37	3.2	98
	15:11	-0.4	-12
	20:58	2.4	73
5 Su	03:03	-0.5	-15
	09:29	3.2	98
	16:02	-0.3	-9
	21:51	2.4	73
6 M	03:55	-0.5	-15
	10:22	3.2	98
	16:55	-0.3	-9
	22:45	2.3	70
7 Tu	04:48	-0.4	-12
	11:17	3.0	91
	17:50	-0.2	-6
	23:42	2.2	67
8 W	05:48	-0.2	-6
	12:14	2.8	85
	18:48	-0.1	-3
9 Th	00:42	2.2	67
	06:53	0.0	0
	13:11	2.6	79
	19:45	0.0	0
10 F	01:43	2.1	64
	08:00	0.1	3
	14:07	2.3	70
	20:41	0.0	0
11 Sa ◑	02:47	2.1	64
	09:09	0.2	6
	15:07	2.1	64
	21:36	0.1	3
12 Su	03:55	2.2	67
	10:16	0.2	6
	16:10	2.0	61
	22:27	0.1	3
13 M	04:59	2.2	67
	11:16	0.2	6
	17:09	1.9	58
	23:15	0.0	0
14 Tu	05:51	2.3	70
	12:10	0.2	6
	17:59	1.9	58
	23:59	0.0	0
15 W	06:35	2.4	73
	12:58	0.1	3
	18:44	1.9	58
16 Th	00:41	0.0	0
	07:15	2.4	73
	13:44	0.1	3
	19:27	1.9	58
17 F	01:22	-0.1	-3
	07:54	2.5	76
	14:25	0.0	0
	20:09	1.9	58
18 Sa	02:02	-0.1	-3
	08:31	2.5	76
	15:03	0.0	0
	20:49	1.9	58
19 Su ○	02:40	-0.1	-3
	09:06	2.5	76
	15:38	-0.1	-3
	21:27	1.9	58
20 M	03:17	-0.1	-3
	09:41	2.5	76
	16:12	-0.1	-3
	22:04	1.9	58
21 Tu	03:53	-0.1	-3
	10:16	2.4	73
	16:47	0.0	0
	22:42	1.9	58
22 W	04:30	0.0	0
	10:53	2.4	73
	17:23	0.0	0
	23:22	1.9	58
23 Th	05:10	0.0	0
	11:32	2.3	70
	18:02	0.0	0
24 F	00:05	1.9	58
	05:56	0.1	3
	12:14	2.2	67
	18:44	0.0	0
25 Sa	00:49	1.9	58
	06:48	0.1	3
	12:58	2.2	67
	19:29	-0.1	-3
26 Su	01:36	1.9	58
	07:46	0.1	3
	13:46	2.1	64
	20:17	-0.1	-3
27 M ◑	02:28	2.0	61
	08:52	0.1	3
	14:41	2.0	61
	21:10	-0.2	-6
28 Tu	03:27	2.2	67
	09:56	0.0	0
	15:43	1.9	58
	22:06	-0.2	-6
29 W	04:31	2.3	70
	11:03	-0.1	-3
	16:49	1.9	58
	23:04	-0.4	-12
30 Th	05:33	2.5	76
	12:05	-0.2	-6
	17:52	2.0	61
31 F	00:01	-0.5	-15
	06:31	2.7	82
	13:06	-0.3	-9
	18:51	2.0	61

StationId: 8651370
Source: NOAA/NOS/CO-OPS
Station Type: Primary
Time Zone: LST_LDT
Datum: MLLW

NOAA Tide Predictions

Duck, NC, 2021

Times and Heights of High and Low Waters

January

Day	Time (h m)	Height (ft)	Height (cm)
1 F	02:14	-0.1	-3
	08:38	3.7	113
	15:10	-0.2	-6
	21:04	2.8	85
2 Sa	03:00	-0.1	-3
	09:20	3.7	113
	15:52	-0.2	-6
	21:50	2.9	88
3 Su	03:49	0.0	0
	10:05	3.6	110
	16:36	-0.2	-6
	22:40	2.9	88
4 M	04:43	0.0	0
	10:54	3.4	104
	17:23	-0.2	-6
	23:34	3.1	94
5 Tu	05:42	0.1	3
	11:47	3.2	98
	18:14	-0.2	-6
6 W ◑	00:33	3.2	98
	06:47	0.1	3
	12:44	3.0	91
	19:08	-0.2	-6
7 Th	01:35	3.4	104
	07:56	0.1	3
	13:46	2.8	85
	20:06	-0.3	-9
8 F	02:38	3.6	110
	09:06	0.0	0
	14:51	2.7	82
	21:05	-0.3	-9
9 Sa	03:40	3.8	116
	10:12	-0.1	-3
	15:56	2.7	82
	22:04	-0.4	-12
10 Su	04:39	4.0	122
	11:13	-0.3	-9
	16:58	2.8	85
	23:02	-0.5	-15
11 M	05:35	4.1	125
	12:08	-0.4	-12
	17:55	2.9	88
	23:57	-0.6	-18
12 Tu	06:28	4.1	125
	13:00	-0.5	-15
	18:48	3.0	91
13 W ●	00:50	-0.6	-18
	07:17	4.1	125
	13:48	-0.5	-15
	19:38	3.0	91
14 Th	01:41	-0.5	-15
	08:04	4.0	122
	14:33	-0.4	-12
	20:26	3.0	91
15 F	02:30	-0.4	-12
	08:49	3.8	116
	15:17	-0.4	-12
	21:13	3.0	91
16 Sa	03:17	-0.2	-6
	09:33	3.6	110
	15:59	-0.2	-6
	21:59	2.9	88
17 Su	04:05	0.0	0
	10:15	3.3	101
	16:39	-0.1	-3
	22:45	2.9	88
18 M	04:54	0.2	6
	10:58	3.0	91
	17:20	0.0	0
	23:33	2.8	85
19 Tu	05:46	0.4	12
	11:42	2.7	82
	18:01	0.2	6
20 W ◐	00:23	2.8	85
	06:42	0.6	18
	12:30	2.5	76
	18:45	0.3	9
21 Th	01:17	2.8	85
	07:44	0.7	21
	13:22	2.3	70
	19:32	0.3	9
22 F	02:13	2.9	88
	08:48	0.7	21
	14:20	2.2	67
	20:24	0.3	9
23 Sa	03:08	2.9	88
	09:48	0.6	18
	15:19	2.2	67
	21:16	0.3	9
24 Su	04:00	3.1	94
	10:39	0.4	12
	16:15	2.3	70
	22:08	0.2	6
25 M	04:48	3.2	98
	11:24	0.3	9
	17:05	2.4	73
	22:57	0.0	0
26 Tu	05:32	3.4	104
	12:06	0.1	3
	17:51	2.6	79
	23:44	-0.1	-3
27 W	06:15	3.6	110
	12:46	-0.1	-3
	18:35	2.7	82
28 Th ○	00:29	-0.2	-6
	06:56	3.7	113
	13:25	-0.2	-6
	19:18	2.9	88
29 F	01:14	-0.4	-12
	07:37	3.8	116
	14:04	-0.4	-12
	20:01	3.0	91
30 Sa	02:00	-0.4	-12
	08:19	3.8	116
	14:45	-0.4	-12
	20:45	3.2	98
31 Su	02:47	-0.4	-12
	09:02	3.7	113
	15:26	-0.5	-15
	21:31	3.3	101

February

Day	Time (h m)	Height (ft)	Height (cm)
1 M	03:37	-0.4	-12
	09:46	3.6	110
	16:09	-0.5	-15
	22:19	3.4	104
2 Tu	04:30	-0.3	-9
	10:34	3.4	104
	16:55	-0.4	-12
	23:12	3.4	104
3 W	05:28	-0.1	-3
	11:25	3.1	94
	17:45	-0.3	-9
4 Th ◑	00:09	3.5	107
	06:31	0.0	0
	12:22	2.8	85
	18:41	-0.2	-6
5 F	01:11	3.5	107
	07:41	0.1	3
	13:26	2.6	79
	19:42	-0.2	-6
6 Sa	02:18	3.5	107
	08:54	0.1	3
	14:36	2.5	76
	20:48	-0.2	-6
7 Su	03:27	3.6	110
	10:03	0.0	0
	15:47	2.6	79
	21:54	-0.2	-6
8 M	04:31	3.7	113
	11:05	-0.1	-3
	16:52	2.7	82
	22:56	-0.3	-9
9 Tu	05:28	3.8	116
	11:59	-0.2	-6
	17:49	2.8	85
	23:52	-0.4	-12
10 W	06:19	3.8	116
	12:46	-0.3	-9
	18:39	3.0	91
11 Th ●	00:43	-0.4	-12
	07:05	3.8	116
	13:30	-0.4	-12
	19:24	3.1	94
12 F	01:30	-0.4	-12
	07:47	3.8	116
	14:09	-0.3	-9
	20:06	3.2	98
13 Sa	02:14	-0.3	-9
	08:27	3.6	110
	14:46	-0.3	-9
	20:46	3.2	98
14 Su	02:56	-0.2	-6
	09:04	3.4	104
	15:21	-0.2	-6
	21:25	3.2	98
15 M	03:37	0.0	0
	09:41	3.2	98
	15:55	-0.1	-3
	22:05	3.1	94
16 Tu	04:19	0.2	6
	10:18	2.9	88
	16:29	0.1	3
	22:45	3.0	91
17 W	05:02	0.4	12
	10:58	2.7	82
	17:07	0.2	6
	23:29	3.0	91
18 Th	05:50	0.6	18
	11:42	2.5	76
	17:49	0.3	9
19 F ◐	00:18	2.9	88
	06:44	0.7	21
	12:31	2.3	70
	18:37	0.4	12
20 Sa	01:12	2.9	88
	07:46	0.7	21
	13:29	2.2	67
	19:32	0.5	15
21 Su	02:12	2.9	88
	08:52	0.7	21
	14:33	2.2	67
	20:32	0.4	12
22 M	03:13	3.0	91
	09:53	0.6	18
	15:36	2.3	70
	21:32	0.3	9
23 Tu	04:10	3.2	98
	10:45	0.4	12
	16:32	2.5	76
	22:28	0.1	3
24 W	05:01	3.4	104
	11:31	0.1	3
	17:22	2.7	82
	23:20	-0.1	-3
25 Th	05:47	3.6	110
	12:13	-0.1	-3
	18:09	3.0	91
26 F	00:09	-0.3	-9
	06:31	3.8	116
	12:54	-0.3	-9
	18:53	3.3	101
27 Sa ○	00:57	-0.5	-15
	07:14	3.9	119
	13:35	-0.5	-15
	19:38	3.5	107
28 Su	01:45	-0.6	-18
	07:58	3.9	119
	14:16	-0.6	-18
	20:23	3.7	113

March

Day	Time (h m)	Height (ft)	Height (cm)
1 M	02:34	-0.6	-18
	08:42	3.8	116
	14:58	-0.6	-18
	21:09	3.9	119
2 Tu	03:24	-0.6	-18
	09:28	3.6	110
	15:42	-0.6	-18
	21:58	3.9	119
3 W	04:17	-0.4	-12
	10:16	3.4	104
	16:30	-0.4	-12
	22:50	3.8	116
4 Th	05:14	-0.2	-6
	11:08	3.1	94
	17:21	-0.3	-9
	23:47	3.7	113
5 F	06:17	0.0	0
	12:07	2.8	85
	18:20	-0.1	-3
6 Sa ◑	00:51	3.6	110
	07:27	0.2	6
	13:14	2.6	79
	19:26	0.1	3
7 Su	02:02	3.5	107
	08:42	0.2	6
	14:29	2.6	79
	20:39	0.1	3
8 M	03:16	3.5	107
	09:52	0.2	6
	15:45	2.7	82
	21:51	0.1	3
9 Tu	04:22	3.5	107
	10:52	0.1	3
	16:49	2.8	85
	22:54	0.0	0
10 W	05:19	3.6	110
	11:42	0.0	0
	17:41	3.0	91
	23:48	-0.1	-3
11 Th	06:07	3.6	110
	12:26	-0.1	-3
	18:26	3.2	98
12 F	00:35	-0.2	-6
	06:49	3.6	110
	13:04	-0.1	-3
	19:06	3.3	101
13 Sa ●	01:18	-0.2	-6
	07:26	3.5	107
	13:38	-0.2	-6
	19:42	3.4	104
14 Su	01:57	-0.2	-6
	09:01	3.4	104
	15:10	-0.1	-3
	21:17	3.5	107
15 M	03:35	-0.1	-3
	09:35	3.3	101
	15:41	-0.1	-3
	21:52	3.5	107
16 Tu	04:11	0.0	0
	10:10	3.1	94
	16:13	0.0	0
	22:27	3.4	104
17 W	04:48	0.2	6
	10:45	2.9	88
	16:47	0.2	6
	23:05	3.3	101
18 Th	05:27	0.4	12
	11:23	2.7	82
	17:23	0.3	9
	23:45	3.2	98
19 F	06:10	0.5	15
	12:05	2.5	76
	18:05	0.5	15
20 Sa	00:30	3.1	94
	06:59	0.7	21
	12:53	2.4	73
	18:53	0.6	18
21 Su ◐	01:22	3.0	91
	07:55	0.7	21
	13:49	2.3	70
	19:50	0.6	18
22 M	02:21	3.0	91
	08:59	0.7	21
	14:52	2.4	73
	20:53	0.6	18
23 Tu	03:25	3.0	91
	10:02	0.6	18
	15:57	2.5	76
	21:58	0.5	15
24 W	04:27	3.2	98
	10:59	0.4	12
	16:57	2.7	82
	22:59	0.2	6
25 Th	05:23	3.4	104
	11:49	0.2	6
	17:50	3.1	94
	23:55	0.0	0
26 F	06:14	3.6	110
	12:35	-0.1	-3
	18:39	3.4	104
27 Sa	00:48	-0.3	-9
	06:59	3.8	116
	13:19	-0.3	-9
	19:26	3.8	116
28 Su ○	01:39	-0.5	-15
	07:49	3.9	119
	14:02	-0.5	-15
	20:13	4.1	125
29 M	02:29	-0.7	-21
	08:35	3.8	116
	14:46	-0.6	-18
	21:00	4.3	131
30 Tu	03:20	-0.7	-21
	09:22	3.7	113
	15:30	-0.6	-18
	21:48	4.4	134
31 W	04:11	-0.6	-18
	10:10	3.6	110
	16:17	-0.5	-15
	22:38	4.3	131

StationId: 8651370
Source: NOAA/NOS/CO-OPS
Station Type: Primary
Time Zone: LST_LDT
Datum: MLLW

NOAA Tide Predictions

Duck, NC, 2021

Times and Heights of High and Low Waters

April

Day	Time	ft	cm
1 Th	05:05	-0.5	-15
	11:00	3.3	101
	17:08	-0.4	-12
	23:31	4.1	125
2 F	06:02	-0.2	-6
	11:55	3.1	94
	18:03	-0.1	-3
3 Sa	00:29	3.9	119
	07:04	0.0	0
	12:56	2.9	88
	19:05	0.1	3
4 Su ◑	01:34	3.6	110
	08:12	0.2	6
	14:06	2.7	82
	20:16	0.3	9
5 M	02:46	3.4	104
	09:24	0.3	9
	15:25	2.7	82
	21:33	0.3	9
6 Tu	04:00	3.3	101
	10:31	0.3	9
	16:37	2.9	88
	22:45	0.3	9
7 W	05:05	3.3	101
	11:28	0.2	6
	17:36	3.0	91
	23:46	0.2	6
8 Th	06:00	3.3	101
	12:15	0.2	6
	18:24	3.2	98
9 F	00:37	0.1	3
	06:45	3.3	101
	12:55	0.1	3
	19:05	3.4	104
10 Sa	01:22	0.0	0
	07:25	3.3	101
	13:30	0.0	0
	19:41	3.5	107
11 Su	02:02	0.0	0
	08:00	3.3	101
	14:02	0.0	0
	20:15	3.6	110
12 M ●	02:38	0.0	0
	08:12	3.2	98
	14:33	0.1	3
	20:47	3.7	113
13 Tu	03:13	0.0	0
	09:07	3.1	94
	15:04	0.1	3
	21:21	3.7	113
14 W	03:47	0.1	3
	09:42	3.0	91
	15:36	0.2	6
	21:55	3.6	110
15 Th	04:22	0.2	6
	10:17	2.8	85
	16:11	0.3	9
	22:31	3.5	107
16 F	05:00	0.3	9
	10:56	2.7	82
	16:49	0.4	12
	23:11	3.4	104
17 Sa	05:40	0.5	15
	11:37	2.6	79
	17:32	0.5	15
	23:54	3.2	98
18 Su	06:26	0.6	18
	12:24	2.5	76
	18:20	0.6	18
19 M	00:44	3.1	94
	07:19	0.6	18
	13:18	2.5	76
	19:17	0.7	21
20 Tu ◐	01:40	3.1	94
	08:17	0.6	18
	14:19	2.6	79
	20:20	0.6	18
21 W	02:42	3.1	94
	09:16	0.5	15
	15:22	2.7	82
	21:26	0.5	15
22 Th	03:44	3.2	98
	10:13	0.3	9
	16:22	3.0	91
	22:31	0.3	9
23 F	04:44	3.3	101
	11:05	0.1	3
	17:18	3.4	104
	23:31	0.0	0
24 Sa	05:39	3.5	107
	11:55	-0.2	-6
	18:10	3.8	116
25 Su	00:27	-0.3	-9
	06:32	3.6	110
	12:42	-0.4	-12
	18:59	4.2	128
26 M	01:21	-0.6	-18
	07:22	3.6	110
	13:29	-0.6	-18
	19:48	4.5	137
27 Tu ○	02:13	-0.7	-21
	08:12	3.6	110
	14:17	-0.6	-18
	20:38	4.6	140
28 W	03:05	-0.7	-21
	09:02	3.6	110
	15:06	-0.6	-18
	21:28	4.6	140
29 Th	03:58	-0.7	-21
	09:53	3.4	104
	15:56	-0.5	-15
	22:19	4.5	137
30 F	04:52	-0.5	-15
	10:47	3.3	101
	16:50	-0.3	-9
	23:14	4.2	128

May

Day	Time	ft	cm
1 Sa	05:49	-0.3	-9
	11:44	3.1	94
	17:48	0.0	0
2 Su	00:12	3.9	119
	06:49	0.0	0
	12:47	3.0	91
	18:53	0.2	6
3 M ◐	01:15	3.6	110
	07:53	0.1	3
	13:56	2.9	88
	20:05	0.4	12
4 Tu	02:23	3.3	101
	08:58	0.3	9
	15:09	2.9	88
	21:20	0.5	15
5 W	03:32	3.2	98
	09:58	0.3	9
	16:15	3.0	91
	22:29	0.4	12
6 Th	04:35	3.1	94
	10:51	0.3	9
	17:11	3.2	98
	23:28	0.4	12
7 F	05:28	3.0	91
	11:36	0.2	6
	17:56	3.3	101
8 Sa	00:19	0.3	9
	06:13	3.0	91
	12:15	0.2	6
	18:36	3.5	107
9 Su	01:03	0.2	6
	06:53	3.0	91
	12:50	0.2	6
	19:11	3.6	110
10 M	01:42	0.1	3
	07:30	2.9	88
	13:23	0.2	6
	19:45	3.7	113
11 Tu ●	02:18	0.1	3
	08:06	2.9	88
	13:56	0.2	6
	20:18	3.7	113
12 W	02:52	0.1	3
	08:41	2.9	88
	14:30	0.2	6
	20:53	3.7	113
13 Th	03:26	0.1	3
	09:18	2.8	85
	15:06	0.3	9
	21:28	3.7	113
14 F	04:01	0.2	6
	09:55	2.7	82
	15:43	0.3	9
	22:05	3.6	110
15 Sa	04:38	0.2	6
	10:34	2.7	82
	16:23	0.4	12
	22:44	3.5	107
16 Su	05:18	0.3	9
	11:16	2.6	79
	17:07	0.5	15
	23:27	3.4	104
17 M	06:02	0.4	12
	12:03	2.6	79
	17:56	0.6	18
18 Tu	00:15	3.3	101
	06:50	0.4	12
	12:55	2.6	79
	18:52	0.6	18
19 W ◐	01:08	3.2	98
	07:42	0.3	9
	13:51	2.8	85
	19:54	0.5	15
20 Th	02:05	3.2	98
	08:36	0.3	9
	14:51	3.0	91
	20:59	0.4	12
21 F	03:06	3.2	98
	09:31	0.1	3
	15:50	3.3	101
	22:05	0.2	6
22 Sa	04:06	3.2	98
	10:24	-0.1	-3
	16:47	3.7	113
	23:08	0.0	0
23 Su	05:05	3.2	98
	11:17	-0.3	-9
	17:41	4.1	125
24 M	00:07	-0.3	-9
	06:02	3.3	101
	12:09	-0.4	-12
	18:34	4.4	134
25 Tu	01:04	-0.5	-15
	06:57	3.3	101
	13:00	-0.6	-18
	19:26	4.6	140
26 W ○	01:58	-0.6	-18
	07:51	3.4	104
	13:52	-0.6	-18
	20:18	4.7	143
27 Th	02:52	-0.7	-21
	08:41	3.3	101
	14:45	-0.6	-18
	21:10	4.6	140
28 F	03:45	-0.6	-18
	09:39	3.3	101
	15:39	-0.4	-12
	22:03	4.4	134
29 Sa	04:38	-0.5	-15
	10:34	3.2	98
	16:35	-0.2	-6
	22:57	4.2	128
30 Su	05:32	-0.3	-9
	11:31	3.1	94
	17:34	0.0	0
	23:53	3.8	116
31 M	06:28	-0.1	-3
	12:31	3.0	91
	18:37	0.2	6

June

Day	Time	ft	cm
1 Tu	00:51	3.5	107
	07:24	0.0	0
	13:35	3.0	91
	19:44	0.4	12
2 W ○	01:51	3.2	98
	08:21	0.2	6
	14:40	3.0	91
	20:54	0.5	15
3 Th	02:52	3.0	91
	09:14	0.2	6
	15:40	3.1	94
	22:01	0.5	15
4 F	03:50	2.8	85
	10:03	0.3	9
	16:33	3.2	98
	23:00	0.5	15
5 Sa	04:44	2.7	82
	10:47	0.3	9
	17:20	3.3	101
	23:52	0.4	12
6 Su	05:33	2.6	79
	11:28	0.3	9
	18:00	3.5	107
7 M	00:37	0.3	9
	06:17	2.6	79
	12:06	0.3	9
	18:38	3.6	110
8 Tu	01:17	0.3	9
	06:58	2.6	79
	12:44	0.2	6
	19:15	3.6	110
9 W	01:54	0.2	6
	07:38	2.7	82
	13:23	0.2	6
	19:51	3.7	113
10 Th ●	02:30	0.1	3
	08:17	2.7	82
	14:01	0.2	6
	20:28	3.7	113
11 F	03:05	0.1	3
	08:56	2.7	82
	14:41	0.3	9
	21:05	3.7	113
12 Sa	03:41	0.1	3
	09:35	2.7	82
	15:21	0.3	9
	21:43	3.6	110
13 Su	04:19	0.1	3
	10:15	2.7	82
	16:03	0.3	9
	22:23	3.6	110
14 M	04:58	0.1	3
	10:57	2.7	82
	16:48	0.4	12
	23:05	3.5	107
15 Tu	05:39	0.1	3
	11:43	2.8	85
	17:38	0.4	12
	23:51	3.4	104
16 W	06:24	0.1	3
	12:32	2.9	88
	18:32	0.4	12
17 Th	00:41	3.3	101
	07:11	0.1	3
	13:26	3.1	94
	19:32	0.4	12
18 F ◐	01:35	3.2	98
	08:01	0.0	0
	14:23	3.3	101
	20:37	0.3	9
19 Sa	02:33	3.1	94
	08:54	-0.1	-3
	15:21	3.6	110
	21:43	0.2	6
20 Su	03:34	3.0	91
	09:49	-0.2	-6
	16:20	3.9	119
	22:48	0.0	0
21 M	04:36	3.0	91
	10:45	-0.3	-9
	17:17	4.2	128
	23:50	-0.2	-6
22 Tu	05:38	3.0	91
	11:42	-0.4	-12
	18:14	4.4	134
23 W	00:49	-0.4	-12
	06:37	3.1	94
	12:38	-0.5	-15
	19:09	4.5	137
24 Th ○	01:44	-0.5	-15
	07:34	3.2	98
	13:34	-0.5	-15
	20:03	4.6	140
25 F	02:38	-0.5	-15
	08:30	3.2	98
	14:29	-0.5	-15
	20:55	4.5	137
26 Sa	03:30	-0.5	-15
	09:24	3.3	101
	15:25	-0.3	-9
	21:47	4.3	131
27 Su	04:20	-0.4	-12
	10:18	3.3	101
	16:20	-0.2	-6
	22:38	4.0	122
28 M	05:10	-0.3	-9
	11:12	3.2	98
	17:16	0.0	0
	23:29	3.7	113
29 Tu	05:59	-0.2	-6
	12:07	3.2	98
	18:14	0.3	9
30 W	00:20	3.4	104
	06:47	0.0	0
	13:02	3.1	94
	19:15	0.5	15

StationId: 8651370
Source: NOAA/NOS/CO-OPS
Station Type: Primary
Time Zone: LST_LDT
Datum: MLLW

NOAA Tide Predictions

Duck, NC,2021

Times and Heights of High and Low Waters

July

Day	Time (h m)	ft	cm	Day	Time (h m)	ft	cm
1 Th ◐	01:11	3.1	94	**16** F	00:17	3.3	101
	07:35	0.2	6		06:41	0.0	0
	13:58	3.1	94		13:01	3.5	107
	20:18	0.6	18		19:15	0.3	9
2 F	02:04	2.8	85	**17** Sa	01:10	3.2	98
	08:21	0.3	9		07:31	0.0	0
	14:53	3.2	98		13:58	3.7	113
	21:22	0.7	21	◑	20:19	0.3	9
3 Sa	02:58	2.6	79	**18** Su	02:08	3.0	91
	09:07	0.4	12		08:25	-0.1	-3
	15:46	3.2	98		14:57	3.8	116
	22:23	0.7	21		21:26	0.3	9
4 Su	03:53	2.5	76	**19** M	03:10	2.9	88
	09:53	0.4	12		09:23	-0.1	-3
	16:35	3.3	101		15:59	4.0	122
	23:17	0.6	18		22:33	0.2	6
5 M	04:47	2.5	76	**20** Tu	04:16	2.9	88
	10:39	0.4	12		10:23	-0.1	-3
	17:21	3.4	104		17:00	4.2	128
					23:37	0.0	0
6 Tu	00:05	0.5	15	**21** W	05:21	2.9	88
	05:38	2.5	76		11:25	-0.2	-6
	11:25	0.4	12		17:59	4.3	131
	18:04	3.5	107				
7 W	00:48	0.4	12	**22** Th	00:36	-0.1	-3
	06:25	2.5	76		06:23	3.1	94
	12:10	0.4	12		12:25	-0.2	-6
	18:45	3.6	110		18:56	4.4	134
8 Th	01:27	0.3	9	**23** F	01:31	-0.3	-9
	07:10	2.6	79		07:21	3.2	98
	12:53	0.3	9		13:22	-0.3	-9
	19:25	3.7	113		19:50	4.4	134
9 F	02:04	0.2	6	**24** Sa ○	02:22	-0.3	-9
	07:52	2.7	82		08:16	3.3	101
	13:36	0.3	9		14:18	-0.3	-9
	20:04	3.7	113		20:40	4.3	131
10 Sa ●	02:41	0.1	3	**25** Su	03:10	-0.3	-9
	08:32	2.8	85		09:07	3.4	104
	14:19	0.2	6		15:11	-0.2	-6
	20:43	3.8	116		21:28	4.2	128
11 Su	03:17	0.1	3	**26** M	03:56	-0.3	-9
	09:13	2.9	88		09:57	3.4	104
	15:01	0.2	6		16:02	0.0	0
	21:22	3.8	116		22:15	3.9	119
12 M	03:55	0.0	0	**27** Tu	04:40	-0.2	-6
	09:54	3.0	91		10:45	3.4	104
	15:45	0.2	6		16:53	0.1	3
	22:02	3.7	113		22:59	3.7	113
13 Tu	04:33	0.0	0	**28** W	05:22	0.0	0
	10:36	3.0	91		11:33	3.4	104
	16:32	0.2	6		17:45	0.4	12
	22:44	3.6	110		23:43	3.4	104
14 W	05:13	0.0	0	**29** Th	06:03	0.1	3
	11:21	3.2	98		12:21	3.4	104
	17:21	0.3	9		18:38	0.6	18
	23:29	3.5	107				
15 Th	05:56	0.0	0	**30** F	00:28	3.1	94
	12:09	3.3	101		06:44	0.3	9
	18:16	0.3	9		13:09	3.3	101
					19:34	0.7	21
				31 Sa ◑	01:15	2.8	85
					07:26	0.4	12
					14:00	3.3	101
					20:34	0.9	27

August

Day	Time (h m)	ft	cm	Day	Time (h m)	ft	cm
1 Su	02:07	2.6	79	**16** M	01:50	3.0	91
	08:12	0.6	18		08:03	0.2	6
	14:53	3.3	101		14:38	4.0	122
	21:36	0.9	27		21:14	0.4	12
2 M	03:03	2.5	76	**17** Tu	02:56	2.9	88
	09:02	0.6	18		09:06	0.2	6
	15:47	3.3	101		15:44	4.1	125
	22:35	0.9	27		22:23	0.4	12
3 Tu	04:02	2.5	76	**18** W	04:06	2.9	88
	09:54	0.6	18		10:12	0.2	6
	16:39	3.4	104		16:49	4.1	125
	23:27	0.8	24		23:27	0.3	9
4 W	05:00	2.5	76	**19** Th	05:15	3.0	91
	10:48	0.6	18		11:18	0.1	3
	17:29	3.5	107		17:50	4.2	128
5 Th	00:13	0.6	18	**20** F	00:25	0.1	3
	05:53	2.6	79		06:16	3.2	98
	11:39	0.5	15		12:19	0.0	0
	18:15	3.6	110		18:46	4.3	131
6 F	00:54	0.5	15	**21** Sa	01:16	0.0	0
	06:40	2.8	85		07:11	3.4	104
	12:27	0.4	12		13:15	0.0	0
	18:57	3.8	116		19:36	4.3	131
7 Sa	01:32	0.3	9	**22** Su ○	02:02	-0.1	-3
	07:24	2.9	88		08:01	3.6	110
	13:13	0.3	9		14:07	0.0	0
	19:38	3.9	119		20:22	4.2	128
8 Su ●	02:10	0.2	6	**23** M	02:45	-0.1	-3
	08:05	3.1	94		08:47	3.7	113
	13:57	0.2	6		14:55	0.0	0
	20:18	3.9	119		21:05	4.0	122
9 M	02:47	0.1	3	**24** Tu	03:25	0.0	0
	08:47	3.3	101		09:30	3.7	113
	14:42	0.1	3		15:42	0.2	6
	20:59	4.0	122		21:46	3.8	116
10 Tu	03:24	0.0	0	**25** W	04:03	0.1	3
	09:28	3.4	104		10:12	3.7	113
	15:28	0.1	3		16:27	0.3	9
	21:40	3.9	119		22:26	3.6	110
11 W	04:03	-0.1	-3	**26** Th	04:39	0.2	6
	10:11	3.6	110		10:54	3.7	113
	16:16	0.1	3		17:12	0.5	15
	22:22	3.8	116		23:06	3.3	101
12 Th	04:44	-0.1	-3	**27** F	05:16	0.4	12
	10:57	3.7	113		11:36	3.6	110
	17:06	0.2	6		17:59	0.7	21
	23:07	3.6	110		23:47	3.1	94
13 F	05:27	-0.1	-3	**28** Sa	05:54	0.5	15
	11:45	3.8	116		12:20	3.5	107
	18:01	0.3	9		18:48	0.9	27
	23:56	3.4	104				
14 Sa	06:13	0.0	0	**29** Su	00:31	2.8	85
	12:38	3.9	119		06:35	0.7	21
	19:00	0.4	12		13:07	3.4	104
					19:42	1.0	30
15 Su ◑	00:50	3.2	98	**30** M ◑	01:22	2.7	82
	07:05	0.1	3		07:22	0.8	24
	13:36	4.0	122		14:00	3.4	104
	20:05	0.4	12		20:43	1.1	34
				31 Tu	02:19	2.6	79
					08:16	0.9	27
					14:57	3.3	101
					21:45	1.1	34

September

Day	Time (h m)	ft	cm	Day	Time (h m)	ft	cm
1 W	03:22	2.6	79	**16** Th	04:06	3.1	94
	09:15	0.9	27		10:11	0.5	15
	15:56	3.4	104		16:42	4.0	122
	22:42	1.0	30		23:16	0.4	12
2 Th	04:24	2.7	82	**17** F	05:13	3.3	101
	10:14	0.8	24		11:17	0.4	12
	16:51	3.5	107		17:41	4.1	125
	23:31	0.8	24				
3 F	05:19	2.8	85	**18** Sa	00:09	0.3	9
	11:09	0.7	21		06:10	3.5	107
	17:40	3.7	113		12:16	0.3	9
					18:33	4.1	125
4 Sa	00:14	0.6	18	**19** Su	00:55	0.2	6
	06:08	3.1	94		06:59	3.7	113
	12:01	0.5	15		13:08	0.2	6
	18:25	3.9	119		19:19	4.0	122
5 Su	00:54	0.4	12	**20** M ○	01:36	0.1	3
	06:52	3.3	101		07:42	3.8	116
	12:49	0.3	9		13:55	0.2	6
	19:08	4.0	122		20:00	4.0	122
6 M	01:32	0.2	6	**21** Tu	02:14	0.1	3
	07:35	3.6	110		08:23	3.9	119
	13:36	0.2	6		14:38	0.2	6
	19:50	4.1	125		20:39	3.8	116
7 Tu ●	02:11	0.0	0	**22** W	02:49	0.2	6
	08:17	3.8	116		09:00	4.0	122
	14:22	0.1	3		15:20	0.3	9
	20:32	4.1	125		21:16	3.6	110
8 W	02:50	-0.1	-3	**23** Th	03:22	0.3	9
	09:01	4.0	122		09:37	4.0	122
	15:10	0.0	0		16:00	0.5	15
	21:15	4.0	122		21:52	3.4	104
9 Th	03:31	-0.1	-3	**24** F	03:56	0.4	12
	09:45	4.2	128		10:15	3.9	119
	15:59	0.0	0		16:40	0.6	18
	22:00	3.9	119		22:30	3.2	98
10 F	04:14	-0.1	-3	**25** Sa	04:31	0.5	15
	10:32	4.3	131		10:53	3.8	116
	16:51	0.1	3		17:21	0.8	24
	22:47	3.7	113		23:10	3.0	91
11 Sa	04:59	0.0	0	**26** Su	05:09	0.7	21
	11:22	4.3	131		11:35	3.7	113
	17:47	0.2	6		18:06	0.9	27
	23:39	3.4	104		23:54	2.9	88
12 Su	05:49	0.1	3	**27** M	05:51	0.9	27
	12:17	4.3	131		12:21	3.5	107
	18:48	0.4	12		18:57	1.1	34
13 M ◑	00:35	3.2	98	**28** Tu	00:44	2.7	82
	06:45	0.3	9		06:40	1.0	30
	13:42	4.2	128		13:13	3.4	104
	19:54	0.5	15		19:54	1.1	34
14 Tu	01:40	3.1	94	**29** W ◑	01:41	2.7	82
	07:49	0.4	12		07:36	1.1	34
	14:24	4.1	125		14:10	3.4	104
	21:05	0.6	18		20:55	1.1	34
15 W	02:52	3.0	91	**30** Th	02:45	2.7	82
	08:59	0.5	15		08:38	1.1	34
	15:35	4.0	122		15:11	3.4	104
	22:14	0.5	15		21:53	1.0	30

StationId: 8651370
Source: NOAA/NOS/CO-OPS
Station Type: Primary
Time Zone: LST_LDT
Datum: MLLW

NOAA Tide Predictions

Duck, NC, 2021

Times and Heights of High and Low Waters

October

Day	Time (h m)	Height (ft)	Height (cm)	Day	Time (h m)	Height (ft)	Height (cm)
1 F	03:48	2.8	85	16 Sa	05:07	3.4	104
	09:41	1.0	30		11:14	0.5	15
	16:09	3.5	107		17:26	3.8	116
	22:44	0.8	24		23:45	0.3	9
2 Sa	04:44	3.1	94	17 Su	05:58	3.6	110
	10:39	0.8	24		12:09	0.4	12
	17:01	3.7	113		18:14	3.7	113
	23:29	0.6	18				
3 Su	05:34	3.4	104	18 M	00:28	0.2	6
	11:34	0.5	15		06:41	3.8	116
	17:49	3.8	116		12:57	0.3	9
					18:56	3.7	113
4 M	00:12	0.3	9	19 Tu	01:05	0.2	6
	06:20	3.7	113		07:20	3.9	119
	12:24	0.3	9		13:40	0.3	9
	18:35	4.0	122		19:34	3.6	110
5 Tu	00:53	0.1	3	20 W	01:39	0.2	6
	07:04	4.0	122		07:56	4.0	122
	13:14	0.1	3		14:20	0.3	9
	19:20	4.1	125	○	20:11	3.5	107
6 W	01:34	-0.1	-3	21 Th	02:12	0.3	9
	07:48	4.3	131		08:30	4.1	125
●	14:03	-0.1	-3		14:58	0.4	12
	20:05	4.0	122		20:46	3.3	101
7 Th	02:16	-0.2	-6	22 F	02:44	0.3	9
	08:34	4.6	140		09:05	4.0	122
	14:53	-0.2	-6		15:34	0.5	15
	20:51	4.0	122		21:22	3.2	98
8 F	03:00	-0.2	-6	23 Sa	03:18	0.4	12
	09:20	4.7	143		09:41	3.9	119
	15:44	-0.1	-3		16:11	0.6	18
	21:39	3.8	116		21:59	3.0	91
9 Sa	03:46	-0.2	-6	24 Su	03:53	0.6	18
	10:10	4.7	143		10:18	3.8	116
	16:37	0.0	0		16:50	0.7	21
	22:29	3.6	110		22:39	2.9	88
10 Su	04:36	0.0	0	25 M	04:32	0.7	21
	11:02	4.6	140		10:58	3.7	113
	17:34	0.1	3		17:32	0.8	24
	23:24	3.4	104		23:23	2.8	85
11 M	05:30	0.2	6	26 Tu	05:15	0.8	24
	11:59	4.4	134		11:43	3.5	107
	18:36	0.3	9		18:19	0.9	27
12 Tu	00:25	3.2	98	27 W	00:12	2.7	82
	06:20	0.4	12		06:04	1.0	30
	13:02	4.2	128		12:32	3.4	104
	19:43	0.5	15		19:12	0.9	27
13 W	01:34	3.1	94	28 Th	01:08	2.6	79
	07:41	0.5	15		07:00	1.0	30
	14:12	4.0	122		13:27	3.3	101
◑	20:53	0.5	15	◑	20:08	0.9	27
14 Th	02:51	3.1	94	29 F	02:09	2.7	82
	08:56	0.6	18		08:03	1.0	30
	15:23	3.8	116		14:25	3.3	101
	21:59	0.5	15		21:04	0.8	24
15 F	04:05	3.2	98	30 Sa	03:10	2.9	88
	10:09	0.6	18		09:07	0.9	27
	16:29	3.8	116		15:24	3.4	104
	22:56	0.4	12		21:56	0.6	18
				31 Su	04:07	3.2	98
					10:09	0.7	21
					16:20	3.5	107
					22:44	0.3	9

November

Day	Time (h m)	Height (ft)	Height (cm)	Day	Time (h m)	Height (ft)	Height (cm)
1 M	04:59	3.5	107	16 Tu	05:18	3.7	113
	11:06	0.4	12		11:42	0.3	9
	17:12	3.6	110		17:30	3.2	98
	23:30	0.1	3		23:31	0.2	6
2 Tu	05:47	3.9	119	17 W	05:55	3.8	116
	12:01	0.1	3		12:23	0.3	9
	18:02	3.7	113		18:08	3.1	94
3 W	00:15	-0.1	-3	18 Th	00:05	0.2	6
	06:35	4.3	131		06:30	3.9	119
	12:53	-0.1	-3		13:01	0.3	9
	18:51	3.8	116		18:44	3.0	91
4 Th	01:00	-0.3	-9	19 F	00:38	0.2	6
	07:04	4.6	140		07:04	3.9	119
	13:45	-0.3	-9		13:37	0.3	9
●	19:40	3.8	116	○	19:20	3.0	91
5 F	01:46	-0.4	-12	20 Sa	01:12	0.2	6
	08:10	4.8	146		07:38	3.9	119
	14:36	-0.4	-12		14:12	0.3	9
	20:30	3.7	113		19:57	2.9	88
6 Sa	02:34	-0.4	-12	21 Su	01:48	0.3	9
	08:59	4.8	146		08:35	3.8	116
	15:29	-0.4	-12		14:48	0.4	12
	21:21	3.6	110		20:35	2.8	85
7 Su	02:24	-0.3	-9	22 M	02:25	0.4	12
	08:51	4.8	146		08:51	3.7	113
	15:23	-0.2	-6		15:25	0.4	12
	21:14	3.4	104		21:15	2.7	82
8 M	03:17	-0.2	-6	23 Tu	03:05	0.5	15
	09:45	4.5	137		09:30	3.6	110
	16:20	-0.1	-3		16:05	0.5	15
	22:11	3.3	101		21:58	2.6	79
9 Tu	04:15	0.0	0	24 W	03:48	0.6	18
	10:43	4.3	131		10:12	3.4	104
	17:21	0.1	3		16:49	0.6	18
	23:15	3.1	94		22:45	2.6	79
10 W	05:19	0.3	9	25 Th	04:36	0.7	21
	11:46	4.0	122		10:58	3.3	101
	18:25	0.2	6		17:36	0.6	18
					23:37	2.6	79
11 Th	00:25	3.1	94	26 F	05:30	0.8	24
	06:31	0.5	15		11:48	3.2	98
	12:53	3.7	113		18:26	0.5	15
◐	19:31	0.3	9				
12 F	01:40	3.1	94	27 Sa	00:33	2.7	82
	07:47	0.5	15		06:30	0.8	24
	14:02	3.5	107		12:43	3.2	98
	20:32	0.3	9	◑	19:18	0.4	12
13 Sa	02:49	3.2	98	28 Su	01:32	2.9	88
	08:59	0.5	15		07:34	0.7	21
	15:05	3.4	104		13:41	3.2	98
	21:27	0.3	9		20:10	0.3	9
14 Su	03:48	3.4	104	29 M	02:29	3.2	98
	10:01	0.5	15		08:38	0.5	15
	16:00	3.3	101		14:39	3.2	98
	22:14	0.2	6		21:01	0.0	0
15 M	04:36	3.6	110	30 Tu	03:24	3.6	110
	10:55	0.4	12		09:40	0.2	6
	16:48	3.2	98		15:36	3.2	98
	22:54	0.2	6		21:51	-0.2	-6

December

Day	Time (h m)	Height (ft)	Height (cm)	Day	Time (h m)	Height (ft)	Height (cm)
1 W	04:17	4.0	122	16 Th	05:29	3.6	110
	10:39	-0.1	-3		12:04	0.2	6
	16:32	3.3	101		17:42	2.6	79
	22:41	-0.4	-12		23:33	0.1	3
2 Th	05:08	4.3	131	17 F	06:05	3.6	110
	11:34	-0.3	-9		12:42	0.2	6
	17:26	3.3	101		18:21	2.6	79
	23:32	-0.6	-18				
3 F	06:00	4.6	140	18 Sa	00:10	0.1	3
	12:28	-0.5	-15		06:41	3.6	110
	18:19	3.4	104		13:17	0.1	3
					18:59	2.7	82
4 Sa	00:22	-0.6	-18	19 Su	00:47	0.1	3
	06:51	4.7	143		07:17	3.6	110
	13:22	-0.6	-18		13:52	0.1	3
●	19:12	3.4	104	○	19:37	2.7	82
5 Su	01:14	-0.7	-21	20 M	01:25	0.1	3
	07:43	4.7	143		07:53	3.6	110
	14:15	-0.6	-18		14:27	0.1	3
	20:05	3.3	101		20:15	2.6	79
6 M	02:08	-0.6	-18	21 Tu	02:04	0.2	6
	08:35	4.6	140		08:29	3.6	110
	15:08	-0.5	-15		15:03	0.1	3
	21:00	3.3	101		20:54	2.6	79
7 Tu	03:03	-0.4	-12	22 W	02:44	0.2	6
	09:29	4.3	131		09:07	3.5	107
	16:03	-0.4	-12		15:40	0.2	6
	21:57	3.2	98		21:36	2.6	79
8 W	04:02	-0.2	-6	23 Th	03:27	0.3	9
	10:25	4.0	122		09:47	3.4	104
	17:00	-0.2	-6		16:20	0.2	6
	22:59	3.1	94		22:19	2.6	79
9 Th	05:04	0.1	3	24 F	04:13	0.4	12
	11:23	3.7	113		10:29	3.3	101
	17:58	-0.1	-3		17:02	0.2	6
					23:07	2.7	82
10 F	00:04	3.0	91	25 Sa	05:04	0.4	12
	06:12	0.3	9		11:15	3.1	94
	12:24	3.4	104		17:47	0.1	3
	18:57	0.0	0		23:59	2.8	85
11 Sa	01:13	3.0	91	26 Su	06:02	0.4	12
	07:24	0.4	12		12:07	3.0	91
	13:26	3.1	94		18:35	0.0	0
◐	19:53	0.1	3				
12 Su	02:19	3.1	94	27 M	00:55	3.0	91
	08:35	0.5	15		07:05	0.4	12
	14:28	2.9	88		13:03	2.9	88
	20:46	0.2	6	◑	19:27	-0.1	-3
13 M	03:17	3.2	98	28 Tu	01:53	3.3	101
	09:39	0.5	15		08:11	0.3	9
	15:25	2.8	85		14:03	2.9	88
	21:34	0.2	6		20:22	-0.2	-6
14 Tu	04:07	3.3	101	29 W	02:52	3.6	110
	10:34	0.4	12		09:16	0.1	3
	16:15	2.7	82		15:05	2.8	85
	22:16	0.2	6		21:18	-0.3	-9
15 W	04:50	3.5	107	30 Th	03:51	3.9	119
	11:22	0.3	9		10:19	-0.1	-3
	17:01	2.6	79		16:06	2.9	88
	22:55	0.1	3		22:14	-0.5	-15
				31 F	04:47	4.2	128
					11:19	-0.4	-12
					17:05	3.0	91
					23:09	-0.6	-18

StationId: 8652587
Source: NOAA/NOS/CO-OPS
Station Type: Primary
Time Zone: LST_LDT
Datum: MLLW

NOAA Tide Predictions

Oregon Inlet Marina, NC,2021

Times and Heights of High and Low Waters

January

Day	Time h m	Height ft	cm	Day	Time h m	Height ft	cm
1 F	03:00 / 09:04 / 16:21 / 21:26	-0.1 / 0.9 / -0.1 / 0.6	-3 / 27 / -3 / 18	16 Sa	04:18 / 10:00 / 17:11 / 22:37	-0.1 / 0.8 / -0.1 / 0.6	-3 / 24 / -3 / 18
2 Sa	03:43 / 09:44 / 17:00 / 22:12	-0.1 / 0.9 / -0.1 / 0.6	-3 / 27 / -3 / 18	17 Su	05:06 / 10:42 / 17:49 / 23:23	0.0 / 0.7 / -0.1 / 0.6	0 / 21 / -3 / 18
3 Su	04:32 / 10:28 / 17:41 / 23:03	0.0 / 0.8 / -0.1 / 0.7	0 / 24 / -3 / 21	18 M	05:56 / 11:25 / 18:25	0.0 / 0.6 / 0.0	0 / 18 / 0
4 M	05:28 / 11:15 / 18:24	0.0 / 0.8 / -0.1	0 / 24 / -3	19 Tu	00:12 / 06:47 / 12:10 / 19:02	0.6 / 0.0 / 0.5 / 0.0	18 / 0 / 15 / 0
5 Tu	00:00 / 06:29 / 12:07 / 19:12	0.7 / 0.0 / 0.7 / -0.1	21 / 0 / 21 / -3	20 W ◑	01:06 / 07:42 / 13:07 / 19:43	0.6 / 0.0 / 0.4 / 0.0	18 / 0 / 12 / 0
6 W ◔	01:04 / 07:38 / 13:08 / 20:06	0.8 / 0.0 / 0.7 / -0.1	24 / 0 / 21 / -3	21 Th	02:04 / 08:43 / 14:35 / 20:31	0.6 / 0.0 / 0.4 / 0.0	18 / 0 / 12 / 0
7 Th	02:14 / 08:54 / 14:21 / 21:05	0.8 / 0.0 / 0.6 / -0.1	24 / 0 / 18 / -3	22 F	03:03 / 09:48 / 15:47 / 21:26	0.6 / 0.0 / 0.4 / 0.0	18 / 0 / 12 / 0
8 F	03:22 / 10:12 / 15:43 / 22:07	0.9 / 0.0 / 0.6 / -0.1	27 / 0 / 18 / -3	23 Sa	03:58 / 10:50 / 16:43 / 22:21	0.6 / -0.1 / 0.4 / -0.1	18 / -3 / 12 / -3
9 Sa	04:24 / 11:24 / 16:54 / 23:09	1.0 / 0.0 / 0.6 / -0.1	30 / 0 / 18 / -3	24 Su	04:47 / 11:44 / 17:29 / 23:12	0.7 / -0.1 / 0.4 / -0.1	21 / -3 / 12 / -3
10 Su	05:20 / 12:26 / 17:54	1.0 / -0.1 / 0.7	30 / -3 / 21	25 M	05:31 / 12:31 / 18:08 / 23:58	0.7 / -0.1 / 0.4 / -0.1	21 / -3 / 12 / -3
11 M	00:07 / 06:11 / 13:22 / 18:46	-0.1 / 1.1 / -0.1 / 0.7	-3 / 34 / -3 / 21	26 Tu	06:11 / 13:14 / 18:41	0.8 / -0.2 / 0.5	24 / -6 / 15
12 Tu	01:01 / 07:00 / 14:12 / 19:35	-0.1 / 1.1 / -0.1 / 0.7	-3 / 34 / -3 / 21	27 W	00:40 / 06:49 / 13:53 / 19:13	-0.2 / 0.8 / -0.2 / 0.5	-6 / 24 / -6 / 15
13 W ●	01:52 / 07:47 / 15:00 / 20:22	-0.1 / 1.1 / -0.1 / 0.7	-3 / 34 / -3 / 21	28 Th ○	01:21 / 07:26 / 14:32 / 19:48	-0.2 / 0.8 / -0.2 / 0.5	-6 / 24 / -6 / 15
14 Th	02:41 / 08:32 / 15:46 / 21:07	-0.1 / 1.0 / -0.1 / 0.7	-3 / 30 / -3 / 21	29 F	02:03 / 08:04 / 15:09 / 20:27	-0.2 / 0.8 / -0.2 / 0.6	-6 / 24 / -6 / 18
15 F	03:30 / 09:16 / 16:30 / 21:52	-0.1 / 0.9 / -0.1 / 0.7	-3 / 27 / -3 / 21	30 Sa	02:48 / 08:43 / 15:48 / 21:10	-0.2 / 0.8 / -0.2 / 0.7	-6 / 24 / -6 / 21
				31 Su	03:36 / 09:25 / 16:27 / 21:57	-0.2 / 0.8 / -0.2 / 0.7	-6 / 24 / -6 / 21

February

Day	Time h m	Height ft	cm	Day	Time h m	Height ft	cm
1 M	04:28 / 10:09 / 17:09 / 22:48	-0.1 / 0.8 / -0.2 / 0.7	-3 / 24 / -6 / 21	16 Tu	05:22 / 10:43 / 17:24 / 23:13	-0.1 / 0.5 / 0.0 / 0.7	-3 / 15 / 0 / 21
2 Tu	05:25 / 10:56 / 17:56 / 23:43	-0.1 / 0.7 / -0.2 / 0.8	-3 / 21 / -6 / 24	17 W	06:06 / 11:20 / 17:57 / 23:54	0.0 / 0.5 / 0.0 / 0.6	0 / 15 / 0 / 18
3 W	06:28 / 11:49 / 18:47	-0.1 / 0.6 / -0.1	-3 / 18 / -3	18 Th	06:55 / 12:02 / 18:38	0.0 / 0.4 / 0.0	0 / 12 / 0
4 Th ◐	00:44 / 07:37 / 12:53 / 19:45	0.8 / 0.0 / 0.6 / -0.1	24 / 0 / 18 / -3	19 F ◐	00:42 / 07:50 / 12:57 / 19:28	0.6 / 0.0 / 0.3 / 0.0	18 / 0 / 9 / 0
5 F	01:52 / 08:53 / 14:17 / 20:50	0.8 / 0.0 / 0.5 / -0.1	24 / 0 / 15 / -3	20 Sa	01:41 / 08:55 / 14:57 / 20:26	0.6 / 0.0 / 0.3 / 0.0	18 / 0 / 9 / 0
6 Sa	03:02 / 10:10 / 15:45 / 21:58	0.9 / 0.0 / 0.5 / -0.1	27 / 0 / 15 / -3	21 Su	02:51 / 10:02 / 16:05 / 21:28	0.6 / 0.0 / 0.3 / 0.0	18 / 0 / 9 / 0
7 Su	04:07 / 11:18 / 16:52 / 23:03	0.9 / -0.1 / 0.6 / -0.1	27 / -3 / 18 / -3	22 M	03:56 / 11:02 / 16:53 / 22:27	0.7 / -0.1 / 0.4 / 0.0	21 / -3 / 12 / 0
8 M	05:05 / 12:16 / 17:48	0.9 / -0.1 / 0.6	27 / -3 / 18	23 Tu	04:49 / 11:52 / 17:32 / 23:21	0.7 / -0.1 / 0.5 / -0.1	21 / -3 / 15 / -3
9 Tu	00:02 / 05:57 / 13:08 / 18:38	-0.1 / 1.0 / -0.1 / 0.7	-3 / 30 / -3 / 21	24 W	05:36 / 12:35 / 18:09	0.8 / -0.1 / 0.5	24 / -3 / 15
10 W	00:55 / 06:45 / 13:54 / 19:23	-0.1 / 1.0 / -0.2 / 0.7	-3 / 30 / -6 / 21	25 Th	00:10 / 06:18 / 13:14 / 18:46	-0.1 / 0.8 / -0.2 / 0.6	-3 / 24 / -6 / 18
11 Th ●	01:43 / 07:30 / 14:37 / 20:05	-0.1 / 1.0 / -0.2 / 0.7	-3 / 30 / -6 / 21	26 F	00:58 / 06:59 / 13:52 / 19:25	-0.2 / 0.9 / -0.2 / 0.7	-6 / 27 / -6 / 21
12 F	02:29 / 08:12 / 15:16 / 20:45	-0.1 / 0.9 / -0.1 / 0.7	-3 / 27 / -3 / 21	27 Sa ○	01:47 / 07:39 / 14:30 / 20:08	-0.2 / 0.9 / -0.2 / 0.8	-6 / 27 / -6 / 24
13 Sa	03:13 / 08:53 / 15:52 / 21:23	-0.1 / 0.8 / -0.1 / 0.7	-3 / 24 / -3 / 21	28 Su	02:37 / 08:21 / 15:09 / 20:52	-0.2 / 0.9 / -0.2 / 0.9	-6 / 27 / -6 / 27
14 Su	03:56 / 09:32 / 16:25 / 22:00	-0.1 / 0.7 / -0.1 / 0.7	-3 / 21 / -3 / 21				
15 M	04:39 / 10:08 / 16:54 / 22:36	-0.1 / 0.6 / 0.0 / 0.7	-3 / 18 / 0 / 21				

March

Day	Time h m	Height ft	cm	Day	Time h m	Height ft	cm
1 M	03:29 / 09:05 / 15:52 / 21:40	-0.1 / 0.8 / -0.2 / 0.9	-3 / 24 / -6 / 27	16 Tu	05:17 / 10:37 / 17:00 / 22:57	0.0 / 0.7 / 0.1 / 0.8	0 / 21 / 3 / 24
2 Tu	04:25 / 09:51 / 16:38 / 22:31	-0.1 / 0.8 / -0.1 / 1.0	-3 / 24 / -3 / 30	17 W	05:57 / 11:08 / 17:28 / 23:30	0.0 / 0.6 / 0.1 / 0.8	0 / 18 / 3 / 24
3 W	05:25 / 10:41 / 17:29 / 23:25	-0.1 / 0.7 / -0.1 / 1.0	-3 / 21 / -3 / 30	18 Th	06:38 / 11:43 / 18:01	0.0 / 0.5 / 0.1	0 / 15 / 3
4 Th	06:29 / 11:39 / 18:27	0.0 / 0.7 / 0.0	0 / 21 / 0	19 F	00:08 / 07:23 / 12:23 / 18:41	0.8 / 0.1 / 0.5 / 0.1	24 / 3 / 15 / 3
5 F	00:25 / 07:38 / 12:52 / 19:30	1.0 / 0.0 / 0.6 / 0.0	30 / 0 / 18 / 0	20 Sa	00:52 / 08:15 / 13:29 / 19:31	0.8 / 0.1 / 0.4 / 0.1	24 / 3 / 12 / 3
6 Sa	01:32 / 08:50 / 14:26 / 20:39	1.0 / 0.0 / 0.6 / 0.1	30 / 0 / 18 / 3	21 Su ◔	01:44 / 09:14 / 14:14 / 20:30	0.8 / 0.1 / 0.4 / 0.1	24 / 3 / 12 / 3
7 Su	02:42 / 10:00 / 15:44 / 21:49	0.9 / 0.0 / 0.6 / 0.1	27 / 0 / 18 / 3	22 M	02:45 / 10:16 / 15:58 / 21:35	0.8 / 0.1 / 0.5 / 0.1	24 / 3 / 15 / 3
8 M	03:48 / 11:03 / 16:46 / 22:55	1.0 / 0.0 / 0.7 / 0.1	30 / 0 / 21 / 3	23 Tu	03:54 / 11:14 / 17:05 / 22:40	0.8 / 0.1 / 0.5 / 0.1	24 / 3 / 15 / 3
9 Tu	04:47 / 11:58 / 17:38 / 23:53	1.0 / 0.0 / 0.7 / 0.0	30 / 0 / 21 / 0	24 W	04:59 / 12:04 / 17:52 / 23:43	0.8 / 0.0 / 0.6 / 0.1	24 / 0 / 18 / 3
10 W	05:39 / 12:46 / 18:24	1.0 / -0.1 / 0.8	30 / -3 / 24	25 Th	05:54 / 12:48 / 18:36	0.9 / 0.0 / 0.8	27 / 0 / 24
11 Th	00:45 / 06:27 / 13:28 / 19:05	0.0 / 1.0 / -0.1 / 0.8	0 / 30 / -3 / 24	26 F	00:41 / 06:42 / 13:28 / 19:19	0.0 / 0.9 / 0.0 / 0.9	0 / 27 / 0 / 27
12 F	01:32 / 07:10 / 14:06 / 19:44	0.0 / 0.9 / -0.1 / 0.9	0 / 27 / -3 / 27	27 Sa	01:36 / 07:28 / 14:07 / 20:03	0.0 / 1.0 / -0.1 / 1.0	0 / 30 / -3 / 30
13 Sa ●	02:16 / 07:51 / 14:39 / 20:20	0.0 / 0.9 / 0.0 / 0.9	0 / 27 / 0 / 27	28 Su ○	02:31 / 08:12 / 14:48 / 20:47	0.0 / 1.0 / -0.1 / 1.1	0 / 30 / -3 / 34
14 Su	03:58 / 09:29 / 16:08 / 21:54	0.0 / 0.8 / 0.0 / 0.9	0 / 24 / 0 / 27	29 M	03:26 / 09:32 / 15:32 / 21:34	0.0 / 0.9 / -0.1 / 1.2	0 / 27 / -3 / 37
15 M	04:38 / 10:04 / 16:35 / 22:26	0.0 / 0.7 / 0.0 / 0.9	0 / 21 / 0 / 27	30 Tu	04:23 / 09:45 / 16:19 / 22:22	0.0 / 0.9 / 0.0 / 1.2	0 / 27 / 0 / 37
				31 W	05:23 / 10:35 / 17:11 / 23:13	0.0 / 0.9 / 0.0 / 1.2	0 / 27 / 0 / 37

NOAA Tide Predictions

Oregon Inlet Marina, NC, 2021

Times and Heights of High and Low Waters

April

Day	Time	ft	cm	Day	Time	ft	cm
1 Th	06:25	0.1	3	16 F	06:24	0.2	6
	11:30	0.8	24		11:13	0.6	18
	18:08	0.1	3		17:16	0.2	6
					23:36	1.0	30
2 F	00:07	1.2	37	17 Sa	07:09	0.2	6
	07:28	0.1	3		11:53	0.6	18
	12:36	0.8	24		17:56	0.2	6
	19:09	0.1	3				
3 Sa	01:06	1.2	37	18 Su	00:19	1.0	30
	08:34	0.1	3		07:57	0.2	6
	13:59	0.7	21		12:41	0.6	18
	20:16	0.2	6		18:45	0.3	9
4 Su	02:11	1.1	34	19 M	01:08	1.0	30
	09:39	0.1	3		08:47	0.2	6
	15:24	0.7	21		13:39	0.6	18
	21:25	0.2	6		19:44	0.3	9
5 M	03:20	1.1	34	20 Tu	02:03	1.0	30
	10:42	0.1	3		09:38	0.2	6
	16:33	0.8	24		14:52	0.6	18
	22:34	0.2	6		20:50	0.3	9
6 Tu	04:26	1.0	30	21 W	03:04	1.0	30
	11:40	0.1	3		10:27	0.2	6
	17:31	0.8	24		16:12	0.7	21
	23:39	0.2	6		21:59	0.2	6
7 W	05:25	1.0	30	22 Th	04:08	1.0	30
	12:30	0.1	3		11:14	0.1	3
	18:20	0.9	27		17:13	0.8	24
					23:07	0.2	6
8 Th	00:38	0.2	6	23 F	05:09	1.0	30
	06:17	1.0	30		11:58	0.1	3
	13:15	0.1	3		18:05	1.0	30
	19:04	1.0	30				
9 F	01:30	0.2	6	24 Sa	00:13	0.2	6
	07:04	1.0	30		06:04	1.0	30
	13:54	0.1	3		12:42	0.0	0
	19:44	1.0	30		18:53	1.1	34
10 Sa	02:18	0.2	6	25 Su	01:16	0.1	3
	07:47	0.9	27		06:56	1.0	30
	14:28	0.1	3		13:26	0.0	0
	20:20	1.0	30		19:40	1.3	40
11 Su	03:01	0.1	3	26 M	02:17	0.1	3
	08:26	0.9	27		07:46	1.0	30
	14:58	0.1	3		14:11	0.0	0
	20:55	1.0	30		20:27	1.4	43
12 M	03:42	0.1	3	27 Tu	03:17	0.1	3
	09:03	0.8	24		08:36	1.0	30
	15:24	0.1	3		15:00	0.0	0
	21:26	1.0	30		21:15	1.4	43
13 Tu	04:22	0.1	3	28 W	04:17	0.1	3
	09:37	0.8	24		09:27	1.0	30
	15:49	0.1	3		15:52	0.1	3
	21:56	1.0	30		22:05	1.4	43
14 W	05:01	0.1	3	29 Th	05:18	0.1	3
	10:08	0.7	21		10:22	0.9	27
	16:15	0.2	6		16:48	0.1	3
	22:26	1.0	30		22:56	1.4	43
15 Th	05:42	0.1	3	30 F	06:20	0.2	6
	10:39	0.6	18		11:22	0.9	27
	16:44	0.2	6		17:49	0.2	6
	22:59	1.0	30		23:50	1.4	43

May

Day	Time	ft	cm	Day	Time	ft	cm
1 Sa	07:21	0.2	6	16 Su	06:59	0.2	6
	12:33	0.8	24		11:30	0.6	18
	18:52	0.2	6		17:25	0.3	9
					23:55	1.1	34
2 Su	00:48	1.3	40	17 M	07:42	0.2	6
	08:21	0.2	6		12:18	0.6	18
	13:53	0.8	24		18:15	0.3	9
	19:57	0.3	9				
3 M	01:50	1.2	37	18 Tu	00:41	1.1	34
	09:20	0.2	6		08:23	0.2	6
	15:07	0.8	24		13:15	0.7	21
	21:04	0.3	9		19:14	0.3	9
4 Tu	02:55	1.1	34	19 W	01:32	1.1	34
	10:16	0.2	6		09:04	0.2	6
	16:11	0.9	27		14:22	0.7	21
	22:10	0.4	12		20:19	0.3	9
5 W	03:58	1.1	34	20 Th	02:27	1.1	34
	11:07	0.2	6		09:46	0.2	6
	17:06	0.9	27		15:34	0.8	24
	23:15	0.4	12		21:28	0.3	9
6 Th	04:56	1.0	30	21 F	03:26	1.0	30
	11:54	0.2	6		10:30	0.1	3
	17:54	1.0	30		16:39	1.0	30
					22:38	0.3	9
7 F	00:15	0.3	9	22 Sa	04:28	1.0	30
	05:49	1.0	30		11:16	0.1	3
	12:36	0.2	6		17:36	1.1	34
	18:38	1.1	34		23:49	0.3	9
8 Sa	01:09	0.3	9	23 Su	05:29	1.0	30
	06:36	0.9	27		12:03	0.1	3
	13:13	0.2	6		18:29	1.3	40
	19:17	1.1	34				
9 Su	01:58	0.3	9	24 M	00:59	0.2	6
	07:20	0.9	27		06:27	1.0	30
	13:46	0.2	6		12:52	0.0	0
	19:54	1.1	34		19:19	1.4	43
10 M	02:42	0.2	6	25 Tu	02:05	0.2	6
	08:00	0.9	27		07:22	1.0	30
	14:17	0.2	6		13:43	0.0	0
	20:28	1.1	34		20:08	1.5	46
11 Tu	03:25	0.2	6	26 W	03:08	0.2	6
	08:38	0.8	24		08:17	1.0	30
	14:45	0.2	6		14:36	0.1	3
	21:01	1.1	34		20:58	1.5	46
12 W	04:06	0.2	6	27 Th	04:10	0.2	6
	09:12	0.8	24		09:12	1.0	30
	15:13	0.2	6		15:31	0.1	3
	21:31	1.1	34		21:48	1.5	46
13 Th	04:48	0.2	6	28 F	05:11	0.2	6
	09:42	0.7	21		10:09	0.9	27
	15:42	0.2	6		16:30	0.2	6
	22:02	1.1	34		22:40	1.5	46
14 F	05:31	0.2	6	29 Sa	06:09	0.2	6
	10:13	0.7	21		11:12	0.9	27
	16:12	0.3	9		17:31	0.2	6
	22:35	1.1	34		23:33	1.4	43
15 Sa	06:16	0.2	6	30 Su	07:06	0.2	6
	10:48	0.6	18		12:20	0.9	27
	16:45	0.3	9		18:33	0.3	9
	23:13	1.1	34				
				31 M	00:28	1.3	40
					08:01	0.2	6
					13:31	0.9	27
					19:34	0.3	9

June

Day	Time	ft	cm	Day	Time	ft	cm
1 Tu	01:26	1.2	37	16 W	00:18	1.1	34
	08:52	0.2	6		07:55	0.2	6
	14:38	0.9	27		12:56	0.8	24
	20:36	0.4	12		18:58	0.3	9
2 W	02:25	1.1	34	17 Th	01:06	1.1	34
	09:41	0.2	6		08:32	0.2	6
	15:39	0.9	27		13:58	0.9	27
	21:39	0.4	12		20:00	0.3	9
3 Th	03:25	1.1	34	18 F	01:57	1.1	34
	10:27	0.2	6		09:12	0.2	6
	16:33	1.0	30		15:05	1.0	30
	22:42	0.4	12		21:06	0.3	9
4 F	04:22	1.0	30	19 Sa	02:55	1.0	30
	11:11	0.2	6		09:56	0.1	3
	17:22	1.0	30		16:11	1.1	34
	23:43	0.4	12		22:17	0.3	9
5 Sa	05:16	0.9	27	20 Su	03:57	1.0	30
	11:51	0.2	6		10:44	0.1	3
	18:06	1.1	34		17:11	1.2	37
					23:32	0.3	9
6 Su	00:40	0.4	12	21 M	05:03	1.0	30
	06:06	0.9	27		11:36	0.1	3
	12:29	0.2	6		18:07	1.3	40
	18:47	1.1	34				
7 M	01:31	0.3	9	22 Tu	00:47	0.3	9
	06:51	0.8	24		06:06	1.0	30
	13:05	0.2	6		12:30	0.1	3
	19:26	1.1	34		19:00	1.4	43
8 Tu	02:18	0.3	9	23 W	01:56	0.3	9
	07:33	0.8	24		07:06	1.0	30
	13:40	0.2	6		13:25	0.1	3
	20:02	1.1	34		19:52	1.5	46
9 W	03:03	0.3	9	24 Th	03:00	0.3	9
	08:11	0.8	24		08:03	1.0	30
	14:13	0.2	6		14:21	0.1	3
	20:36	1.1	34		20:42	1.5	46
10 Th	03:47	0.3	9	25 F	04:00	0.2	6
	08:45	0.7	21		08:59	1.0	30
	14:46	0.2	6		15:18	0.1	3
	21:09	1.1	34		21:32	1.5	46
11 F	04:32	0.2	6	26 Sa	04:56	0.2	6
	09:16	0.7	21		09:56	0.9	27
	15:18	0.2	6		16:16	0.2	6
	21:41	1.1	34		22:23	1.4	43
12 Sa	05:16	0.2	6	27 Su	05:51	0.2	6
	09:48	0.7	21		10:54	0.9	27
	15:51	0.2	6		17:14	0.2	6
	22:16	1.2	37		23:14	1.4	43
13 Su	06:00	0.2	6	28 M	06:43	0.2	6
	10:26	0.7	21		11:55	0.9	27
	16:27	0.2	6		18:11	0.3	9
	22:54	1.2	37				
14 M	06:41	0.2	6	29 Tu	00:05	1.3	40
	11:10	0.7	21		07:31	0.2	6
	17:10	0.3	9		12:57	0.9	27
	23:34	1.1	34		19:08	0.3	9
15 Tu	07:19	0.2	6	30 W	00:57	1.2	37
	12:00	0.7	21		08:17	0.2	6
	18:01	0.3	9		13:58	0.9	27
					20:04	0.4	12

StationId: 8652587
Source: NOAA/NOS/CO-OPS
Station Type: Primary
Time Zone: LST_LDT
Datum: MLLW

NOAA Tide Predictions

Oregon Inlet Marina, NC,2021

Times and Heights of High and Low Waters

July

Day	Time	ft	cm	Day	Time	ft	cm
1 Th ☽	01:51	1.1	34	16 F	00:43	1.1	34
	09:00	0.3	9		08:01	0.2	6
	14:56	1.0	30		13:36	1.0	30
	21:01	0.4	12		19:50	0.4	12
2 F	02:46	1.0	30	17 Sa ☾	01:34	1.1	34
	09:42	0.3	9		08:44	0.2	6
	15:50	1.0	30		14:40	1.1	34
	22:00	0.4	12		20:55	0.4	12
3 Sa	03:44	0.9	27	18 Su	02:32	1.1	34
	10:22	0.3	9		09:32	0.2	6
	16:42	1.0	30		15:46	1.2	37
	23:01	0.4	12		22:06	0.4	12
4 Su	04:41	0.9	27	19 M	03:38	1.0	30
	11:04	0.2	6		10:25	0.2	6
	17:29	1.0	30		16:50	1.3	40
					23:24	0.4	12
5 M	00:00	0.4	12	20 Tu	04:49	1.0	30
	05:33	0.8	24		11:22	0.2	6
	11:45	0.2	6		17:49	1.4	43
	18:14	1.1	34				
6 Tu	00:56	0.4	12	21 W	00:40	0.4	12
	06:21	0.8	24		05:57	1.0	30
	12:27	0.2	6		12:20	0.2	6
	18:56	1.1	34		18:45	1.4	43
7 W	01:47	0.3	9	22 Th	01:48	0.4	12
	07:04	0.8	24		06:59	1.0	30
	13:07	0.2	6		13:18	0.2	6
	19:35	1.1	34		19:37	1.5	46
8 Th	02:35	0.3	9	23 F	02:48	0.3	9
	07:43	0.8	24		07:54	1.0	30
	13:45	0.2	6		14:14	0.2	6
	20:12	1.2	37		20:27	1.5	46
9 F	03:21	0.3	9	24 Sa ○	03:43	0.3	9
	08:16	0.8	24		08:47	1.0	30
	14:22	0.2	6		15:08	0.2	6
	20:47	1.2	37		21:16	1.5	46
10 Sa ●	04:06	0.3	9	25 Su	04:35	0.3	9
	08:49	0.8	24		09:39	1.0	30
	14:58	0.2	6		16:02	0.2	6
	21:21	1.2	37		22:04	1.4	43
11 Su	04:49	0.3	9	26 M	05:24	0.3	9
	09:25	0.8	24		10:30	1.0	30
	15:36	0.2	6		16:55	0.3	9
	21:56	1.2	37		22:52	1.3	40
12 M	05:31	0.3	9	27 Tu	06:10	0.3	9
	10:06	0.8	24		11:22	1.0	30
	16:17	0.2	6		17:47	0.3	9
	22:34	1.2	37		23:39	1.3	40
13 Tu	06:09	0.3	9	28 W	06:54	0.3	9
	10:52	0.8	24		12:14	1.0	30
	17:03	0.3	9		18:38	0.4	12
	23:14	1.2	37				
14 W	06:46	0.2	6	29 Th	00:26	1.2	37
	11:42	0.9	27		07:35	0.3	9
	17:54	0.3	9		13:07	1.0	30
	23:57	1.2	37		19:28	0.4	12
15 Th	07:23	0.2	6	30 F	01:13	1.1	34
	12:36	1.0	30		08:14	0.4	12
	18:50	0.3	9		14:01	1.0	30
					20:18	0.4	12
				31 Sa ☾	02:03	1.0	30
					08:52	0.4	12
					14:57	1.0	30
					21:10	0.5	15

August

Day	Time	ft	cm	Day	Time	ft	cm
1 Su	03:00	0.9	27	16 M	02:20	1.1	34
	09:33	0.4	12		09:17	0.3	9
	15:53	1.0	30		15:25	1.3	40
	22:07	0.5	15		22:05	0.5	15
2 M	04:02	0.9	27	17 Tu	03:34	1.1	34
	10:17	0.3	9		10:16	0.3	9
	16:46	1.0	30		16:32	1.4	43
	23:10	0.5	15		23:22	0.5	15
3 Tu	04:59	0.9	27	18 W	04:51	1.1	34
	11:03	0.3	9		11:18	0.3	9
	17:36	1.1	34		17:34	1.4	43
4 W	00:12	0.5	15	19 Th	00:33	0.5	15
	05:49	0.9	27		05:57	1.1	34
	11:50	0.3	9		12:18	0.3	9
	18:22	1.1	34		18:30	1.5	46
5 Th	01:09	0.4	12	20 F	01:35	0.5	15
	06:33	0.9	27		06:54	1.1	34
	12:35	0.3	9		13:16	0.3	9
	19:05	1.2	37		19:22	1.5	46
6 F	01:59	0.4	12	21 Sa	02:29	0.4	12
	07:11	0.9	27		07:45	1.2	37
	13:17	0.2	6		14:09	0.3	9
	19:44	1.2	37		20:11	1.5	46
7 Sa	02:45	0.4	12	22 Su ○	03:19	0.4	12
	07:46	0.9	27		08:33	1.2	37
	13:58	0.2	6		15:00	0.3	9
	20:21	1.2	37		20:58	1.5	46
8 Su ●	03:28	0.4	12	23 M	04:05	0.4	12
	08:23	0.9	27		09:18	1.2	37
	14:39	0.2	6		15:50	0.3	9
	20:57	1.3	40		21:43	1.4	43
9 M	04:09	0.3	9	24 Tu	04:49	0.4	12
	09:02	1.0	30		10:02	1.2	37
	15:22	0.2	6		16:37	0.4	12
	21:33	1.3	40		22:27	1.3	40
10 Tu	04:49	0.3	9	25 W	05:30	0.5	15
	09:46	1.0	30		10:45	1.2	37
	16:09	0.3	9		17:24	0.4	12
	22:12	1.3	40		23:10	1.2	37
11 W	05:28	0.3	9	26 Th	06:09	0.5	15
	10:32	1.1	34		11:28	1.2	37
	16:58	0.3	9		18:09	0.4	12
	22:53	1.2	37		23:52	1.2	37
12 Th	06:08	0.3	9	27 F	06:46	0.5	15
	11:22	1.1	34		12:10	1.1	34
	17:51	0.3	9		18:52	0.5	15
	23:37	1.2	37				
13 F	06:49	0.3	9	28 Sa	00:33	1.1	34
	12:16	1.2	37		07:23	0.5	15
	18:47	0.4	12		12:56	1.1	34
					19:36	0.5	15
14 Sa	00:25	1.2	37	29 Su	01:14	1.0	30
	07:34	0.3	9		08:01	0.5	15
	13:14	1.2	37		13:46	1.1	34
	19:47	0.4	12		20:23	0.5	15
15 Su ☾	01:19	1.1	34	30 M ☾	02:02	1.0	30
	08:23	0.3	9		08:44	0.5	15
	14:17	1.3	40		14:45	1.1	34
	20:52	0.5	15		21:16	0.5	15
				31 Tu	03:07	0.9	27
					09:31	0.5	15
					15:49	1.1	34
					22:17	0.5	15

September

Day	Time	ft	cm	Day	Time	ft	cm
1 W	04:17	0.9	27	16 Th	04:55	1.2	37
	10:21	0.5	15		11:15	0.5	15
	16:50	1.1	34		17:18	1.4	43
	23:23	0.5	15				
2 Th	05:12	0.9	27	17 F	00:20	0.5	15
	11:11	0.4	12		05:54	1.2	37
	17:42	1.2	37		12:16	0.5	15
					18:15	1.5	46
3 F	00:23	0.5	15	18 Sa	01:15	0.5	15
	05:57	1.0	30		06:46	1.3	40
	12:01	0.4	12		13:12	0.4	12
	18:29	1.2	37		19:06	1.5	46
4 Sa	01:14	0.5	15	19 Su	02:04	0.5	15
	06:37	1.0	30		07:32	1.3	40
	12:48	0.3	9		14:04	0.4	12
	19:10	1.3	40		19:53	1.4	43
5 Su	01:59	0.5	15	20 M ○	02:49	0.5	15
	07:16	1.1	34		08:15	1.3	40
	13:34	0.3	9		14:52	0.4	12
	19:49	1.3	40		20:38	1.4	43
6 M	02:40	0.4	12	21 Tu	03:29	0.5	15
	07:57	1.2	37		08:55	1.3	40
	14:21	0.3	9		15:37	0.4	12
	20:28	1.3	40		21:21	1.3	40
7 Tu ●	03:20	0.4	12	22 W	04:07	0.5	15
	08:40	1.2	37		09:33	1.3	40
	15:09	0.3	9		16:20	0.4	12
	21:07	1.3	40		22:02	1.3	40
8 W	04:00	0.4	12	23 Th	04:43	0.5	15
	09:25	1.3	40		10:10	1.3	40
	16:00	0.3	9		17:01	0.5	15
	21:49	1.3	40		22:41	1.2	37
9 Th	04:43	0.4	12	24 F	05:17	0.6	18
	10:12	1.4	43		10:45	1.3	40
	16:53	0.4	12		17:41	0.5	15
	22:33	1.3	40		23:18	1.1	34
10 F	05:28	0.4	12	25 Sa	05:52	0.6	18
	11:02	1.4	43		11:22	1.3	40
	17:49	0.4	12		18:21	0.5	15
	23:20	1.3	40		23:53	1.1	34
11 Sa	06:18	0.4	12	26 Su	06:29	0.6	18
	11:54	1.4	43		12:00	1.2	37
	18:47	0.5	15		19:01	0.5	15
12 Su	00:12	1.2	37	27 M	00:28	1.0	30
	07:10	0.4	12		07:09	0.6	18
	12:53	1.4	43		12:44	1.2	37
	19:49	0.5	15		19:46	0.5	15
13 M ☾	01:11	1.2	37	28 Tu ☽	01:08	1.0	30
	08:07	0.5	15		07:53	0.6	18
	13:57	1.4	43		13:35	1.2	37
	20:56	0.5	15		20:37	0.6	18
14 Tu	02:23	1.2	37	29 W ☽	01:59	1.0	30
	09:08	0.5	15		08:42	0.6	18
	15:06	1.4	43		14:36	1.1	34
	22:06	0.6	18		21:35	0.6	18
15 W	03:44	1.2	37	30 Th	03:07	1.0	30
	10:11	0.5	15		09:35	0.5	15
	16:15	1.4	43		15:45	1.2	37
	23:16	0.6	18		22:35	0.6	18

StationId: 8652587
Source: NOAA/NOS/CO-OPS
Station Type: Primary
Time Zone: LST_LDT
Datum: MLLW

NOAA Tide Predictions

Oregon Inlet Marina, NC,2021

Times and Heights of High and Low Waters

October

Day	Time	ft	cm
1 F	04:20	1.0	30
	10:30	0.5	15
	16:50	1.2	37
	23:32	0.5	15
2 Sa	05:16	1.1	34
	11:25	0.4	12
	17:44	1.2	37
3 Su	00:22	0.5	15
	06:03	1.1	34
	12:19	0.4	12
	18:31	1.3	40
4 M	01:06	0.5	15
	06:48	1.2	37
	13:12	0.4	12
	19:15	1.3	40
5 Tu	01:47	0.4	12
	07:32	1.3	40
	14:04	0.3	9
	19:58	1.3	40
6 W ●	02:29	0.4	12
	08:18	1.4	43
	14:56	0.3	9
	20:41	1.3	40
7 Th	03:14	0.4	12
	09:04	1.5	46
	15:50	0.4	12
	21:26	1.3	40
8 F	04:02	0.4	12
	09:52	1.5	46
	16:46	0.4	12
	22:14	1.3	40
9 Sa	04:54	0.4	12
	10:43	1.6	49
	17:45	0.4	12
	23:05	1.2	37
10 Su	05:50	0.4	12
	11:36	1.5	46
	18:45	0.5	15
11 M	00:03	1.2	37
	06:50	0.5	15
	12:34	1.5	46
	19:48	0.5	15
12 Tu	01:10	1.2	37
	07:52	0.5	15
	13:37	1.4	43
	20:52	0.5	15
13 W	02:29	1.2	37
	08:57	0.5	15
	14:46	1.4	43
	21:57	0.5	15
14 Th	03:44	1.2	37
	10:02	0.5	15
	15:56	1.4	43
	23:00	0.5	15
15 F	04:48	1.2	37
	11:07	0.5	15
	16:59	1.4	43
	23:57	0.5	15
16 Sa	05:42	1.3	40
	12:08	0.5	15
	17:56	1.3	40
17 Su	00:48	0.5	15
	06:31	1.3	40
	13:04	0.5	15
	18:47	1.3	40
18 M	01:33	0.5	15
	07:14	1.3	40
	13:55	0.4	12
	19:34	1.3	40
19 Tu	02:14	0.5	15
	07:54	1.4	43
	14:41	0.4	12
	20:18	1.2	37
20 W ○	02:51	0.5	15
	08:31	1.4	43
	15:23	0.4	12
	20:59	1.2	37
21 Th	03:24	0.5	15
	09:06	1.4	43
	16:03	0.4	12
	21:38	1.1	34
22 F	03:57	0.5	15
	09:39	1.3	40
	16:41	0.4	12
	22:14	1.1	34
23 Sa	04:29	0.5	15
	10:11	1.3	40
	17:19	0.4	12
	22:47	1.0	30
24 Su	05:03	0.5	15
	10:45	1.2	37
	17:57	0.4	12
	23:17	1.0	30
25 M	05:39	0.5	15
	11:22	1.2	37
	18:37	0.4	12
	23:50	0.9	27
26 Tu	06:19	0.5	15
	12:03	1.2	37
	19:21	0.5	15
27 W	00:30	0.9	27
	07:03	0.5	15
	12:50	1.1	34
	20:08	0.5	15
28 Th	01:18	0.9	27
	07:52	0.5	15
	13:43	1.1	34
	20:58	0.5	15
29 F	02:17	0.9	27
	08:48	0.5	15
	14:43	1.1	34
	21:50	0.5	15
30 Sa	03:27	1.0	30
	09:48	0.4	12
	15:49	1.1	34
	22:40	0.4	12
31 Su	04:34	1.0	30
	10:50	0.4	12
	16:53	1.1	34
	23:29	0.4	12

November

Day	Time	ft	cm
1 M	05:30	1.1	34
	11:52	0.3	9
	17:50	1.1	34
2 Tu	00:15	0.3	9
	06:21	1.3	40
	12:51	0.3	9
	18:41	1.2	37
3 W	01:01	0.3	9
	07:09	1.4	43
	13:48	0.3	9
	19:30	1.2	37
4 Th ●	01:48	0.3	9
	07:57	1.5	46
	14:45	0.3	9
	20:18	1.2	37
5 F	02:38	0.3	9
	08:45	1.5	46
	15:41	0.3	9
	21:07	1.2	37
6 Sa	03:31	0.3	9
	09:34	1.5	46
	16:38	0.3	9
	21:58	1.1	34
7 Su	03:28	0.3	9
	09:38	1.5	46
	16:37	0.3	9
	21:53	1.1	34
8 M	04:28	0.3	9
	10:18	1.5	46
	17:37	0.3	9
	22:54	1.1	34
9 Tu	05:30	0.4	12
	11:14	1.4	43
	18:37	0.3	9
10 W	00:04	1.1	34
	06:34	0.4	12
	12:16	1.3	40
	19:37	0.4	12
11 Th ◐	01:19	1.0	30
	07:39	0.4	12
	13:23	1.3	40
	20:36	0.4	12
12 F	02:28	1.1	34
	08:46	0.4	12
	14:32	1.2	37
	21:33	0.4	12
13 Sa ◑	03:29	1.1	34
	09:52	0.4	12
	15:36	1.1	34
	22:26	0.4	12
14 Su	04:22	1.1	34
	10:54	0.4	12
	16:34	1.1	34
	23:15	0.3	9
15 M	05:09	1.2	37
	11:50	0.3	9
	17:27	1.0	30
	23:59	0.3	9
16 Tu	05:52	1.2	37
	12:41	0.3	9
	18:14	1.0	30
17 W	00:38	0.3	9
	06:31	1.2	37
	13:26	0.3	9
	18:58	1.0	30
18 Th	01:15	0.3	9
	07:08	1.2	37
	14:07	0.2	6
	19:38	0.9	27
19 F ○	01:49	0.3	9
	07:42	1.2	37
	14:45	0.2	6
	20:16	0.9	27
20 Sa	02:21	0.3	9
	08:14	1.2	37
	15:23	0.2	6
	20:50	0.8	24
21 Su	02:54	0.3	9
	08:45	1.1	34
	16:00	0.2	6
	21:19	0.8	24
22 M	03:26	0.3	9
	09:18	1.1	34
	16:39	0.2	6
	21:47	0.8	24
23 Tu	04:00	0.3	9
	09:53	1.1	34
	17:18	0.2	6
	22:19	0.7	21
24 W	04:36	0.3	9
	10:33	1.0	30
	17:58	0.2	6
	22:59	0.7	21
25 Th	05:19	0.3	9
	11:17	1.0	30
	18:38	0.3	9
	23:47	0.7	21
26 F ◐	06:09	0.3	9
	12:05	1.0	30
	19:20	0.3	9
27 Sa ◑	00:43	0.8	24
	07:07	0.3	9
	12:59	0.9	27
	20:05	0.2	6
28 Su	01:47	0.8	24
	08:11	0.3	9
	14:00	0.9	27
	20:52	0.2	6
29 M	02:56	0.9	27
	09:19	0.2	6
	15:06	0.9	27
	21:42	0.2	6
30 Tu	03:59	1.0	30
	10:28	0.2	6
	16:12	0.9	27
	22:34	0.1	3

December

Day	Time	ft	cm
1 W	04:55	1.2	37
	11:34	0.1	3
	17:12	0.9	27
	23:27	0.1	3
2 Th	05:48	1.3	40
	12:36	0.1	3
	18:07	0.9	27
3 F	00:20	0.0	0
	06:38	1.4	43
	13:35	0.1	3
	19:00	0.9	27
4 Sa ●	01:15	0.0	0
	07:28	1.4	43
	14:32	0.1	3
	19:52	0.9	27
5 Su	02:11	0.0	0
	08:18	1.4	43
	15:28	0.1	3
	20:45	0.9	27
6 M	03:09	0.1	3
	09:08	1.4	43
	16:25	0.1	3
	21:41	0.9	27
7 Tu	04:09	0.1	3
	10:00	1.3	40
	17:21	0.1	3
	22:40	0.9	27
8 W	05:10	0.1	3
	10:54	1.2	37
	18:16	0.1	3
	23:45	0.9	27
9 Th	06:12	0.2	6
	11:51	1.1	34
	19:11	0.1	3
10 F	00:52	0.9	27
	07:16	0.2	6
	12:54	1.0	30
	20:04	0.1	3
11 Sa ◐	01:58	0.9	27
	08:22	0.2	6
	14:02	0.9	27
	20:57	0.2	6
12 Su	02:58	0.9	27
	09:28	0.2	6
	15:09	0.8	24
	21:48	0.2	6
13 M	03:52	0.9	27
	10:32	0.2	6
	16:10	0.8	24
	22:37	0.1	3
14 Tu	04:41	0.9	27
	11:30	0.2	6
	17:05	0.7	21
	23:22	0.1	3
15 W	05:25	1.0	30
	12:21	0.1	3
	17:54	0.7	21
16 Th	00:05	0.1	3
	06:06	1.0	30
	13:06	0.1	3
	18:38	0.7	21
17 F	00:45	0.1	3
	06:44	1.0	30
	13:46	0.0	0
	19:18	0.7	21
18 Sa	01:21	0.1	3
	07:20	1.0	30
	14:25	0.0	0
	19:55	0.6	18
19 Su ○	01:56	0.1	3
	07:53	0.9	27
	15:03	0.0	0
	20:27	0.6	18
20 M	02:29	0.1	3
	08:24	0.9	27
	15:41	0.0	0
	20:54	0.6	18
21 Tu	03:01	0.1	3
	08:56	0.9	27
	16:18	0.0	0
	21:21	0.6	18
22 W	03:33	0.1	3
	09:30	0.9	27
	16:54	0.0	0
	21:54	0.6	18
23 Th	04:08	0.1	3
	10:08	0.8	24
	17:29	0.0	0
	22:34	0.6	18
24 F	04:50	0.1	3
	10:49	0.8	24
	18:03	0.0	0
	23:21	0.6	18
25 Sa	05:40	0.1	3
	11:34	0.8	24
	18:40	0.0	0
26 Su	00:15	0.7	21
	06:38	0.1	3
	12:24	0.7	21
	19:22	0.0	0
27 M ◐	01:16	0.7	21
	07:44	0.1	3
	13:22	0.7	21
	20:10	0.0	0
28 Tu	02:23	0.8	24
	08:56	0.1	3
	14:29	0.6	18
	21:06	0.0	0
29 W	03:31	0.9	27
	10:11	0.0	0
	15:43	0.6	18
	22:05	-0.1	-3
30 Th	04:33	1.0	30
	11:23	0.0	0
	16:53	0.7	21
	23:05	-0.1	-3
31 F	05:29	1.1	34
	12:27	-0.1	-3
	17:53	0.7	21

StationId: 8654400
Source: NOAA/NOS/CO-OPS
Station Type: Primary
Time Zone: LST_LDT
Datum: MLLW

Cape Hatteras Fishing Pier, NC, 2021

Times and Heights of High and Low Waters

January

Day	Time (h m)	Height (ft)	Height (cm)	Day	Time (h m)	Height (ft)	Height (cm)
1 F	02:02	-0.2	-6	16 Sa	03:05	-0.3	-9
	08:36	3.6	110		09:31	3.4	104
	15:08	-0.1	-3		15:57	-0.2	-6
	20:54	2.4	73		21:56	2.6	79
2 Sa	02:46	-0.2	-6	17 Su	03:54	-0.1	-3
	09:18	3.5	107		10:16	3.1	94
	15:49	-0.1	-3		16:39	-0.1	-3
	21:41	2.5	76		22:44	2.6	79
3 Su	03:35	-0.1	-3	18 M	04:45	0.1	3
	10:03	3.4	104		11:00	2.8	85
	16:32	-0.1	-3		17:21	0.0	0
	22:31	2.6	79		23:34	2.5	76
4 M	04:29	0.0	0	19 Tu	05:39	0.3	9
	10:51	3.2	98		11:45	2.5	76
	17:18	-0.1	-3		18:03	0.1	3
	23:27	2.7	82				
5 Tu	05:29	0.0	0	20 W	00:26	2.5	76
	11:44	3.0	91		06:38	0.4	12
	18:07	-0.2	-6		12:34	2.2	67
				☽	18:46	0.2	6
6 W	00:27	2.9	88	21 Th	01:21	2.5	76
	06:36	0.1	3		07:42	0.5	15
☽	12:42	2.8	85		13:27	2.1	64
	19:00	-0.2	-6		19:33	0.3	9
7 Th	01:30	3.1	94	22 F	02:16	2.6	79
	07:48	0.1	3		08:46	0.5	15
	13:44	2.6	79		14:23	1.9	58
	19:56	-0.3	-9		20:22	0.2	6
8 F	02:33	3.3	101	23 Sa	03:10	2.7	82
	09:00	0.0	0		09:45	0.4	12
	14:48	2.5	76		15:20	1.9	58
	20:53	-0.4	-12		21:13	0.2	6
9 Sa	03:35	3.5	107	24 Su	04:00	2.9	88
	10:07	-0.1	-3		10:37	0.3	9
	15:51	2.5	76		16:12	2.0	61
	21:51	-0.5	-15		22:02	0.1	3
10 Su	04:34	3.7	113	25 M	04:47	3.1	94
	11:07	-0.2	-6		11:23	0.2	6
	16:52	2.5	76		17:00	2.1	64
	22:48	-0.6	-18		22:50	-0.1	-3
11 M	05:29	3.9	119	26 Tu	05:31	3.2	98
	12:03	-0.4	-12		12:05	0.0	0
	17:48	2.5	76		17:45	2.2	67
	23:43	-0.6	-18		23:35	-0.2	-6
12 Tu	06:22	3.9	119	27 W	06:13	3.4	104
	12:54	-0.4	-12		12:45	-0.1	-3
	18:41	2.6	79		18:27	2.3	70
13 W	00:36	-0.6	-18	28 Th	00:20	-0.3	-9
	07:12	3.9	119		06:55	3.5	107
●	13:43	-0.4	-12		13:23	-0.2	-6
	19:32	2.6	79	○	19:09	2.5	76
14 Th	01:27	-0.6	-18	29 F	01:04	-0.4	-12
	08:00	3.8	116		07:36	3.6	110
	14:29	-0.4	-12		14:02	-0.3	-9
	20:20	2.7	82		19:52	2.6	79
15 F	02:16	-0.5	-15	30 Sa	01:49	-0.5	-15
	08:46	3.6	110		08:17	3.6	110
	15:14	-0.3	-9		14:41	-0.4	-12
	21:08	2.6	79		20:36	2.8	85
				31 Su	02:36	-0.5	-15
					08:59	3.5	107
					15:20	-0.4	-12
					21:22	2.9	88

February

Day	Time (h m)	Height (ft)	Height (cm)	Day	Time (h m)	Height (ft)	Height (cm)
1 M	03:25	-0.4	-12	16 Tu	04:13	0.0	0
	09:44	3.3	101		10:18	2.6	79
	16:02	-0.5	-15		16:27	0.0	0
	22:12	3.0	91		22:46	2.7	82
2 Tu	04:19	-0.3	-9	17 W	05:00	0.2	6
	10:31	3.1	94		10:58	2.4	73
	16:47	-0.4	-12		17:04	0.1	3
	23:06	3.1	94		23:31	2.7	82
3 W	05:18	-0.2	-6	18 Th	05:51	0.4	12
	11:22	2.8	85		11:41	2.1	64
	17:35	-0.4	-12		17:44	0.3	9
4 Th	00:04	3.1	94	19 F	00:20	2.6	79
	06:24	0.0	0		06:49	0.5	15
	12:19	2.5	76		12:30	2.0	61
◐	18:29	-0.3	-9	◐	18:30	0.3	9
5 F	01:08	3.2	98	20 Sa	01:16	2.6	79
	07:36	0.1	3		07:54	0.6	18
	13:24	2.3	70		13:29	1.8	55
	19:29	-0.3	-9		19:25	0.4	12
6 Sa	02:15	3.3	101	21 Su	02:17	2.7	82
	08:50	0.1	3		08:59	0.5	15
	14:33	2.2	67		14:32	1.8	55
	20:33	-0.3	-9		20:25	0.3	9
7 Su	03:21	3.4	104	22 M	03:16	2.8	85
	09:58	0.0	0		09:57	0.4	12
	15:41	2.2	67		15:33	1.9	58
	21:38	-0.3	-9		21:24	0.2	6
8 M	04:23	3.5	107	23 Tu	04:11	3.0	91
	10:59	-0.1	-3		10:47	0.3	9
	16:44	2.3	70		16:27	2.1	64
	22:40	-0.4	-12		22:20	0.0	0
9 Tu	05:20	3.6	110	24 W	05:00	3.2	98
	11:52	-0.2	-6		11:31	0.1	3
	17:40	2.5	76		17:15	2.3	70
	23:36	-0.5	-15		23:11	-0.2	-6
10 W	06:12	3.6	110	25 Th	05:45	3.4	104
	12:40	-0.3	-9		12:11	-0.1	-3
	18:31	2.6	79		18:01	2.6	79
11 Th	00:28	-0.5	-15	26 F	00:00	-0.4	-12
	06:59	3.6	110		06:29	3.5	107
●	13:23	-0.4	-12		12:51	-0.3	-9
	19:17	2.7	82		18:45	2.8	85
12 F	01:16	-0.5	-15	27 Sa	00:48	-0.6	-18
	07:42	3.5	107		07:12	3.6	110
	14:04	-0.4	-12		13:30	-0.5	-15
	20:01	2.8	85	○	19:30	3.1	94
13 Sa	02:02	-0.4	-12	28 Su	01:36	-0.7	-21
	08:24	3.3	101		07:54	3.6	110
	14:42	-0.3	-9		14:09	-0.6	-18
	20:43	2.8	85		20:15	3.3	101
14 Su	02:45	-0.3	-9				
	09:03	3.1	94				
	15:18	-0.2	-6				
	21:23	2.8	85				
15 M	03:29	-0.2	-6				
	09:41	2.9	88				
	15:53	-0.1	-3				
	22:04	2.8	85				

March

Day	Time (h m)	Height (ft)	Height (cm)	Day	Time (h m)	Height (ft)	Height (cm)
1 M	02:25	-0.7	-21	16 Tu	04:05	-0.1	-3
	08:38	3.4	104		10:07	2.8	85
	14:50	-0.6	-18		16:08	0.0	0
	21:02	3.5	107		22:26	3.1	94
2 Tu	03:16	-0.6	-18	17 W	04:45	0.1	3
	09:24	3.2	98		10:42	2.5	76
	15:32	-0.6	-18		16:40	0.1	3
	21:52	3.5	107		23:04	3.0	91
3 W	04:10	-0.4	-12	18 Th	05:27	0.2	6
	10:12	3.0	91		11:19	2.3	70
	16:18	-0.5	-15		17:14	0.2	6
	22:45	3.5	107		23:44	2.9	88
4 Th	05:09	-0.2	-6	19 F	06:13	0.4	12
	11:04	2.7	82		11:59	2.2	67
	17:08	-0.4	-12		17:53	0.4	12
	23:44	3.5	107				
5 F	06:14	0.0	0	20 Sa	00:30	2.9	88
	12:04	2.4	73		07:05	0.5	15
	18:06	-0.2	-6		12:47	2.0	61
					18:39	0.5	15
6 Sa	00:49	3.4	104	21 Su	01:23	2.8	85
	07:25	0.1	3		08:05	0.6	18
☽	13:12	2.3	70		13:44	1.9	58
	19:11	-0.1	-3	◐	19:35	0.5	15
7 Su	01:59	3.3	101	22 M	02:25	2.8	85
	08:39	0.1	3		09:10	0.6	18
	14:26	2.2	67		14:49	2.0	61
	20:22	0.0	0		20:40	0.5	15
8 M	03:09	3.3	101	23 Tu	03:29	2.9	88
	09:47	0.1	3		10:11	0.5	15
	15:36	2.3	70		15:54	2.1	64
	21:33	0.0	0		21:47	0.3	9
9 Tu	04:12	3.3	101	24 W	04:29	3.0	91
	11:03	0.0	0		11:03	0.0	0
	16:38	2.5	76		16:53	2.3	70
	22:36	-0.1	-3		22:50	0.1	3
10 W	05:08	3.4	104	25 Th	05:23	3.2	98
	11:35	-0.1	-3		11:49	0.1	3
	17:31	2.6	79		17:44	2.7	82
	23:31	-0.2	-6		23:46	-0.1	-3
11 Th	05:57	3.4	104	26 F	06:12	3.4	104
	12:18	-0.2	-6		12:32	-0.1	-3
	18:17	2.8	85		18:33	3.0	91
12 F	00:20	-0.3	-9	27 Sa	00:39	-0.3	-9
	06:46	3.3	101		06:59	3.5	107
	12:57	-0.2	-6		13:13	-0.3	-9
	18:59	3.0	91		19:20	3.4	104
13 Sa	01:04	-0.3	-9	28 Su	01:31	-0.5	-15
	07:20	3.3	101		07:44	3.5	107
●	13:33	-0.2	-6		13:54	-0.5	-15
	19:38	3.1	94	○	20:06	3.7	113
14 Su	01:46	-0.3	-9	29 M	02:21	-0.7	-21
	08:57	3.1	94		08:30	3.5	107
	15:06	-0.2	-6		14:36	-0.6	-18
	21:15	3.1	94		20:53	3.9	119
15 M	03:26	-0.2	-6	30 Tu	03:13	-0.7	-21
	09:32	3.0	91		09:16	3.4	104
	15:37	-0.1	-3		15:19	-0.7	-21
	21:50	3.1	94		21:42	4.0	122
				31 W	04:05	-0.6	-18
					10:04	3.2	98
					16:05	-0.6	-18
					22:33	4.0	122

StationId: 8654400
Source: NOAA/NOS/CO-OPS
Station Type: Primary
Time Zone: LST_LDT
Datum: MLLW

NOAA Tide Predictions

Cape Hatteras Fishing Pier, NC, 2021

Times and Heights of High and Low Waters

April

Day	Time (h m)	Height (ft)	Height (cm)	Day	Time (h m)	Height (ft)	Height (cm)
1 Th	05:00	-0.4	-12	16 F	05:02	0.3	9
	10:55	2.9	88		10:48	2.3	70
	16:53	-0.4	-12		16:35	0.4	12
	23:27	3.9	119		23:09	3.2	98
2 F	05:59	-0.2	-6	17 Sa	05:45	0.4	12
	11:51	2.7	82		11:29	2.2	67
	17:47	-0.2	-6		17:15	0.5	15
					23:53	3.1	94
3 Sa	00:26	3.7	113	18 Su	06:33	0.5	15
	07:04	0.0	0		12:16	2.1	64
	12:53	2.5	76		18:02	0.5	15
	18:49	0.0	0				
4 Su	01:32	3.5	107	19 M	00:43	3.0	91
	08:13	0.2	6		07:27	0.6	18
	14:05	2.4	73		13:11	2.1	64
	19:59	0.2	6		18:58	0.6	18
5 M	02:42	3.3	101	20 Tu	01:41	3.0	91
	09:23	0.2	6		08:26	0.6	18
	15:19	2.4	73		14:14	2.1	64
	21:14	0.2	6		20:04	0.6	18
6 Tu	03:51	3.2	98	21 W	02:44	3.0	91
	10:27	0.2	6		09:23	0.5	15
	16:27	2.5	76		15:19	2.3	70
	22:26	0.2	6		21:14	0.4	12
7 W	04:54	3.2	98	22 Th	03:45	3.1	94
	11:21	0.1	3		10:16	0.3	9
	17:25	2.7	82		16:19	2.6	79
	23:27	0.2	6		22:21	0.2	6
8 Th	05:48	3.2	98	23 F	04:42	3.2	98
	12:08	0.1	3		11:04	0.1	3
	18:15	2.9	88		17:13	3.0	91
					23:22	0.0	0
9 F	00:20	0.1	3	24 Sa	05:36	3.3	101
	06:34	3.1	94		11:49	-0.2	-6
	12:48	0.0	0		18:05	3.5	107
	18:57	3.1	94				
10 Sa	01:07	0.0	0	25 Su	00:19	-0.3	-9
	07:15	3.1	94		06:26	3.4	104
	13:23	0.0	0		12:34	-0.4	-12
	19:36	3.2	98		18:54	3.8	116
11 Su	01:49	0.0	0	26 M	01:14	-0.5	-15
	07:53	3.0	91		07:16	3.4	104
	13:56	0.0	0		13:19	-0.6	-18
	20:12	3.3	101		19:43	4.2	128
12 M	02:28	0.0	0	27 Tu	02:07	-0.6	-18
	08:28	2.9	88		08:05	3.3	101
	14:27	0.0	0		14:05	-0.7	-21
	20:46	3.4	104		20:33	4.4	134
13 Tu	03:06	0.0	0	28 W	03:00	-0.6	-18
	09:02	2.8	85		08:55	3.2	98
	14:57	0.0	0		14:52	-0.7	-21
	21:20	3.4	104		21:23	4.4	134
14 W	03:44	0.1	3	29 Th	03:54	-0.5	-15
	09:37	2.6	79		09:46	3.0	91
	15:28	0.1	3		15:41	-0.6	-18
	21:54	3.4	104		22:16	4.3	131
15 Th	04:22	0.2	6	30 F	04:50	-0.4	-12
	10:11	2.5	76		10:40	2.9	88
	16:00	0.2	6		16:34	-0.4	-12
	22:30	3.3	101		23:11	4.1	125

May

Day	Time (h m)	Height (ft)	Height (cm)	Day	Time (h m)	Height (ft)	Height (cm)
1 Sa	05:48	-0.2	-6	16 Su	05:23	0.4	12
	11:39	2.7	82		11:06	2.2	67
	17:31	-0.1	-3		16:48	0.4	12
					23:26	3.3	101
2 Su	00:10	3.8	116	17 M	06:08	0.4	12
	06:50	0.0	0		11:53	2.2	67
	12:43	2.6	79		17:36	0.5	15
	18:35	0.1	3				
3 M	01:14	3.5	107	18 Tu	00:14	3.2	98
	07:54	0.1	3		06:56	0.4	12
	13:53	2.5	76		12:46	2.2	67
	19:46	0.3	9		18:32	0.5	15
4 Tu	02:20	3.3	101	19 W	01:07	3.1	94
	08:58	0.2	6		07:47	0.4	12
	15:04	2.6	79		13:46	2.4	73
	21:00	0.4	12		19:37	0.5	15
5 W	03:25	3.1	94	20 Th	02:05	3.1	94
	09:56	0.2	6		08:39	0.3	9
	16:08	2.7	82		14:48	2.6	79
	22:10	0.4	12		20:46	0.4	12
6 Th	04:25	3.0	91	21 F	03:04	3.1	94
	10:47	0.2	6		09:30	0.1	3
	17:03	2.9	88		15:47	3.0	91
	23:10	0.4	12		21:55	0.3	9
7 F	05:17	2.9	88	22 Sa	04:03	3.1	94
	11:31	0.2	6		10:20	-0.1	-3
	17:50	3.1	94		16:44	3.4	104
					23:00	0.0	0
8 Sa	00:02	0.3	9	23 Su	05:00	3.1	94
	06:03	2.8	85		11:10	-0.3	-9
	12:09	0.1	3		17:38	3.8	116
	18:31	3.2	98				
9 Su	00:48	0.2	6	24 M	00:00	-0.2	-6
	06:44	2.8	85		05:55	3.1	94
	12:44	0.1	3		11:59	-0.5	-15
	19:09	3.4	104		18:31	4.1	125
10 M	01:30	0.2	6	25 Tu	00:58	-0.4	-12
	07:22	2.7	82		06:52	3.1	94
	13:16	0.1	3		12:48	-0.6	-18
	19:44	3.5	107		19:23	4.4	134
11 Tu	02:09	0.1	3	26 W	01:53	-0.5	-15
	07:58	2.6	79		07:42	3.0	91
	13:48	0.1	3		13:38	-0.7	-21
	20:18	3.5	107		20:14	4.5	137
12 W	02:47	0.1	3	27 Th	02:48	-0.5	-15
	08:34	2.5	76		08:34	3.0	91
	14:21	0.1	3		14:29	-0.6	-18
	20:52	3.6	110		21:07	4.5	137
13 Th	03:25	0.2	6	28 F	03:42	-0.5	-15
	09:10	2.5	76		09:30	2.9	88
	14:54	0.2	6		15:22	-0.5	-15
	21:27	3.5	107		22:00	4.3	131
14 F	04:03	0.2	6	29 Sa	04:37	-0.4	-12
	09:46	2.4	73		10:26	2.8	85
	15:29	0.3	9		16:17	-0.3	-9
	22:04	3.5	107		22:55	4.1	125
15 Sa	04:42	0.3	9	30 Su	05:32	-0.2	-6
	10:24	2.3	70		11:25	2.7	82
	16:07	0.3	9		17:16	-0.1	-3
	22:43	3.4	104		23:51	3.8	116
				31 M	06:29	-0.1	-3
					12:27	2.6	79
					18:19	0.1	3

June

Day	Time (h m)	Height (ft)	Height (cm)	Day	Time (h m)	Height (ft)	Height (cm)
1 Tu	00:50	3.5	107	16 W	06:26	0.2	6
	07:27	0.1	3		12:24	2.5	76
	13:32	2.6	79		18:14	0.4	12
	19:26	0.4	12				
2 W	01:50	3.2	98	17 Th	00:39	3.2	98
	08:23	0.1	3		07:12	0.1	3
	14:37	2.7	82		13:20	2.6	79
	20:36	0.5	15		19:17	0.4	12
3 Th	02:49	2.9	88	18 F	01:32	3.1	94
	09:16	0.2	6		08:00	0.0	0
	15:37	2.8	85		14:20	2.9	88
	21:43	0.5	15		20:25	0.4	12
4 F	03:45	2.7	82	19 Sa	02:30	3.0	91
	10:03	0.2	6		08:51	-0.1	-3
	16:31	3.0	91		15:20	3.2	98
	22:44	0.5	15		21:34	0.3	9
5 Sa	04:37	2.6	79	20 Su	03:30	2.9	88
	10:46	0.2	6		09:43	-0.2	-6
	17:18	3.1	94		16:19	3.6	110
	23:37	0.5	15		22:42	0.1	3
6 Su	05:24	2.5	76	21 M	04:30	2.8	85
	11:25	0.2	6		10:36	-0.4	-12
	18:00	3.3	101		17:16	3.9	119
					23:45	-0.1	-3
7 M	00:25	0.4	12	22 Tu	05:30	2.8	85
	06:08	2.4	73		11:30	-0.5	-15
	12:02	0.1	3		18:11	4.2	128
	18:38	3.4	104				
8 Tu	01:08	0.3	9	23 W	00:44	-0.2	-6
	06:49	2.4	73		06:28	2.8	85
	12:38	0.1	3		12:24	-0.6	-18
	19:16	3.5	107		19:06	4.3	131
9 W	01:48	0.2	6	24 Th	01:40	-0.3	-9
	07:28	2.4	73		07:24	2.8	85
	13:14	0.1	3		13:18	-0.6	-18
	19:52	3.6	110		19:59	4.4	134
10 Th	02:27	0.2	6	25 F	02:34	-0.4	-12
	08:07	2.4	73		08:19	2.8	85
	13:51	0.1	3		14:13	-0.6	-18
	20:29	3.6	110		20:52	4.4	134
11 F	03:05	0.2	6	26 Sa	03:27	-0.4	-12
	08:45	2.3	70		09:14	2.8	85
	14:28	0.1	3		15:07	-0.5	-15
	21:05	3.6	110		21:44	4.2	128
12 Sa	03:43	0.2	6	27 Su	04:18	-0.3	-9
	09:24	2.3	70		10:09	2.8	85
	15:06	0.2	6		16:02	-0.3	-9
	21:43	3.5	107		22:36	3.9	119
13 Su	04:22	0.2	6	28 M	05:10	-0.2	-6
	10:03	2.3	70		11:05	2.8	85
	15:46	0.2	6		16:58	-0.1	-3
	22:23	3.5	107		23:28	3.6	110
14 M	05:01	0.2	6	29 Tu	06:00	-0.1	-3
	10:46	2.3	70		12:02	2.8	85
	16:30	0.3	9		17:57	0.2	6
	23:04	3.4	104				
15 Tu	05:43	0.2	6	30 W	00:20	3.3	101
	11:33	2.4	73		06:50	0.0	0
	17:18	0.3	9		13:01	2.8	85
	23:49	3.3	101		18:58	0.4	12

StationId: 8654400
Source: NOAA/NOS/CO-OPS
Station Type: Primary
Time Zone: LST_LDT
Datum: MLLW

NOAA Tide Predictions

Cape Hatteras Fishing Pier, NC,2021

Times and Heights of High and Low Waters

July

Day	Time	ft	cm	Day	Time	ft	cm
1 Th ☽	01:12	3.0	91	16 F	00:13	3.2	98
	07:39	0.1	3		06:37	0.0	0
	13:59	2.8	85		12:56	3.0	91
	20:02	0.5	15		19:01	0.3	9
2 F	02:05	2.7	82	17 Sa ◐	01:06	3.0	91
	08:26	0.2	6		07:25	-0.1	-3
	14:56	2.9	88		13:55	3.2	98
	21:08	0.6	18		20:09	0.4	12
3 Sa	02:58	2.5	76	18 Su	02:03	2.8	85
	09:12	0.3	9		08:18	-0.1	-3
	15:50	3.0	91		14:56	3.5	107
	22:10	0.7	21		21:19	0.3	9
4 Su	03:51	2.4	73	19 M	03:05	2.7	82
	09:57	0.3	9		09:14	-0.2	-6
	16:39	3.1	94		15:58	3.7	113
	23:06	0.6	18		22:28	0.2	6
5 M	04:42	2.3	70	20 Tu	04:09	2.6	79
	10:40	0.3	9		10:12	-0.3	-9
	17:25	3.2	98		16:59	3.9	119
	23:56	0.5	15		23:33	0.1	3
6 Tu	05:31	2.2	67	21 W	05:13	2.6	79
	11:22	0.2	6		11:12	-0.4	-12
	18:07	3.3	101		17:58	4.1	125
7 W	00:41	0.4	12	22 Th	00:32	0.0	0
	06:16	2.3	70		06:13	2.7	82
	12:04	0.2	6		12:10	-0.4	-12
	18:48	3.4	104		18:53	4.2	128
8 Th	01:23	0.3	9	23 F	01:27	-0.1	-3
	06:59	2.3	70		07:10	2.8	85
	12:45	0.1	3		13:06	-0.5	-15
	19:27	3.5	107		19:46	4.2	128
9 F	02:03	0.3	9	24 Sa ○	02:18	-0.2	-6
	07:40	2.3	70		08:05	2.9	88
	13:26	0.1	3		14:01	-0.5	-15
	20:06	3.6	110		20:37	4.2	128
10 Sa ●	02:41	0.2	6	25 Su	03:07	-0.2	-6
	08:20	2.4	73		08:57	3.0	91
	14:06	0.1	3		15:54	-0.4	-12
	20:44	3.6	110		21:26	4.0	122
11 Su	03:19	0.1	3	26 M	03:54	-0.2	-6
	09:00	2.5	76		09:48	3.0	91
	14:47	0.1	3		15:46	-0.2	-6
	21:23	3.6	110		22:13	3.8	116
12 M	03:56	0.1	3	27 Tu	04:39	-0.1	-3
	09:42	2.5	76		10:39	3.0	91
	15:30	0.1	3		16:37	0.0	0
	22:02	3.6	110		22:59	3.5	107
13 Tu	04:34	0.1	3	28 W	05:22	0.0	0
	10:25	2.6	79		11:29	3.0	91
	16:15	0.1	3		17:30	0.2	6
	22:43	3.5	107		23:44	3.2	98
14 W	05:13	0.1	3	29 Th	06:05	0.1	3
	11:11	2.7	82		12:20	2.9	88
	17:05	0.2	6		18:24	0.5	15
	23:26	3.4	104				
15 Th	05:53	0.0	0	30 F	00:30	2.9	88
	12:01	2.8	85		06:48	0.3	9
	18:00	0.3	9		13:12	2.9	88
					19:23	0.7	21
				31 Sa ◐	01:17	2.6	79
					07:31	0.4	12
					14:06	2.9	88
					20:25	0.8	24

August

Day	Time	ft	cm	Day	Time	ft	cm
1 Su	02:09	2.4	73	16 M	01:45	2.8	85
	08:17	0.5	15		07:53	0.0	0
	15:01	3.0	91		14:38	3.7	113
	21:29	0.8	24		21:09	0.5	15
2 M	03:04	2.3	70	17 Tu	02:51	2.6	79
	09:05	0.5	15		08:55	0.0	0
	15:55	3.1	94		15:44	3.8	116
	22:29	0.8	24		22:20	0.4	12
3 Tu	04:00	2.2	67	18 W	03:59	2.6	79
	09:56	0.5	15		10:00	0.0	0
	16:47	3.2	98		16:48	3.9	119
	23:23	0.7	21		23:23	0.3	9
4 W	04:54	2.2	67	19 Th	05:05	2.7	82
	10:46	0.4	12		11:04	-0.1	-3
	17:35	3.3	101		17:48	4.0	122
5 Th	00:10	0.6	18	20 F	00:20	0.2	6
	05:44	2.3	70		06:05	2.9	88
	11:34	0.3	9		12:03	-0.2	-6
	18:19	3.5	107		18:42	4.1	125
6 F	00:53	0.5	15	21 Sa	01:11	0.1	3
	06:29	2.4	73		07:00	3.0	91
	12:19	0.2	6		12:59	-0.2	-6
	19:00	3.6	110		19:32	4.1	125
7 Sa	01:32	0.4	12	22 Su ○	01:58	0.0	0
	07:12	2.6	79		07:50	3.2	98
	13:03	0.1	3		13:51	-0.2	-6
	19:40	3.7	113		20:19	4.0	122
8 Su ●	02:10	0.2	6	23 M	02:41	0.0	0
	07:53	2.7	82		08:38	3.3	101
	13:47	0.0	0		14:40	-0.1	-3
	20:19	3.8	116		21:03	3.9	119
9 M	02:46	0.1	3	24 Tu	03:22	0.0	0
	08:35	2.8	85		09:23	3.3	101
	14:30	0.0	0		15:27	0.0	0
	20:58	3.8	116		21:45	3.6	110
10 Tu	03:23	0.1	3	25 W	04:01	0.1	3
	09:17	3.0	91		10:07	3.3	101
	15:13	0.0	0		16:13	0.2	6
	21:38	3.7	113		22:25	3.4	104
11 W	04:00	0.0	0	26 Th	04:38	0.2	6
	10:01	3.1	94		10:51	3.3	101
	16:02	0.0	0		17:00	0.4	12
	22:20	3.6	110		23:05	3.1	94
12 Th	04:39	0.0	0	27 F	05:15	0.3	9
	10:48	3.3	101		11:35	3.2	98
	16:53	0.1	3		17:49	0.6	18
	23:04	3.4	104		23:47	2.8	85
13 F	05:20	0.0	0	28 Sa	05:53	0.5	15
	11:38	3.4	104		12:21	3.2	98
	17:48	0.2	6		18:42	0.8	24
	23:51	3.2	98				
14 Sa	06:06	0.0	0	29 Su	00:31	2.6	79
	12:33	3.5	107		06:34	0.6	18
	18:50	0.4	12		13:12	3.1	94
					19:40	0.9	27
15 Su ◐	00:45	3.0	91	30 M ◐	01:21	2.4	73
	06:56	0.0	0		07:21	0.7	21
	13:33	3.6	110		14:08	3.1	94
	19:57	0.4	12		20:44	1.0	30
				31 Tu	02:18	2.3	70
					08:15	0.8	24
					15:08	3.1	94
					21:48	1.0	30

September

Day	Time	ft	cm	Day	Time	ft	cm
1 W	03:20	2.3	70	16 Th	03:57	2.8	85
	09:14	0.7	21		09:56	0.3	9
	16:06	3.2	98		16:39	3.8	116
	22:44	0.9	27		23:11	0.5	15
2 Th	04:19	2.4	73	17 F	05:02	2.9	88
	10:11	0.7	21		11:02	0.2	6
	16:58	3.3	101		17:37	3.9	119
	23:33	0.8	24				
3 F	05:11	2.5	76	18 Sa	00:03	0.3	9
	11:05	0.5	15		05:58	3.1	94
	17:46	3.5	107		12:00	0.1	3
					18:28	3.9	119
4 Sa	00:15	0.6	18	19 Su	00:49	0.2	6
	05:58	2.7	82		06:48	3.3	101
	11:54	0.3	9		12:52	0.1	3
	18:29	3.7	113		19:14	3.9	119
5 Su	00:54	0.4	12	20 M ○	01:31	0.2	6
	06:42	2.9	88		07:33	3.5	107
	12:41	0.2	6		13:40	0.1	3
	19:10	3.8	116		19:56	3.8	116
6 M	01:31	0.3	9	21 Tu	02:09	0.2	6
	07:25	3.2	98		08:15	3.6	110
	13:26	0.0	0		14:24	0.1	3
	19:50	3.9	119		20:36	3.6	110
7 Tu ●	02:08	0.1	3	22 W	02:45	0.2	6
	08:07	3.4	104		08:55	3.6	110
	14:12	-0.1	-3		15:07	0.2	6
	20:31	3.9	119		21:14	3.4	104
8 W	02:46	0.0	0	23 Th	03:19	0.3	9
	08:51	3.6	110		09:34	3.6	110
	14:59	-0.1	-3		15:49	0.3	9
	21:13	3.8	116		21:51	3.2	98
9 Th	03:24	-0.1	-3	24 F	03:52	0.4	12
	09:36	3.8	116		10:12	3.6	110
	15:49	0.0	0		16:32	0.5	15
	21:56	3.6	110		22:28	3.0	91
10 F	04:05	-0.1	-3	25 Sa	04:26	0.5	15
	10:24	3.9	119		10:52	3.5	107
	16:41	0.1	3		17:16	0.7	21
	22:42	3.4	104		22:58	2.8	85
11 Sa	04:49	0.0	0	26 Su	05:03	0.7	21
	11:16	3.9	119		11:34	3.4	104
	17:38	0.2	6		18:04	0.9	27
	23:33	3.2	98		23:49	2.6	79
12 Su	05:38	0.1	3	27 M	05:43	0.8	24
	12:13	3.9	119		12:22	3.3	101
	18:40	0.4	12		18:58	1.0	30
13 M ◐	00:30	2.9	88	28 Tu	00:38	2.4	73
	06:33	0.2	6		06:31	0.9	27
	13:15	3.9	119		13:17	3.2	98
	19:49	0.5	15		19:59	1.1	34
14 Tu	01:35	2.8	85	29 W ☽	01:36	2.4	73
	07:36	0.3	9		07:28	1.0	30
	14:24	3.8	116		14:18	3.2	98
	21:02	0.6	18		21:03	1.1	34
15 W	02:46	2.7	82	30 Th	02:41	2.4	73
	08:46	0.3	9		08:32	0.9	27
	15:33	3.8	116		15:20	3.2	98
	22:10	0.6	18		22:00	1.0	30

StationId: 8654400
Source: NOAA/NOS/CO-OPS
Station Type: Primary
Time Zone: LST_LDT
Datum: MLLW

NOAA Tide Predictions

Cape Hatteras Fishing Pier, NC,2021

Times and Heights of High and Low Waters

October

Day	Time (h m)	Height (ft)	Height (cm)
1 F	03:43	2.5	76
	09:36	0.8	24
	16:16	3.4	104
	22:49	0.8	24
2 Sa	04:37	2.7	82
	10:34	0.6	18
	17:06	3.5	107
	23:31	0.6	18
3 Su	05:26	3.0	91
	11:27	0.4	12
	17:52	3.7	113
4 M	00:11	0.4	12
	06:11	3.3	101
	12:17	0.2	6
	18:36	3.8	116
5 Tu	00:50	0.2	6
	06:56	3.7	113
	13:06	0.0	0
	19:19	3.8	116
6 ● W	01:28	0.0	0
	07:40	4.0	122
	13:55	-0.1	-3
	20:03	3.8	116
7 Th	02:09	-0.1	-3
	08:26	4.2	128
	14:44	-0.2	-6
	20:47	3.7	113
8 F	02:51	-0.2	-6
	09:13	4.3	131
	15:36	-0.1	-3
	21:34	3.5	107
9 Sa	03:35	-0.2	-6
	10:03	4.4	134
	16:30	0.0	0
	22:24	3.3	101
10 Su	04:23	-0.1	-3
	10:57	4.3	131
		0.2	6
	23:18	3.1	94
11 M	05:16	0.1	3
	11:55	4.1	125
	18:31	0.4	12
12 Tu	00:19	2.9	88
	06:17	0.3	9
	13:00	4.0	122
	19:39	0.5	15
13 W	01:29	2.8	85
	07:26	0.4	12
	14:10	3.8	116
	20:49	0.6	18
14 Th	02:43	2.8	85
	08:41	0.5	15
	15:20	3.7	113
	21:54	0.5	15
15 F	03:53	2.9	88
	09:53	0.5	15
	16:24	3.7	113
	22:51	0.5	15

Day	Time (h m)	Height (ft)	Height (cm)
16 Sa	04:54	3.1	94
	10:57	0.4	12
	17:19	3.6	110
	23:39	0.4	12
17 Su	05:46	3.3	101
	11:53	0.3	9
	18:08	3.6	110
18 M	00:22	0.3	9
	06:32	3.5	107
	12:42	0.3	9
	18:51	3.5	107
19 Tu	01:00	0.3	9
	07:13	3.7	113
	13:26	0.3	9
	19:31	3.4	104
20 ○ W	01:34	0.3	9
	07:51	3.8	116
	14:08	0.3	9
	20:08	3.3	101
21 Th	02:07	0.3	9
	08:27	3.8	116
	14:48	0.3	9
	20:44	3.1	94
22 F	02:39	0.4	12
	09:02	3.8	116
	15:27	0.4	12
	21:19	3.0	91
23 Sa	03:11	0.5	15
	09:38	3.7	113
	16:06	0.5	15
	21:56	2.8	85
24 Su	03:45	0.6	18
	10:16	3.6	110
	16:48	0.7	21
	22:34	2.6	79
25 M	04:22	0.7	21
	10:56	3.5	107
	17:32	0.8	24
	23:16	2.5	76
26 Tu	05:03	0.8	24
	11:42	3.3	101
	18:22	0.9	27
27 W	00:03	2.4	73
	05:51	0.9	27
	12:33	3.2	98
	19:17	1.0	30
28 Th	01:00	2.4	73
	06:47	0.9	27
	13:31	3.2	98
	20:15	1.0	30
29 F	02:02	2.4	73
	07:52	0.9	27
	14:31	3.2	98
	21:10	0.9	27
30 Sa	03:05	2.6	79
	08:59	0.8	24
	15:29	3.3	101
	21:59	0.7	21
31 Su	04:01	2.9	88
	10:02	0.6	18
	16:23	3.4	104
	22:44	0.5	15

November

Day	Time (h m)	Height (ft)	Height (cm)
1 M	04:52	3.2	98
	11:00	0.4	12
	17:13	3.4	104
	23:26	0.2	6
2 Tu	05:41	3.6	110
	11:55	0.1	3
	18:01	3.5	107
3 W	00:09	0.0	0
	06:28	4.0	122
	12:47	-0.1	-3
	18:48	3.5	107
4 ● Th	00:52	-0.2	-6
	07:15	4.3	131
	13:38	-0.2	-6
	19:36	3.5	107
5 F	01:36	-0.3	-9
	08:04	4.5	137
	14:30	-0.3	-9
	20:24	3.4	104
6 Sa	02:22	-0.4	-12
	08:54	4.6	140
	15:23	-0.2	-6
	21:15	3.3	101
7 Su	02:11	-0.3	-9
	08:46	4.5	137
	15:18	-0.1	-3
	21:08	3.1	94
8 M	03:03	-0.2	-6
	09:41	4.4	134
	16:16	0.0	0
	22:05	3.0	91
9 Tu	04:00	0.0	0
	10:40	4.1	125
	17:17	0.2	6
	23:09	2.8	85
10 W	05:04	0.2	6
	11:44	3.9	119
	18:22	0.3	9
11 ◐ Th	00:19	2.8	85
	06:15	0.4	12
	12:51	3.6	110
	19:27	0.4	12
12 F	01:31	2.8	85
	07:30	0.5	15
	13:57	3.4	104
	20:28	0.4	12
13 Sa	02:38	3.0	91
	08:42	0.5	15
	14:59	3.3	101
	21:21	0.3	9
14 Su	03:36	3.1	94
	09:45	0.5	15
	15:53	3.2	98
	22:08	0.3	9
15 M	04:26	3.3	101
	10:40	0.4	12
	16:41	3.1	94
	22:48	0.2	6

Day	Time (h m)	Height (ft)	Height (cm)
16 Tu	05:10	3.5	107
	11:28	0.3	9
	17:24	3.0	91
	23:25	0.2	6
17 W	05:49	3.6	110
	12:11	0.3	9
	18:04	2.9	88
	23:59	0.2	6
18 Th	06:26	3.7	113
	12:51	0.3	9
	18:41	2.8	85
19 ○ F	00:32	0.2	6
	07:01	3.7	113
	13:29	0.3	9
	19:17	2.7	82
20 Sa	01:06	0.3	9
	07:36	3.7	113
	14:07	0.3	9
	19:53	2.6	79
21 Su	01:40	0.3	9
	08:12	3.6	110
	14:45	0.4	12
	20:30	2.5	76
22 M	02:15	0.4	12
	08:49	3.5	107
	15:25	0.5	15
	21:08	2.4	73
23 Tu	02:53	0.5	15
	09:29	3.4	104
	16:06	0.5	15
	21:49	2.4	73
24 W	03:34	0.6	18
	10:11	3.3	101
	16:51	0.6	18
	22:35	2.3	70
25 Th	04:20	0.7	21
	10:58	3.2	98
	17:38	0.6	18
	23:27	2.3	70
26 F	05:15	0.7	21
	11:49	3.1	94
	18:28	0.6	18
27 ◐ Sa	00:25	2.4	73
	06:17	0.7	21
	12:45	3.0	91
	19:18	0.5	15
28 Su	01:25	2.6	79
	07:24	0.6	18
	13:42	3.0	91
	20:08	0.4	12
29 M	02:24	2.9	88
	08:31	0.5	15
	14:39	3.0	91
	20:56	0.1	3
30 Tu	03:19	3.3	101
	09:39	0.2	6
	15:35	3.0	91
	21:44	-0.1	-3

December

Day	Time (h m)	Height (ft)	Height (cm)
1 W	04:12	3.7	113
	10:33	0.0	0
	16:29	3.1	94
	22:32	-0.3	-9
2 Th	05:03	4.1	125
	11:29	-0.2	-6
	17:21	3.1	94
	23:20	-0.5	-15
3 F	05:54	4.3	131
	12:24	-0.4	-12
	18:13	3.1	94
4 ● Sa	00:10	-0.6	-18
	06:46	4.5	137
	13:17	-0.4	-12
	19:05	3.1	94
5 Su	01:01	-0.7	-21
	07:38	4.5	137
	14:10	-0.4	-12
	19:58	3.0	91
6 M	01:54	-0.6	-18
	08:31	4.4	134
	15:04	-0.4	-12
	20:53	2.9	88
7 Tu	02:49	-0.5	-15
	09:26	4.2	128
	16:00	-0.2	-6
	21:51	2.8	85
8 W	03:47	-0.3	-9
	10:23	3.9	119
	16:57	-0.1	-3
	22:53	2.8	85
9 Th	04:50	0.0	0
	11:22	3.6	110
	17:55	0.0	0
	23:59	2.7	82
10 F	05:57	0.2	6
	12:23	3.3	101
	18:54	0.1	3
11 ◐ Sa	01:06	2.8	85
	07:09	0.4	12
	13:24	3.0	91
	19:50	0.2	6
12 Su	02:10	2.9	88
	08:19	0.4	12
	14:24	2.8	85
	20:41	0.2	6
13 M	03:08	3.0	91
	09:23	0.4	12
	15:20	2.6	79
	21:28	0.2	6
14 Tu	03:58	3.1	94
	10:20	0.4	12
	16:10	2.5	76
	22:11	0.1	3
15 W	04:43	3.3	101
	11:09	0.3	9
	16:55	2.5	76
	22:50	0.1	3

Day	Time (h m)	Height (ft)	Height (cm)
16 Th	05:24	3.4	104
	11:53	0.2	6
	17:37	2.4	73
	23:27	0.1	3
17 F	06:02	3.4	104
	12:33	0.2	6
	18:16	2.4	73
18 Sa	00:04	0.1	3
	06:39	3.5	107
	13:11	0.1	3
	18:54	2.4	73
19 ○ Su	00:40	0.1	3
	07:15	3.5	107
	13:49	0.1	3
	19:31	2.4	73
20 M	01:17	0.1	3
	07:52	3.5	107
	14:26	0.1	3
	20:08	2.3	70
21 Tu	01:54	0.1	3
	08:29	3.4	104
	15:03	0.2	6
	20:46	2.3	70
22 W	02:33	0.2	6
	09:07	3.3	101
	15:41	0.2	6
	21:26	2.3	70
23 Th	03:14	0.2	6
	09:46	3.2	98
	16:20	0.2	6
	22:10	2.3	70
24 F	03:59	0.3	9
	10:28	3.1	94
	17:00	0.2	6
	22:57	2.4	73
25 Sa	04:50	0.3	9
	11:14	3.0	91
	17:44	0.2	6
	23:51	2.5	76
26 Su	05:49	0.4	12
	12:05	2.8	85
	18:30	0.1	3
27 ◐ M	00:48	2.7	82
	06:54	0.3	9
	13:01	2.7	82
	19:20	0.0	0
28 Tu	01:48	3.0	91
	08:04	0.3	9
	14:00	2.6	79
	20:13	-0.2	-6
29 W	02:48	3.3	101
	09:12	0.1	3
	15:01	2.6	79
	21:07	-0.3	-9
30 Th	03:46	3.6	110
	10:15	-0.1	-3
	16:01	2.6	79
	22:02	-0.5	-15
31 F	04:43	3.9	119
	11:15	-0.3	-9
	17:00	2.7	82
	22:55	-0.6	-18

StationId: 8658120
Source: NOAA/NOS/CO-OPS
Station Type: Primary
Time Zone: LST_LDT
Datum: MLLW

Wilmington, NC, 2021

Times and Heights of High and Low Waters

January

Day	Time	ft	cm	Day	Time	ft	cm
1 F	05:03	-0.1	-3	**16** Sa	06:08	0.0	0
	10:31	4.6	140		12:05	4.6	140
	17:56	0.2	6		18:43	0.1	3
	22:53	3.9	119				
2 Sa	05:46	-0.1	-3	**17** Su	00:24	4.0	122
	11:08	4.6	140		06:53	0.1	3
	18:38	0.2	6		12:52	4.4	134
	23:35	4.0	122		19:25	0.2	6
3 Su	06:32	-0.1	-3	**18** M	01:14	4.0	122
	11:55	4.6	140		07:40	0.3	9
	19:22	0.2	6		13:38	4.2	128
					20:07	0.2	6
4 M	00:30	4.0	122	**19** Tu	02:04	3.9	119
	07:25	0.0	0		08:29	0.4	12
	12:51	4.5	137		14:25	4.0	122
	20:10	0.2	6		20:49	0.3	9
5 Tu	01:34	4.1	125	**20** W	02:53	3.9	119
	08:26	0.1	3		09:21	0.5	15
	13:53	4.4	134		15:13	3.9	119
	21:04	0.1	3		21:34	0.3	9
6 W	02:42	4.2	128	**21** Th	03:42	4.0	122
	09:35	0.2	6		10:17	0.6	18
	14:59	4.2	128		16:02	3.8	116
	22:03	0.1	3		22:21	0.3	9
7 Th	03:49	4.4	134	**22** F	04:33	4.0	122
	10:44	0.3	9		11:13	0.6	18
	16:04	4.1	125		16:53	3.7	113
	23:04	0.0	0		23:11	0.3	9
8 F	04:54	4.5	137	**23** Sa	05:25	4.1	125
	11:50	0.2	6		12:07	0.5	15
	17:09	4.1	125		17:45	3.7	113
9 Sa	00:03	-0.1	-3	**24** Su	00:02	0.2	6
	05:58	4.7	143		06:16	4.2	128
	12:52	0.1	3		12:59	0.4	12
	18:12	4.1	125		18:35	3.8	116
10 Su	01:01	-0.2	-6	**25** M	00:52	0.2	6
	06:59	4.8	146		07:05	4.3	131
	13:50	0.0	0		13:49	0.4	12
	19:12	4.1	125		19:24	3.9	119
11 M	01:58	-0.3	-9	**26** Tu	01:42	0.1	3
	07:56	5.0	152		07:52	4.4	134
	14:46	-0.1	-3		14:37	0.3	9
	20:08	4.2	128		20:09	4.0	122
12 Tu	02:52	-0.4	-12	**27** W	02:31	0.0	0
	08:50	5.0	152		08:34	4.6	140
	15:38	-0.1	-3		15:24	0.2	6
	21:01	4.2	128		20:50	4.1	125
13 W ●	03:45	-0.4	-12	**28** Th ○	03:18	-0.1	-3
	09:41	5.0	152		09:12	4.7	143
	16:28	-0.1	-3		16:08	0.2	6
	21:52	4.2	128		21:29	4.2	128
14 Th	04:34	-0.3	-9	**29** F	04:05	-0.2	-6
	10:30	4.9	149		09:48	4.8	146
	17:15	-0.1	-3		16:51	0.1	3
	22:43	4.2	128		22:06	4.3	131
15 F	05:22	-0.2	-6	**30** Sa	04:51	-0.2	-6
	11:18	4.7	143		10:24	4.8	146
	18:00	0.0	0		17:33	0.1	3
	23:33	4.1	125		22:45	4.4	134
				31 Su	05:38	-0.2	-6
					11:04	4.8	146
					18:15	0.1	3
					23:30	4.4	134

February

Day	Time	ft	cm	Day	Time	ft	cm
1 M	06:26	-0.1	-3	**16** Tu	00:35	4.3	131
	11:50	4.7	143		07:08	0.4	12
	18:59	0.1	3		12:59	4.2	128
					19:18	0.4	12
2 Tu	00:23	4.5	137	**17** W	01:19	4.2	128
	07:19	0.0	0		07:51	0.5	15
	12:43	4.5	137		13:43	4.0	122
	19:46	0.1	3		19:51	0.5	15
3 W	01:23	4.5	137	**18** Th	02:04	4.2	128
	08:18	0.2	6		08:38	0.7	21
	13:43	4.4	134		14:30	3.9	119
	20:39	0.1	3		20:28	0.5	15
4 Th ◐	02:28	4.6	140	**19** F ◐	02:50	4.1	125
	09:23	0.3	9		09:31	0.8	24
	14:46	4.2	128		15:18	3.8	116
	21:38	0.1	3		21:14	0.6	18
5 F	03:33	4.6	140	**20** Sa	03:39	4.1	125
	10:29	0.4	12		10:28	0.8	24
	15:51	4.1	125		16:09	3.7	113
	22:42	0.1	3		22:11	0.6	18
6 Sa	04:38	4.6	140	**21** Su	04:32	4.1	125
	11:34	0.3	9		11:26	0.8	24
	16:55	4.0	122		17:03	3.8	116
	23:44	0.1	3		23:13	0.5	15
7 Su	05:43	4.7	143	**22** M	05:28	4.2	128
	12:35	0.3	9		12:22	0.7	21
	17:58	4.0	122		17:57	3.8	116
8 M	00:44	0.0	0	**23** Tu	00:13	0.4	12
	06:45	4.8	146		06:24	4.3	131
	13:32	0.1	3		13:15	0.6	18
	18:59	4.1	125		18:49	4.0	122
9 Tu	01:42	-0.1	-3	**24** W	01:11	0.3	9
	07:42	4.8	146		07:15	4.5	137
	14:26	0.1	3		14:05	0.5	15
	19:55	4.3	131		19:37	4.2	128
10 W	02:36	-0.2	-6	**25** Th	02:05	0.1	3
	08:35	4.9	149		08:03	4.7	143
	15:17	0.0	0		14:53	0.4	12
	20:47	4.4	134		20:23	4.4	134
11 Th ●	03:28	-0.2	-6	**26** F	02:57	0.0	0
	09:23	4.9	149		08:46	4.8	146
	16:04	0.0	0		15:40	0.2	6
	21:35	4.4	134		21:06	4.6	140
12 F	04:16	-0.2	-6	**27** Sa ○	03:48	-0.1	-3
	10:08	4.9	149		09:27	4.9	149
	16:48	0.0	0		16:24	0.1	3
	22:22	4.4	134		21:48	4.8	146
13 Sa	05:01	-0.1	-3	**28** Su	04:37	-0.2	-6
	10:51	4.7	143		10:09	5.0	152
	17:30	0.1	3		17:08	0.1	3
	23:07	4.4	134		22:32	4.9	149
14 Su	05:44	0.1	3				
	11:33	4.6	140				
	18:08	0.2	6				
	23:51	4.4	134				
15 M	06:26	0.2	6				
	12:16	4.4	134				
	18:44	0.3	9				

March

Day	Time	ft	cm	Day	Time	ft	cm
1 M	05:27	-0.2	-6	**16** Tu	00:18	4.7	143
	10:52	4.9	149		07:00	0.3	9
	17:51	0.0	0		12:41	4.4	134
	23:19	5.0	152		19:03	0.4	12
2 Tu	06:17	-0.1	-3	**17** W	00:55	4.6	140
	11:40	4.8	146		07:39	0.5	15
	18:36	0.0	0		13:21	4.2	128
					19:31	0.5	15
3 W	00:13	5.0	152	**18** Th	01:30	4.5	137
	07:11	0.1	3		08:17	0.6	18
	12:35	4.6	140		14:02	4.0	122
	19:24	0.1	3		19:58	0.6	18
4 Th	01:12	5.0	152	**19** F	02:01	4.4	134
	08:08	0.2	6		08:58	0.7	21
	13:34	4.4	134		14:44	3.9	119
	20:17	0.2	6		20:30	0.6	18
5 F	02:15	4.9	149	**20** Sa	02:33	4.3	131
	09:10	0.4	12		09:46	0.8	24
	14:37	4.2	128		15:31	3.8	116
	21:18	0.3	9		21:14	0.7	21
6 Sa	03:19	4.8	146	**21** Su ◐	03:18	4.3	131
	10:13	0.5	15		10:42	0.9	27
	15:40	4.1	125		16:22	3.8	116
	22:23	0.4	12		22:13	0.7	21
7 Su	04:23	4.7	143	**22** M	04:18	4.3	131
	11:16	0.5	15		11:43	0.9	27
	16:44	4.1	125		17:17	3.8	116
	23:27	0.3	9		23:25	0.7	21
8 M	05:27	4.7	143	**23** Tu	05:26	4.3	131
	12:15	0.4	12		12:42	0.8	24
	17:46	4.2	128		18:14	4.0	122
9 Tu	00:28	0.3	9	**24** W	00:36	0.6	18
	06:27	4.7	143		06:33	4.4	134
	13:11	0.3	9		13:38	0.7	21
	18:45	4.3	131		19:11	4.2	128
10 W	01:25	0.1	3	**25** Th	01:40	0.5	15
	07:23	4.8	146		07:33	4.6	140
	14:03	0.2	6		14:30	0.5	15
	19:40	4.5	137		20:04	4.4	134
11 Th	02:18	0.1	3	**26** F	02:40	0.3	9
	08:13	4.8	146		08:26	4.7	143
	14:51	0.1	3		15:20	0.4	12
	20:29	4.6	140		20:54	4.7	143
12 F	03:08	0.0	0	**27** Sa	03:36	0.1	3
	08:59	4.9	149		09:15	4.9	149
	15:36	0.1	3		16:08	0.2	6
	21:16	4.7	143		21:41	5.0	152
13 Sa ●	03:55	0.0	0	**28** Su ○	04:30	0.0	0
	09:41	4.8	146		10:01	5.0	152
	16:18	0.1	3		16:55	0.1	3
	21:59	4.8	146		22:28	5.3	162
14 Su	05:39	0.1	3	**29** M	05:22	-0.1	-3
	11:22	4.7	143		10:47	5.0	152
	17:56	0.2	6		17:41	0.0	0
	23:40	4.8	146		23:15	5.4	165
15 M	06:20	0.2	6	**30** Tu	06:14	-0.1	-3
	12:02	4.6	140		11:35	4.9	149
	18:31	0.3	9		18:27	0.0	0
				31 W	00:05	5.4	165
					07:06	-0.1	-3
					12:27	4.7	143
					19:14	0.1	3

StationId: 8658120
Source: NOAA/NOS/CO-OPS
Station Type: Primary
Time Zone: LST_LDT
Datum: MLLW

April

Day	Time	ft	cm
1 Th	01:00	5.4	165
	07:59	0.1	3
	13:24	4.5	137
	20:04	0.2	6
2 F	02:00	5.2	158
	08:55	0.2	6
	14:25	4.3	131
	20:59	0.3	9
3 Sa	03:03	5.0	152
	09:54	0.4	12
	15:28	4.2	128
	22:00	0.5	15
4 Su ◑	04:05	4.9	149
	10:55	0.4	12
	16:30	4.2	128
	23:05	0.5	15
5 M	05:06	4.7	143
	11:55	0.4	12
	17:31	4.2	128
6 Tu	00:08	0.5	15
	06:06	4.7	143
	12:52	0.3	9
	18:30	4.3	131
7 W	01:08	0.4	12
	07:04	4.6	140
	13:45	0.2	6
	19:27	4.5	137
8 Th	02:04	0.3	9
	07:56	4.7	143
	14:34	0.1	3
	20:20	4.6	140
9	02:56	0.2	6
	08:45	4.7	143
	15:21	0.1	3
	21:08	4.8	146
10 Sa	03:45	0.2	6
	09:30	4.7	143
	15:36	0.1	3
	21:52	4.9	149
11 Su	04:31	0.2	6
	10:12	4.6	140
	16:44	0.2	6
	22:33	5.0	152
12 M	05:15	0.2	6
	10:52	4.5	137
	17:21	0.3	9
	23:11	4.9	149
13 Tu	05:56	0.3	9
	11:31	4.4	134
	17:55	0.4	12
	23:47	4.9	149
14 W	06:35	0.4	12
	12:09	4.2	128
	18:25	0.5	15
15 Th	00:17	4.8	146
	07:13	0.5	15
	12:46	4.1	125
	18:52	0.5	15
16 F	00:38	4.7	143
	07:50	0.6	18
	13:22	3.9	119
	19:19	0.6	18
17 Sa	00:57	4.6	140
	08:28	0.7	21
	13:57	3.8	116
	19:54	0.6	18
18 Su	01:32	4.5	137
	09:11	0.8	24
	14:39	3.8	116
	20:38	0.6	18
19 M	02:21	4.5	137
	10:02	0.8	24
	15:31	3.8	116
	21:35	0.7	21
20 Tu ◑	03:20	4.4	134
	11:02	0.8	24
	16:31	3.9	119
	22:46	0.7	21
21 W	04:27	4.4	134
	12:02	0.7	21
	17:32	4.1	125
22 Th	00:03	0.6	18
	05:40	4.5	137
	12:59	0.6	18
	18:33	4.3	131
23 F	01:13	0.5	15
	06:47	4.5	137
	13:53	0.4	12
	19:31	4.6	140
24 Sa	02:16	0.3	9
	07:48	4.6	140
	14:45	0.2	6
	20:26	5.0	152
25 Su	03:15	0.1	3
	08:42	4.7	143
	15:36	0.1	3
	21:17	5.3	162
26 M	04:12	0.0	0
	09:34	4.7	143
	16:25	-0.1	-3
	22:07	5.5	168
27 Tu ○	05:06	-0.1	-3
	10:25	4.7	143
	17:15	-0.1	-3
	22:58	5.6	171
28 W	05:59	-0.2	-6
	11:17	4.6	140
	18:04	-0.1	-3
	23:51	5.5	168
29 Th	06:52	-0.1	-3
	12:12	4.5	137
	18:54	0.0	0
30 F	00:47	5.4	165
	07:45	0.0	0
	13:12	4.3	131
	19:46	0.1	3

May

Day	Time	ft	cm
1 Sa	01:48	5.2	158
	08:39	0.1	3
	14:14	4.2	128
	20:42	0.3	9
2 Su	02:48	5.0	152
	09:35	0.2	6
	15:15	4.1	125
	21:42	0.4	12
3 M ◑	03:47	4.8	146
	10:32	0.3	9
	16:15	4.1	125
	22:44	0.5	15
4 Tu	04:44	4.6	140
	11:29	0.2	6
	17:13	4.2	128
	23:46	0.5	15
5 W	05:39	4.5	137
	12:23	0.2	6
	18:09	4.3	131
6 Th	00:44	0.4	12
	06:33	4.4	134
	13:13	0.1	3
	19:03	4.5	137
7 F	01:39	0.3	9
	07:24	4.4	134
	14:01	0.0	0
	19:54	4.6	140
8 Sa	02:31	0.3	9
	08:12	4.4	134
	14:46	0.0	0
	20:41	4.8	146
9 Su	03:19	0.2	6
	08:58	4.4	134
	15:28	0.0	0
	21:25	4.9	149
10 M	04:06	0.2	6
	09:41	4.3	131
	16:08	0.1	3
	22:06	4.9	149
11 Tu ●	04:50	0.2	6
	10:23	4.2	128
	16:46	0.2	6
	22:43	4.9	149
12 W	05:31	0.2	6
	11:02	4.1	125
	17:20	0.3	9
	23:17	4.8	146
13 Th	06:11	0.3	9
	11:40	4.0	122
	17:52	0.4	12
	23:44	4.7	143
14 F	06:50	0.4	12
	12:15	3.8	116
	18:23	0.4	12
15 Sa	00:00	4.6	140
	07:27	0.5	15
	12:45	3.7	113
	18:55	0.4	12
16 Su	00:22	4.6	140
	08:05	0.5	15
	13:15	3.7	113
	19:32	0.4	12
17 M	01:01	4.6	140
	08:45	0.5	15
	13:56	3.7	113
	20:17	0.4	12
18 Tu ◑	01:51	4.5	137
	09:32	0.5	15
	14:51	3.8	116
	21:12	0.5	15
19 W ◑	02:49	4.5	137
	10:26	0.5	15
	15:53	3.9	119
	22:22	0.5	15
20 Th	03:53	4.4	134
	11:24	0.4	12
	16:57	4.1	125
	23:38	0.5	15
21 F	05:01	4.4	134
	12:21	0.2	6
	18:00	4.4	134
22 Sa	00:49	0.4	12
	05:40	4.4	134
	13:17	0.1	3
	19:01	4.7	143
23 Su	01:54	0.2	6
	07:13	4.4	134
	14:12	-0.1	-3
	19:59	5.0	152
24 M	02:56	0.1	3
	08:12	4.4	134
	15:05	-0.2	-6
	20:55	5.3	162
25 Tu	03:54	-0.1	-3
	09:09	4.4	134
	15:59	-0.2	-6
	21:49	5.4	165
26 W ○	04:50	-0.2	-6
	10:04	4.4	134
	16:52	-0.3	-9
	22:42	5.5	168
27 Th	05:43	-0.2	-6
	10:59	4.3	131
	17:44	-0.2	-6
	23:37	5.4	165
28 F	06:36	-0.2	-6
	11:56	4.2	128
	18:36	-0.1	-3
29 Sa	00:33	5.2	158
	07:27	-0.2	-6
	12:57	4.1	125
	19:29	0.0	0
30 Su	01:32	5.0	152
	08:19	-0.1	-3
	13:58	4.0	122
	20:23	0.2	6
31 M	02:29	4.8	146
	09:11	0.0	0
	14:57	4.0	122
	21:20	0.3	9

June

Day	Time	ft	cm
1 Tu	03:24	4.6	140
	10:04	0.0	0
	15:54	4.0	122
	22:19	0.4	12
2 W ◑	04:16	4.4	134
	10:57	0.0	0
	16:49	4.1	125
	23:18	0.4	12
3 Th	05:07	4.3	131
	11:48	0.0	0
	17:42	4.2	128
4 F	00:15	0.4	12
	05:57	4.2	128
	12:37	-0.1	-3
	18:33	4.3	131
5 Sa	01:09	0.3	9
	06:47	4.1	125
	13:23	-0.1	-3
	19:23	4.5	137
6 Su	02:01	0.3	9
	07:37	4.0	122
	14:07	-0.1	-3
	20:11	4.6	140
7 M	02:50	0.2	6
	08:24	4.0	122
	14:50	-0.1	-3
	20:56	4.7	143
8 Tu	03:37	0.1	3
	09:10	3.9	119
	15:31	0.0	0
	21:38	4.7	143
9 W	04:22	0.1	3
	09:53	3.9	119
	16:11	0.1	3
	22:16	4.7	143
10 Th ●	05:06	0.2	6
	10:34	3.8	116
	16:50	0.1	3
	22:51	4.7	143
11 F	05:47	0.2	6
	11:12	3.7	113
	17:26	0.2	6
	23:19	4.6	140
12 Sa	06:26	0.2	6
	11:47	3.7	113
	18:02	0.2	6
	23:38	4.6	140
13 Su	07:05	0.3	9
	12:16	3.6	110
	18:39	0.2	6
14 M	00:02	4.6	140
	07:43	0.3	9
	12:46	3.7	113
	19:19	0.2	6
15 Tu	00:42	4.6	140
	08:23	0.3	9
	13:29	3.7	113
	20:05	0.2	6
16 W	01:31	4.5	137
	09:06	0.2	6
	14:25	3.8	116
	21:00	0.3	9
17 Th	02:27	4.5	137
	09:55	0.1	3
	15:27	4.0	122
	22:07	0.4	12
18 F	03:29	4.4	134
	10:50	0.1	3
	16:31	4.2	128
	23:21	0.4	12
19 Sa	04:34	4.3	131
	11:47	0.0	0
	17:34	4.5	137
20 Su	00:31	0.3	9
	05:40	4.2	128
	12:45	-0.2	-6
	18:37	4.7	143
21 M	01:36	0.2	6
	06:46	4.1	125
	13:43	-0.2	-6
	19:38	5.0	152
22 Tu	02:38	0.1	3
	07:49	4.1	125
	14:41	-0.3	-9
	20:37	5.2	158
23 W	03:36	-0.1	-3
	08:49	4.1	125
	15:37	-0.4	-12
	21:33	5.3	162
24 Th ○	04:32	-0.2	-6
	09:46	4.1	125
	16:33	-0.4	-12
	22:28	5.3	162
25 F	05:26	-0.2	-6
	10:43	4.1	125
	17:27	-0.3	-9
	23:22	5.2	158
26 Sa	06:17	-0.3	-9
	11:40	4.0	122
	18:19	-0.2	-6
27 Su	00:16	5.0	152
	07:06	-0.2	-6
	12:38	4.0	122
	19:10	-0.1	-3
28 M	01:10	4.8	146
	07:55	-0.2	-6
	13:36	4.0	122
	20:02	0.1	3
29 Tu	02:03	4.6	140
	08:43	-0.1	-3
	14:33	4.0	122
	20:54	0.2	6
30 W	02:53	4.4	134
	09:31	-0.1	-3
	15:26	4.0	122
	21:49	0.4	12

Station Id: 8658120
Source: NOAA/NOS/CO-OPS
Station Type: Primary
Time Zone: LST_LDT
Datum: MLLW

NOAA Tide Predictions

Wilmington, NC, 2021

Times and Heights of High and Low Waters

July

Day	Time (h m)	Height ft	Height cm	Day	Time (h m)	Height ft	Height cm
1 Th ☽	03:43	4.2	128	**16** F	02:11	4.4	134
	10:19	-0.1	-3		09:28	0.0	0
	16:18	4.1	125		15:08	4.3	131
	22:45	0.4	12		21:58	0.3	9
2 F	04:31	4.1	125	**17** Sa ◐	03:11	4.3	131
	11:07	0.0	0		10:21	-0.1	-3
	17:08	4.1	125		16:12	4.4	134
	23:41	0.5	15		23:07	0.4	12
3 Sa	05:20	3.9	119	**18** Su	04:16	4.2	128
	11:54	0.0	0		11:20	-0.1	-3
	17:59	4.2	128		17:15	4.6	140
4 Su	00:36	0.4	12	**19** M	00:15	0.4	12
	06:10	3.8	116		05:22	4.0	122
	12:40	-0.1	-3		12:22	-0.2	-6
	18:48	4.3	131		18:20	4.8	146
5 M	01:28	0.3	9	**20** Tu	01:20	0.3	9
	07:01	3.8	116		06:29	4.0	122
	13:26	0.0	0		13:23	-0.2	-6
	19:37	4.4	134		19:22	4.9	149
6 Tu	02:18	0.3	9	**21** W	02:20	0.1	3
	07:50	3.8	116		07:33	4.0	122
	14:11	0.0	0		14:23	-0.3	-9
	20:24	4.5	137		20:23	5.0	152
7 W	03:07	0.2	6	**22** Th	03:18	0.0	0
	08:38	3.8	116		08:34	4.0	122
	14:56	0.0	0		15:21	-0.3	-9
	21:08	4.6	140		21:20	5.1	155
8 Th	03:53	0.2	6	**23** F	04:13	-0.1	-3
	09:24	3.8	116		09:32	4.1	125
	15:40	0.0	0		16:16	-0.3	-9
	21:49	4.6	140		22:13	5.1	155
9 F	04:38	0.2	6	**24** Sa ○	05:05	-0.2	-6
	10:06	3.7	113		10:27	4.1	125
	16:22	0.0	0		17:10	-0.3	-9
	22:26	4.6	140		23:04	5.1	155
10 Sa ●	05:20	0.2	6	**25** Su	05:54	-0.2	-6
	10:45	3.7	113		11:21	4.2	128
	17:04	0.0	0		18:02	-0.2	-6
	22:57	4.6	140		23:54	4.9	149
11 Su	06:01	0.2	6	**26** M	06:41	-0.2	-6
	11:20	3.7	113		12:15	4.2	128
	17:45	0.1	3		18:49	0.0	0
	23:23	4.6	140				
12 M	06:41	0.2	6	**27** Tu	00:43	4.8	146
	11:52	3.8	116		07:26	-0.1	-3
	18:27	0.1	3		13:08	4.1	125
	23:50	4.6	140		19:38	0.1	3
13 Tu	07:19	0.1	3	**28** W	01:31	4.6	140
	12:26	3.9	119		08:09	-0.1	-3
	19:10	0.1	3		14:01	4.1	125
					20:26	0.3	9
14 W	00:28	4.6	140	**29** Th	02:18	4.4	134
	07:59	0.1	3		08:52	0.0	0
	13:11	4.0	122		14:52	4.1	125
	19:58	0.2	6		21:16	0.5	15
15 Th	01:16	4.6	140	**30** F	03:06	4.2	128
	08:41	0.0	0		09:35	0.1	3
	14:06	4.1	125		15:41	4.1	125
	20:54	0.2	6		22:09	0.6	18
				31 Sa ☽	03:54	4.0	122
					10:19	0.2	6
					16:30	4.1	125
					23:04	0.6	18

August

Day	Time (h m)	Height ft	Height cm	Day	Time (h m)	Height ft	Height cm
1 Su	04:43	3.9	119	**16** M	04:06	4.1	125
	11:05	0.2	6		11:01	0.1	3
	17:20	4.2	128		17:03	4.7	143
	23:59	0.6	18				
2 M	05:33	3.8	116	**17** Tu	00:01	0.5	15
	11:53	0.2	6		05:13	4.0	122
	18:10	4.2	128		12:06	0.1	3
					18:07	4.8	146
3 Tu	00:52	0.6	18	**18** W	01:04	0.4	12
	06:25	3.7	113		06:20	4.0	122
	12:43	0.2	6		13:09	0.0	0
	19:01	4.3	131		19:11	4.9	149
4 W	01:44	0.5	15	**19** Th	02:03	0.3	9
	07:16	3.7	113		07:23	4.1	125
	13:32	0.2	6		14:09	-0.1	-3
	19:50	4.4	134		20:10	5.0	152
5 Th	02:33	0.4	12	**20** F	02:59	0.1	3
	08:06	3.8	116		08:23	4.2	128
	14:22	0.1	3		15:06	-0.1	-3
	20:37	4.5	137		21:05	5.1	155
6 F	03:21	0.4	12	**21** Sa	03:52	0.0	0
	08:53	3.9	119		09:19	4.3	131
	15:10	0.1	3		16:00	-0.1	-3
	21:20	4.6	140		21:55	5.1	155
7 Sa	04:07	0.3	9	**22** Su ○	04:41	0.0	0
	09:37	3.9	119		10:11	4.4	134
	15:57	0.1	3		16:52	-0.1	-3
	21:59	4.7	143		22:42	5.1	155
8 Su ●	04:51	0.2	6	**23** M	05:28	-0.1	-3
	10:17	4.0	122		11:01	4.5	137
	16:43	0.0	0		17:40	0.0	0
	22:33	4.8	146		23:27	4.9	149
9 M	05:33	0.2	6	**24** Tu	06:11	0.0	0
	10:54	4.1	125		11:49	4.5	137
	17:29	0.0	0		18:27	0.1	3
	23:04	4.8	146				
10 Tu	06:13	0.1	3	**25** W	00:11	4.8	146
	11:29	4.2	128		06:52	0.1	3
	18:14	0.0	0		12:36	4.4	134
	23:37	4.8	146		19:12	0.3	9
11 W	06:53	0.1	3	**26** Th	00:55	4.6	140
	12:08	4.3	131		07:31	0.2	6
	19:01	0.1	3		13:24	4.4	134
					19:56	0.5	15
12 Th	00:15	4.7	143	**27** F	01:40	4.3	131
	07:33	0.0	0		08:08	0.3	9
	12:54	4.4	134		14:11	4.3	131
	19:51	0.2	6		20:42	0.7	21
13 F	01:02	4.6	140	**28** Sa	02:27	4.1	125
	08:16	0.0	0		08:45	0.4	12
	13:50	4.5	137		14:58	4.3	131
	20:47	0.3	9		21:30	0.8	24
14 Sa	01:58	4.5	137	**29** Su	03:15	4.0	122
	09:04	0.0	0		09:23	0.5	15
	14:53	4.6	140		15:46	4.2	128
	21:49	0.4	12		22:23	0.9	27
15 Su ◐	03:00	4.3	131	**30** M ◐	04:04	3.8	116
	09:59	0.1	3		10:07	0.5	15
	15:58	4.7	143		16:36	4.2	128
	22:55	0.5	15		23:18	0.9	27
				31 Tu	04:55	3.8	116
					11:00	0.5	15
					17:28	4.2	128

September

Day	Time (h m)	Height ft	Height cm	Day	Time (h m)	Height ft	Height cm
1 W	00:14	0.9	27	**16** Th	00:47	0.5	15
	05:48	3.8	116		06:12	4.2	128
	11:57	0.5	15		12:55	0.2	6
	18:20	4.3	131		18:58	4.9	149
2 Th	01:07	0.8	24	**17** F	01:44	0.3	9
	06:41	3.8	116		07:14	4.3	131
	12:54	0.4	12		13:54	0.1	3
	19:12	4.4	134		19:54	5.0	152
3 F	01:58	0.7	21	**18** Sa	02:37	0.2	6
	07:33	3.9	119		08:11	4.5	137
	13:49	0.3	9		14:50	0.1	3
	20:01	4.6	140		20:46	5.0	152
4 Sa	02:47	0.5	15	**19** Su	03:27	0.1	3
	08:21	4.1	125		09:04	4.6	140
	14:41	0.2	6		15:42	0.0	0
	20:46	4.7	143		21:33	5.1	155
5 Su	03:33	0.4	12	**20** M ○	04:14	0.0	0
	09:06	4.3	131		09:52	4.7	143
	15:32	0.1	3		16:32	0.1	3
	21:27	4.9	149		22:16	5.0	152
6 M	04:18	0.3	9	**21** Tu	04:58	0.0	0
	09:48	4.5	137		10:38	4.8	146
	16:22	0.1	3		17:18	0.2	6
	22:05	5.0	152		22:58	4.9	149
7 Tu ●	05:01	0.2	6	**22** W	05:39	0.1	3
	10:27	4.6	140		11:21	4.8	146
	17:11	0.1	3		18:03	0.3	9
	22:41	5.0	152		23:39	4.7	143
8 W	05:43	0.1	3	**23** Th	06:17	0.2	6
	11:07	4.8	146		12:03	4.7	143
	18:00	0.1	3		18:45	0.4	12
	23:18	4.9	149				
9 Th	06:25	0.1	3	**24** F	00:20	4.5	137
	11:49	4.9	149		06:52	0.4	12
	18:50	0.1	3		12:44	4.6	140
					19:27	0.6	18
10 F	00:01	4.8	146	**25** Sa	01:03	4.3	131
	07:08	0.1	3		07:24	0.5	15
	12:38	4.9	149		14:08	4.5	137
	19:42	0.3	9		20:08	0.8	24
11 Sa	00:50	4.6	140	**26** Su	01:47	4.1	125
	07:53	0.1	3		07:54	0.6	18
	13:36	4.9	149		14:08	4.4	134
	20:38	0.4	12		20:52	0.9	27
12 Su	01:49	4.4	134	**27** M	02:33	3.9	119
	08:44	0.2	6		08:26	0.6	18
	14:41	4.9	149		14:54	4.3	131
	21:38	0.6	18		21:41	1.0	30
13 M ◐	02:55	4.3	131	**28** Tu	03:23	3.8	116
	09:42	0.2	6		09:08	0.7	21
	15:47	4.9	149		15:44	4.2	128
	22:42	0.6	18		22:35	1.0	30
14 Tu	04:02	4.1	125	**29** W ◐	04:15	3.8	116
	10:47	0.3	9		10:03	0.7	21
	16:53	4.8	146		16:38	4.2	128
	23:46	0.6	18		23:32	1.0	30
15 W	05:08	4.1	125	**30** Th	05:08	3.8	116
	11:53	0.3	9		11:10	0.7	21
	17:57	4.9	149		17:33	4.3	131

StationId: 8658120
Source: NOAA/NOS/CO-OPS
Station Type: Primary
Time Zone: LST_LDT
Datum: MLLW

NOAA Tide Predictions

Wilmington, NC, 2021

Times and Heights of High and Low Waters

October

	Time	ft	cm		Time	ft	cm
1 F	00:27 06:03 12:16 18:28	0.9 3.9 0.6 4.4	27 119 18 134	**16** Sa	01:20 07:00 13:37 19:32	0.2 4.4 0.2 4.8	6 134 6 146
2 Sa	01:20 06:56 13:17 19:20	0.7 4.1 0.5 4.6	21 125 15 140	**17** Su	02:11 07:55 14:31 20:21	0.1 4.6 0.1 4.9	3 140 3 149
3 Su	02:09 07:46 14:14 20:08	0.6 4.3 0.3 4.8	18 131 9 146	**18** M	02:59 08:45 15:21 21:06	0.0 4.8 0.1 4.8	0 146 3 146
4 M	02:57 08:34 15:08 20:52	0.4 4.6 0.2 4.9	12 140 6 149	**19** Tu	03:44 09:31 16:09 21:49	0.0 4.9 0.1 4.8	0 149 3 146
5 Tu	03:43 09:19 16:02 21:34	0.2 4.8 0.1 5.0	6 146 3 152	**20** W O	04:26 10:13 16:55 22:30	0.0 4.9 0.2 4.7	0 149 6 143
6 W ●	04:29 10:02 16:54 22:16	0.1 5.1 0.0 5.0	3 155 0 152	**21** Th	05:05 10:54 17:38 23:10	0.1 4.9 0.3 4.5	3 149 9 137
7 Th	05:13 10:45 17:45 22:59	0.0 5.2 0.0 4.9	0 158 0 149	**22** F	05:41 11:32 18:20 23:49	0.2 4.8 0.4 4.3	6 146 12 131
8 F	05:58 11:32 18:37 23:46	0.0 5.3 0.1 4.7	0 162 3 143	**23** Sa	06:14 12:08 18:59	0.4 4.7 0.6	12 143 18
9 Sa	06:45 12:24 19:30	0.0 5.3 0.2	0 162 6	**24** Su	00:28 06:44 12:41 19:38	4.1 0.5 4.5 0.7	125 15 137 21
10 Su	00:39 07:34 13:25 20:25	4.5 0.1 5.2 0.4	137 3 158 12	**25** M	01:07 07:12 13:10 20:18	3.9 0.5 4.4 0.8	119 15 134 24
11 M	01:42 08:27 14:31 21:25	4.3 0.2 5.0 0.5	131 6 152 15	**26** Tu	01:48 07:45 13:40 21:02	3.8 0.6 4.3 0.9	116 18 131 27
12 Tu	02:50 09:28 15:37 22:26	4.2 0.3 4.9 0.6	128 9 149 18	**27** W	02:33 08:26 14:26 21:52	3.7 0.6 4.3 1.0	113 18 131 30
13 W ◐	03:56 10:33 16:41 23:28	4.1 0.4 4.8 0.5	125 12 146 15	**28** Th ◐	03:26 09:19 15:27 22:48	3.7 0.6 4.2 0.9	113 18 128 27
14 Th	05:00 11:38 17:41	4.1 0.4 4.8	125 12 146	**29** F	04:22 10:26 16:33 23:44	3.7 0.6 4.3 0.8	113 18 131 24
15 F	00:26 06:02 12:40 18:38	0.4 4.2 0.3 4.8	12 128 9 146	**30** Sa	05:19 11:39 17:35	3.9 0.6 4.4	119 18 134
				31 Su	00:39 06:15 12:46 18:32	0.6 4.1 0.4 4.5	18 125 12 137

November

	Time	ft	cm		Time	ft	cm
1 M	01:30 07:10 13:47 19:26	0.4 4.4 0.3 4.6	12 134 9 140	**16** Tu	01:27 07:21 13:58 19:37	-0.1 4.7 0.1 4.5	-3 143 3 137
2 Tu	02:20 08:01 14:46 20:17	0.2 4.7 0.1 4.7	6 143 3 143	**17** W	02:11 08:06 14:45 20:21	-0.1 4.8 0.1 4.4	-3 146 3 134
3 W	03:09 08:51 15:42 21:05	0.0 5.0 0.0 4.8	0 152 0 146	**18** Th	02:52 08:48 15:31 21:03	-0.1 4.8 0.1 4.3	-3 146 3 131
4 Th ●	03:57 09:39 16:36 21:52	-0.1 5.3 0.0 4.8	-3 162 0 146	**19** F O	03:32 09:28 16:14 21:43	0.0 4.8 0.2 4.2	0 146 6 128
5 F	04:46 10:27 17:30 22:40	-0.2 5.4 -0.1 4.7	-6 165 -3 143	**20** Sa	04:08 10:05 16:55 22:22	0.1 4.7 0.3 4.1	3 143 9 125
6 Sa	05:35 11:17 18:23 23:32	-0.2 5.4 0.0 4.5	-6 165 0 137	**21** Su	04:42 10:43 17:34 22:58	0.2 4.6 0.4 3.9	6 140 12 119
7 Su	05:25 11:13 18:16 23:29	-0.2 5.3 0.1 4.3	-6 162 3 131	**22** M	05:14 11:06 18:12 23:32	0.3 4.5 0.5 3.8	9 137 15 116
8 M	06:17 12:15 19:10	-0.1 5.1 0.2	-3 155 6	**23** Tu	05:45 11:24 18:49	0.3 4.4 0.6	9 134 18
9 Tu	00:33 07:12 13:20 20:07	4.2 0.1 5.0 0.3	128 3 152 9	**24** W	00:01 06:19 11:53 19:28	3.7 0.3 4.3 0.7	113 9 131 21
10 W	01:40 08:12 14:22 21:05	4.1 0.2 4.8 0.3	125 6 146 9	**25** Th	00:35 07:00 12:37 20:12	3.6 0.4 4.3 0.7	110 12 131 21
11 Th ◑	02:44 09:15 15:22 22:03	4.1 0.3 4.7 0.3	125 9 143 9	**26** F	01:25 07:50 13:33 21:03	3.6 0.4 4.3 0.6	110 12 131 18
12 F	03:45 10:18 16:18 22:59	4.1 0.3 4.6 0.2	125 9 140 6	**27** Sa ◑	02:26 08:53 14:36 21:59	3.7 0.4 4.3 0.5	113 12 131 15
13 Sa	04:44 11:19 17:12 23:52	4.2 0.3 4.5 0.0	128 9 137 0	**28** Su	03:30 10:07 15:41 22:55	3.9 0.4 4.3 0.3	119 12 131 9
14 Su	05:40 12:15 18:03	4.4 0.2 4.5	134 6 137	**29** M	04:32 11:18 16:45 23:50	4.1 0.4 4.3 0.2	125 12 131 6
15 M	00:41 06:32 13:08 18:51	-0.1 4.5 0.1 4.5	-3 137 3 137	**30** Tu	05:32 12:23 17:47	4.4 0.2 4.4	134 6 134

December

	Time	ft	cm		Time	ft	cm
1 W	00:44 06:30 13:25 18:44	0.0 4.8 0.1 4.4	0 146 3 134	**16** Th	01:37 07:39 14:19 19:53	-0.1 4.6 0.1 4.1	-3 140 3 125
2 Th	01:37 07:26 14:23 19:39	-0.2 5.0 0.0 4.5	-6 152 0 137	**17** F	02:20 08:23 15:05 20:37	-0.1 4.6 0.1 4.1	-3 140 3 125
3 F	02:31 08:19 15:19 20:32	-0.3 5.2 -0.1 4.5	-9 158 -3 137	**18** Sa	03:01 09:04 15:48 21:19	-0.1 4.6 0.1 4.0	-3 140 3 122
4 Sa ●	03:24 09:12 16:14 21:25	-0.4 5.3 -0.2 4.4	-12 162 -6 134	**19** Su O	03:40 09:42 16:30 21:58	0.0 4.6 0.2 3.9	0 140 6 119
5 Su	04:17 10:06 17:07 22:20	-0.4 5.3 -0.2 4.3	-12 162 -6 131	**20** M	04:17 10:16 17:09 22:33	0.0 4.5 0.3 3.8	0 137 9 116
6 M	05:09 11:03 17:59 23:18	-0.4 5.2 -0.1 4.2	-12 158 -3 128	**21** Tu	04:52 10:44 17:47 23:04	0.1 4.4 0.3 3.7	3 134 9 113
7 Tu	06:02 12:02 18:51	-0.3 5.0 0.0	-9 152 0	**22** W	05:27 11:02 18:23 23:28	0.1 4.4 0.4 3.7	3 134 12 113
8 W	00:20 06:57 13:02 19:44	4.1 -0.1 4.8 0.0	125 -3 146 0	**23** Th	06:03 11:29 18:59 23:59	0.1 4.4 0.4 3.7	3 134 12 113
9 Th	01:24 07:53 14:00 20:38	4.0 0.0 4.6 0.1	122 0 140 3	**24** F	06:44 12:11 19:38	0.1 4.4 0.4	3 134 12
10 F	02:24 08:53 14:55 21:33	4.0 0.2 4.5 0.1	122 6 137 3	**25** Sa	00:45 07:32 13:02 20:22	3.8 0.2 4.3 0.3	116 6 131 9
11 Sa ◑	03:22 09:53 15:47 22:26	4.0 0.3 4.3 0.0	122 9 131 0	**26** Su	01:42 08:31 13:59 21:14	3.9 0.3 4.3 0.2	119 9 131 6
12 Su	04:18 10:52 16:39 23:18	4.1 0.3 4.2 -0.1	125 9 128 -3	**27** M ◑	02:46 09:42 15:02 22:13	4.1 0.3 4.2 0.1	125 9 128 3
13 M	05:12 11:48 17:29	4.2 0.2 4.2	128 6 128	**28** Tu	03:53 10:55 16:08 23:13	4.3 0.3 4.1 0.0	131 9 125 0
14 Tu	00:06 06:03 12:41 18:19	-0.1 4.4 0.1 4.1	-3 134 3 125	**29** W	04:59 12:03 17:15	4.5 0.2 4.1	137 6 125
15 W	00:52 06:53 13:31 19:07	-0.1 4.5 0.1 4.1	-3 137 3 125	**30** Th	00:13 06:04 13:06 18:19	-0.1 4.7 0.1 4.2	-3 143 3 128
				31 F	01:12 07:06 14:05 18:59	-0.2 4.9 0.0 4.2	-6 149 0 128

131

StationId: 8660642
Source: NOAA/NOS/CO-OPS
Station Type: Subordinate
Time Zone: LST_LDT
Datum: MLLW

NOAA Tide Predictions

NORTH MYRTLE BEACH, SC,2021

Times and Heights of High and Low Waters

January

Day	Time (h m)	Height (ft)	Height (cm)
1 F	06:04	-0.3	-9
	11:24	2.1	64
	18:49	0.0	0
	23:44	1.7	52
2 Sa	06:49	-0.3	-9
	12:05	2.1	64
	19:31	0.0	0
3 Su	00:28	1.7	52
	07:37	-0.2	-6
	12:49	2.0	61
	20:17	0.0	0
4 M	01:18	1.7	52
	08:29	-0.1	-3
	13:37	2.0	61
	21:05	0.0	0
5 Tu	02:14	1.7	52
	09:28	0.1	3
	14:31	1.9	58
	21:59	-0.1	-3
6 W ◖	03:16	1.8	55
	10:32	0.1	3
	15:30	1.8	55
	22:56	-0.1	-3
7 Th	04:22	1.9	58
	11:40	0.1	3
	16:33	1.8	55
	23:56	-0.2	-6
8 F	05:28	2.0	61
	12:48	0.1	3
	17:38	1.7	52
9 Sa	00:57	-0.3	-9
	06:33	2.1	64
	13:52	-0.1	-3
	18:41	1.7	52
10 Su	01:57	-0.5	-15
	07:34	2.2	67
	14:51	-0.3	-9
	19:42	1.8	55
11 M	02:54	-0.6	-18
	08:31	2.2	67
	15:46	-0.4	-12
	20:39	1.8	55
12 Tu	03:49	-0.7	-21
	09:25	2.3	70
	16:38	-0.5	-15
	21:32	1.8	55
13 W ●	04:41	-0.7	-21
	10:16	2.3	70
	17:27	-0.5	-15
	22:23	1.8	55
14 Th	05:30	-0.7	-21
	11:04	2.2	67
	18:14	-0.4	-12
	23:11	1.8	55
15 F	06:18	-0.5	-15
	11:50	2.1	64
	18:59	-0.3	-9
	23:57	1.8	55
16 Sa	07:04	-0.3	-9
	12:33	2.0	61
	19:42	-0.1	-3
17 Su	00:43	1.7	52
	07:51	0.0	0
	13:16	1.9	58
	20:25	0.0	0
18 M	01:29	1.7	52
	08:38	0.3	9
	13:59	1.8	55
	21:07	0.2	6
19 Tu	02:16	1.7	52
	09:27	0.5	15
	14:43	1.7	52
	21:50	0.3	9
20 W ◐	03:06	1.6	49
	10:21	0.7	21
	15:31	1.6	49
	22:36	0.4	12
21 Th	03:58	1.7	52
	11:18	0.8	24
	16:22	1.5	46
	23:25	0.4	12
22 F	04:52	1.7	52
	12:18	0.8	24
	17:16	1.5	46
23 Sa	00:16	0.4	12
	05:46	1.7	52
	13:15	0.7	21
	18:10	1.5	46
24 Su	01:08	0.3	9
	06:39	1.8	55
	14:07	0.6	18
	19:03	1.5	46
25 M	01:59	0.1	3
	07:30	1.9	58
	14:55	0.4	12
	19:52	1.5	46
26 Tu	02:48	-0.1	-3
	08:18	2.0	61
	15:40	0.2	6
	20:39	1.6	49
27 W	03:34	-0.3	-9
	09:03	2.0	61
	16:22	0.0	0
	21:22	1.7	52
28 Th ○	04:19	-0.4	-12
	09:45	2.1	64
	17:04	-0.1	-3
	22:04	1.7	52
29 F	05:04	-0.6	-18
	10:27	2.1	64
	17:45	-0.3	-9
	22:46	1.8	55
30 Sa	05:49	-0.6	-18
	11:07	2.1	64
	18:26	-0.4	-12
	23:29	1.8	55
31 Su	06:36	-0.6	-18
	11:49	2.1	64
	19:09	-0.4	-12

February

Day	Time (h m)	Height (ft)	Height (cm)
1 M	00:14	1.8	55
	07:25	-0.5	-15
	12:33	2.0	61
	19:53	-0.4	-12
2 Tu	01:03	1.9	58
	08:17	-0.4	-12
	13:20	1.9	58
	20:41	-0.4	-12
3 W	01:58	1.9	58
	09:15	-0.2	-6
	14:12	1.8	55
	21:33	-0.3	-9
4 Th ◑	02:58	1.9	58
	10:18	0.0	0
	15:11	1.7	52
	22:31	-0.2	-6
5 F	04:04	1.9	58
	11:25	0.1	3
	16:15	1.7	52
	23:34	-0.2	-6
6 Sa	05:13	2.0	61
	12:33	0.1	3
	17:22	1.6	49
7 Su	00:39	-0.2	-6
	06:21	2.0	61
	13:37	0.0	0
	18:29	1.6	49
8 M	01:43	-0.3	-9
	07:24	2.1	64
	14:36	-0.1	-3
	19:31	1.7	52
9 Tu	02:42	-0.4	-12
	08:21	2.1	64
	15:30	-0.3	-9
	20:27	1.7	52
10 W	03:37	-0.5	-15
	09:13	2.1	64
	16:20	-0.4	-12
	21:19	1.8	55
11 Th ●	04:28	-0.6	-18
	10:00	2.1	64
	17:06	-0.4	-12
	22:06	1.8	55
12 F	05:15	-0.5	-15
	10:43	2.1	64
	17:48	-0.4	-12
	22:50	1.8	55
13 Sa ○	05:59	-0.4	-12
	11:23	2.0	61
	18:29	-0.3	-9
	23:31	1.8	55
14 Su	06:41	-0.2	-6
	12:02	1.9	58
	19:07	-0.2	-6
15 M	00:11	1.8	55
	07:23	0.0	0
	12:39	1.8	55
	19:43	0.0	0
16 Tu	00:50	1.8	55
	08:04	0.3	9
	13:17	1.7	52
	20:20	0.1	3
17 W	01:30	1.8	55
	08:47	0.5	15
	13:56	1.6	49
	20:58	0.3	9
18 Th	02:13	1.7	52
	09:33	0.7	21
	14:40	1.5	46
	21:39	0.4	12
19 F ◐	03:01	1.7	52
	10:26	0.8	24
	15:30	1.5	46
	22:28	0.5	15
20 Sa	03:55	1.7	52
	11:25	0.9	27
	16:27	1.4	43
	23:23	0.5	15
21 Su	04:54	1.7	52
	12:26	0.9	27
	17:26	1.4	43
22 M	00:23	0.5	15
	05:54	1.8	55
	13:25	0.7	21
	18:24	1.5	46
23 Tu	01:21	0.3	9
	06:52	1.8	55
	14:18	0.5	15
	19:18	1.6	49
24 W	02:17	0.0	0
	07:45	1.9	58
	15:06	0.2	6
	20:08	1.7	52
25 Th	03:08	-0.3	-9
	08:34	2.0	61
	15:52	0.0	0
	20:56	1.8	55
26 F	03:58	-0.5	-15
	09:19	2.1	64
	16:35	-0.3	-9
	21:41	1.9	58
27 Sa ○	04:46	-0.7	-21
	10:03	2.2	67
	17:18	-0.5	-15
	22:26	2.0	61
28 Su	05:34	-0.8	-24
	10:47	2.2	67
	18:01	-0.6	-18
	23:11	2.1	64

March

Day	Time (h m)	Height (ft)	Height (cm)
1 M	06:23	-0.8	-24
	11:30	2.1	64
	18:44	-0.6	-18
	23:58	2.1	64
2 Tu	07:13	-0.7	-21
	12:16	2.0	61
	19:30	-0.6	-18
3 W	00:48	2.1	64
	08:06	-0.5	-15
	13:04	1.9	58
	20:18	-0.5	-15
4 Th	01:43	2.1	64
	09:03	-0.2	-6
	13:58	1.8	55
	21:11	-0.3	-9
5 F	02:43	2.0	61
	10:04	0.0	0
	14:57	1.7	52
	22:11	-0.1	-3
6 Sa ◖	03:50	2.0	61
	11:10	0.2	6
	16:03	1.6	49
	23:16	0.1	3
7 Su	05:00	2.0	61
	12:17	0.3	9
	17:12	1.6	49
8 M	00:25	0.1	3
	06:08	2.0	61
	13:21	0.2	6
	18:19	1.6	49
9 Tu	01:31	0.0	0
	07:10	2.0	61
	14:18	0.1	3
	19:20	1.7	52
10 W	02:31	-0.1	-3
	08:05	2.0	61
	15:10	-0.1	-3
	20:14	1.8	55
11 Th	03:24	-0.2	-6
	08:54	2.1	64
	15:57	-0.2	-6
	21:02	1.9	58
12 F	04:12	-0.3	-9
	09:37	2.1	64
	16:39	-0.2	-6
	21:45	1.9	58
13 Sa ●	04:57	-0.3	-9
	10:17	2.0	61
	17:19	-0.3	-9
	22:25	2.0	61
14 Su	06:38	-0.2	-6
	11:54	2.0	61
	18:55	-0.2	-6
15 M	00:03	2.0	61
	07:18	-0.1	-3
	12:30	1.9	58
	19:30	-0.1	-3
16 Tu	00:38	2.0	61
	07:56	0.1	3
	13:05	1.8	55
	20:03	0.1	3
17 W	01:13	1.9	58
	08:34	0.3	9
	13:40	1.7	52
	20:36	0.2	6
18 Th	01:49	1.9	58
	09:12	0.5	15
	14:17	1.6	49
	21:12	0.4	12
19 F ◐	02:27	1.8	55
	09:53	0.7	21
	14:57	1.5	46
	21:52	0.5	15
20 Sa	03:11	1.8	55
	10:41	0.8	24
	15:45	1.5	46
	22:40	0.6	18
21 Su ◑	04:03	1.8	55
	11:36	0.9	27
	16:40	1.4	43
	23:36	0.7	21
22 M	05:03	1.8	55
	12:38	0.9	27
	17:41	1.5	46
23 Tu	00:40	0.6	18
	06:07	1.8	55
	13:40	0.8	24
	18:43	1.5	46
24 W	01:45	0.4	12
	07:09	1.9	58
	14:37	0.6	18
	19:42	1.6	49
25 Th	02:46	0.2	6
	08:07	2.0	61
	15:29	0.2	6
	20:36	1.8	55
26 F	03:42	-0.2	-6
	08:59	2.1	64
	16:17	-0.1	-3
	21:27	2.0	61
27 Sa	04:35	-0.5	-15
	09:49	2.1	64
	16:55	-0.4	-12
	22:16	2.1	64
28 Su ○	05:27	-0.7	-21
	10:36	2.2	67
	17:48	-0.6	-18
	23:04	2.2	67
29 M	06:18	-0.8	-24
	11:23	2.2	67
	18:33	-0.7	-21
	23:52	2.3	70
30 Tu	07:09	-0.8	-24
	12:10	2.1	64
	19:19	-0.7	-21
31 W	00:41	2.3	70
	08:00	-0.7	-21
	12:59	2.0	61
	20:07	-0.6	-18

StationId: 8660642
Source: NOAA/NOS/CO-OPS
Station Type: Subordinate
Time Zone: LST_LDT
Datum: MLLW

NOAA Tide Predictions

NORTH MYRTLE BEACH, SC, 2021

Times and Heights of High and Low Waters

April

Day	Time	ft	cm
1 Th	01:33	2.3	70
	08:54	-0.5	-15
	13:50	1.9	58
	20:58	-0.4	-12
2 F	02:29	2.2	67
	09:51	-0.2	-6
	14:46	1.8	55
	21:53	-0.1	-3
3 Sa	03:30	2.1	64
	10:51	0.1	3
	15:47	1.7	52
	22:55	0.1	3
4 Su	04:36	2.0	61
		0.3	9
	16:54	1.7	52
5 M	00:02	0.3	9
	05:44	2.0	61
	12:58	0.3	9
	18:01	1.7	52
6 Tu	01:11	0.4	12
	06:49	2.0	61
	13:59	0.3	9
	19:05	1.7	52
7 W	02:16	0.3	9
	07:48	2.0	61
	14:54	0.2	6
	20:03	1.8	55
8 Th	03:15	0.2	6
	08:40	2.0	61
	15:43	0.1	3
	20:54	1.9	58
9 F	04:06	0.1	3
	09:26	2.0	61
	16:27	0.0	0
	21:39	2.0	61
10 Sa	04:53	0.0	0
	10:07	2.0	61
	17:07	-0.1	-3
	22:20	2.0	61
11 Su	05:36	0.0	0
	10:46	1.9	58
	17:45	-0.1	-3
	22:58	2.1	64
12 M	06:16	0.1	3
	11:23	1.9	58
	18:20	0.0	0
	23:34	2.1	64
13 Tu	06:54	0.1	3
	11:59	1.8	55
	18:53	0.1	3
14 W	00:08	2.1	64
	07:31	0.3	9
	12:34	1.7	52
	19:26	0.2	6
15 Th	00:41	2.0	61
	08:07	0.4	12
	13:09	1.7	52
	20:00	0.3	9
16 F	01:15	2.0	61
	08:44	0.5	15
	13:45	1.6	49
	20:36	0.5	15
17 Sa	01:51	1.9	58
	09:23	0.7	21
	14:24	1.5	46
	21:17	0.6	18
18 Su	02:33	1.9	58
	10:08	0.8	24
	15:08	1.5	46
	22:05	0.7	21
19 M	03:23	1.9	58
	10:59	0.8	24
	16:02	1.5	46
	23:01	0.7	21
20 Tu	04:20	1.9	58
	11:57	0.8	24
	17:03	1.5	46
21 W	00:04	0.7	21
	05:23	1.9	58
	12:57	0.7	21
	18:06	1.6	49
22 Th	01:11	0.5	15
	06:26	1.9	58
	13:55	0.4	12
	19:07	1.8	55
23 F	02:16	0.3	9
	07:26	2.0	61
	14:50	0.1	3
	20:04	1.9	58
24 Sa	03:16	-0.1	-3
	08:22	2.0	61
	15:41	-0.2	-6
	20:58	2.1	64
25 Su	04:13	-0.4	-12
	09:15	2.1	64
	16:30	-0.5	-15
	21:50	2.3	70
26 M	05:08	-0.6	-18
	10:07	2.1	64
	17:19	-0.7	-21
	22:41	2.4	73
27 Tu	06:01	-0.7	-21
	10:58	2.1	64
	18:07	-0.8	-24
	23:33	2.5	76
28 W	06:54	-0.7	-21
	11:50	2.0	61
	18:56	-0.7	-21
29 Th	00:25	2.5	76
	07:44	-0.6	-18
	12:42	2.0	61
	19:47	-0.6	-18
30 F	01:19	2.4	73
	08:41	-0.4	-12
	13:37	1.9	58
	20:40	-0.3	-9

May

Day	Time	ft	cm
1 Sa	02:17	2.3	70
	09:36	-0.2	-6
	14:35	1.8	55
	21:37	0.0	0
2 Su	03:17	2.2	67
	10:34	0.0	0
	15:37	1.7	52
	22:39	0.2	6
3 M	04:19	2.1	64
	11:34	0.2	6
	16:41	1.7	52
	23:45	0.4	12
4 Tu	05:21	2.0	61
	12:34	0.3	9
	17:44	1.7	52
5 W	00:52	0.5	15
	06:20	1.9	58
	13:30	0.3	9
	18:44	1.8	55
6 Th	01:55	0.5	15
	07:15	1.9	58
	14:22	0.2	6
	19:38	1.9	58
7 F	02:52	0.5	15
	08:04	1.9	58
	15:09	0.1	3
	20:26	1.9	58
8 Sa	03:43	0.4	12
	08:49	1.8	55
	15:51	0.1	3
	21:10	2.0	61
9 Su	04:29	0.3	9
	09:32	1.8	55
	16:31	0.0	0
	21:51	2.1	64
10 M	05:12	0.3	9
	10:12	1.8	55
	17:09	0.0	0
	22:29	2.1	64
11 Tu	05:52	0.2	6
	10:51	1.8	55
	17:45	0.1	3
	23:05	2.1	64
12 W	06:30	0.3	9
	11:30	1.7	52
	18:20	0.1	3
	23:40	2.1	64
13 Th	07:07	0.3	9
	12:07	1.7	52
	18:55	0.2	6
14 F	00:15	2.1	64
	07:44	0.4	12
	12:43	1.6	49
	19:31	0.3	9
15 Sa	00:49	2.0	61
	08:21	0.5	15
	13:20	1.6	49
	20:09	0.4	12
16 Su	01:26	2.0	61
	09:00	0.6	18
	13:58	1.5	46
	20:51	0.5	15
17 M	02:07	2.0	61
	09:43	0.6	18
	14:42	1.5	46
	21:39	0.6	18
18 Tu	02:54	1.9	58
	10:31	0.6	18
	15:34	1.6	49
	22:35	0.6	18
19 W	03:48	1.9	58
	11:24	0.5	15
	16:33	1.6	49
	23:37	0.6	18
20 Th	04:47	1.9	58
	12:21	0.4	12
	17:34	1.7	52
21 F	00:43	0.5	15
	05:47	1.9	58
	13:17	0.2	6
	18:36	1.9	58
22 Sa	01:50	0.2	6
	06:48	1.9	58
	14:13	-0.1	-3
	19:35	2.1	64
23 Su	02:53	0.0	0
	07:46	2.0	61
	15:07	-0.4	-12
	20:31	2.2	67
24 M	03:52	-0.3	-9
	08:44	2.0	61
	16:00	-0.6	-18
	21:27	2.4	73
25 Tu	04:49	-0.5	-15
	09:40	2.0	61
	16:52	-0.7	-21
	22:21	2.5	76
26 W	05:44	-0.6	-18
	10:35	2.0	61
	17:44	-0.8	-24
	23:16	2.5	76
27 Th	06:38	-0.6	-18
	11:30	1.9	58
	18:36	-0.7	-21
28 F	00:11	2.5	76
	07:31	-0.6	-18
	12:26	1.9	58
	19:29	-0.5	-15
29 Sa	01:06	2.4	73
	08:25	-0.4	-12
	13:23	1.8	55
	20:24	-0.3	-9
30 Su	02:02	2.3	70
	09:19	-0.2	-6
	14:21	1.8	55
	21:21	0.0	0
31 M	02:59	2.2	67
	10:13	0.0	0
	15:20	1.8	55
	22:20	0.3	9

June

Day	Time	ft	cm
1 Tu	03:55	2.0	61
	11:08	0.1	3
	16:20	1.7	52
	23:22	0.5	15
2 W	04:50	1.9	58
	12:02	0.2	6
	17:18	1.8	55
3 Th	00:25	0.6	18
	05:43	1.8	55
	12:54	0.2	6
	18:13	1.8	55
4 F	01:25	0.7	21
	06:34	1.8	55
	13:43	0.2	6
	19:04	1.9	58
5 Sa	02:22	0.7	21
	07:22	1.7	52
	14:28	0.2	6
	19:52	1.9	58
6 Su	03:13	0.6	18
	08:08	1.7	52
	15:11	0.1	3
	20:36	2.0	61
7 M	04:00	0.5	15
	08:54	1.7	52
	15:53	0.1	3
	21:18	2.1	64
8 Tu	04:44	0.4	12
	09:37	1.7	52
	16:33	0.1	3
	21:59	2.1	64
9 W	05:26	0.4	12
	10:20	1.7	52
	17:12	0.1	3
	22:38	2.1	64
10 Th	06:05	0.3	9
	11:02	1.6	49
	17:50	0.1	3
	23:16	2.1	64
11 F	06:43	0.3	9
	11:41	1.6	49
	18:28	0.2	6
	23:53	2.1	64
12 Sa	07:21	0.4	12
	12:20	1.6	49
	19:07	0.2	6
13 Su	00:29	2.1	64
	07:59	0.4	12
	12:58	1.6	49
	19:48	0.3	9
14 M	01:07	2.0	61
	08:39	0.4	12
	13:38	1.6	49
	20:32	0.3	9
15 Tu	01:47	2.0	61
	09:21	0.4	12
	14:22	1.6	49
	21:21	0.4	12
16 W	02:33	2.0	61
	10:06	0.3	9
	15:13	1.6	49
	22:16	0.4	12
17 Th	03:23	2.0	61
	10:56	0.2	6
	16:09	1.7	52
	23:16	0.4	12
18 F	04:18	1.9	58
	11:48	0.1	3
	17:09	1.8	55
19 Sa	00:21	0.4	12
	05:16	1.9	58
	12:44	-0.1	-3
	18:10	2.0	61
20 Su	01:28	0.2	6
	06:16	1.9	58
	13:41	-0.3	-9
	19:10	2.1	64
21 M	02:32	0.1	3
	07:17	1.9	58
	14:38	-0.5	-15
	20:10	2.3	70
22 Tu	03:34	-0.2	-6
	08:18	1.9	58
	15:34	-0.6	-18
	21:08	2.4	73
23 W	04:32	-0.3	-9
	09:17	1.9	58
	16:30	-0.7	-21
	22:05	2.4	73
24 Th	05:27	-0.5	-15
	10:16	1.9	58
	17:25	-0.7	-21
	23:01	2.4	73
25 F	06:21	-0.5	-15
	11:13	1.9	58
	18:19	-0.6	-18
	23:57	2.4	73
26 Sa	07:14	-0.5	-15
	12:09	1.8	55
	19:13	-0.5	-15
27 Su	00:50	2.3	70
	08:05	-0.4	-12
	13:05	1.8	55
	20:07	-0.2	-6
28 M	01:43	2.2	67
	08:56	-0.2	-6
	14:00	1.8	55
	21:01	0.0	0
29 Tu	02:34	2.1	64
	09:46	-0.1	-3
	14:55	1.8	55
	21:56	0.3	9
30 W	03:24	2.0	61
	10:35	0.1	3
	15:49	1.8	55
	22:53	0.6	18

StationId: 8660642
Source: NOAA/NOS/CO-OPS
Station Type: Subordinate
Time Zone: LST_LDT
Datum: MLLW

NOAA Tide Predictions

NORTH MYRTLE BEACH, SC,2021

Times and Heights of High and Low Waters

July

Day	Time	ft	cm	Day	Time	ft	cm
1 Th ◐	04:12	1.9	58	**16** F	03:01	2.0	61
	11:23	0.2	6		10:29	0.0	0
	16:42	1.8	55		15:48	1.9	58
	23:51	0.7	21		23:00	0.4	12
2 F	05:01	1.8	55	**17** Sa ◑	03:54	1.9	58
	12:11	0.2	6		11:21	-0.1	-3
	17:34	1.8	55		16:48	2.0	61
3 Sa	00:49	0.8	24	**18** Su	00:04	0.4	12
	05:49	1.7	52		04:52	1.9	58
	12:58	0.3	9		12:17	-0.2	-6
	18:24	1.9	58		17:49	2.1	64
4 Su	01:45	0.8	24	**19** M	01:10	0.3	9
	06:38	1.6	49		05:53	1.8	55
	13:44	0.3	9		13:16	-0.2	-6
	19:12	1.9	58		18:52	2.2	67
5 M	02:38	0.8	24	**20** Tu	02:15	0.2	6
	07:27	1.6	49		06:56	1.8	55
	14:29	0.2	6		14:16	-0.3	-9
	19:59	2.0	61		19:54	2.3	70
6 Tu	03:27	0.7	21	**21** W	03:17	0.1	3
	08:16	1.6	49		07:59	1.8	55
	15:14	0.2	6		15:16	-0.4	-12
	20:45	2.0	61		20:55	2.3	70
7 W	04:13	0.6	18	**22** Th	04:15	-0.1	-3
	09:03	1.6	49		09:01	1.8	55
	15:58	0.2	6		16:15	-0.5	-15
	21:29	2.1	64		21:53	2.4	73
8 Th	04:56	0.5	15	**23** F	05:10	-0.2	-6
	09:49	1.6	49		10:00	1.9	58
	16:41	0.1	3		17:11	-0.5	-15
	22:11	2.1	64		22:48	2.4	73
9 F	05:37	0.4	12	**24** Sa ○	06:03	-0.3	-9
	10:33	1.6	49		10:57	1.9	58
	17:24	0.1	3		18:04	-0.5	-15
	22:52	2.1	64		23:40	2.4	73
10 Sa ●	06:17	0.3	9	**25** Su	06:52	-0.3	-9
	11:16	1.6	49		11:51	1.9	58
	18:05	0.1	3		18:56	-0.3	-9
	23:32	2.1	64				
11 Su	06:56	0.3	9	**26** M	00:30	2.3	70
	11:56	1.6	49		07:40	-0.2	-6
	18:47	0.1	3		12:43	1.9	58
					19:47	-0.1	-3
12 M	00:10	2.1	64	**27** Tu	01:17	2.2	67
	07:35	0.2	6		08:27	-0.1	-3
	12:36	1.7	52		13:33	1.9	58
	19:31	0.1	3		20:37	0.2	6
13 Tu	00:48	2.1	64	**28** W	02:02	2.1	64
	08:15	0.2	6		09:11	0.0	0
	13:18	1.7	52		14:22	1.9	58
	20:16	0.2	6		21:27	0.5	15
14 W	01:29	2.1	64	**29** Th	02:46	2.0	61
	08:57	0.1	3		09:55	0.2	6
	14:03	1.7	52		15:11	1.8	55
	21:06	0.2	6		22:18	0.7	21
15 Th	02:13	2.0	61	**30** F	03:31	1.8	55
	09:41	0.1	3		10:38	0.3	9
	14:53	1.8	55		15:59	1.8	55
	22:00	0.3	9		23:12	0.9	27
				31 Sa ◐	04:16	1.7	52
					11:23	0.4	12
					16:48	1.9	58

August

Day	Time	ft	cm	Day	Time	ft	cm
1 Su	00:07	1.0	30	**16** M	04:36	1.8	55
	05:05	1.7	52		11:56	0.0	0
	12:09	0.5	15		17:35	2.2	67
	17:39	1.9	58				
2 M	01:03	1.1	34	**17** Tu	00:56	0.5	15
	05:56	1.6	49		05:40	1.8	55
	12:57	0.5	15		12:59	0.0	0
	18:30	1.9	58		18:41	2.2	67
3 Tu	01:58	1.0	30	**18** W	02:01	0.5	15
	06:48	1.6	49		06:45	1.8	55
	13:47	0.5	15		14:03	0.0	0
	19:21	2.0	61		19:45	2.3	70
4 W	02:50	0.9	27	**19** Th	03:03	0.3	9
	07:40	1.6	49		07:50	1.8	55
	14:37	0.4	12		15:05	-0.1	-3
	20:10	2.0	61		20:45	2.3	70
5 Th	03:38	0.8	24	**20** F	03:59	0.2	6
	08:30	1.6	49		08:50	1.9	58
	15:26	0.3	9		16:03	-0.2	-6
	20:58	2.1	64		21:41	2.3	70
6 F	04:23	0.7	21	**21** Sa	04:52	0.0	0
	09:18	1.7	52		09:47	1.9	58
	16:13	0.2	6		16:58	-0.2	-6
	21:44	2.1	64		22:32	2.4	73
7 Sa	05:06	0.5	15	**22** Su ○	05:41	0.0	0
	10:04	1.7	52		10:40	2.0	61
	16:59	0.1	3		17:49	-0.2	-6
	22:26	2.2	67		23:19	2.3	70
8 Su ●	05:47	0.4	12	**23** M	06:27	-0.1	-3
	10:48	1.8	55		11:29	2.0	61
	17:43	0.0	0		18:38	0.0	0
	23:07	2.2	67				
9 M	06:27	0.2	6	**24** Tu	00:03	2.3	70
	11:30	1.8	55		07:10	0.0	0
	18:28	0.0	0		12:16	2.0	61
	23:47	2.2	67		19:24	0.2	6
10 Tu	07:07	0.1	3	**25** W	00:45	2.2	67
	12:13	1.9	58		07:52	0.1	3
	19:14	0.0	0		13:00	2.0	61
					20:10	0.4	12
11 W	00:27	2.2	67	**26** Th	01:26	2.1	64
	07:48	0.0	0		08:32	0.2	6
	12:56	1.9	58		13:43	2.0	61
	20:01	0.1	3		20:55	0.7	21
12 Th	01:08	2.2	67	**27** F	02:06	1.9	58
	08:30	0.0	0		09:11	0.4	12
	13:43	2.0	61		14:27	2.0	61
	20:52	0.2	6		21:41	0.9	27
13 F	01:53	2.1	64	**28** Sa	02:48	1.8	55
	09:15	0.0	0		09:50	0.6	18
	14:34	2.0	61		15:11	1.9	58
	21:47	0.3	9		22:30	1.1	34
14 Sa	02:42	2.0	61	**29** Su	03:32	1.7	52
	10:03	0.0	0		10:32	0.7	21
	15:30	2.1	64		15:59	1.9	58
	22:46	0.4	12		23:22	1.3	40
15 Su ◑	03:36	1.9	58	**30** M ◐	04:21	1.7	52
	10:57	0.0	0		11:19	0.8	24
	16:31	2.1	64		16:51	1.9	58
	23:50	0.5	15				
				31 Tu	00:17	1.3	40
					05:14	1.6	49
					12:10	0.9	27
					17:45	1.9	58

September

Day	Time	ft	cm	Day	Time	ft	cm
1 W	01:14	1.3	40	**16** Th	01:47	0.7	21
	06:09	1.6	49		06:40	1.9	58
	13:06	0.8	24		13:54	0.3	9
	18:41	2.0	61		19:36	2.3	70
2 Th	02:09	1.2	37	**17** F	02:47	0.5	15
	07:04	1.7	52		07:43	1.9	58
	14:01	0.7	21		14:56	0.3	9
	19:34	2.0	61		20:32	2.3	70
3 F	03:00	1.0	30	**18** Sa	03:41	0.4	12
	07:57	1.7	52		08:41	2.0	61
	14:55	0.5	15		15:53	0.2	6
	20:25	2.1	64		21:24	2.3	70
4 Sa	03:47	0.8	24	**19** Su	04:30	0.2	6
	08:47	1.8	55		09:33	2.1	64
	15:45	0.3	9		16:44	0.1	3
	21:12	2.2	67		22:10	2.3	70
5 Su	04:31	0.6	18	**20** M ○	05:15	0.1	3
	09:34	1.9	58		10:21	2.1	64
	16:34	0.2	6		17:32	0.2	6
	21:56	2.3	70		22:53	2.3	70
6 M	05:14	0.3	9	**21** Tu	05:57	0.1	3
	10:19	2.0	61		11:05	2.2	67
	17:22	0.0	0		18:18	0.3	9
	22:38	2.3	70		23:33	2.2	67
7 Tu ●	05:55	0.1	3	**22** W	06:37	0.2	6
	11:03	2.1	64		11:46	2.2	67
	18:09	-0.1	-3		19:01	0.4	12
	23:20	2.3	70				
8 W	06:37	0.0	0	**23** Th	00:11	2.1	64
	11:48	2.2	67		07:15	0.3	9
	18:57	-0.1	-3		12:25	2.2	67
					19:42	0.6	18
9 Th	00:02	2.3	70	**24** F	00:49	2.0	61
	07:19	-0.1	-3		07:19	0.5	15
	12:34	2.2	67		13:04	2.1	64
	19:47	0.0	0		20:23	0.8	24
10 F	00:47	2.2	67	**25** Sa	01:27	1.9	58
	08:03	-0.1	-3		08:27	0.6	18
	13:23	2.3	70		13:43	2.1	64
	20:39	0.1	3		21:05	1.0	30
11 Sa	01:34	2.1	64	**26** Su	02:07	1.8	55
	08:50	0.0	0		09:04	0.8	24
	14:16	2.3	70		14:24	2.0	61
	21:34	0.3	9		21:48	1.2	37
12 Su	02:26	2.0	61	**27** M	02:50	1.7	52
	09:41	0.1	3		09:45	1.0	30
	15:10	2.2	67		15:10	2.0	61
	22:34	0.5	15		22:36	1.4	43
13 M ◐	03:23	1.9	58	**28** Tu	03:38	1.7	52
	10:38	0.2	6		10:31	1.1	34
	16:18	2.2	67		16:02	2.0	61
	23:38	0.7	21		23:30	1.5	46
14 Tu	04:26	1.9	58	**29** W ◐	04:32	1.6	49
	11:41	0.3	9		11:25	1.1	34
	17:26	2.2	67		16:59	2.0	61
15 W	00:43	0.7	21	**30** Th	00:28	1.4	43
	05:33	1.8	55		05:30	1.7	52
	12:48	0.4	12		12:25	1.1	34
	18:33	2.2	67		17:58	2.0	61

StationId: 8660642
Source: NOAA/NOS/CO-OPS
Station Type: Subordinate
Time Zone: LST_LDT
Datum: MLLW

NOAA Tide Predictions

NORTH MYRTLE BEACH, SC, 2021

Times and Heights of High and Low Waters

October

Day	Time	ft	cm
1 F	01:25	1.3	40
	06:28	1.7	52
	13:25	0.9	27
	18:54	2.1	64
2 Sa	02:19	1.1	34
	07:23	1.8	55
	14:23	0.7	21
	19:47	2.1	64
3 Su	03:08	0.8	24
	08:15	1.9	58
	15:18	0.4	12
	20:36	2.2	67
4 M	03:54	0.5	15
	09:03	2.1	64
	16:10	0.2	6
	21:22	2.3	70
5 Tu	04:39	0.2	6
	09:50	2.2	67
	17:00	0.0	0
	22:07	2.3	70
6 W ●	05:22	0.0	0
	10:37	2.3	70
	17:50	-0.1	-3
	22:52	2.3	70
7 Th	06:06	-0.2	-6
	11:24	2.4	73
	18:40	-0.2	-6
	23:38	2.3	70
8 F	06:51	-0.2	-6
	12:13	2.5	76
	19:31	-0.1	-3
9 Sa	00:26	2.2	67
	07:38	-0.2	-6
	13:04	2.5	76
	20:25	0.1	3
10 Su	01:17	2.1	64
	08:28	-0.1	-3
	14:00	2.4	73
	21:21	0.3	9
11 M	02:12	2.0	61
	09:23	0.1	3
	15:01	2.3	70
	22:20	0.5	15
12 Tu	03:13	1.9	58
	10:23	0.4	12
	16:07	2.3	70
	23:24	0.7	21
13 W ◑	04:19	1.9	58
	11:29	0.5	15
	17:15	2.2	67
14 Th	00:28	0.7	21
	05:27	1.9	58
	12:38	0.6	18
	18:20	2.2	67
15 F	01:30	0.7	21
	06:33	1.9	58
	13:44	0.6	18
	19:19	2.2	67
16 Sa	02:26	0.5	15
	07:33	2.0	61
	14:44	0.5	15
	20:12	2.2	67
17 Su	03:18	0.4	12
	08:27	2.1	64
	15:39	0.4	12
	21:00	2.2	67
18 M	04:04	0.3	9
	09:15	2.1	64
	16:28	0.4	12
	21:43	2.2	67
19 Tu	04:46	0.2	6
	09:59	2.2	67
	17:14	0.4	12
	22:23	2.1	64
20 W ○	05:26	0.2	6
	10:39	2.2	67
	17:57	0.4	12
	23:02	2.1	64
21 Th	06:03	0.2	6
	11:17	2.2	67
	18:37	0.5	15
	23:39	2.0	61
22 F	06:38	0.4	12
	11:53	2.2	67
	19:16	0.7	21
23 Sa	00:16	1.9	58
	07:13	0.5	15
	12:29	2.2	67
	19:54	0.8	24
24 Su	00:53	1.8	55
	07:48	0.7	21
	13:05	2.1	64
	20:32	1.0	30
25 M	01:31	1.8	55
	08:25	0.8	24
	13:44	2.1	64
	21:13	1.1	34
26 Tu	02:11	1.7	52
	09:05	0.9	27
	14:27	2.0	61
	21:57	1.3	40
27 W	02:57	1.6	49
	09:51	1.0	30
	15:17	2.0	61
	22:47	1.3	40
28 Th ◐	03:50	1.6	49
	10:45	1.1	34
	16:12	2.0	61
	23:43	1.3	40
29 F	04:49	1.6	49
	11:46	1.1	34
	17:11	2.0	61
30 Sa	00:40	1.1	34
	05:49	1.7	52
	12:49	0.9	27
	18:10	2.0	61
31 Su	01:35	0.9	27
	06:47	1.8	55
	13:52	0.7	21
	19:05	2.1	64

November

Day	Time	ft	cm
1 M	02:27	0.6	18
	07:41	2.0	61
	14:50	0.4	12
	19:57	2.1	64
2 Tu	03:17	0.2	6
	08:33	2.2	67
	15:46	0.1	3
	20:48	2.2	67
3 W	04:04	-0.1	-3
	09:23	2.3	70
	16:40	-0.1	-3
	21:37	2.2	67
4 Th ●	04:51	-0.3	-9
	09:47	2.5	76
	17:32	-0.3	-9
	22:27	2.2	67
5 F	05:39	-0.5	-15
	11:03	2.5	76
	18:24	-0.3	-9
	23:17	2.2	67
6 Sa	06:27	-0.5	-15
	11:55	2.6	79
	19:16	-0.3	-9
7 Su	00:08	2.1	64
	06:18	-0.4	-12
	11:49	2.5	76
	19:10	-0.1	-3
8 M	00:02	2.0	61
	07:11	-0.2	-6
	12:47	2.4	73
	20:06	0.1	3
9 Tu	00:59	1.9	58
	07:35	0.0	0
	13:48	2.3	70
	21:04	0.3	9
10 W	02:02	1.9	58
	09:08	0.3	9
	14:52	2.2	67
	22:05	0.5	15
11 Th ◑	03:07	1.8	55
	10:14	0.5	15
	15:55	2.1	64
	23:06	0.5	15
12 F	04:14	1.8	55
	11:22	0.6	18
	16:56	2.1	64
13 Sa	00:05	0.5	15
	05:17	1.9	58
	12:27	0.6	18
	17:53	2.0	61
14 Su	00:59	0.4	12
	06:15	2.0	61
	13:27	0.6	18
	18:43	2.0	61
15 M	01:48	0.3	9
	07:06	2.0	61
	14:20	0.5	15
	19:30	2.0	61
16 Tu	02:33	0.2	6
	07:52	2.1	64
	15:09	0.4	12
	20:13	2.0	61
17 W	03:15	0.1	3
	08:34	2.2	67
	15:53	0.4	12
	20:54	1.9	58
18 Th	03:54	0.1	3
	09:13	2.2	67
	16:35	0.4	12
	21:33	1.9	58
19 F ○	04:31	0.2	6
	09:50	2.2	67
	17:14	0.4	12
	22:11	1.8	55
20 Sa	05:07	0.2	6
	10:26	2.2	67
	17:52	0.5	15
	22:49	1.8	55
21 Su	05:42	0.3	9
	11:02	2.1	64
	18:28	0.6	18
	23:25	1.7	52
22 M	06:18	0.4	12
	11:38	2.1	64
	19:05	0.7	21
23 Tu	00:02	1.7	52
	06:55	0.6	18
	12:15	2.0	61
	19:43	0.8	24
24 W	00:40	1.6	49
	07:35	0.7	21
	12:54	2.0	61
	20:24	0.9	27
25 Th	01:22	1.6	49
	08:20	0.7	21
	13:39	1.9	58
	21:10	0.9	27
26 F	02:11	1.6	49
	09:12	0.8	24
	14:30	1.9	58
	22:01	0.9	27
27 Sa ◐	03:08	1.6	49
	10:11	0.8	24
	15:26	1.9	58
	22:56	0.7	21
28 Su	04:09	1.7	52
	11:16	0.7	21
	16:25	1.9	58
	23:52	0.5	15
29 M	05:10	1.8	55
	12:21	0.5	15
	17:23	1.9	58
30 Tu	00:47	0.2	6
	06:08	2.0	61
	13:24	0.3	9
	18:21	2.0	61

December

Day	Time	ft	cm
1 W	01:41	-0.1	-3
	07:05	2.2	67
	14:24	0.0	0
	19:16	2.0	61
2 Th	02:33	-0.4	-12
	07:59	2.3	70
	15:20	-0.3	-9
	20:11	2.0	61
3 F	03:25	-0.6	-18
	08:53	2.5	76
	16:15	-0.5	-15
	21:05	2.0	61
4 Sa ●	04:17	-0.7	-21
	09:47	2.5	76
	17:08	-0.5	-15
	21:58	2.0	61
5 Su	05:09	-0.8	-24
	10:41	2.5	76
	18:01	-0.5	-15
	22:52	2.0	61
6 M	06:01	-0.7	-21
	11:36	2.5	76
	18:54	-0.4	-12
	23:48	1.9	58
7 Tu	06:55	-0.5	-15
	12:33	2.4	73
	19:48	-0.2	-6
8 W	00:45	1.9	58
	07:52	-0.2	-6
	13:30	2.2	67
	20:43	0.0	0
9 Th	01:45	1.8	55
	08:51	0.0	0
	14:28	2.1	64
	21:39	0.1	3
10 F	02:47	1.8	55
	09:53	0.3	9
	15:26	2.0	61
	22:35	0.2	6
11 Sa ◑	03:49	1.8	55
	10:57	0.5	15
	16:22	1.9	58
	23:31	0.3	9
12 Su	04:49	1.8	55
	12:01	0.6	18
	17:16	1.8	55
13 M	00:23	0.2	6
	05:45	1.9	58
	13:01	0.6	18
	18:07	1.8	55
14 Tu	01:18	0.2	6
	06:36	1.9	58
	13:56	0.5	15
	18:56	1.7	52
15 W	01:59	0.1	3
	07:23	2.0	61
	14:45	0.5	15
	19:41	1.7	52
16 Th	02:42	0.1	3
	08:06	2.0	61
	15:30	0.4	12
	20:25	1.7	52
17 F	03:23	0.0	0
	08:47	2.1	64
	16:11	0.3	9
	21:07	1.7	52
18 Sa	04:02	0.0	0
	09:27	2.1	64
	16:51	0.3	9
	21:47	1.7	52
19 Su ○	04:41	0.0	0
	10:05	2.1	64
	17:28	0.3	9
	22:26	1.7	52
20 M	05:18	0.0	0
	10:42	2.1	64
	18:05	0.3	9
	23:03	1.6	49
21 Tu	05:55	0.1	3
	11:17	2.0	61
	18:41	0.4	12
	23:39	1.6	49
22 W	06:33	0.2	6
	11:53	2.0	61
	19:17	0.4	12
23 Th	00:15	1.6	49
	07:13	0.2	6
	12:29	2.0	61
	19:56	0.4	12
24 F	00:57	1.6	49
	07:57	0.3	9
	13:10	1.9	58
	20:38	0.4	12
25 Sa	01:39	1.6	49
	08:47	0.4	12
	13:55	1.9	58
	21:24	0.3	9
26 Su	02:32	1.6	49
	09:44	0.4	12
	14:47	1.8	55
	22:16	0.2	6
27 M ◐	03:31	1.7	52
	10:47	0.4	12
	15:45	1.8	55
	23:11	0.1	3
28 Tu	04:34	1.8	55
	11:55	0.3	9
	16:46	1.8	55
29 W	00:10	-0.1	-3
	05:38	2.0	61
	13:01	0.1	3
	17:48	1.8	55
30 Th	01:09	-0.3	-9
	06:40	2.1	64
	14:04	-0.1	-3
	18:50	1.8	55
31 F	02:08	-0.6	-18
	07:40	2.2	67
	15:03	-0.4	-12
	19:50	1.8	55

StationId: 8665530
Source: NOAA/NOS/CO-OPS
Station Type: Primary
Time Zone: LST_LDT
Datum: MLLW

NOAA Tide Predictions

Charleston, Cooper River Entrance, SC, 2021

Times and Heights of High and Low Waters

January

Day	Time	ft	cm	Day	Time	ft	cm
1 F	02:52	-0.3	-9	16 Sa	03:52	-0.3	-9
	09:09	5.8	177		10:18	5.6	171
	15:37	0.0	0		16:30	-0.2	-6
	21:29	4.6	140		22:28	4.8	146
2 Sa	03:37	-0.3	-9	17 Su	04:39	0.0	0
	09:50	5.8	177		11:01	5.3	162
	16:19	0.0	0		17:13	0.0	0
	22:13	4.7	143		23:14	4.7	143
3 Su	04:25	-0.2	-6	18 M	05:26	0.3	9
	10:34	5.7	174		11:44	4.9	149
	17:05	0.0	0		17:55	0.2	6
	23:03	4.7	143				
4 M	05:17	-0.1	-3	19 Tu	00:01	4.6	140
	11:22	5.5	168		06:15	0.6	18
	17:53	0.0	0		12:28	4.6	140
	23:59	4.8	146		18:38	0.3	9
5 Tu	06:16	0.1	3	20 W ☽	00:51	4.6	140
	12:16	5.3	162		07:09	0.9	27
	18:47	-0.1	-3		13:16	4.4	134
					19:24	0.4	12
6 W ☽	01:01	5.0	152	21 Th	01:43	4.6	140
	07:20	0.2	6		08:06	1.0	30
	13:15	5.1	155		14:07	4.2	128
	19:44	-0.1	-3		20:13	0.5	15
7 Th	02:07	5.2	158	22 F	02:37	4.7	143
	08:28	0.2	6		09:06	1.0	30
	14:18	4.9	149		15:01	4.1	125
	20:44	-0.3	-9		21:04	0.4	12
8 F	03:13	5.5	168	23 Sa	03:31	4.8	146
	09:36	0.1	3		10:03	0.9	27
	15:23	4.8	146		15:55	4.1	125
	21:45	-0.4	-12		21:56	0.3	9
9 Sa	04:18	5.8	177	24 Su	04:24	5.0	152
	10:40	-0.1	-3		10:55	0.7	21
	16:26	4.8	146		16:48	4.2	128
	22:45	-0.6	-18		22:47	0.1	3
10 Su	05:19	6.0	183	25 M	05:15	5.2	158
	11:39	-0.3	-9		11:43	0.5	15
	17:27	4.9	149		17:37	4.3	131
	23:42	-0.7	-21		23:36	-0.1	-3
11 M	06:16	6.2	189	26 Tu	06:03	5.4	165
	12:34	-0.5	-15		12:28	0.2	6
	18:24	5.0	152		18:24	4.5	137
12 Tu	00:37	-0.8	-24	27 W	00:22	-0.3	-9
	07:10	6.3	192		06:48	5.6	171
	13:26	-0.6	-18		13:10	0.0	0
	19:17	5.0	152		19:07	4.6	140
13 W ●	01:29	-0.9	-27	28 Th ○	01:07	-0.5	-15
	08:01	6.3	192		07:30	5.8	177
	14:15	-0.6	-18		13:52	-0.2	-6
	20:08	5.0	152		19:49	4.8	146
14 Th	02:18	-0.8	-24	29 F	01:52	-0.7	-21
	08:49	6.1	186		08:12	5.9	180
	15:02	-0.5	-15		14:33	-0.3	-9
	20:56	5.0	152		20:31	4.9	149
15 F	03:06	-0.6	-18	30 Sa	02:37	-0.8	-24
	09:35	5.9	180		08:52	5.9	180
	15:47	-0.4	-12		15:14	-0.4	-12
	21:42	4.9	149		21:14	5.0	152
				31 Su	03:24	-0.7	-21
					09:34	5.8	177
					15:57	-0.5	-15
					21:59	5.1	155

February

Day	Time	ft	cm	Day	Time	ft	cm
1 M	04:13	-0.6	-18	16 Tu	04:52	0.3	9
	10:18	5.7	174		11:02	4.8	146
	16:41	-0.5	-15		17:08	0.2	6
	22:48	5.2	158		23:15	4.9	149
2 Tu	05:05	-0.4	-12	17 W	05:35	0.6	18
	11:05	5.4	165		11:41	4.5	137
	17:29	-0.4	-12		17:46	0.3	9
	23:43	5.3	162		23:58	4.8	146
3 W	06:03	-0.2	-6	18 Th	06:21	0.8	24
	11:57	5.1	155		12:25	4.2	128
	18:21	-0.4	-12		18:27	0.5	15
4 Th ☽	00:43	5.3	162	19 F ◐	00:46	4.7	143
	07:06	0.0	0		07:14	1.0	30
	12:56	4.8	146		13:15	4.0	122
	19:19	-0.3	-9		19:16	0.6	18
5 F	01:49	5.3	162	20 Sa	01:40	4.7	143
	08:13	0.1	3		08:13	1.1	34
	14:00	4.6	140		14:12	3.9	119
	20:22	-0.2	-6		20:11	0.6	18
6 Sa	02:58	5.4	165	21 Su	02:39	4.7	143
	09:21	0.1	3		09:14	1.0	30
	15:07	4.5	137		15:11	4.0	122
	21:27	-0.2	-6		21:11	0.5	15
7 Su	04:06	5.6	171	22 M	03:39	4.9	149
	10:25	0.0	0		10:13	0.9	27
	16:14	4.5	137		16:09	4.1	125
	22:31	-0.3	-9		22:09	0.3	9
8 M	05:09	5.7	174	23 Tu	04:37	5.1	155
	11:24	-0.1	-3		11:06	0.6	18
	17:16	4.7	143		17:03	4.3	131
	23:30	-0.5	-15		23:05	0.0	0
9 Tu	06:06	5.9	180	24 W	05:30	5.4	165
	12:18	-0.3	-9		11:54	0.3	9
	18:12	4.8	146		17:53	4.6	140
					23:56	-0.3	-9
10 W	00:25	-0.6	-18	25 Th	06:19	5.7	174
	06:58	5.9	180		12:40	0.0	0
	13:08	-0.4	-12		18:41	4.9	149
	19:04	5.0	152				
11 Th ●	01:16	-0.7	-21	26 F	00:46	-0.6	-18
	07:45	5.9	180		07:04	5.9	180
	13:54	-0.5	-15		13:23	-0.3	-9
	19:51	5.1	155		19:26	5.2	158
12 F	02:03	-0.6	-18	27 Sa ○	01:34	-0.8	-24
	08:28	5.8	177		07:48	6.0	183
	14:36	-0.5	-15		14:06	-0.6	-18
	20:35	5.1	155		20:11	5.5	168
13 Sa	02:47	-0.5	-15	28 Su	02:22	-1.0	-30
	09:08	5.7	174		08:32	6.0	183
	15:17	-0.4	-12		14:49	-0.7	-21
	21:16	5.1	155		20:56	5.7	174
14 Su	03:29	-0.3	-9				
	09:47	5.4	165				
	15:55	-0.2	-6				
	21:56	5.0	152				
15 M	04:11	0.0	0				
	10:24	5.1	155				
	16:31	0.0	0				
	22:35	5.0	152				

March

Day	Time	ft	cm	Day	Time	ft	cm
1 M	03:11	-0.9	-27	16 Tu	04:44	0.1	3
	09:15	5.9	180		10:50	5.0	152
	15:32	-0.8	-24		16:51	0.1	3
	21:43	5.8	177		22:58	5.4	165
2 Tu	04:01	-0.8	-24	17 W	05:22	0.4	12
	10:01	5.7	174		11:25	4.7	143
	16:18	-0.7	-21		17:24	0.3	9
	22:33	5.9	180		23:34	5.3	162
3 W	04:54	-0.6	-18	18 Th	06:00	0.6	18
	10:49	5.4	165		12:02	4.5	137
	17:06	-0.6	-18		18:00	0.5	15
	23:28	5.8	177				
4 Th	05:51	-0.3	-9	19 F	00:12	5.1	155
	11:43	5.0	152		06:41	0.8	24
	17:59	-0.3	-9		12:42	4.3	131
					18:40	0.6	18
5 F	00:28	5.7	174	20 Sa	00:56	5.0	152
	06:52	0.0	0		07:29	1.0	30
	12:42	4.7	143		13:41	4.1	125
	18:59	-0.1	-3		19:28	0.8	24
6 Sa	01:35	5.5	168	21 Su ◐	01:48	4.9	149
	07:58	0.2	6		08:24	1.1	34
	13:48	4.5	137		14:25	4.0	122
	20:04	0.1	3		20:24	0.8	24
7 Su	02:45	5.4	165	22 M	02:48	4.9	149
	09:05	0.3	9		09:26	1.1	34
	14:57	4.5	137		15:26	4.1	125
	21:13	0.1	3		21:28	0.7	21
8 M	03:53	5.5	168	23 Tu	03:52	5.0	152
	10:09	0.2	6		10:28	0.9	27
	16:04	4.6	140		16:28	4.3	131
	22:19	0.0	0		22:33	0.5	15
9 Tu	04:55	5.5	168	24 W	04:54	5.2	158
	11:06	0.1	3		11:25	0.7	21
	17:05	4.8	146		17:27	4.6	140
	23:19	-0.1	-3		23:34	0.2	6
10 W	05:50	5.6	171	25 Th	05:52	5.5	168
	11:58	-0.1	-3		12:17	0.3	9
	17:59	5.0	152		18:21	5.0	152
11 Th	00:12	-0.3	-9	26 F	00:30	-0.2	-6
	06:39	5.7	174		06:44	5.7	174
	12:45	-0.2	-6		13:05	-0.1	-3
	18:47	5.2	158		19:12	5.4	165
12 F	01:00	-0.3	-9	27 Sa	01:23	-0.5	-15
	07:22	5.7	174		07:34	5.9	180
	13:27	-0.3	-9		13:51	-0.4	-12
	19:30	5.3	162		20:01	5.8	177
13 Sa ●	01:45	-0.3	-9	28 Su ○	02:15	-0.8	-24
	08:02	5.6	171		08:21	6.0	183
	14:07	-0.3	-9		14:36	-0.7	-21
	20:10	5.4	165		20:49	6.2	189
14 Su	03:26	-0.2	-6	29 M	03:06	-1.0	-30
	09:39	5.5	168		09:08	6.0	183
	15:43	-0.2	-6		15:21	-0.9	-27
	21:48	5.5	168		21:37	6.4	195
15 M	04:06	-0.1	-3	30 Tu	03:57	-1.0	-30
	10:15	5.3	162		09:55	5.9	180
	16:18	-0.1	-3		16:07	-0.9	-27
	22:23	5.4	165		22:26	6.5	198
				31 W	04:48	-0.8	-24
					10:44	5.6	171
					16:55	-0.7	-21
					23:18	6.4	195

StationId: 8665530
Source: NOAA/NOS/CO-OPS
Station Type: Primary
Time Zone: LST_LDT
Datum: MLLW

NOAA Tide Predictions

Charleston, Cooper River Entrance, SC, 2021

Times and Heights of High and Low Waters

April

Day	Time	ft	cm	Day	Time	ft	cm
1 Th	05:42	-0.6	-18	16 F	05:32	0.6	18
	11:35	5.3	162		11:30	4.4	134
	17:46	-0.5	-15		17:24	0.6	18
					23:36	5.4	165
2 F	00:14	6.2	189	17 Sa	06:11	0.8	24
	06:39	-0.2	-6		12:09	4.3	131
	12:31	5.0	152		18:05	0.7	21
	18:41	-0.2	-6				
3 Sa	01:15	5.9	180	18 Su	00:18	5.3	162
	07:39	0.1	3		06:56	0.9	27
	13:32	4.8	146		12:53	4.2	128
	19:43	0.1	3		18:53	0.8	24
4 Su	02:21	5.7	174	19 M	01:08	5.2	158
	08:42	0.3	9		07:47	1.0	30
	14:39	4.6	140		13:47	4.2	128
	20:50	0.4	12		19:49	0.9	27
5 M	03:29	5.5	168	20 Tu	02:05	5.1	155
	09:46	0.4	12		08:45	1.0	30
	15:46	4.6	140		14:48	4.3	131
	21:59	0.4	12		20:52	0.8	24
6 Tu	04:34	5.4	165	21 W	03:08	5.2	158
	10:47	0.4	12		09:45	0.8	24
	16:50	4.8	146		15:51	4.5	137
	23:04	0.4	12		21:59	0.6	18
7 W	05:33	5.4	165	22 Th	04:11	5.3	162
	11:42	0.3	9		10:43	0.5	15
	17:48	5.0	152		16:52	4.9	149
					23:04	0.3	9
8 Th	00:03	0.3	9	23 F	05:11	5.5	168
	06:25	5.5	168		11:38	0.1	3
	12:31	0.1	3		17:49	5.4	165
	18:39	5.2	158				
9 F	00:54	0.1	3	24 Sa	00:04	-0.1	-3
	07:11	5.5	168		06:07	5.7	174
	13:15	0.0	0		12:29	-0.2	-6
	19:24	5.5	168		18:43	5.9	180
10 Sa	01:41	0.1	3	25 Su	01:01	-0.4	-12
	07:52	5.4	165		07:00	5.8	177
	13:55	-0.1	-3		13:18	-0.6	-18
	20:05	5.6	171		19:35	6.4	195
11 Su	02:24	0.0	0	26 M	01:56	-0.7	-21
	08:31	5.4	165		07:52	5.8	177
	14:33	-0.1	-3		14:07	-0.8	-24
	20:43	5.7	174		20:26	6.7	204
12 M	03:04	0.1	3	27 Tu	02:49	-0.9	-27
	09:08	5.2	158		08:43	5.8	177
	15:08	0.0	0		14:55	-0.9	-27
	21:19	5.8	177		21:18	6.9	210
13 Tu	03:42	0.2	6	28 W	03:42	-0.9	-27
	09:44	5.0	152		09:35	5.7	174
	15:41	0.1	3		15:44	-0.9	-27
	21:53	5.7	174		22:10	6.9	210
14 W	04:19	0.3	9	29 Th	04:35	-0.8	-24
	10:19	4.8	146		10:27	5.5	168
	16:14	0.2	6		16:35	-0.7	-21
	22:26	5.7	174		23:04	6.7	204
15 Th	04:55	0.5	15	30 F	05:29	-0.5	-15
	10:54	4.6	140		11:22	5.2	158
	16:48	0.4	12		17:28	-0.4	-12
	23:00	5.5	168				

May

Day	Time	ft	cm	Day	Time	ft	cm
1 Sa	00:02	6.4	195	16 Su	05:48	0.7	21
	06:24	-0.2	-6		11:43	4.3	131
	12:20	5.0	152		17:39	0.6	18
	18:25	0.0	0		23:52	5.5	168
2 Su	01:02	6.0	183	17 M	06:31	0.7	21
	07:22	0.1	3		12:27	4.3	131
	13:22	4.8	146		18:27	0.7	21
	19:27	0.3	9				
3 M	02:04	5.7	174	18 Tu	00:39	5.4	165
	08:22	0.3	9		07:19	0.7	21
	14:26	4.8	146		13:19	4.3	131
	20:33	0.5	15		19:23	0.7	21
4 Tu	03:06	5.5	168	19 W	01:33	5.3	162
	09:22	0.4	12		08:12	0.6	18
	15:29	4.8	146		14:18	4.5	137
	21:40	0.6	18		20:25	0.7	21
5 W	04:05	5.3	162	20 Th	02:32	5.3	162
	10:18	0.3	9		09:09	0.4	12
	16:29	4.9	149		15:19	4.8	146
	22:43	0.6	18		21:31	0.5	15
6 Th	05:00	5.2	158	21 F	03:32	5.4	165
	11:10	0.3	9		10:05	0.2	6
	17:23	5.2	158		16:21	5.2	158
	23:40	0.6	18		22:38	0.3	9
7 F	05:49	5.2	158	22 Sa	04:33	5.4	165
	11:57	0.2	6		11:01	-0.1	-3
	18:11	5.4	165		17:20	5.7	174
					23:41	0.0	0
8 Sa	00:31	0.5	15	23 Su	05:31	5.5	168
	06:34	5.1	155		11:55	-0.4	-12
	12:39	0.1	3		18:16	6.2	189
	18:55	5.6	171				
9 Su	01:17	0.4	12	24 M	00:40	-0.3	-9
	07:17	5.1	155		06:29	5.5	168
	13:19	0.0	0		12:48	-0.7	-21
	19:36	5.8	177		19:12	6.6	201
10 M	02:00	0.3	9	25 Tu	01:37	-0.6	-18
	07:57	5.0	152		07:25	5.5	168
	13:57	0.0	0		13:40	-0.9	-27
	20:14	5.9	180		20:06	6.9	210
11 Tu	02:40	0.3	9	26 W	02:32	-0.7	-21
	08:36	4.9	149		08:20	5.4	165
	14:33	0.1	3		14:32	-0.9	-27
	20:50	5.9	180		21:01	6.9	210
12 W	03:18	0.3	9	27 Th	03:26	-0.8	-24
	09:15	4.8	146		09:15	5.4	165
	15:08	0.2	6		15:24	-0.8	-24
	21:25	5.9	180		21:56	6.9	210
13 Th	03:55	0.4	12	28 F	04:19	-0.7	-21
	09:52	4.6	140		10:11	5.2	158
	15:43	0.3	9		16:17	-0.6	-18
	22:00	5.8	177		22:51	6.7	204
14 F	04:32	0.5	15	29 Sa	05:13	-0.5	-15
	10:28	4.5	137		11:08	5.1	155
	16:19	0.4	12		17:12	-0.3	-9
	22:34	5.7	174		23:47	6.3	192
15 Sa	05:09	0.6	18	30 Su	06:07	-0.3	-9
	11:05	4.3	131		12:06	5.0	152
	16:57	0.5	15		18:09	0.0	0
	23:11	5.5	168				
				31 M	00:44	6.0	183
					07:01	-0.1	-3
					13:05	4.9	149
					19:08	0.3	9

June

Day	Time	ft	cm	Day	Time	ft	cm
1 Tu	01:40	5.7	174	16 W	00:18	5.5	168
	07:56	0.1	3		06:54	0.4	12
	14:05	4.8	146		12:58	4.6	140
	20:10	0.6	18		19:04	0.5	15
2 W	02:35	5.4	165	17 Th	01:08	5.5	168
	08:50	0.2	6		07:44	0.2	6
	15:03	4.9	149		13:54	4.8	146
	21:13	0.8	24		20:04	0.5	15
3 Th	03:28	5.1	155	18 F	02:03	5.4	165
	09:42	0.2	6		08:36	0.1	3
	15:58	5.0	152		14:54	5.1	155
	22:13	0.8	24		21:09	0.4	12
4 F	04:19	4.9	149	19 Sa	03:01	5.3	162
	10:31	0.2	6		09:32	-0.1	-3
	16:49	5.2	158		15:55	5.5	168
	23:10	0.8	24		22:16	0.3	9
5 Sa	05:07	4.8	146	20 Su	04:01	5.2	158
	11:16	0.2	6		10:29	-0.3	-9
	17:37	5.4	165		16:55	5.9	180
					23:20	0.1	3
6 Su	00:01	0.7	21	21 M	05:02	5.2	158
	05:53	4.7	143		11:26	-0.5	-15
	11:59	0.1	3		17:55	6.3	192
	18:21	5.6	171				
7 M	00:48	0.6	18	22 Tu	00:22	-0.2	-6
	06:39	4.7	143		06:03	5.2	158
	12:41	0.1	3		12:22	-0.7	-21
	19:03	5.7	174		18:53	6.6	201
8 Tu	01:32	0.5	15	23 W	01:20	-0.4	-12
	07:22	4.6	140		07:02	5.2	158
	13:21	0.1	3		13:18	-0.8	-24
	19:44	5.8	177		19:50	6.8	207
9 W	02:14	0.4	12	24 Th	02:15	-0.5	-15
	08:05	4.6	140		08:01	5.2	158
	14:00	0.1	3		14:13	-0.8	-24
	20:23	5.9	180		20:46	6.8	207
10 Th	02:53	0.4	12	25 F	03:09	-0.6	-18
	08:47	4.5	137		08:58	5.2	158
	14:38	0.1	3		15:07	-0.8	-24
	21:01	5.8	177		21:42	6.7	204
11 F	03:31	0.4	12	26 Sa	04:02	-0.5	-15
	09:26	4.5	137		09:54	5.1	155
	15:16	0.2	6		16:01	-0.6	-18
	21:38	5.8	177		22:35	6.5	198
12 Sa	04:09	0.4	12	27 Su	04:53	-0.4	-12
	10:05	4.4	134		10:50	5.1	155
	15:55	0.3	9		16:55	-0.3	-9
	22:14	5.7	174		23:28	6.2	189
13 Su	04:47	0.5	15	28 M	05:44	-0.3	-9
	10:43	4.3	131		11:45	5.0	152
	16:36	0.3	9		17:49	0.0	0
	22:52	5.7	174				
14 M	05:27	0.5	15	29 Tu	00:19	5.9	180
	11:23	4.3	131		06:34	-0.1	-3
	17:20	0.4	12		12:40	4.9	149
	23:32	5.6	171		18:44	0.4	12
15 Tu	06:09	0.4	12	30 W	01:09	5.5	168
	12:07	4.4	134		07:23	0.1	3
	18:09	0.5	15		13:34	4.9	149
					19:41	0.7	21

StationId: 8665530
Source: NOAA/NOS/CO-OPS
Station Type: Primary
Time Zone: LST_LDT
Datum: MLLW

NOAA Tide Predictions

Charleston, Cooper River Entrance, SC,2021

Times and Heights of High and Low Waters

July

Day	Time (h m)	Height (ft)	Height (cm)	Day	Time (h m)	Height (ft)	Height (cm)
1 Th ◑	01:57	5.2	158	16 F	00:46	5.5	168
	08:11	0.2	6		07:17	0.0	0
	14:27	5.0	152		13:33	5.2	158
	20:39	0.9	27		19:48	0.4	12
2 F	02:46	4.9	149	17 Sa ◑	01:39	5.3	162
	08:59	0.3	9		08:09	-0.1	-3
	15:19	5.0	152		14:33	5.5	168
	21:37	1.0	30		20:52	0.5	15
3 Sa	03:34	4.7	143	18 Su	02:37	5.2	158
	09:46	0.3	9		09:05	-0.2	-6
	16:09	5.2	158		15:34	5.8	177
	22:33	1.0	30		21:58	0.4	12
4 Su	04:23	4.6	140	19 M	03:38	5.1	155
	10:32	0.3	9		10:04	-0.3	-9
	16:57	5.3	162		16:37	6.0	183
	23:26	0.9	27		23:03	0.3	9
5 M	05:12	4.5	137	20 Tu	04:41	5.0	152
	11:17	0.3	9		11:04	-0.4	-12
	17:44	5.5	168		17:39	6.3	192
6 Tu	00:15	0.8	24	21 W	00:05	0.1	3
	06:01	4.5	137		05:44	5.0	152
	12:02	0.2	6		12:04	-0.5	-15
	18:30	5.6	171		18:40	6.5	198
7 W	01:01	0.7	21	22 Th	01:03	-0.1	-3
	06:48	4.5	137		06:46	5.1	155
	12:46	0.2	6		13:03	-0.6	-18
	19:14	5.7	174		19:38	6.6	201
8 Th	01:44	0.6	18	23 F	01:58	-0.3	-9
	07:34	4.5	137		07:45	5.1	155
	13:29	0.1	3		13:59	-0.6	-18
	19:56	5.8	177		20:33	6.6	201
9 F	02:25	0.5	15	24 Sa ○	02:51	-0.3	-9
	08:18	4.5	137		08:42	5.2	158
	14:12	0.1	3		14:52	-0.5	-15
	20:37	5.9	180		21:25	6.6	201
10 Sa ●	03:05	0.4	12	25 Su	03:40	-0.3	-9
	09:01	4.5	137		09:36	5.2	158
	14:53	0.1	3		15:44	-0.4	-12
	21:17	5.9	180		22:15	6.4	195
11 Su	03:44	0.3	9	26 M	04:28	-0.3	-9
	09:41	4.5	137		10:28	5.2	158
	15:35	0.1	3		16:35	-0.1	-3
	21:55	5.9	180		23:02	6.1	186
12 M	04:23	0.3	9	27 Tu	05:15	-0.1	-3
	10:21	4.6	140		11:18	5.2	158
	16:19	0.1	3		17:25	0.2	6
	22:33	5.8	177		23:47	5.8	177
13 Tu	05:03	0.2	6	28 W	05:59	0.0	0
	11:03	4.7	143		12:07	5.2	158
	17:04	0.2	6		18:15	0.5	15
	23:14	5.8	177				
14 W	05:45	0.1	3	29 Th	00:31	5.4	165
	11:48	4.8	146		06:43	0.2	6
	17:54	0.3	9		12:56	5.1	155
	23:58	5.7	174		19:06	0.8	24
15 Th	06:29	0.1	3	30 F	01:16	5.1	155
	12:38	5.0	152		07:26	0.4	12
	18:48	0.4	12		13:44	5.1	155
					20:00	1.1	34
				31 Sa ◑	02:01	4.8	146
					08:11	0.5	15
					14:33	5.2	158
					20:55	1.2	37

August

Day	Time (h m)	Height (ft)	Height (cm)	Day	Time (h m)	Height (ft)	Height (cm)
1 Su	02:50	4.6	140	16 M	02:21	5.1	155
	08:57	0.6	18		08:44	0.1	3
	15:24	5.2	158		15:20	6.0	183
	21:51	1.3	40		21:44	0.6	18
2 M	03:41	4.5	137	17 Tu	03:25	5.0	152
	09:45	0.6	18		09:47	0.1	3
	16:15	5.3	162		16:26	6.1	186
	22:46	1.2	37		22:49	0.5	15
3 Tu	04:33	4.4	134	18 W	04:30	5.0	152
	10:35	0.6	18		10:51	0.0	0
	17:06	5.5	168		17:30	6.3	192
	23:38	1.1	34		23:51	0.4	12
4 W	05:25	4.5	137	19 Th	05:35	5.1	155
	11:25	0.5	15		11:53	-0.1	-3
	17:55	5.6	171		18:30	6.4	195
5 Th	00:26	1.0	30	20 F	00:47	0.2	6
	06:15	4.5	137		06:35	5.2	158
	12:14	0.4	12		12:51	-0.2	-6
	18:43	5.8	177		19:26	6.5	198
6 F	01:11	0.8	24	21 Sa	01:40	0.1	3
	07:03	4.7	143		07:32	5.4	165
	13:01	0.3	9		13:46	-0.2	-6
	19:29	5.9	180		20:17	6.5	198
7 Sa	01:54	0.6	18	22 Su ○	02:29	0.0	0
	07:49	4.8	146		08:25	5.5	168
	13:47	0.1	3		14:37	-0.2	-6
	20:11	6.0	183		21:04	6.5	198
8 Su ●	02:35	0.4	12	23 M	03:15	-0.1	-3
	08:33	4.9	149		09:14	5.6	171
	14:31	0.0	0		15:26	0.0	0
	20:52	6.1	186		21:48	6.3	192
9 M	03:15	0.3	9	24 Tu	03:58	0.0	0
	09:15	5.0	152		10:01	5.6	171
	15:16	0.0	0		16:12	0.2	6
	21:32	6.1	186		22:30	6.0	183
10 Tu	03:55	0.1	3	25 W	04:40	0.1	3
	09:58	5.2	158		10:45	5.6	171
	16:02	0.0	0		16:58	0.5	15
	22:12	6.1	186		23:11	5.7	174
11 W	04:36	0.0	0	26 Th	05:20	0.3	9
	10:41	5.3	162		11:28	5.5	168
	16:49	0.1	3		17:43	0.8	24
	22:53	6.0	183		23:51	5.4	165
12 Th	05:18	0.0	0	27 F	05:59	0.5	15
	11:28	5.5	168		12:12	5.5	168
	17:25	0.2	6		18:29	1.1	34
	23:38	5.8	177				
13 F	06:03	-0.1	-3	28 Sa	00:33	5.1	155
	12:19	5.6	171		06:38	0.7	21
	18:35	0.3	9		12:56	5.4	165
					19:18	1.3	40
14 Sa	00:27	5.6	171	29 Su	01:17	4.8	146
	06:51	0.0	0		07:20	0.9	27
	13:15	5.8	177		13:44	5.3	162
	19:34	0.5	15		20:10	1.5	46
15 Su	01:21	5.3	162	30 M ◑	02:06	4.6	140
	07:45	0.0	0		08:07	1.0	30
	14:16	5.9	180		14:36	5.3	162
	20:38	0.6	18		21:05	1.6	49
				31 Tu	02:59	4.5	137
					08:58	1.0	30
					15:30	5.4	165
					22:02	1.6	49

September

Day	Time (h m)	Height (ft)	Height (cm)	Day	Time (h m)	Height (ft)	Height (cm)
1 W	03:54	4.5	137	16 Th	04:25	5.2	158
	09:54	1.0	30		10:42	0.4	12
	16:26	5.5	168		17:21	6.3	192
	22:57	1.4	43		23:35	0.6	18
2 Th	04:49	4.6	140	17 F	05:28	5.3	162
	10:49	0.9	27		11:44	0.3	9
	17:19	5.7	174		18:17	6.4	195
	23:48	1.2	37				
3 F	05:42	4.8	146	18 Sa	00:29	0.4	12
	11:43	0.7	21		06:26	5.5	168
	18:10	5.9	180		12:41	0.2	6
					19:09	6.4	195
4 Sa	00:35	1.0	30	19 Su	01:18	0.3	9
	06:32	5.0	152		07:18	5.7	174
	12:33	0.4	12		13:32	0.1	3
	18:57	6.1	186		19:55	6.4	195
5 Su	01:19	0.7	21	20 M ○	02:03	0.2	6
	07:19	5.3	162		08:06	5.9	180
	13:22	0.2	6		14:20	0.2	6
	19:41	6.3	192		20:38	6.3	192
6 M	02:02	0.4	12	21 Tu	02:45	0.1	3
	08:04	5.5	168		08:50	6.0	183
	14:10	0.0	0		15:06	0.3	9
	20:23	6.4	195		21:18	6.1	186
7 Tu ●	02:43	0.2	6	22 W	03:25	0.2	6
	08:48	5.8	177		09:31	6.0	183
	14:57	-0.1	-3		15:49	0.5	15
	21:05	6.4	195		21:56	5.9	180
8 W	03:25	0.0	0	23 Th	04:03	0.4	12
	09:33	6.0	183		10:10	6.0	183
	15:45	-0.1	-3		16:30	0.7	21
	21:47	6.3	192		22:34	5.6	171
9 Th	04:07	-0.1	-3	24 F	04:39	0.5	15
	10:19	6.2	189		11:11	5.9	180
	16:35	0.0	0		17:11	1.0	30
	22:32	6.1	186		23:12	5.3	162
10 F	04:51	-0.1	-3	25 Sa	05:15	0.8	24
	11:08	6.3	192		11:28	5.8	177
	17:27	0.2	6		17:53	1.2	37
	23:19	5.9	180		23:52	5.0	152
11 Sa	05:38	0.0	0	26 Su	05:52	1.0	30
	12:01	6.3	192		12:09	5.6	171
	18:22	0.4	12		18:36	1.5	46
12 Su	00:11	5.6	171	27 M	00:35	4.8	146
	06:29	0.1	3		06:29	1.1	34
	12:59	6.2	189		12:55	5.5	168
	19:22	0.6	18		19:24	1.6	49
13 M ◑	01:08	5.3	162	28 Tu	01:23	4.6	140
	07:26	0.3	9		07:19	1.3	40
	14:03	6.2	189		13:47	5.4	165
	20:26	0.8	24		20:18	1.7	52
14 Tu	02:11	5.2	158	29 W ◑	02:17	4.6	140
	08:29	0.4	12		08:13	1.3	40
	15:11	6.2	189		14:44	5.4	165
	21:31	0.8	24		21:16	1.7	52
15 W	03:18	5.1	155	30 Th	03:15	4.6	140
	09:36	0.5	15		09:13	1.3	40
	16:18	6.2	189		15:43	5.5	168
	22:35	0.8	24		22:13	1.6	49

StationId: 8665530
Source: NOAA/NOS/CO-OPS
Station Type: Primary
Time Zone: LST_LDT
Datum: MLLW

NOAA Tide Predictions

Charleston, Cooper River Entrance, SC, 2021

Times and Heights of High and Low Waters

October

Day	Time	ft	cm	Day	Time	ft	cm
1 F	04:13	4.8	146	**16** Sa	05:18	5.5	168
	10:13	1.1	34		11:32	0.6	18
	16:39	5.7	174		17:57	6.1	186
	23:07	1.3	40				
2 Sa	05:08	5.0	152	**17** Su	00:06	0.5	15
	11:11	0.8	24		06:12	5.7	174
	17:32	6.0	183		12:27	0.5	15
	23:56	1.0	30		18:45	6.1	186
3 Su	06:00	5.4	165	**18** M	00:52	0.3	9
	12:06	0.5	15		07:00	5.9	180
	18:21	6.2	189		13:16	0.4	12
					19:28	6.0	183
4 M	00:42	0.6	18	**19** Tu	01:34	0.2	6
	06:48	5.7	174		07:44	6.1	186
	12:58	0.2	6		14:02	0.4	12
	19:07	6.4	195		20:08	5.9	180
5 Tu	01:27	0.2	6	**20** W	02:14	0.2	6
	07:35	6.1	186		08:24	6.2	189
	13:48	0.0	0		14:45	0.5	15
	19:52	6.4	195	○	20:47	5.8	177
6 W	02:10	0.0	0	**21** Th	02:51	0.3	9
	08:22	6.5	198		09:02	6.2	189
	14:38	-0.2	-6		15:25	0.6	18
●	20:37	6.4	195		21:24	5.6	171
7 Th	02:54	-0.2	-6	**22** F	03:26	0.4	12
	09:09	6.7	204		09:38	6.2	189
	15:28	-0.2	-6		16:04	0.8	24
	21:23	6.3	192		22:01	5.3	162
8 F	03:39	-0.3	-9	**23** Sa	04:01	0.6	18
	09:58	6.8	207		10:14	6.0	183
	16:19	-0.1	-3		16:42	1.0	30
	22:11	6.1	186		22:38	5.1	155
9 Sa	04:26	-0.2	-6	**24** Su	04:36	0.8	24
	10:49	6.8	207		10:50	5.9	180
	17:13	0.1	3		17:20	1.2	37
	23:02	5.8	177		23:16	4.9	149
10 Su	05:16	-0.1	-3	**25** M	05:13	1.0	30
	11:45	6.7	204		11:29	5.7	174
	18:09	0.3	9		18:01	1.4	43
	23:57	5.6	171		23:56	4.7	143
11 M	06:11	0.2	6	**26** Tu	05:53	1.1	34
	12:46	6.5	198		12:12	5.6	171
	19:08	0.6	18		18:45	1.5	46
12 Tu	00:58	5.3	162	**27** W	00:42	4.5	137
	07:11	0.4	12		06:39	1.2	37
	13:52	6.3	192		13:02	5.5	168
	20:12	0.8	24		19:35	1.6	49
13 W	02:04	5.2	158	**28** Th	01:35	4.5	137
	08:17	0.6	18		07:33	1.3	40
	15:00	6.2	189		13:57	5.4	165
	21:16	0.9	27	◑	20:31	1.5	46
14 Th	03:12	5.2	158	**29** F	02:34	4.6	140
	09:26	0.7	21		08:34	1.3	40
	16:05	6.1	186		14:56	5.5	168
	22:18	0.8	24		21:28	1.4	43
15 F	04:18	5.3	162	**30** Sa	03:34	4.8	146
	10:32	0.7	21		09:37	1.1	34
	17:04	6.1	186		15:55	5.6	171
	23:14	0.7	21		22:23	1.1	34
				31 Su	04:32	5.1	155
					10:40	0.8	24
					16:50	5.8	177
					23:15	0.7	21

November

Day	Time	ft	cm	Day	Time	ft	cm
1 M	05:26	5.6	171	**16** Tu	05:37	5.9	180
	11:38	0.5	15		11:57	0.5	15
	17:42	6.0	183		17:58	5.5	168
2 Tu	00:05	0.3	9	**17** W	00:03	0.2	6
	06:18	6.0	183		06:19	6.0	183
	12:34	0.1	3		12:41	0.5	15
	18:33	6.1	186		18:39	5.4	165
3 W	00:52	-0.1	-3	**18** Th	00:42	0.1	3
	07:08	6.5	198		06:58	6.1	186
	13:28	-0.2	-6		13:23	0.5	15
	19:22	6.2	189		19:18	5.3	162
4 Th	01:39	-0.4	-12	**19** F	01:19	0.2	6
	07:58	6.8	207		07:35	6.1	186
	14:20	-0.3	-9		14:02	0.5	15
●	20:12	6.1	186	○	19:56	5.1	155
5 F	02:27	-0.5	-15	**20** Sa	01:55	0.3	9
	08:48	7.1	216		08:11	6.0	183
	15:12	-0.4	-12		14:40	0.6	18
	21:02	6.0	183		20:34	5.0	152
6 Sa	03:15	-0.6	-18	**21** Su	02:30	0.4	12
	09:40	7.1	216		08:47	5.9	180
	16:04	-0.3	-9		15:16	0.7	21
	21:53	5.8	177		21:10	4.8	146
7 Su	03:06	-0.5	-15	**22** M	03:06	0.5	15
	09:33	7.0	213		09:23	5.8	177
	15:58	-0.1	-3		15:53	0.9	27
	21:47	5.6	171		21:47	4.6	140
8 M	03:59	-0.3	-9	**23** Tu	03:43	0.7	21
	10:32	6.8	207		10:00	5.6	171
	16:54	0.1	3		16:31	1.0	30
	22:44	5.4	165		22:25	4.5	137
9 Tu	04:55	0.0	0	**24** W	04:23	0.8	24
	11:33	6.5	198		10:39	5.5	168
	17:52	0.4	12		17:12	1.1	34
	23:47	5.2	158		23:07	4.4	134
10 W	05:56	0.3	9	**25** Th	05:08	0.9	27
	12:37	6.2	189		11:24	5.4	165
	18:53	0.6	18		17:58	1.1	34
					23:56	4.4	134
11 Th	00:52	5.1	155	**26** F	06:00	0.9	27
	07:02	0.6	18		12:15	5.3	162
	13:40	5.9	180		18:49	1.0	30
◐	19:54	0.6	18				
12 F	01:59	5.1	155	**27** Sa	00:53	4.5	137
	08:10	0.7	21		06:59	0.9	27
	14:41	5.8	177		13:11	5.3	162
	20:53	0.6	18	◑	19:44	0.9	27
13 Sa	03:02	5.2	158	**28** Su	01:54	4.7	143
	09:15	0.7	21		08:04	0.8	24
	15:38	5.7	174		14:10	5.4	165
	21:47	0.5	15		20:40	0.6	18
14 Su	04:00	5.4	165	**29** M	02:55	5.1	155
	10:15	0.7	21		09:09	0.6	18
	16:28	5.6	171		15:08	5.4	165
	22:36	0.3	9		21:35	0.3	9
15 M	04:51	5.6	171	**30** Tu	03:53	5.6	171
	11:08	0.6	18		10:12	0.3	9
	17:15	5.5	168		16:06	5.5	168
	23:21	0.2	6		22:29	-0.1	-3

December

Day	Time	ft	cm	Day	Time	ft	cm
1 W	04:50	6.1	186	**16** Th	05:51	5.7	174
	11:12	0.0	0		12:18	0.4	12
	17:01	5.6	171		18:10	4.8	146
	23:21	-0.4	-12				
2 Th	05:44	6.5	198	**17** F	00:11	0.0	0
	12:08	-0.3	-9		06:32	5.8	177
	17:56	5.6	171		12:59	0.4	12
					18:52	4.8	146
3 F	00:13	-0.7	-21	**18** Sa	00:50	0.0	0
	06:38	6.8	207		07:12	5.8	177
	13:03	-0.5	-15		13:39	0.3	9
	18:50	5.7	174		19:32	4.7	143
4 Sa	01:05	-0.9	-27	**19** Su	01:29	0.0	0
	07:32	7.0	213		07:50	5.8	177
	13:56	-0.6	-18		14:16	0.3	9
●	19:43	5.6	171	○	20:11	4.6	140
5 Su	01:57	-0.9	-27	**20** M	02:06	0.1	3
	08:26	7.0	213		08:27	5.7	174
	14:49	-0.6	-18		14:53	0.4	12
	20:37	5.5	168		20:48	4.5	137
6 M	02:49	-0.8	-24	**21** Tu	02:43	0.1	3
	09:21	6.8	207		09:02	5.6	171
	15:42	-0.5	-15		15:29	0.5	15
	21:33	5.4	165		21:24	4.5	137
7 Tu	03:43	-0.6	-18	**22** W	03:21	0.2	6
	10:18	6.6	201		09:38	5.5	168
	16:36	-0.3	-9		16:05	0.5	15
	22:30	5.2	158		22:00	4.4	134
8 W	04:40	-0.3	-9	**23** Th	04:01	0.3	9
	11:15	6.2	189		10:14	5.4	165
	17:31	0.0	0		16:44	0.5	15
	23:30	5.1	155		22:39	4.4	134
9 Th	05:39	0.1	3	**24** F	04:45	0.4	12
	12:13	5.9	180		10:55	5.3	162
	18:27	0.2	6		17:26	0.5	15
					23:24	4.4	134
10 F	00:32	5.0	152	**25** Sa	05:35	0.5	15
	06:41	0.4	12		11:40	5.2	158
	13:11	5.5	168		18:12	0.4	12
	19:23	0.3	9				
11 Sa	01:34	4.9	149	**26** Su	00:17	4.6	140
	07:45	0.6	18		06:32	0.5	15
	14:07	5.3	162		12:32	5.1	155
○	20:19	0.3	9		19:04	0.3	9
12 Su	02:34	5.0	152	**27** M	01:16	4.8	146
	08:49	0.7	21		07:35	0.5	15
	15:01	5.1	155		13:30	5.0	152
	21:11	0.3	9	◑	19:59	0.1	3
13 M	03:30	5.2	158	**28** Tu	02:19	5.1	155
	09:49	0.7	21		08:43	0.4	12
	15:52	4.9	149		14:31	5.0	152
	22:01	0.2	6		20:58	-0.1	-3
14 Tu	04:21	5.3	162	**29** W	03:23	5.5	168
	10:44	0.6	18		09:49	0.2	6
	16:41	4.8	146		15:33	5.0	152
	22:47	0.2	6		21:57	-0.4	-12
15 W	05:08	5.5	168	**30** Th	04:25	5.9	180
	11:33	0.5	15		10:52	-0.1	-3
	17:26	4.8	146		16:35	5.0	152
	23:30	0.1	3		22:56	-0.7	-21
				31 F	05:25	6.2	189
					11:51	-0.4	-12
					17:35	5.1	155
					23:52	-0.8	-24

StationId: 8720030
Source: NOAA/NOS/CO-OPS
Station Type: Primary
Time Zone: LST_LDT
Datum: MLLW

NOAA Tide Predictions

Fernandina Beach, FL, 2021

Times and Heights of High and Low Waters

January

Day	Time	ft	cm	Day	Time	ft	cm
1 F	03:31	-0.3	-9	**16** Sa	04:28	-0.3	-9
	10:13	6.7	204		11:11	6.5	198
	16:12	0.0	0		17:06	-0.1	-3
	22:30	5.5	168		23:26	5.7	174
2 Sa	04:13	-0.3	-9	**17** Su	05:15	0.1	3
	10:55	6.6	201		11:53	6.1	186
	16:54	0.0	0		17:50	0.1	3
	23:15	5.6	171				
3 Su	05:00	-0.1	-3	**18** M	00:10	5.5	168
	11:38	6.5	198		06:05	0.5	15
	17:39	0.0	0		12:33	5.7	174
					18:35	0.3	9
4 M	00:02	5.6	171	**19** Tu	00:55	5.4	165
	05:53	0.0	0		06:58	0.8	24
	12:25	6.3	192		13:15	5.3	162
	18:30	0.0	0		19:22	0.5	15
5 Tu	00:54	5.8	177	**20** W ◐	01:41	5.4	165
	06:53	0.2	6		07:54	1.0	30
	13:16	6.1	186		14:00	5.1	155
	19:25	-0.1	-3		20:10	0.6	18
6 W ◑	01:51	5.9	180	**21** Th	02:31	5.4	165
	07:59	0.3	9		08:51	1.1	34
	14:12	5.9	180		14:50	4.9	149
	20:23	-0.2	-6		20:59	0.6	18
7 Th	02:54	6.1	186	**22** F	03:26	5.4	165
	09:06	0.2	6		09:47	1.1	34
	15:14	5.7	174		15:46	4.8	146
	21:22	-0.3	-9		21:49	0.5	15
8 F	04:02	6.3	192	**23** Sa	04:23	5.6	171
	10:11	0.1	3		10:40	0.9	27
	16:20	5.6	171		16:43	4.8	146
	22:21	-0.5	-15		22:39	0.4	12
9 Sa	05:09	6.6	201	**24** Su	05:19	5.8	177
	11:14	-0.1	-3		11:31	0.8	24
	17:25	5.7	174		17:37	4.9	149
	23:20	-0.6	-18		23:29	0.2	6
10 Su	06:12	6.9	210	**25** M	06:11	6.0	183
	12:14	-0.3	-9		12:20	0.5	15
	18:26	5.8	177		18:28	5.1	155
11 M	00:18	-0.8	-24	**26** Tu	00:18	0.0	0
	07:09	7.1	216		06:59	6.3	192
	13:11	-0.5	-15		13:06	0.3	9
	19:22	5.9	180		19:15	5.3	162
12 Tu	01:14	-0.9	-27	**27** W	01:04	-0.3	-9
	08:03	7.2	219		07:44	6.5	198
	14:04	-0.6	-18		13:49	0.0	0
	20:15	6.0	183		20:00	5.5	168
13 W ●	02:06	-0.9	-27	**28** Th ○	01:49	-0.5	-15
	08:54	7.2	219		08:28	6.7	204
	14:52	-0.6	-18		14:30	-0.2	-6
	21:06	6.0	183		20:44	5.6	171
14 Th	02:55	-0.8	-24	**29** F	02:32	-0.7	-21
	09:42	7.1	216		09:11	6.8	207
	15:38	-0.5	-15		15:09	-0.4	-12
	21:55	5.9	180		21:28	5.8	177
15 F	03:42	-0.6	-18	**30** Sa	03:16	-0.8	-24
	10:28	6.8	207		09:53	6.8	207
	16:23	-0.4	-12		15:49	-0.5	-15
	22:41	5.8	177		22:12	5.9	180
				31 Su	04:00	-0.8	-24
					10:36	6.7	204
					16:31	-0.6	-18
					22:57	6.0	183

February

Day	Time	ft	cm	Day	Time	ft	cm
1 M	04:48	-0.6	-18	**16** Tu	05:31	0.4	12
	11:20	6.5	198		11:55	5.5	168
	17:16	-0.6	-18		17:48	0.2	6
	23:45	6.1	186				
2 Tu	05:41	-0.4	-12	**17** W	00:13	5.7	174
	12:07	6.3	192		06:17	0.7	21
	18:05	-0.5	-15		12:33	5.2	158
					18:29	0.5	15
3 W	00:37	6.2	189	**18** Th	00:55	5.6	171
	06:39	-0.1	-3		07:08	0.9	27
	12:57	6.0	183		13:15	5.0	152
	18:59	-0.4	-12		19:15	0.6	18
4 Th ◐	01:33	6.2	189	**19** F ◐	01:41	5.5	168
	07:43	0.1	3		08:02	1.1	34
	13:52	5.7	174		14:02	4.8	146
	19:58	-0.3	-9		20:06	0.7	21
5 F	02:36	6.2	189	**20** Sa	02:33	5.4	165
	08:50	0.2	6		08:59	1.1	34
	14:54	5.4	165		14:57	4.7	143
	20:59	-0.3	-9		21:00	0.7	21
6 Sa	03:45	6.2	189	**21** Su	03:33	5.4	165
	09:55	0.2	6		09:55	1.1	34
	16:02	5.3	162		15:57	4.7	143
	22:02	-0.3	-9		21:56	0.6	18
7 Su	04:55	6.3	192	**22** M	04:36	5.6	171
	10:59	0.1	3		10:50	0.9	27
	17:10	5.4	165		16:58	4.8	146
	23:04	-0.4	-12		22:52	0.4	12
8 M	06:00	6.5	198	**23** Tu	05:34	5.9	180
	11:59	-0.1	-3		11:42	0.6	18
	18:12	5.5	168		17:54	5.1	155
					23:46	0.1	3
9 Tu	00:04	-0.5	-15	**24** W	06:27	6.2	189
	06:57	6.7	204		12:31	0.3	9
	12:55	-0.3	-9		18:45	5.4	165
	19:09	5.7	174				
10 W	01:01	-0.6	-18	**25** Th	00:37	-0.2	-6
	07:49	6.8	207		07:16	6.5	198
	13:46	-0.4	-12		13:17	-0.1	-3
	20:00	5.9	180		19:34	5.8	177
11 Th ●	01:53	-0.7	-21	**26** F	01:26	-0.6	-18
	08:37	6.8	207		08:02	6.8	207
	14:32	-0.5	-15		14:01	-0.4	-12
	20:48	6.0	183		20:20	6.1	186
12 F	02:40	-0.7	-21	**27** Sa ○	02:13	-0.8	-24
	09:21	6.7	204		08:47	6.9	210
	15:15	-0.5	-15		14:43	-0.7	-21
	21:33	6.0	183		21:06	6.4	195
13 Sa	03:24	-0.5	-15	**28** Su	03:00	-1.0	-30
	10:02	6.5	198		09:31	6.9	210
	15:54	-0.4	-12		15:25	-0.9	-27
	22:15	5.9	180		21:52	6.6	201
14 Su	04:07	-0.2	-6				
	10:41	6.2	189				
	16:32	-0.2	-6				
	22:55	5.9	180				
15 M	04:48	0.1	3				
	11:18	5.9	180				
	17:10	0.0	0				
	23:34	5.8	177				

March

Day	Time	ft	cm	Day	Time	ft	cm
1 M	03:47	-1.0	-30	**16** Tu	05:22	0.2	6
	10:16	6.8	207		11:44	5.8	177
	16:07	-0.9	-27		17:31	0.1	3
	22:40	6.7	204		23:58	6.1	186
2 Tu	04:36	-0.8	-24	**17** W	06:01	0.4	12
	11:02	6.6	201		12:20	5.5	168
	16:52	-0.9	-27		18:05	0.4	12
	23:29	6.8	207				
3 W	05:28	-0.6	-18	**18** Th	00:35	6.0	183
	11:50	6.3	192		06:41	0.7	21
	17:42	-0.7	-21		12:57	5.3	162
					18:42	0.6	18
4 Th	00:21	6.7	204	**19** F ◐	01:14	5.9	180
	06:26	-0.2	-6		07:26	0.9	27
	12:41	6.0	183		13:37	5.1	155
	18:36	-0.4	-12		19:25	0.8	24
5 F	01:18	6.5	198	**20** Sa	01:58	5.7	174
	07:29	0.1	3		08:17	1.1	34
	13:37	5.6	171		14:23	4.9	149
	19:37	-0.2	-6		20:16	0.9	27
6 Sa ◑	02:21	6.3	192	**21** Su ◐	02:48	5.6	171
	08:34	0.3	9		09:13	1.2	37
	14:40	5.4	165		15:15	4.8	146
	20:42	0.0	0		21:14	0.9	27
7 Su	03:31	6.2	189	**22** M	03:46	5.6	171
	09:40	0.3	9		10:10	1.2	37
	15:49	5.3	162		16:14	4.8	146
	21:47	0.1	3		22:15	0.8	24
8 M	04:41	6.2	189	**23** Tu	04:51	5.7	174
	10:42	0.3	9		11:07	1.0	30
	16:57	5.4	165		17:18	5.0	152
	22:51	0.0	0		23:15	0.6	18
9 Tu	05:45	6.4	195	**24** W	05:54	5.9	180
	11:41	0.2	6		12:02	0.7	21
	17:59	5.6	171		18:19	5.4	165
	23:52	-0.1	-3				
10 W	06:40	6.5	198	**25** Th	00:14	0.3	9
	12:35	0.0	0		06:51	6.2	189
	18:54	5.8	177		12:53	0.3	9
					19:14	5.8	177
11 Th	00:48	-0.2	-6	**26** F	01:10	-0.1	-3
	07:30	6.6	201		07:43	6.5	198
	13:24	-0.2	-6		13:42	-0.1	-3
	19:43	6.0	183		20:05	6.3	192
12 F	01:38	-0.3	-9	**27** Sa	02:03	-0.5	-15
	08:14	6.6	201		08:32	6.8	207
	14:07	-0.3	-9		14:29	-0.5	-15
	20:27	6.2	189		20:54	6.7	204
13 Sa ●	02:23	-0.3	-9	**28** Su ○	02:54	-0.8	-24
	08:55	6.5	198		09:19	6.9	210
	14:46	-0.3	-9		15:11	-0.8	-24
	21:08	6.3	192		21:43	7.1	216
14 Su	04:05	-0.2	-6	**29** M	03:43	-1.0	-30
	10:33	6.3	192		10:07	6.9	210
	16:22	-0.2	-6		15:58	-1.0	-30
	22:46	6.3	192		22:31	7.3	223
15 M	04:44	-0.1	-3	**30** Tu	04:32	-1.0	-30
	11:09	6.0	183		10:55	6.8	207
	16:57	-0.1	-3		16:43	-1.1	-34
	23:23	6.2	189		23:21	7.4	226
				31 W	05:22	-0.9	-27
					11:44	6.6	201
					17:30	-0.9	-27

NOAA Tide Predictions

Fernandina Beach, FL, 2021

Times and Heights of High and Low Waters

April

Day	Time	ft	cm	Day	Time	ft	cm
1 Th	00:13	7.3	223	**16** F	00:03	6.3	192
	06:15	-0.6	-18		06:11	0.7	21
	12:35	6.3	192		12:27	5.2	158
	18:21	-0.6	-18		18:05	0.7	21
2 F	01:07	7.1	216	**17** Sa	00:42	6.1	186
	07:12	-0.2	-6		06:52	0.9	27
	13:28	6.0	183		13:08	5.1	155
	19:17	-0.2	-6		18:46	0.8	24
3 Sa	02:04	6.8	207	**18** Su	01:25	6.0	183
	08:14	0.1	3		07:39	1.0	30
	14:25	5.7	174		13:52	5.0	152
	20:20	0.1	3		19:36	0.9	27
4 Su	03:07	6.5	198	**19** M	02:13	5.9	180
	09:19	0.3	9		08:33	1.1	34
	15:28	5.5	168		14:41	5.0	152
	21:27	0.3	9		20:35	1.0	30
5 M	04:14	6.3	192	**20** Tu	03:08	5.8	177
	10:22	0.4	12		09:31	1.0	30
	16:35	5.5	168		15:39	5.1	155
	22:34	0.4	12		21:39	0.9	27
6 Tu	05:21	6.2	189	**21** W	04:08	5.9	180
	11:22	0.4	12		10:27	0.8	24
	17:41	5.6	171		16:41	5.3	162
	23:38	0.4	12		22:43	0.7	21
7 W	06:22	6.2	189	**22** Th	05:12	6.0	183
	12:18	0.3	9		11:22	0.5	15
	18:41	5.8	177		17:44	5.7	174
					23:44	0.4	12
8 Th	00:37	0.3	9	**23** F	06:12	6.2	189
	07:15	6.3	192		12:15	0.1	3
	13:09	0.2	6		18:43	6.2	189
	19:33	6.1	186				
9 F	01:31	0.2	6	**24** Sa	00:43	0.0	0
	08:02	6.3	192		07:08	6.4	195
	13:54	0.0	0		13:06	-0.3	-9
	20:19	6.3	192		19:37	6.7	204
10 Sa	02:20	0.1	3	**25** Su	01:40	-0.4	-12
	08:45	6.2	189		08:00	6.6	201
	14:36	-0.1	-3		13:56	-0.7	-21
	21:01	6.5	198		20:29	7.2	219
11 Su	03:03	0.1	3	**26** M	02:34	-0.8	-24
	09:24	6.1	186		08:51	6.7	204
	15:14	-0.1	-3		14:45	-1.0	-30
	21:39	6.6	201		21:20	7.6	232
12	03:43	0.1	3	**27** Tu	03:26	-1.0	-30
	10:01	6.0	183		09:42	6.7	204
	15:49	0.0	0		15:33	-1.1	-34
	22:16	6.6	201		22:12	7.8	238
13	04:21	0.1	3	**28** W	04:16	-1.0	-30
	10:38	5.8	177		10:34	6.6	201
	16:22	0.1	3		16:21	-1.1	-34
	22:51	6.5	198		23:04	7.8	238
14	04:57	0.3	9	**29** Th	05:08	-0.9	-27
	11:14	5.6	171		11:26	6.4	195
	16:55	0.3	9		17:10	-0.9	-27
	23:27	6.4	195		23:58	7.6	232
15	05:33	0.5	15	**30** F	06:01	-0.6	-18
	11:50	5.4	165		12:20	6.2	189
	17:29	0.5	15		18:03	-0.5	-15

May

Day	Time	ft	cm	Day	Time	ft	cm
1 Sa	00:53	7.3	223	**16** Su	00:18	6.2	189
	06:57	-0.2	-6		06:25	0.7	21
	13:15	6.0	183		12:43	5.0	152
	19:00	-0.1	-3		18:18	0.7	21
2 Su	01:50	6.9	210	**17** M	01:00	6.1	186
	07:58	0.1	3		07:10	0.8	24
	14:12	5.7	174		13:27	5.0	152
	20:04	0.3	9		19:07	0.8	24
3 M	02:49	6.5	198	**18** Tu	01:46	6.0	183
	09:00	0.3	9		08:01	0.8	24
	15:13	5.6	171		14:16	5.1	155
	21:11	0.5	15		20:06	0.8	24
4 Tu	03:51	6.2	189	**19** W	02:37	6.0	183
	10:00	0.4	12		08:56	0.6	18
	16:16	5.6	171		15:10	5.3	162
	22:17	0.7	21		21:10	0.7	21
5 W	04:52	6.0	183	**20** Th	03:33	5.9	180
	10:56	0.3	9		09:51	0.4	12
	17:18	5.7	174		16:10	5.6	171
	23:19	0.7	21		22:15	0.6	18
6 Th	05:49	5.9	180	**21** F	04:33	6.0	183
	11:48	0.3	9		10:46	0.1	3
	18:15	5.9	180		17:12	6.0	183
					23:18	0.3	9
7 F	00:16	0.6	18	**22** Sa	05:34	6.0	183
	06:41	5.9	180		11:39	-0.3	-9
	12:35	0.2	6		18:13	6.5	198
	19:05	6.2	189				
8 Sa	01:08	0.5	15	**23** Su	00:18	-0.1	-3
	07:27	5.8	177		06:33	6.2	189
	13:19	0.1	3		12:33	-0.6	-18
	19:50	6.4	195		19:10	7.0	213
9 Su	01:55	0.4	12	**24** M	01:17	-0.4	-12
	08:10	5.8	177		07:30	6.3	192
	14:00	0.0	0		13:26	-0.9	-27
	20:30	6.6	201		20:05	7.4	226
10 M	02:39	0.3	9	**25** Tu	02:14	-0.7	-21
	08:50	5.7	174		08:25	6.3	192
	14:38	0.0	0		14:18	-1.1	-34
	21:09	6.7	204		21:00	7.7	235
11 Tu	03:19	0.2	6	**26** W	03:08	-0.9	-27
	09:29	5.6	171		09:19	6.3	192
	15:15	0.1	3		15:10	-1.2	-37
	21:46	6.7	204		21:54	7.8	238
12 W	03:56	0.2	6	**27** Th	04:00	-0.9	-27
	10:07	5.5	168		10:14	6.3	192
	15:50	0.1	3		16:01	-1.1	-34
	22:23	6.6	201		22:49	7.7	235
13 Th	04:32	0.3	9	**28** F	04:52	-0.8	-24
	10:45	5.4	165		11:09	6.2	189
	16:24	0.3	9		16:52	-0.9	-27
	23:00	6.5	198		23:44	7.5	229
14 F	05:08	0.4	12	**29** Sa	05:45	-0.6	-18
	11:23	5.3	162		12:04	6.0	183
	16:59	0.4	12		17:46	-0.5	-15
	23:38	6.4	195				
15 Sa	05:45	0.6	18	**30** Su	00:38	7.2	219
	12:03	5.1	155		06:40	-0.3	-9
	17:36	0.5	15		12:59	5.8	177
					18:43	-0.1	-3
				31 M	01:32	6.8	207
					07:37	-0.1	-3
					13:55	5.7	174
					19:45	0.3	9

June

Day	Time	ft	cm	Day	Time	ft	cm
1 Tu	02:26	6.4	195	**16** W	01:24	6.1	186
	08:35	0.1	3		07:33	0.3	9
	14:52	5.6	171		13:55	5.3	162
	20:50	0.6	18		19:44	0.5	15
2 W	03:21	6.0	183	**17** Th	02:12	6.0	183
	09:31	0.2	6		08:25	0.2	6
	15:50	5.6	171		14:47	5.5	168
	21:54	0.7	21		20:48	0.5	15
3 Th	04:15	5.7	174	**18** F	03:04	5.9	180
	10:23	0.2	6		09:19	-0.1	-3
	16:47	5.7	174		15:44	5.8	177
	22:53	0.8	24		21:52	0.4	12
4 F	05:08	5.5	168	**19** Sa	04:01	5.9	180
	11:11	0.2	6		10:13	-0.3	-9
	17:41	5.9	180		16:45	6.2	189
	23:47	0.7	21		22:55	0.2	6
5 Sa	05:59	5.4	165	**20** Su	05:02	5.8	177
	11:56	0.1	3		11:08	-0.6	-18
	18:30	6.1	186		17:47	6.6	201
					23:57	-0.1	-3
6 Su	00:38	0.6	18	**21** M	06:04	5.8	177
	06:46	5.3	162		12:04	-0.8	-24
	12:39	0.1	3		18:48	7.0	213
	19:15	6.3	192				
7 M	01:26	0.5	15	**22** Tu	00:57	-0.3	-9
	07:31	5.3	162		07:04	5.9	180
	13:22	0.1	3		13:00	-1.0	-30
	19:57	6.4	195		19:46	7.3	223
8 Tu	02:10	0.4	12	**23** W	01:55	-0.6	-18
	08:14	5.3	162		08:02	6.0	183
	14:03	0.0	0		13:56	-1.1	-34
	20:38	6.5	198		20:43	7.5	229
9 W	02:51	0.3	9	**24** Th	02:50	-0.7	-21
	08:56	5.3	162		08:59	6.0	183
	14:43	0.0	0		14:50	-1.1	-34
	21:18	6.6	201		21:39	7.6	232
10 Th	03:30	0.2	6	**25** F	03:44	-0.8	-24
	09:38	5.3	162		09:56	6.0	183
	15:21	0.1	3		15:44	-1.0	-30
	21:58	6.5	198		22:34	7.5	229
11 F	04:08	0.2	6	**26** Sa	04:35	-0.7	-21
	10:19	5.2	158		10:52	6.0	183
	15:58	0.1	3		16:36	-0.8	-24
	22:37	6.5	198		23:28	7.3	223
12 Sa	04:44	0.3	9	**27** Su	05:26	-0.6	-18
	10:59	5.1	155		11:46	5.9	180
	16:35	0.2	6		17:29	-0.5	-15
	23:17	6.4	195				
13 Su	05:22	0.3	9	**28** M	00:19	7.0	213
	11:41	5.1	155		06:17	-0.4	-12
	17:14	0.3	9		12:40	5.8	177
	23:58	6.3	192		18:23	0.0	0
14 M	06:01	0.4	12	**29** Tu	01:09	6.6	201
	12:23	5.1	155		07:10	-0.2	-6
	17:57	0.4	12		13:32	5.7	174
					19:21	0.4	12
15 Tu	00:40	6.2	189	**30** W	01:57	6.2	189
	06:45	0.4	12		08:02	0.0	0
	13:07	5.1	155		14:24	5.6	171
	18:47	0.5	15		20:22	0.7	21

141

StationId: 8720030
Source: NOAA/NOS/CO-OPS
Station Type: Primary
Time Zone: LST_LDT
Datum: MLLW

NOAA Tide Predictions

Fernandina Beach, FL, 2021

Times and Heights of High and Low Waters

July

Day	Time	ft	cm	Day	Time	ft	cm
1 Th ☽	02:45	5.8	177	16 F	01:50	6.1	186
	08:54	0.1	3		07:56	-0.2	-6
	15:16	5.6	171		14:26	6.0	183
	21:23	0.8	24		20:29	0.4	12
2 F	03:33	5.5	168	17 Sa ☾	02:40	5.9	180
	09:43	0.2	6		08:50	-0.3	-9
	16:07	5.7	174		15:22	6.2	189
	22:19	0.9	27		21:33	0.3	9
3 Sa	04:22	5.2	158	18 Su	03:36	5.8	177
	10:29	0.2	6		09:46	-0.4	-12
	16:59	5.8	177		16:23	6.4	195
	23:12	0.9	27		22:36	0.2	6
4 Su	05:13	5.1	155	19 M	04:37	5.7	174
	11:14	0.2	6		10:44	-0.5	-15
	17:49	6.0	183		17:28	6.7	204
					23:38	0.1	3
5 M	00:03	0.8	24	20 Tu	05:41	5.7	174
	06:03	5.0	152		11:42	-0.7	-21
	11:59	0.2	6		18:32	7.0	213
	18:37	6.1	186				
6 Tu	00:51	0.7	21	21 W	00:39	-0.1	-3
	06:52	5.1	155		06:45	5.7	174
	12:44	0.2	6		12:41	-0.8	-24
	19:23	6.3	192		19:32	7.2	219
7 W	01:37	0.6	18	22 Th	01:37	-0.3	-9
	07:39	5.1	155		07:45	5.8	177
	13:29	0.1	3		13:39	-0.8	-24
	20:08	6.4	195		20:30	7.4	226
8 Th	02:21	0.4	12	23 F	02:33	-0.4	-12
	08:24	5.2	158		08:43	5.9	180
	14:12	0.1	3		14:35	-0.8	-24
	20:51	6.5	198		21:25	7.4	226
9 F	03:02	0.3	9	24 Sa ○	03:26	-0.5	-15
	09:09	5.2	158		09:39	6.0	183
	14:54	0.0	0		15:29	-0.8	-24
	21:34	6.6	201		22:17	7.3	223
10 Sa ●	03:41	0.2	6	25 Su	04:16	-0.5	-15
	09:52	5.2	158		10:33	6.0	183
	15:35	0.0	0		16:20	-0.6	-18
	22:15	6.6	201		23:07	7.1	216
11 Su	04:19	0.2	6	26 M	05:03	-0.4	-12
	10:35	5.3	162		11:25	6.0	183
	16:15	0.0	0		17:10	-0.2	-6
	22:57	6.5	198		23:55	6.8	207
12 M	04:58	0.1	3	27 Tu	05:49	-0.3	-9
	11:18	5.3	162		12:15	6.0	183
	16:56	0.0	0		18:01	0.1	3
	23:38	6.5	198				
13 Tu	05:37	0.1	3	28 W	00:40	6.4	195
	12:02	5.4	165		06:35	0.0	0
	17:41	0.1	3		13:10	5.9	180
					18:53	0.5	15
14 W	00:20	6.4	195	29 Th	01:23	6.1	186
	06:19	0.0	0		07:22	0.2	6
	12:47	5.5	168		13:49	5.8	177
	18:31	0.2	6		19:48	0.9	27
15 Th	01:03	6.3	192	30 F	02:05	5.7	174
	07:05	-0.1	-3		08:09	0.4	12
	13:35	5.7	174		14:35	5.8	177
	19:27	0.3	9		20:44	1.1	34
				31 Sa ☽	02:49	5.4	165
					08:56	0.5	15
					15:22	5.8	177
					21:40	1.2	37

August

Day	Time	ft	cm	Day	Time	ft	cm
1 Su	03:36	5.2	158	16 M	03:18	5.9	180
	09:44	0.6	18		09:24	-0.1	-3
	16:12	5.8	177		16:07	6.7	204
	22:33	1.2	37		22:20	0.5	15
2 M	04:27	5.0	152	17 Tu	04:21	5.8	177
	10:31	0.6	18		10:25	-0.1	-3
	17:05	5.9	180		17:15	6.9	210
	23:24	1.1	34		23:23	0.4	12
3 Tu	05:20	5.0	152	18 W	05:27	5.8	177
	11:19	0.5	15		11:26	-0.2	-6
	17:58	6.1	186		18:20	7.0	213
4 W	00:13	1.0	30	19 Th	00:23	0.3	9
	06:13	5.1	155		06:32	5.9	180
	12:08	0.5	15		12:27	-0.3	-9
	18:49	6.3	192		19:21	7.2	219
5 Th	01:01	0.9	27	20 F	01:21	0.1	3
	06:57	5.2	158		07:33	6.0	183
	12:56	0.4	12		13:26	-0.3	-9
	19:37	6.5	198		20:17	7.3	223
6 F	01:47	0.7	21	21 Sa	02:16	0.0	0
	07:54	5.4	165		08:29	6.2	189
	13:43	0.2	6		14:22	-0.3	-9
	20:23	6.6	201		21:08	7.3	223
7 Sa	02:31	0.5	15	22 Su ○	03:06	-0.1	-3
	08:40	5.5	168		09:22	6.3	192
	14:29	0.1	3		15:14	-0.3	-9
	21:08	6.8	207		21:57	7.2	219
8 Su ●	03:12	0.3	9	23 M	03:52	-0.2	-6
	09:26	5.7	174		10:12	6.4	195
	15:12	0.0	0		16:03	-0.1	-3
	21:50	6.8	207		22:42	7.0	213
9 M	03:52	0.1	3	24 Tu	04:35	-0.1	-3
	10:10	5.8	177		11:00	6.4	195
	15:56	-0.1	-3		16:50	0.1	3
	22:33	6.9	210		23:25	6.7	204
10 Tu	04:31	0.0	0	25 W	05:16	0.1	3
	10:55	6.0	183		11:44	6.4	195
	16:20	-0.1	-3		17:35	0.5	15
	23:15	6.8	207				
11 W	05:10	-0.1	-3	26 Th	00:06	6.4	195
	11:40	6.1	186		05:57	0.3	9
	17:26	0.0	0		12:27	6.3	192
	23:58	6.7	204		18:22	0.8	24
12 Th	05:53	-0.2	-6	27 F	00:46	6.0	183
	12:26	6.3	192		06:38	0.6	18
	18:16	0.1	3		13:09	6.2	189
					19:10	1.1	34
13 F	00:43	6.5	198	28 Sa	01:25	5.7	174
	06:39	-0.2	-6		07:20	0.8	24
	13:15	6.4	195		13:51	6.1	186
	19:12	0.3	9		20:02	1.4	43
14 Sa	01:30	6.3	192	29 Su	02:07	5.5	168
	07:29	-0.2	-6		08:06	1.0	30
	14:07	6.6	201		14:36	6.1	186
	20:13	0.4	12		20:55	1.5	46
15 Su ☽	02:22	6.1	186	30 M ☽	02:53	5.3	162
	08:25	-0.1	-3		08:56	1.1	34
	15:04	6.6	201		15:25	6.0	183
	21:17	0.5	15		21:49	1.6	49
				31 Tu	03:43	5.2	158
					09:47	1.1	34
					16:20	6.1	186
					22:42	1.5	46

September

Day	Time	ft	cm	Day	Time	ft	cm
1 W	04:38	5.2	158	16 Th	05:18	6.0	183
	10:40	1.0	30		11:15	0.4	12
	17:17	6.2	189		18:08	7.1	216
	23:33	1.4	43				
2 Th	05:36	5.3	162	17 F	00:08	0.7	21
	11:32	0.9	27		06:23	6.2	189
	18:13	6.4	195		12:17	0.3	9
					19:07	7.2	219
3 F	00:23	1.2	37	18 Sa	01:03	0.5	15
	06:31	5.5	168		07:21	6.4	195
	12:24	0.7	21		13:15	0.3	9
	19:05	6.6	201		19:59	7.3	223
4 Sa	01:11	0.9	27	19 Su	01:55	0.3	9
	07:23	5.8	177		08:15	6.6	201
	13:15	0.5	15		14:09	0.2	6
	19:53	6.9	210		20:47	7.2	219
5 Su	01:57	0.7	21	20 M ○	02:42	0.2	6
	08:11	6.1	186		09:03	6.8	207
	14:04	0.3	9		14:59	0.2	6
	20:38	7.1	216		21:32	7.1	216
6 M	02:40	0.3	9	21 Tu	03:25	0.2	6
	08:58	6.4	195		09:49	6.9	210
	14:51	0.1	3		15:45	0.3	9
	21:22	7.2	219		22:13	6.9	210
7 Tu ●	03:21	0.1	3	22 W	04:04	0.2	6
	09:44	6.6	201		10:31	6.9	210
	15:37	-0.1	-3		16:28	0.5	15
	22:06	7.2	219		22:53	6.7	204
8 W	04:02	-0.1	-3	23 Th	04:42	0.4	12
	10:30	6.9	210		11:11	6.9	210
	16:23	-0.1	-3		17:09	0.8	24
	22:50	7.1	216		23:31	6.4	195
9 Th	04:43	-0.2	-6	24 F	05:18	0.6	18
	11:16	7.1	216		11:50	6.8	207
	17:10	0.0	0		17:50	1.1	34
	23:36	7.0	213				
10 F	05:26	-0.2	-6	25 Sa	00:09	6.1	186
	12:05	7.2	219		05:55	0.9	27
	18:01	0.1	3		12:29	6.6	201
					18:32	1.4	43
11 Sa	00:23	6.7	204	26 Su	00:47	5.8	177
	06:14	-0.1	-3		06:33	1.1	34
	12:56	7.2	219		13:09	6.5	198
	18:57	0.4	12		19:19	1.6	49
12 Su	01:13	6.5	198	27 M	01:28	5.6	171
	07:06	0.0	0		07:17	1.3	40
	13:51	7.1	216		13:53	6.3	192
	19:58	0.6	18		20:09	1.8	55
13 M ☽	02:07	6.3	192	28 Tu	02:13	5.5	168
	08:04	0.2	6		08:07	1.5	46
	14:41	7.1	216		14:41	6.3	192
	21:02	0.8	24		21:04	1.9	58
14 Tu	03:06	6.1	186	29 W	03:03	5.4	165
	09:07	0.3	9		09:02	1.5	46
	15:55	7.0	213		15:36	6.2	189
	22:06	0.8	24		21:59	1.8	55
15 W	04:10	6.0	183	30 Th	03:59	5.4	165
	10:12	0.4	12		10:00	1.4	43
	17:03	7.0	213		16:35	6.3	192
	23:08	0.8	24		22:52	1.6	49

StationId: 8720030
Source: NOAA/NOS/CO-OPS
Station Type: Primary
Time Zone: LST_LDT
Datum: MLLW

NOAA Tide Predictions

Fernandina Beach, FL,2021

Times and Heights of High and Low Waters

October

	Time	Height ft	cm		Time	Height ft	cm
1 F	04:58 10:57 17:33 23:43	5.6 1.3 6.5 1.4	171 40 198 43	**16** Sa	06:10 12:06 18:46	6.4 0.8 7.0	195 24 213
2 Sa	05:57 11:52 18:28	5.9 1.0 6.7	180 30 204	**17** Su	00:41 07:06 13:02 19:36	0.6 6.7 0.7 7.0	18 204 21 213
3 Su	00:32 06:51 12:46 19:19	1.0 6.2 0.7 7.0	30 189 21 213	**18** M	01:30 07:56 13:55 20:21	0.5 6.9 0.6 6.9	15 210 18 210
4 M	01:20 07:42 13:39 20:06	0.7 6.7 0.4 7.2	21 204 12 219	**19** Tu	02:14 08:41 14:42 21:03	0.4 7.1 0.6 6.8	12 216 18 207
5 Tu	02:05 14:29 20:52	0.3 7.1 0.1 7.3	9 216 3 223	**20** W	02:54 09:22 15:25 21:43	0.4 7.2 0.6 6.6	12 219 18 201
6 W	02:49 09:17 15:18 21:38	0.0 7.4 -0.1 7.3	0 226 -3 223	**21** Th	03:32 10:01 16:05 22:22	0.4 7.2 0.7 6.4	12 219 21 195
7 Th	03:33 10:05 16:06 22:26	-0.3 7.7 -0.2 7.3	-9 235 -6 223	**22** F	04:08 10:39 16:43 22:58	0.6 7.1 0.9 6.2	18 216 27 189
8 F	04:17 10:54 16:55 23:14	-0.4 7.8 -0.1 7.1	-12 238 -3 216	**23** Sa	04:42 11:16 17:21 23:35	0.7 7.0 1.1 6.0	21 213 34 183
9 Sa	05:03 11:46 17:46	-0.3 7.8 0.1	-9 238 3	**24** Su	05:17 11:53 17:59	0.9 6.8 1.3	27 207 40
10 Su	00:05 12:39 18:42	6.9 -0.1 7.7 0.4	210 -3 235 12	**25** M	00:14 05:54 12:33 18:40	5.8 1.2 6.6 1.5	177 37 201 46
11 M	00:58 06:46 13:36 19:42	6.6 0.2 7.5 0.7	201 6 229 21	**26** Tu	00:54 06:34 13:16 19:27	5.6 1.4 6.5 1.7	171 43 198 52
12 Tu	01:54 07:47 14:37 20:46	6.4 0.5 7.3 0.9	195 15 223 27	**27** W	01:38 07:22 14:03 20:19	5.5 1.5 6.4 1.8	168 46 195 55
13 W	02:55 08:53 15:41 21:51	6.2 0.7 7.1 1.0	189 21 216 30	**28** Th	02:26 08:19 14:54 21:15	5.4 1.6 6.3 1.7	165 49 192 52
14 Th	04:00 10:00 16:48 22:52	6.1 0.8 7.0 0.9	186 24 213 27	**29** F	03:21 09:20 15:51 22:09	5.5 1.5 6.3 1.5	168 46 192 46
15 F	05:07 11:05 17:50 23:49	6.2 0.8 7.0 0.8	189 24 213 24	**30** Sa	04:21 10:22 16:50 23:02	5.7 1.3 6.4 1.2	174 40 195 37
				31 Su	05:21 11:21 17:48 23:53	6.0 1.1 6.6 0.8	183 34 201 24

November

	Time	Height ft	cm		Time	Height ft	cm
1 M	06:19 12:18 18:42	6.5 0.7 6.8	198 21 207	**16** Tu	06:32 12:35 18:52	6.8 0.7 6.3	207 21 192
2 Tu	00:42 07:12 13:14 19:34	0.4 7.0 0.4 7.0	12 213 12 213	**17** W	00:43 07:15 13:21 19:33	0.4 7.0 0.7 6.2	12 213 21 189
3 W	01:31 08:03 14:07 20:23	0.0 7.5 0.0 7.1	0 229 0 216	**18** Th	01:23 07:55 14:03 20:13	0.3 7.1 0.6 6.1	9 216 18 186
4 Th ●	02:19 08:53 14:59 21:13	-0.3 7.9 -0.3 7.1	-9 241 -9 216	**19** F ○	02:01 08:33 14:42 20:51	0.4 7.1 0.6 6.0	12 216 18 183
5 F	03:06 09:44 15:49 22:03	-0.6 8.1 -0.4 7.1	-18 247 -12 216	**20** Sa	02:38 09:11 15:19 21:29	0.4 7.0 0.7 5.9	12 213 21 180
6 Sa	03:54 10:36 16:39 22:54	-0.7 8.2 -0.3 6.9	-21 250 -9 210	**21** Su	03:13 09:48 15:55 22:07	0.5 6.9 0.8 5.7	15 210 24 174
7 Su	03:42 10:29 16:31 22:48	-0.6 8.1 -0.1 6.7	-18 247 -3 204	**22** M	03:48 10:27 16:31 22:45	0.7 6.7 1.0 5.6	21 204 30 171
8 M	04:34 11:25 17:26 23:43	-0.3 7.8 0.2 6.5	-9 238 6 198	**23** Tu	04:23 11:05 17:09 23:25	0.8 6.6 1.1 5.4	24 201 34 165
9 Tu	05:29 12:22 18:25	0.1 7.5 0.5	3 229 15	**24** W	05:02 11:46 17:51	1.0 6.4 1.2	30 195 37
10 W	00:40 06:30 13:21 19:28	6.3 0.4 7.2 0.7	192 12 219 21	**25** Th	00:07 05:48 12:30 18:39	5.3 1.1 6.3 1.3	162 34 192 40
11 Th ◐	01:41 07:37 14:22 20:30	6.1 0.7 6.9 0.8	186 21 210 24	**26** F	00:54 06:42 13:17 19:32	5.3 1.2 6.2 1.2	162 37 189 37
12 F	02:45 08:45 15:23 21:29	6.1 0.9 6.7 0.7	186 27 204 21	**27** Sa ◗	01:46 07:44 14:10 20:26	5.4 1.2 6.1 1.0	165 37 186 30
13 Sa	03:49 09:50 16:23 22:23	6.2 1.0 6.5 0.6	189 30 198 18	**28** Su	02:43 08:48 15:07 21:20	5.6 1.1 6.1 0.7	171 34 186 21
14 Su	04:50 10:50 17:18 23:13	6.3 0.9 6.4 0.5	192 27 195 15	**29** M	03:45 09:51 16:07 22:14	6.0 0.8 6.2 0.3	183 24 189 9
15 M	05:44 11:45 18:07 23:59	6.6 0.8 6.4 0.4	201 24 195 12	**30** Tu	04:46 10:51 17:06 23:07	6.5 0.5 6.3 0.0	198 15 192 0

December

	Time	Height ft	cm		Time	Height ft	cm
1 W	05:44 11:50 18:03	7.0 0.1 6.4	213 3 195	**16** Th	00:10 06:47 12:57 19:03	0.3 6.5 0.6 5.6	9 198 18 171
2 Th	00:00 06:39 12:46 18:57	-0.4 7.4 -0.2 6.6	-12 226 -6 201	**17** F	00:52 07:28 13:39 19:44	0.2 6.6 0.5 5.6	6 201 15 171
3 F	00:52 07:33 13:40 19:50	-0.7 7.8 -0.5 6.7	-21 238 -15 204	**18** Sa	01:33 08:08 14:18 20:25	0.2 6.7 0.4 5.6	6 204 12 171
4 Sa ●	01:44 08:27 14:33 20:43	-0.9 8.0 -0.6 6.7	-27 244 -18 204	**19** Su ○	02:12 08:47 14:55 21:04	0.1 6.7 0.4 5.5	3 204 12 168
5 Su	02:35 09:21 15:24 21:37	-1.0 8.0 -0.6 6.6	-30 244 -18 201	**20** M	02:49 09:26 15:31 21:43	0.1 6.6 0.4 5.4	3 201 12 165
6 M	03:26 10:15 16:15 22:32	-0.9 7.9 -0.5 6.5	-27 241 -15 198	**21** Tu	03:24 10:04 16:06 22:21	0.2 6.5 0.5 5.4	6 198 15 165
7 Tu	04:18 11:10 17:08 23:27	-0.7 7.6 -0.2 6.3	-21 232 -6 192	**22** W	04:01 10:42 16:42 23:01	0.3 6.4 0.5 5.3	9 195 15 162
8 W	05:13 12:04 18:04	-0.3 7.3 0.0	-9 223 0	**23** Th	04:39 11:21 17:21 23:41	0.4 6.3 0.6 5.3	12 192 18 162
9 Th	00:23 06:13 12:59 19:03	6.1 0.2 6.9 0.3	186 6 210 9	**24** F	05:23 12:01 18:05	0.5 6.2 0.6	15 189 18
10 F	01:21 07:17 13:54 20:01	6.0 0.5 6.5 0.4	183 15 198 12	**25** Sa	00:25 06:14 12:45 18:53	5.3 0.7 6.0 0.5	162 21 183 15
11 Sa ◐	02:20 08:23 14:50 20:58	5.9 0.8 6.1 0.4	180 24 186 12	**26** Su	01:14 07:14 13:34 19:46	5.5 0.7 5.9 0.3	168 21 180 9
12 Su	03:21 09:27 15:47 21:50	5.9 0.9 5.8 0.4	180 27 177 12	**27** M ◗	02:09 08:18 14:29 20:42	5.7 0.7 5.8 0.1	174 21 177 3
13 M	04:20 10:26 16:42 22:39	6.0 0.9 5.7 0.4	183 27 174 12	**28** Tu	03:10 09:23 15:30 21:38	5.9 0.5 5.7 -0.1	180 15 174 -3
14 Tu	05:14 11:20 17:33 23:25	6.2 0.8 5.6 0.3	189 24 171 9	**29** W	04:15 10:26 16:33 22:36	6.3 0.3 5.7 -0.4	192 9 174 -12
15 W	06:03 12:11 18:19	6.4 0.7 5.6	195 21 171	**30** Th	05:19 11:28 17:36 23:33	6.7 0.0 5.8 -0.7	204 0 177 -21
				31 F	06:20 12:27 18:35	7.1 -0.3 6.0	216 -9 183

143

NOAA Tide Predictions

Mayport (Ferry Depot), FL, 2021

Times and Heights of High and Low Waters

January

Day	Time	ft	cm	Day	Time	ft	cm
1 F	03:10	-0.3	-9	**16** Sa	04:22	-0.5	-15
	10:02	4.8	146		11:02	4.6	140
	16:01	-0.1	-3		17:03	-0.4	-12
	22:19	4.0	122		23:21	4.0	122
2 Sa	03:54	-0.2	-6	**17** Su	05:11	-0.1	-3
	10:44	4.8	146		11:45	4.4	134
	16:44	-0.1	-3		17:48	-0.2	-6
	23:04	4.0	122				
3 Su	04:43	-0.1	-3	**18** M	00:06	4.0	122
	11:28	4.7	143		06:02	0.2	6
	17:30	-0.1	-3		12:28	4.1	125
	23:52	4.1	125		18:32	0.1	3
4 M	05:37	0.1	3	**19** Tu	00:52	3.9	119
	12:16	4.6	140		06:55	0.5	15
	18:20	-0.1	-3		13:12	3.9	119
					19:18	0.2	6
5 Tu	00:46	4.2	128	**20** W	01:41	3.9	119
	06:38	0.2	6		07:51	0.7	21
	13:09	4.4	134		13:59	3.7	113
	19:15	-0.1	-3	◐	20:04	0.4	12
6 W	01:45	4.3	131	**21** Th	02:32	4.0	122
	07:46	0.3	9		08:49	0.8	24
	14:08	4.2	128		14:49	3.6	110
◑	20:13	-0.2	-6		20:53	0.4	12
7 Th	02:49	4.5	137	**22** F	03:26	4.0	122
	08:57	0.3	9		09:45	0.8	24
	15:12	4.0	122		15:43	3.5	107
	21:13	-0.3	-9		21:42	0.4	12
8 F	03:55	4.6	140	**23** Sa	04:21	4.1	125
	10:06	0.1	3		10:38	0.7	21
	16:19	3.9	119		16:37	3.4	104
	22:13	-0.4	-12		22:30	0.3	9
9 Sa	05:01	4.8	146	**24** Su	05:15	4.2	128
	11:10	-0.1	-3		11:27	0.5	15
	17:24	3.9	119		17:30	3.5	107
	23:11	-0.6	-18		23:17	0.1	3
10 Su	06:03	4.9	149	**25** M	06:06	4.3	131
	12:09	-0.3	-9		12:13	0.3	9
	18:24	3.9	119		18:20	3.5	107
11 M	00:08	-0.8	-24	**26** Tu	00:02	-0.1	-3
	07:01	5.0	152		06:53	4.4	134
	13:03	-0.5	-15		12:56	0.1	3
	19:20	3.9	119		19:07	3.6	110
12 Tu	01:02	-0.9	-27	**27** W	00:45	-0.3	-9
	07:54	5.1	155		07:38	4.6	140
	13:55	-0.6	-18		13:36	-0.2	-6
	20:13	4.0	122		19:51	3.7	113
13 W	01:54	-0.9	-27	**28** Th	01:28	-0.5	-15
	08:44	5.0	152		08:21	4.7	143
	14:45	-0.7	-21		14:17	-0.4	-12
● 21:02		4.0	122	○ 20:34		3.9	119
14 Th	02:44	-0.9	-27	**29** F	02:12	-0.7	-21
	09:32	5.0	152		09:02	4.8	146
	15:32	-0.7	-21		14:57	-0.6	-18
	21:50	4.0	122		21:18	4.0	122
15 F	03:33	-0.7	-21	**30** Sa	02:56	-0.7	-21
	10:18	4.8	146		09:44	4.8	146
	16:18	-0.5	-15		15:38	-0.7	-21
	22:36	4.0	122		22:01	4.2	128
				31 Su	03:43	-0.7	-21
					10:27	4.7	143
					16:21	-0.7	-21
					22:47	4.3	131

February

Day	Time	ft	cm	Day	Time	ft	cm
1 M	04:32	-0.6	-18	**16** Tu	05:24	0.1	3
	11:11	4.6	140		11:46	4.0	122
	17:07	-0.7	-21		17:40	0.0	0
	23:35	4.4	134				
2 Tu	05:27	-0.4	-12	**17** W	00:06	4.1	125
	11:59	4.4	134		06:09	0.4	12
	17:56	-0.6	-18		12:25	3.8	116
					18:19	0.2	6
3 W	00:28	4.4	134	**18** Th	00:48	4.0	122
	06:27	-0.1	-3		06:58	0.6	18
	12:52	4.1	125		13:06	3.6	110
	18:49	-0.4	-12		19:01	0.4	12
4 Th	01:27	4.4	134	**19** F	01:35	4.0	122
	07:34	0.1	3		07:52	0.8	24
	13:51	3.9	119		13:53	3.5	107
◐	19:49	-0.3	-9	◐	19:50	0.6	18
5 F	02:32	4.4	134	**20** Sa	02:29	3.9	119
	08:45	0.2	6		08:52	0.9	27
	14:57	3.7	113		14:47	3.4	104
	20:53	-0.3	-9		20:45	0.6	18
6 Sa	03:42	4.4	134	**21** Su	03:30	3.9	119
	09:55	0.1	3		09:51	0.9	27
	16:07	3.6	110		15:48	3.3	101
	21:58	-0.3	-9		21:42	0.5	15
7 Su	04:51	4.5	137	**22** M	04:32	4.0	122
	11:00	0.0	0		09:44	0.7	21
	17:14	3.6	110		16:48	3.4	104
	23:00	-0.4	-12		22:38	0.3	9
8 M	05:55	4.6	140	**23** Tu	05:30	4.2	128
	11:58	-0.2	-6		11:36	0.4	12
	18:15	3.7	113		17:44	3.6	110
	23:59	-0.6	-18		23:30	0.0	0
9 Tu	06:51	4.7	143	**24** W	06:21	4.4	134
	12:51	-0.4	-12		12:22	0.1	3
	19:09	3.8	116		18:36	3.8	116
10 W	00:53	-0.8	-24	**25** Th	00:19	-0.3	-9
	07:42	4.8	146		07:09	4.6	140
	13:40	-0.6	-18		13:05	-0.3	-9
	19:59	4.0	122		19:24	4.0	122
11 Th	01:43	-0.8	-24	**26** F	01:07	-0.6	-18
	08:29	4.8	146		07:54	4.8	146
	14:25	-0.7	-21		13:47	-0.6	-18
● 20:44		4.0	122		20:09	4.3	131
12 F	02:30	-0.8	-24	**27** Sa	01:54	-0.8	-24
	09:12	4.7	143		08:38	4.9	149
	15:07	-0.7	-21		14:29	-0.8	-24
	21:27	4.1	125	○ 20:55		4.5	137
13 Sa	03:15	-0.7	-21	**28** Su	02:42	-0.9	-27
	09:52	4.6	140		09:22	4.9	149
	15:47	-0.6	-18		15:12	-1.0	-30
	22:08	4.1	125		21:40	4.7	143
14 Su	03:58	-0.5	-15				
	10:31	4.4	134				
	16:26	-0.5	-15				
	22:47	4.1	125				
15 M	04:41	-0.2	-6				
	11:09	4.2	128				
	17:03	-0.2	-6				
	23:26	4.1	125				

March

Day	Time	ft	cm	Day	Time	ft	cm
1 M	03:30	-0.9	-27	**16** Tu	05:12	-0.1	-3
	10:07	4.8	146		11:34	4.2	128
	15:56	-1.0	-30		17:19	-0.1	-3
	22:28	4.8	146		23:48	4.4	134
2 Tu	04:21	-0.8	-24	**17** W	05:49	0.2	6
	10:53	4.6	140		12:09	4.0	122
	16:42	-0.9	-27		17:52	0.1	3
	23:17	4.8	146				
3 W	05:16	-0.5	-15	**18** Th	00:24	4.3	131
	11:43	4.4	134		06:28	0.5	15
	17:32	-0.7	-21		12:44	3.8	116
					18:26	0.4	12
4 Th	00:11	4.8	146	**19** F	01:02	4.3	131
	06:16	-0.2	-6		07:10	0.7	21
	12:37	4.1	125		13:22	3.7	113
	18:27	-0.4	-12		19:06	0.6	18
5 F	01:12	4.6	140	**20** Sa	01:46	4.2	128
	07:23	0.1	3		08:00	0.9	27
	13:38	3.8	116		14:06	3.6	110
	19:30	-0.2	-6		19:54	0.8	24
6 Sa	02:19	4.5	137	**21** Su	02:37	4.1	125
	08:35	0.2	6		08:58	1.1	34
	14:47	3.7	113		14:59	3.5	107
◑	20:39	0.0	0	◐	20:51	0.8	24
7 Su	03:31	4.5	137	**22** M	03:38	4.1	125
	09:44	0.3	9		10:01	1.0	30
	15:57	3.7	113		16:01	3.5	107
	21:49	0.0	0		21:56	0.7	21
8 M	04:41	4.5	137	**23** Tu	04:45	4.2	128
	10:48	0.2	6		11:01	0.8	24
	17:04	3.7	113		17:06	3.6	110
	22:53	-0.1	-3		23:00	0.5	15
9 Tu	05:43	4.6	140	**24** W	05:48	4.3	131
	11:44	0.0	0		11:55	0.5	15
	18:03	3.9	119		18:08	3.9	119
	23:51	-0.3	-9		23:59	0.2	6
10 W	06:37	4.7	143	**25** Th	06:44	4.5	137
	12:34	-0.2	-6		12:44	0.1	3
	18:55	4.1	125		19:03	4.2	128
11 Th	00:43	-0.4	-12	**26** F	00:54	-0.2	-6
	07:24	4.7	143		07:36	4.7	143
	13:24	-0.4	-12		13:30	-0.3	-9
	19:40	4.2	128		19:54	4.5	137
12 F	01:30	-0.5	-15	**27** Sa	01:45	-0.5	-15
	08:07	4.7	143		08:24	4.9	149
	13:59	-0.5	-15		14:15	-0.7	-21
	20:22	4.4	134		20:43	4.8	146
13 Sa	02:14	-0.6	-18	**28** Su	02:36	-0.8	-24
	08:47	4.6	140		09:11	4.9	149
	14:35	-0.5	-15		15:04	-0.9	-27
● 21:01		4.4	134	○ 21:31		5.1	155
14 Su	03:55	-0.5	-15	**29** M	03:26	-1.0	-30
	10:24	4.5	137		09:58	4.9	149
	16:13	-0.4	-12		15:44	-1.0	-30
	22:38	4.5	137		22:19	5.3	162
15 M	04:34	-0.3	-9	**30** Tu	04:16	-0.9	-27
	11:00	4.3	131		10:46	4.8	146
	16:47	-0.3	-9		16:30	-1.0	-30
	23:13	4.5	137		23:08	5.3	162
				31 W	05:09	-0.8	-24
					11:35	4.6	140
					17:19	-0.8	-24

StationId: 8720220
Source: NOAA/NOS/CO-OPS
Station Type: Primary
Time Zone: LST_LDT
Datum: MLLW

NOAA Tide Predictions

Mayport (Ferry Depot), FL,2021

Times and Heights of High and Low Waters

April

Day	Time	ft	cm	Day	Time	ft	cm
1 Th	00:00	5.2	158	16 F	05:55	0.5	15
	06:05	-0.5	-15		12:11	3.9	119
	12:28	4.4	134		17:46	0.5	15
	18:11	-0.5	-15				
2 F	00:57	5.1	155	17 Sa	00:27	4.5	137
	07:06	-0.2	-6		06:35	0.7	21
	13:25	4.1	125		12:49	3.8	116
	19:10	-0.2	-6		18:25	0.7	21
3 Sa	01:59	4.9	149	18 Su	01:09	4.4	134
	08:13	0.1	3		07:21	0.9	27
	14:28	4.0	122		13:32	3.7	113
	20:16	0.1	3		19:13	0.8	24
4 Su	03:06	4.7	143	19 M	01:58	4.3	131
	09:22	0.3	9		08:16	1.0	30
	15:36	3.9	119		14:24	3.7	113
	21:29	0.3	9		20:11	0.9	27
5 M	04:16	4.6	140	20 Tu	02:56	4.3	131
	10:29	0.4	12		09:17	1.0	30
	16:45	3.9	119		15:25	3.8	116
	22:39	0.3	9		21:17	0.8	24
6 Tu	05:23	4.6	140	21 W	04:00	4.3	131
	11:29	0.3	9		10:18	0.7	21
	17:49	4.0	122		16:29	3.9	119
	23:43	0.2	6		22:26	0.6	18
7 W	06:22	4.6	140	22 Th	05:04	4.4	134
	12:22	0.2	6		11:14	0.4	12
	18:45	4.2	128		17:32	4.2	128
					23:30	0.3	9
8 Th	00:38	0.1	3	23 F	06:05	4.5	137
	07:14	4.6	140		12:05	0.0	0
	13:08	0.0	0		18:30	4.6	140
	19:33	4.4	134				
9 F	01:28	-0.1	-3	24 Sa	00:29	-0.1	-3
	07:59	4.6	140		07:00	4.7	143
	13:50	-0.2	-6		12:54	-0.4	-12
	20:17	4.6	140		19:25	4.9	149
10 Sa	02:12	-0.2	-6	25 Su	01:24	-0.5	-15
	08:40	4.6	140		07:53	4.8	146
	14:28	-0.2	-6		13:42	-0.7	-21
	20:56	4.7	143		20:17	5.2	158
11 Su	02:54	-0.2	-6	26 M	02:17	-0.8	-24
	09:18	4.5	137		08:44	4.8	146
	15:04	-0.3	-9		14:29	-1.0	-30
	21:33	4.7	143		21:08	5.5	168
12 M	03:32	-0.2	-6	27 Tu	03:09	-0.9	-27
	09:54	4.4	134		09:35	4.7	143
	15:37	-0.2	-6		15:17	-1.1	-34
	22:08	4.7	143		21:59	5.6	171
13 Tu	04:09	-0.1	-3	28 W	04:02	-0.9	-27
	10:29	4.2	128		10:26	4.6	140
	16:08	-0.1	-3		16:06	-1.0	-30
	22:42	4.7	143		22:51	5.6	171
14 W	04:44	0.1	3	29 Th	04:56	-0.7	-21
	11:03	4.1	125		11:19	4.5	137
	16:39	0.1	3		16:58	-0.8	-24
	23:16	4.6	140		23:46	5.4	165
15 Th	05:19	0.3	9	30 F	05:53	-0.5	-15
	11:37	4.0	122		12:14	4.3	131
	17:11	0.3	9		17:53	-0.5	-15
	23:51	4.6	140				

May

Day	Time	ft	cm	Day	Time	ft	cm
1 Sa	00:43	5.2	158	16 Su	00:03	4.6	140
	06:54	-0.2	-6		06:09	0.6	18
	13:12	4.2	128		12:25	3.7	113
	18:55	-0.1	-3		17:56	0.6	18
2 Su	01:44	5.0	152	17 M	00:44	4.5	137
	07:58	0.1	3		06:54	0.7	21
	14:14	4.0	122		13:09	3.7	113
	20:03	0.2	6		18:45	0.7	21
3 M	02:48	4.7	143	18 Tu	01:30	4.4	134
	09:03	0.3	9		07:45	0.7	21
	15:19	4.0	122		13:59	3.8	116
	21:14	0.4	12		19:42	0.8	24
4 Tu	03:53	4.6	140	19 W	02:23	4.4	134
	10:05	0.3	9		08:41	0.6	18
	16:24	4.1	125		14:56	3.9	119
	22:23	0.5	15		20:48	0.7	21
5 W	04:55	4.5	137	20 Th	03:22	4.4	134
	11:01	0.3	9		09:39	0.4	12
	17:24	4.3	131		15:58	4.2	128
	23:24	0.5	15		21:57	0.6	18
6 Th	05:51	4.5	137	21 F	04:24	4.4	134
	11:51	0.2	6		10:35	0.1	3
	18:18	4.4	134		17:00	4.5	137
					23:04	0.3	9
7 F	00:18	0.3	9	22 Sa	05:27	4.4	134
	06:41	4.4	134		11:29	-0.2	-6
	12:35	0.1	3		18:01	4.8	146
	19:05	4.6	140				
8 Sa	01:06	0.2	6	23 Su	00:06	-0.1	-3
	07:27	4.4	134		06:27	4.4	134
	13:16	0.0	0		12:21	-0.6	-18
	19:48	4.7	143		18:58	5.1	155
9 Su	01:50	0.1	3	24 M	01:04	-0.4	-12
	08:08	4.3	131		07:24	4.4	134
	13:53	-0.1	-3		13:12	-0.8	-24
	20:27	4.8	146		19:54	5.4	165
10 M	02:30	0.0	0	25 Tu	02:00	-0.7	-21
	08:47	4.2	128		08:20	4.4	134
	14:28	-0.1	-3		14:03	-1.0	-30
	21:04	4.8	146		20:48	5.5	168
11 Tu	03:08	0.0	0	26 W	02:54	-0.8	-24
	09:24	4.1	125		09:15	4.4	134
	15:02	-0.1	-3		14:54	-1.1	-34
	21:40	4.8	146		21:43	5.6	171
12 W	03:45	0.0	0	27 Th	03:48	-0.9	-27
	10:00	4.0	122		10:09	4.3	131
	15:34	0.0	0		15:47	-1.0	-30
	22:15	4.8	146		22:37	5.5	168
13 Th	04:20	0.1	3	28 F	04:43	-0.8	-24
	10:36	3.9	119		11:03	4.3	131
	16:06	0.1	3		16:41	-0.8	-24
	22:50	4.7	143		23:32	5.4	165
14 F	04:54	0.3	9	29 Sa	05:39	-0.6	-18
	11:11	3.8	116		11:58	4.2	128
	16:39	0.3	9		17:38	-0.5	-15
	23:26	4.6	140				
15 Sa	05:30	0.4	12	30 Su	00:27	5.1	155
	11:47	3.8	116		06:37	-0.3	-9
	17:15	0.4	12		12:55	4.1	125
					18:39	-0.1	-3
				31 M	01:24	4.9	149
					07:36	-0.1	-3
					13:54	4.1	125
					19:44	0.2	6

June

Day	Time	ft	cm	Day	Time	ft	cm
1 Tu	02:22	4.7	143	16 W	01:08	4.5	137
	08:35	0.1	3		07:18	0.3	9
	14:54	4.1	125		13:38	4.0	122
	20:51	0.4	12		19:21	0.5	15
2 W	03:20	4.4	134	17 Th	01:57	4.4	134
	09:32	0.2	6		08:09	0.2	6
	15:53	4.2	128		14:32	4.1	125
	21:56	0.6	18		20:26	0.5	15
3 Th	04:17	4.3	131	18 F	02:51	4.3	131
	10:24	0.2	6		09:04	0.1	3
	16:50	4.3	131		15:31	4.4	134
	22:55	0.6	18		21:34	0.4	12
4 F	05:11	4.2	128	19 Sa	03:51	4.2	128
	11:12	0.2	6		10:01	-0.1	-3
	17:43	4.4	134		16:34	4.6	140
	23:49	0.5	15		22:43	0.3	9
5 Sa	06:02	4.1	125	20 Su	04:55	4.1	125
	11:56	0.1	3		10:57	-0.4	-12
	18:31	4.6	140		17:37	4.9	149
					23:47	0.0	0
6 Su	00:38	0.4	12	21 M	05:59	4.1	125
	06:49	4.0	122		11:53	-0.6	-18
	12:38	0.1	3		18:38	5.1	155
	19:15	4.7	143				
7 M	01:22	0.3	9	22 Tu	00:48	-0.3	-9
	07:33	3.9	119		07:02	4.1	125
	13:17	0.0	0		12:48	-0.8	-24
	19:56	4.7	143		19:38	5.3	162
8 Tu	02:04	0.2	6	23 W	01:45	-0.5	-15
	08:14	3.9	119		08:01	4.1	125
	13:54	0.0	0		13:43	-1.0	-30
	20:36	4.8	146		20:35	5.4	165
9 W	02:43	0.1	3	24 Th	02:40	-0.7	-21
	08:54	3.8	116		08:58	4.1	125
	14:30	0.0	0		14:37	-1.0	-30
	21:15	4.8	146		21:30	5.4	165
10 Th	03:21	0.1	3	25 F	03:34	-0.8	-24
	09:33	3.8	116		09:53	4.2	128
	15:04	0.0	0		15:31	-1.0	-30
	21:53	4.7	143		22:23	5.4	165
11 F	03:57	0.1	3	26 Sa	04:28	-0.7	-21
	10:11	3.7	113		10:47	4.2	128
	15:39	0.0	0		16:26	-0.8	-24
	22:30	4.7	143		23:16	5.2	158
12 Sa	04:32	0.2	6	27 Su	05:21	-0.6	-18
	10:48	3.7	113		11:40	4.2	128
	16:14	0.1	3		17:21	-0.5	-15
	23:07	4.6	140				
13 Su	05:09	0.2	6	28 M	00:07	5.0	152
	11:26	3.7	113		06:13	-0.5	-15
	16:53	0.2	6		12:33	4.1	125
	23:44	4.6	140		18:18	-0.2	-6
14 M	05:48	0.3	9	29 Tu	00:58	4.8	146
	12:06	3.8	116		07:06	-0.2	-6
	17:36	0.3	9		13:26	4.1	125
					19:18	0.2	6
15 Tu	00:24	4.6	140	30 W	01:49	4.5	137
	06:31	0.3	9		07:58	0.0	0
	12:50	3.8	116		14:20	4.2	128
	18:25	0.4	12		20:19	0.4	12

StationId: 8720220
Source: NOAA/NOS/CO-OPS
Station Type: Primary
Time Zone: LST_LDT
Datum: MLLW

NOAA Tide Predictions

Mayport (Ferry Depot), FL,2021

Times and Heights of High and Low Waters

July

Day	Time (h m)	Height ft	Height cm
1 Th ◐	02:40	4.3	131
	08:50	0.1	3
	15:14	4.2	128
	21:20	0.6	18
2 F	03:32	4.1	125
	09:39	0.3	9
	16:08	4.3	131
	22:19	0.7	21
3 Sa	04:25	3.9	119
	10:28	0.3	9
	17:01	4.4	134
	23:14	0.7	21
4 Su	05:16	3.8	116
	11:14	0.3	9
	17:51	4.5	137
5 M	00:05	0.7	21
	06:07	3.7	113
	11:58	0.3	9
	18:40	4.5	137
6 Tu	00:51	0.5	15
	06:55	3.7	113
	12:41	0.2	6
	19:25	4.6	140
7 W	01:35	0.4	12
	07:41	3.7	113
	13:21	0.1	3
	20:09	4.7	143
8 Th	02:16	0.3	9
	08:24	3.7	113
	14:00	0.0	0
	20:51	4.7	143
9 F	02:55	0.2	6
	09:06	3.8	116
	14:38	0.0	0
	21:31	4.8	146
10 Sa ●	03:32	0.1	3
	09:46	3.8	116
	15:16	-0.1	-3
	22:09	4.8	146
11 Su	04:09	0.0	0
	10:26	3.9	119
	15:55	-0.1	-3
	22:47	4.8	146
12 M	04:46	0.0	0
	11:05	3.9	119
	16:36	0.0	0
	23:25	4.8	146
13 Tu	05:24	0.0	0
	11:46	4.0	122
	17:20	0.1	3
14 W	00:05	4.7	143
	06:06	0.0	0
	12:30	4.2	128
	18:10	0.2	6
15 Th	00:48	4.6	140
	06:51	0.0	0
	13:18	4.3	131
	19:06	0.4	12
16 F	01:35	4.5	137
	07:40	0.0	0
	14:11	4.5	137
	20:08	0.5	15
17 Sa ◐	02:28	4.3	131
	08:34	-0.1	-3
	15:09	4.6	140
	21:17	0.5	15
18 Su	03:28	4.1	125
	09:32	-0.1	-3
	16:14	4.8	146
	22:27	0.4	12
19 M	04:34	4.0	122
	10:33	-0.2	-6
	17:21	4.9	149
	23:34	0.2	6
20 Tu	05:42	4.0	122
	11:34	-0.4	-12
	18:26	5.1	155
21 W	00:36	0.0	0
	06:48	4.0	122
	12:33	-0.5	-15
	19:28	5.2	158
22 Th	01:33	-0.2	-6
	07:49	4.1	125
	13:30	-0.7	-21
	20:25	5.3	162
23 F	02:28	-0.4	-12
	08:45	4.2	128
	14:25	-0.8	-24
	21:18	5.4	165
24 Sa ○	03:19	-0.6	-18
	09:38	4.3	131
	15:19	-0.7	-21
	22:08	5.3	162
25 Su	04:09	-0.6	-18
	10:29	4.3	131
	16:14	-0.6	-18
	22:56	5.2	158
26 M	04:56	-0.5	-15
	11:17	4.4	134
	17:02	-0.4	-12
	23:42	5.0	152
27 Tu	05:43	-0.4	-12
	12:05	4.4	134
	17:53	0.0	0
28 W	00:27	4.8	146
	06:28	-0.1	-3
	12:52	4.4	134
	18:46	0.3	9
29 Th	01:11	4.5	137
	07:14	0.1	3
	13:39	4.4	134
	19:40	0.6	18
30 F	01:56	4.3	131
	08:00	0.4	12
	14:28	4.4	134
	20:37	0.9	27
31 Sa ◐	02:44	4.1	125
	08:48	0.6	18
	15:19	4.4	134
	21:36	1.1	34

August

Day	Time (h m)	Height ft	Height cm
1 Su	03:34	3.9	119
	09:37	0.7	21
	16:13	4.4	134
	22:33	1.1	34
2 M	04:27	3.8	116
	10:27	0.7	21
	17:08	4.5	137
	23:27	1.1	34
3 Tu	05:22	3.8	116
	11:17	0.7	21
	18:02	4.6	140
4 W	00:17	1.0	30
	06:16	3.8	116
	12:05	0.6	18
	18:53	4.7	143
5 Th	01:03	0.8	24
	07:06	3.9	119
	12:50	0.4	12
	19:40	4.8	146
6 F	01:45	0.6	18
	07:53	4.0	122
	13:32	0.3	9
	20:24	4.9	149
7 Sa	02:25	0.4	12
	08:37	4.1	125
	14:14	0.1	3
	21:05	5.0	152
8 Su ●	03:03	0.2	6
	09:19	4.2	128
	15:00	0.0	0
	21:45	5.1	155
9 M	03:40	0.0	0
	10:01	4.4	134
	15:36	-0.1	-3
	22:24	5.1	155
10 Tu	04:18	-0.1	-3
	10:42	4.5	137
	16:20	-0.1	-3
	23:03	5.1	155
11 W	04:57	-0.2	-6
	11:24	4.7	143
	17:06	0.0	0
	23:44	5.0	152
12 Th	05:38	-0.2	-6
	12:09	4.8	146
	17:57	0.2	6
13 F	00:28	4.9	149
	06:24	-0.1	-3
	12:57	4.9	149
	18:52	0.4	12
14 Sa	01:16	4.7	143
	07:13	0.0	0
	13:52	5.0	152
	19:55	0.6	18
15 Su ◐	02:11	4.4	134
	08:09	0.2	6
	14:53	5.0	152
	21:05	0.7	21
16 M	03:14	4.2	128
	09:12	0.2	6
	16:02	5.0	152
	22:17	0.7	21
17 Tu	04:24	4.1	125
	10:18	0.2	6
	17:13	5.1	155
	23:25	0.6	18
18 W	05:34	4.1	125
	11:24	0.1	3
	18:20	5.2	158
19 Th	00:26	0.4	12
	06:40	4.2	128
	12:25	0.0	0
	19:20	5.4	165
20 F	01:22	0.2	6
	07:39	4.4	134
	13:23	-0.2	-6
	20:14	5.5	168
21 Sa	02:13	0.0	0
	08:32	4.6	140
	14:16	-0.3	-9
	21:03	5.5	168
22 Su ○	03:00	-0.2	-6
	09:21	4.7	143
	15:06	-0.3	-9
	21:49	5.4	165
23 M	03:44	-0.2	-6
	10:07	4.8	146
	15:53	-0.2	-6
	22:32	5.3	162
24 Tu	04:26	-0.2	-6
	10:50	4.9	149
	16:40	0.0	0
	23:13	5.1	155
25 W	05:07	0.0	0
	11:32	4.9	149
	17:22	0.3	9
	23:52	4.9	149
26 Th	05:46	0.2	6
	12:14	4.8	146
	18:11	0.6	18
27 F	00:32	4.7	143
	06:26	0.5	15
	12:56	4.8	146
	18:58	0.9	27
28 Sa	01:12	4.4	134
	07:06	0.8	24
	12:57	4.7	143
	19:50	1.3	40
29 Su	01:55	4.3	131
	07:51	1.0	30
	14:28	4.7	143
	20:46	1.5	46
30 M ◑	02:43	4.1	125
	08:46	1.2	37
	15:22	4.6	140
	21:46	1.6	49
31 Tu	03:38	4.0	122
	09:36	1.3	40
	16:22	4.7	143
	22:45	1.6	49

September

Day	Time (h m)	Height ft	Height cm
1 W	04:37	4.0	122
	10:33	1.3	40
	17:21	4.7	143
	23:38	1.5	46
2 Th	05:36	4.1	125
	11:27	1.1	34
	18:17	4.9	149
3 F	00:26	1.2	37
	06:31	4.2	128
	12:17	0.9	27
	19:06	5.1	155
4 Sa	01:09	0.9	27
	07:20	4.4	134
	13:04	0.6	18
	19:52	5.3	162
5 Su	01:49	0.6	18
	08:06	4.6	140
	13:49	0.3	9
	20:34	5.4	165
6 M	02:28	0.3	9
	08:50	4.9	149
	14:33	0.1	3
	21:16	5.5	168
7 Tu ●	03:07	0.0	0
	09:33	5.1	155
	15:18	0.0	0
	21:57	5.5	168
8 W	03:47	-0.1	-3
	10:16	5.3	162
	16:04	0.0	0
	22:39	5.4	165
9 Th	04:28	-0.2	-6
	11:01	5.5	168
	16:52	0.1	3
	23:23	5.3	162
10 F	05:12	-0.1	-3
	11:48	5.5	168
	17:44	0.3	9
11 Sa	00:10	5.1	155
	05:59	0.1	3
	12:39	5.5	168
	18:41	0.6	18
12 Su	01:02	4.8	146
	06:51	0.3	9
	13:37	5.5	168
	19:46	0.8	24
13 M ◐	02:00	4.6	140
	07:51	0.5	15
	14:46	5.4	165
	20:57	1.0	30
14 Tu	03:07	4.5	137
	08:59	0.7	21
	15:54	5.3	162
	22:09	1.1	34
15 W	04:19	4.4	134
	10:11	0.8	24
	17:06	5.3	162
	23:15	1.0	30
16 Th	05:29	4.5	137
	11:19	0.7	21
	18:10	5.4	165
17 F	00:14	0.8	24
	06:32	4.7	143
	12:20	0.5	15
	19:07	5.5	168
18 Sa	01:06	0.5	15
	07:27	4.9	149
	13:15	0.3	9
	19:58	5.6	171
19 Su	01:53	0.3	9
	08:16	5.1	155
	14:05	0.2	6
	20:43	5.6	171
20 M ○	02:36	0.2	6
	09:01	5.2	158
	14:51	0.2	6
	21:25	5.5	168
21 Tu	03:15	0.1	3
	09:42	5.3	162
	15:35	0.2	6
	22:04	5.3	162
22 W	03:53	0.2	6
	10:21	5.3	162
	16:16	0.4	12
	22:42	5.2	158
23 Th	04:29	0.3	9
	10:59	5.3	162
	16:57	0.6	18
	23:18	5.0	152
24 F	05:04	0.6	18
	11:36	5.2	158
	17:37	0.9	27
	23:55	4.8	146
25 Sa	05:39	0.8	24
	12:14	5.2	158
	18:19	1.2	37
26 Su	00:32	4.6	140
	06:15	1.1	34
	12:55	5.0	152
	19:04	1.5	46
27 M	01:12	4.4	134
	06:56	1.4	43
	13:40	4.9	149
	19:56	1.8	55
28 Tu	01:58	4.3	131
	07:44	1.6	49
	14:33	4.7	143
	20:55	1.9	58
29 W ◐	02:51	4.3	131
	08:41	1.7	52
	15:33	4.9	149
	21:56	1.9	58
30 Th	03:52	4.3	131
	09:45	1.7	52
	16:35	4.9	149
	22:53	1.7	52

StationId: 8720220
Source: NOAA/NOS/CO-OPS
Station Type: Primary
Time Zone: LST_LDT
Datum: MLLW

NOAA Tide Predictions

Mayport (Ferry Depot), FL,2021

Times and Heights of High and Low Waters

October

Day	Time (h m)	Height (ft)	Height (cm)	Day	Time (h m)	Height (ft)	Height (cm)
1 F	04:54	4.4	134	16 Sa	06:17	5.0	152
	10:47	1.5	46		12:11	0.8	24
	17:34	5.1	155		18:47	5.5	168
	23:43	1.4	43				
2 Sa	05:52	4.6	140	17 Su	00:43	0.7	21
	11:43	1.2	37		07:09	5.2	158
	18:26	5.3	162		13:03	0.6	18
					19:35	5.5	168
3 Su	00:28	1.1	34	18 M	01:27	0.5	15
	06:44	4.9	149		07:55	5.4	165
	12:35	0.8	24		13:50	0.5	15
	19:14	5.4	165		20:18	5.4	165
4 M	01:10	0.7	21	19 Tu	02:07	0.4	12
	07:33	5.2	158		08:37	5.5	168
	13:23	0.5	15		14:33	0.5	15
	20:00	5.6	171		20:58	5.3	162
5 Tu	01:52	0.3	9	20 W	02:44	0.3	9
	08:19	5.5	168		09:16	5.5	168
	14:11	0.2	6		15:14	0.5	15
	20:45	5.6	171	○	21:36	5.1	155
6 W ●	02:34	0.0	0	21 Th	03:19	0.4	12
	09:05	5.8	177		09:53	5.5	168
	14:59	0.0	0		15:53	0.6	18
	21:30	5.6	171		22:12	5.0	152
7 Th	03:16	-0.2	-6	22 F	03:53	0.5	15
	09:51	6.0	183		10:29	5.5	168
	15:48	0.0	0		16:30	0.7	21
	22:16	5.5	168		22:47	4.8	146
8 F	04:00	-0.2	-6	23 Sa	04:26	0.7	21
	10:39	6.0	183		11:04	5.4	165
	16:38	0.1	3		17:07	1.0	30
	23:03	5.3	162		23:22	4.7	143
9 Sa	04:47	-0.1	-3	24 Su	04:59	0.9	27
	11:30	6.0	183		11:41	5.3	162
	17:32	0.3	9		17:45	1.2	37
	23:54	5.1	155		23:58	4.5	137
10 Su	05:38	0.1	3	25 M	05:34	1.1	34
	12:25	5.9	180		12:19	5.1	155
	18:31	0.6	18		18:26	1.5	46
11 M	00:50	4.9	149	26 Tu	00:37	4.4	134
	06:34	0.5	15		06:13	1.4	43
	13:26	5.7	174		13:02	5.0	152
	19:37	0.9	27		19:13	1.7	52
12 Tu	01:52	4.7	143	27 W	01:21	4.3	131
	07:38	0.8	24		06:59	1.6	49
	14:33	5.5	168		13:51	4.9	149
	20:48	1.1	34		20:06	1.8	55
13 W	03:01	4.6	140	28 Th	02:12	4.3	131
	08:51	1.0	30		07:55	1.7	52
	15:43	5.4	165		14:46	4.9	149
	21:57	1.1	34	◑	21:05	1.8	55
14 Th	04:11	4.7	143	29 F	03:10	4.4	134
	10:05	1.0	30		08:59	1.7	52
	16:51	5.4	165		15:46	4.9	149
	23:00	1.0	30		22:03	1.6	49
15 F	05:18	4.8	146	30 Sa	04:12	4.5	137
	11:12	1.0	30		10:06	1.5	46
	17:53	5.4	165		16:45	5.0	152
	23:55	0.9	27		22:56	1.2	37
				31 Su	05:12	4.8	146
					11:08	1.2	37
					17:42	5.1	155
					23:44	0.9	27

November

Day	Time (h m)	Height (ft)	Height (cm)	Day	Time (h m)	Height (ft)	Height (cm)
1 M	06:07	5.1	155	16 Tu	06:30	5.3	162
	12:05	0.8	24		12:30	0.6	18
	18:35	5.2	158		18:49	4.9	149
2 Tu	00:31	0.4	12	17 W	00:36	0.3	9
	06:59	5.4	165		07:11	5.3	162
	12:58	0.4	12		13:13	0.5	15
	19:25	5.3	162		19:29	4.8	146
3 W	01:17	0.0	0	18 Th	01:13	0.3	9
	07:50	5.8	177		07:50	5.3	162
	13:50	0.1	3		13:53	0.5	15
	20:15	5.3	162		20:08	4.6	140
4 Th	02:02	-0.3	-9	19 F	01:48	0.3	9
	08:40	6.0	183		08:27	5.3	162
	14:41	-0.1	-3		14:31	0.5	15
●	21:04	5.3	162	○	20:44	4.5	137
5 F	02:49	-0.4	-12	20 Sa	02:22	0.4	12
	09:30	6.1	186		09:04	5.2	158
	15:32	-0.2	-6		15:07	0.6	18
	21:55	5.2	158		21:20	4.4	134
6 Sa	03:37	-0.4	-12	21 Su	02:55	0.5	15
	10:22	6.2	189		09:40	5.1	155
	16:25	-0.1	-3		15:43	0.7	21
	22:46	5.1	155		21:56	4.3	131
7 Su	03:27	-0.3	-9	22 M	03:28	0.6	18
	10:16	6.1	186		10:16	5.0	152
	16:21	0.1	3		16:19	0.9	27
	22:41	4.9	149		22:32	4.2	128
8 M	04:21	0.0	0	23 Tu	04:03	0.8	24
	11:13	5.9	180		10:54	4.9	149
	17:20	0.4	12		16:57	1.1	34
	23:39	4.8	146		23:10	4.1	125
9 Tu	05:20	0.3	9	24 W	04:42	1.0	30
	12:14	5.6	171		11:33	4.9	149
	18:24	0.6	18		17:39	1.2	37
					23:52	4.1	125
10 W	00:41	4.6	140	25 Th	05:27	1.1	34
	06:27	0.6	18		12:17	4.8	146
	13:18	5.4	165		18:27	1.2	37
	19:31	0.8	24				
11 Th	01:47	4.6	140	26 F	00:40	4.2	128
	07:40	0.9	27		06:20	1.2	37
	14:23	5.3	162		13:05	4.7	143
◐	20:35	0.8	24	◐	19:19	1.2	37
12 F	02:54	4.7	143	27 Sa	01:33	4.3	131
	08:51	1.0	30		07:21	1.2	37
	15:27	5.2	158		13:59	4.7	143
	21:34	0.8	24	◑	20:14	1.0	30
13 Sa	03:57	4.8	146	28 Su	02:32	4.4	134
	09:56	0.9	27		08:29	1.1	34
	16:25	5.1	155		14:59	4.7	143
	22:27	0.7	21		21:09	0.7	21
14 Su	04:54	5.0	152	29 M	03:32	4.7	143
	10:53	0.8	24		09:35	0.9	27
	17:18	5.0	152		15:57	4.7	143
	23:14	0.5	15		22:02	0.4	12
15 M	05:44	5.1	155	30 Tu	04:31	5.0	152
	11:44	0.7	21		10:37	0.5	15
	18:06	4.9	149		16:56	4.7	143
	23:56	0.4	12		22:54	0.0	0

December

Day	Time (h m)	Height (ft)	Height (cm)	Day	Time (h m)	Height (ft)	Height (cm)
1 W	05:29	5.3	162	16 Th	00:04	0.2	6
	11:35	0.2	6		06:44	4.9	149
	17:53	4.7	143		12:49	0.4	12
	23:45	-0.4	-12		19:00	4.1	125
2 Th	06:25	5.6	171	17 F	00:43	0.1	3
	12:31	-0.2	-6		07:25	4.9	149
	18:49	4.7	143		13:30	0.3	9
					19:41	4.0	122
3 F	00:35	-0.6	-18	18 Sa	01:20	0.1	3
	07:20	5.8	177		08:04	4.9	149
	13:25	-0.4	-12		14:09	0.2	6
	19:43	4.7	143		20:19	4.0	122
4 Sa	01:26	-0.8	-24	19 Su	01:56	0.1	3
	08:14	5.9	180		08:43	4.8	146
	14:18	-0.5	-15		14:46	0.3	9
●	20:37	4.7	143	○	20:57	3.9	119
5 Su	02:18	-0.8	-24	20 M	02:31	0.1	3
	09:09	5.9	180		09:20	4.8	146
	15:13	-0.5	-15		15:21	0.3	9
	21:32	4.6	140		21:34	3.9	119
6 M	03:12	-0.7	-21	21 Tu	03:05	0.2	6
	10:04	5.7	174		09:57	4.7	143
	16:08	-0.4	-12		15:56	0.4	12
	22:27	4.6	140		22:11	3.9	119
7 Tu	04:08	-0.5	-15	22 W	03:41	0.3	9
	11:00	5.5	168		10:33	4.7	143
	17:06	-0.2	-6		16:32	0.4	12
	23:24	4.5	137		22:48	3.9	119
8 W	05:07	-0.1	-3	23 Th	04:20	0.4	12
	11:57	5.3	162		11:09	4.6	140
	18:05	0.0	0		17:11	0.5	15
					23:28	3.9	119
9 Th	00:23	4.4	134	24 F	05:04	0.5	15
	06:12	0.2	6		11:49	4.5	137
	12:55	5.1	155		17:53	0.5	15
	19:05	0.2	6				
10 F	01:24	4.4	134	25 Sa	00:12	4.0	122
	07:20	0.5	15		05:54	0.6	18
	13:54	4.8	146		12:32	4.5	137
	20:04	0.3	9		18:40	0.4	12
11 Sa	02:26	4.4	134	26 Su	01:01	4.1	125
	08:27	0.6	18		06:52	0.6	18
	14:52	4.6	140		13:21	4.4	134
◐	20:59	0.4	12	◐	19:32	0.3	9
12 Su	03:26	4.5	137	27 M	01:56	4.3	131
	09:30	0.7	21		07:58	0.6	18
	15:49	4.5	137		14:17	4.2	128
	21:51	0.4	12	◑	20:27	0.1	3
13 M	04:22	4.6	140	28 Tu	02:57	4.5	137
	10:28	0.7	21		09:06	0.5	15
	16:42	4.3	131		15:19	4.1	125
	22:38	0.3	9		21:25	-0.1	-3
14 Tu	05:13	4.7	143	29 W	04:00	4.7	143
	11:19	0.6	18		10:13	0.2	6
	17:32	4.2	128		16:23	4.1	125
	23:23	0.2	6		22:22	-0.4	-12
15 W	06:00	4.8	146	30 Th	05:05	4.9	149
	12:06	0.5	15		11:16	-0.1	-3
	18:17	4.2	128		17:28	4.1	125
					23:19	-0.7	-21
				31 F	06:07	5.1	155
					12:15	-0.4	-12
					18:29	4.1	125

StationId: 8721604
Source: NOAA/NOS/CO-OPS
Station Type: Primary
Time Zone: LST_LDT
Datum: MLLW

NOAA Tide Predictions

Trident Pier, Port Canaveral, FL,2021

Times and Heights of High and Low Waters

January

Day	Time	ft	cm		Day	Time	ft	cm
1 F	02:31	-0.3	-9		**16** Sa	03:30	-0.3	-9
	09:10	4.1	125			10:00	3.8	116
	15:29	0.1	3			16:18	-0.1	-3
	21:25	2.9	88			22:19	3.0	91
2 Sa	03:17	-0.2	-6		**17** Su	04:20	-0.1	-3
	09:52	4.0	122			10:42	3.5	107
	16:14	0.1	3			17:03	0.0	0
	22:10	3.0	91			23:06	3.0	91
3 Su	04:07	-0.1	-3		**18** M	05:13	0.2	6
	10:35	3.9	119			11:24	3.2	98
	17:01	0.0	0			17:48	0.1	3
	23:00	3.1	94			23:56	2.9	88
4 M	05:03	0.0	0		**19** Tu	06:07	0.4	12
	11:22	3.7	113			12:08	2.9	88
	17:50	-0.1	-3			18:31	0.1	3
	23:54	3.2	98					
5 Tu	06:03	0.1	3		**20** W	00:49	2.9	88
	12:12	3.5	107			07:03	0.6	18
	18:40	-0.2	-6			12:56	2.7	82
					☽	19:15	0.2	6
6 W	00:55	3.4	104		**21** Th	01:47	2.9	88
	07:07	0.1	3			08:00	0.7	21
	13:09	3.3	101			13:50	2.5	76
☾	19:32	-0.3	-9			20:01	0.2	6
7 Th	02:00	3.6	110		**22** F	02:45	3.0	91
	08:12	0.2	6			08:58	0.7	21
	14:11	3.1	94			14:46	2.4	73
	20:26	-0.4	-12			20:49	0.1	3
8 F	03:04	3.8	116		**23** Sa	03:39	3.1	94
	09:18	0.1	3			09:55	0.6	18
	15:13	3.0	91			15:41	2.4	73
	21:23	-0.5	-15			21:39	0.1	3
9 Sa	04:05	4.1	125		**24** Su	04:28	3.3	101
	10:23	0.0	0			10:48	0.5	15
	16:14	3.0	91			16:32	2.4	73
	22:20	-0.6	-18			22:28	0.0	0
10 Su	05:03	4.3	131		**25** M	05:14	3.5	107
	11:24	-0.1	-3			11:36	0.3	9
	17:13	3.0	91			17:19	2.5	76
	23:16	-0.7	-21			23:17	-0.2	-6
11 M	05:59	4.4	134		**26** Tu	05:58	3.6	110
	12:20	-0.2	-6			12:19	0.2	6
	18:09	3.1	94			18:05	2.6	79
12 Tu	00:11	-0.8	-24		**27** W	00:02	-0.4	-12
	06:52	4.4	134			06:41	3.8	116
	13:11	-0.3	-9			13:00	0.0	0
	19:03	3.1	94			18:50	2.8	85
13 W	01:02	-0.8	-24		**28** Th	00:46	-0.5	-15
	07:43	4.4	134			07:24	3.9	119
	14:00	-0.3	-9			13:40	-0.1	-3
●	19:55	3.1	94		○	19:34	2.9	88
14 Th	01:52	-0.7	-21		**29** F	01:30	-0.6	-18
	08:32	4.3	131			08:06	4.0	122
	14:46	-0.3	-9			14:20	-0.2	-6
	20:45	3.1	94			20:19	3.1	94
15 F	02:41	-0.5	-15		**30** Sa	02:15	-0.6	-18
	09:17	4.1	125			08:48	4.0	122
	15:33	-0.2	-6			15:02	-0.3	-9
	21:33	3.1	94			21:05	3.2	98
					31 Su	03:02	-0.6	-18
						09:30	3.9	119
						15:45	-0.4	-12
						21:52	3.4	104

February

Day	Time	ft	cm		Day	Time	ft	cm
1 M	03:54	-0.5	-15		**16** Tu	04:40	0.2	6
	10:14	3.8	116			10:45	3.0	91
	16:31	-0.4	-12			16:57	0.0	0
	22:42	3.5	107			23:13	3.1	94
2 Tu	04:49	-0.3	-9		**17** W	05:29	0.4	12
	11:00	3.5	107			11:24	2.8	85
	17:20	-0.5	-15			17:39	0.1	3
	23:35	3.5	107			23:59	3.0	91
3 W	05:50	-0.1	-3		**18** Th	06:21	0.5	15
	11:50	3.3	101			12:08	2.5	76
	18:11	-0.5	-15			18:23	0.2	6
4 Th	00:34	3.6	110		**19** F	00:50	3.0	91
	06:53	0.0	0			07:15	0.6	18
	12:46	3.0	91			12:58	2.4	73
◐	19:05	-0.4	-12		◐	19:11	0.3	9
5 F	01:39	3.6	110		**20** Sa	01:47	3.0	91
	07:58	0.1	3			08:12	0.7	21
	13:50	2.8	85			13:57	2.3	70
	20:03	-0.4	-12			20:03	0.3	9
6 Sa	02:47	3.7	113		**21** Su	02:48	3.0	91
	09:05	0.1	3			09:09	0.7	21
	14:58	2.7	82			14:58	2.3	70
	21:04	-0.4	-12			20:57	0.2	6
7 Su	03:52	3.8	116		**22** M	03:45	3.2	98
	10:12	0.1	3			10:06	0.6	18
	16:03	2.7	82			15:55	2.4	73
	22:06	-0.5	-15			21:53	0.1	3
8 M	04:53	3.9	119		**23** Tu	04:37	3.4	104
	11:14	0.0	0			10:58	0.4	12
	17:04	2.8	85			16:46	2.6	79
	23:06	-0.6	-18			22:46	-0.1	-3
9 Tu	05:49	4.0	122		**24** W	05:25	3.6	110
	12:09	-0.1	-3			11:44	0.2	6
	18:00	2.9	88			17:35	2.8	85
						23:36	-0.4	-12
10 W	00:02	-0.6	-18		**25** Th	06:11	3.8	116
	06:41	4.0	122			12:27	0.0	0
	12:57	-0.2	-6			18:23	3.1	94
	18:52	3.1	94					
11 Th	00:52	-0.6	-18		**26** F	00:24	-0.6	-18
	07:28	4.0	122			06:55	3.9	119
	13:40	-0.3	-9			13:08	-0.3	-9
●	19:40	3.1	94			19:10	3.3	101
12 F	01:39	-0.6	-18		**27** Sa	01:11	-0.7	-21
	08:12	3.9	119			07:39	4.0	122
	14:21	-0.3	-9			13:49	-0.4	-12
	20:26	3.2	98		○	19:57	3.6	110
13 Sa	02:23	-0.5	-15		**28** Su	01:59	-0.8	-24
	08:53	3.8	116			08:23	4.0	122
	15:00	-0.2	-6			14:31	-0.6	-18
	21:09	3.2	98			20:45	3.8	116
14 Su	03:08	-0.3	-9					
	09:31	3.6	110					
	15:38	-0.2	-6					
	21:50	3.2	98					
15 M	03:53	-0.1	-3					
	10:08	3.3	101					
	16:17	-0.1	-3					
	22:31	3.2	98					

March

Day	Time	ft	cm		Day	Time	ft	cm
1 M	02:48	-0.7	-21		**16** Tu	04:27	0.1	3
	09:07	3.9	119			10:35	3.2	98
	15:15	-0.6	-18			16:33	0.0	0
	21:33	4.0	122			22:58	3.5	107
2 Tu	03:41	-0.6	-18		**17** W	05:11	0.2	6
	09:53	3.7	113			11:11	3.0	91
	16:01	-0.6	-18			17:11	0.1	3
	22:23	4.0	122			23:36	3.4	104
3 W	04:37	-0.4	-12		**18** Th	05:57	0.4	12
	10:40	3.5	107			11:49	2.7	82
	16:51	-0.6	-18			17:52	0.2	6
	23:16	4.0	122					
4 Th	05:37	-0.2	-6		**19** F	00:17	3.3	101
	11:31	3.2	98			06:45	0.6	18
	17:46	-0.5	-15			12:31	2.6	79
						18:37	0.4	12
5 F	00:14	3.9	119		**20** Sa	01:04	3.2	98
	06:41	0.0	0			07:37	0.7	21
	12:29	2.9	88			13:18	2.4	73
	18:44	-0.3	-9			19:28	0.4	12
6 Sa	01:20	3.8	116		**21** Su	01:57	3.2	98
	07:46	0.2	6			08:31	0.7	21
	13:36	2.7	82			14:15	2.4	73
◐	19:46	-0.2	-6		◐	20:22	0.4	12
7 Su	02:31	3.7	113		**22** M	02:58	3.2	98
	08:53	0.2	6			09:27	0.7	21
	14:49	2.7	82			15:17	2.4	73
	20:51	-0.2	-6			21:19	0.4	12
8 M	03:40	3.7	113		**23** Tu	04:00	3.3	101
	10:00	0.2	6			10:23	0.6	18
	15:57	2.8	85			16:18	2.6	79
	21:57	-0.2	-6			22:17	0.2	6
9 Tu	04:42	3.8	116		**24** W	04:56	3.4	104
	11:01	0.1	3			11:16	0.4	12
	16:58	2.9	88			17:14	2.8	85
	22:59	-0.2	-6			23:15	0.0	0
10 W	05:36	3.8	116		**25** Th	05:47	3.6	110
	11:52	0.0	0			12:05	0.2	6
	17:51	3.1	94			18:05	3.1	94
	23:53	-0.3	-9					
11 Th	06:24	3.8	116		**26** F	00:10	-0.2	-6
	12:36	-0.1	-3			06:36	3.8	116
	18:39	3.2	98			12:50	-0.1	-3
						18:55	3.5	107
12 F	00:41	-0.3	-9		**27** Sa	01:02	-0.5	-15
	07:07	3.8	116			07:23	3.9	119
	13:14	-0.1	-3			13:34	-0.4	-12
	19:23	3.4	104		○	19:45	3.9	119
13 Sa	01:25	-0.3	-9		**28** Su	01:53	-0.6	-18
	07:47	3.7	113			08:10	4.0	122
	13:50	-0.2	-6			14:06	-0.6	-18
●	20:04	3.5	107		○	20:34	4.2	128
14 Su	03:06	-0.2	-6		**29** M	02:43	-0.7	-21
	09:24	3.5	107			08:57	3.9	119
	15:24	-0.2	-6			15:00	-0.7	-21
	21:43	3.5	107			21:24	4.4	134
15 M	03:46	-0.1	-3		**30** Tu	03:34	-0.7	-21
	10:00	3.4	104			09:44	3.8	116
	15:58	-0.1	-3			16:15	-0.8	-24
	22:20	3.5	107			22:14	4.5	137
					31 W	04:28	-0.5	-15
						10:32	3.6	110
						16:34	-0.7	-21
						23:05	4.5	137

StationId: 8721604
Source: NOAA/NOS/CO-OPS
Station Type: Primary
Time Zone: LST_LDT
Datum: MLLW

Trident Pier, Port Canaveral, FL,2021

Times and Heights of High and Low Waters

April

Day	Time	ft	cm	Day	Time	ft	cm
1 Th	05:25	-0.3	-9	**16** F	05:29	0.4	12
	11:23	3.4	104		11:21	2.7	82
	17:27	-0.5	-15		17:14	0.3	9
	23:59	4.4	134		23:45	3.6	110
2 F	06:26	-0.1	-3	**17** Sa	06:16	0.6	18
	12:16	3.2	98		12:02	2.6	79
	18:25	-0.3	-9		18:00	0.4	12
3 Sa	00:57	4.2	128	**18** Su	00:29	3.5	107
	07:29	0.1	3		07:06	0.6	18
	13:17	2.9	88		12:48	2.5	76
	19:27	-0.1	-3		18:51	0.5	15
4 Su	02:02	3.9	119	**19** M	01:19	3.4	104
	08:33	0.2	6		07:57	0.7	21
	14:26	2.8	85		13:42	2.5	76
	20:33	0.0	0		19:47	0.5	15
5 M	03:14	3.7	113	**20** Tu	02:16	3.3	101
	09:38	0.3	9		08:50	0.6	18
	15:41	2.8	85		14:43	2.6	79
	21:40	0.1	3		20:45	0.4	12
6 Tu	04:23	3.6	110	**21** W	03:16	3.4	104
	10:41	0.3	9		09:42	0.5	15
	16:50	3.0	91		15:45	2.8	85
	22:47	0.1	3		21:45	0.3	9
7 W	05:23	3.6	110	**22** Th	04:14	3.5	107
	11:38	0.2	6		10:34	0.3	9
	17:48	3.1	94		16:43	3.1	94
	23:48	0.1	3		22:45	0.1	3
8 Th	06:14	3.6	110	**23** F	05:08	3.6	110
	12:25	0.1	3		11:24	0.0	0
	18:37	3.3	101		17:37	3.5	107
					23:44	-0.1	-3
9 F	00:41	0.1	3	**24** Sa	05:59	3.7	113
	06:59	3.5	107		12:11	-0.3	-9
	13:05	0.0	0		18:29	3.9	119
	19:21	3.5	107				
10 Sa	01:27	0.0	0	**25** Su	00:40	-0.4	-12
	07:39	3.5	107		06:49	3.8	116
	13:40	0.0	0		12:58	-0.6	-18
	20:01	3.6	110		19:20	4.3	131
11 Su	02:08	0.0	0	**26** M	01:34	-0.5	-15
	08:17	3.4	104		07:39	3.8	116
	14:13	-0.1	-3		13:44	-0.8	-24
	20:39	3.7	113		20:12	4.6	140
12 M	02:47	0.1	3	**27** Tu	02:27	-0.6	-18
	08:53	3.3	101		08:30	3.7	113
	14:46	-0.1	-3		14:31	-0.9	-27
	21:15	3.8	116		21:04	4.8	146
13 Tu	03:25	0.1	3	**28** W	03:20	-0.6	-18
	09:29	3.1	94		09:22	3.6	110
	15:19	0.0	0		15:19	-0.8	-24
	21:52	3.8	116		21:56	4.8	146
14 W	04:05	0.2	6	**29** Th	04:15	-0.5	-15
	10:06	3.0	91		10:14	3.5	107
	15:55	0.1	3		16:11	-0.7	-21
	22:28	3.8	116		22:48	4.7	143
15 Th	04:46	0.3	9	**30** F	05:12	-0.3	-9
	10:43	2.8	85		11:07	3.3	101
	16:32	0.2	6		17:06	-0.5	-15
	23:05	3.7	113		23:43	4.5	137

May

Day	Time	ft	cm	Day	Time	ft	cm
1 Sa	06:13	-0.1	-3	**16** Su	05:52	0.4	12
	12:03	3.1	94		11:39	2.5	76
	18:07	-0.3	-9		17:31	0.3	9
2 Su	00:40	4.2	128	**17** M	00:03	3.6	110
	07:15	0.0	0		06:40	0.5	15
	13:04	3.0	91		12:24	2.5	76
	19:12	0.0	0		18:23	0.4	12
3 M	01:43	3.9	119	**18** Tu	00:49	3.5	107
	08:16	0.1	3		07:28	0.4	12
	14:13	2.9	88		13:16	2.6	79
	20:18	0.1	3		19:18	0.4	12
4 Tu	02:50	3.7	113	**19** W	01:41	3.4	104
	09:16	0.2	6		08:17	0.3	9
	15:27	2.9	88		14:14	2.7	82
	21:24	0.3	9		20:17	0.3	9
5 W	03:55	3.5	107	**20** Th	02:37	3.4	104
	10:12	0.2	6		09:06	0.2	6
	16:33	3.1	94		15:15	3.0	91
	22:28	0.3	9		21:17	0.2	6
6 Th	04:52	3.4	104	**21** F	03:34	3.4	104
	11:03	0.2	6		09:55	0.0	0
	17:28	3.2	98		16:14	3.4	104
	23:28	0.3	9		22:19	0.1	3
7 F	05:41	3.3	101	**22** Sa	04:30	3.4	104
	11:47	0.1	3		10:45	-0.3	-9
	18:15	3.4	104		17:10	3.8	116
					23:20	-0.1	-3
8 Sa	00:21	0.3	9	**23** Su	05:24	3.5	107
	06:24	3.2	98		11:35	-0.5	-15
	12:26	0.0	0		18:04	4.2	128
	18:56	3.6	110				
9 Su	01:07	0.3	9	**24** M	00:20	-0.3	-9
	07:04	3.1	94		06:18	3.4	104
	13:01	0.0	0		12:25	-0.8	-24
	19:34	3.7	113		18:58	4.5	137
10 M	01:48	0.2	6	**25** Tu	01:16	-0.4	-12
	07:42	3.0	91		07:12	3.4	104
	13:36	-0.1	-3		13:15	-0.9	-27
	20:11	3.8	116		19:51	4.8	146
11 Tu	02:27	0.2	6	**26** W	02:11	-0.5	-15
	08:21	2.9	88		08:06	3.4	104
	14:10	-0.1	-3		14:06	-1.0	-30
	20:48	3.9	119		20:45	4.9	149
12 W	03:04	0.2	6	**27** Th	03:05	-0.5	-15
	09:00	2.8	85		09:01	3.3	101
	14:46	0.0	0		14:57	-0.9	-27
	21:25	3.9	119		21:39	4.8	146
13 Th	03:43	0.2	6	**28** F	04:00	-0.5	-15
	09:39	2.8	85		09:57	3.3	101
	15:23	0.1	3		15:51	-0.8	-24
	22:02	3.8	116		22:33	4.7	143
14 F	04:23	0.3	9	**29** Sa	04:57	-0.3	-9
	10:18	2.7	82		10:52	3.2	98
	16:02	0.2	6		16:49	-0.5	-15
	22:40	3.8	116		23:27	4.4	134
15 Sa	05:06	0.4	12	**30** Su	05:56	-0.2	-6
	10:57	2.6	79		11:48	3.1	94
	16:44	0.3	9		17:50	-0.3	-9
	23:20	3.7	113				
				31 M	00:21	4.1	125
					06:55	-0.1	-3
					12:48	3.0	91
					18:53	0.0	0

June

Day	Time	ft	cm	Day	Time	ft	cm
1 Tu	01:18	3.8	116	**16** W	00:24	3.6	110
	07:52	0.0	0		06:59	0.1	3
	13:53	2.9	88		12:53	2.8	85
	19:57	0.2	6		18:56	0.2	6
2 W	02:17	3.5	107	**17** Th	01:11	3.5	107
	08:44	0.0	0		07:45	0.0	0
	15:01	3.0	91		13:49	3.0	91
	20:59	0.3	9		19:54	0.2	6
3 Th	03:16	3.2	98	**18** F	02:04	3.4	104
	09:33	0.1	3		08:32	-0.2	-6
	16:04	3.1	94		14:49	3.2	98
	22:00	0.4	12		20:55	0.2	6
4 F	04:10	3.0	91	**19** Sa	03:00	3.3	101
	10:19	0.0	0		09:20	-0.3	-9
	16:58	3.2	98		15:49	3.6	110
	22:59	0.5	15		21:57	0.1	3
5 Sa	04:59	2.9	88	**20** Su	03:57	3.2	98
	11:01	0.0	0		10:11	-0.5	-15
	17:43	3.4	104		16:47	4.0	122
	23:53	0.5	15		23:00	0.0	0
6 Su	05:43	2.8	85	**21** M	04:55	3.2	98
	11:42	0.0	0		11:04	-0.7	-21
	18:24	3.5	107		17:43	4.3	131
7 M	00:41	0.4	12	**22** Tu	00:01	-0.2	-6
	06:25	2.7	82		05:52	3.1	94
	12:21	-0.1	-3		11:58	-0.8	-24
	19:03	3.7	113		18:39	4.5	137
8 Tu	01:24	0.3	9	**23** W	01:00	-0.3	-9
	07:07	2.7	82		06:49	3.1	94
	13:00	-0.1	-3		12:53	-0.9	-27
	19:42	3.8	116		19:34	4.7	143
9 W	02:03	0.3	9	**24** Th	01:56	-0.4	-12
	07:49	2.6	79		07:46	3.2	98
	13:38	-0.1	-3		13:47	-0.9	-27
	20:21	3.8	116		20:29	4.7	143
10 Th	02:42	0.2	6	**25** F	02:50	-0.4	-12
	08:31	2.6	79		08:44	3.2	98
	14:17	-0.1	-3		14:40	-0.9	-27
	21:00	3.8	116		21:24	4.6	140
11 F	03:21	0.2	6	**26** Sa	03:44	-0.4	-12
	09:13	2.6	79		09:40	3.2	98
	14:56	-0.1	-3		15:35	-0.7	-21
	21:39	3.8	116		22:17	4.5	137
12 Sa	04:01	0.2	6	**27** Su	04:38	-0.3	-9
	09:54	2.6	79		10:35	3.2	98
	15:37	0.0	0		16:31	-0.5	-15
	22:19	3.8	116		23:07	4.2	128
13 Su	04:43	0.3	9	**28** M	05:33	-0.2	-6
	10:35	2.6	79		11:29	3.1	94
	16:20	0.1	3		17:30	-0.2	-6
	22:59	3.7	113		23:57	4.0	122
14 M	05:27	0.3	9	**29** Tu	06:26	-0.1	-3
	11:18	2.6	79		12:25	3.1	94
	17:08	0.1	3		18:29	0.0	0
	23:40	3.7	113				
15 Tu	06:13	0.2	6	**30** W	00:47	3.6	110
	12:03	2.7	82		07:17	-0.1	-3
	18:00	0.2	6		13:23	3.0	91
					19:29	0.3	9

StationId: 8721604
Source: NOAA/NOS/CO-OPS
Station Type: Primary
Time Zone: LST_LDT
Datum: MLLW

July

Day	Time	ft	cm	Day	Time	ft	cm
1 Th ◑	01:37	3.3	101	**16** F	00:45	3.5	107
	08:04	0.0	0		07:13	-0.2	-6
	14:23	3.0	91		13:26	3.4	104
	20:27	0.5	15		19:37	0.2	6
2 F	02:29	3.0	91	**17** Sa ◑	01:36	3.4	104
	08:48	0.0	0		08:01	-0.3	-9
	15:23	3.1	94		14:25	3.6	110
	21:25	0.6	18		20:38	0.2	6
3 Sa	03:22	2.8	85	**18** Su	02:32	3.2	98
	09:31	0.1	3		08:51	-0.4	-12
	16:17	3.2	98		15:27	3.9	119
	22:22	0.6	18		21:40	0.2	6
4 Su	04:13	2.6	79	**19** M	03:33	3.1	94
	10:14	0.1	3		09:45	-0.5	-15
	17:05	3.4	104		16:28	4.1	125
	23:17	0.6	18		22:44	0.2	6
5 M	05:01	2.6	79	**20** Tu	04:34	3.1	94
	10:58	0.1	3		10:42	-0.6	-18
	17:48	3.5	107		17:27	4.3	131
					23:47	0.1	3
6 Tu	00:08	0.6	18	**21** W	05:34	3.1	94
	05:47	2.5	76		11:40	-0.6	-18
	11:43	0.0	0		18:24	4.5	137
	18:30	3.6	110				
7 W	00:54	0.5	15	**22** Th	00:46	0.0	0
	06:33	2.5	76		06:33	3.1	94
	12:27	0.0	0		12:38	-0.7	-21
	19:12	3.7	113		19:21	4.6	140
8 Th	01:36	0.4	12	**23** F	01:42	-0.1	-3
	07:17	2.6	79		07:31	3.2	98
	13:10	-0.1	-3		13:33	-0.7	-21
	19:54	3.8	116		20:15	4.6	140
9 F	02:16	0.3	9	**24** Sa ○	02:34	-0.2	-6
	08:02	2.6	79		08:28	3.3	101
	13:52	-0.1	-3		14:27	-0.6	-18
	20:35	3.9	119		21:08	4.5	137
10 Sa ●	02:55	0.3	9	**25** Su	03:24	-0.2	-6
	08:46	2.7	82		09:23	3.3	101
	14:34	-0.1	-3		15:19	-0.5	-15
	21:16	3.9	119		21:57	4.4	134
11 Su	03:35	0.2	6	**26** M	04:12	-0.1	-3
	09:29	2.7	82		10:15	3.4	104
	15:16	-0.1	-3		16:12	-0.3	-9
	21:56	3.9	119		22:43	4.2	128
12 M	04:16	0.2	6	**27** Tu	05:00	-0.1	-3
	10:12	2.8	85		11:05	3.4	104
	16:00	-0.1	-3		17:05	0.0	0
	22:36	3.9	119		23:27	3.9	119
13 Tu	04:58	0.1	3	**28** W	05:47	0.0	0
	10:56	2.9	88		11:55	3.3	101
	16:48	0.0	0		18:00	0.3	9
	23:17	3.8	116				
14 W	05:42	0.0	0	**29** Th	00:11	3.6	110
	11:42	3.1	94		06:33	0.1	3
	17:41	0.1	3		12:45	3.3	101
	23:59	3.7	113		18:56	0.5	15
15 Th	06:26	0.0	0	**30** F	00:55	3.3	101
	12:32	3.2	98		07:17	0.2	6
	18:37	0.2	6		13:37	3.3	101
					19:51	0.7	21
				31 Sa ◑	01:41	3.0	91
					08:00	0.3	9
					14:32	3.3	101
					20:46	0.8	24

August

Day	Time	ft	cm	Day	Time	ft	cm
1 Su	02:32	2.8	85	**16** M	02:13	3.3	101
	08:44	0.3	9		08:29	-0.1	-3
	15:28	3.4	104		15:08	4.2	128
	21:41	0.9	27		21:28	0.5	15
2 M	03:27	2.6	79	**17** Tu	03:17	3.2	98
	09:30	0.3	9		09:27	-0.1	-3
	16:21	3.4	104		16:13	4.3	131
	22:37	0.9	27		22:32	0.5	15
3 Tu	04:21	2.6	79	**18** W	04:23	3.2	98
	10:18	0.3	9		10:28	-0.1	-3
	17:10	3.6	110		17:16	4.4	134
	23:30	0.8	24		23:35	0.4	12
4 W	05:12	2.6	79	**19** Th	05:25	3.3	101
	11:08	0.3	9		11:30	-0.2	-6
	17:57	3.7	113		18:14	4.5	137
5 Th	00:19	0.7	21	**20** F	00:34	0.3	9
	06:00	2.7	82		06:24	3.4	104
	11:57	0.2	6		12:29	-0.2	-6
	18:41	3.8	116		19:08	4.6	140
6 F	01:03	0.6	18	**21** Sa	01:26	0.2	6
	06:47	2.8	85		07:20	3.5	107
	12:44	0.1	3		13:23	-0.2	-6
	19:24	3.9	119		20:00	4.5	137
7 Sa	01:44	0.5	15	**22** Su ○	02:14	0.2	6
	07:33	3.0	91		08:14	3.7	113
	13:28	0.0	0		14:14	-0.2	-6
	20:07	4.1	125		20:48	4.5	137
8 Su ●	02:24	0.4	12	**23** M	02:58	0.1	3
	08:18	3.1	94		09:04	3.8	116
	14:12	-0.1	-3		15:03	-0.1	-3
	20:49	4.1	125		21:32	4.3	131
9 M	03:03	0.3	9	**24** Tu	03:40	0.2	6
	09:03	3.3	101		09:52	3.8	116
	14:56	-0.1	-3		15:51	0.1	3
	21:30	4.2	128		22:14	4.1	125
10 Tu	03:43	0.2	6	**25** W	04:21	0.2	6
	09:48	3.4	104		10:37	3.8	116
	15:42	-0.1	-3		16:39	0.4	12
	22:10	4.1	125		22:54	3.9	119
11 W	04:24	0.1	3	**26** Th	05:02	0.3	9
	10:33	3.6	110		11:20	3.8	116
	16:31	0.0	0		17:29	0.6	18
	22:52	4.0	122		23:34	3.6	110
12 Th	05:07	0.0	0	**27** F	05:44	0.4	12
	11:20	3.8	116		12:04	3.8	116
	17:25	0.1	3		18:21	0.8	24
	23:36	3.9	119				
13 F	05:53	0.0	0	**28** Sa	00:14	3.3	101
	12:10	3.9	119		06:26	0.6	18
	18:22	0.3	9		12:50	3.7	113
					19:13	1.0	30
14 Sa	00:22	3.7	113	**29** Su	00:58	3.1	94
	06:42	-0.1	-3		07:11	0.7	21
	13:04	4.0	122		13:40	3.6	110
	19:22	0.4	12		20:07	1.1	34
15 Su ◑	01:14	3.4	104	**30** M ◑	01:47	2.9	88
	07:34	-0.1	-3		07:59	0.7	21
	14:04	4.1	125		14:35	3.6	110
	20:24	0.5	15		21:00	1.2	37
				31 Tu	02:43	2.8	85
					08:49	0.8	24
					15:34	3.6	110
					21:55	1.2	37

September

Day	Time	ft	cm	Day	Time	ft	cm
1 W	03:42	2.8	85	**16** Th	04:18	3.5	107
	09:41	0.8	24		10:21	0.3	9
	16:30	3.7	113		17:06	4.5	137
	22:49	1.1	34		23:24	0.7	21
2 Th	04:38	2.9	88	**17** F	05:22	3.6	110
	10:35	0.7	21		11:24	0.3	9
	17:20	3.9	119		18:02	4.5	137
	23:40	1.0	30				
3 F	05:29	3.1	94	**18** Sa	00:18	0.6	18
	11:27	0.5	15		06:18	3.8	116
	18:07	4.0	122		12:22	0.3	9
					18:53	4.5	137
4 Sa	00:26	0.9	27	**19** Su	01:06	0.5	15
	06:17	3.3	101		07:10	4.0	122
	12:17	0.4	12		13:14	0.3	9
	18:51	4.2	128		19:40	4.5	137
5 Su	01:08	0.7	21	**20** M ○	01:48	0.4	12
	07:03	3.5	107		07:58	4.1	125
	13:04	0.2	6		14:02	0.3	9
	19:34	4.3	131		20:23	4.4	134
6 M	01:48	0.5	15	**21** Tu	02:27	0.4	12
	07:49	3.8	116		08:43	4.2	128
	13:50	0.1	3		14:46	0.4	12
	20:17	4.4	134		21:03	4.2	128
7 Tu ●	02:28	0.3	9	**22** W	03:04	0.4	12
	08:36	4.0	122		09:25	4.3	131
	14:37	0.1	3		15:29	0.5	15
	21:00	4.4	134		21:42	4.0	122
8 W	03:08	0.2	6	**23** Th	03:40	0.5	15
	09:22	4.2	128		10:06	4.3	131
	15:24	0.1	3		16:13	0.7	21
	21:43	4.4	134		22:20	3.8	116
9 Th	03:49	0.1	3	**24** F	04:17	0.6	18
	10:10	4.4	134		10:45	4.2	128
	16:15	0.2	6		16:58	0.9	27
	22:27	4.2	128		22:58	3.6	110
10 F	04:34	0.0	0	**25** Sa	04:56	0.7	21
	10:58	4.6	140		11:25	4.1	125
	17:10	0.3	9		17:46	1.1	34
	23:13	4.0	122		23:37	3.4	104
11 Sa	05:22	0.1	3	**26** Su	05:38	0.9	27
	11:49	4.6	140		12:07	4.0	122
	18:08	0.5	15		18:36	1.2	37
12 Su	00:03	3.8	116	**27** M	00:20	3.2	98
	06:15	0.1	3		06:25	1.0	30
	12:45	4.6	140		12:54	3.9	119
	19:10	0.6	18		19:28	1.3	40
13 M ◑	00:58	3.6	110	**28** Tu	01:08	3.1	94
	07:12	0.2	6		07:16	1.1	34
	13:41	4.5	137		13:47	3.8	116
	20:13	0.7	21		20:22	1.4	43
14 Tu	02:00	3.4	104	**29** W ◑	02:03	3.0	91
	08:13	0.3	9		08:10	1.1	34
	14:54	4.5	137		14:46	3.8	116
	21:18	0.8	24		21:15	1.4	43
15 W	03:09	3.4	104	**30** Th	03:05	3.0	91
	09:05	0.3	9		09:05	1.1	34
	16:02	4.5	137		15:46	3.9	119
	22:22	0.8	24		22:08	1.3	40

StationId: 8721604
Source: NOAA/NOS/CO-OPS
Station Type: Primary
Time Zone: LST_LDT
Datum: MLLW

NOAA Tide Predictions

Trident Pier, Port Canaveral, FL, 2021

Times and Heights of High and Low Waters

October

Day	Time	ft	cm	Day	Time	ft	cm
1 F	04:04	3.2	98	16 Sa	05:17	3.8	116
	10:01	1.0	30		11:17	0.6	18
	16:40	4.0	122		17:45	4.3	131
	22:59	1.1	34		23:56	0.7	21
2 Sa	04:58	3.4	104	17 Su	06:10	4.0	122
	10:56	0.8	24		12:14	0.6	18
	17:28	4.2	128		18:32	4.3	131
	23:45	0.9	27				
3 Su	05:47	3.7	113	18 M	00:40	0.6	18
	11:49	0.6	18		06:57	4.2	128
	18:14	4.3	131		13:04	0.6	18
					19:14	4.2	128
4 M	00:29	0.7	21	19 Tu	01:18	0.5	15
	06:34	4.0	122		07:40	4.3	131
	12:40	0.4	12		13:48	0.6	18
	18:58	4.4	134		19:54	4.0	122
5 Tu	01:10	0.4	12	20 W	01:53	0.5	15
	07:22	4.4	134		08:20	4.4	134
	13:29	0.2	6		14:29	0.7	21
	19:43	4.5	137 ○		20:33	3.9	119 ○
6 W	01:52	0.2	6	21 Th	02:27	0.5	15
	08:09	4.7	143		08:58	4.5	137
	14:18	0.1	3		15:09	0.7	21
	20:29	4.5	137		21:11	3.7	113
7 Th	02:33	0.0	0	22 F	03:02	0.5	15
	08:58	4.9	149		09:36	4.5	137
	15:08	0.1	3		15:49	0.8	24
	21:16	4.4	134		21:49	3.6	110
8 F	03:17	0.0	0	23 Sa	03:37	0.6	18
	09:47	5.1	155		10:13	4.4	134
	16:00	0.2	6		16:30	1.0	30
	22:04	4.2	128		22:27	3.4	104
9 Sa	04:04	0.0	0	24 Su	04:16	0.8	24
	10:38	5.1	155		10:52	4.3	131
	16:55	0.4	12		17:15	1.1	34
	22:53	4.0	122		23:06	3.3	101
10 Su	04:56	0.1	3	25 M	04:58	0.9	27
	11:30	5.1	155		11:32	4.2	128
	17:54	0.5	15		18:03	1.2	37
	23:46	3.8	116		23:48	3.2	98
11 M	05:53	0.3	9	26 Tu	05:45	1.0	30
	12:27	4.9	149		12:16	4.0	122
	18:57	0.7	21		18:53	1.3	40
12 Tu	00:44	3.6	110	27 W	00:34	3.1	94
	06:55	0.4	12		06:37	1.1	34
	13:30	4.7	143		13:06	3.9	119
	20:02	0.8	24		19:45	1.3	40
13 W	01:50	3.5	107	28 Th	01:27	3.0	91
	08:01	0.5	15		07:32	1.1	34
	14:39	4.5	137		14:01	3.8	116
	21:06	0.9	27		20:37	1.3	40 ◑
14 Th	03:03	3.5	107	29 F	02:27	3.1	94
	09:07	0.6	18		08:29	1.1	34
	15:48	4.4	134		14:59	3.9	119
	22:08	0.9	27		21:27	1.1	34
15 F	04:15	3.6	110	30 Sa	03:28	3.3	101
	10:14	0.7	21		09:27	1.0	30
	16:51	4.4	134		15:55	3.9	119
	23:06	0.8	24		22:16	0.9	27
				31 Su	04:25	3.6	110
					10:24	0.8	24
					16:47	4.0	122
					23:03	0.7	21

November

Day	Time	ft	cm	Day	Time	ft	cm
1 M	05:17	3.9	119	16 Tu	05:38	4.1	125
	11:21	0.6	18		11:50	0.7	21
	17:35	4.1	125		17:45	3.6	110
	23:48	0.4	12		23:45	0.3	9
2 Tu	06:06	4.3	131	17 W	06:18	4.2	128
	12:16	0.4	12		12:32	0.7	21
	18:23	4.2	128		18:25	3.5	107
3 W	00:33	0.1	3	18 Th	00:20	0.3	9
	06:55	4.7	143		06:55	4.3	131
	13:09	0.2	6		13:12	0.6	18
	19:12	4.2	128		19:04	3.4	104
4 Th	01:18	-0.1	-3	19 F	00:55	0.3	9
	07:45	5.1	155		07:32	4.3	131
	14:00	0.1	3		13:49	0.6	18
	20:01	4.2	128 ●		19:42	3.3	101 ○
5 F	02:03	-0.3	-9	20 Sa	01:30	0.4	12
	08:36	5.3	162		08:10	4.3	131
	14:51	0.0	0		14:27	0.7	21
	20:51	4.1	125		20:21	3.2	98
6 Sa	02:50	-0.3	-9	21 Su	02:07	0.4	12
	09:27	5.4	165		08:47	4.3	131
	15:44	0.1	3		15:06	0.7	21
	21:43	4.0	122		21:00	3.1	94
7 Su	02:40	-0.3	-9	22 M	02:45	0.5	15
	09:20	5.3	162		09:25	4.2	128
	15:40	0.2	6		15:48	0.8	24
	21:36	3.9	119		21:40	3.0	91
8 M	03:35	-0.1	-3	23 Tu	03:27	0.6	18
	10:14	5.1	155		10:05	4.0	122
	16:39	0.4	12		16:33	0.9	27
	22:31	3.7	113		22:21	3.0	91
9 Tu	04:34	0.1	3	24 W	04:12	0.7	21
	11:10	4.8	146		10:46	3.9	119
	17:42	0.5	15		17:21	0.9	27
	23:31	3.6	110		23:05	2.9	88
10 W	05:39	0.3	9	25 Th	05:02	0.8	24
	12:11	4.5	137		11:31	3.8	116
	18:45	0.6	18		18:09	0.9	27
					23:55	2.9	88
11 Th	00:37	3.5	107	26 F	05:57	0.8	24
	06:46	0.5	15		12:20	3.7	113
	13:18	4.3	131		18:58	0.8	24
	19:47	0.6	18 ◐				
12 F	01:52	3.5	107	27 Sa	00:51	3.0	91
	07:54	0.6	18		06:55	0.8	24
	14:25	4.1	125		13:14	3.6	110
	20:45	0.6	18		19:45	0.7	21 ◑
13 Sa	03:03	3.6	110	28 Su	01:52	3.2	98
	09:00	0.7	21		07:54	0.7	21
	15:26	3.9	119		14:10	3.6	110
	21:38	0.6	18		20:33	0.5	15
14 Su	04:04	3.8	116	29 M	02:52	3.5	107
	10:04	0.7	21		08:55	0.6	18
	16:18	3.8	116		15:05	3.6	110
	22:25	0.5	15		21:21	0.2	6
15 M	04:54	4.0	122	30 Tu	03:47	3.9	119
	11:00	0.7	21		09:55	0.4	12
	17:04	3.7	113		15:59	3.7	113
	23:07	0.4	12		22:10	-0.1	-3

December

Day	Time	ft	cm	Day	Time	ft	cm
1 W	04:40	4.3	131	16 Th	05:53	3.9	119
	10:54	0.2	6		12:14	0.5	15
	16:51	3.7	113		17:56	2.9	88
	23:00	-0.3	-9		23:49	0.1	3
2 Th	05:32	4.7	143	17 F	06:31	4.0	122
	11:50	0.0	0		12:52	0.4	12
	17:44	3.7	113		18:37	2.9	88
	23:49	-0.5	-15				
3 F	06:24	5.0	152	18 Sa	00:27	0.1	3
	12:43	-0.2	-6		07:09	4.0	122
	18:37	3.7	113		13:29	0.4	12
					19:17	2.9	88
4 Sa	00:39	-0.7	-21	19 Su	01:06	0.0	0
	07:17	5.2	158		07:47	4.0	122
	13:36	-0.2	-6		14:05	0.4	12
	19:31	3.7	113 ●		19:57	2.9	88 ○
5 Su	01:30	-0.7	-21	20 M	01:44	0.1	3
	08:10	5.2	158		08:25	4.0	122
	14:29	-0.2	-6		14:43	0.4	12
	20:25	3.7	113		20:37	2.8	85
6 M	02:23	-0.6	-18	21 Tu	02:23	0.1	3
	09:04	5.1	155		09:03	3.9	119
	15:24	-0.1	-3		15:23	0.4	12
	21:20	3.6	110		21:16	2.8	85
7 Tu	03:18	-0.5	-15	22 W	03:03	0.2	6
	09:58	4.8	146		09:41	3.8	116
	16:21	0.0	0		16:04	0.4	12
	22:15	3.5	107		21:57	2.8	85
8 W	04:18	-0.2	-6	23 Th	03:47	0.3	9
	10:52	4.5	137		10:20	3.7	113
	17:21	0.1	3		16:48	0.4	12
	23:14	3.4	104		22:40	2.8	85
9 Th	05:21	0.1	3	24 F	04:35	0.3	9
	11:48	4.2	128		11:01	3.6	110
	18:20	0.2	6		17:32	0.4	12
					23:26	2.8	85
10 F	00:18	3.3	101	25 Sa	05:28	0.4	12
	06:27	0.3	9		11:45	3.5	107
	12:47	3.8	116		18:18	0.3	9
	19:17	0.2	6				
11 Sa	01:28	3.3	101	26 Su	00:19	3.0	91
	07:32	0.5	15		06:26	0.4	12
	13:49	3.6	110		12:34	3.4	104
	20:10	0.3	9 ◐		19:04	0.1	3
12 Su	02:38	3.4	104	27 M	01:18	3.2	98
	08:38	0.6	18		07:26	0.4	12
	14:49	3.3	101		13:29	3.2	98
	21:00	0.2	6		19:53	0.0	0 ◑
13 M	03:39	3.5	107	28 Tu	02:19	3.5	107
	09:41	0.7	21		08:28	0.3	9
	15:43	3.2	98		14:28	3.2	98
	21:46	0.2	6		20:44	-0.2	-6
14 Tu	04:29	3.7	113	29 W	03:19	3.8	116
	10:40	0.7	21		09:32	0.2	6
	16:31	3.0	91		15:27	3.1	94
	22:29	0.2	6		21:38	-0.4	-12
15 W	05:13	3.8	116	30 Th	04:16	4.2	128
	11:30	0.6	18		10:34	0.0	0
	17:15	3.0	91		16:25	3.2	98
	23:10	0.1	3		22:33	-0.7	-21
				31 F	05:12	4.5	137
					11:33	-0.2	-6
					17:22	3.2	98
					23:26	-0.8	-24

StationId: 8723178
Source: NOAA/NOS/CO-OPS
Station Type: Primary
Time Zone: LST_LDT
Datum: MLLW

NOAA Tide Predictions

MIAMI BEACH, GOVERNMENT CUT, FL,2021

Times and Heights of High and Low Waters

January

Day	Time	ft	cm
1 F	03:14	-0.3	-9
	10:09	2.5	76
	15:45	0.1	3
	22:15	2.2	67
2 Sa	03:58	-0.2	-6
	10:52	2.4	73
	16:30	0.1	3
	23:02	2.2	67
3 Su	04:45	-0.2	-6
	11:35	2.4	73
	17:18	0.0	0
	23:54	2.2	67
4 M	05:37	-0.1	-3
	12:22	2.3	70
	18:12	0.0	0
5 Tu	00:50	2.2	67
	06:35	0.0	0
	13:12	2.2	67
	19:10	-0.1	-3
6 W	01:51	2.2	67
	07:38	0.1	3
	14:07	2.2	67
	20:12	-0.2	-6
7 Th	02:56	2.2	67
	08:44	0.2	6
	15:07	2.2	67
	21:14	-0.3	-9
8 F	04:03	2.3	70
	09:49	0.2	6
	16:10	2.2	67
	22:15	-0.4	-12
9 Sa	05:07	2.4	73
	10:50	0.1	3
	17:13	2.2	67
	23:13	-0.5	-15
10 Su	06:07	2.5	76
	11:47	0.0	0
	18:13	2.3	70
11 M	00:09	-0.6	-18
	07:03	2.6	79
	12:42	-0.1	-3
	19:08	2.4	73
12 Tu	01:02	-0.6	-18
	07:54	2.6	79
	13:33	-0.1	-3
	20:01	2.4	73
13 W	01:53	-0.6	-18
	08:43	2.6	79
	14:23	-0.2	-6
	20:50	2.4	73
14 Th	02:42	-0.6	-18
	09:28	2.6	79
	15:11	-0.2	-6
	21:38	2.4	73
15 F	03:29	-0.5	-15
	10:12	2.5	76
	15:59	-0.1	-3
	22:24	2.3	70
16 Sa	04:16	-0.3	-9
	10:54	2.4	73
	16:46	-0.1	-3
	23:10	2.2	67
17 Su	05:03	-0.2	-6
	11:34	2.3	70
	17:32	-0.1	-3
	23:55	2.1	64
18 M	05:50	0.0	0
	12:15	2.1	64
	18:20	0.0	0
19 Tu	00:42	2.0	61
	06:39	0.2	6
	12:56	2.0	61
	19:08	0.1	3
20 W	01:31	1.9	58
	07:31	0.3	9
	13:40	1.9	58
	19:59	0.1	3
21 Th	02:24	1.8	55
	08:26	0.4	12
	14:28	1.8	55
	20:51	0.1	3
22 F	03:21	1.8	55
	09:21	0.4	12
	15:22	1.7	52
	21:44	0.1	3
23 Sa	04:19	1.8	55
	10:16	0.4	12
	16:19	1.7	52
	22:34	0.0	0
24 Su	05:16	1.9	58
	11:06	0.4	12
	17:15	1.8	55
	23:22	-0.1	-3
25 M	06:08	2.0	61
	11:53	0.3	9
	18:08	1.9	58
26 Tu	00:07	-0.2	-6
	06:56	2.1	64
	12:38	0.2	6
	18:57	2.0	61
27 W	00:51	-0.3	-9
	07:41	2.2	67
	13:20	0.1	3
	19:44	2.1	64
28 Th	01:33	-0.4	-12
	08:24	2.3	70
	14:02	0.0	0
	20:29	2.2	67
29 F	02:15	-0.5	-15
	09:06	2.4	73
	14:43	-0.2	-6
	21:15	2.3	70
30 Sa	02:59	-0.5	-15
	09:47	2.4	73
	15:26	-0.3	-9
	22:01	2.3	70
31 Su	03:43	-0.5	-15
	10:29	2.4	73
	16:11	-0.3	-9
	22:48	2.3	70

February

Day	Time	ft	cm
1 M	04:30	-0.4	-12
	11:12	2.4	73
	16:58	-0.4	-12
	23:38	2.3	70
2 Tu	05:21	-0.3	-9
	11:57	2.3	70
	17:49	-0.4	-12
3 W	00:33	2.3	70
	06:16	-0.1	-3
	12:46	2.2	67
	18:46	-0.4	-12
4 Th	01:32	2.2	67
	07:17	0.0	0
	13:41	2.1	64
	19:48	-0.4	-12
5 F	02:36	2.1	64
	08:23	0.1	3
	14:44	2.0	61
	20:53	-0.4	-12
6 Sa	03:45	2.1	64
	09:31	0.2	6
	15:52	2.0	61
	21:59	-0.4	-12
7 Su	04:53	2.2	67
	10:35	0.1	3
	17:00	2.0	61
	23:01	-0.4	-12
8 M	05:56	2.3	70
	11:35	0.0	0
	18:03	2.1	64
	23:58	-0.5	-15
9 Tu	06:51	2.3	70
	12:30	-0.1	-3
	18:59	2.2	67
10 W	00:51	-0.5	-15
	07:41	2.4	73
	13:20	-0.2	-6
	19:50	2.3	70
11 Th	01:40	-0.5	-15
	08:25	2.4	73
	14:07	-0.2	-6
	20:36	2.3	70
12 F	02:26	-0.5	-15
	09:06	2.4	73
	14:51	-0.3	-9
	21:19	2.3	70
13 Sa	03:09	-0.4	-12
	09:45	2.4	73
	15:33	-0.3	-9
	22:01	2.3	70
14 Su	03:50	-0.3	-9
	10:21	2.3	70
	16:13	-0.2	-6
	22:41	2.2	67
15 M	04:31	-0.2	-6
	10:57	2.2	67
	16:53	-0.2	-6
	23:20	2.1	64
16 Tu	05:11	0.0	0
	11:32	2.1	64
	17:32	-0.1	-3
17 W	00:01	2.0	61
	05:52	0.2	6
	12:08	1.9	58
	18:14	0.0	0
18 Th	00:44	1.9	58
	06:37	0.3	9
	12:48	1.8	55
	19:00	0.1	3
19 F	01:32	1.8	55
	07:27	0.4	12
	13:34	1.7	52
	19:52	0.1	3
20 Sa	02:28	1.8	55
	08:25	0.5	15
	14:28	1.7	52
	20:50	0.1	3
21 Su	03:31	1.7	52
	09:27	0.5	15
	15:32	1.7	52
	21:50	0.1	3
22 M	04:35	1.8	55
	10:26	0.5	15
	16:37	1.7	52
	22:45	0.0	0
23 Tu	05:34	1.9	58
	11:19	0.3	9
	17:37	1.9	58
	23:37	-0.1	-3
24 W	06:26	2.1	64
	12:08	0.2	6
	18:32	2.0	61
25 Th	00:25	-0.3	-9
	07:13	2.3	70
	12:53	0.0	0
	19:22	2.2	67
26 F	01:10	-0.4	-12
	07:57	2.4	73
	13:37	-0.2	-6
	20:10	2.4	73
27 Sa	01:55	-0.5	-15
	08:39	2.5	76
	14:20	-0.4	-12
	20:56	2.5	76
28 Su	02:40	-0.5	-15
	09:21	2.6	79
	15:04	-0.5	-15
	21:43	2.6	79

March

Day	Time	ft	cm
1 M	03:26	-0.5	-15
	10:04	2.6	79
	15:49	-0.6	-18
	22:31	2.6	79
2 Tu	04:14	-0.4	-12
	10:48	2.5	76
	16:37	-0.6	-18
	23:22	2.6	79
3 W	05:04	-0.2	-6
	11:34	2.4	73
	17:28	-0.5	-15
4 Th	00:15	2.5	76
	05:59	-0.1	-3
	12:25	2.3	70
	18:25	-0.4	-12
5 F	01:13	2.3	70
	06:59	0.1	3
	13:22	2.1	64
	19:28	-0.3	-9
6 Sa	02:18	2.2	67
	08:06	0.2	6
	14:28	2.1	64
	20:37	-0.2	-6
7 Su	03:28	2.1	64
	09:16	0.3	9
	15:39	2.0	61
	21:46	-0.2	-6
8 M	04:38	2.2	67
	10:23	0.2	6
	16:50	2.1	64
	22:50	-0.2	-6
9 Tu	05:41	2.2	67
	11:23	0.1	3
	17:53	2.2	67
	23:47	-0.2	-6
10 W	06:35	2.3	70
	12:17	0.0	0
	18:47	2.3	70
11 Th	00:38	-0.3	-9
	07:21	2.4	73
	13:04	-0.1	-3
	19:35	2.4	73
12 F	01:24	-0.3	-9
	08:02	2.4	73
	13:47	-0.2	-6
	20:18	2.4	73
13 Sa	02:06	-0.3	-9
	08:39	2.4	73
	14:26	-0.2	-6
	20:57	2.4	73
14 Su	03:45	-0.2	-6
	10:14	2.4	73
	16:04	-0.2	-6
	22:35	2.4	73
15 M	04:23	-0.1	-3
	10:48	2.3	70
	16:39	-0.2	-6
	23:11	2.4	73
16 Tu	04:59	0.0	0
	11:21	2.3	70
	17:14	-0.2	-6
	23:48	2.3	70
17 W	05:35	0.1	3
	11:54	2.2	67
	17:49	-0.1	-3
18 Th	00:25	2.2	67
	06:11	0.3	9
	12:29	2.0	61
	18:26	0.0	0
19 F	01:05	2.1	64
	06:50	0.4	12
	13:07	1.9	58
	19:08	0.1	3
20 Sa	01:51	2.0	61
	07:36	0.5	15
	13:51	1.8	55
	19:57	0.2	6
21 Su	02:44	1.9	58
	08:32	0.6	18
	20:58	0.3	9
22 M	03:46	1.9	58
	09:38	0.6	18
	15:50	1.8	55
	22:04	0.3	9
23 Tu	04:53	1.9	58
	10:44	0.6	18
	17:01	1.8	55
	23:07	0.2	6
24 W	05:55	2.0	61
	11:43	0.4	12
	18:07	2.0	61
25 Th	00:04	0.0	0
	06:50	2.2	67
	12:35	0.2	6
	19:05	2.2	67
26 F	00:56	-0.1	-3
	07:39	2.4	73
	13:22	0.0	0
	19:58	2.4	73
27 Sa	01:45	-0.3	-9
	08:25	2.5	76
	14:08	-0.3	-9
	20:48	2.6	79
28 Su	02:33	-0.3	-9
	09:09	2.6	79
	14:54	-0.5	-15
	21:36	2.8	85
29 M	03:20	-0.4	-12
	09:54	2.7	82
	15:40	-0.6	-18
	22:25	2.9	88
30 Tu	04:07	-0.4	-12
	10:39	2.7	82
	16:27	-0.7	-21
	23:14	2.9	88
31 W	04:56	-0.3	-9
	11:25	2.7	82
	17:16	-0.6	-18

StationId: 8723178
Source: NOAA/NOS/CO-OPS
Station Type: Primary
Time Zone: LST_LDT
Datum: MLLW

MIAMI BEACH, GOVERNMENT CUT, FL,2021

Times and Heights of High and Low Waters

April

Day	Time	ft	cm
1 Th	00:05	2.8	85
	05:48	-0.1	-3
	12:14	2.5	76
	18:09	-0.5	-15
2 F	00:58	2.7	82
	06:43	0.1	3
	13:08	2.4	73
	19:08	-0.3	-9
3 Sa	01:57	2.5	76
	07:44	0.2	6
	14:08	2.3	70
	20:12	-0.1	-3
4 Su	03:01	2.3	70
	08:52	0.3	9
	15:14	2.2	67
	21:22	0.0	0
5 M	04:09	2.2	67
	10:02	0.4	12
	16:26	2.1	64
	22:31	0.0	0
6 Tu	05:17	2.2	67
	11:08	0.3	9
	17:36	2.2	67
	23:34	0.1	3
7 W	06:17	2.3	70
	12:06	0.2	6
	18:37	2.2	67
8 Th	00:30	0.0	0
	07:09	2.3	70
	12:56	0.1	3
	19:30	2.3	70
9 F	01:18	0.0	0
	07:53	2.4	73
	13:40	0.0	0
	20:15	2.4	73
10 Sa	02:02	0.0	0
	08:32	2.4	73
	14:20	-0.1	-3
	20:55	2.5	76
11 Su	02:42	0.0	0
	09:08	2.4	73
	14:57	-0.1	-3
	21:32	2.5	76
12 M	03:19	0.0	0
	09:42	2.4	73
	15:32	-0.1	-3
	22:08	2.5	76
13 Tu	03:55	0.1	3
	10:15	2.4	73
	16:06	-0.1	-3
	22:43	2.5	76
14 W	04:30	0.2	6
	10:48	2.3	70
	16:39	-0.1	-3
	23:19	2.4	73
15 Th	05:04	0.3	9
	11:22	2.2	67
	17:13	0.0	0
	23:56	2.3	70
16 F	05:39	0.4	12
	11:58	2.1	64
	17:49	0.1	3
17 Sa	00:36	2.2	67
	06:16	0.5	15
	12:37	2.0	61
	18:29	0.2	6
18 Su	01:21	2.1	64
	07:00	0.6	18
	13:21	2.0	61
	19:18	0.3	9
19 M	02:12	2.1	64
	07:55	0.6	18
	14:15	1.9	58
	20:17	0.3	9
20 Tu	03:10	2.0	61
	09:00	0.6	18
	15:19	1.9	58
	21:24	0.3	9
21 W	04:12	2.1	64
	10:06	0.5	15
	16:29	2.0	61
	22:30	0.3	9
22 Th	05:13	2.2	67
	11:06	0.3	9
	17:36	2.2	67
	23:31	0.1	3
23 F	06:10	2.3	70
	12:00	0.1	3
	18:37	2.4	73
24 Sa	00:26	0.0	0
	07:02	2.4	73
	12:51	-0.2	-6
	19:33	2.6	79
25 Su	01:19	-0.1	-3
	07:51	2.6	79
	13:39	-0.4	-12
	20:25	2.8	85
26 M	02:09	-0.2	-6
	08:39	2.7	82
	14:28	-0.6	-18
	21:16	3.0	91
27 Tu	02:58	-0.2	-6
	09:27	2.8	85
	15:16	-0.7	-21
	22:06	3.0	91
28 W	03:48	-0.2	-6
	10:16	2.8	85
	16:06	-0.7	-21
	22:57	3.0	91
29 Th	04:39	-0.1	-3
	11:06	2.7	82
	16:58	-0.6	-18
	23:48	2.9	88
30 F	05:32	0.0	0
	11:58	2.6	79
	17:53	-0.4	-12

May

Day	Time	ft	cm
1 Sa	00:42	2.7	82
	06:28	0.1	3
	12:53	2.5	76
	18:52	-0.2	-6
2 Su	01:39	2.6	79
	07:30	0.2	6
	13:53	2.3	70
	19:56	-0.1	-3
3 M	02:40	2.4	73
	08:37	0.3	9
	14:58	2.2	67
	21:04	0.1	3
4 Tu	03:43	2.3	70
	09:43	0.3	9
	16:07	2.2	67
	22:10	0.2	6
5 W	04:45	2.3	70
	10:45	0.3	9
	17:13	2.2	67
	23:10	0.2	6
6 Th	05:42	2.2	67
	11:39	0.2	6
	18:12	2.2	67
7 F	00:03	0.2	6
	06:32	2.3	70
	12:27	0.1	3
	19:03	2.3	70
8 Sa	00:51	0.2	6
	07:16	2.3	70
	13:09	0.0	0
	19:47	2.4	73
9 Su	01:34	0.2	6
	07:56	2.3	70
	13:48	-0.1	-3
	20:27	2.5	76
10 M	02:13	0.2	6
	08:33	2.3	70
	14:25	-0.1	-3
	21:05	2.5	76
11 Tu	02:51	0.2	6
	09:09	2.3	70
	15:01	-0.1	-3
	21:41	2.5	76
12 W	03:27	0.2	6
	09:44	2.3	70
	15:35	-0.1	-3
	22:18	2.5	76
13 Th	04:02	0.3	9
	10:20	2.2	67
	16:09	-0.1	-3
	22:56	2.4	73
14 F	04:37	0.3	9
	10:57	2.2	67
	16:44	0.0	0
	23:34	2.4	73
15 Sa	05:13	0.4	12
	11:35	2.1	64
	17:21	0.1	3
16 Su	00:15	2.3	70
	05:52	0.5	15
	12:16	2.0	61
	18:03	0.1	3
17 M	00:59	2.2	67
	06:37	0.5	15
	13:02	2.0	61
	18:51	0.2	6
18 Tu	01:47	2.2	67
	07:30	0.5	15
	13:55	2.0	61
	19:47	0.2	6
19 W	02:39	2.1	64
	08:30	0.4	12
	14:56	2.0	61
	20:51	0.3	9
20 Th	03:34	2.2	67
	09:32	0.3	9
	16:02	2.1	64
	21:57	0.2	6
21 F	04:32	2.2	67
	10:31	0.1	3
	17:08	2.2	67
	22:59	0.2	6
22 Sa	05:29	2.3	70
	11:27	-0.1	-3
	18:11	2.4	73
	23:58	0.1	3
23 Su	06:25	2.4	73
	12:21	-0.3	-9
	19:09	2.6	79
24 M	00:53	0.0	0
	07:19	2.5	76
	13:13	-0.5	-15
	20:04	2.8	85
25 Tu	01:46	-0.1	-3
	08:12	2.6	79
	14:04	-0.7	-21
	20:57	2.9	88
26 W	02:37	-0.2	-6
	09:04	2.7	82
	14:56	-0.7	-21
	21:49	3.0	91
27 Th	03:29	-0.2	-6
	09:56	2.7	82
	15:48	-0.7	-21
	22:40	2.9	88
28 F	04:22	-0.1	-3
	10:49	2.6	79
	16:42	-0.6	-18
	23:32	2.8	85
29 Sa	05:16	0.0	0
	11:43	2.6	79
	17:37	-0.4	-12
30 Su	00:25	2.7	82
	06:13	0.0	0
	12:38	2.4	73
	18:35	-0.2	-6
31 M	01:19	2.5	76
	07:13	0.1	3
	13:36	2.3	70
	19:36	-0.1	-3

June

Day	Time	ft	cm
1 Tu	02:13	2.4	73
	08:14	0.2	6
	14:36	2.2	67
	20:38	0.1	3
2 W	03:09	2.3	70
	09:15	0.2	6
	15:38	2.1	64
	21:39	0.2	6
3 Th	04:04	2.2	67
	10:12	0.2	6
	16:40	2.1	64
	22:36	0.3	9
4 F	04:57	2.1	64
	11:04	0.1	3
	17:37	2.1	64
	23:29	0.3	9
5 Sa	05:47	2.1	64
	11:51	0.1	3
	18:28	2.2	67
6 Su	00:17	0.3	9
	06:33	2.1	64
	12:34	0.0	0
	19:14	2.2	67
7 M	01:01	0.3	9
	07:16	2.1	64
	13:14	-0.1	-3
	19:56	2.3	70
8 Tu	01:42	0.3	9
	07:57	2.1	64
	13:53	-0.1	-3
	20:36	2.4	73
9 W	02:22	0.3	9
	08:37	2.1	64
	14:31	-0.1	-3
	21:16	2.4	73
10 Th	02:59	0.3	9
	09:17	2.2	67
	15:08	-0.1	-3
	21:55	2.4	73
11 F	03:37	0.3	9
	09:56	2.1	64
	15:44	-0.1	-3
	22:35	2.4	73
12 Sa	04:14	0.3	9
	10:36	2.1	64
	16:22	-0.1	-3
	23:15	2.4	73
13 Su	04:52	0.3	9
	11:18	2.1	64
	17:01	-0.1	-3
	23:57	2.3	70
14 M	05:33	0.3	9
	12:01	2.1	64
	17:43	0.0	0
15 Tu	00:39	2.3	70
	06:18	0.3	9
	12:48	2.1	64
	18:31	0.1	3
16 W	01:23	2.2	67
	07:08	0.3	9
	13:39	2.1	64
	19:25	0.1	3
17 Th	02:10	2.2	67
	08:03	0.2	6
	14:37	2.1	64
	20:25	0.2	6
18 F	03:01	2.2	67
	09:01	0.1	3
	15:39	2.2	67
	21:29	0.2	6
19 Sa	03:56	2.2	67
	10:01	-0.1	-3
	16:43	2.3	70
	22:32	0.2	6
20 Su	04:54	2.2	67
	10:59	-0.3	-9
	17:47	2.4	73
	23:32	0.1	3
21 M	05:54	2.3	70
	11:56	-0.4	-12
	18:48	2.6	79
22 Tu	00:30	0.0	0
	06:53	2.4	73
	12:51	-0.6	-18
	19:46	2.7	82
23 W	01:25	0.0	0
	07:51	2.5	76
	13:46	-0.7	-21
	20:41	2.8	85
24 Th	02:19	-0.1	-3
	08:46	2.6	79
	14:40	-0.7	-21
	21:33	2.8	85
25 F	03:12	-0.1	-3
	09:41	2.6	79
	15:33	-0.7	-21
	22:25	2.8	85
26 Sa	04:05	-0.1	-3
	10:34	2.6	79
	16:26	-0.6	-18
	23:15	2.7	82
27 Su	04:59	-0.1	-3
	11:26	2.5	76
	17:19	-0.4	-12
28 M	00:04	2.6	79
	05:53	0.0	0
	12:19	2.4	73
	18:13	-0.2	-6
29 Tu	00:52	2.5	76
	06:48	0.0	0
	13:12	2.3	70
	19:08	0.0	0
30 W	01:40	2.4	73
	07:43	0.1	3
	14:06	2.2	67
	20:04	0.1	3

StationId: 8723178
Source: NOAA/NOS/CO-OPS
Station Type: Primary
Time Zone: LST_LDT
Datum: MLLW

NOAA Tide Predictions

MIAMI BEACH, GOVERNMENT CUT, FL,2021

Times and Heights of High and Low Waters

July

Day	Time (h m)	Height (ft)	Height (cm)	Day	Time (h m)	Height (ft)	Height (cm)
1 Th ◑	02:28	2.2	67	**16** F	01:42	2.3	70
	08:38	0.1	3		07:37	0.0	0
	15:01	2.1	64		14:18	2.3	70
	21:00	0.3	9		20:02	0.2	6
2 F	03:16	2.1	64	**17** Sa ◑	02:32	2.3	70
	09:31	0.1	3		08:34	-0.1	-3
	15:57	2.1	64		15:18	2.3	70
	21:56	0.4	12		21:05	0.3	9
3 Sa	04:06	2.0	61	**18** Su	03:27	2.3	70
	10:22	0.1	3		09:35	-0.2	-6
	16:53	2.0	61		16:23	2.4	73
	22:49	0.5	15		22:09	0.3	9
4 Su	04:56	2.0	61	**19** M	04:28	2.3	70
	11:10	0.1	3		10:37	-0.2	-6
	17:46	2.1	64		17:28	2.4	73
	23:39	0.5	15		23:12	0.3	9
5 M	05:46	2.0	61	**20** Tu	05:33	2.3	70
	11:56	0.1	3		11:37	-0.3	-9
	18:36	2.1	64		18:32	2.5	76
6 Tu	00:26	0.4	12	**21** W	00:12	0.2	6
	06:35	2.0	61		06:36	2.4	73
	12:40	0.0	0		12:36	-0.4	-12
	19:23	2.2	67		19:31	2.6	79
7 W	01:10	0.4	12	**22** Th	01:10	0.1	3
	07:22	2.0	61		07:37	2.5	76
	13:23	0.0	0		13:32	-0.5	-15
	20:08	2.3	70		20:27	2.7	82
8 Th	01:52	0.4	12	**23** F	02:04	0.0	0
	08:08	2.1	64		08:34	2.6	79
	14:03	-0.1	-3		14:26	-0.5	-15
	20:51	2.3	70		21:18	2.8	85
9 F	02:33	0.3	9	**24** Sa ○	02:57	0.0	0
	08:52	2.1	64		09:27	2.6	79
	14:43	-0.1	-3		15:18	-0.5	-15
	21:32	2.4	73		22:06	2.8	85
10 Sa ●	03:12	0.3	9	**25** Su	03:48	-0.1	-3
	09:34	2.2	67		10:18	2.6	79
	15:22	-0.1	-3		16:08	-0.4	-12
	22:13	2.4	73		22:52	2.8	85
11 Su	03:51	0.3	9	**26** M	04:38	-0.1	-3
	10:17	2.2	67		11:07	2.6	79
	16:01	-0.1	-3		16:57	-0.2	-6
	22:54	2.4	73		23:37	2.7	82
12 M	04:31	0.2	6	**27** Tu	05:27	0.0	0
	11:00	2.2	67		11:55	2.5	76
	16:42	-0.1	-3		17:46	-0.1	-3
	23:34	2.4	73				
13 Tu	05:12	0.2	6	**28** W	00:19	2.6	79
	11:45	2.2	67		06:15	0.0	0
	17:25	-0.1	-3		12:42	2.4	73
					18:35	0.1	3
14 W	00:15	2.4	73	**29** Th	01:01	2.4	73
	05:56	0.1	3		07:03	0.1	3
	12:32	2.3	70		13:29	2.3	70
	18:12	0.0	0		19:24	0.3	9
15 Th	00:57	2.4	73	**30** F	01:43	2.3	70
	06:44	0.1	3		07:52	0.2	6
	13:23	2.3	70		14:18	2.2	67
	19:05	0.1	3		20:16	0.5	15
				31 Sa ◑	02:27	2.2	67
					08:43	0.3	9
					15:09	2.1	64
					21:10	0.6	18

August

Day	Time (h m)	Height (ft)	Height (cm)	Day	Time (h m)	Height (ft)	Height (cm)
1 Su	03:13	2.1	64	**16** M	03:07	2.4	73
	09:35	0.3	9		09:16	0.0	0
	16:04	2.1	64		16:07	2.5	76
	22:05	0.7	21		21:53	0.5	15
2 M	04:05	2.0	61	**17** Tu	04:13	2.4	73
	10:27	0.3	9		10:22	0.0	0
	17:01	2.1	64		17:15	2.6	79
	22:58	0.7	21		22:59	0.5	15
3 Tu	05:00	2.0	61	**18** W	05:22	2.4	73
	11:18	0.3	9		11:26	0.0	0
	17:57	2.1	64		18:20	2.6	79
	23:50	0.7	21				
4 W	05:57	2.0	61	**19** Th	00:01	0.5	15
	12:07	0.2	6		06:28	2.5	76
	18:50	2.2	67		12:26	-0.1	-3
					19:19	2.7	82
5 Th	00:38	0.6	18	**20** F	00:58	0.4	12
	06:50	2.1	64		07:28	2.7	82
	12:53	0.2	6		13:22	-0.1	-3
	19:38	2.3	70		20:12	2.8	85
6 F	01:23	0.5	15	**21** Sa	01:51	0.2	6
	07:40	2.2	67		08:22	2.8	85
	13:36	0.1	3		14:13	-0.1	-3
	20:23	2.4	73		21:00	2.9	88
7 Sa	02:05	0.4	12	**22** Su ○	02:41	0.2	6
	08:27	2.3	70		09:13	2.8	85
	14:18	0.0	0		15:02	-0.1	-3
	21:06	2.6	79		21:44	2.9	88
8 Su ●	02:46	0.3	9	**23** M	03:27	0.1	3
	09:12	2.4	73		09:59	2.9	88
	14:59	0.0	0		15:48	0.0	0
	21:47	2.6	79		22:25	2.9	88
9 M	03:26	0.2	6	**24** Tu	04:12	0.1	3
	09:56	2.5	76		10:44	2.8	85
	15:40	-0.1	-3		16:32	0.1	3
	22:27	2.7	82		23:04	2.8	85
10 Tu	04:06	0.2	6	**25** W	04:55	0.1	3
	10:41	2.6	79		11:26	2.8	85
	16:22	0.0	0		17:15	0.2	6
	23:07	2.7	82		23:42	2.7	82
11 W	04:48	0.1	3	**26** Th	05:37	0.2	6
	11:26	2.6	79		12:08	2.7	82
	17:06	0.0	0		17:58	0.4	12
	23:48	2.7	82				
12 Th	05:32	0.0	0	**27** F	00:20	2.6	79
	12:14	2.6	79		06:19	0.3	9
	17:54	0.1	3		12:50	2.6	79
					18:42	0.6	18
13 F	00:31	2.6	79	**28** Sa	00:58	2.4	73
	06:20	0.0	0		07:03	0.4	12
	13:05	2.6	79		13:34	2.4	73
	18:45	0.3	9		19:29	0.8	24
14 Sa	01:17	2.5	76	**29** Su	01:39	2.3	70
	07:13	0.0	0		07:50	0.5	15
	14:00	2.6	79		14:22	2.3	70
	19:43	0.4	12		20:20	0.9	27
15 Su ◑	02:09	2.5	76	**30** M ◑	02:25	2.2	67
	08:02	0.0	0		08:43	0.6	18
	15:01	2.5	76		15:16	2.3	70
	20:46	0.5	15		21:17	1.0	30
				31 Tu	03:18	2.2	67
					09:41	0.6	18
					16:15	2.3	70
					22:16	1.0	30

September

Day	Time (h m)	Height (ft)	Height (cm)	Day	Time (h m)	Height (ft)	Height (cm)
1 W	04:18	2.2	67	**16** Th	05:15	2.7	82
	10:39	0.6	18		11:17	0.3	9
	17:17	2.3	70		18:07	2.8	85
	23:13	0.9	27		23:52	0.7	21
2 Th	05:21	2.2	67	**17** F	06:21	2.8	85
	11:33	0.6	18		12:17	0.3	9
	18:14	2.4	73		19:03	2.9	88
3 F	00:05	0.9	27	**18** Sa	00:47	0.5	15
	06:19	2.3	70		07:18	2.9	88
	12:22	0.5	15		13:10	0.3	9
	19:05	2.5	76		19:52	3.0	91
4 Sa	00:51	0.7	21	**19** Su	01:36	0.4	12
	07:13	2.5	76		08:09	3.0	91
	13:08	0.3	9		13:58	0.2	6
	19:52	2.7	82		20:36	3.0	91
5 Su	01:35	0.6	18	**20** M ○	02:21	0.3	9
	08:02	2.7	82		08:55	3.1	94
	13:51	0.2	6		14:42	0.3	9
	20:35	2.8	85		21:17	3.0	91
6 M	02:16	0.4	12	**21** Tu	03:03	0.3	9
	08:48	2.8	85		09:38	3.1	94
	14:34	0.2	6		15:24	0.3	9
	21:16	2.9	88		21:54	3.0	91
7 Tu ●	02:57	0.3	9	**22** W	03:42	0.3	9
	09:34	2.9	88		10:18	3.1	94
	15:17	0.1	3		16:04	0.4	12
	21:57	3.0	91		22:30	2.9	88
8 W	03:38	0.1	3	**23** Th	04:20	0.3	9
	10:19	3.0	91		10:56	3.0	91
	16:00	0.1	3		16:43	0.6	18
	22:38	3.0	91		23:05	2.9	88
9 Th	04:21	0.0	0	**24** F	04:58	0.4	12
	11:06	3.1	94		11:34	2.9	88
	16:46	0.2	6		17:22	0.7	21
	23:21	3.0	91		23:40	2.7	82
10 F	05:07	0.0	0	**25** Sa	05:36	0.5	15
	11:55	3.1	94		12:13	2.8	85
	17:35	0.3	9		18:01	0.8	24
11 Sa	00:06	2.9	88	**26** Su	00:17	2.6	79
	05:57	0.0	0		06:15	0.6	18
	12:46	3.0	91		12:54	2.7	82
	18:27	0.5	15		18:43	1.0	30
12 Su	00:55	2.8	85	**27** M	00:57	2.5	76
	06:52	0.1	3		06:59	0.7	21
	13:43	2.9	88		13:41	2.5	76
	19:26	0.6	18		19:31	1.1	34
13 M ◑	01:51	2.7	82	**28** Tu	01:43	2.4	73
	07:54	0.2	6		07:51	0.8	24
	14:45	2.8	85		14:34	2.5	76
	20:32	0.8	24		20:29	1.2	37
14 Tu	02:54	2.6	79	**29** W ◑	02:38	2.3	70
	09:02	0.3	9		08:52	0.9	27
	15:53	2.7	82		15:34	2.4	73
	21:42	0.8	24		21:33	1.2	37
15 W	04:04	2.6	79	**30** Th	03:41	2.3	70
	10:12	0.3	9		09:56	0.9	27
	17:02	2.8	85		16:36	2.5	76
	22:50	0.8	24		22:35	1.1	34

StationId: 8723178
Source: NOAA/NOS/CO-OPS
Station Type: Primary
Time Zone: LST_LDT
Datum: MLLW

MIAMI BEACH, GOVERNMENT CUT, FL, 2021

Times and Heights of High and Low Waters

October

Day	Time (h m)	Height (ft)	Height (cm)	Day	Time (h m)	Height (ft)	Height (cm)
1 F	04:47	2.4	73	16 Sa	06:09	2.9	88
	10:55	0.8	24		12:03	0.5	15
	17:35	2.6	79		18:40	2.9	88
	23:29	1.0	30				
2 Sa	05:48	2.5	76	17 Su	00:30	0.6	18
	11:48	0.7	21		07:04	3.0	91
	18:28	2.7	82		12:53	0.5	15
					19:27	3.0	91
3 Su	00:17	0.8	24	18 M	01:15	0.5	15
	06:44	2.7	82		07:52	3.0	91
	12:37	0.6	18		13:38	0.5	15
	19:15	2.9	88		20:08	3.0	91
4 M	01:02	0.6	18	19 Tu	01:57	0.4	12
	07:35	2.9	88		08:34	3.1	94
	13:23	0.4	12		14:20	0.5	15
	19:59	3.0	91		20:46	3.0	91
5 Tu	01:44	0.4	12	20 W ○	02:35	0.3	9
	08:23	3.1	94		09:13	3.1	94
	14:08	0.3	9		14:59	0.6	18
	20:42	3.1	94		21:22	2.9	88
6 W ●	02:27	0.2	6	21 Th	03:12	0.3	9
	09:10	3.3	101		09:51	3.1	94
	14:53	0.3	9		15:36	0.6	18
	21:26	3.2	98		21:57	2.9	88
7 Th	03:11	0.0	0	22 F	03:48	0.4	12
	09:57	3.4	104		10:27	3.0	91
	15:39	0.3	9		16:13	0.7	21
	22:10	3.2	98		22:31	2.8	85
8 F	03:57	0.0	0	23 Sa	04:23	0.4	12
	10:46	3.4	104		11:04	2.9	88
	16:26	0.4	12		16:49	0.8	24
	22:56	3.2	98		23:06	2.7	82
9 Sa	04:45	0.0	0	24 Su	04:59	0.5	15
	11:36	3.3	101		11:42	2.8	85
	17:16	0.5	15		17:25	0.9	27
	23:45	3.1	94		23:43	2.6	79
10 Su	05:37	0.1	3	25 M	05:36	0.6	18
	12:29	3.2	98		12:22	2.7	82
	18:11	0.6	18		18:05	1.0	30
11 M	00:38	3.0	91	26 Tu	00:24	2.5	76
	06:34	0.2	6		06:17	0.7	21
	13:27	3.1	94		13:08	2.6	79
	19:12	0.8	24		18:50	1.1	34
12 Tu	01:38	2.8	85	27 W	01:10	2.4	73
	07:39	0.4	12		07:05	0.8	24
	14:30	2.9	88		13:58	2.5	76
	20:20	0.9	27		19:46	1.2	37
13 W	02:44	2.8	85	28 Th ◑	02:04	2.4	73
	08:50	0.5	15		08:04	0.9	27
	15:38	2.9	88		14:55	2.5	76
	21:32	0.9	27		20:50	1.2	37
14 Th	03:56	2.7	82	29 F	03:07	2.4	73
	10:00	0.6	18		09:10	0.9	27
	16:45	2.8	85		15:54	2.5	76
	22:39	0.8	24		21:53	1.0	30
15 F	05:06	2.8	85	30 Sa	04:13	2.4	73
	11:05	0.6	18		10:14	0.8	24
	17:46	2.9	88		16:52	2.6	79
	23:38	0.7	21		22:50	0.9	27
				31 Su	05:16	2.6	79
					11:12	0.7	21
					17:45	2.7	82
					23:40	0.6	18

November

Day	Time (h m)	Height (ft)	Height (cm)	Day	Time (h m)	Height (ft)	Height (cm)
1 M	06:14	2.8	85	16 Tu	06:29	2.8	85
	12:04	0.6	18		12:14	0.6	18
	18:35	2.8	85		18:36	2.7	82
2 Tu	00:28	0.4	12	17 W	00:29	0.2	6
	07:08	3.0	91		07:10	2.9	88
	12:54	0.5	15		12:55	0.5	15
	19:23	3.0	91		19:15	2.7	82
3 W	01:14	0.1	3	18 Th	01:07	0.2	6
	07:58	3.2	98		07:48	2.9	88
	13:42	0.3	9		13:33	0.5	15
	20:10	3.1	94		19:51	2.7	82
4 Th ●	02:00	-0.1	-3	19 F ○	01:44	0.2	6
	08:48	3.4	104		08:25	2.9	88
	14:30	0.3	9		14:10	0.6	18
	20:57	3.1	94		20:27	2.6	79
5 F	02:47	-0.2	-6	20 Sa	02:19	0.2	6
	09:37	3.4	104		09:02	2.8	85
	15:18	0.3	9		14:46	0.6	18
	21:45	3.2	98		21:03	2.6	79
6 Sa	03:35	-0.2	-6	21 Su	02:54	0.3	9
	10:27	3.4	104		09:39	2.8	85
	16:08	0.3	9		15:22	0.7	21
	22:35	3.1	94		21:40	2.5	76
7 Su	03:26	-0.2	-6	22 M	03:30	0.3	9
	10:19	3.3	101		10:18	2.7	82
	16:00	0.4	12		15:58	0.7	21
	22:27	3.0	91		22:19	2.4	73
8 M	04:21	-0.1	-3	23 Tu	04:07	0.4	12
	11:13	3.2	98		10:58	2.6	79
	16:56	0.5	15		16:37	0.8	24
	23:24	2.9	88		23:00	2.3	70
9 Tu	05:20	0.1	3	24 W	04:46	0.5	15
	12:11	3.0	91		11:41	2.5	76
	17:58	0.6	18		17:21	0.8	24
					23:45	2.3	70
10 W	00:25	2.8	85	25 Th	05:32	0.6	18
	06:24	0.3	9		12:28	2.4	73
	13:12	2.9	88		18:11	0.8	24
	19:06	0.7	21				
11 Th ◐	01:30	2.7	82	26 F	00:37	2.2	67
	07:33	0.4	12		06:26	0.6	18
	14:15	2.8	85		13:18	2.4	73
	20:15	0.7	21		19:09	0.8	24
12 F	02:39	2.6	79	27 Sa ◑	01:36	2.2	67
	08:42	0.5	15		07:27	0.6	18
	15:18	2.7	82		14:11	2.4	73
	21:19	0.6	18		20:10	0.7	21
13 Sa	03:47	2.6	79	28 Su	02:40	2.3	70
	09:45	0.6	18		08:32	0.6	18
	16:22	2.7	82		15:06	2.4	73
	22:16	0.5	15		21:08	0.5	15
14 Su	04:49	2.7	82	29 M	03:43	2.4	73
	10:41	0.6	18		09:34	0.5	15
	17:09	2.7	82		16:02	2.5	76
	23:05	0.4	12		22:03	0.3	9
15 M	05:42	2.8	85	30 Tu	04:44	2.6	79
	11:30	0.6	18		10:32	0.4	12
	17:55	2.7	82		16:56	2.6	79
	23:49	0.3	9		22:55	0.0	0

December

Day	Time (h m)	Height (ft)	Height (cm)	Day	Time (h m)	Height (ft)	Height (cm)
1 W	05:41	2.8	85	16 Th	00:00	0.0	0
	11:26	0.3	9		06:43	2.5	76
	17:50	2.7	82		12:29	0.4	12
	23:46	-0.2	-6		18:43	2.3	70
2 Th	06:36	3.0	91	17 F	00:40	0.0	0
	12:18	0.2	6		07:23	2.5	76
	18:42	2.8	85		13:08	0.4	12
					19:23	2.3	70
3 F	00:36	-0.4	-12	18 Sa	01:19	0.0	0
	07:28	3.1	94		08:02	2.5	76
	13:09	0.1	3		13:46	0.4	12
	19:34	2.9	88		20:02	2.3	70
4 Sa ●	01:27	-0.5	-15	19 Su ○	01:56	0.0	0
	08:20	3.2	98		08:40	2.5	76
	14:00	0.1	3		14:24	0.4	12
	20:26	2.9	88		20:41	2.3	70
5 Su	02:19	-0.5	-15	20 M	02:32	0.0	0
	09:12	3.2	98		09:19	2.5	76
	14:52	0.1	3		15:00	0.4	12
	21:19	2.9	88		21:20	2.2	67
6 M	03:12	-0.5	-15	21 Tu	03:08	0.0	0
	10:04	3.1	94		09:58	2.4	73
	15:45	0.1	3		15:37	0.4	12
	22:13	2.8	85		22:00	2.2	67
7 Tu	04:06	-0.3	-9	22 W	03:45	0.0	0
	10:57	3.0	91		10:37	2.4	73
	16:41	0.2	6		16:15	0.4	12
	23:09	2.7	82		22:41	2.1	64
8 W	05:04	-0.1	-3	23 Th	04:24	0.1	3
	11:51	2.8	85		11:17	2.3	70
	17:41	0.3	9		16:56	0.4	12
					23:26	2.1	64
9 Th	00:08	2.6	79	24 F	05:07	0.2	6
	06:05	0.0	0		11:59	2.3	70
	12:46	2.7	82		17:42	0.3	9
	18:44	0.3	9				
10 F	01:09	2.5	76	25 Sa	00:14	2.1	64
	07:09	0.2	6		05:56	0.2	6
	13:43	2.5	76		12:43	2.2	67
	19:48	0.3	9		18:33	0.3	9
11 Sa ◐	02:13	2.4	73	26 Su	01:09	2.1	64
	08:13	0.4	12		06:53	0.3	9
	14:40	2.4	73		13:31	2.2	67
	20:48	0.3	9		19:30	0.2	6
12 Su	03:17	2.3	70	27 M ◑	02:08	2.1	64
	09:14	0.4	12		07:55	0.3	9
	15:36	2.3	70		14:23	2.2	67
	21:43	0.2	6		20:29	0.0	0
13 M	04:18	2.3	70	28 Tu	03:12	2.2	67
	10:10	0.5	15		09:00	0.3	9
	16:29	2.3	70		15:21	2.2	67
	22:33	0.2	6		21:29	-0.1	-3
14 Tu	05:12	2.4	73	29 W	04:16	2.3	70
	11:01	0.5	15		10:02	0.2	6
	17:17	2.3	70		16:22	2.2	67
	23:18	0.1	3		22:27	-0.3	-9
15 W	06:00	2.4	73	30 Th	05:19	2.5	76
	11:46	0.5	15		11:01	0.1	3
	18:02	2.3	70		17:22	2.3	70
					23:23	-0.5	-15
				31 F	06:17	2.6	79
					11:58	0.0	0
					18:21	2.4	73

StationId: 8723970
Source: NOAA/NOS/CO-OPS
Station Type: Primary
Time Zone: LST_LDT
Datum: MLLW

Vaca Key, Florida Bay, FL, 2021

Times and Heights of High and Low Waters

January

Day	Time	ft	cm
1 F	01:46	1.0	30
	08:02	-0.3	-9
2 Sa	02:39	1.0	30
	08:47	-0.2	-6
	18:05	0.6	18
	20:25	0.5	15
3 Su	03:30	0.9	27
	09:33	-0.2	-6
	18:09	0.5	15
	21:24	0.4	12
4 M	04:21	0.9	27
	10:20	-0.1	-3
	18:03	0.6	18
	22:28	0.3	9
5 Tu	05:14	0.7	21
	11:06	0.0	0
	18:24	0.6	18
	23:35	0.2	6
6 W ◑	06:13	0.6	18
	11:51	0.2	6
	18:54	0.7	21
7 Th	00:45	0.1	3
	07:28	0.4	12
	12:36	0.3	9
	19:27	0.7	21
8 F	01:54	-0.1	-3
	20:04	0.8	24
9 Sa	03:01	-0.2	-6
	20:43	0.9	27
10 Su	04:01	-0.3	-9
	21:25	0.9	27
11 M	04:53	-0.3	-9
	22:15	0.9	27
12 Tu	05:40	-0.4	-12
	23:19	0.9	27
13 W ●	06:25	-0.3	-9
14 Th	00:31	0.9	27
	07:08	-0.3	-9
15 F	01:38	0.8	24
	07:52	-0.3	-9
	17:09	0.4	12
	19:24	0.3	9
16 Sa	02:35	0.8	24
	08:35	-0.2	-6
	17:34	0.4	12
	20:23	0.2	6
17 Su	03:26	0.7	21
	09:19	-0.2	-6
	17:33	0.4	12
	21:24	0.2	6
18 M	04:15	0.6	18
	10:03	-0.1	-3
	17:09	0.5	15
	22:29	0.1	3
19 Tu	05:04	0.5	15
	10:47	0.0	0
	17:35	0.6	18
	23:35	0.0	0
20 W ◑	05:56	0.3	9
	11:30	0.0	0
	18:11	0.6	18
21 Th	00:41	-0.1	-3
	09:41	0.2	6
	12:14	0.1	3
	18:52	0.6	18
22 F	01:47	-0.2	-6
	19:35	0.6	18
23 Sa	02:48	-0.3	-9
	20:20	0.6	18
24 Su	03:38	-0.4	-12
	21:06	0.6	18
25 M	04:19	-0.4	-12
	21:51	0.7	21
26 Tu	04:57	-0.4	-12
	22:40	0.7	21
27 W	05:36	-0.4	-12
	23:36	0.7	21
28 Th ○	06:16	-0.4	-12
29 F	00:39	0.7	21
	06:58	-0.4	-12
30 Sa	01:41	0.8	24
	07:40	-0.3	-9
	16:49	0.4	12
	19:21	0.2	6
31 Su	02:37	0.7	21
	08:23	-0.2	-6
	16:53	0.4	12
	20:17	0.1	3

February

Day	Time	ft	cm
1 M	03:30	0.7	21
	09:06	-0.2	-6
	16:48	0.4	12
	21:15	0.0	0
2 Tu	04:22	0.6	18
	09:48	-0.1	-3
	17:05	0.5	15
	22:16	-0.1	-3
3 W	05:15	0.4	12
	10:29	0.0	0
	17:32	0.6	18
	23:19	-0.2	-6
4 Th ◐	06:15	0.2	6
	11:09	0.1	3
	18:06	0.6	18
5 F	00:25	-0.3	-9
	18:44	0.6	18
6 Sa	01:32	-0.4	-12
	19:28	0.7	21
7 Su	02:40	-0.4	-12
	20:18	0.7	21
8 M	03:43	-0.5	-15
	21:13	0.7	21
9 Tu	04:38	-0.4	-12
	22:15	0.7	21
10 W	05:24	-0.4	-12
	23:27	0.7	21
11 Th ●	06:06	-0.3	-9
	15:25	0.3	9
	17:31	0.2	6
12 F ○	00:46	0.6	18
	06:45	-0.3	-9
	15:54	0.3	9
	18:25	0.1	3
13 Sa	01:52	0.6	18
	07:25	-0.2	-6
	16:18	0.3	9
	19:19	0.1	3
14 Su	02:43	0.6	18
	08:05	-0.2	-6
	16:20	0.4	12
	20:12	0.0	0
15 M	03:28	0.5	15
	08:46	-0.1	-3
	15:58	0.4	12
	21:06	-0.1	-3
16 Tu	04:10	0.4	12
	09:26	-0.1	-3
	16:19	0.5	15
	22:00	-0.2	-6
17 W	04:54	0.3	9
	10:06	-0.1	-3
	16:52	0.5	15
	22:54	-0.3	-9
18 Th	05:41	0.2	6
	10:45	0.0	0
	17:29	0.5	15
	23:49	-0.4	-12
19 F ◐	18:10	0.5	15
20 Sa	00:45	-0.5	-15
	18:55	0.5	15
21 Su	01:43	-0.5	-15
	19:42	0.5	15
22 M	02:42	-0.5	-15
	20:31	0.5	15
23 Tu	03:37	-0.5	-15
	21:24	0.5	15
24 W	04:26	-0.4	-12
	22:21	0.6	18
25 Th	05:11	-0.4	-12
	23:29	0.6	18
26 F	05:52	-0.3	-9
	15:16	0.3	9
	17:29	0.2	6
27 Sa ○	00:42	0.7	21
	06:33	-0.2	-6
	15:37	0.4	12
	18:20	0.1	3
28 Su	01:51	0.7	21
	07:14	-0.1	-3
	15:44	0.4	12
	19:13	0.0	0

March

Day	Time	ft	cm
1 M	02:51	0.6	18
	07:54	0.0	0
	15:37	0.4	12
	20:07	-0.1	-3
2 Tu	03:45	0.6	18
	08:33	0.0	0
	15:51	0.5	15
	21:03	-0.3	-9
3 W	04:38	0.4	12
	09:12	0.0	0
	16:17	0.6	18
	22:01	-0.4	-12
4 Th	05:37	0.3	9
	09:49	0.1	3
	16:49	0.6	18
	23:00	-0.5	-15
5 F	17:27	0.7	21
6 Sa ○	00:02	-0.5	-15
	18:11	0.7	21
7 Su	01:07	-0.5	-15
	19:03	0.6	18
8 M	02:15	-0.5	-15
	20:01	0.6	18
9 Tu	03:21	-0.4	-12
	21:07	0.6	18
10 W	07:34	-0.3	-9
	22:27	0.5	15
11 Th	05:02	-0.2	-6
	14:09	0.3	9
	16:39	0.2	6
12 F	00:55	0.5	15
	05:41	-0.1	-3
	14:39	0.4	12
	17:33	0.1	3
13 Sa ●	01:56	0.6	18
	06:17	-0.1	-3
	15:04	0.4	12
	18:23	0.0	0
14 Su	03:45	0.5	15
	07:54	0.0	0
	16:12	0.4	12
	20:10	0.0	0
15 M	04:26	0.5	15
	08:31	0.0	0
	15:45	0.5	15
	20:56	-0.1	-3
16 Tu	04:58	0.4	12
	09:09	0.0	0
	16:04	0.6	18
	21:42	-0.3	-9
17 W	05:24	0.4	12
	09:47	0.1	3
	16:35	0.6	18
	22:29	-0.4	-12
18 Th	05:55	0.3	9
	10:24	0.1	3
	17:12	0.6	18
	23:16	-0.5	-15
19 F	06:35	0.2	6
	11:01	0.1	3
	17:51	0.6	18
20 Sa	00:06	-0.5	-15
	18:32	0.6	18
21 Su ◐	00:58	-0.5	-15
	19:17	0.5	15
22 M	01:54	-0.5	-15
	20:06	0.5	15
23 Tu	02:54	-0.4	-12
	21:00	0.5	15
24 W	03:55	-0.3	-9
	22:00	0.6	18
25 Th	04:51	-0.2	-6
	23:10	0.6	18
26 F	05:40	-0.1	-3
	14:59	0.4	12
	17:27	0.3	9
27 Sa	00:36	0.6	18
	06:22	0.0	0
	15:20	0.4	12
	18:20	0.2	6
28 Su ○	02:25	0.7	21
	07:02	0.1	3
	15:28	0.5	15
	19:11	0.0	0
29 M	03:39	0.7	21
	07:40	0.2	6
	15:17	0.5	15
	20:02	-0.1	-3
30 Tu	04:40	0.6	18
	08:17	0.3	9
	15:31	0.6	18
	20:55	-0.3	-9
31 W	05:40	0.5	15
	08:55	0.3	9
	15:59	0.7	21
	21:48	-0.4	-12

StationId: 8723970
Source: NOAA/NOS/CO-OPS
Station Type: Primary
Time Zone: LST_LDT
Datum: MLLW

NOAA Tide Predictions

Vaca Key, Florida Bay, FL,2021

Times and Heights of High and Low Waters

April

Day	Time	ft	cm	Day	Time	ft	cm
1 Th	06:48	0.4	12	16 F	07:04	0.4	12
	09:31	0.3	9		09:42	0.3	9
	16:34	0.8	24		16:35	0.7	21
	22:43	-0.5	-15		22:43	-0.5	-15
2 F	17:13	0.8	24	17 Sa	17:15	0.7	21
	23:40	-0.5	-15		23:30	-0.5	-15
3 Sa	17:57	0.8	24	18 Su	17:57	0.7	21
4 Su	00:39	-0.5	-15	19 M	00:21	-0.5	-15
	18:47	0.7	21		18:42	0.7	21
5 M	01:40	-0.4	-12	20 Tu	01:15	-0.4	-12
	19:43	0.7	21		19:33	0.7	21
6 Tu	02:44	-0.3	-9	21 W	02:14	-0.3	-9
	20:48	0.6	18		20:32	0.6	18
7 W	03:49	-0.2	-6	22 Th	03:14	-0.1	-3
	13:16	0.3	9		13:10	0.5	15
	15:33	0.3	9		15:14	0.4	12
	22:09	0.5	15		21:42	0.6	18
8 Th	04:46	-0.1	-3	23 F	04:12	0.0	0
	13:49	0.4	12		13:35	0.5	15
	16:51	0.2	6		16:20	0.3	9
					23:08	0.6	18
9	01:16	0.6	18	24 Sa	05:01	0.2	6
	05:31	0.0	0		13:55	0.6	18
	14:21	0.5	15		17:18	0.2	6
	17:50	0.2	6				
10 Sa	02:18	0.6	18	25 Su	02:04	0.7	21
	06:09	0.1	3		05:44	0.3	9
	14:47	0.5	15		13:54	0.6	18
	18:36	0.1	3		18:10	0.1	3
11 Su	03:12	0.6	18	26 M	03:12	0.7	21
	06:44	0.2	6		06:23	0.4	12
	15:00	0.6	18		13:32	0.7	21
	19:17	0.0	0		19:00	-0.1	-3
12	04:01	0.6	18	27 Tu	04:12	0.7	21
	07:19	0.3	9		07:00	0.5	15
	14:20	0.6	18		13:54	0.8	24
	19:55	-0.1	-3		19:50	-0.2	-6
13	04:47	0.6	18	28 W	05:09	0.7	21
	07:54	0.3	9		07:37	0.5	15
	14:42	0.7	21		14:30	0.9	27
	20:35	-0.2	-6		20:40	-0.3	-9
14	05:31	0.5	15	29 Th	06:06	0.6	18
	08:30	0.3	9		08:13	0.5	15
	15:17	0.7	21		15:13	1.0	30
	21:16	-0.3	-9		21:32	-0.4	-12
15	06:14	0.4	12	30 F	15:59	1.0	30
	09:06	0.3	9		22:25	-0.4	-12
	15:55	0.7	21				
	21:58	-0.4	-12				

May

Day	Time	ft	cm	Day	Time	ft	cm
1 Sa	16:46	1.0	30	16 Su	16:45	0.9	27
	23:18	-0.4	-12		23:01	-0.4	-12
2 Su	17:35	0.9	27	17 M	17:29	0.8	24
					23:50	-0.3	-9
3 M	00:14	-0.3	-9	18 Tu	18:15	0.8	24
	18:28	0.8	24				
4 Tu	01:11	-0.2	-6	19 W	00:43	-0.2	-6
	19:26	0.7	21		19:09	0.7	21
5 W	02:10	-0.1	-3	20 Th	01:38	-0.1	-3
	11:47	0.4	12		11:31	0.5	15
	14:15	0.3	9		13:46	0.4	12
	20:35	0.6	18		20:12	0.7	21
6 Th	03:09	0.0	0	21 F	02:34	0.1	3
	12:23	0.5	15		11:57	0.6	18
	15:57	0.3	9		15:00	0.4	12
					21:30	0.6	18
7 F	00:07	0.5	15	22 Sa	03:29	0.2	6
	04:05	0.2	6		12:05	0.6	18
	12:56	0.6	18		16:07	0.2	6
	17:24	0.2	6				
8 Sa	01:20	0.6	18	23 Su	01:09	0.6	18
	04:52	0.3	9		04:17	0.4	12
	13:24	0.7	21		11:16	0.7	21
	18:06	0.1	3		17:05	0.1	3
9 Su	02:20	0.6	18	24 M	02:23	0.7	21
	05:32	0.3	9		05:01	0.5	15
	13:34	0.7	21		11:36	0.8	24
	18:35	0.0	0		17:58	-0.1	-3
10 M	03:13	0.6	18	25 Tu	03:24	0.7	21
	06:07	0.4	12		05:40	0.6	18
	12:39	0.8	24		12:03	0.9	27
	19:04	-0.1	-3		18:47	-0.2	-6
11 Tu	04:03	0.6	18	26 W	10:33	1.0	30
	06:42	0.4	12		19:36	-0.3	-9
	13:12	0.8	24				
	19:36	-0.1	-3				
12 W	04:50	0.6	18	27 Th	13:39	1.1	34
	07:15	0.5	15		20:25	-0.3	-9
	13:53	0.8	24				
	20:11	-0.2	-6				
13 Th	05:36	0.6	18	28 F	14:39	1.1	34
	07:50	0.5	15		21:14	-0.4	-12
	14:35	0.9	27				
	20:49	-0.3	-9				
14 F	06:22	0.5	15	29 Sa	15:35	1.1	34
	08:26	0.4	12		22:04	-0.3	-9
	15:19	0.9	27				
	21:30	-0.4	-12				
15 Sa	16:02	0.9	27	30 Su	16:27	1.0	30
	22:14	-0.4	-12		22:55	-0.3	-9
				31 M	17:19	0.9	27
					23:46	-0.2	-6

June

Day	Time	ft	cm	Day	Time	ft	cm
1 Tu	18:12	0.8	24	16 W	08:37	0.6	18
					11:12	0.5	15
					17:59	0.9	27
2 W	00:38	-0.1	-3	17 Th	00:12	-0.1	-3
	10:05	0.5	15		08:06	0.6	18
	12:44	0.4	12		12:19	0.4	12
	19:11	0.7	21		18:54	0.8	24
3 Th	01:31	0.1	3	18 F	01:02	0.1	3
	10:44	0.6	18		08:31	0.6	18
	14:21	0.3	9		13:31	0.3	9
	20:21	0.5	15		20:00	0.6	18
4 F	02:26	0.2	6	19 Sa	01:53	0.2	6
	11:18	0.6	18		09:03	0.7	21
	16:57	0.2	6		14:42	0.2	6
					23:54	0.5	15
5 Sa	00:06	0.5	15	20 Su	02:42	0.4	12
	03:20	0.3	9		09:35	0.8	24
	11:42	0.7	21		15:49	0.1	3
	17:58	0.1	3				
6 Su	01:15	0.6	18	21 M	01:23	0.6	18
	04:09	0.4	12		03:30	0.5	15
	10:33	0.8	24		10:08	0.9	27
	18:15	0.0	0		16:50	0.0	0
7 M	02:15	0.6	18	22 Tu	10:40	1.0	30
	04:52	0.5	15		17:44	-0.2	-6
	11:08	0.8	24				
	18:22	-0.1	-3				
8 Tu	03:08	0.6	18	23 W	11:16	1.1	34
	05:29	0.5	15		18:33	-0.2	-6
	11:47	0.9	27				
	18:44	-0.1	-3				
9 W	03:58	0.6	18	24 Th	12:05	1.1	34
	06:04	0.5	15		19:21	-0.3	-9
	12:28	0.9	27				
	19:13	-0.2	-6				
10 Th	13:13	0.9	27	25 F	13:13	1.2	37
	19:47	-0.2	-6		20:07	-0.3	-9
11 F	14:01	0.9	27	26 Sa	14:21	1.1	34
	20:25	-0.3	-9		20:54	-0.2	-6
12 Sa	14:49	0.9	27	27 Su	15:22	1.1	34
	21:06	-0.3	-9		21:41	-0.1	-3
13 Su	15:37	1.0	30	28 M	16:16	1.0	30
	21:49	-0.3	-9		22:28	-0.1	-3
14 M	16:23	0.9	27	29 Tu	07:39	0.5	15
	22:35	-0.3	-9		10:05	0.4	12
					17:08	0.9	27
					23:15	0.0	0
15 Tu	08:09	0.5	15	30 W	08:05	0.6	18
	10:11	0.5	15		11:15	0.4	12
	17:10	0.9	27		18:00	0.8	24
	23:23	-0.2	-6				

StationId: 8723970
Source: NOAA/NOS/CO-OPS
Station Type: Primary
Time Zone: LST_LDT
Datum: MLLW

NOAA Tide Predictions

Vaca Key, Florida Bay, FL,2021

Times and Heights of High and Low Waters

July

Day	Time	ft	cm
1 Th ◐	00:03	0.1	3
	07:13	0.6	18
	12:32	0.3	9
	18:55	0.6	18
2 F	00:51	0.2	6
	07:38	0.7	21
	14:00	0.2	6
	20:04	0.5	15
3 Sa	01:41	0.3	9
	08:17	0.8	24
	15:58	0.1	3
	23:57	0.5	15
4 Su	02:33	0.4	12
	09:00	0.8	24
	17:24	0.0	0
5 M	01:07	0.5	15
	03:24	0.5	15
	09:44	0.9	27
	17:49	0.0	0
6 Tu	02:06	0.6	18
	04:10	0.5	15
	10:27	0.9	27
	17:56	-0.1	-3
7 W	11:11	0.9	27
	18:19	-0.1	-3
8 Th	11:56	1.0	30
	18:49	-0.1	-3
9 F ○	12:44	1.0	30
	19:23	-0.2	-6
10 Sa ●	13:36	1.0	30
	20:01	-0.2	-6
11 Su	14:30	1.0	30
	20:42	-0.1	-3
12 M	15:22	1.0	30
	21:25	-0.1	-3
13 Tu	06:37	0.7	21
	09:04	0.5	15
	16:12	1.0	30
	22:10	0.0	0
14 W	06:32	0.7	21
	10:00	0.5	15
	17:01	1.0	30
	22:55	0.1	3
15 Th	06:35	0.7	21
	11:00	0.4	12
	17:52	0.9	27
	23:40	0.2	6
16 F	07:00	0.8	24
	12:05	0.3	9
	18:48	0.7	21
17 Sa ◑	00:24	0.3	9
	07:31	0.8	24
	13:12	0.2	6
	19:55	0.6	18
18 Su	01:09	0.4	12
	08:07	0.9	27
	14:21	0.1	3
19 M	08:45	1.0	30
	15:29	0.0	0
20 Tu	09:27	1.0	30
	16:33	-0.1	-3
21 W	10:11	1.1	34
	17:29	-0.1	-3
22 Th	11:02	1.2	37
	18:19	-0.1	-3
23 F	12:01	1.2	37
	19:04	-0.1	-3
24 Sa ○	13:11	1.2	37
	19:48	0.0	0
25 Su	14:19	1.2	37
	20:31	0.1	3
26 M	05:46	0.7	21
	07:58	0.5	15
	15:19	1.1	34
	21:14	0.1	3
27 Tu	06:11	0.7	21
	08:56	0.5	15
	16:12	1.0	30
	21:57	0.2	6
28 W	06:13	0.7	21
	09:56	0.4	12
	17:01	0.9	27
	22:41	0.2	6
29 Th	05:48	0.8	24
	10:59	0.4	12
	17:50	0.8	24
	23:25	0.3	9
30 F	06:13	0.9	27
	12:05	0.3	9
	18:42	0.7	21
31 Sa ◐	00:09	0.4	12
	06:49	0.9	27
	13:13	0.2	6
	22:18	0.5	15

August

Day	Time	ft	cm
1 Su	00:55	0.4	12
	07:31	0.9	27
	14:23	0.1	3
2 M	08:17	0.9	27
	15:33	0.1	3
3 Tu	09:05	0.9	27
	16:33	0.0	0
4 W	09:53	1.0	30
	17:14	0.0	0
5 Th	10:42	1.0	30
	17:49	0.0	0
6 F	11:33	1.0	30
	18:23	0.0	0
7 Sa	12:26	1.1	34
	18:59	0.1	3
8 Su ●	13:24	1.1	34
	19:38	0.1	3
9 M	05:03	0.8	24
	07:13	0.7	21
	14:23	1.2	37
	20:18	0.2	6
10 Tu	05:23	0.8	24
	08:02	0.6	18
	15:18	1.2	37
	20:59	0.3	9
11 W	05:22	0.8	24
	08:54	0.6	18
	16:11	1.1	34
	21:41	0.3	9
12 Th	05:21	0.9	27
	09:48	0.4	12
	17:02	1.1	34
	22:22	0.4	12
13 F	05:41	0.9	27
	10:46	0.3	9
	17:54	0.9	27
	23:03	0.5	15
14 Sa	06:09	1.0	30
	11:47	0.2	6
	18:52	0.8	24
	23:43	0.6	18
15 Su ◐	06:43	1.1	34
	12:51	0.1	3
16 M	07:23	1.1	34
	13:58	0.1	3
17 Tu	08:08	1.2	37
	15:07	0.1	3
18 W	09:00	1.2	37
	16:14	0.1	3
19 Th	09:57	1.2	37
	17:13	0.1	3
20 F	11:00	1.2	37
	18:02	0.2	6
21 Sa	12:10	1.2	37
	18:44	0.3	9
22 Su ○	03:59	0.8	24
	06:07	0.7	21
	13:30	1.2	37
	19:24	0.3	9
23 M ●	04:28	0.8	24
	07:02	0.7	21
	14:43	1.2	37
	20:03	0.4	12
24 Tu	04:52	0.9	27
	07:55	0.6	18
	15:38	1.2	37
	20:42	0.5	15
25 W	04:55	0.9	27
	08:47	0.5	15
	16:23	1.1	34
	21:22	0.5	15
26 Th	04:31	1.0	30
	09:41	0.4	12
	17:04	1.0	30
	22:03	0.6	18
27 F	04:54	1.1	34
	10:35	0.3	9
	17:47	0.9	27
	22:44	0.6	18
28 Sa	05:28	1.1	34
	11:29	0.3	9
	18:33	0.8	24
	23:26	0.6	18
29 Su	06:07	1.1	34
	12:26	0.2	6
	22:06	0.7	21
30 M ◐	00:08	0.7	21
	06:50	1.1	34
	13:24	0.2	6
31 Tu	07:37	1.1	34
	14:24	0.2	6

September

Day	Time	ft	cm
1 W	08:28	1.1	34
	15:26	0.2	6
2 Th	09:21	1.1	34
	16:24	0.2	6
3 F	10:17	1.1	34
	17:13	0.3	9
4 Sa	11:14	1.2	37
	17:54	0.3	9
5 Su	03:20	1.0	30
	05:29	0.9	27
	12:17	1.2	37
	18:33	0.4	12
6 M	03:48	1.0	30
	06:15	0.8	24
	13:25	1.3	40
	19:11	0.5	15
7 Tu ●	04:07	1.0	30
	07:03	0.8	24
	14:32	1.3	40
	19:49	0.6	18
8 W	04:10	1.0	30
	07:51	0.7	21
	15:32	1.3	40
	20:28	0.7	21
9 Th	04:04	1.1	34
	08:42	0.5	15
	16:27	1.2	37
	21:07	0.7	21
10 F	04:22	1.2	37
	09:35	0.4	12
	17:21	1.1	34
	21:45	0.8	24
11 Sa	04:51	1.3	40
	10:31	0.3	9
	18:21	1.0	30
	22:22	0.8	24
12 Su	05:24	1.3	40
	11:29	0.2	6
13 M ◐	06:03	1.3	40
	12:30	0.2	6
14 Tu	06:48	1.3	40
	13:34	0.2	6
15 W	07:41	1.3	40
	14:42	0.3	9
16 Th	08:42	1.3	40
	15:50	0.3	9
17 F	09:50	1.3	40
	16:51	0.4	12
18 Sa	02:09	1.0	30
	04:12	0.9	27
	11:13	1.3	40
	17:38	0.5	15
19 Su	02:41	1.0	30
	05:17	0.8	24
	13:37	1.3	40
	18:18	0.6	18
20 M ○	03:10	1.1	34
	06:11	0.8	24
	14:42	1.3	40
	18:54	0.7	21
21 Tu	03:35	1.1	34
	07:01	0.7	21
	15:36	1.3	40
	19:31	0.8	24
22 W	03:41	1.1	34
	07:48	0.6	18
	16:24	1.3	40
	20:08	0.8	24
23 Th	03:09	1.2	37
	08:34	0.5	15
	17:09	1.2	37
	20:46	0.8	24
24 F	03:33	1.3	40
	09:20	0.4	12
	17:51	1.1	34
	21:24	0.8	24
25 Sa	04:08	1.3	40
	10:06	0.3	9
	18:40	1.0	30
	22:03	0.8	24
26 Su	04:47	1.3	40
	10:54	0.3	9
	20:15	0.9	27
	22:42	0.8	24
27 M	05:29	1.3	40
	11:44	0.2	6
28 Tu	06:13	1.3	40
	12:37	0.2	6
29 W ◐	07:00	1.2	37
	13:33	0.3	9
30 Th	07:53	1.2	37
	14:34	0.3	9

StationId: 8723970
Source: NOAA/NOS/CO-OPS
Station Type: Primary
Time Zone: LST_LDT
Datum: MLLW

Vaca Key, Florida Bay, FL, 2021

Times and Heights of High and Low Waters

October

Day	Time (h m)	Height (ft)	Height (cm)	Day	Time (h m)	Height (ft)	Height (cm)
1 F	08:50	1.2	37	16 Sa	00:46	1.0	30
	15:35	0.4	12		03:07	0.9	27
					09:51	1.2	37
					16:17	0.7	21
2 Sa	09:52	1.2	37	17 Su	01:19	1.1	34
	16:31	0.5	15		04:26	0.9	27
					12:53	1.3	40
					17:04	0.8	24
3 Su	02:01	1.1	34	18 M	01:50	1.2	37
	04:26	1.0	30		05:28	0.8	24
	11:00	1.3	40		13:59	1.3	40
	17:18	0.6	18		17:44	0.8	24
4 M	02:28	1.1	34	19 Tu	02:15	1.2	37
	05:17	0.9	27		06:16	0.7	21
	12:21	1.3	40		14:55	1.3	40
	17:59	0.7	21		18:21	0.9	27
5 Tu	02:47	1.2	37	20 W ○	02:21	1.3	40
	06:05	0.8	24		06:57	0.6	18
	14:13	1.3	40		15:47	1.3	40
	18:37	0.9	27		18:56	1.0	30
6 W ●	02:46	1.2	37	21 Th	01:33	1.3	40
	06:52	0.7	21		07:36	0.5	15
	15:26	1.4	43		16:37	1.2	37
	19:14	0.9	27		19:32	1.0	30
7 Th	02:35	1.3	40	22 F	02:05	1.4	43
	07:40	0.6	18		08:15	0.4	12
	16:27	1.3	40		17:24	1.2	37
	19:51	1.0	30		20:08	1.0	30
8 F	02:56	1.4	43	23 Sa	02:45	1.4	43
	08:29	0.4	12		08:56	0.3	9
	17:26	1.3	40		18:12	1.1	34
	20:28	1.0	30		20:45	1.0	30
9 Sa	03:27	1.4	43	24 Su	03:28	1.4	43
	09:21	0.3	9		09:38	0.2	6
	18:32	1.2	37		19:05	1.0	30
	21:04	1.0	30		21:22	1.0	30
10 Su	04:05	1.5	46	25 M	04:11	1.4	43
	10:14	0.2	6		10:22	0.2	6
11 M	04:46	1.5	46	26 Tu	04:54	1.3	40
	11:10	0.2	6		11:09	0.2	6
12 Tu	05:32	1.5	46	27 W	05:39	1.3	40
	12:08	0.2	6		11:59	0.2	6
13 W	06:23	1.5	46	28 Th ◗	06:27	1.3	40
	13:09	0.3	9		12:53	0.3	9
14 Th	07:21	1.4	43	29 F	07:20	1.2	37
	14:13	0.4	12		13:50	0.4	12
15 F	08:28	1.3	40	30 Sa	08:20	1.2	37
	15:18	0.5	15		14:49	0.5	15
				31 Su	00:35	1.1	34
					03:07	1.0	30
					09:28	1.2	37
					15:46	0.6	18

November

Day	Time (h m)	Height (ft)	Height (cm)	Day	Time (h m)	Height (ft)	Height (cm)
1 M	01:01	1.1	34	16 Tu	04:42	0.5	15
	04:09	0.9	27		13:01	1.1	34
	10:51	1.2	37		16:06	0.8	24
	16:36	0.8	24		22:33	1.2	37
2 Tu	01:16	1.2	37	17 W	05:16	0.4	12
	05:02	0.8	24		13:57	1.1	34
	13:48	1.2	37		16:44	0.9	27
	17:19	0.9	27		22:59	1.2	37
3 W	00:35	1.2	37	18 Th	05:47	0.4	12
	05:51	0.6	18		14:48	1.1	34
	14:56	1.3	40		17:20	0.9	27
	17:58	1.0	30		23:36	1.3	40
4 Th ●	00:45	1.3	40	19 F ○	06:19	0.3	9
	06:39	0.5	15		15:37	1.1	34
	15:56	1.3	40		17:55	0.9	27
	18:34	1.1	34				
5 F	01:11	1.4	43	20 Sa	00:18	1.3	40
	07:26	0.3	9		06:54	0.2	6
	16:53	1.2	37		16:24	1.0	30
	19:10	1.1	34		18:31	0.9	27
6 Sa	01:49	1.5	46	21 Su	01:05	1.3	40
	08:15	0.2	6		07:32	0.1	3
7 Su	01:37	1.5	46	22 M	01:53	1.3	40
	08:05	0.1	3		08:12	0.0	0
8 M	02:28	1.5	46	23 Tu	02:40	1.2	37
	08:57	0.1	3		08:55	0.0	0
9 Tu	03:19	1.5	46	24 W	03:26	1.2	37
	09:51	0.1	3		09:40	0.0	0
10 W	04:12	1.5	46	25 Th	04:13	1.2	37
	10:46	0.2	6		10:28	0.1	3
11 Th ◖	05:06	1.4	43	26 F ◗	05:01	1.1	34
	11:42	0.3	9		11:18	0.2	6
					21:12	0.9	27
					23:20	0.8	24
12 F	06:06	1.2	37	27 Sa ◗	05:54	1.1	34
	12:40	0.4	12		12:11	0.3	9
	22:14	0.9	27		21:46	0.9	27
13 Sa	00:45	0.8	24	28 Su	00:32	0.8	24
	07:15	1.1	34		06:55	1.0	30
	13:38	0.6	18		13:05	0.4	12
	22:50	1.0	30		22:00	0.9	27
14 Su	02:23	0.8	24	29 M	01:42	0.7	21
	10:41	1.0	30		08:08	0.9	27
	14:34	0.7	21		13:59	0.6	18
	23:23	1.1	34		21:13	1.0	30
15 M	03:51	0.7	21	30 Tu	02:47	0.5	15
	11:59	1.1	34		11:49	0.9	27
	15:23	0.8	24		14:48	0.7	21
	23:49	1.1	34		21:37	1.1	34

December

Day	Time (h m)	Height (ft)	Height (cm)	Day	Time (h m)	Height (ft)	Height (cm)
1 W	03:44	0.4	12	16 Th	05:07	0.1	3
	13:05	1.0	30		13:52	0.8	24
	15:33	0.8	24		16:07	0.6	18
	22:03	1.1	34		22:16	1.0	30
2 Th	04:35	0.2	6	17 F	05:31	0.0	0
	14:08	1.0	30		14:43	0.8	24
	16:13	0.9	27		16:45	0.7	21
	22:26	1.2	37		22:58	1.0	30
3 F	05:24	0.1	3	18 Sa	05:59	-0.1	-3
	21:04	1.3	40		23:44	1.0	30
4 Sa ●	06:12	0.0	0	19 Su ○	06:32	-0.1	-3
	21:47	1.4	43				
5 Su	07:01	-0.1	-3	20 M	00:35	1.0	30
	22:38	1.4	43		07:08	-0.2	-6
6 M	07:50	-0.1	-3	21 Tu	01:28	1.0	30
					07:48	-0.2	-6
7 Tu	02:07	1.3	40	22 W	02:19	1.0	30
	08:39	-0.1	-3		08:30	-0.2	-6
					18:07	0.7	21
					20:08	0.6	18
8 W	03:05	1.3	40	23 Th	03:08	1.0	30
	09:30	0.0	0		09:14	-0.2	-6
					18:30	0.6	18
					21:01	0.5	15
9 Th	04:00	1.2	37	24 F	03:55	0.9	27
	10:21	0.1	3		10:00	-0.1	-3
	19:49	0.7	21		18:11	0.6	18
	21:57	0.6	18		21:59	0.5	15
10 F	04:54	1.1	34	25 Sa	04:44	0.9	27
	11:11	0.2	6		10:47	0.0	0
	20:26	0.7	21		18:26	0.7	21
	23:16	0.6	18		23:03	0.4	12
11 Sa ◖	05:52	0.9	27	26 Su ◗	05:37	0.8	24
	12:03	0.3	9		11:35	0.1	3
	21:01	0.8	24		18:56	0.7	21
12 Su	00:45	0.5	15	27 M ◗	00:09	0.3	9
	07:01	0.7	21		06:38	0.6	18
	12:55	0.4	12		12:22	0.2	6
	19:51	0.8	24		19:30	0.7	21
13 M	02:33	0.4	12	28 Tu	01:16	0.2	6
	10:42	0.7	21		07:54	0.5	15
	13:47	0.5	15		13:10	0.4	12
	20:21	0.9	27		20:04	0.8	24
14 Tu	04:13	0.3	9	29 W	02:21	0.1	3
	11:55	0.7	21		20:37	0.9	27
	14:38	0.6	18				
	20:58	1.0	30				
15 W	04:48	0.1	3	30 Th	03:22	-0.1	-3
	12:57	0.7	21		21:08	1.0	30
	15:25	0.6	18				
	21:36	1.0	30				
				31 F	04:18	-0.2	-6
					20:36	1.0	30

159

StationId: 8724580
Source: NOAA/NOS/CO-OPS
Station Type: Primary
Time Zone: LST_LDT
Datum: MLLW

NOAA Tide Predictions

Key West, FL,2021

Times and Heights of High and Low Waters

January

Day	Time	ft	cm	Day	Time	ft	cm
1 F	05:16	-0.4	-12	16 Sa	06:01	-0.3	-9
	11:59	1.0	30		12:28	1.0	30
	16:21	0.4	12		17:29	0.2	6
	23:05	1.9	58				
2 Sa	05:56	-0.3	-9	17 Su	00:04	1.6	49
	12:40	1.1	34		06:40	-0.1	-3
	17:10	0.4	12		13:04	1.1	34
	23:52	1.8	55		18:25	0.2	6
3 Su	06:38	-0.2	-6	18 M	00:49	1.4	43
	13:22	1.1	34		07:19	0.0	0
	18:08	0.4	12		13:40	1.2	37
					19:27	0.3	9
4 M	00:44	1.7	52	19 Tu	01:38	1.2	37
	07:21	-0.1	-3		07:57	0.2	6
	14:04	1.2	37		14:19	1.2	37
	19:16	0.3	9		20:36	0.2	6
5 Tu	01:45	1.5	46	20 W	02:37	1.0	30
	08:06	0.1	3		08:37	0.3	9
	14:49	1.3	40		15:01	1.2	37
	20:34	0.3	9		21:51	0.2	6
6 W	03:00	1.3	40	21 Th	03:53	0.9	27
	08:54	0.2	6		09:21	0.4	12
	15:37	1.4	43		15:48	1.3	40
	21:57	0.1	3		23:03	0.1	3
7 Th	04:30	1.1	34	22 F	05:26	0.8	24
	09:45	0.3	9		10:09	0.5	15
	16:29	1.6	49		16:41	1.3	40
	23:15	-0.1	-3				
8 F	06:03	1.0	30	23 Sa	00:07	0.0	0
	10:38	0.4	12		06:50	0.7	21
	17:25	1.7	52		11:00	0.5	15
					17:37	1.4	43
9 Sa	00:24	-0.3	-9	24 Su	01:01	-0.2	-6
	07:21	0.9	27		07:49	0.7	21
	11:31	0.4	12		11:49	0.5	15
	18:21	1.8	55		18:30	1.5	46
10 Su	01:25	-0.5	-15	25 M	01:48	-0.3	-9
	08:22	0.9	27		08:32	0.8	24
	12:25	0.3	9		12:36	0.4	12
	19:17	1.9	58		19:20	1.6	49
11 M	02:19	-0.6	-18	26 Tu	02:29	-0.4	-12
	09:13	0.9	27		09:10	0.8	24
	13:17	0.3	9		13:19	0.3	9
	20:11	2.0	61		20:07	1.7	52
12 Tu	03:09	-0.6	-18	27 W	03:06	-0.5	-15
	09:57	0.9	27		09:44	0.9	27
	14:08	0.2	6		14:02	0.3	9
	21:02	2.0	61		20:51	1.8	55
13 W	03:56	-0.6	-18	28 Th	03:42	-0.5	-15
	10:38	0.9	27		10:18	0.9	27
	14:58	0.2	6		14:45	0.2	6
	21:50	2.0	61		21:34	1.8	55
14 Th	04:40	-0.5	-15	29 F	04:17	-0.5	-15
	11:16	0.9	27		10:52	1.0	30
	15:47	0.1	3		15:30	0.1	3
	22:36	1.9	58		22:17	1.9	58
15 F	05:21	-0.4	-12	30 Sa	04:52	-0.5	-15
	11:52	1.0	30		11:27	1.1	34
	16:37	0.1	3		16:18	0.1	3
	23:20	1.8	55		23:02	1.8	55
				31 Su	05:28	-0.4	-12
					12:01	1.2	37
					17:10	0.0	0
					23:49	1.7	52

February

Day	Time	ft	cm	Day	Time	ft	cm
1 M	06:04	-0.2	-6	16 Tu	00:25	1.3	40
	12:36	1.3	40		06:25	0.1	3
	18:07	0.0	0		12:39	1.3	40
					18:54	0.0	0
2 Tu	00:42	1.5	46	17 W	01:09	1.1	34
	06:42	-0.1	-3		06:55	0.2	6
	13:13	1.4	43		13:12	1.3	40
	19:10	-0.1	-3		19:50	0.0	0
3 W	01:42	1.2	37	18 Th	02:00	0.9	27
	07:22	0.1	3		07:26	0.3	9
	13:55	1.4	43		13:50	1.3	40
	20:22	-0.1	-3		20:55	0.0	0
4 Th	02:55	1.0	30	19 F	03:07	0.8	24
	08:06	0.2	6		08:01	0.4	12
	14:45	1.5	46		14:36	1.3	40
	21:42	-0.2	-6		22:10	0.0	0
5 F	04:28	0.8	24	20 Sa	04:41	0.6	18
	08:57	0.3	9		08:47	0.5	15
	15:45	1.6	49		15:34	1.3	40
	23:03	-0.3	-9		23:24	-0.1	-3
6 Sa	06:07	0.7	21	21 Su	06:25	0.6	18
	09:57	0.4	12		09:54	0.5	15
	16:56	1.6	49		16:45	1.3	40
7 Su	00:18	-0.4	-12	22 M	00:29	-0.2	-6
	07:24	0.7	21		07:29	0.7	21
	11:04	0.3	9		11:05	0.5	15
	18:09	1.7	52		17:56	1.4	43
8 M	01:22	-0.5	-15	23 Tu	01:21	-0.2	-6
	08:20	0.7	21		08:10	0.7	21
	12:09	0.3	9		12:06	0.4	12
	19:15	1.7	52		18:58	1.5	46
9 Tu	02:15	-0.5	-15	24 W	02:03	-0.3	-9
	09:03	0.8	24		08:43	0.8	24
	13:09	0.2	6		12:59	0.3	9
	20:12	1.8	55		19:50	1.7	52
10 W	03:01	-0.5	-15	25 Th	02:40	-0.4	-12
	09:41	0.8	24		09:14	0.9	27
	14:04	0.1	3		13:48	0.2	6
	21:02	1.8	55		20:38	1.8	55
11 Th	03:41	-0.5	-15	26 F	03:13	-0.4	-12
	10:14	0.9	27		09:45	1.1	34
	21:46	1.8	55		14:36	0.1	3
					21:24	1.8	55
12 F	04:17	-0.4	-12	27 Sa	03:46	-0.4	-12
	10:45	1.0	30		10:15	1.2	37
	15:43	0.0	0		15:24	-0.1	-3
	22:27	1.7	52		22:10	1.8	55
13 Sa	04:50	-0.3	-9	28 Su	04:19	-0.3	-9
	11:14	1.1	34		10:46	1.3	40
	16:30	0.0	0		16:14	-0.2	-6
	23:06	1.6	49		22:58	1.7	52
14 Su	05:23	-0.2	-6				
	11:42	1.2	37				
	17:16	0.0	0				
	23:44	1.5	46				
15 M	05:54	-0.1	-3				
	12:10	1.3	40				
	18:04	0.0	0				

March

Day	Time	ft	cm	Day	Time	ft	cm
1 M	04:53	-0.2	-6	16 Tu	00:27	1.4	43
	11:18	1.5	46		06:08	0.1	3
	17:06	-0.3	-9		12:20	1.5	46
	23:47	1.6	49		18:41	-0.1	-3
2 Tu	05:27	-0.1	-3	17 W	01:06	1.3	40
	11:52	1.6	49		06:34	0.2	6
	18:01	-0.4	-12		12:48	1.5	46
					19:24	-0.1	-3
3 W	00:41	1.3	40	18 Th	01:48	1.1	34
	06:03	0.1	3		07:01	0.3	9
	12:29	1.7	52		13:19	1.5	46
	19:02	-0.4	-12		20:11	-0.1	-3
4 Th	01:41	1.1	34	19 F	02:37	0.9	27
	06:42	0.2	6		07:27	0.4	12
	13:13	1.7	52		13:55	1.4	43
	20:10	-0.4	-12		21:07	-0.1	-3
5 F	02:55	0.8	24	20 Sa	03:39	0.8	24
	07:25	0.3	9		07:57	0.5	15
	14:06	1.6	49		14:40	1.4	43
	21:28	-0.3	-9		22:17	0.0	0
6 Sa	04:29	0.7	21	21 Su	05:06	0.7	21
	08:19	0.4	12		08:39	0.6	18
	15:15	1.6	49		15:39	1.3	40
	22:51	-0.3	-9		23:36	0.0	0
7 Su	06:07	0.7	21	22 M	06:50	0.7	21
	09:32	0.4	12		09:55	0.6	18
	16:41	1.6	49		16:57	1.3	40
8 M	00:09	-0.3	-9	23 Tu	00:46	0.0	0
	07:16	0.7	21		07:54	0.8	24
	10:54	0.4	12		11:29	0.6	18
	18:07	1.6	49		18:21	1.4	43
9 Tu	01:12	-0.3	-9	24 W	01:41	-0.1	-3
	08:04	0.8	24		08:32	0.9	27
	12:08	0.3	9		12:44	0.5	15
	19:16	1.7	52		19:31	1.6	49
10 W	02:00	-0.3	-9	25 Th	02:23	-0.1	-3
	08:41	0.9	27		09:04	1.0	30
	13:11	0.2	6		13:48	0.4	12
	20:11	1.7	52		20:30	1.7	52
11 Th	02:39	-0.2	-6	26 F	03:00	-0.2	-6
	09:13	1.1	34		09:33	1.2	37
	14:05	0.1	3		14:37	0.2	6
	20:57	1.7	52		21:23	1.8	55
12 F	03:12	-0.2	-6	27 Sa	03:33	-0.1	-3
	09:41	1.2	37		10:03	1.4	43
	14:53	0.0	0		15:27	-0.1	-3
	21:38	1.7	52		22:14	1.8	55
13 Sa	03:43	-0.1	-3	28 Su	04:07	-0.1	-3
	10:06	1.3	40		10:33	1.6	49
	15:37	-0.1	-3		16:17	-0.3	-9
	22:15	1.6	49		23:03	1.8	55
14 Su	05:12	0.0	0	29 M	04:40	0.0	0
	11:30	1.4	43		11:04	1.7	52
	17:19	-0.1	-3		17:07	-0.4	-12
	23:51	1.5	46		23:53	1.6	49
15 M	05:40	0.0	0	30 Tu	05:15	0.1	3
	11:55	1.5	46		11:38	1.9	58
	18:00	-0.1	-3		17:59	-0.6	-18
				31 W	00:45	1.4	43
					05:50	0.2	6
					12:14	1.9	58
					18:54	-0.6	-18

StationId: 8724580
Source: NOAA/NOS/CO-OPS
Station Type: Primary
Time Zone: LST_LDT
Datum: MLLW

NOAA Tide Predictions

Key West, FL, 2021

Times and Heights of High and Low Waters

April

Day	Time	ft	cm	Day	Time	ft	cm
1 Th	01:40	1.2	37	16 F	01:34	1.1	34
	06:27	0.3	9		06:16	0.5	15
	12:56	1.9	58		12:40	1.6	49
	19:53	-0.5	-15		19:42	-0.2	-6
2 F	02:41	1.0	30	17 Sa	02:24	1.0	30
	07:08	0.3	9		06:44	0.5	15
	13:44	1.9	58		13:17	1.6	49
	20:59	-0.4	-12		20:34	-0.1	-3
3 Sa	03:54	0.8	24	18 Su	03:24	0.9	27
	07:56	0.4	12		07:17	0.6	18
	14:43	1.8	55		14:03	1.5	46
	22:14	-0.3	-9		21:37	0.0	0
4 Su	05:23	0.7	21	19 M	04:41	0.8	24
	08:59	0.5	15		08:06	0.7	21
	15:59	1.6	49		15:01	1.5	46
	23:35	-0.2	-6		22:48	0.0	0
5 M	06:48	0.8	24	20 Tu	06:03	0.9	27
	10:25	0.5	15		09:28	0.7	21
	17:32	1.6	49		16:18	1.4	43
					23:54	0.0	0
6 Tu	00:47	-0.1	-3	21 W	07:01	1.0	30
	07:49	0.9	27		11:05	0.7	21
	11:56	0.5	15		17:44	1.5	46
	19:00	1.6	49				
7 W	01:44	0.0	0	22 Th	00:47	0.0	0
	08:32	1.0	30		07:41	1.1	34
	13:12	0.4	12		12:25	0.5	15
	20:08	1.6	49		19:03	1.5	46
8 Th	02:26	0.0	0	23 F	01:31	0.1	3
	09:06	1.2	37		08:14	1.3	40
	14:12	0.3	9		13:29	0.3	9
	21:01	1.6	49		20:10	1.6	49
9 F	03:01	0.1	3	24 Sa	02:10	0.1	3
	09:35	1.3	40		08:45	1.5	46
	15:03	0.1	3		14:25	0.0	0
	21:46	1.6	49		21:09	1.6	49
10 Sa	03:32	0.1	3	25 Su	02:47	0.1	3
	10:00	1.5	46		09:16	1.7	52
	15:47	0.0	0		15:17	-0.2	-6
	22:25	1.5	46		22:04	1.6	49
11 Su	04:00	0.2	6	26 M	03:23	0.2	6
	10:23	1.6	49		09:50	1.9	58
	16:27	-0.1	-3		16:08	-0.5	-15
	23:01	1.5	46		22:57	1.5	46
12 M	04:28	0.2	6	27 Tu	04:00	0.2	6
	10:46	1.7	52		10:25	2.0	61
	17:05	-0.2	-6		16:59	-0.6	-18
	23:37	1.4	43		23:49	1.4	43
13 Tu	04:56	0.3	9	28 W	04:37	0.3	9
	11:11	1.7	52		11:04	2.1	64
	17:42	-0.2	-6		17:51	-0.7	-21
14 W	00:13	1.3	40	29 Th	00:42	1.3	40
	05:22	0.3	9		05:16	0.3	9
	11:37	1.7	52		11:47	2.2	67
	18:19	-0.2	-6		18:45	-0.7	-21
15 Th	00:52	1.2	37	30 F	01:37	1.1	34
	05:49	0.4	12		05:58	0.4	12
	12:07	1.7	52		12:34	2.1	64
	18:59	-0.2	-6		19:44	-0.5	-15

May

Day	Time	ft	cm	Day	Time	ft	cm
1 Sa	02:37	0.9	27	16 Su	02:14	0.9	27
	06:44	0.4	12		06:15	0.6	18
	13:28	2.0	61		12:54	1.7	52
	20:47	-0.4	-12		20:11	-0.2	-6
2 Su	03:44	0.9	27	17 M	03:10	0.9	27
	07:40	0.5	15		06:58	0.6	18
	14:30	1.8	55		13:41	1.6	49
	21:56	-0.2	-6		21:06	-0.1	-3
3 M	04:59	0.9	27	18 Tu	04:11	0.9	27
	08:54	0.6	18		07:57	0.7	21
	15:46	1.6	49		14:38	1.6	49
	23:06	0.0	0		22:03	0.0	0
4 Tu	06:09	1.0	30	19 W	05:10	1.0	30
	09:19	0.6	18		09:19	0.7	21
	17:14	1.5	46		15:50	1.5	46
					22:59	0.1	3
5 W	00:07	0.1	3	20 Th	06:00	1.1	34
	07:05	1.1	34		10:49	0.6	18
	11:55	0.5	15		17:13	1.4	43
	18:39	1.4	43		23:50	0.1	3
6 Th	00:57	0.2	6	21 F	06:41	1.3	40
	07:47	1.3	40		12:08	0.4	12
	13:08	0.4	12		18:37	1.4	43
	19:48	1.4	43				
7 F	01:38	0.2	6	22 Sa	00:36	0.2	6
	08:21	1.4	43		07:18	1.5	46
	14:05	0.2	6		13:14	0.1	3
	20:44	1.4	43		19:52	1.4	43
8 Sa	02:13	0.3	9	23 Su	01:18	0.2	6
	08:49	1.6	49		07:55	1.7	52
	14:53	0.1	3		14:12	-0.2	-6
	21:30	1.3	40		20:58	1.4	43
9 Su	02:44	0.3	9	24 M	02:00	0.3	9
	09:15	1.7	52		08:33	1.9	58
	15:35	-0.1	-3		15:06	-0.4	-12
	22:10	1.3	40		21:57	1.3	40
10 M	03:15	0.4	12	25 Tu	02:40	0.3	9
	09:40	1.7	52		09:13	2.1	64
	16:13	-0.2	-6		15:59	-0.7	-21
	22:48	1.3	40		22:52	1.2	37
11 Tu	03:44	0.4	12	26 W	03:22	0.3	9
	10:06	1.8	55		09:56	2.2	67
	16:49	-0.3	-9		16:51	-0.8	-24
	23:25	1.2	37		23:45	1.2	37
12 W	04:13	0.4	12	27 Th	04:04	0.3	9
	10:34	1.8	55		10:42	2.2	67
	17:24	-0.3	-9		17:43	-0.8	-24
13 Th	00:02	1.1	34	28 F	00:36	1.1	34
	04:41	0.5	15		04:49	0.3	9
	11:05	1.8	55		11:31	2.2	67
	18:01	-0.3	-9		18:37	-0.7	-21
14 F	00:42	1.1	34	29 Sa	01:28	1.0	30
	05:10	0.5	15		05:37	0.3	9
	11:38	1.8	55		12:23	2.1	64
	18:40	-0.3	-9		19:33	-0.5	-15
15 Sa	01:25	1.0	30	30 Su	02:22	0.9	27
	05:41	0.5	15		06:30	0.4	12
	12:14	1.7	52		13:19	2.0	61
	19:23	-0.2	-6		20:30	-0.3	-9
				31 M	03:19	0.9	27
					07:33	0.5	15
					14:19	1.8	55
					21:28	-0.1	-3

June

Day	Time	ft	cm	Day	Time	ft	cm
1 Tu	04:18	1.0	30	16 W	03:30	1.1	34
	08:50	0.5	15		07:55	0.6	18
	15:26	1.6	49		14:25	1.6	49
	22:23	0.0	0		21:20	0.0	0
2 W	05:16	1.1	34	17 Th	04:15	1.2	37
	10:17	0.5	15		09:12	0.6	18
	16:42	1.4	43		15:32	1.4	43
	23:15	0.2	6		22:07	0.1	3
3 Th	06:07	1.3	40	18 F	04:59	1.3	40
	11:40	0.4	12		10:35	0.4	12
	18:03	1.3	40		16:52	1.3	40
					22:55	0.2	6
4 F	00:01	0.3	9	19 Sa	05:42	1.5	46
	06:50	1.4	43		11:52	0.2	6
	12:51	0.3	9		18:19	1.2	37
	19:18	1.2	37		23:42	0.3	9
5 Sa	00:42	0.4	12	20 Su	06:26	1.7	52
	07:26	1.5	46		13:00	-0.1	-3
	13:48	0.2	6		19:42	1.1	34
	20:20	1.1	34				
6 Su	01:20	0.4	12	21 M	00:30	0.4	12
	07:58	1.6	49		07:11	1.8	55
	14:36	0.0	0		14:01	-0.3	-9
	21:12	1.1	34		20:53	1.1	34
7 M	01:55	0.4	12	22 Tu	01:17	0.4	12
	08:29	1.7	52		07:59	2.0	61
	15:18	-0.1	-3		14:57	-0.5	-15
	21:55	1.1	34		21:53	1.0	30
8 Tu	02:29	0.5	15	23 W	02:04	0.4	12
	09:00	1.7	52		08:49	2.1	64
	15:56	-0.2	-6		15:51	-0.7	-21
	22:35	1.0	30		22:47	1.0	30
9 W	03:02	0.5	15	24 Th	02:52	0.3	9
	09:33	1.8	55		09:40	2.2	67
	16:33	-0.3	-9		16:44	-0.7	-21
	23:12	1.0	30		23:36	1.0	30
10 Th	03:34	0.5	15	25 F	03:41	0.3	9
	10:07	1.8	55		10:32	2.2	67
	17:09	-0.3	-9		17:35	-0.7	-21
	23:51	1.0	30				
11 F	04:07	0.5	15	26 Sa	00:23	1.0	30
	10:44	1.8	55		04:32	0.3	9
	17:47	-0.4	-12		11:24	2.2	67
					18:25	-0.5	-15
12 Sa	00:30	1.0	30	27 Su	01:08	1.0	30
	04:41	0.5	15		05:25	0.3	9
	11:21	1.8	55		12:16	2.1	64
	18:25	-0.3	-9		19:14	-0.4	-12
13 Su	01:12	1.0	30	28 M	01:54	1.0	30
	05:18	0.5	15		06:22	0.3	9
	12:01	1.8	55		13:08	1.9	58
	19:06	-0.3	-9		20:01	-0.2	-6
14 M	01:57	1.0	30	29 Tu	02:40	1.1	34
	06:01	0.5	15		07:25	0.4	12
	12:43	1.8	55		14:01	1.7	52
	19:49	-0.2	-6		20:48	0.0	0
15 Tu	02:43	1.0	30	30 W	03:26	1.2	37
	06:52	0.6	18		08:36	0.4	12
	13:30	1.7	52		14:58	1.5	46
	20:33	-0.1	-3		21:33	0.1	3

StationId: 8724580
Source: NOAA/NOS/CO-OPS
Station Type: Primary
Time Zone: LST_LDT
Datum: MLLW

NOAA Tide Predictions

Key West, FL,2021

Times and Heights of High and Low Waters

July

Day	Time (h m)	Height (ft)	(cm)	Day	Time (h m)	Height (ft)	(cm)
1 Th ◑	04:12	1.3	40	16 F	03:20	1.4	43
	09:54	0.4	12		09:02	0.4	12
	16:02	1.3	40		15:22	1.4	43
	22:17	0.3	9		21:19	0.2	6
2 F	04:57	1.4	43	17 Sa ◐	04:02	1.6	49
	11:12	0.4	12		10:19	0.2	6
	17:18	1.1	34		16:42	1.2	37
	23:01	0.4	12		22:05	0.4	12
3 Sa	05:41	1.5	46	18 Su	04:49	1.7	52
	12:21	0.3	9		11:36	0.1	3
	18:40	1.0	30		18:13	1.0	30
	23:44	0.5	15		22:55	0.5	15
4 Su	06:24	1.6	49	19 M	05:42	1.8	55
	13:21	0.1	3		12:48	-0.1	-3
	19:54	1.0	30		19:41	1.0	30
					23:49	0.5	15
5 M	00:27	0.5	15	20 Tu	06:41	2.0	61
	07:05	1.6	49		13:53	-0.3	-9
	14:13	0.0	0		20:52	1.0	30
	20:53	0.9	27				
6 Tu	01:08	0.5	15	21 W	00:45	0.5	15
	07:47	1.7	52		07:41	2.1	64
	14:58	-0.1	-3		14:52	-0.4	-12
	21:39	0.9	27		21:49	1.0	30
7 W	01:48	0.5	15	22 Th	01:41	0.5	15
	08:28	1.7	52		08:40	2.2	67
	15:39	-0.2	-6		15:45	-0.5	-15
	22:19	0.9	27		22:36	1.0	30
8 Th	02:27	0.5	15	23 F	02:37	0.4	12
	09:10	1.8	55		09:36	2.2	67
	16:17	-0.3	-9		16:35	-0.5	-15
	22:56	1.0	30		23:19	1.0	30
9 F	03:05	0.5	15	24 Sa ○	03:31	0.3	9
	09:50	1.9	58		10:29	2.3	70
	16:54	-0.3	-9		17:20	-0.4	-12
	23:33	1.0	30		23:59	1.1	34
10 Sa ●	03:43	0.5	15	25 Su	04:24	0.3	9
	10:31	1.9	58		11:18	2.2	67
	17:30	-0.3	-9		18:03	-0.3	-9
11 Su	00:10	1.0	30	26 M	00:37	1.2	37
	04:24	0.5	15		05:18	0.3	9
	11:11	1.9	58		12:06	2.1	64
	18:06	-0.3	-9		18:43	-0.1	-3
12 M	00:47	1.1	34	27 Tu	01:13	1.3	40
	05:07	0.5	15		06:13	0.3	9
	11:52	1.9	58		12:52	1.9	58
	18:42	-0.2	-6		19:22	0.0	0
13 Tu	01:25	1.2	37	28 W	01:50	1.4	43
	05:55	0.5	15		07:11	0.4	12
	12:36	1.9	58		13:38	1.7	52
	19:18	-0.1	-3		20:00	0.2	6
14 W	02:03	1.2	37	29 Th	02:26	1.5	46
	06:49	0.5	15		08:13	0.4	12
	13:23	1.8	55		14:27	1.5	46
	19:57	0.0	0		20:37	0.3	9
15 Th	02:41	1.3	40	30 F	03:04	1.5	46
	07:51	0.4	12		09:20	0.4	12
	14:18	1.6	49		15:23	1.3	40
	20:36	0.1	3		21:16	0.5	15
				31 Sa ◑	03:44	1.6	49
					10:31	0.4	12
					16:31	1.1	34
					21:57	0.6	18

August

Day	Time (h m)	Height (ft)	(cm)	Day	Time (h m)	Height (ft)	(cm)
1 Su	04:29	1.6	49	16 M	04:08	2.0	61
	11:42	0.3	9		11:24	0.1	3
	17:58	1.0	30		18:18	1.0	30
	22:43	0.7	21		22:17	0.7	21
2 M	05:20	1.6	49	17 Tu	05:14	2.0	61
	12:48	0.2	6		12:40	0.0	0
	19:28	0.9	27		19:45	1.0	30
	23:34	0.7	21		23:23	0.7	21
3 Tu	06:16	1.7	52	18 W	06:28	2.1	64
	13:46	0.1	3		13:48	-0.1	-3
	20:33	1.0	30		20:48	1.1	34
4 W	00:26	0.7	21	19 Th	00:31	0.7	21
	07:12	1.7	52		07:39	2.2	67
	14:36	0.1	3		14:46	-0.1	-3
	21:19	1.0	30		21:36	1.1	34
5 Th	01:16	0.7	21	20 F	01:35	0.6	18
	08:05	1.8	55		08:42	2.3	70
	15:19	0.0	0		15:35	-0.1	-3
	21:57	1.0	30		22:16	1.2	37
6 F	02:02	0.6	18	21 Sa	02:34	0.5	15
	08:52	1.9	58		09:36	2.3	70
	15:56	-0.1	-3		16:17	-0.1	-3
	22:30	1.1	34		22:52	1.3	40
7 Sa	02:46	0.6	18	22 Su ○	03:29	0.5	15
	09:36	2.0	61		10:25	2.3	70
	16:31	-0.1	-3		16:55	0.0	0
	23:03	1.2	37		23:25	1.5	46
8 Su ●	03:29	0.5	15	23 M	04:21	0.4	12
	10:19	2.1	64		11:10	2.2	67
	16:17	-0.1	-3		17:30	0.1	3
	23:36	1.3	40		23:56	1.6	49
9 M	04:13	0.5	15	24 Tu	05:11	0.4	12
	11:01	2.1	64		11:52	2.1	64
	17:35	-0.1	-3		18:03	0.2	6
10 Tu	00:09	1.4	43	25 W	00:26	1.7	52
	05:00	0.4	12		06:00	0.4	12
	11:44	2.1	64		12:33	1.9	58
	18:08	0.0	0		18:36	0.4	12
11 W	00:41	1.5	46	26 Th	00:55	1.8	55
	05:49	0.4	12		06:50	0.4	12
	12:29	2.0	61		13:14	1.8	55
	18:41	0.1	3		19:08	0.5	15
12 Th	01:15	1.6	49	27 F	01:26	1.8	55
	06:43	0.3	9		07:42	0.4	12
	13:18	1.8	55		13:59	1.6	49
	19:16	0.2	6		19:40	0.6	18
13 F	01:50	1.7	52	28 Sa	01:59	1.8	55
	07:43	0.3	9		08:39	0.4	12
	14:14	1.6	49		14:50	1.4	43
	19:53	0.4	12		20:13	0.8	24
14 Sa	02:28	1.8	55	29 Su	02:37	1.8	55
	08:50	0.2	6		09:44	0.5	15
	15:20	1.4	43		15:53	1.2	37
	20:34	0.5	15		20:50	0.9	27
15 Su ◐	03:13	1.9	58	30 M ◐	03:24	1.8	55
	10:04	0.2	6		10:04	0.5	15
	16:42	1.2	37		17:21	1.1	34
	21:21	0.6	18		21:37	0.9	27
				31 Tu ◑	04:22	1.7	52
					12:11	0.4	12
					19:02	1.1	34
					22:41	1.0	30

September

Day	Time (h m)	Height (ft)	(cm)	Day	Time (h m)	Height (ft)	(cm)
1 W	05:32	1.8	55	16 Th	06:28	2.2	67
	13:16	0.4	12		13:39	0.2	6
	20:09	1.1	34		20:31	1.3	40
	23:51	1.0	30				
2 Th	06:42	1.9	58	17 F	00:33	0.9	27
	14:08	0.3	9		07:42	2.2	67
	20:51	1.2	37		14:30	0.3	9
					21:12	1.5	46
3 F	00:52	0.9	27	18 Sa	01:40	0.8	24
	07:42	2.0	61		08:42	2.3	70
	14:50	0.3	9		15:12	0.3	9
	21:24	1.3	40		21:46	1.6	49
4 Sa	01:45	0.8	24	19 Su	02:38	0.6	18
	08:34	2.1	64		09:33	2.3	70
	15:24	0.2	6		15:47	0.4	12
	21:54	1.4	43		22:17	1.7	52
5 Su	02:32	0.7	21	20 M ○	03:29	0.5	15
	09:20	2.2	67		10:17	2.3	70
	15:56	0.2	6		16:19	0.4	12
	22:24	1.6	49		22:45	1.9	58
6 M	03:18	0.6	18	21 Tu	04:16	0.5	15
	10:05	2.3	70		10:57	2.2	67
	16:26	0.2	6		16:49	0.5	15
	22:53	1.7	52		23:11	2.0	61
7 Tu ●	04:05	0.5	15	22 W	05:00	0.4	12
	10:49	2.3	70		11:36	2.1	64
	16:56	0.3	9		17:19	0.6	18
	23:23	1.8	55		23:36	2.1	64
8 W	04:52	0.3	9	23 Th	05:43	0.4	12
	11:35	2.2	67		12:13	1.9	58
	17:28	0.4	12		17:48	0.7	21
	23:54	2.0	61				
9 Th	05:42	0.2	6	24 F	00:03	2.1	64
	12:23	2.0	61		06:26	0.4	12
	18:01	0.5	15		12:53	1.8	55
					18:17	0.8	24
10 F	00:27	2.1	64	25 Sa	00:32	2.1	64
	06:35	0.2	6		07:11	0.4	12
	13:15	1.8	55		13:35	1.6	49
	18:35	0.6	18		18:45	0.9	27
11 Sa	01:03	2.2	67	26 Su	01:04	2.0	61
	07:33	0.1	3		08:00	0.4	12
	14:13	1.6	49		14:24	1.5	46
	19:13	0.7	21		19:14	1.0	30
12 Su	01:45	2.2	67	27 M	01:43	2.0	61
	08:38	0.2	6		08:58	0.5	15
	15:21	1.4	43		15:26	1.3	40
	19:55	0.8	24		19:46	1.1	34
13 M ◐	02:36	2.2	67	28 Tu	02:31	1.9	58
	09:52	0.2	6		10:10	0.6	18
	16:41	1.2	37		16:51	1.3	40
	20:46	0.9	27		20:31	1.1	34
14 Tu	03:41	2.2	67	29 W ◑	03:32	1.9	58
	11:14	0.2	6		11:28	0.6	18
	18:23	1.2	37		18:30	1.3	40
	21:54	0.9	27		21:50	1.2	37
15 W	05:02	2.2	67	30 Th	04:49	1.9	58
	12:33	0.2	6		12:37	0.5	15
	19:39	1.2	37		19:33	1.3	40
	23:15	0.9	27		23:22	1.2	37

StationId: 8724580
Source: NOAA/NOS/CO-OPS
Station Type: Primary
Time Zone: LST_LDT
Datum: MLLW

NOAA Tide Predictions

Key West, FL, 2021

Times and Heights of High and Low Waters

October

Day	Time (h m)	Height (ft)	Height (cm)
1 F	06:08	1.9	58
	13:28	0.5	15
	20:11	1.4	43
2 Sa	00:33	1.1	34
	07:15	2.1	64
	14:07	0.5	15
	20:42	1.6	49
3 Su	01:30	0.9	27
	08:12	2.2	67
	14:40	0.5	15
	21:10	1.7	52
4 M	02:20	0.7	21
	09:02	2.2	67
	15:11	0.5	15
	21:38	1.9	58
5 Tu	03:07	0.5	15
	09:51	2.3	70
	15:42	0.5	15
	22:07	2.1	64
6 W	03:54	0.3	9
	10:39	2.2	67
	16:14	0.6	18
	22:37	2.2	67
7 Th	04:42	0.1	3
	11:27	2.1	64
	16:47	0.6	18
	23:10	2.4	73
8 F	05:32	0.0	0
	12:18	1.9	58
	17:21	0.7	21
	23:46	2.5	76
9 Sa	06:25	0.0	0
	13:12	1.7	52
	17:58	0.8	24
10 Su	00:27	2.5	76
	07:22	0.0	0
	14:11	1.5	46
	18:38	0.9	27
11 M	01:15	2.4	73
	08:27	0.1	3
	15:21	1.4	43
	19:25	0.9	27
12 Tu	02:14	2.4	73
	09:21	0.2	6
	16:45	1.3	40
	20:25	1.0	30
13 W	03:27	2.2	67
	11:02	0.3	9
	18:10	1.3	40
	21:48	1.0	30
14 Th	04:57	2.2	67
	12:16	0.4	12
	19:14	1.4	43
	23:21	1.0	30
15 F	06:25	2.1	64
	13:14	0.5	15
	20:01	1.6	49
16 Sa	00:41	0.9	27
	07:38	2.1	64
	13:59	0.5	15
	20:38	1.7	52
17 Su	01:45	0.8	24
	08:36	2.1	64
	14:35	0.6	18
	21:10	1.9	58
18 M	02:39	0.6	18
	09:24	2.1	64
	15:07	0.6	18
	21:38	2.0	61
19 Tu	03:25	0.5	15
	10:06	2.0	61
	15:37	0.7	21
	22:03	2.1	64
20 W	04:08	0.4	12
	10:44	1.9	58
	16:06	0.7	21
	22:27	2.2	67
21 Th	04:47	0.3	9
	11:21	1.9	58
	16:35	0.8	24
	22:52	2.2	67
22 F	05:25	0.3	9
	11:57	1.7	52
	17:03	0.8	24
	23:19	2.2	67
23 Sa	06:04	0.2	6
	12:35	1.6	49
	17:31	0.9	27
	23:50	2.2	67
24 Su	06:44	0.3	9
	13:17	1.5	46
	17:59	0.9	27
25 M	00:24	2.1	64
	07:29	0.3	9
	14:06	1.4	43
	18:28	1.0	30
26 Tu	01:04	2.0	61
	08:22	0.4	12
	15:05	1.3	40
	19:02	1.1	34
27 W	01:52	2.0	61
	09:27	0.5	15
	16:21	1.3	40
	19:50	1.1	34
28 Th	02:52	1.9	58
	10:38	0.6	18
	17:42	1.3	40
	21:14	1.2	37
29 F	04:07	1.9	58
	11:43	0.6	18
	18:40	1.4	43
	22:54	1.2	37
30 Sa	05:29	1.9	58
	12:33	0.6	18
	19:19	1.6	49
31 Su	00:12	1.0	30
	06:44	1.9	58
	13:13	0.6	18
	19:51	1.7	52

November

Day	Time (h m)	Height (ft)	Height (cm)
1 M	01:13	0.8	24
	07:48	2.0	61
	13:49	0.6	18
	20:21	1.9	58
2 Tu	02:05	0.5	15
	08:45	2.0	61
	14:23	0.6	18
	20:51	2.1	64
3 W	02:55	0.2	6
	09:39	2.0	61
	14:57	0.6	18
	21:23	2.3	70
4 Th ●	03:43	0.0	0
	10:31	1.9	58
	15:33	0.7	21
	21:58	2.4	73
5 F	04:32	-0.2	-6
	11:22	1.8	55
	16:09	0.7	21
	22:37	2.5	76
6 Sa	05:23	-0.3	-9
	12:13	1.7	52
	16:48	0.7	21
	23:19	2.6	79
7 Su	05:16	-0.3	-9
	12:07	1.5	46
	16:29	0.7	21
	23:07	2.5	76
8 M	06:14	-0.2	-6
	13:05	1.3	40
	17:14	0.8	24
9 Tu	00:00	2.4	73
	07:16	0.0	0
	14:10	1.3	40
	18:08	0.8	24
10 W	01:03	2.3	70
	08:25	0.2	6
	15:22	1.2	37
	19:19	0.9	27
11 Th ◐	02:17	2.1	64
	09:36	0.3	9
	16:34	1.3	40
	20:49	0.9	27
12 F	03:44	2.0	61
	10:39	0.4	12
	17:33	1.5	46
	22:23	0.9	27
13 Sa	05:10	1.9	58
	11:32	0.5	15
	18:19	1.6	49
	23:41	0.7	21
14 Su	06:24	1.8	55
	12:14	0.6	18
	18:57	1.8	55
15 M	00:43	0.6	18
	07:23	1.8	55
	12:51	0.6	18
	19:29	1.9	58
16 Tu	01:34	0.4	12
	08:13	1.7	52
	13:24	0.7	21
	19:57	2.0	61
17 W	02:17	0.3	9
	08:55	1.6	49
	13:55	0.7	21
	20:23	2.1	64
18 Th	02:56	0.1	3
	09:33	1.6	49
	14:26	0.7	21
	20:50	2.1	64
19 F ○	03:33	0.1	3
	10:09	1.5	46
	14:56	0.7	21
	21:19	2.1	64
20 Sa	04:09	0.0	0
	10:44	1.4	43
	15:26	0.7	21
	21:50	2.1	64
21 Su	04:46	0.0	0
	11:22	1.4	43
	15:56	0.8	24
	22:24	2.1	64
22 M	05:25	0.1	3
	12:03	1.3	40
	16:26	0.8	24
	23:00	2.0	61
23 Tu	06:08	0.1	3
	12:50	1.2	37
	17:00	0.8	24
	23:41	1.9	58
24 W	06:55	0.2	6
	13:43	1.2	37
	17:40	0.9	27
25 Th	00:27	1.9	58
	07:47	0.3	9
	14:42	1.2	37
	18:35	1.0	30
26 F	01:22	1.8	55
	08:43	0.3	9
	15:42	1.3	40
	19:54	1.0	30
27 Sa ◐	02:30	1.7	52
	09:38	0.4	12
	16:33	1.4	43
	21:27	0.9	27
28 Su	03:50	1.6	49
	10:28	0.5	15
	17:16	1.5	46
	22:47	0.7	21
29 M	05:13	1.6	49
	11:13	0.5	15
	17:53	1.7	52
	23:53	0.4	12
30 Tu	06:28	1.6	49
	11:55	0.5	15
	18:30	1.9	58

December

Day	Time (h m)	Height (ft)	Height (cm)
1 W	00:50	0.1	3
	07:33	1.6	49
	12:35	0.6	18
	19:07	2.1	64
2 Th	01:42	-0.2	-6
	08:32	1.5	46
	13:16	0.6	18
	19:47	2.3	70
3 F	02:33	-0.4	-12
	09:25	1.5	46
	13:57	0.5	15
	20:30	2.4	73
4 Sa ●	03:24	-0.5	-15
	10:17	1.4	43
	14:39	0.5	15
	21:17	2.5	76
5 Su	04:16	-0.6	-18
	11:06	1.3	40
	15:23	0.5	15
	22:06	2.5	76
6 M	05:09	-0.5	-15
	11:56	1.2	37
	16:10	0.5	15
	22:58	2.4	73
7 Tu	06:03	-0.4	-12
	12:48	1.1	34
	17:02	0.5	15
	23:54	2.2	67
8 W	06:59	-0.2	-6
	13:43	1.1	34
	18:02	0.6	18
9 Th	00:54	2.0	61
	07:57	0.0	0
	14:41	1.2	37
	19:15	0.6	18
10 F	02:01	1.8	55
	08:53	0.2	6
	15:40	1.3	40
	20:41	0.6	18
11 Sa ◐	03:17	1.6	49
	09:47	0.3	9
	16:36	1.4	43
	22:10	0.6	18
12 Su	04:41	1.4	43
	10:37	0.4	12
	17:25	1.5	46
	23:27	0.4	12
13 M	06:01	1.3	40
	11:21	0.5	15
	18:07	1.7	52
14 Tu	00:29	0.3	9
	07:07	1.3	40
	12:02	0.6	18
	18:43	1.7	52
15 W	01:20	0.1	3
	08:01	1.2	37
	12:41	0.6	18
	19:17	1.8	55
16 Th	02:04	0.0	0
	08:45	1.2	37
	13:17	0.6	18
	19:50	1.8	55
17 F	02:43	-0.1	-3
	09:23	1.1	34
	13:52	0.5	15
	20:23	1.9	58
18 Sa	03:20	-0.2	-6
	09:58	1.1	34
	14:26	0.5	15
	20:58	1.9	58
19 Su ○	03:56	-0.2	-6
	10:32	1.1	34
	14:59	0.5	15
	21:33	1.9	58
20 M	04:32	-0.2	-6
	11:08	1.1	34
	15:33	0.5	15
	22:11	1.9	58
21 Tu	05:09	-0.2	-6
	11:47	1.1	34
	16:08	0.5	15
	22:49	1.8	55
22 W	05:47	-0.2	-6
	12:28	1.1	34
	16:47	0.5	15
	23:29	1.8	55
23 Th	06:27	-0.1	-3
	13:10	1.1	34
	17:33	0.6	18
24 F	00:13	1.7	52
	07:08	0.0	0
	13:55	1.1	34
	18:29	0.6	18
25 Sa	01:03	1.6	49
	07:51	0.1	3
	14:39	1.2	37
	19:40	0.6	18
26 Su	02:04	1.5	46
	08:36	0.2	6
	15:23	1.3	40
	21:01	0.5	15
27 M ◐	03:20	1.3	40
	09:24	0.3	9
	16:08	1.4	43
	22:21	0.3	9
28 Tu	04:49	1.2	37
	10:13	0.4	12
	16:54	1.6	49
	23:32	0.0	0
29 W	06:15	1.1	34
	11:02	0.4	12
	17:42	1.7	52
30 Th	00:35	-0.3	-9
	07:28	1.1	34
	11:52	0.4	12
	18:32	1.9	58
31 F	01:32	-0.5	-15
	08:29	1.0	30
	12:41	0.4	12
	18:59	2.1	64

StationId: 8725110
Source: NOAA/NOS/CO-OPS
Station Type: Primary
Time Zone: LST_LDT
Datum: MLLW

NOAA Tide Predictions

Naples, Gulf of Mexico, FL, 2021

Times and Heights of High and Low Waters

January

Day	Time	ft	cm	Day	Time	ft	cm
1 F	00:06	2.7	82	**16** Sa	01:30	2.6	79
	07:53	-0.8	-24		08:30	-0.5	-15
	14:46	2.1	64		15:07	2.1	64
	19:39	1.2	37		20:42	0.8	24
2 Sa	00:47	2.7	82	**17** Su	02:21	2.4	73
	08:34	-0.7	-21		09:09	-0.1	-3
	15:27	2.1	64		15:43	2.1	64
	20:26	1.1	34		21:32	0.7	21
3 Su	01:39	2.6	79	**18** M	03:16	2.1	64
	09:16	-0.4	-12		09:48	0.2	6
	16:07	2.2	67		16:21	2.2	67
	21:21	1.0	30		22:21	0.7	21
4 M	02:43	2.4	73	**19** Tu	04:18	1.9	58
	10:02	-0.1	-3		10:30	0.6	18
	16:48	2.2	67		17:02	2.1	64
	22:29	0.8	24		23:39	0.6	18
5 Tu	04:07	2.1	64	**20** W	05:31	1.6	49
	10:56	0.2	6		11:21	0.9	27
	17:29	2.3	70		17:47	2.1	64
	23:47	0.6	18	◐			
6 W	05:49	1.9	58	**21** Th	00:45	0.4	12
	11:56	0.6	18		06:50	1.5	46
	18:11	2.3	70		12:24	1.1	34
◑					18:35	2.1	64
7 Th	00:59	0.2	6	**22** F	01:46	0.2	6
	07:23	1.8	55		08:23	1.5	46
	12:58	0.9	27		13:28	1.3	40
	18:55	2.4	73		19:26	2.1	64
8 F	02:03	-0.2	-6	**23** Sa	02:41	-0.1	-3
	09:01	1.8	55		11:05	1.6	49
	14:00	1.1	34		14:30	1.4	43
	19:46	2.5	76		20:20	2.2	67
9 Sa	03:04	-0.6	-18	**24** Su	03:31	-0.3	-9
	10:26	1.9	58		11:07	1.7	52
	15:00	1.2	37		15:25	1.4	43
	20:41	2.7	82		21:12	2.3	70
10 Su	04:00	-0.9	-27	**25** M	04:16	-0.5	-15
	11:25	2.0	61		11:29	1.8	55
	15:57	1.3	40		16:10	1.4	43
	21:36	2.8	85		21:55	2.4	73
11 M	04:51	-1.1	-34	**26** Tu	04:56	-0.7	-21
	12:11	2.0	61		11:56	1.9	58
	16:47	1.2	37		16:49	1.3	40
	22:25	2.9	88		22:33	2.6	79
12 Tu	05:39	-1.2	-37	**27** W	05:35	-0.9	-27
	12:51	2.0	61		12:26	2.0	61
	17:35	1.1	34		17:26	1.2	37
	23:10	2.9	88		23:06	2.7	82
13 W	06:24	-1.1	-34	**28** Th	06:14	-0.9	-27
	13:26	2.0	61		12:59	2.1	64
	18:22	1.0	30		18:04	1.0	30
● 23:55		2.9	88	○ 23:39		2.8	85
14 Th	07:08	-1.0	-30	**29** F	06:53	-0.9	-27
	14:00	2.0	61		13:33	2.1	64
	19:09	0.9	27		18:45	0.9	27
15 F	00:41	2.8	85	**30** Sa	00:16	2.8	85
	07:50	-0.8	-24		07:31	-0.8	-24
	14:33	2.1	64		14:07	2.2	67
	19:55	0.9	27		19:28	0.7	21
				31 Su	01:01	2.7	82
					08:10	-0.6	-18
					14:39	2.2	67
					20:15	0.5	15

February

Day	Time	ft	cm	Day	Time	ft	cm
1 M	01:54	2.6	79	**16** Tu	02:49	2.1	64
	08:49	-0.3	-9		09:01	0.4	12
	15:12	2.3	70		15:15	2.3	70
	21:06	0.4	12		21:44	0.3	9
2 Tu	02:57	2.3	70	**17** W	03:42	1.9	58
	09:29	0.1	3		09:24	0.8	24
	15:44	2.3	70		15:47	2.2	67
	22:07	0.2	6		22:41	0.3	9
3 W	04:12	2.0	61	**18** Th	04:48	1.6	49
	10:14	0.5	15		09:26	1.0	30
	16:20	2.3	70		16:23	2.1	64
	23:19	0.1	3		23:50	0.3	9
4 Th	05:46	1.7	52	**19** F	06:10	1.5	46
	11:10	0.9	27		09:14	1.2	37
	17:07	2.4	73		17:14	2.1	64
◑				◐			
5 F	00:35	-0.2	-6	**20** Sa	00:59	0.2	6
	07:28	1.6	49		18:27	2.1	64
	12:23	1.2	37				
	18:07	2.4	73				
6 Sa	01:46	-0.4	-12	**21** Su	02:02	0.0	0
	10:02	1.6	49		19:39	2.1	64
	13:37	1.4	43				
	19:18	2.4	73				
7 Su	02:51	-0.6	-18	**22** M	02:58	-0.2	-6
	11:12	1.8	55		11:24	1.7	52
	14:48	1.4	43		14:58	1.5	46
	20:33	2.5	76		20:45	2.3	70
8 M	03:50	-0.8	-24	**23** Tu	03:47	-0.4	-12
	11:47	1.9	58		11:07	1.9	58
	15:49	1.3	40		15:48	1.4	43
	21:38	2.7	82		21:37	2.5	76
9 Tu	04:40	-0.9	-27	**24** W	04:30	-0.6	-18
	12:11	2.0	61		11:27	2.0	61
	16:41	1.1	34		16:29	1.2	37
	22:30	2.8	85		22:21	2.7	82
10 W	05:26	-0.9	-27	**25** Th	05:10	-0.7	-21
	12:32	2.0	61		11:53	2.1	64
	17:27	0.9	27		17:08	1.0	30
	23:15	2.8	85		22:59	2.8	85
11 Th	06:07	-0.8	-24	**26** F	05:49	-0.7	-21
	12:53	2.1	64		12:20	2.3	70
	18:10	0.7	21		17:47	0.7	21
● 23:56		2.8	85		23:38	2.9	88
12 F	06:46	-0.7	-21	**27** Sa	06:27	-0.7	-21
	13:17	2.2	67		12:48	2.4	73
	18:53	0.6	18		18:29	0.5	15
				○			
13 Sa	00:37	2.7	82	**28** Su	00:20	2.9	88
	07:24	-0.4	-12		07:05	-0.5	-15
	13:44	2.2	67		13:16	2.5	76
	19:34	0.5	15		19:13	0.2	6
14 Su	01:19	2.5	76				
	07:59	-0.2	-6				
	14:13	2.3	70				
	20:15	0.4	12				
15 M	02:03	2.3	70				
	08:31	0.1	3				
	14:44	2.3	70				
	20:57	0.4	12				

March

Day	Time	ft	cm	Day	Time	ft	cm
1 M	01:08	2.8	85	**16** Tu	02:46	2.4	73
	07:43	-0.2	-6		08:54	0.6	18
	13:44	2.5	76		14:43	2.5	76
	19:59	0.0	0		21:26	0.1	3
2 Tu	02:03	2.6	79	**17** W	03:30	2.2	67
	08:21	0.2	6		09:17	0.8	24
	14:13	2.6	79		15:07	2.5	76
	20:50	-0.2	-6		22:07	0.1	3
3 W	03:05	2.3	70	**18** Th	04:19	2.0	61
	08:58	0.6	18		09:29	1.1	34
	14:43	2.6	79		15:27	2.4	73
	21:47	-0.2	-6		22:55	0.2	6
4 Th	04:19	2.0	61	**19** F	05:22	1.8	55
	09:37	1.0	30		09:29	1.3	40
	15:20	2.6	79		15:49	2.3	70
	22:57	-0.2	-6		23:58	0.2	6
5 F	05:52	1.7	52	**20** Sa	06:43	1.6	49
	10:25	1.3	40		09:37	1.4	43
	16:10	2.5	76		16:20	2.2	67
6 Sa	00:15	-0.3	-9	**21** Su	01:12	0.2	6
	07:59	1.6	49		17:17	2.2	67
	12:00	1.6	49	◐			
◑ 17:36		2.4	73				
7 Su	01:29	-0.3	-9	**22** M	02:20	0.1	3
	10:39	1.8	55		19:55	2.2	67
	13:30	1.6	49				
	19:13	2.4	73				
8 M	02:36	-0.4	-12	**23** Tu	03:19	0.0	0
	11:09	2.0	61		11:06	1.9	58
	14:44	1.5	46		15:30	1.6	49
	20:36	2.5	76		21:13	2.3	70
9 Tu	03:35	-0.4	-12	**24** W	04:11	-0.1	-3
	11:28	2.1	64		11:21	2.1	64
	15:44	1.2	37		16:22	1.4	43
	21:42	2.6	79		22:14	2.5	76
10 W	04:24	-0.4	-12	**25** Th	04:57	-0.3	-9
	11:40	2.1	64		11:44	2.3	70
	16:33	1.0	30		17:05	1.1	34
	22:32	2.7	82		23:04	2.8	85
11 Th	05:06	-0.4	-12	**26** F	05:39	-0.3	-9
	11:52	2.2	67		12:09	2.4	73
	17:15	0.7	21		17:46	0.8	24
	23:13	2.8	85		23:48	2.9	88
12 F	05:44	-0.3	-9	**27** Sa	06:19	-0.3	-9
	12:08	2.3	70		12:34	2.6	79
	17:55	0.5	15		18:27	0.4	12
	23:51	2.7	82				
13 Sa	06:19	-0.1	-3	**28** Su	00:32	3.0	91
	12:29	2.4	73		06:58	-0.1	-3
	18:33	0.4	12		12:59	2.7	82
●				○ 19:10		0.0	0
14 Su	00:27	2.7	82	**29** M	01:18	3.0	91
	06:53	0.1	3		07:36	0.1	3
	13:53	2.5	76		13:24	2.8	85
	20:10	0.2	6		19:56	-0.3	-9
15 M	02:05	2.5	76	**30** Tu	02:10	2.8	85
	08:25	0.3	9		08:15	0.4	12
	14:18	2.5	76		13:50	2.9	88
	20:48	0.1	3		20:44	-0.5	-15
				31 W	03:08	2.6	79
					08:53	0.8	24
					14:20	2.9	88
					21:35	-0.5	-15

StationId: 8725110
Source: NOAA/NOS/CO-OPS
Station Type: Primary
Time Zone: LST_LDT
Datum: MLLW

Naples, Gulf of Mexico, FL, 2021

Times and Heights of High and Low Waters

April

Day	Time	ft	cm
1 Th	04:13	2.3	70
	09:31	1.1	34
	14:56	2.9	88
	22:32	-0.5	-15
2 F	05:28	2.0	61
	10:10	1.4	43
	15:39	2.8	85
	23:38	-0.3	-9
3 Sa	07:03	1.9	58
	11:06	1.6	49
	16:40	2.6	79
4 Su	00:54	-0.2	-6
	10:08	1.9	58
	12:55	1.8	55
	18:33	2.5	76
5 M	02:08	-0.1	-3
	11:03	2.0	61
	14:26	1.6	49
	20:11	2.4	73
6	03:13	0.0	0
	11:27	2.2	67
	15:37	1.4	43
	21:32	2.5	76
7 W	04:10	0.0	0
	11:39	2.3	70
	16:33	1.1	34
	22:37	2.6	79
8 Th	04:57	0.1	3
	11:50	2.4	73
	17:18	0.8	24
	23:26	2.6	79
9	05:38	0.2	6
	12:04	2.5	76
	17:58	0.6	18
10 Sa	00:05	2.7	82
	06:15	0.4	12
	12:22	2.6	79
	18:35	0.3	9
11 Su	00:41	2.6	79
	06:48	0.5	15
	12:43	2.7	82
	19:11	0.1	3
12	01:16	2.6	79
	07:20	0.7	21
	13:05	2.8	85
	19:46	0.0	0
13	01:53	2.5	76
	07:50	0.9	27
	13:27	2.8	85
	20:23	-0.1	-3
14	02:33	2.4	73
	08:17	1.1	34
	13:46	2.7	82
	21:00	-0.1	-3
15	03:18	2.2	67
	08:37	1.2	37
	14:04	2.7	82
	21:40	-0.1	-3
16 F	04:10	2.1	64
	08:48	1.4	43
	14:25	2.6	79
	22:25	0.0	0
17 Sa	05:12	1.9	58
	09:00	1.5	46
	14:55	2.5	76
	23:20	0.1	3
18 Su	06:27	1.9	58
	09:22	1.7	52
	15:34	2.4	73
19 M	00:28	0.2	6
	07:44	1.9	58
	09:59	1.8	55
	16:32	2.3	70
20 Tu	01:36	0.2	6
	08:53	2.0	61
	13:48	1.8	55
	19:04	2.3	70
21 W	02:35	0.2	6
	09:45	2.2	67
	14:58	1.6	49
	20:37	2.4	73
22 Th	03:29	0.1	3
	10:23	2.3	70
	15:51	1.3	40
	21:47	2.6	79
23 F	04:18	0.1	3
	10:53	2.5	76
	16:38	0.9	27
	22:46	2.8	85
24 Sa	05:03	0.2	6
	11:20	2.7	82
	17:23	0.4	12
	23:37	2.9	88
25 Su	05:45	0.3	9
	11:46	2.9	88
	18:07	0.0	0
26 M	00:26	2.9	88
	06:26	0.5	15
	12:11	3.0	91
	18:53	-0.4	-12
27 Tu	01:17	2.9	88
	07:06	0.7	21
	12:38	3.2	98
	19:41	-0.7	-21
28 W	02:13	2.7	82
	07:47	1.0	30
	13:08	3.2	98
	20:31	-0.8	-24
29 Th	03:14	2.5	76
	08:28	1.2	37
	13:43	3.2	98
	21:23	-0.8	-24
30 F	04:20	2.3	70
	09:10	1.4	43
	14:27	3.1	94
	22:18	-0.6	-18

May

Day	Time	ft	cm
1 Sa	05:33	2.1	64
	09:59	1.6	49
	15:22	2.9	88
	23:20	-0.3	-9
2 Su	06:57	2.0	61
	11:08	1.8	55
	16:42	2.7	82
3 M	00:29	-0.1	-3
	08:20	2.1	64
	12:47	1.7	52
	18:28	2.5	76
4 Tu	01:38	0.1	3
	09:29	2.2	67
	14:12	1.5	46
	19:56	2.4	73
5 W	02:40	0.3	9
	10:06	2.3	70
	15:18	1.3	40
	21:13	2.4	73
6 Th	03:34	0.5	15
	10:30	2.4	73
	16:12	0.9	27
	22:22	2.4	73
7 F	04:22	0.6	18
	10:52	2.6	79
	16:57	0.6	18
	23:14	2.4	73
8 Sa	05:04	0.8	24
	11:15	2.7	82
	17:36	0.4	12
	23:54	2.5	76
9 Su	05:41	0.9	27
	11:39	2.8	85
	18:13	0.1	3
10 M	00:30	2.4	73
	06:16	1.0	30
	12:03	2.9	88
	18:48	0.0	0
11 Tu	01:06	2.4	73
	06:47	1.2	37
	12:25	2.9	88
	19:25	-0.2	-6
12 W	01:44	2.3	70
	07:17	1.3	40
	12:46	2.9	88
	20:02	-0.2	-6
13 Th	02:27	2.3	70
	07:43	1.4	43
	13:04	2.9	88
	20:40	-0.3	-9
14 F	03:15	2.2	67
	08:05	1.5	46
	13:23	2.8	85
	21:20	-0.2	-6
15 Sa	04:07	2.1	64
	08:26	1.6	49
	13:50	2.8	85
	22:03	-0.1	-3
16 Su	05:05	2.1	64
	08:55	1.7	52
	14:26	2.7	82
	22:52	0.0	0
17 M	06:08	2.1	64
	09:37	1.8	55
	15:15	2.6	79
	23:49	0.1	3
18 Tu	07:07	2.2	67
	10:59	1.8	55
	16:21	2.5	76
19 W	00:51	0.2	6
	07:57	2.3	70
	13:13	1.7	52
	18:24	2.4	73
20 Th	01:50	0.3	9
	08:41	2.4	73
	14:23	1.4	43
	20:04	2.4	73
21 F	02:45	0.4	12
	09:21	2.5	76
	15:20	1.0	30
	21:22	2.5	76
22 Sa	03:36	0.5	15
	09:56	2.7	82
	16:12	0.5	15
	22:31	2.6	79
23 Su	04:25	0.7	21
	10:29	2.9	88
	17:02	0.0	0
	23:30	2.7	82
24 M	05:11	0.9	27
	11:01	3.1	94
	17:50	-0.4	-12
25 Tu	00:24	2.7	82
	05:55	1.1	34
	11:32	3.2	98
	18:39	-0.8	-24
26 W	01:19	2.6	79
	06:38	1.2	37
	12:06	3.4	104
	19:28	-0.9	-27
27 Th	02:17	2.5	76
	07:22	1.4	43
	12:43	3.4	104
	20:19	-1.0	-30
28 F	03:18	2.4	73
	08:08	1.5	46
	13:26	3.3	101
	21:10	-0.8	-24
29 Sa	04:19	2.2	67
	08:57	1.5	46
	14:18	3.2	98
	22:02	-0.6	-18
30 Su	05:19	2.2	67
	09:52	1.6	49
	15:24	2.9	88
	22:57	-0.3	-9
31 M	06:19	2.2	67
	11:00	1.6	49
	16:44	2.7	82
	23:57	0.1	3

June

Day	Time	ft	cm
1 Tu	07:12	2.2	67
	12:24	1.6	49
	18:09	2.5	76
2 W	00:59	0.4	12
	07:58	2.3	70
	13:43	1.3	40
	19:27	2.3	70
3 Th	01:57	0.6	18
	08:38	2.4	73
	14:47	1.1	34
	20:41	2.2	67
4 F	02:50	0.8	24
	09:17	2.6	79
	15:41	0.8	24
	21:55	2.2	67
5 Sa	03:40	1.0	30
	09:53	2.7	82
	16:29	0.5	15
	22:58	2.2	67
6 Su	04:25	1.2	37
	10:28	2.7	82
	17:11	0.2	6
	23:44	2.2	67
7 M	05:07	1.3	40
	11:00	2.8	85
	17:50	0.0	0
8 Tu	00:23	2.2	67
	05:44	1.4	43
	11:29	2.9	88
	18:27	-0.2	-6
9 W	01:00	2.2	67
	06:17	1.5	46
	11:56	2.9	88
	19:05	-0.3	-9
10 Th	01:40	2.2	67
	06:48	1.5	46
	12:20	2.9	88
	19:43	-0.3	-9
11 F	02:23	2.2	67
	07:18	1.6	49
	12:42	2.9	88
	20:22	-0.4	-12
12 Sa	03:10	2.2	67
	07:49	1.6	49
	13:05	2.9	88
	21:02	-0.3	-9
13 Su	03:58	2.2	67
	08:25	1.7	52
	13:37	2.9	88
	21:43	-0.3	-9
14 M	04:46	2.2	67
	09:08	1.7	52
	14:19	2.8	85
	22:26	-0.1	-3
15 Tu	05:34	2.3	70
	10:00	1.7	52
	15:15	2.7	82
	23:14	0.1	3
16 W	06:21	2.4	73
	11:11	1.6	49
	16:25	2.6	79
17 Th	00:08	0.3	9
	07:03	2.4	73
	12:38	1.4	43
	18:06	2.4	73
18 F	01:05	0.5	15
	07:43	2.5	76
	13:50	1.1	34
	19:41	2.3	70
19 Sa	02:01	0.7	21
	08:21	2.7	82
	14:51	0.6	18
	21:05	2.3	70
20 Su	02:55	1.0	30
	09:00	2.8	85
	15:49	0.2	6
	22:24	2.3	70
21 M	03:49	1.2	37
	09:42	3.0	91
	16:44	-0.3	-9
	23:32	2.4	73
22 Tu	04:41	1.3	40
	10:25	3.2	98
	17:36	-0.6	-18
23 W	00:29	2.4	73
	05:30	1.4	43
	11:08	3.3	101
	18:27	-0.8	-24
24 Th	01:24	2.4	73
	06:17	1.5	46
	11:51	3.5	107
	19:17	-0.9	-27
25 F	02:19	2.3	70
	07:05	1.5	46
	12:36	3.5	107
	20:06	-0.9	-27
26 Sa	03:10	2.3	70
	07:55	1.5	46
	13:25	3.4	104
	20:55	-0.7	-21
27 Su	03:57	2.3	70
	08:46	1.4	43
	14:21	3.2	98
	21:42	-0.4	-12
28 M	04:41	2.3	70
	09:40	1.4	43
	15:23	3.0	91
	22:29	-0.1	-3
29 Tu	05:25	2.4	73
	10:39	1.4	43
	16:28	2.7	82
	23:19	0.3	9
30 W	06:08	2.4	73
	11:47	1.3	40
	17:37	2.5	76

StationId: 8725110
Source: NOAA/NOS/CO-OPS
Station Type: Primary
Time Zone: LST_LDT
Datum: MLLW

NOAA Tide Predictions

Naples, Gulf of Mexico, FL, 2021

Times and Heights of High and Low Waters

July

Day	Time (h m)	Height (ft)	Height (cm)
1 Th ◐	00:12	0.7	21
	06:51	2.5	76
	13:01	1.2	37
	18:50	2.2	67
2 F	01:08	1.0	30
	07:33	2.6	79
	14:06	1.0	30
	20:02	2.1	64
3 Sa	02:03	1.2	37
	08:16	2.6	79
	15:03	0.7	21
	21:19	2.0	61
4 Su	02:56	1.4	43
	09:00	2.7	82
	15:56	0.5	15
	22:43	2.0	61
5 M	03:46	1.5	46
	09:44	2.7	82
	16:43	0.2	6
	23:41	2.1	64
6 Tu	04:34	1.6	49
	10:27	2.8	85
	17:26	0.0	0
7 W	00:20	2.1	64
	05:16	1.7	52
	11:06	2.9	88
	18:07	-0.1	-3
8 Th	00:55	2.2	67
	05:53	1.7	52
	11:40	3.0	91
	18:46	-0.2	-6
9 F	01:31	2.2	67
	06:27	1.7	52
	12:10	3.0	91
	19:24	-0.3	-9
10 Sa ●	02:10	2.3	70
	07:02	1.6	49
	12:37	3.1	94
	20:03	-0.3	-9
11 Su	02:50	2.3	70
	07:39	1.6	49
	13:06	3.1	94
	20:41	-0.3	-9
12 M	03:30	2.4	73
	08:20	1.6	49
	13:41	3.1	94
	21:20	-0.2	-6
13 Tu	04:08	2.5	76
	09:05	1.5	46
	14:27	3.0	91
	21:59	0.0	0
14 W	04:47	2.5	76
	09:54	1.4	43
	15:24	2.9	88
	22:41	0.2	6
15 Th	05:25	2.6	79
	10:53	1.3	40
	16:32	2.7	82
	23:27	0.6	18
16 F	06:03	2.6	79
	12:06	1.1	34
	17:59	2.5	76
17 Sa ◑	00:21	0.9	27
	06:43	2.7	82
	13:20	0.8	24
	19:31	2.3	70
18 Su	01:20	1.2	37
	07:25	2.8	85
	14:27	0.4	12
	21:01	2.2	67
19 M	02:21	1.4	43
	08:14	2.9	88
	15:31	0.1	3
	22:34	2.2	67
20 Tu	03:21	1.6	49
	09:09	3.1	94
	16:30	-0.3	-9
	23:47	2.3	70
21 W	04:20	1.7	52
	10:08	3.3	101
	17:25	-0.5	-15
22 Th	00:39	2.3	70
	05:15	1.6	49
	11:03	3.4	104
	18:16	-0.6	-18
23 F	01:23	2.4	73
	06:05	1.6	49
	11:52	3.5	107
	19:04	-0.6	-18
24 Sa ○	02:03	2.4	73
	06:54	1.5	46
	12:39	3.5	107
	19:50	-0.5	-15
25 Su	02:39	2.4	73
	07:43	1.3	40
	13:27	3.4	104
	20:34	-0.3	-9
26 M	03:14	2.5	76
	08:31	1.3	40
	14:18	3.3	101
	21:16	0.0	0
27 Tu	03:49	2.6	79
	09:20	1.2	37
	15:11	3.1	94
	21:56	0.3	9
28 W	04:25	2.6	79
	10:10	1.1	34
	16:05	2.8	85
	22:37	0.7	21
29 Th	05:04	2.6	79
	11:05	1.1	34
	17:03	2.5	76
	23:20	1.0	30
30 F	05:45	2.7	82
	12:10	1.0	30
	18:09	2.3	70
31 Sa ◐	00:10	1.3	40
	06:31	2.7	82
	13:18	0.9	27
	19:22	2.1	64

August

Day	Time (h m)	Height (ft)	Height (cm)
1 Su	01:10	1.6	49
	07:20	2.7	82
	14:21	0.8	24
	20:42	2.0	61
2 M	02:12	1.8	55
	08:12	2.7	82
	15:20	0.6	18
	22:50	2.0	61
3 Tu	03:12	1.9	58
	09:08	2.7	82
	16:14	0.4	12
	23:55	2.1	64
4 W	04:07	1.9	58
	10:02	2.8	85
	17:01	0.2	6
5 Th	00:12	2.2	67
	04:54	1.8	55
	10:49	3.0	91
	17:44	0.1	3
6 F	00:37	2.3	70
	05:33	1.8	55
	11:28	3.1	94
	18:23	-0.1	-3
7 Sa	01:06	2.4	73
	06:09	1.7	52
	12:03	3.2	98
	19:01	-0.1	-3
8 Su ●	01:37	2.5	76
	06:46	1.6	49
	12:35	3.3	101
	19:38	-0.1	-3
9 M	02:10	2.6	79
	07:24	1.4	43
	13:09	3.4	104
	20:15	0.0	0
10 Tu	02:44	2.7	82
	08:06	1.3	40
	13:48	3.3	101
	20:53	0.1	3
11 W	03:16	2.7	82
	08:50	1.1	34
	14:36	3.2	98
	21:30	0.4	12
12 Th	03:48	2.8	85
	09:38	1.0	30
	15:32	3.0	91
	22:08	0.7	21
13 F	04:19	2.8	85
	10:33	0.8	24
	16:39	2.8	85
	22:49	1.1	34
14 Sa	04:53	2.9	88
	11:39	0.7	21
	18:01	2.5	76
	23:38	1.4	43
15 Su ◖	05:36	2.9	88
	12:55	0.5	15
	19:33	2.3	70
16 M	00:45	1.7	52
	06:35	3.0	91
	14:08	0.3	9
	21:16	2.2	67
17 Tu	01:59	1.9	58
	07:46	3.0	91
	15:16	0.1	3
	23:11	2.3	70
18 W	03:09	1.9	58
	09:01	3.2	98
	16:19	0.0	0
19 Th	00:03	2.4	73
	04:13	1.8	55
	10:11	3.3	101
	17:14	-0.2	-6
20 F	00:34	2.5	76
	05:09	1.7	52
	11:08	3.5	107
	18:02	-0.2	-6
21 Sa	01:00	2.6	79
	05:58	1.5	46
	11:57	3.6	110
	18:47	-0.1	-3
22 Su ○	01:25	2.6	79
	06:43	1.3	40
	12:41	3.6	110
	19:28	0.1	3
23 M	01:52	2.7	82
	07:28	1.1	34
	13:24	3.5	107
	20:07	0.3	9
24 Tu	02:20	2.8	85
	08:11	1.0	30
	14:07	3.3	101
	20:45	0.5	15
25 W	02:51	2.9	88
	08:55	0.9	27
	14:53	3.1	94
	21:20	0.8	24
26 Th	03:23	2.9	88
	09:38	0.9	27
	15:40	2.9	88
	21:54	1.1	34
27 F	03:56	2.9	88
	10:24	0.9	27
	16:32	2.7	82
	22:26	1.4	43
28 Sa	04:32	2.8	85
	11:19	0.9	27
	17:34	2.4	73
	22:54	1.7	52
29 Su	05:16	2.7	82
	12:26	0.9	27
	18:48	2.2	67
	22:37	1.9	58
30 M ◐	06:17	2.7	82
	13:37	0.9	27
	20:11	2.2	67
31 Tu	01:29	2.1	64
	07:27	2.7	82
	14:42	0.8	24

September

Day	Time (h m)	Height (ft)	Height (cm)
1 W	00:17	2.2	67
	02:46	2.1	64
	08:35	2.8	85
	15:40	0.6	18
	23:39	2.3	70
2 Th	03:45	2.1	64
	09:38	2.9	88
	16:31	0.5	15
	23:39	2.5	76
3 F	04:33	1.9	58
	10:30	3.1	94
	17:15	0.3	9
4 Sa	00:01	2.6	79
	05:13	1.8	55
	11:13	3.3	101
	17:54	0.2	6
5 Su	00:27	2.7	82
	05:49	1.6	49
	11:51	3.4	104
	18:31	0.2	6
6 M	00:54	2.8	85
	06:26	1.3	40
	12:27	3.5	107
	19:08	0.3	9
7 Tu ●	01:21	2.9	88
	07:06	1.1	34
	13:05	3.5	107
	19:45	0.4	12
8 W	01:47	3.0	91
	07:48	0.8	24
	13:49	3.5	107
	20:23	0.6	18
9 Th	02:14	3.1	94
	08:33	0.6	18
	14:40	3.3	101
	21:00	0.9	27
10 F	02:41	3.1	94
	09:21	0.5	15
	15:38	3.1	94
	21:38	1.2	37
11 Sa	03:11	3.1	94
	10:15	0.4	12
	16:47	2.8	85
	22:16	1.6	49
12 Su	03:48	3.1	94
	11:19	0.4	12
	18:11	2.5	76
	23:03	1.9	58
13 M ◐	04:37	3.1	94
	12:35	0.4	12
	19:47	2.4	73
14 Tu	00:24	2.1	64
	06:01	3.0	91
	13:52	0.4	12
	22:04	2.4	73
15 W ◐	01:55	2.1	64
	07:42	3.1	94
	15:01	0.3	9
	23:18	2.5	76
16 Th	03:08	2.0	61
	09:06	3.2	98
	16:03	0.3	9
	23:43	2.6	79
17 F	04:10	1.8	55
	10:16	3.3	101
	16:57	0.3	9
18 Sa	00:02	2.7	82
	05:02	1.5	46
	11:12	3.4	104
	17:42	0.4	12
19 Su	00:20	2.8	85
	05:48	1.2	37
	11:57	3.5	107
	18:23	0.5	15
20 M ○	00:40	2.9	88
	06:30	1.0	30
	12:37	3.5	107
	19:01	0.7	21
21 Tu	01:02	3.0	91
	07:10	0.8	24
	13:15	3.4	104
	19:37	0.9	27
22 W	01:26	3.1	94
	07:49	0.7	21
	13:54	3.2	98
	20:11	1.1	34
23 Th	01:51	3.1	94
	08:28	0.6	18
	14:35	3.1	94
	20:43	1.3	40
24 F	02:17	3.1	94
	09:08	0.6	18
	15:20	2.9	88
	21:13	1.5	46
25 Sa	02:43	3.0	91
	09:50	0.6	18
	16:10	2.7	82
	21:36	1.8	55
26 Su	03:08	2.9	88
	10:37	0.7	21
	17:10	2.5	76
	21:43	1.9	58
27 M	03:36	2.8	85
	11:37	0.8	24
	18:24	2.4	73
	21:41	2.1	64
28 Tu	04:16	2.7	82
	12:50	0.9	27
	19:45	2.3	70
	21:57	2.2	67
29 W ◐	06:32	2.6	79
	13:59	0.8	24
	23:42	2.3	70
30 Th	02:21	2.2	67
	08:00	2.7	82
	14:59	0.7	21
	22:13	2.5	76

StationId: 8725110
Source: NOAA/NOS/CO-OPS
Station Type: Primary
Time Zone: LST_LDT
Datum: MLLW

October

Day	Time	ft	cm	Day	Time	ft	cm
1 F	03:21	2.1	64	16 Sa	04:02	1.5	46
	09:08	2.8	85		10:15	3.1	94
	15:52	0.7	21		16:31	0.7	21
	22:47	2.6	79		23:14	2.8	85
2 Sa	04:07	1.9	58	17 Su	04:51	1.1	34
	10:06	3.0	91		11:10	3.1	94
	16:38	0.6	18		17:15	0.8	24
	23:15	2.8	85		23:34	2.9	88
3 Su	04:48	1.6	49	18 M	05:34	0.8	24
	10:54	3.2	98		11:53	3.2	98
	17:19	0.5	15		17:54	0.9	27
	23:42	2.9	88		23:56	3.0	91
4 M	05:26	1.2	37	19 Tu	06:13	0.6	18
	11:36	3.4	104		12:30	3.1	94
	17:58	0.6	18		18:30	1.1	34
5 Tu	00:06	3.1	94	20 W	00:18	3.1	94
	06:05	0.9	27		06:50	0.4	12
	12:17	3.5	107		13:06	3.0	91
	18:36	0.7	21		19:05	1.3	40
6 W	00:30	3.2	98	21 Th	00:40	3.1	94
	06:46	0.5	15		07:27	0.3	9
	13:00	3.5	107		13:42	2.9	88
	19:14	0.8	24		19:37	1.4	43
7 Th	00:53	3.3	101	22 F	01:01	3.1	94
	07:30	0.2	6		08:04	0.2	6
	13:48	3.4	104		14:22	2.8	85
	19:52	1.1	34		20:08	1.6	49
8 F	01:17	3.3	101	23 Sa	01:21	3.1	94
	08:16	0.0	0		08:43	0.2	6
	14:43	3.2	98		15:07	2.7	82
	20:31	1.3	40		20:35	1.7	52
9 Sa	01:45	3.4	104	24 Su	01:41	3.0	91
	09:06	-0.1	-3		09:23	0.3	9
	15:45	2.9	88		15:57	2.5	76
	21:10	1.6	49		20:56	1.9	58
10 Su	02:20	3.4	104	25 M	02:05	2.9	88
	10:00	0.0	0		10:06	0.4	12
	16:56	2.7	82		16:56	2.4	73
	21:52	1.9	58		21:08	2.0	61
11 M	03:05	3.3	101	26 Tu	02:35	2.8	85
	11:02	0.1	3		10:58	0.5	15
	18:21	2.5	76		18:05	2.3	70
	22:46	2.1	64		21:28	2.1	64
12 Tu	04:05	3.1	94	27 W	03:17	2.7	82
	12:16	0.3	9		12:03	0.6	18
	19:53	2.4	73		19:15	2.3	70
					22:14	2.2	67
13 W	00:20	2.2	67	28 Th	04:21	2.5	76
	05:57	3.0	91		13:11	0.7	21
	13:32	0.4	12		20:16	2.4	73
	21:35	2.5	76				
14 Th	01:53	2.1	64	29 F	01:45	2.1	64
	07:42	2.9	88		07:14	2.5	76
	14:40	0.5	15		14:12	0.7	21
	22:29	2.6	79		21:08	2.5	76
15 F	03:04	1.8	55	30 Sa	02:46	1.9	58
	09:05	3.0	91		08:30	2.6	79
	15:39	0.6	18		15:06	0.7	21
	22:54	2.7	82		21:49	2.7	82
				31 Su	03:35	1.5	46
					09:35	2.8	85
					15:55	0.7	21
					22:23	2.8	85

November

Day	Time	ft	cm	Day	Time	ft	cm
1 M	04:19	1.1	34	16 Tu	04:15	0.4	12
	10:32	2.9	88		10:49	2.6	79
	16:40	0.7	21		16:23	1.2	37
	22:52	2.9	88		22:15	2.9	88
2 Tu	05:02	0.7	21	17 W	04:54	0.1	3
	11:22	3.1	94		11:25	2.6	79
	17:22	0.8	24		17:01	1.3	40
	23:18	3.1	94		22:41	3.0	91
3 W	05:44	0.2	6	18 Th	05:31	-0.1	-3
	12:09	3.2	98		12:00	2.6	79
	18:03	1.0	30		17:35	1.4	43
	23:43	3.2	98		23:05	3.0	91
4 Th	06:28	-0.2	-6	19 F	06:07	-0.2	-6
	12:57	3.1	94		12:36	2.5	76
	18:43	1.2	37		18:08	1.5	46
				○	23:27	3.0	91
5 F	00:09	3.4	104	20 Sa	06:45	-0.2	-6
	07:14	-0.5	-15		13:16	2.4	73
	13:49	3.0	91		18:39	1.6	49
	19:23	1.3	40		23:47	2.9	88
6 Sa	00:37	3.4	104	21 Su	07:23	-0.2	-6
	08:03	-0.6	-18		14:01	2.4	73
	14:48	2.8	85		19:07	1.7	52
	20:05	1.5	46				
7 Su	01:11	3.4	104	22 M	00:08	2.8	85
	07:54	-0.6	-18		08:02	-0.2	-6
	14:52	2.6	79		14:50	2.3	70
	19:49	1.7	52		19:35	1.7	52
8 M	00:53	3.3	101	23 Tu	00:34	2.8	85
	08:43	-0.5	-15		08:43	-0.1	-3
	15:59	2.5	76		15:42	2.3	70
	20:38	1.8	55		20:05	1.8	55
9 Tu	01:47	3.2	98	24 W	01:09	2.7	82
	09:46	-0.2	-6		09:28	0.1	3
	17:13	2.4	73		16:38	2.2	67
	21:42	1.9	58		20:48	1.8	55
10 W	03:04	2.9	88	25 Th	01:56	2.5	76
	10:53	0.1	3		10:19	0.2	6
	18:24	2.4	73		17:34	2.3	70
	23:11	1.9	58		22:07	1.8	55
11 Th	04:56	2.7	82	26 F	03:01	2.4	73
	12:03	0.3	9		11:19	0.4	12
	19:24	2.4	73		18:24	2.3	70
					23:56	1.7	52
12 F	00:39	1.7	52	27 Sa	05:11	2.3	70
	06:30	2.6	79		12:20	0.5	15
	13:08	0.6	18		19:08	2.4	73
	20:11	2.5	76				
13 Sa	01:48	1.3	40	28 Su	01:05	1.4	43
	07:51	2.6	79		06:49	2.3	70
	14:05	0.7	21		13:16	0.6	18
	20:49	2.6	79		19:48	2.5	76
14 Su	02:45	1.0	30	29 M	02:00	1.0	30
	09:05	2.6	79		08:04	2.3	70
	14:57	0.9	27		14:08	0.8	24
	21:20	2.7	82		20:24	2.6	79
15 M	03:33	0.7	21	30 Tu	02:50	0.5	15
	10:05	2.6	79		09:14	2.4	73
	15:43	1.1	34		14:59	0.9	27
	21:48	2.8	85		20:59	2.8	85

December

Day	Time	ft	cm	Day	Time	ft	cm
1 W	03:39	0.0	0	16 Th	04:34	-0.3	-9
	10:14	2.6	79		11:29	2.1	64
	15:47	1.0	30		16:35	1.3	40
	21:32	3.0	91		22:13	2.7	82
2 Th	04:26	-0.5	-15	17 F	05:13	-0.4	-12
	11:07	2.6	79		12:01	2.1	64
	16:32	1.2	37		17:12	1.4	43
	22:05	3.1	94		22:43	2.7	82
3 F	05:14	-0.8	-24	18 Sa	05:50	-0.6	-18
	11:59	2.6	79		12:35	2.1	64
	17:16	1.3	40		17:46	1.4	43
	22:40	3.3	101		23:11	2.7	82
4 Sa	06:02	-1.1	-34	19 Su	06:28	-0.6	-18
	12:54	2.5	76		13:12	2.1	64
	18:00	1.4	43		18:19	1.4	43
●	23:17	3.3	101	○	23:36	2.7	82
5 Su	06:52	-1.1	-34	20 M	07:06	-0.6	-18
	13:51	2.4	73		13:53	2.1	64
	18:46	1.4	43		18:52	1.4	43
	23:59	3.3	101				
6 M	07:43	-1.0	-30	21 Tu	00:00	2.6	79
	14:48	2.3	70		07:44	-0.6	-18
	19:36	1.4	43		14:34	2.1	64
					19:27	1.4	43
7 Tu	00:49	3.2	98	22 W	00:28	2.6	79
	08:34	-0.8	-24		08:22	-0.5	-15
	15:43	2.2	67		15:17	2.1	64
	20:30	1.4	43		20:05	1.4	43
8 W	01:52	2.9	88	23 Th	01:06	2.5	76
	09:26	-0.5	-15		09:00	-0.3	-9
	16:38	2.2	67		16:00	2.1	64
	21:32	1.4	43		20:51	1.4	43
9 Th	03:11	2.6	79	24 F	01:55	2.4	73
	10:23	-0.1	-3		09:42	-0.1	-3
	17:30	2.2	67		16:43	2.2	67
	22:48	1.3	40		21:49	1.3	40
10 F	04:38	2.4	73	25 Sa	02:57	2.2	67
	11:24	0.3	9		10:28	0.1	3
	18:18	2.3	70		17:25	2.2	67
					23:06	1.1	34
11 Sa	00:10	1.1	34	26 Su	04:27	2.0	61
	06:04	2.2	67		11:23	0.4	12
	12:26	0.6	18		18:05	2.3	70
●	19:02	2.3	70				
12 Su	01:19	0.8	24	27 M	00:21	0.8	24
	07:24	2.1	64		06:13	1.9	58
	13:23	0.8	24		12:23	0.6	18
◑	19:43	2.4	73	◑	18:43	2.3	70
13 M	02:17	0.5	15	28 Tu	01:25	0.4	12
	08:49	2.0	61		07:41	1.9	58
	14:17	1.0	30		13:23	0.9	27
	20:24	2.5	76		19:23	2.5	76
14 Tu	03:09	0.2	6	29 W	02:23	-0.1	-3
	10:05	2.0	61		09:06	1.9	58
	15:08	1.2	37		14:19	1.1	34
	21:03	2.6	79		20:06	2.6	79
15 W	03:54	0.0	0	30 Th	03:19	-0.5	-15
	10:54	2.1	64		10:17	2.0	61
	15:54	1.3	40		15:15	1.2	37
	21:39	2.6	79		20:53	2.8	85
				31 F	04:12	-0.9	-27
					11:15	2.1	64
					16:08	1.2	37
					21:36	2.9	88

StationId: 8726520
Source: NOAA/NOS/CO-OPS
Station Type: Primary
Time Zone: LST_LDT
Datum: MLLW

NOAA Tide Predictions

St. Petersburg, Tampa Bay, FL, 2021

Times and Heights of High and Low Waters

January

Day	Time (h m)	Height ft	Height cm	Day	Time (h m)	Height ft	Height cm
1 F	01:52	2.4	73	16 Sa	02:52	2.0	61
	10:02	-0.7	-21		10:34	-0.5	-15
	17:20	1.1	34		17:24	1.2	37
	20:05	1.0	30		21:40	0.8	24
2 Sa	02:39	2.3	70	17 Su	03:41	1.8	55
	10:42	-0.6	-18		11:06	-0.3	-9
	17:46	1.1	34		17:46	1.3	40
	21:11	0.9	27		22:49	0.7	21
3 Su	03:31	2.1	64	18 M	04:35	1.5	46
	11:23	-0.5	-15		11:37	-0.1	-3
	18:15	1.2	37		18:11	1.4	43
	22:28	0.9	27				
4 M	04:32	1.9	58	19 Tu	00:04	0.6	18
	12:05	-0.3	-9		05:41	1.3	40
	18:46	1.3	40		12:09	0.2	6
	23:57	0.7	21		18:40	1.5	46
5 Tu	05:45	1.6	49	20 W	01:23	0.4	12
	12:48	0.0	0		07:08	1.0	30
	19:19	1.5	46		12:41	0.4	12
					19:12	1.6	49
6 W	01:31	0.5	15	21 Th	02:42	0.2	6
	07:20	1.3	40		09:06	0.9	27
	13:30	0.3	9		13:14	0.7	21
	19:55	1.7	52		19:49	1.7	52
7 Th	03:01	0.1	3	22 F	03:54	-0.1	-3
	09:17	1.1	34		11:16	0.9	27
	14:11	0.6	18		13:49	0.9	27
	20:34	1.9	58		20:31	1.8	55
8 F	04:18	-0.2	-6	23 Sa	04:55	-0.3	-9
	11:18	1.1	34		21:17	1.9	58
	14:50	0.8	24				
	21:17	2.0	61				
9 Sa	05:25	-0.6	-18	24 Su	05:48	-0.5	-15
	13:02	1.1	34		22:06	1.9	58
	15:28	1.0	30				
	22:03	2.2	67				
10 Su	06:23	-0.8	-24	25 M	06:34	-0.6	-18
	22:52	2.3	70		22:54	2.0	61
11 M	07:15	-1.0	-30	26 Tu	07:16	-0.7	-21
	23:41	2.4	73		15:13	1.1	34
					17:14	1.1	34
					23:42	2.1	64
12 Tu	08:03	-1.0	-30	27 W	07:54	-0.8	-24
					15:31	1.1	34
					18:02	1.0	30
13 W	00:31	2.4	73	28 Th	00:27	2.2	67
	08:46	-0.9	-27		08:30	-0.8	-24
	16:31	1.1	34		15:45	1.1	34
	18:36	1.0	30		18:49	0.9	27
14 Th	01:19	2.3	70	29 F	01:13	2.3	70
	09:26	-0.8	-24		09:05	-0.8	-24
	16:49	1.1	34		15:59	1.1	34
	19:35	0.9	27		19:39	0.8	24
15 F	02:06	2.2	67	30 Sa	01:59	2.2	67
	10:01	-0.7	-21		09:39	-0.7	-21
	17:06	1.1	34		16:15	1.1	34
	20:36	0.9	27		20:33	0.7	21
				31 Su	02:48	2.1	64
					10:12	-0.5	-15
					16:35	1.2	37
					21:32	0.5	15

February

Day	Time (h m)	Height ft	Height cm	Day	Time (h m)	Height ft	Height cm
1 M	03:41	1.9	58	16 Tu	04:27	1.4	43
	10:45	-0.3	-9		10:33	0.2	6
	16:59	1.4	43		16:43	1.7	52
	22:37	0.3	9		23:24	0.2	6
2 Tu	04:41	1.7	52	17 W	05:24	1.2	37
	11:17	0.0	0		10:55	0.4	12
	17:28	1.5	46		17:09	1.7	52
	23:51	0.2	6				
3 W	05:55	1.3	40	18 Th	00:27	0.1	3
	11:48	0.3	9		06:41	1.0	30
	18:01	1.7	52		11:15	0.7	21
					17:41	1.8	55
4 Th	01:14	0.0	0	19 F	01:39	0.0	0
	07:37	1.0	30		08:52	0.9	27
	12:15	0.6	18		11:20	0.8	24
	18:41	1.9	58		18:20	1.8	55
5 F	02:45	-0.2	-6	20 Sa	02:59	-0.1	-3
	10:19	0.9	27		19:10	1.8	55
	12:30	0.9	27				
	19:31	2.0	61				
6 Sa	04:11	-0.5	-15	21 Su	04:15	-0.3	-9
	20:31	2.1	64		20:17	1.9	58
7 Su	05:24	-0.7	-21	22 M	05:18	-0.4	-12
	21:41	2.1	64		21:32	1.9	58
8 M	06:23	-0.8	-24	23 Tu	06:09	-0.5	-15
	22:50	2.2	67		14:18	1.2	37
					16:22	1.2	37
					22:40	2.0	61
9 Tu	07:12	-0.9	-27	24 W	06:51	-0.6	-18
	15:08	1.2	37		14:24	1.2	37
	17:16	1.1	34		17:28	1.1	34
	23:51	2.2	67		23:38	2.1	64
10 W	07:54	-0.8	-24	25 Th	07:29	-0.7	-21
	15:18	1.2	37		14:33	1.2	37
	18:21	1.0	30		18:19	0.9	27
11 Th	00:43	2.2	67	26 F	00:29	2.2	67
	08:29	-0.7	-21		08:03	-0.6	-18
	15:29	1.2	37		14:44	1.3	40
	19:14	0.8	24		19:06	0.7	21
12 F	01:30	2.1	64	27 Sa	01:18	2.2	67
	08:58	-0.6	-18		08:34	-0.5	-15
	15:39	1.2	37		14:56	1.3	40
	20:03	0.7	21		19:53	0.5	15
13 Sa	02:13	2.0	61	28 Su	02:06	2.2	67
	09:24	-0.4	-12		09:04	-0.3	-9
	15:50	1.3	40		15:11	1.5	46
	20:51	0.5	15		20:43	0.3	9
14 Su	02:55	1.8	55				
	09:48	-0.2	-6				
	16:03	1.4	43				
	21:39	0.4	12				
15 M	03:38	1.6	49				
	10:11	0.0	0				
	16:21	1.5	46				
	22:29	0.3	9				

March

Day	Time (h m)	Height ft	Height cm	Day	Time (h m)	Height ft	Height cm
1 M	02:57	2.0	61	16 Tu	04:37	1.6	49
	09:32	-0.1	-3		10:14	0.5	15
	15:30	1.6	49		16:13	2.0	61
	21:36	0.1	3		23:07	0.0	0
2 Tu	03:52	1.8	55	17 W	05:23	1.4	43
	09:59	0.2	6		10:31	0.6	18
	15:54	1.8	55		16:35	2.1	64
	22:35	-0.1	-3		23:52	-0.1	-3
3 W	04:56	1.5	46	18 Th	06:18	1.2	37
	10:22	0.5	15		10:47	0.8	24
	16:23	2.0	61		17:01	2.1	64
	23:42	-0.2	-6				
4 Th	06:18	1.2	37	19 F	00:45	-0.1	-3
	10:39	0.8	24		07:34	1.1	34
	16:57	2.1	64		10:55	1.0	30
					17:34	2.1	64
5 F	01:01	-0.3	-9	20 Sa	01:51	-0.1	-3
	17:41	2.1	64		18:14	2.1	64
6 Sa	02:33	-0.3	-9	21 Su	03:09	-0.1	-3
	18:39	2.1	64		19:08	2.0	61
7 Su	04:03	-0.4	-12	22 M	04:30	-0.1	-3
	20:03	2.1	64		20:27	1.9	58
8 M	05:15	-0.5	-15	23 Tu	05:37	-0.2	-6
	21:42	2.0	61		22:04	2.0	61
9 Tu	06:10	-0.6	-18	24 W	06:29	-0.3	-9
	14:05	1.3	40		14:13	1.4	43
	16:51	1.2	37		17:32	1.3	40
	23:04	2.1	64		23:26	2.0	61
10 W	06:53	-0.5	-15	25 Th	07:12	-0.4	-12
	14:09	1.4	43		14:18	1.5	46
	18:00	1.0	30		18:33	1.0	30
11 Th	00:05	2.1	64	26 F	00:31	2.1	64
	07:27	-0.4	-12		07:49	-0.3	-9
	14:17	1.4	43		14:27	1.5	46
	18:50	0.8	24		19:22	0.8	24
12 F	00:54	2.0	61	27 Sa	01:27	2.2	67
	07:55	-0.3	-9		08:22	-0.2	-6
	14:25	1.5	46		14:38	1.6	49
	19:32	0.6	18		20:08	0.5	15
13 Sa	01:37	2.0	61	28 Su	02:20	2.1	64
	08:18	-0.1	-3		08:52	0.0	0
	14:33	1.6	49		14:53	1.8	55
	20:11	0.4	12		20:54	0.1	3
14 Su	03:17	1.8	55	29 M	03:13	2.0	61
	09:38	0.1	3		09:19	0.3	9
	15:43	1.7	52		15:11	2.0	61
	21:48	0.2	6		21:42	-0.1	-3
15 M	03:56	1.7	52	30 Tu	04:08	1.9	58
	09:56	0.3	9		09:44	0.6	18
	15:56	1.8	55		15:33	2.2	67
	22:26	0.1	3		22:34	-0.3	-9
				31 W	05:09	1.6	49
					10:04	0.8	24
					16:00	2.3	70
					23:31	-0.4	-12

StationId: 8726520
Source: NOAA/NOS/CO-OPS
Station Type: Primary
Time Zone: LST_LDT
Datum: MLLW

NOAA Tide Predictions

St. Petersburg, Tampa Bay, FL, 2021

Times and Heights of High and Low Waters

April

Day	Time	ft	cm	Day	Time	ft	cm
1 Th	06:23	1.4	43	16 F	06:26	1.3	40
	10:18	1.0	30		09:41	1.1	34
	16:33	2.5	76		16:13	2.4	73
2 F	00:36	-0.4	-12	17 Sa	00:20	-0.2	-6
	17:11	2.5	76		16:49	2.4	73
3 Sa	01:53	-0.4	-12	18 Su	01:20	-0.1	-3
	17:59	2.4	73		17:33	2.3	70
4 Su	03:20	-0.3	-9	19 M	02:31	-0.1	-3
	19:06	2.2	67		18:31	2.2	67
5 M	04:43	-0.3	-9	20 Tu	03:43	-0.1	-3
	20:56	2.0	61		19:56	2.0	61
6 Tu	05:48	-0.3	-9	21 W	04:46	-0.1	-3
	13:57	1.5	46		12:53	1.5	46
	17:02	1.4	43		15:59	1.4	43
	22:50	2.0	61		21:38	2.0	61
7 W	06:36	-0.2	-6	22 Th	05:38	-0.1	-3
	13:56	1.6	49		12:54	1.6	49
	18:23	1.1	34		17:26	1.2	37
					23:07	2.0	61
8 Th	00:10	1.9	58	23 F	06:22	0.0	0
	07:14	-0.1	-3		13:05	1.7	52
	14:04	1.6	49		18:25	0.8	24
	19:14	0.9	27				
9 F	01:09	1.9	58	24 Sa	00:20	2.0	61
	07:44	0.1	3		06:59	0.1	3
	14:14	1.7	52		13:18	1.9	58
	19:56	0.6	18		19:15	0.5	15
10 Sa	01:57	1.9	58	25 Su	01:24	2.0	61
	08:08	0.3	9		07:32	0.3	9
	14:23	1.9	58		13:35	2.0	61
	20:32	0.4	12		20:03	0.1	3
11 Su	02:40	1.8	55	26 M	02:25	1.9	58
	08:28	0.4	12		08:01	0.6	18
	14:32	2.0	61		13:55	2.3	70
	21:05	0.2	6		20:51	-0.2	-6
12 M	03:21	1.7	52	27 Tu	03:25	1.8	55
	08:45	0.6	18		08:26	0.9	27
	14:43	2.1	64		14:19	2.5	76
	21:38	0.0	0		21:40	-0.5	-15
13 Tu	04:01	1.6	49	28 W	04:28	1.7	52
	09:00	0.8	24		08:47	1.1	34
	14:58	2.2	67		14:47	2.7	82
	22:12	-0.1	-3		22:32	-0.6	-18
14 W	04:42	1.5	46	29 Th	05:40	1.5	46
	09:15	0.9	27		09:01	1.2	37
	15:17	2.3	70		15:21	2.8	85
	22:49	-0.2	-6		23:29	-0.6	-18
15 Th	05:28	1.4	43	30 F	15:59	2.8	85
	09:29	1.0	30				
	15:42	2.4	73				
	23:30	-0.2	-6				

May

Day	Time	ft	cm	Day	Time	ft	cm
1 Sa	00:33	-0.5	-15	16 Su	00:06	-0.2	-6
	16:44	2.6	79		16:24	2.5	76
2 Su	01:43	-0.4	-12	17 M	01:00	-0.2	-6
	17:39	2.4	73		17:14	2.4	73
3 M	02:57	-0.2	-6	18 Tu	01:58	-0.2	-6
	18:56	2.2	67		18:16	2.2	67
4 Tu	04:04	-0.1	-3	19 W	02:56	-0.1	-3
	12:42	1.6	49		11:04	1.6	49
	15:13	1.5	46		13:48	1.5	46
	20:53	1.9	58		19:39	2.1	64
5 W	04:59	0.0	0	20 Th	03:51	0.0	0
	12:34	1.7	52		11:14	1.7	52
	17:15	1.3	40		15:48	1.3	40
	22:41	1.8	55		21:17	1.9	58
6 Th	05:43	0.2	6	21 F	04:40	0.1	3
	12:44	1.8	55		11:31	1.8	55
	18:20	0.9	27		17:09	1.0	30
					22:51	1.8	55
7 F	00:00	1.8	55	22 Sa	05:23	0.3	9
	06:18	0.3	9		11:51	2.0	61
	12:57	1.9	58		18:11	0.6	18
	19:07	0.6	18				
8 Sa	01:03	1.7	52	23 Su	00:14	1.8	55
	06:47	0.5	15		06:01	0.6	18
	13:10	2.0	61		12:13	2.2	67
	19:46	0.4	12		19:06	0.1	3
9 Su	01:58	1.6	49	24 M	01:29	1.7	52
	07:11	0.7	21		06:34	0.8	24
	13:22	2.2	67		12:38	2.4	73
	20:21	0.1	3		19:57	-0.2	-6
10 M	02:47	1.6	49	25 Tu	02:39	1.7	52
	07:31	0.9	27		07:03	1.1	34
	13:35	2.3	70		13:07	2.6	79
	20:54	-0.1	-3		20:48	-0.5	-15
11 Tu	03:32	1.5	46	26 W	03:50	1.6	49
	07:47	1.1	34		07:26	1.3	40
	13:51	2.4	73		13:40	2.8	85
	21:27	-0.2	-6		21:39	-0.6	-18
12 W	04:17	1.5	46	27 Th	05:04	1.5	46
	08:01	1.2	37		07:42	1.4	43
	14:11	2.5	76		14:17	2.9	88
	22:00	-0.3	-9		22:33	-0.7	-21
13 Th	05:02	1.4	43	28 F	14:59	2.9	88
	08:14	1.2	37		23:28	-0.6	-18
	14:36	2.6	79				
	22:37	-0.3	-9				
14 F	05:52	1.3	40	29 Sa	15:45	2.8	85
	08:26	1.3	40				
	15:07	2.6	79				
	23:19	-0.3	-9				
15 Sa	15:42	2.6	79	30 Su	00:25	-0.5	-15
					16:36	2.6	79
				31 M	01:23	-0.3	-9
					17:37	2.4	73

June

Day	Time	ft	cm	Day	Time	ft	cm
1 Tu	02:18	-0.1	-3	16 W	01:23	-0.1	-3
	18:54	2.1	64		08:46	1.5	46
					12:07	1.4	43
					18:13	2.2	67
2 W	03:09	0.1	3	17 Th	02:10	0.0	0
	10:51	1.7	52		09:14	1.7	52
	15:14	1.4	43		13:52	1.3	40
	20:34	1.8	55		19:31	2.0	61
3 Th	03:55	0.3	9	18 F	02:55	0.2	6
	11:08	1.8	55		09:43	1.8	55
	16:51	1.1	34		15:29	1.0	30
	22:16	1.6	49		21:05	1.8	55
4 F	04:35	0.5	15	19 Sa	03:39	0.5	15
	11:27	2.0	61		10:12	2.0	61
	17:55	0.7	21		16:49	0.7	21
	23:43	1.5	46		22:45	1.6	49
5 Sa	05:11	0.7	21	20 Su	04:20	0.7	21
	11:47	2.1	64		10:43	2.2	67
	18:45	0.4	12		17:58	0.3	9
6 Su	00:58	1.5	46	21 M	00:23	1.5	46
	05:42	0.9	27		04:58	1.0	30
	12:06	2.2	67		11:17	2.5	76
	19:27	0.2	6		18:58	-0.1	-3
7 M	02:03	1.5	46	22 Tu	01:53	1.5	46
	06:09	1.1	34		05:30	1.2	37
	12:26	2.3	70		11:54	2.7	82
	20:06	0.0	0		19:55	-0.4	-12
8 Tu	03:02	1.5	46	23 W	03:16	1.5	46
	06:30	1.2	37		05:58	1.4	43
	12:47	2.5	76		12:35	2.9	88
	20:42	-0.2	-6		20:48	-0.6	-18
9 W	03:57	1.4	43	24 Th	13:19	3.0	91
	06:47	1.3	40		21:41	-0.6	-18
	13:11	2.6	79				
	21:17	-0.3	-9				
10 Th	04:49	1.4	43	25 F	14:06	3.0	91
	07:01	1.4	43		22:31	-0.6	-18
	13:39	2.6	79				
	21:53	-0.3	-9				
11 F	14:12	2.7	82	26 Sa	14:54	2.9	88
	22:31	-0.3	-9		23:19	-0.5	-15
12 Sa	14:49	2.7	82	27 Su	15:45	2.8	85
	23:11	-0.3	-9				
13 Su	15:31	2.7	82	28 M	00:04	-0.3	-9
	23:53	-0.3	-9		16:38	2.6	79
14 M	16:17	2.6	79	29 Tu	00:47	-0.1	-3
					08:13	1.5	46
					11:17	1.4	43
					17:36	2.3	70
15 Tu	00:38	-0.2	-6	30 W	01:27	0.1	3
	08:17	1.4	43		08:36	1.6	49
	10:26	1.4	43		12:58	1.3	40
	17:10	2.5	76		18:44	2.0	61

169

StationId: 8726520
Source: NOAA/NOS/CO-OPS
Station Type: Primary
Time Zone: LST_LDT
Datum: MLLW

NOAA Tide Predictions

St. Petersburg, Tampa Bay, FL, 2021

Times and Heights of High and Low Waters

July

Day	Time (h:m)	ft	cm
1 Th ◑	02:05	0.3	9
	09:03	1.8	55
	14:37	1.1	34
	20:07	1.7	52
2 F	02:43	0.6	18
	09:32	1.9	58
	16:05	0.9	27
	21:46	1.5	46
3 Sa	03:20	0.8	24
	10:02	2.1	64
	17:15	0.6	18
	23:28	1.4	43
4 Su	03:56	1.0	30
	10:32	2.2	67
	18:13	0.4	12
5 M	01:00	1.4	43
	04:31	1.2	37
	11:04	2.3	70
	19:03	0.1	3
6 Tu	02:20	1.5	46
	05:03	1.4	43
	11:38	2.4	73
	19:47	0.0	0
7 W	03:27	1.5	46
	05:32	1.4	43
	12:12	2.5	76
	20:29	-0.1	-3
8 Th	12:48	2.6	79
	21:08	-0.2	-6
9 F	13:26	2.7	82
	21:44	-0.2	-6
10 Sa ●	14:06	2.7	82
	22:20	-0.3	-9
11 Su	05:50	1.4	43
	07:52	1.4	43
	14:48	2.8	85
	22:55	-0.2	-6
12 M	06:05	1.4	43
	08:48	1.3	40
	15:32	2.7	82
	23:31	-0.2	-6
13 Tu	06:24	1.5	46
	09:51	1.3	40
	16:20	2.6	79
14 W	00:07	-0.1	-3
	06:47	1.6	49
	11:00	1.2	37
	17:13	2.4	73
15 Th	00:44	0.1	3
	07:15	1.7	52
	12:17	1.1	34
	18:16	2.2	67
16 F	01:21	0.4	12
	07:47	1.9	58
	13:41	0.9	27
	19:32	1.9	58
17 Sa ◐	01:59	0.6	18
	08:22	2.1	64
	15:08	0.7	21
	21:08	1.6	49
18 Su	02:36	0.9	27
	09:01	2.3	70
	16:32	0.4	12
	23:05	1.5	46
19 M	03:12	1.2	37
	09:45	2.5	76
	17:49	0.1	3
20 Tu	01:07	1.5	46
	03:46	1.4	43
	10:35	2.7	82
	18:56	-0.1	-3
21 W	11:29	2.8	85
	19:55	-0.3	-9
22 Th	12:24	2.9	88
	20:48	-0.4	-12
23 F	13:19	3.0	91
	21:35	-0.4	-12
24 Sa ○	14:11	3.0	91
	22:17	-0.3	-9
25 Su	05:32	1.5	46
	08:10	1.4	43
	15:01	2.9	88
	22:54	-0.2	-6
26 M	05:48	1.5	46
	09:13	1.3	40
	15:49	2.7	82
	23:28	0.0	0
27 Tu	06:05	1.6	49
	10:17	1.2	37
	16:38	2.5	76
	23:59	0.3	9
28 W	06:25	1.7	52
	11:24	1.1	34
	17:30	2.2	67
29 Th	00:28	0.5	15
	06:49	1.9	58
	12:34	1.0	30
	18:29	1.9	58
30 F	00:58	0.7	21
	07:18	2.0	61
	13:48	0.9	27
	19:43	1.7	52
31 Sa ◑	01:28	1.0	30
	07:51	2.1	64
	15:07	0.8	24
	21:22	1.5	46

August

Day	Time (h:m)	ft	cm
1 Su	02:00	1.2	37
	08:29	2.2	67
	16:24	0.6	18
	23:26	1.5	46
2 M	02:34	1.4	43
	09:14	2.3	70
	17:34	0.4	12
3 Tu	10:06	2.4	73
	18:34	0.2	6
4 W	11:00	2.5	76
	19:25	0.1	3
5 Th	11:53	2.6	79
	20:10	0.0	0
6 F	03:56	1.6	49
	05:59	1.6	49
	12:41	2.7	82
	20:48	-0.1	-3
7 Sa	04:14	1.6	49
	06:47	1.5	46
	13:26	2.7	82
	21:23	-0.1	-3
8 Su ●	04:26	1.6	49
	07:34	1.4	43
	14:09	2.8	85
	21:55	0.0	0
9 M	04:37	1.6	49
	08:22	1.3	40
	14:52	2.8	85
	22:26	0.0	0
10 Tu	04:51	1.7	52
	09:12	1.2	37
	15:37	2.7	82
	22:56	0.2	6
11 W	05:08	1.8	55
	10:06	1.0	30
	16:25	2.6	79
	23:27	0.4	12
12 Th	05:31	1.9	58
	11:05	0.9	27
	17:20	2.4	73
	23:57	0.6	18
13 F	05:58	2.1	64
	12:11	0.7	21
	18:24	2.1	64
14 Sa	00:28	0.9	27
	06:31	2.3	70
	13:26	0.6	18
	19:45	1.8	55
15 Su ◐	00:57	1.2	37
	07:10	2.4	73
	14:52	0.5	15
	21:43	1.6	49
16 M	01:23	1.4	43
	07:59	2.5	76
	16:23	0.3	9
17 Tu	09:01	2.6	79
	17:45	0.1	3
18 W	10:14	2.7	82
	18:54	0.0	0
19 Th	11:28	2.8	85
	19:50	-0.1	-3
20 F	03:37	1.7	52
	05:38	1.6	49
	12:34	2.9	88
	20:36	-0.1	-3
21 Sa	03:49	1.7	52
	06:50	1.5	46
	13:31	2.9	88
	21:15	0.0	0
22 Su ○	04:02	1.7	52
	07:48	1.3	40
	14:21	2.8	85
	21:47	0.1	3
23 M	04:13	1.7	52
	08:40	1.2	37
	15:07	2.7	82
	22:14	0.3	9
24 Tu	04:25	1.8	55
	09:29	1.0	30
	15:50	2.6	79
	22:39	0.5	15
25 W	04:40	2.0	61
	10:18	0.9	27
	16:34	2.4	73
	23:02	0.7	21
26 Th	04:58	2.1	64
	11:08	0.8	24
	17:22	2.1	64
	23:25	0.9	27
27 F	05:20	2.2	67
	12:01	0.7	21
	18:17	1.9	58
	23:48	1.1	34
28 Sa	05:48	2.3	70
	13:01	0.7	21
	19:28	1.7	52
29 Su	00:12	1.3	40
	06:21	2.4	73
	14:11	0.6	18
	21:14	1.6	49
30 M ◑	00:33	1.5	46
	07:02	2.4	73
	15:31	0.6	18
31 Tu	07:58	2.4	73
	16:51	0.5	15

September

Day	Time (h:m)	ft	cm
1 W	09:11	2.4	73
	17:59	0.4	12
2 Th	10:32	2.4	73
	18:53	0.3	9
3 F	02:36	1.8	55
	05:20	1.7	52
	11:41	2.5	76
	19:37	0.2	6
4 Sa	02:50	1.8	55
	06:17	1.6	49
	12:36	2.7	82
	20:14	0.2	6
5 Su	03:03	1.8	55
	07:04	1.4	43
	13:24	2.7	82
	20:47	0.2	6
6 M	03:13	1.8	55
	07:48	1.2	37
	14:09	2.8	85
	21:17	0.3	9
7 Tu ●	03:25	1.9	58
	08:32	1.0	30
	14:54	2.8	85
	21:45	0.4	12
8 W	03:40	2.0	61
	09:18	0.8	24
	15:41	2.6	79
	22:12	0.7	21
9 Th	03:59	2.2	67
	10:07	0.6	18
	16:33	2.5	76
	22:38	0.9	27
10 F	04:23	2.4	73
	11:02	0.5	15
	17:32	2.2	67
	23:04	1.2	37
11 Sa	04:52	2.5	76
	12:03	0.4	12
	18:44	1.9	58
	23:26	1.4	43
12 Su	05:27	2.6	79
	13:16	0.3	9
	20:29	1.7	52
	23:38	1.6	49
13 M ◐	06:12	2.7	82
	14:44	0.3	9
14 Tu	07:11	2.7	82
	16:17	0.2	6
15 W	08:35	2.6	79
	17:38	0.2	6
16 Th	10:17	2.6	79
	18:40	0.1	3
17 F	02:21	1.8	55
	05:15	1.7	52
	11:43	2.7	82
	19:28	0.2	6
18 Sa	02:30	1.8	55
	06:28	1.5	46
	12:49	2.7	82
	20:06	0.3	9
19 Su	02:42	1.9	58
	07:22	1.3	40
	13:42	2.7	82
	20:37	0.4	12
20 M ○	02:52	2.0	61
	08:08	1.0	30
	14:28	2.6	79
	21:02	0.6	18
21 Tu	03:02	2.1	64
	08:48	0.8	24
	15:10	2.5	76
	21:23	0.8	24
22 W ●	03:14	2.2	67
	09:27	0.7	21
	15:51	2.3	70
	21:42	1.0	30
23 Th	03:28	2.3	70
	10:06	0.5	15
	16:32	2.2	67
	22:00	1.2	37
24 F	03:46	2.5	76
	10:47	0.5	15
	17:18	2.0	61
	22:19	1.3	40
25 Sa	04:09	2.5	76
	11:31	0.4	12
	18:13	1.9	58
	22:37	1.5	46
26 Su	04:37	2.6	79
	12:23	0.4	12
	19:27	1.7	52
	22:53	1.6	49
27 M	05:11	2.5	76
	13:26	0.5	15
28 Tu	05:53	2.5	76
	14:44	0.5	15
29 W ◑	06:54	2.4	73
	16:05	0.5	15
30 Th	08:24	2.3	70
	17:14	0.4	12

StationId: 8726520
Source: NOAA/NOS/CO-OPS
Station Type: Primary
Time Zone: LST_LDT
Datum: MLLW

St. Petersburg, Tampa Bay, FL, 2021

Times and Heights of High and Low Waters

October

Day	Time	ft	cm	Day	Time	ft	cm
1 F	01:19	1.9	58	16 Sa	01:14	1.9	58
	04:10	1.8	55		05:51	1.4	43
	10:05	2.3	70		11:52	2.3	70
	18:08	0.3	9		18:48	0.4	12
2 Sa	01:28	1.9	58	17 Su	01:25	2.0	61
	05:27	1.6	49		06:46	1.1	34
	11:23	2.4	73		12:54	2.3	70
	18:51	0.3	9		19:21	0.6	18
3 Su	01:39	1.9	58	18 M	01:38	2.1	64
	06:20	1.4	43		07:31	0.8	24
	12:24	2.5	76		13:46	2.3	70
	19:28	0.4	12		19:47	0.8	24
4 M	01:51	2.0	61	19 Tu	01:49	2.2	67
	07:04	1.1	34		08:09	0.6	18
	13:17	2.6	79		14:32	2.2	67
	20:00	0.5	15		20:08	1.0	30
5 Tu	02:04	2.1	64	20 W	02:00	2.3	70
	07:47	0.8	24		08:45	0.4	12
	14:07	2.6	79		15:15	2.1	64
	20:29	0.7	21		20:26	1.1	34
6 W	02:19	2.2	67	21 Th	02:13	2.4	73
	08:30	0.5	15		09:18	0.2	6
	14:57	2.5	76		15:56	2.0	61
	20:56	0.9	27		20:43	1.3	40
7 Th	02:37	2.4	73	22 F	02:29	2.5	76
	09:15	0.3	9		09:52	0.1	3
	15:50	2.4	73		16:39	1.9	58
	21:20	1.1	34		20:58	1.4	43
8	03:00	2.6	79	23 Sa	02:50	2.6	79
	10:03	0.1	3		10:28	0.1	3
	16:47	2.2	67		17:25	1.8	55
	21:43	1.3	40		21:14	1.5	46
9	03:28	2.7	82	24 Su	03:16	2.6	79
	10:57	0.0	0		11:09	0.1	3
	17:55	1.9	58		18:22	1.7	52
	22:01	1.5	46		21:28	1.5	46
10	04:01	2.8	85	25 M	03:47	2.6	79
	11:59	0.0	0		11:57	0.1	3
	19:31	1.7	52				
	22:06	1.6	49				
11	04:41	2.8	85	26 Tu	04:24	2.5	76
	13:12	0.0	0		12:56	0.2	6
12	05:31	2.7	82	27 W	05:10	2.4	73
	14:37	0.1	3		14:05	0.3	9
13	06:41	2.6	79	28 Th	06:13	2.3	70
	16:03	0.2	6		15:16	0.3	9
14	08:32	2.4	73	29 F	07:46	2.1	64
	17:13	0.2	6		16:19	0.3	9
15	01:08	1.9	58	30 Sa	00:00	1.8	55
	04:28	1.7	52		04:04	1.6	49
	10:29	2.4	73		09:33	2.1	64
	18:07	0.3	9		17:11	0.3	9
				31 Su	00:13	1.9	58
					05:16	1.3	40
					11:00	2.1	64
					17:55	0.4	12

November

Day	Time	ft	cm	Day	Time	ft	cm
1 M	00:27	2.0	61	16 Tu	06:25	0.3	9
	06:08	0.9	27		12:52	1.7	52
	12:09	2.1	64		17:51	0.9	27
	18:33	0.5	15		23:52	2.3	70
2 Tu	00:43	2.1	64	17 W	07:02	0.0	0
	06:54	0.6	18		13:43	1.7	52
	13:10	2.2	67		18:12	1.1	34
	19:06	0.7	21				
3 W	01:01	2.3	70	18 Th	00:07	2.4	73
	07:39	0.2	6		07:35	-0.1	-3
	14:08	2.1	64		14:30	1.6	49
	19:35	0.9	27		18:30	1.2	37
4 Th	01:21	2.4	73	19 F	00:25	2.4	73
	08:24	-0.1	-3		08:08	-0.2	-6
	15:06	2.0	61		15:15	1.6	49
●	20:01	1.2	37	○	18:46	1.3	40
5 F	01:46	2.6	79	20 Sa	00:46	2.5	76
	09:11	-0.3	-9		08:41	-0.3	-9
	16:07	1.9	58		16:00	1.5	46
	20:24	1.3	40		19:00	1.4	43
6 Sa	02:15	2.8	85	21 Su	01:12	2.5	76
	10:01	-0.5	-15		09:17	-0.3	-9
	17:15	1.7	52		16:47	1.4	43
	20:41	1.5	46		19:15	1.4	43
7 Su	01:50	2.9	88	22 M	01:43	2.5	76
	09:56	-0.5	-15		09:57	-0.3	-9
	17:42	1.6	49				
	19:48	1.5	46				
8 M	02:29	2.9	88	23 Tu	02:19	2.5	76
	10:58	-0.4	-12		10:42	-0.2	-6
9 Tu	03:16	2.8	85	24 W	03:01	2.4	73
	12:07	-0.3	-9		11:33	-0.2	-6
10 W	04:13	2.6	79	25 Th	03:51	2.2	67
	13:20	-0.1	-3		12:28	-0.1	-3
11 Th	05:33	2.3	70	26 F	04:55	2.1	64
	14:30	0.0	0		13:24	0.0	0
◐	22:49	1.7	52		21:08	1.5	46
12 F	01:49	1.6	49	27 Sa	00:54	1.4	43
	07:33	2.0	61		06:20	1.9	58
	15:28	0.2	6		14:18	0.1	3
	22:51	1.8	55	◐	21:30	1.6	49
13 Sa	03:46	1.3	40	28 Su	02:38	1.1	34
	09:25	1.9	58		08:01	1.7	52
	16:16	0.4	12		15:07	0.2	6
◑	23:05	1.9	58		21:52	1.8	55
14 Su	04:54	0.9	27	29 M	03:52	0.8	24
	10:48	1.8	55		09:37	1.6	49
	16:54	0.6	18		15:52	0.4	12
	23:21	2.0	61		22:15	1.9	58
15 M	05:43	0.6	18	30 Tu	04:50	0.4	12
	11:55	1.8	55		11:00	1.6	49
	17:25	0.8	24		16:32	0.6	18
	23:37	2.1	64		22:39	2.1	64

December

Day	Time	ft	cm	Day	Time	ft	cm
1 W	05:41	0.0	0	16 Th	06:49	-0.4	-12
	12:14	1.6	49		14:04	1.3	40
	17:07	0.9	27		17:18	1.1	34
	23:06	2.3	70		23:25	2.2	67
2 Th	06:31	-0.4	-12	17 F	07:25	-0.5	-15
	13:23	1.6	49		14:57	1.3	40
	17:38	1.1	34		17:40	1.2	37
	23:36	2.5	76		23:51	2.3	70
3 F	07:20	-0.7	-21	18 Sa	08:00	-0.6	-18
	14:30	1.5	46		15:43	1.3	40
	18:05	1.2	37		18:00	1.2	37
4 Sa	00:10	2.7	82	19 Su	00:20	2.3	70
	08:10	-0.8	-24		08:35	-0.6	-18
	15:39	1.4	43	○			
●	18:26	1.3	40				
5 Su	00:48	2.8	85	20 M	00:54	2.3	70
	09:02	-0.9	-27		09:11	-0.6	-18
6 M	01:31	2.8	85	21 Tu	01:31	2.3	70
	09:56	-0.8	-24		09:47	-0.6	-18
					17:26	1.2	37
					19:32	1.1	34
7 Tu	02:19	2.7	82	22 W	02:12	2.3	70
	10:52	-0.7	-21		10:26	-0.5	-15
					17:53	1.2	37
					20:27	1.1	34
8 W	03:12	2.5	76	23 Th	02:57	2.2	67
	11:49	-0.5	-15		11:06	-0.4	-12
					18:22	1.2	37
					21:37	1.1	34
9 Th	04:14	2.2	67	24 F	03:48	2.0	61
	12:44	-0.3	-9		11:48	-0.3	-9
	20:46	1.3	40		18:53	1.3	40
	23:32	1.3	40		23:01	1.0	30
10 F	05:33	1.9	58	25 Sa	04:49	1.8	55
	13:37	0.0	0		12:31	-0.2	-6
	21:04	1.5	46		19:24	1.4	43
11 Sa	01:48	1.1	34	26 Su	00:34	0.9	27
	07:18	1.6	49		06:05	1.6	49
	14:24	0.2	6		13:15	0.0	0
◑	21:26	1.6	49		19:56	1.5	46
12 Su	03:27	0.8	24	27 M	02:04	0.6	18
	09:08	1.4	43		07:40	1.3	40
	15:07	0.4	12		13:59	0.3	9
◐	21:49	1.8	55	◐	20:29	1.7	52
13 M	04:35	0.4	12	28 Tu	03:23	0.3	9
	10:42	1.3	40		09:27	1.2	37
	15:46	0.7	21		14:43	0.5	15
	22:13	1.9	58		21:04	1.9	58
14 Tu	05:27	0.1	3	29 W	04:31	-0.1	-3
	11:59	1.3	40		11:10	1.2	37
	16:21	0.8	24		15:25	0.8	24
	22:37	2.0	61		21:41	2.1	64
15 W	06:10	-0.2	-6	30 Th	05:31	-0.5	-15
	13:06	1.3	40		12:41	1.2	37
	16:51	1.0	30		16:03	1.0	30
	23:00	2.1	64		22:21	2.3	70
				31 F	06:27	-0.8	-24
					14:00	1.2	37
					16:39	1.1	34
					22:59	2.5	76

StationId: 8727520
Source: NOAA/NOS/CO-OPS
Station Type: Primary
Time Zone: LST_LDT
Datum: MLLW

Cedar Key, FL, 2021

Times and Heights of High and Low Waters

January

Day	Time	ft	cm	Day	Time	ft	cm
1 F	02:11	3.7	113	16 Sa	03:02	3.5	107
	09:29	-1.0	-30		10:04	-0.6	-18
	16:05	2.8	85		16:28	2.8	85
	21:20	1.1	34		22:05	0.7	21
2 Sa	02:52	3.7	113	17 Su	03:46	3.2	98
	10:06	-0.9	-27		10:36	-0.3	-9
	16:38	2.8	85		16:57	2.8	85
	22:03	1.0	30		22:49	0.6	18
3 Su	03:39	3.5	107	18 M	04:33	2.9	88
	10:45	-0.7	-21		11:07	0.0	0
	17:12	2.8	85		17:27	2.8	85
	22:51	0.9	27		23:36	0.6	18
4 M	04:31	3.3	101	19 Tu	05:23	2.6	79
	11:27	-0.3	-9		11:39	0.4	12
	17:49	2.8	85		17:59	2.8	85
	23:47	0.7	21				
5 Tu	05:32	3.0	91	20 W	00:30	0.6	18
	12:13	0.0	0		06:22	2.2	67
	18:31	2.9	88		12:15	0.7	21
					18:37	2.8	85
6 W	00:54	0.6	18	21 Th	01:36	0.5	15
	06:47	2.6	79		07:41	2.0	61
	13:06	0.5	15		13:00	1.0	30
	19:21	2.9	88		19:25	2.8	85
7 Th	02:14	0.3	9	22 F	02:54	0.3	9
	08:25	2.3	70		09:24	1.9	58
	14:11	0.9	27		14:06	1.3	40
	20:18	3.1	94		20:23	2.9	88
8 F	03:36	-0.1	-3	23 Sa	04:09	0.1	3
	10:09	2.3	70		10:56	2.0	61
	15:21	1.2	37		15:22	1.5	46
	21:18	3.2	98		21:24	3.0	91
9 Sa	04:48	-0.5	-15	24 Su	05:10	-0.2	-6
	11:36	2.5	76		12:05	2.2	67
	16:27	1.3	40		16:30	1.5	46
	22:15	3.5	107		22:20	3.1	94
10 Su	05:51	-0.9	-27	25 M	06:02	-0.5	-15
	12:42	2.6	79		12:53	2.4	73
	17:28	1.4	43		17:30	1.5	46
	23:08	3.6	110		23:11	3.3	101
11 M	06:45	-1.2	-37	26 Tu	06:45	-0.8	-24
	13:33	2.8	85		13:31	2.6	79
	18:23	1.3	40		18:21	1.3	40
					23:58	3.4	104
12 Tu	00:00	3.8	116	27 W	07:24	-1.0	-30
	07:32	-1.4	-43		14:05	2.7	82
	14:15	2.8	85		19:06	1.2	37
	19:12	1.2	37				
13 W	00:48	3.8	116	28 Th	00:42	3.6	110
	08:14	-1.3	-40		08:00	-1.1	-34
	14:52	2.8	85		14:36	2.8	85
	19:57	1.0	30		19:47	1.0	30
14 Th	01:34	3.8	116	29 F	01:25	3.7	113
	08:53	-1.2	-37		08:36	-1.1	-34
	15:26	2.8	85		15:06	2.8	85
	20:40	0.9	27		20:27	0.8	24
15 F	02:18	3.7	113	30 Sa	02:08	3.7	113
	09:29	-0.9	-27		09:12	-1.0	-30
	15:58	2.8	85		15:35	2.9	88
	21:22	0.8	24		21:08	0.6	18
				31 Su	02:52	3.7	113
					09:49	-0.8	-24
					16:05	2.9	88
					21:52	0.4	12

February

Day	Time	ft	cm	Day	Time	ft	cm
1 M	03:40	3.5	107	16 Tu	04:16	2.9	88
	10:25	-0.5	-15		10:29	0.2	6
	16:35	3.0	91		16:34	3.1	94
	22:40	0.3	9		23:03	0.2	6
2 Tu	04:32	3.2	98	17 W	05:01	2.7	82
	11:03	-0.1	-3		10:57	0.5	15
	17:09	3.1	94		17:03	3.1	94
	23:33	0.2	6		23:47	0.2	6
3 W	05:31	2.8	85	18 Th	05:51	2.4	73
	11:42	0.3	9		11:26	0.8	24
	17:46	3.1	94		17:35	3.1	94
4 Th	00:35	0.1	3	19 F	00:39	0.3	9
	06:43	2.4	73		06:55	2.1	64
	12:27	0.8	24		12:01	1.1	34
	18:30	3.2	98		18:15	3.1	94
5 F	01:52	0.0	0	20 Sa	01:49	0.3	9
	08:22	2.1	64		08:30	1.9	58
	13:24	1.2	37		12:53	1.4	43
	19:27	3.2	98		19:09	3.0	91
6 Sa	03:18	-0.2	-6	21 Su	03:11	0.2	6
	10:16	2.1	64		10:16	2.0	61
	14:42	1.5	46		14:22	1.6	49
	20:38	3.2	98		20:23	3.0	91
7 Su	04:38	-0.5	-15	22 M	04:26	0.0	0
	11:46	2.3	70		11:33	2.2	67
	16:01	1.6	49		15:51	1.7	52
	21:51	3.3	101		21:40	3.1	94
8 M	05:44	-0.8	-24	23 Tu	05:27	-0.3	-9
	12:43	2.5	76		12:23	2.4	73
	17:12	1.5	46		17:00	1.5	46
	22:57	3.5	107		22:45	3.3	101
9 Tu	06:38	-1.0	-30	24 W	06:16	-0.5	-15
	13:23	2.6	79		13:00	2.6	79
	18:12	1.2	37		17:57	1.3	40
	23:56	3.6	110		23:41	3.5	107
10 W	07:22	-1.0	-30	25 Th	06:58	-0.7	-21
	13:56	2.8	85		13:31	2.8	85
	19:03	1.0	30		18:46	1.0	30
11 Th	00:48	3.6	110	26 F	00:32	3.7	113
	08:00	-0.9	-27		07:37	-0.8	-24
	14:25	2.8	85		14:00	2.9	88
	19:47	0.7	21		19:29	0.7	21
12 F	01:33	3.6	110	27 Sa	01:19	3.8	116
	08:34	-0.8	-24		08:14	-0.8	-24
	14:52	2.9	88		14:28	3.0	91
	20:27	0.5	15		20:12	0.4	12
13 Sa	02:15	3.5	107	28 Su	02:05	3.8	116
	09:05	-0.6	-18		08:50	-0.6	-18
	15:18	2.9	88		14:55	3.1	94
	21:06	0.4	12		20:54	0.1	3
14 Su	02:55	3.4	104				
	09:34	-0.3	-9				
	15:43	3.0	91				
	21:44	0.3	9				
15 M	03:35	3.2	98				
	10:02	-0.1	-3				
	16:08	3.1	94				
	22:23	0.2	6				

March

Day	Time	ft	cm	Day	Time	ft	cm
1 M	02:52	3.8	116	16 Tu	04:23	3.2	98
	09:26	-0.4	-12		10:27	0.4	12
	15:24	3.3	101		16:20	3.4	104
	21:39	-0.1	-3		22:56	0.0	0
2 Tu	03:41	3.5	107	17 W	05:02	3.1	94
	10:01	0.0	0		10:54	0.7	21
	15:54	3.4	104		16:45	3.5	107
	22:26	-0.2	-6		23:32	0.0	0
3 W	04:34	3.2	98	18 Th	05:43	2.8	85
	10:37	0.4	12		11:21	0.9	27
	16:28	3.5	107		17:13	3.5	107
	23:18	-0.3	-9				
4 Th	05:33	2.8	85	19 F	00:10	0.1	3
	11:14	0.8	24		06:30	2.6	79
	17:05	3.5	107		11:51	1.1	34
					17:45	3.4	104
5 F	00:17	-0.2	-6	20 Sa	00:56	0.2	6
	06:44	2.4	73		07:26	2.4	73
	11:55	1.2	37		12:53	1.4	43
	17:50	3.5	107		18:24	3.3	101
6 Sa	01:31	-0.1	-3	21 Su	01:55	0.3	9
	08:24	2.1	64		08:45	2.2	67
	12:50	1.6	49		13:15	1.6	49
	18:48	3.3	101		19:16	3.2	98
7 Su	03:00	-0.1	-3	22 M	03:13	0.3	9
	10:19	2.2	67		10:26	2.2	67
	14:17	1.8	55		14:41	1.8	55
	20:09	3.2	98		20:33	3.1	94
8 M	04:25	-0.2	-6	23 Tu	04:35	0.2	6
	11:37	2.4	73		11:42	2.4	73
	15:49	1.7	52		16:19	1.8	55
	21:40	3.2	98		22:05	3.1	94
9 Tu	05:32	-0.3	-9	24 W	05:42	0.1	3
	12:34	2.6	79		12:34	2.6	79
	17:05	1.4	43		17:33	1.5	46
	22:57	3.4	104		23:22	3.3	101
10 W	06:23	-0.4	-12	25 Th	06:37	-0.1	-3
	12:54	2.8	85		13:12	2.9	88
	18:05	1.1	34		18:32	1.2	37
	23:58	3.5	107				
11 Th	07:04	-0.4	-12	26 F	00:25	3.6	110
	13:22	2.9	88		07:24	-0.3	-9
	18:53	0.8	24		13:45	3.1	94
					19:23	0.8	24
12 F	00:48	3.6	110	27 Sa	01:21	3.8	116
	07:37	-0.3	-9		08:06	-0.3	-9
	13:48	3.1	94		14:15	3.2	98
	19:34	0.5	15		20:10	0.4	12
13 Sa	01:30	3.6	110	28 Su	02:12	3.9	119
	08:07	-0.1	-3		08:45	-0.2	-6
	14:11	3.2	98		14:43	3.4	104
	20:11	0.3	9		20:54	0.0	0
14 Su	03:09	3.5	107	29 M	03:01	3.9	119
	09:35	0.0	0		09:22	0.1	3
	15:34	3.3	101		15:12	3.6	110
	21:47	0.1	3		21:38	-0.3	-9
15 M	03:46	3.4	104	30 Tu	03:50	3.8	116
	10:01	0.2	6		09:59	0.4	12
	15:57	3.3	101		15:42	3.7	113
	22:21	0.1	3		22:24	-0.5	-15
				31 W	04:43	3.6	110
					10:35	0.7	21
					16:14	3.9	119
					23:13	-0.6	-18

StationId: 8727520
Source: NOAA/NOS/CO-OPS
Station Type: Primary
Time Zone: LST_LDT
Datum: MLLW

NOAA Tide Predictions

Cedar Key, FL,2021

Times and Heights of High and Low Waters

April

Day	Time	ft	cm
1 Th	05:38	3.2	98
	11:12	1.1	34
	16:51	3.9	119
2 F	00:05	-0.5	-15
	06:38	2.9	88
	11:51	1.4	43
	17:32	3.8	116
3 Sa	01:02	-0.3	-9
	07:48	2.6	79
	12:35	1.7	52
	18:21	3.7	113
4 Su	02:11	0.0	0
	09:20	2.4	73
	13:37	1.9	58
	19:25	3.4	104
5 M	03:36	0.2	6
	10:54	2.4	73
	15:08	1.9	58
	20:55	3.2	98
6 Tu	04:59	0.2	6
	11:55	2.6	79
	16:43	1.7	52
	22:37	3.2	98
7 W	06:04	0.3	9
	12:37	2.8	85
	17:56	1.3	40
	23:55	3.3	101
8 Th	06:53	0.3	9
	13:09	3.0	91
	18:52	0.9	27
9 F	00:55	3.4	104
	07:32	0.3	9
	13:37	3.2	98
	19:38	0.5	15
10 Sa	01:42	3.5	107
	08:04	0.4	12
	14:03	3.4	104
	20:17	0.3	9
11 Su	02:23	3.5	107
	08:33	0.6	18
	14:26	3.5	107
	20:52	0.1	3
12 M	03:00	3.5	107
	09:00	0.7	21
	14:49	3.6	110
	21:26	0.0	0
13 Tu	03:36	3.4	104
	09:27	0.9	27
	15:12	3.7	113
	21:59	-0.1	-3
14 W	04:13	3.3	101
	09:55	1.0	30
	15:36	3.7	113
	22:32	-0.1	-3
15 Th	04:51	3.1	94
	10:23	1.2	37
	16:02	3.7	113
	23:06	-0.1	-3
16 F	05:32	3.0	91
	10:52	1.4	43
	16:31	3.7	113
	23:43	0.0	0
17 Sa	06:17	2.8	85
	11:26	1.5	46
	17:06	3.7	113
18 Su	00:26	0.1	3
	07:09	2.7	82
	12:06	1.7	52
	17:49	3.6	110
19 M	01:19	0.2	6
	08:14	2.6	79
	13:01	1.8	55
	18:45	3.4	104
20 Tu	02:27	0.4	12
	09:34	2.6	79
	14:22	1.9	58
	20:01	3.3	101
21 W	03:44	0.4	12
	10:43	2.7	82
	15:53	1.7	52
	21:36	3.2	98
22 Th	04:53	0.3	9
	11:34	2.9	88
	17:06	1.4	43
	23:00	3.4	104
23 F	05:52	0.3	9
	12:15	3.2	98
	18:06	0.9	27
24 Sa	00:08	3.6	110
	06:43	0.3	9
	12:51	3.4	104
	19:00	0.5	15
25 Su	01:08	3.8	116
	07:29	0.4	12
	13:24	3.6	110
	19:49	0.0	0
26 M	02:04	3.9	119
	08:11	0.6	18
	13:57	3.8	116
	20:37	-0.4	-12
27 Tu	02:57	3.9	119
	08:51	0.8	24
	14:29	4.0	122
	21:23	-0.7	-21
28 W	03:50	3.7	113
	09:30	1.1	34
	15:04	4.2	128
	22:11	-0.8	-24
29 Th	04:45	3.5	107
	10:09	1.4	43
	15:41	4.2	128
	23:01	-0.7	-21
30 F	05:43	3.2	98
	10:50	1.6	49
	16:22	4.2	128
	23:53	-0.5	-15

May

Day	Time	ft	cm
1 Sa	06:41	3.0	91
	11:35	1.8	55
	17:09	4.0	122
2 Su	00:48	-0.2	-6
	07:43	2.8	85
	12:27	1.9	58
	18:05	3.7	113
3 M	01:49	0.1	3
	08:53	2.7	82
	13:34	1.9	58
	19:14	3.4	104
4 Tu	03:00	0.5	15
	10:02	2.7	82
	15:00	1.8	55
	20:45	3.1	94
5 W	04:14	0.7	21
	10:56	2.9	88
	16:27	1.5	46
	22:24	3.1	94
6 Th	05:15	0.8	24
	11:37	3.1	94
	17:36	1.1	34
	23:41	3.1	94
7 F	06:04	0.9	27
	12:13	3.3	101
	18:31	0.7	21
8 Sa	00:40	3.2	98
	06:44	1.0	30
		3.5	107
	19:16	0.4	12
9 Su	01:29	3.3	101
	07:20	1.1	34
	13:13	3.7	113
	19:56	0.1	3
10 M	02:12	3.4	104
	07:53	1.2	37
	13:40	3.8	116
	20:32	0.0	0
11 Tu	02:51	3.3	101
	08:24	1.3	40
	14:06	3.8	116
	21:06	-0.1	-3
12 W	03:29	3.3	101
	08:55	1.4	43
	14:31	3.9	119
	21:39	-0.2	-6
13 Th	04:07	3.2	98
	09:25	1.6	49
	14:58	3.9	119
	22:12	-0.2	-6
14 F	04:46	3.1	94
	09:57	1.7	52
	15:27	3.9	119
	22:47	-0.1	-3
15 Sa	05:27	3.1	94
	10:32	1.7	52
	16:01	3.9	119
	23:25	-0.1	-3
16 Su	06:10	3.0	91
	11:11	1.8	55
	16:41	3.8	116
17 M	00:07	0.0	0
	06:55	2.9	88
	11:58	1.8	55
	17:29	3.7	113
18 Tu	00:56	0.2	6
	07:47	2.9	88
	12:56	1.9	58
	18:29	3.5	107
19 W	01:53	0.3	9
	08:45	3.0	91
	14:07	1.8	55
	19:43	3.4	104
20 Th	02:58	0.5	15
	09:44	3.1	94
	15:27	1.6	49
	21:13	3.3	101
21 F	04:05	0.6	18
	10:34	3.3	101
	16:39	1.1	34
	22:38	3.4	104
22 Sa	05:04	0.7	21
	11:18	3.5	107
	17:41	0.6	18
	23:52	3.5	107
23 Su	05:58	0.9	27
	11:58	3.8	116
	18:38	0.1	3
24 M	00:58	3.6	110
	06:48	1.0	30
	12:36	4.0	122
	19:31	-0.3	-9
25 Tu	01:58	3.7	113
	07:35	1.3	40
	13:14	4.2	128
	20:22	-0.7	-21
26 W	02:55	3.6	110
	08:20	1.5	46
	13:53	4.4	134
	21:11	-0.9	-27
27 Th	03:50	3.5	107
	09:03	1.7	52
	14:34	4.4	134
	22:00	-0.9	-27
28 F	04:46	3.4	104
	09:47	1.8	55
	15:17	4.4	134
	22:50	-0.7	-21
29 Sa	05:41	3.2	98
	10:33	1.9	58
	16:04	4.3	131
	23:40	-0.4	-12
30 Su	06:32	3.1	94
	11:24	1.9	58
	16:57	4.0	122
31 M	00:30	-0.1	-3
	07:20	3.0	91
	12:20	1.8	55
	17:57	3.7	113

June

Day	Time	ft	cm
1 Tu	01:21	0.3	9
	08:08	3.0	91
	13:24	1.8	55
	19:04	3.4	104
2 W	02:15	0.7	21
	08:58	3.0	91
	14:38	1.6	49
	20:24	3.1	94
3 Th	03:13	1.0	30
	09:48	3.2	98
	15:56	1.3	40
	21:54	2.9	88
4 F	04:10	1.2	37
	10:32	3.3	101
	17:04	1.0	30
	23:12	3.0	91
5 Sa	05:00	1.4	43
	11:12	3.5	107
	18:01	0.6	18
6 Su	00:16	3.0	91
	05:46	1.5	46
	11:48	3.7	113
	18:49	0.3	9
7 M	01:11	3.1	94
	06:29	1.6	49
	12:22	3.8	116
	19:32	0.1	3
8 Tu	01:58	3.2	98
	07:09	1.7	52
	12:55	3.9	119
	20:11	-0.1	-3
9 W	02:41	3.2	98
	07:48	1.8	55
	13:27	4.0	122
	20:47	-0.2	-6
10 Th	03:22	3.2	98
	08:25	1.8	55
	13:58	4.0	122
	21:22	-0.2	-6
11 F	04:02	3.2	98
	09:02	1.9	58
	14:31	4.0	122
	21:57	-0.2	-6
12 Sa	04:41	3.2	98
	09:39	1.9	58
	15:06	4.0	122
	22:33	-0.2	-6
13 Su	05:20	3.1	94
	10:19	1.9	58
	15:45	4.0	122
	23:11	-0.1	-3
14 M	05:57	3.2	98
	11:03	1.9	58
	16:30	3.9	119
	23:52	0.0	0
15 Tu	06:35	3.2	98
	11:51	1.8	55
	17:22	3.8	116
16 W	00:36	0.1	3
	07:15	3.2	98
	12:46	1.7	52
	18:22	3.6	110
17 Th	01:24	0.4	12
	07:59	3.3	101
	13:49	1.5	46
	19:31	3.4	104
18 F	02:18	0.6	18
	08:47	3.4	104
	15:01	1.2	37
	20:54	3.3	101
19 Sa	03:18	0.9	27
	09:36	3.6	110
	16:13	0.8	24
	22:21	3.2	98
20 Su	04:18	1.2	37
	10:24	3.8	116
	17:19	0.4	12
	23:40	3.3	101
21 M	05:15	1.4	43
	11:10	4.1	125
	18:20	-0.1	-3
22 Tu	00:52	3.4	104
	06:09	1.6	49
	11:56	4.3	131
	19:18	-0.5	-15
23 W	01:57	3.4	104
	07:02	1.8	55
	12:42	4.5	137
	20:11	-0.7	-21
24 Th	02:54	3.4	104
	07:54	1.9	58
	13:29	4.5	137
	21:02	-0.8	-24
25 F	03:48	3.4	104
	08:43	1.9	58
	14:17	4.5	137
	21:50	-0.7	-21
26 Sa	04:38	3.3	101
	09:31	1.9	58
	15:06	4.4	134
	22:37	-0.5	-15
27 Su	05:24	3.3	101
	10:21	1.8	55
	15:56	4.2	128
	23:23	-0.2	-6
28 M	06:05	3.2	98
	11:12	1.7	52
	16:51	4.0	122
29 Tu	00:05	0.1	3
	06:41	3.2	98
	12:06	1.6	49
	17:48	3.7	113
30 W	00:46	0.5	15
	07:17	3.3	101
	13:02	1.5	46
	18:48	3.4	104

StationId: 8727520
Source: NOAA/NOS/CO-OPS
Station Type: Primary
Time Zone: LST_LDT
Datum: MLLW

NOAA Tide Predictions

Cedar Key, FL, 2021

Times and Heights of High and Low Waters

July

Day	Time (h m)	Height ft	Height cm		Day	Time (h m)	Height ft	Height cm
1 Th ☽	01:26	0.9	27		16 F	00:55	0.6	18
	07:54	3.4	104			07:12	3.7	113
	14:03	1.4	43			13:29	1.1	34
	19:53	3.1	94			19:22	3.5	107
2 F	02:10	1.2	37		17 Sa ☾	01:41	0.9	27
	08:36	3.4	104			07:54	3.8	116
	15:12	1.2	37			14:36	0.9	27
	21:11	2.9	88			20:40	3.2	98
3 Sa	02:59	1.5	46		18 Su	02:34	1.3	40
	09:21	3.5	107			08:42	3.9	119
	16:21	1.0	30			15:49	0.6	18
	22:33	2.8	85			22:10	3.1	94
4 Su	03:53	1.7	52		19 M	03:35	1.6	49
	10:08	3.7	113			09:37	4.1	125
	17:22	0.7	21			17:00	0.3	9
	23:45	2.8	85			23:36	3.1	94
5 M	04:46	1.9	58		20 Tu	04:38	1.9	58
	10:52	3.8	116			10:33	4.2	128
	18:17	0.4	12			18:07	-0.1	-3
6 Tu	00:49	2.9	88		21 W	00:53	3.2	98
	05:38	2.0	61			05:40	2.0	61
	11:35	3.9	119			11:28	4.4	134
	19:06	0.2	6			19:09	-0.3	-9
7 W	01:44	3.0	91		22 Th	01:57	3.3	101
	06:29	2.0	61			06:40	2.1	64
	12:16	4.0	122			12:24	4.5	137
	19:49	0.0	0			20:04	-0.5	-15
8 Th	02:30	3.1	94		23 F	02:49	3.3	101
	07:17	2.1	64			07:38	2.0	61
	12:56	4.0	122			13:19	4.5	137
	20:29	-0.1	-3			20:53	-0.5	-15
9 F	03:11	3.2	98		24 Sa ○	03:33	3.4	104
	08:02	2.0	61			08:31	1.9	58
	13:36	4.1	125			14:12	4.5	137
	21:06	-0.1	-3			21:38	-0.3	-9
10 Sa ●	03:49	3.2	98		25 Su	04:13	3.4	104
	08:44	2.0	61			09:20	1.7	52
	14:16	4.1	125			15:03	4.4	134
	21:42	-0.1	-3			22:19	-0.1	-3
11 Su	04:25	3.2	98		26 M	04:48	3.4	104
	09:26	1.9	58			10:08	1.5	46
	14:57	4.1	125			15:53	4.2	128
	22:19	-0.1	-3			22:58	0.2	6
12 M	04:58	3.3	101		27 Tu	05:21	3.4	104
	10:08	1.8	55			10:55	1.4	43
	15:40	4.1	125			16:43	4.0	122
	22:56	0.0	0			23:33	0.5	15
13 Tu	05:30	3.3	101		28 W	05:51	3.5	107
	10:52	1.7	52			11:43	1.3	40
	16:27	4.1	125			17:33	3.8	116
	23:34	0.1	3					
14 W	06:02	3.4	104		29 Th	00:06	0.8	24
	11:39	1.5	46			06:21	3.6	110
	17:20	3.9	119			12:31	1.2	37
						18:25	3.5	107
15 Th	00:13	0.3	9		30 F	00:39	1.1	34
	06:36	3.5	107			06:53	3.7	113
	12:31	1.3	40			13:21	1.1	34
	18:17	3.7	113			19:20	3.2	98
					31 Sa ☽	01:14	1.4	43
						07:28	3.7	113
						14:19	1.1	34
						20:26	2.9	88

August

Day	Time (h m)	Height ft	Height cm		Day	Time (h m)	Height ft	Height cm
1 Su	01:53	1.7	52		16 M	01:55	1.8	55
	08:09	3.7	113			07:55	4.1	125
	15:26	1.0	30			15:28	0.5	15
	21:47	2.8	85			22:08	3.0	91
2 M	02:45	1.9	58		17 Tu	02:58	2.1	64
	08:59	3.8	116			08:57	4.2	128
	16:35	0.8	24			16:46	0.4	12
	23:11	2.8	85			23:40	3.0	91
3 Tu	03:49	2.1	64		18 W	04:12	2.2	67
	09:56	3.8	116			10:07	4.2	128
	17:39	0.7	21			17:59	0.2	6
4 W	00:24	2.9	88		19 Th	00:55	3.1	94
	04:54	2.2	67			05:25	2.2	67
	10:52	3.9	119			11:17	4.3	131
	18:36	0.5	15			19:03	0.0	0
5 Th	01:23	3.0	91		20 F	01:49	3.3	101
	05:56	2.2	67			06:32	2.1	64
	11:46	4.0	122			12:22	4.4	134
	19:25	0.3	9			19:56	0.0	0
6 F	02:09	3.2	98		21 Sa	02:29	3.4	104
	06:53	2.1	64			07:32	1.8	55
	12:36	4.1	125			13:22	4.4	134
	20:08	0.1	3			20:40	0.0	0
7 Sa	02:47	3.3	101		22 Su ○	03:04	3.5	107
	07:43	2.0	61			08:23	1.6	49
	13:24	4.2	128			14:15	4.4	134
	20:46	0.1	3			21:19	0.2	6
8 Su ●	03:20	3.3	101		23 M	03:34	3.6	110
	08:28	1.9	58			09:09	1.3	40
	14:10	4.3	131			15:03	4.3	131
	21:23	0.0	0			21:54	0.4	12
9 M	03:51	3.4	104		24 Tu	04:03	3.6	110
	09:11	1.7	52			10:19	1.1	34
	14:54	4.3	131			15:48	4.2	128
	21:58	0.1	3			22:26	0.6	18
10 Tu	04:20	3.5	107		25 W	04:30	3.7	113
	09:53	1.5	46			10:33	1.0	30
	15:39	4.3	131			16:31	4.0	122
	22:34	0.2	6			22:56	0.8	24
11 W	04:49	3.6	110		26 Th	04:57	3.8	116
	10:37	1.3	40			11:14	0.9	27
	16:26	4.2	128			17:15	3.8	116
	23:11	0.4	12			23:25	1.1	34
12 Th	05:19	3.7	113		27 F	05:24	3.9	119
	11:23	1.1	34			11:56	0.9	27
	17:18	4.0	122			18:01	3.6	110
	23:48	0.6	18			23:55	1.3	40
13 F	05:51	3.9	119		28 Sa	05:54	3.9	119
	12:13	0.9	27			12:38	0.9	27
	18:14	3.8	116			18:49	3.3	101
14 Sa	00:26	1.0	30		29 Su	00:26	1.6	49
	06:26	4.0	122			06:26	3.9	119
	13:07	0.7	21			13:26	0.9	27
	19:16	3.5	107			19:45	3.0	91
15 Su ☽	01:07	1.4	43		30 M ☽	01:01	1.9	58
	07:07	4.1	125			07:04	3.9	119
	14:12	0.6	18			14:26	1.0	30
	20:32	3.1	94			21:01	2.9	88
					31 Tu	01:47	2.1	64
						07:53	3.8	116
						15:39	1.0	30
						22:31	2.8	85

September

Day	Time (h m)	Height ft	Height cm		Day	Time (h m)	Height ft	Height cm
1 W	02:57	2.3	70		16 Th	04:03	2.3	70
	08:58	3.7	113			09:56	3.9	119
	16:54	0.9	27			17:49	0.5	15
	23:50	2.9	88					
2 Th	04:20	2.4	73		17 F	00:39	3.1	94
	10:14	3.8	116			05:24	2.1	64
	17:59	0.7	21			11:20	4.0	122
						18:51	0.4	12
3 F	00:50	3.1	94		18 Sa	01:22	3.3	101
	05:31	2.2	67			06:32	1.8	55
	11:22	3.9	119			12:31	4.1	125
	18:54	0.5	15			19:39	0.4	12
4 Sa	01:34	3.3	101		19 Su	01:56	3.5	107
	06:32	2.0	61			07:27	1.4	43
	12:22	4.1	125			13:29	4.2	128
	19:39	0.4	12			20:19	0.5	15
5 Su	02:09	3.4	104		20 M ○	02:25	3.6	110
	07:25	1.8	55			08:14	1.1	34
	13:16	4.2	128			14:17	4.2	128
	20:19	0.3	9			20:52	0.7	21
6 M	02:39	3.5	107		21 Tu	02:51	3.8	116
	08:11	1.5	46			08:55	0.8	24
	14:04	4.4	134			15:00	4.2	128
	20:56	0.3	9			21:22	0.8	24
7 Tu ●	03:07	3.6	110		22 W	03:16	3.9	119
	08:54	1.2	37			09:33	0.6	18
	14:50	4.4	134			15:39	4.1	125
	21:32	0.4	12			21:51	1.0	30
8 W	03:35	3.8	116		23 Th	03:40	3.9	119
	09:36	0.9	27			10:10	0.5	15
	15:37	4.4	134			16:18	3.9	119
	22:08	0.6	18			22:19	1.2	37
9 Th	04:03	3.9	119		24 F	04:05	4.0	122
	10:19	0.7	21			10:46	0.5	15
	16:25	4.2	128			16:58	3.7	113
	22:43	0.8	24			22:47	1.4	43
10 F	04:33	4.1	125		25 Sa	04:31	4.0	122
	11:05	0.5	15			11:21	0.5	15
	17:17	4.0	122			17:39	3.5	107
	23:20	1.1	34			23:15	1.6	49
11 Sa	05:06	4.2	128		26 Su	05:00	4.0	122
	11:54	0.4	12			11:59	0.6	18
	18:12	3.7	113			18:23	3.3	101
	23:57	1.5	46			23:46	1.8	55
12 Su	05:43	4.3	131		27 M	05:32	4.0	122
	12:48	0.4	12			12:41	0.7	21
	19:14	3.4	104			19:14	3.1	94
13 M ☽	00:37	1.8	55		28 Tu	00:21	2.0	61
	06:26	4.3	131			06:10	3.9	119
	13:51	0.4	12			13:32	0.8	24
	20:31	3.1	94			20:18	2.9	88
14 Tu	01:25	2.1	64		29 W ☾	01:07	2.2	67
	07:18	4.2	128			06:58	3.8	116
	15:08	0.5	15			14:40	0.9	27
	22:09	2.9	88			21:45	2.8	85
15 W	02:34	2.3	70		30 Th	02:18	2.3	70
	08:27	4.0	122			08:06	3.6	110
	16:33	0.6	18			16:01	0.9	27
	23:38	3.0	91			23:04	2.9	88

StationId: 8727520
Source: NOAA/NOS/CO-OPS
Station Type: Primary
Time Zone: LST_LDT
Datum: MLLW

NOAA Tide Predictions

Cedar Key, FL, 2021

Times and Heights of High and Low Waters

October

Day	Time	ft	cm	Day	Time	ft	cm
1 F	03:51	2.3	70	**16** Sa	00:02	3.1	94
	09:38	3.6	110		05:24	1.7	52
	17:13	0.8	24		11:27	3.6	110
					18:25	0.8	24
2 Sa	00:02	3.1	94	**17** Su	00:41	3.3	101
	05:09	2.1	64		06:28	1.3	40
	11:01	3.7	113		12:36	3.7	113
	18:12	0.7	21		19:11	0.8	24
3 Su	00:46	3.3	101	**18** M	01:13	3.5	107
	06:11	1.7	52		07:19	0.8	24
	12:08	3.9	119		13:30	3.8	116
	19:02	0.6	18		19:47	0.9	27
4 M	01:21	3.5	107	**19** Tu	01:42	3.7	113
	07:04	1.3	40		08:02	0.5	15
	13:05	4.1	125		14:15	3.8	116
	19:45	0.5	15		20:19	1.0	30
5 Tu	01:51	3.7	113	**20** W	02:08	3.8	116
	07:51	0.9	27		08:40	0.3	9
	13:57	4.3	131		14:54	3.8	116
	20:25	0.6	18		20:48	1.2	37
6 W	02:20	3.8	116	**21** Th	02:32	3.9	119
	08:35	0.5	15		09:14	0.1	3
	14:45	4.3	131		15:31	3.7	113
	21:02	0.7	21		21:17	1.3	40
7 Th	02:49	4.0	122	**22** F	02:57	4.0	122
	09:18	0.2	6		09:47	0.0	0
	15:34	4.2	128		16:07	3.6	110
	21:38	1.0	30		21:45	1.4	43
8 F	03:19	4.2	128	**23** Sa	03:21	4.0	122
	10:03	-0.1	-3		10:20	0.0	0
	16:24	4.1	125		16:45	3.5	107
	22:15	1.2	37		22:14	1.5	46
9 Sa	03:51	4.3	131	**24** Su	03:48	4.0	122
	10:49	-0.2	-6		10:53	0.1	3
	17:16	3.8	116		17:23	3.4	104
	22:52	1.5	46		22:44	1.7	52
10 Su	04:26	4.4	134	**25** M	04:17	4.0	122
	11:38	-0.2	-6		11:28	0.1	3
	18:12	3.5	107		18:04	3.2	98
	23:31	1.8	55		23:16	1.8	55
11 M	05:07	4.4	134	**26** Tu	04:50	3.9	119
	12:31	0.0	0		12:06	0.3	9
	19:13	3.2	98		18:49	3.0	91
					23:54	1.9	58
12 Tu	00:14	2.0	61	**27** W	05:30	3.8	116
	05:54	4.2	128		12:52	0.4	12
	13:32	0.2	6		19:43	2.9	88
	20:26	2.9	88				
13 W	01:08	2.2	67	**28** Th	00:42	2.0	61
	06:52	4.0	122		06:20	3.6	110
	14:46	0.5	15		13:50	0.6	18
	21:56	2.8	85		20:51	2.8	85
14 Th	02:26	2.2	67	**29** F	01:51	2.0	61
	08:10	3.7	113		07:28	3.4	104
	16:12	0.7	21		15:05	0.8	24
	23:11	2.9	88		22:06	2.9	88
15 F	04:01	2.1	64	**30** Sa	03:22	1.9	58
	09:55	3.5	107		09:03	3.2	98
	17:27	0.8	24		16:20	0.8	24
					23:04	3.0	91
				31 Su	04:43	1.6	49
					10:36	3.3	101
					17:24	0.8	24
					23:49	3.2	98

November

Day	Time	ft	cm	Day	Time	ft	cm
1 M	05:47	1.2	37	**16** Tu	06:05	0.3	9
	11:51	3.5	107		12:26	3.2	98
	18:18	0.7	21		18:08	1.2	37
					23:57	3.6	110
2 Tu	00:27	3.5	107	**17** W	06:47	-0.1	-3
	06:42	0.7	21		13:09	3.3	101
	12:53	3.7	113		18:43	1.3	40
	19:06	0.8	24				
3 W	01:01	3.7	113	**18** Th	00:26	3.7	113
	07:31	0.1	3		07:23	-0.3	-9
	13:49	3.9	119		13:48	3.3	101
	19:50	0.9	27		19:15	1.3	40
4 Th	01:34	3.9	119	**19** F	00:54	3.8	116
	08:18	-0.3	-9		07:57	-0.4	-12
	14:41	3.9	119		14:24	3.3	101
●	20:31	1.0	30	○	19:47	1.4	43
5 F	02:08	4.1	125	**20** Sa	01:21	3.8	116
	09:03	-0.6	-18		08:29	-0.5	-15
	15:32	3.9	119		15:00	3.2	98
	21:10	1.2	37		20:18	1.5	46
6 Sa	02:42	4.3	131	**21** Su	01:48	3.8	116
	09:49	-0.8	-24		09:00	-0.4	-12
	16:23	3.7	113		15:35	3.2	98
	21:49	1.4	43		20:49	1.5	46
7 Su	02:19	4.4	134	**22** M	02:17	3.8	116
	09:36	-0.8	-24		09:32	-0.4	-12
	16:16	3.5	107		16:11	3.1	94
	21:29	1.6	49		21:21	1.6	49
8 M	02:58	4.4	134	**23** Tu	02:48	3.8	116
	10:25	-0.7	-21		10:06	-0.3	-9
	17:10	3.2	98		16:48	3.0	91
	22:11	1.7	52		21:57	1.6	49
9 Tu	03:43	4.2	128	**24** W	03:24	3.7	113
	11:16	-0.4	-12		10:43	-0.2	-6
	18:05	3.0	91		17:26	2.9	88
	23:00	1.8	55		22:37	1.6	49
10 W	04:35	3.9	119	**25** Th	04:06	3.5	107
	12:12	0.0	0		11:24	0.0	0
	19:04	2.8	85		18:09	2.8	85
	23:59	1.9	58		23:26	1.6	49
11 Th	05:38	3.6	110	**26** F	04:58	3.3	101
	13:16	0.4	12		12:13	0.2	6
	20:13	2.7	82		19:00	2.8	85
◐							
12 F	01:17	1.8	55	**27** Sa	00:30	1.6	49
	06:59	3.2	98		06:03	3.1	94
	14:31	0.7	21		13:13	0.4	12
◑	21:18	2.8	85	◑	19:59	2.8	85
13 Sa	02:51	1.6	49	**28** Su	01:51	1.4	43
	08:48	3.0	91		07:31	2.9	88
	15:43	0.9	27		14:24	0.6	18
◑	22:09	3.0	91		20:58	2.9	88
14 Su	04:13	1.1	34	**29** M	03:12	1.1	34
	10:23	3.0	91		09:10	2.9	88
	16:41	1.1	34		15:32	0.7	21
	22:50	3.2	98		21:49	3.1	94
15 M	05:15	0.7	21	**30** Tu	04:20	0.6	18
	11:32	3.1	94		10:33	3.0	91
	17:28	1.1	34		16:32	0.8	24
	23:25	3.4	104		22:33	3.4	104

December

Day	Time	ft	cm	Day	Time	ft	cm
1 W	05:20	0.0	0	**16** Th	06:29	-0.4	-12
	11:44	3.2	98		13:03	2.8	85
	17:26	1.0	30		18:06	1.4	43
	23:14	3.7	113		23:48	3.5	107
2 Th	06:13	-0.5	-15	**17** F	07:06	-0.6	-18
	12:45	3.3	101		13:42	2.9	88
	18:16	1.1	34		18:46	1.4	43
	23:54	3.9	119				
3 F	07:03	-1.0	-30	**18** Sa	00:22	3.5	107
	13:39*	3.4	104		07:41	-0.8	-24
	19:02	1.2	37		14:17	2.9	88
					19:22	1.4	43
4 Sa	00:35	4.1	125	**19** Su	00:54	3.6	110
	07:51	-1.3	-40		08:13	-0.8	-24
	14:31	3.4	104		14:51	2.9	88
●	19:45	1.3	40	○	19:57	1.3	40
5 Su	01:16	4.2	128	**20** M	01:26	3.6	110
	08:38	-1.4	-43		08:45	-0.8	-24
	15:21	3.2	98		15:24	2.9	88
	20:28	1.4	43		20:32	1.3	40
6 M	01:58	4.3	131	**21** Tu	01:59	3.6	110
	09:24	-1.3	-40		09:16	-0.7	-21
	16:10	3.1	94		15:56	2.8	85
	21:11	1.4	43		21:06	1.3	40
7 Tu	02:43	4.1	125	**22** W	02:34	3.5	107
	10:12	-1.0	-30		09:49	-0.7	-21
	16:57	2.9	88		16:28	2.8	85
	21:58	1.4	43		21:43	1.2	37
8 W	03:32	3.9	119	**23** Th	03:12	3.5	107
	10:59	-0.6	-18		10:24	-0.5	-15
	17:41	2.8	85		17:00	2.8	85
	22:49	1.4	43		22:24	1.1	34
9 Th	04:26	3.6	110	**24** F	03:55	3.3	101
	11:46	-0.2	-6		11:01	-0.4	-12
	18:25	2.7	82		17:34	2.8	85
	23:48	1.3	40		23:12	1.1	34
10 F	05:28	3.1	94	**25** Sa	04:46	3.1	94
	12:36	0.3	9		11:43	-0.1	-3
	19:12	2.7	82		18:13	2.8	85
11 Sa	00:57	1.2	37	**26** Su	00:08	1.0	30
	06:43	2.7	82		05:48	2.9	88
	13:32	0.7	21		12:31	0.2	6
◐	20:06	2.7	82		18:59	2.9	88
12 Su	02:23	1.0	30	**27** M	01:18	0.8	24
	08:22	2.4	73		07:06	2.6	79
	14:36	1.0	30		13:30	0.5	15
	21:01	2.8	85	◑	19:52	2.9	88
13 M	03:46	0.7	21	**28** Tu	02:39	0.5	15
	10:02	2.4	73		08:46	2.4	73
	15:38	1.2	37		14:38	0.8	24
	21:50	3.0	91		20:48	3.1	94
14 Tu	04:52	0.3	9	**29** W	03:54	0.0	0
	11:19	2.5	76		10:20	2.5	76
	16:33	1.3	40		15:46	1.0	30
	22:33	3.2	98		21:43	3.3	101
15 W	05:45	-0.1	-3	**30** Th	05:00	-0.5	-15
	12:17	2.6	79		11:40	2.7	82
	17:22	1.3	40		16:48	1.2	37
	23:12	3.3	101		22:34	3.6	110
				31 F	05:59	-1.0	-30
					12:45	2.8	85
					17:46	1.3	40
					23:21	3.8	116

StationId: 8728142
Source: NOAA/NOS/CO-OPS
Station Type: Subordinate
Time Zone: LST_LDT
Datum: MLLW

NOAA Tide Predictions

St. Marks, St. Marks River, FL, 2021

Times and Heights of High and Low Waters

January

Day	Time (h m)	Height (ft)	Height (cm)
1 F	02:59	3.2	98
	10:39	-0.8	-24
	16:51	2.8	85
	22:31	0.9	27
2 Sa	03:41	3.2	98
	11:14	-0.7	-21
	17:26	2.7	82
	23:16	0.8	24
3 Su	04:27	3.0	91
	11:52	-0.5	-15
	18:03	2.7	82
4 M	00:09	0.7	21
	05:22	2.8	85
	12:34	-0.2	-6
	18:43	2.7	82
5 Tu	01:11	0.6	18
	06:29	2.5	76
	13:21	0.2	6
	19:26	2.7	82
6 W	02:25	0.4	12
	07:57	2.2	67
	14:17	0.6	18
	20:16	2.7	82
7 Th	03:45	0.1	3
	09:41	2.1	64
	15:22	1.0	30
	21:12	2.7	82
8 F	05:02	-0.3	-9
	11:15	2.3	70
	16:33	1.2	37
	22:13	2.8	85
9 Sa	06:09	-0.7	-21
	12:29	2.5	76
	17:43	1.3	40
	23:13	2.9	88
10 Su	07:08	-1.0	-30
	13:26	2.6	79
	18:45	1.4	43
11 M	00:09	3.1	94
	08:01	-1.2	-37
	14:15	2.7	82
	19:38	1.3	40
12 Tu	01:01	3.2	98
	08:49	-1.3	-40
	14:57	2.8	85
	20:25	1.2	37
13 W ●	01:49	3.2	98
	09:33	-1.2	-37
	15:35	2.7	82
	21:09	1.0	30
14 Th	02:34	3.2	98
	10:13	-1.0	-30
	16:10	2.7	82
	21:50	0.9	27
15 F	03:16	3.1	94
	10:49	-0.8	-24
	16:42	2.6	79
	22:31	0.8	24
16 Sa	03:57	2.9	88
	11:22	-0.5	-15
	17:12	2.5	76
	23:13	0.7	21
17 Su	04:39	2.7	82
	11:52	-0.1	-3
	17:40	2.5	76
	23:58	0.6	18
18 M	05:24	2.4	73
	12:21	0.3	9
	18:08	2.4	73
19 Tu	00:51	0.6	18
	06:19	2.1	64
	12:51	0.6	18
	18:37	2.4	73
20 W ◖	01:56	0.6	18
	07:18	1.8	55
	13:28	0.9	27
	19:11	2.3	70
21 Th	03:19	0.5	15
	09:29	1.7	52
	14:21	1.2	37
	19:58	2.3	70
22 F	04:46	0.3	9
	11:14	1.8	55
	15:37	1.4	43
	21:05	2.2	67
23 Sa	05:56	0.0	0
	12:21	2.0	61
	17:02	1.5	46
	22:22	2.3	70
24 Su	06:49	-0.2	-6
	13:07	2.2	67
	18:12	1.4	43
	23:26	2.4	73
25 M	07:33	-0.5	-15
	13:45	2.4	73
	19:04	1.3	40
26 Tu	00:15	2.6	79
	08:11	-0.7	-21
	14:20	2.6	79
	19:47	1.2	37
27 W	00:58	2.8	85
	08:46	-0.8	-24
	14:53	2.7	82
	20:26	1.0	30
28 Th ○	01:39	3.0	91
	09:18	-0.9	-27
	15:24	2.8	85
	21:04	0.8	24
29 F	02:18	3.1	94
	09:50	-1.0	-30
	15:53	2.9	88
	21:42	0.6	18
30 Sa	03:00	3.2	98
	10:21	-0.9	-27
	16:22	2.9	88
	22:22	0.4	12
31 Su	03:43	3.2	98
	10:52	-0.7	-21
	16:50	2.9	88
	23:06	0.2	6

February

Day	Time (h m)	Height (ft)	Height (cm)
1 M	04:30	3.0	91
	11:25	-0.4	-12
	17:18	2.9	88
	23:54	0.1	3
2 Tu	05:23	2.8	85
	11:59	0.0	0
	17:48	2.9	88
3 W	00:49	0.0	0
	06:25	2.4	73
	12:36	0.5	15
	18:21	2.9	88
4 Th ◐	01:57	-0.1	-3
	07:47	2.1	64
	13:20	0.9	27
	19:02	2.8	85
5 F	03:18	-0.2	-6
	09:36	1.9	58
	14:18	1.3	40
	19:59	2.7	82
6 Sa	04:45	-0.4	-12
	11:23	2.0	61
	15:43	1.6	49
	21:23	2.7	82
7 Su	06:02	-0.7	-21
	12:36	2.3	70
	17:22	1.6	49
	22:56	2.7	82
8 M	07:04	-0.9	-27
	13:26	2.5	76
	18:41	1.4	43
9 Tu	00:09	2.9	88
	07:56	-1.0	-30
	14:05	2.6	79
	19:39	1.2	37
10 W	01:06	3.0	91
	08:39	-1.0	-30
	14:39	2.7	82
	20:25	0.9	27
11 Th ●	01:54	3.1	94
	09:17	-0.9	-27
	15:10	2.8	85
	21:05	0.7	21
12 F	02:36	3.1	94
	09:50	-0.8	-24
	15:38	2.8	85
	21:43	0.5	15
13 Sa	03:15	3.1	94
	10:19	-0.5	-15
	16:03	2.8	85
	22:19	0.3	9
14 Su	03:52	2.9	88
	10:45	-0.3	-9
	16:26	2.8	85
	22:55	0.2	6
15 M	04:28	2.7	82
	11:08	0.0	0
	16:47	2.8	85
	23:32	0.2	6
16 Tu	05:08	2.5	76
	11:31	0.3	9
	17:08	2.8	85
17 W	00:12	0.2	6
	05:52	2.2	67
	11:56	0.6	18
	17:29	2.7	82
18 Th	00:59	0.3	9
	06:50	1.9	58
	12:25	1.0	30
	17:53	2.6	79
19 F ◖	02:04	0.4	12
	08:21	1.7	52
	13:04	1.3	40
	18:25	2.4	73
20 Sa	03:37	0.4	12
	10:32	1.8	55
	14:12	1.6	49
	19:14	2.3	70
21 Su	05:13	0.2	6
	12:02	2.0	61
	16:08	1.7	52
	20:55	2.2	67
22 M	06:20	-0.1	-3
	12:50	2.3	70
	17:51	1.6	49
	22:51	2.3	70
23 Tu	07:09	-0.3	-9
	13:27	2.5	76
	18:52	1.4	43
	23:59	2.6	79
24 W	07:48	-0.6	-18
	13:58	2.7	82
	19:37	1.2	37
25 Th	00:49	2.9	88
	08:23	-0.7	-21
	14:28	2.9	88
	20:15	0.9	27
26 F	01:33	3.1	94
	08:56	-0.8	-24
	14:55	3.0	91
	20:53	0.6	18
27 Sa ○	02:16	3.3	101
	09:27	-0.8	-24
	15:20	3.1	94
	21:31	0.2	6
28 Su	03:00	3.4	104
	09:56	-0.6	-18
	15:45	3.2	98
	22:11	-0.1	-3

March

Day	Time (h m)	Height (ft)	Height (cm)
1 M	03:44	3.3	101
	10:26	-0.3	-9
	16:09	3.2	98
	22:52	-0.3	-9
2 Tu	04:31	3.1	94
	10:55	0.1	3
	16:33	3.3	101
	23:38	-0.4	-12
3 W	05:23	2.8	85
	11:25	0.5	15
	16:59	3.3	101
4 Th	00:30	-0.4	-12
	06:23	2.4	73
	11:56	0.9	27
	17:28	3.2	98
5 F	01:34	-0.3	-9
	07:42	2.1	64
	12:30	1.3	40
	18:04	3.0	91
6 Sa ◖	02:57	-0.2	-6
	09:39	1.9	58
	13:18	1.7	52
	18:55	2.8	85
7 Su	04:33	-0.2	-6
	11:38	2.1	64
	15:02	1.9	58
	20:45	2.6	79
8 M	05:55	-0.3	-9
	12:37	2.3	70
	17:29	1.8	55
	23:02	2.6	79
9 Tu	06:56	-0.5	-15
	13:13	2.5	76
	18:51	1.4	43
10 W	00:18	2.8	85
	07:42	-0.5	-15
	13:43	2.7	82
	19:40	1.0	30
11 Th	01:11	3.0	91
	08:20	-0.5	-15
	14:11	2.9	88
	20:20	0.7	21
12 F	01:54	3.1	94
	08:52	-0.4	-12
	14:36	3.0	91
	20:56	0.4	12
13 Sa ●	02:32	3.1	94
	09:20	-0.2	-6
	15:00	3.1	94
	21:30	0.2	6
14 Su	04:07	3.1	94
	10:44	0.0	0
	16:21	3.2	98
	23:03	0.0	0
15 M	04:41	3.0	91
	11:06	0.2	6
	16:41	3.2	98
	23:34	-0.1	-3
16 Tu	05:15	2.9	88
	11:29	0.4	12
	17:01	3.2	98
17 W	00:06	-0.1	-3
	05:51	2.7	82
	11:52	0.6	18
	17:20	3.1	94
18 Th	00:39	0.0	0
	06:32	2.5	76
	12:18	0.9	27
	17:41	3.0	91
19 F	01:18	0.1	3
	07:22	2.2	67
	12:48	1.1	34
	18:05	2.9	88
20 Sa	02:08	0.3	9
	08:36	2.0	61
	13:25	1.4	43
	18:35	2.8	85
21 Su ◖	03:26	0.4	12
	10:36	2.0	61
	14:25	1.7	52
	19:19	2.6	79
22 M	05:12	0.4	12
	12:24	2.2	67
	16:25	1.9	58
	20:45	2.4	73
23 Tu	06:34	0.1	3
	13:17	2.5	76
	18:25	1.8	55
	23:13	2.4	73
24 W	07:30	-0.1	-3
	13:53	2.7	82
	19:32	1.5	46
25 Th	00:38	2.7	82
	07:42	-0.3	-9
	14:23	2.9	88
	20:18	1.1	34
26 F	01:35	3.0	91
	08:50	-0.4	-12
	14:50	3.1	94
	20:58	0.6	18
27 Sa	02:25	3.3	101
	09:25	-0.4	-12
	15:16	3.3	101
	21:37	0.2	
28 Su ○	03:12	3.5	10
	09:57	-0.2	
	15:40	3.4	10
	22:16	-0.2	
29 M	03:58	3.5	10
	10:28	0.1	
	16:04	3.5	10
	22:57	-0.6	-1
30 Tu	04:45	3.4	10
	10:58	0.4	
	16:28	3.6	11
	23:40	-0.7	-2
31 W	05:33	3.2	9
	11:27	0.7	2
	16:53	3.6	11

StationId: 8728142
Source: NOAA/NOS/CO-OPS
Station Type: Subordinate
Time Zone: LST_LDT
Datum: MLLW

April

Day	Time	ft	cm
1 Th	00:25	-0.8	-24
	06:24	2.9	88
	11:55	1.1	34
	17:21	3.6	110
2 F	01:17	-0.6	-18
	07:23	2.5	76
	12:24	1.4	43
	17:51	3.5	107
3 Sa	02:19	-0.3	-9
	08:40	2.2	67
	12:55	1.7	52
	18:26	3.2	98
4 Su	03:40	-0.1	-3
	10:37	2.1	64
	13:42	1.9	58
	19:17	2.9	88
5 M	05:14	0.1	3
	12:26	2.2	67
	15:58	2.0	61
	21:39	2.5	76
6 Tu	06:35	0.1	3
	13:11	2.4	73
	18:43	1.8	55
7 W	00:08	2.6	79
	07:33	0.1	3
	13:41	2.7	82
	19:50	1.3	40
8 Th	01:17	2.8	85
	08:16	0.1	3
	14:08	2.9	88
	20:32	0.9	27
9 F	02:06	2.9	88
	08:50	0.2	6
	14:33	3.1	94
	21:08	0.5	15
10	02:46	3.0	91
	09:19	0.3	9
	14:57	3.2	98
	21:42	0.2	6
11	03:22	3.1	94
	09:44	0.4	12
	15:19	3.3	101
	22:14	0.0	0
12	03:56	3.1	94
	10:07	0.6	18
	15:40	3.4	104
	22:44	-0.2	-6
13	04:29	3.1	94
	10:31	0.7	21
	16:00	3.5	107
	23:14	-0.2	-6
14	05:03	3.0	91
	10:55	0.8	24
	16:21	3.4	104
	23:44	-0.2	-6
15	05:38	2.9	88
	11:22	1.0	30
	16:42	3.4	104
16 F	00:15	-0.1	-3
	06:18	2.7	82
	11:51	1.2	37
	17:07	3.3	101
17 Sa	00:51	0.0	0
	07:06	2.5	76
	12:25	1.4	43
	17:35	3.2	98
18 Su	01:37	0.2	6
	08:11	2.4	73
	13:07	1.6	49
	18:10	3.0	91
19 M	02:40	0.3	9
	09:43	2.3	70
	14:10	1.9	58
	18:58	2.8	85
20 Tu	04:06	0.4	12
	11:20	2.4	73
	15:57	2.0	61
	20:22	2.6	79
21 W	05:30	0.3	9
	12:21	2.7	82
	17:48	1.8	55
	22:36	2.6	79
22 Th	06:35	0.2	6
	13:02	2.9	88
	18:59	1.4	43
23 F	00:12	2.8	85
	07:26	0.1	3
	13:34	3.1	94
	19:51	0.9	27
24 Sa	01:19	3.1	94
	08:09	0.2	6
	14:03	3.3	101
	20:36	0.3	9
25 Su	02:15	3.3	101
	08:48	0.3	9
	14:31	3.5	107
	21:19	-0.2	-6
26 M	03:06	3.5	107
	09:24	0.5	15
	14:58	3.6	110
	22:01	-0.6	-18
27 Tu	03:56	3.5	107
	09:58	0.8	24
	15:25	3.8	116
	22:45	-0.9	-27
28 W	04:45	3.4	104
	10:31	1.1	34
	15:54	3.9	119
	23:30	-1.0	-30
29 Th	05:34	3.2	98
	11:02	1.3	40
	16:24	3.9	119
30 F	00:17	-0.9	-27
	06:25	2.9	88
	11:33	1.5	46
	16:56	3.8	116

May

Day	Time	ft	cm
1 Sa	01:09	-0.6	-18
	07:22	2.6	79
	12:06	1.7	52
	17:32	3.6	110
2 Su	02:08	-0.3	-9
	08:31	2.4	73
	12:46	1.9	58
	18:13	3.2	98
3 M	03:19	0.1	3
	10:01	2.3	70
	13:53	2.0	61
	19:13	2.8	85
4 Tu	04:38	0.4	12
	11:27	2.4	73
	16:12	2.0	61
	21:42	2.5	76
5 W	05:53	0.6	18
	12:18	2.6	79
	18:27	1.6	49
	23:55	2.5	76
6 Th	06:50	0.7	21
	12:53	2.8	85
	19:31	1.2	37
7 F	01:04	2.7	82
	07:34	0.8	24
	13:22	3.0	91
	20:14	0.7	21
8 Sa	01:54	2.8	85
	08:08	0.9	27
	13:49	3.2	98
	20:50	0.4	12
9 Su	02:35	2.9	88
	08:37	1.0	30
	14:14	3.3	101
	21:24	0.1	3
10 M	03:11	3.0	91
	09:05	1.0	30
	14:38	3.4	104
	21:57	-0.1	-3
11 Tu	03:45	3.0	91
	09:32	1.1	34
	15:01	3.5	107
	22:28	-0.2	-6
12 W	04:19	3.0	91
	09:59	1.1	34
	15:25	3.6	110
	22:58	-0.2	-6
13 Th	04:54	3.0	91
	10:29	1.2	37
	15:49	3.6	110
	23:29	-0.2	-6
14 F	05:30	3.0	91
	11:00	1.3	40
	16:16	3.5	107
15 Sa	00:01	-0.2	-6
	06:10	2.9	88
	11:34	1.4	43
	16:45	3.5	107
16 Su	00:37	-0.1	-3
	06:55	2.8	85
	12:13	1.6	49
	17:19	3.4	104
17 M	01:19	0.0	0
	07:50	2.7	82
	13:00	1.7	52
	18:01	3.2	98
18 Tu	02:11	0.1	3
	08:56	2.7	82
	14:05	1.8	55
	18:55	3.0	91
19 W	03:14	0.3	9
	10:08	2.7	82
	15:33	1.8	55
	20:17	2.8	85
20 Th	04:24	0.4	12
	11:09	2.8	85
	17:06	1.6	49
	22:08	2.7	82
21 F	05:30	0.5	15
	11:56	3.0	91
	18:22	1.1	34
	23:47	2.8	85
22 Sa	06:29	0.6	18
	12:35	3.2	98
	19:21	0.5	15
23 Su	01:03	3.0	91
	07:21	0.8	24
	13:10	3.4	104
	20:13	0.0	0
24 M	02:05	3.2	98
	08:08	1.0	30
	13:45	3.6	110
	21:02	-0.5	-15
25 Tu	03:02	3.4	104
	08:50	1.2	37
	14:59	3.8	116
	21:49	-0.8	-24
26 W	03:54	3.4	104
	09:30	1.4	43
	14:54	3.9	119
	22:37	-1.0	-30
27 Th	04:44	3.3	101
	10:08	1.5	46
	15:31	4.0	122
	23:24	-1.0	-30
28 F	05:33	3.1	94
	10:45	1.6	49
	16:08	4.0	122
29 Sa	00:12	-0.8	-24
	06:21	2.9	88
	11:23	1.7	52
	16:48	3.8	116
30 Su	01:01	-0.5	-15
	07:11	2.7	82
	12:05	1.8	55
	17:30	3.6	110
31 M	01:52	-0.1	-3
	08:04	2.6	79
	12:56	1.8	55
	18:19	3.2	98

June

Day	Time	ft	cm
1 Tu	02:46	0.3	9
	09:03	2.5	76
	14:08	1.8	55
	19:24	2.8	85
2 W	03:44	0.6	18
	10:05	2.5	76
	15:53	1.7	52
	21:16	2.5	76
3 Th	04:44	0.9	27
	11:02	2.6	79
	17:43	1.4	43
	23:19	2.4	73
4 F	05:42	1.2	37
	11:47	2.8	85
	18:57	1.0	30
5 Sa	00:40	2.5	76
	06:32	1.3	40
	12:26	3.0	91
	19:47	0.7	21
6 Su	01:36	2.6	79
	07:14	1.4	43
	12:59	3.1	94
	20:29	0.3	9
7 M	02:21	2.7	82
	07:52	1.5	46
	13:31	3.3	101
	21:07	0.1	3
8 Tu	03:00	2.8	85
	08:27	1.5	46
	14:01	3.4	104
	21:42	-0.1	-3
9 W	03:36	2.9	88
	09:01	1.5	46
	14:30	3.5	107
	22:15	-0.2	-6
10 Th	04:11	3.0	91
	09:35	1.5	46
	14:59	3.5	107
	22:48	-0.2	-6
11 F	04:46	3.0	91
	10:10	1.5	46
	15:29	3.6	110
	23:19	-0.2	-6
12 Sa	05:22	3.0	91
	10:46	1.5	46
	16:01	3.6	110
	23:51	-0.3	-9
13 Su	06:00	3.0	91
	11:24	1.5	46
	16:35	3.6	110
14 M	00:25	-0.2	-6
	06:40	3.0	91
	12:06	1.5	46
	17:14	3.6	110
15 Tu	01:02	-0.2	-6
	07:23	3.0	91
	12:55	1.6	49
	18:00	3.4	104
16 W	00:00	0.0	0
	08:09	3.0	91
	13:55	1.5	46
	18:57	3.2	98
17 Th	02:32	0.2	6
	10:05	3.0	91
	15:07	1.4	43
	20:12	2.9	88
18 F	03:27	0.5	15
	09:51	3.0	91
	16:28	1.2	37
	21:48	2.7	82
19 Sa	04:28	0.8	24
	10:42	3.1	94
	17:46	0.7	21
	23:27	2.7	82
20 Su	05:31	1.1	34
	11:31	3.3	101
	18:54	0.2	6
21 M	00:51	2.9	88
	06:32	1.4	43
	12:18	3.5	107
	19:54	-0.2	-6
22 Tu	02:00	3.1	94
	07:29	1.5	46
	13:05	3.7	113
	20:49	-0.6	-18
23 W	02:59	3.2	98
	08:21	1.7	52
	13:51	3.8	116
	21:41	-0.9	-27
24 Th	03:51	3.2	98
	09:09	1.7	52
	14:36	4.0	122
	22:30	-1.0	-30
25 F	04:39	3.2	98
	09:54	1.7	52
	15:22	4.0	122
	23:17	-0.9	-27
26 Sa	05:23	3.1	94
	10:37	1.7	52
	16:06	3.9	119
27 Su	00:02	-0.7	-21
	06:04	3.0	91
	11:21	1.6	49
	16:50	3.8	116
28 M	00:44	-0.4	-12
	06:43	2.9	88
	12:06	1.6	49
	17:35	3.5	107
29 Tu	01:24	0.0	0
	07:22	2.8	85
	12:57	1.5	46
	18:23	3.2	98
30 W	02:03	0.4	12
	08:00	2.7	82
	13:58	1.5	46
	19:20	2.8	85

StationId: 8728142
Source: NOAA/NOS/CO-OPS
Station Type: Subordinate
Time Zone: LST_LDT
Datum: MLLW

NOAA Tide Predictions

St. Marks, St. Marks River, FL,2021

Times and Heights of High and Low Waters

July

Day	Time (h m)	Height (ft)	Height (cm)	Day	Time (h m)	Height (ft)	Height (cm)
1 Th ◑	02:41	0.8	24	**16** F	01:54	0.4	12
	08:41	2.7	82		07:56	3.2	98
	15:14	1.4	43		14:41	0.9	27
	20:39	2.5	76		20:06	3.0	91
2 F	03:23	1.2	37	**17** Sa ◐	02:40	0.8	24
	09:26	2.8	85		08:39	3.3	101
	16:44	1.3	40		15:56	0.7	21
	22:26	2.3	70		21:34	2.7	82
3 Sa	04:11	1.5	46	**18** Su	03:34	1.2	37
	10:18	2.8	85		09:29	3.3	101
	18:10	1.0	30		17:17	0.5	15
					23:15	2.6	79
4 Su	00:05	2.3	70	**19** M	04:38	1.6	49
	05:09	1.7	52		10:30	3.4	104
	11:13	2.9	88		18:34	0.1	3
	19:16	0.7	21				
5 M	01:15	2.4	73	**20** Tu	00:46	2.8	85
	06:10	1.8	55		05:49	1.8	55
	12:04	3.0	91		11:36	3.5	107
	20:07	0.4	12		19:42	-0.2	-6
6 Tu	02:07	2.6	79	**21** W	01:57	2.9	88
	07:06	1.8	55		07:00	1.9	58
	12:50	3.1	94		12:41	3.6	110
	20:50	0.2	6		20:41	-0.5	-15
7 W	02:48	2.7	82	**22** Th	02:53	3.1	94
	07:55	1.8	55		08:03	1.9	58
	13:32	3.3	101		13:40	3.8	116
	21:28	0.0	0		21:34	-0.7	-21
8 Th	03:26	2.9	88	**23** F	03:41	3.1	94
	08:39	1.7	52		08:58	1.7	52
	14:09	3.4	104		14:33	3.9	119
	22:03	-0.1	-3		22:21	-0.7	-21
9 F	04:01	3.0	91	**24** Sa ○	04:22	3.2	98
	09:20	1.6	49		09:47	1.6	49
	14:44	3.5	107		15:22	4.0	122
	22:36	-0.2	-6		23:04	-0.6	-18
10 Sa ●	04:35	3.1	94	**25** Su	04:59	3.2	98
	09:58	1.5	46		10:32	1.4	43
	15:19	3.6	110		16:07	3.9	119
	23:06	-0.3	-9		23:42	-0.4	-12
11 Su	05:08	3.1	94	**26** M	05:33	3.1	94
	10:37	1.5	46		11:15	1.3	40
	15:54	3.7	113		16:50	3.8	116
	23:36	-0.3	-9				
12 M	05:40	3.2	98	**27** Tu	00:16	-0.1	-3
	11:16	1.4	43		06:03	3.1	94
	16:32	3.7	113		11:58	1.2	37
					17:32	3.5	107
13 Tu	00:06	-0.3	-9	**28** W	00:47	0.3	9
	06:13	3.2	98		06:31	3.1	94
	11:58	1.3	40		12:42	1.1	34
	17:14	3.7	113		18:15	3.2	98
14 W	00:39	-0.1	-3	**29** Th	01:15	0.6	18
	06:45	3.2	98		06:57	3.0	91
	12:45	1.2	37		13:31	1.1	34
	18:01	3.5	107		19:03	2.9	88
15 Th	01:14	0.1	3	**30** F	01:42	1.0	30
	07:19	3.2	98		07:24	3.0	91
	13:38	1.1	34		14:28	1.1	34
	18:57	3.3	101		20:03	2.6	79
				31 Sa ◑	02:13	1.3	40
					07:55	3.0	91
					15:41	1.1	34
					21:29	2.3	70

August

Day	Time (h m)	Height (ft)	Height (cm)	Day	Time (h m)	Height (ft)	Height (cm)
1 Su	02:52	1.6	49	**16** M	02:48	1.6	49
	08:35	2.9	88		08:28	3.4	104
	17:12	1.0	30		16:57	0.4	12
	23:20	2.3	70		23:14	2.6	79
2 M	03:49	1.9	58	**17** Tu	03:54	1.9	58
	09:35	2.9	88		09:41	3.4	104
	18:38	0.9	27		18:22	0.2	6
3 Tu	00:51	2.4	73	**18** W	00:47	2.7	82
	05:09	2.0	61		05:22	2.1	64
	11:01	2.9	88		11:15	3.4	104
	19:42	0.6	18		19:34	-0.1	-3
4 W	01:49	2.6	79	**19** Th	01:51	2.9	88
	06:31	2.0	61		06:50	2.0	61
	12:17	3.0	91		12:38	3.6	110
	20:30	0.4	12		20:33	-0.3	-9
5 Th	02:32	2.8	85	**20** F	02:39	3.0	91
	07:35	1.9	58		08:00	1.8	55
	13:12	3.2	98		13:43	3.7	113
	21:10	0.2	6		21:21	-0.3	-9
6 F	03:08	2.9	88	**21** Sa	03:18	3.1	94
	08:25	1.8	55		08:54	1.5	46
	13:55	3.4	104		14:36	3.9	119
	21:44	0.0	0		22:03	-0.3	-9
7 Sa	03:41	3.1	94	**22** Su ○	03:52	3.2	98
	09:08	1.6	49		09:41	1.3	40
	14:34	3.6	110		15:22	3.9	119
	22:15	-0.1	-3		22:40	-0.1	-3
8 Su ●	04:12	3.2	98	**23** M	04:23	3.3	101
	09:47	1.4	43		10:23	1.1	34
	15:12	3.7	113		16:03	3.9	119
	22:44	-0.2	-6		23:11	0.1	3
9 M	04:40	3.3	101	**24** Tu	04:50	3.3	101
	10:25	1.2	37		11:02	0.9	27
	15:50	3.9	119		16:43	3.8	116
	23:12	-0.2	-6		23:39	0.3	9
10 Tu	05:08	3.4	104	**25** W	05:15	3.3	101
	11:04	1.0	30		11:40	0.8	24
	16:30	3.9	119		17:21	3.6	110
	23:41	-0.1	-3				
11 W	05:34	3.4	104	**26** Th	00:04	0.6	18
	11:44	0.9	27		05:37	3.3	101
	17:13	3.8	116		12:17	0.7	21
					18:00	3.3	101
12 Th	00:11	0.1	3	**27** F	00:28	0.9	27
	06:00	3.5	107		05:58	3.3	101
	12:28	0.7	21		12:57	0.8	24
	18:01	3.6	110		18:42	3.0	91
13 F	00:43	0.5	15	**28** Sa	00:53	1.2	37
	06:28	3.5	107		06:20	3.2	98
	13:18	0.6	18		13:42	0.9	27
	18:55	3.3	101		19:33	2.7	82
14 Sa	01:18	0.8	24	**29** Su	01:22	1.5	46
	07:00	3.5	107		06:45	3.1	94
	14:17	0.5	15		14:41	1.0	30
	20:02	3.0	91		20:44	2.5	76
15 Su ◐	01:58	1.2	37	**30** M ◑	01:59	1.7	52
	07:38	3.5	107		07:19	3.0	91
	15:30	0.5	15		16:09	1.1	34
	21:28	2.7	82		22:33	2.3	70
				31 Tu	02:55	2.0	61
					08:10	2.9	88
					17:52	1.0	30

September

Day	Time (h m)	Height (ft)	Height (cm)	Day	Time (h m)	Height (ft)	Height (cm)
1 W	00:19	2.4	73	**16** Th	00:41	2.7	82
	04:28	2.1	64		05:24	2.1	64
	09:50	2.8	85		11:21	3.2	98
	19:08	0.8	24		19:23	0.2	6
2 Th	01:21	2.7	82	**17** F	01:33	2.9	88
	06:11	2.1	64		06:58	1.9	58
	11:47	2.9	88		12:46	3.4	104
	19:59	0.5	15		20:16	0.1	3
3 F	02:03	2.9	88	**18** Sa	02:11	3.1	94
	07:21	1.9	58		08:00	1.5	46
	12:53	3.2	98		13:46	3.6	110
	20:39	0.3	9		20:59	0.1	3
4 Sa	02:38	3.0	91	**19** Su	02:43	3.2	98
	08:11	1.7	52		08:48	1.1	34
	13:40	3.4	104		14:34	3.7	113
	21:13	0.1	3		21:35	0.2	6
5 Su	03:08	3.2	98	**20** M ○	03:12	3.3	101
	08:52	1.4	43		09:30	0.8	24
	14:22	3.7	113		15:15	3.8	116
	21:44	0.0	0		22:06	0.4	12
6 M	03:35	3.3	101	**21** Tu	03:39	3.4	104
	09:31	1.1	34		10:07	0.6	18
	15:03	3.8	116		15:54	3.7	113
	22:13	0.1	3		22:33	0.6	18
7 Tu ●	04:01	3.4	104	**22** W	04:03	3.5	107
	10:09	0.8	24		10:43	0.4	12
	15:44	4.0	122		16:30	3.6	110
	22:42	0.2	6		22:58	0.8	24
8 W	04:25	3.5	107	**23** Th	04:25	3.5	107
	10:47	0.5	15		11:16	0.4	12
	16:26	4.0	122		17:05	3.5	107
	23:11	0.4	12		23:22	1.0	30
9 Th	04:48	3.6	110	**24** F	04:45	3.5	107
	11:28	0.3	9		11:50	0.4	12
	17:11	3.8	116		17:42	3.3	101
	23:40	0.6	18		23:46	1.2	37
10 F	05:13	3.7	113	**25** Sa	05:06	3.4	104
	12:11	0.1	3		12:24	0.5	15
	18:00	3.6	110		18:22	3.1	94
11 Sa	00:11	1.0	30	**26** Su	00:14	1.4	43
	05:40	3.7	113		05:29	3.3	101
	13:00	0.1	3		13:03	0.6	18
	18:54	3.3	101		19:09	2.8	85
12 Su	00:44	1.3	40	**27** M	00:45	1.6	49
	06:11	3.7	113		05:56	3.2	98
	13:59	0.2	6		13:53	0.8	24
	20:01	2.9	88		20:13	2.6	79
13 M ◐	01:22	1.7	52	**28** Tu	01:26	1.8	55
	06:49	3.6	110		06:30	3.1	94
	15:13	0.3	9		15:10	1.0	30
	21:29	2.6	79		21:51	2.5	76
14 Tu	02:11	1.9	58	**29** W ◑	02:27	2.0	61
	07:20	3.4	104		07:20	2.9	88
	16:45	0.4	12		16:53	1.0	30
	23:18	2.6	79		23:35	2.5	76
15 W	03:30	2.1	64	**30** Th	04:08	2.1	64
	09:14	3.2	98		08:57	2.7	82
	18:13	0.3	9		18:16	0.8	24

StationId: 8728142
Source: NOAA/NOS/CO-OPS
Station Type: Subordinate
Time Zone: LST_LDT
Datum: MLLW

NOAA Tide Predictions

St. Marks, St. Marks River, FL, 2021

Times and Heights of High and Low Waters

October

Day	Time	ft	cm	Day	Time	ft	cm
1 F	00:39	2.7	82	16 Sa	00:58	2.9	88
	05:53	2.0	61		07:02	1.5	46
	11:12	2.8	85		12:49	3.2	98
	19:13	0.6	18		19:48	0.5	15
2 Sa	01:21	2.9	88	17 Su	01:32	3.0	91
	07:01	1.7	52		07:54	1.0	30
	12:28	3.1	94		13:42	3.3	101
	19:56	0.4	12		20:27	0.6	18
3 Su	01:54	3.1	94	18 M	02:02	3.2	98
	07:49	1.4	43		08:37	0.7	21
	13:21	3.4	104		14:26	3.4	104
	20:32	0.3	9		20:59	0.7	21
4 M	02:23	3.3	101	19 Tu	02:28	3.3	101
	08:31	1.0	30		09:14	0.4	12
	14:07	3.6	110		15:05	3.5	107
	21:05	0.3	9		21:27	0.8	24
5 Tu	02:49	3.4	104	20 W	02:53	3.4	104
	09:10	0.6	18		09:49	0.1	3
	14:52	3.8	116		15:41	3.4	104
	21:37	0.4	12	○	21:53	0.9	27
6 W	03:14	3.5	107	21 Th	03:16	3.5	107
	09:49	0.2	6		10:22	0.0	0
	15:37	3.9	119		16:16	3.4	104
	22:08	0.6	18		22:18	1.1	34
7 Th	03:38	3.6	110	22 F	03:39	3.5	107
	10:29	-0.1	-3		10:54	0.0	0
	16:23	3.9	119		16:51	3.3	101
	22:39	0.9	27		22:45	1.2	37
8 F	04:03	3.7	113	23 Sa	04:02	3.5	107
	11:12	-0.3	-9		11:26	0.1	3
	17:10	3.7	113		17:26	3.2	98
	23:10	1.1	34		23:13	1.3	40
9 Sa	04:30	3.8	116	24 Su	04:26	3.4	104
	11:57	-0.4	-12		11:59	0.2	6
	17:59	3.4	104		18:06	3.0	91
	23:41	1.4	43		23:45	1.4	43
10 Su	05:00	3.8	116	25 M	04:52	3.3	101
	12:48	-0.3	-9		12:36	0.3	9
	18:55	3.1	94		18:51	2.8	85
11 M	00:15	1.6	49	26 Tu	00:21	1.6	49
	05:34	3.7	113		05:23	3.2	98
	13:47	-0.1	-3		13:21	0.5	15
	20:02	2.7	82		19:50	2.6	79
12 Tu	00:55	1.9	58	27 W	01:07	1.7	52
	06:16	3.5	107		06:02	3.0	91
	15:02	0.2	6		14:24	0.6	18
	21:30	2.5	76		21:10	2.5	76
13 W	01:52	2.0	61	28 Th	02:13	1.9	58
	07:17	3.2	98		06:55	2.8	85
	16:31	0.4	12		15:46	0.7	21
	23:08	2.5	76	◐	22:38	2.6	79
14 Th	03:34	2.1	64	29 F	03:48	1.9	58
	09:19	2.9	88		08:27	2.6	79
	17:55	0.5	15		17:08	0.7	21
					23:42	2.7	82
15 F	00:15	2.7	82	30 Sa	05:24	1.7	52
	05:41	1.9	58		10:31	2.6	79
	11:33	3.0	91		18:11	0.6	18
	18:59	0.5	15				
				31 Su	00:27	2.9	88
					06:31	1.3	40
					11:58	2.9	88
					19:02	0.5	15

November

Day	Time	ft	cm	Day	Time	ft	cm
1 M	01:01	3.1	94	16 Tu	00:16	3.0	91
	07:22	0.9	27		07:21	0.2	6
	13:00	3.2	98		13:17	3.0	91
	19:45	0.5	15		19:18	1.1	34
2 Tu	01:31	3.2	98	17 W	00:45	3.2	98
	08:06	0.4	12		07:58	-0.1	-3
	13:53	3.4	104		13:55	3.0	91
	20:24	0.6	18		19:48	1.1	34
3 W	01:59	3.4	104	18 Th	01:11	3.3	101
	08:49	-0.1	-3		08:33	-0.2	-6
	14:43	3.6	110		14:30	3.0	91
	21:00	0.8	24		20:17	1.2	37
4 Th	02:27	3.5	107	19 F	01:37	3.3	101
	09:31	-0.5	-15		09:06	-0.3	-9
	15:32	3.7	113		15:04	3.0	91
●	21:35	1.0	30	○	20:46	1.2	37
5 F	02:55	3.7	113	20 Sa	02:03	3.3	101
	10:15	-0.8	-24		09:38	-0.3	-9
	16:20	3.6	110		15:39	3.0	91
	22:10	1.2	37		21:17	1.2	37
6 Sa	03:25	3.8	116	21 Su	02:30	3.3	101
	11:00	-0.9	-27		10:10	-0.2	-6
	17:09	3.4	104		16:14	2.9	88
	22:44	1.4	43		21:50	1.2	37
7 Su	02:58	3.8	116	22 M	02:59	3.2	98
	10:48	-0.8	-24		10:42	-0.2	-6
	16:59	3.1	94		16:53	2.8	85
	22:19	1.6	49		22:26	1.3	40
8 M	03:34	3.7	113	23 Tu	03:31	3.1	94
	11:40	-0.6	-18		11:18	-0.1	-3
	17:53	2.8	85		17:36	2.7	82
	22:58	1.7	52		23:06	1.4	43
9 Tu	04:15	3.5	107	24 W	04:06	3.0	91
	12:39	-0.3	-9		12:09	0.1	3
	18:56	2.6	79		18:26	2.6	79
	23:45	1.8	55		23:55	1.5	46
10 W	05:04	3.2	98	25 Th	04:49	2.9	88
	13:46	0.1	3		12:48	0.2	6
	20:09	2.4	73		19:25	2.6	79
11 Th	00:55	1.8	55	26 F	00:58	1.5	46
	06:16	2.9	88		05:45	2.7	82
	15:03	0.4	12		13:47	0.3	9
◐	21:27	2.4	73		20:29	2.6	79
12 F	02:46	1.7	52	27 Sa	02:19	1.5	46
	08:28	2.6	79		07:09	2.5	76
	16:17	0.6	18		14:55	0.4	12
	22:27	2.5	76	◐	21:29	2.6	79
13 Sa	04:39	1.4	43	28 Su	03:43	1.2	37
	10:29	2.6	79		08:54	2.4	73
	17:19	0.8	24		16:02	0.6	18
	23:11	2.7	82		22:19	2.7	82
14 Su	05:50	1.0	30	29 M	04:54	0.8	24
	11:42	2.7	82		10:29	2.6	79
	18:08	0.9	27		17:02	0.7	21
	23:46	2.9	88		22:59	2.9	88
15 M	06:40	0.5	15	30 Tu	05:51	0.3	9
	12:34	2.9	88		11:42	2.8	85
	18:46	1.0	30		17:55	0.8	24
					23:36	3.1	94

December

Day	Time	ft	cm	Day	Time	ft	cm
1 W	06:42	-0.3	-9	16 Th	00:04	2.8	85
	12:43	3.1	94		07:44	-0.3	-9
	18:43	0.9	27		13:47	2.6	79
					19:15	1.3	40
2 Th	00:11	3.2	98	17 F	00:38	2.9	88
	07:30	-0.7	-21		08:20	-0.5	-15
	13:37	3.2	98		14:22	2.7	82
	19:27	1.1	34		19:51	1.2	37
3 F	00:46	3.4	104	18 Sa	01:10	3.0	91
	08:18	-1.1	-34		08:55	-0.5	-15
	14:29	3.3	101		14:56	2.7	82
	20:08	1.2	37		20:26	1.1	34
4 Sa	01:23	3.5	107	19 Su	01:42	3.0	91
	09:06	-1.3	-40		09:28	-0.6	-18
	15:18	3.2	98		15:29	2.7	82
●	20:48	1.3	40	○	21:02	1.1	34
5 Su	02:03	3.6	110	20 M	02:14	3.0	91
	09:54	-1.3	-40		09:59	-0.5	-15
	16:06	3.1	94		16:03	2.7	82
	21:28	1.4	43		21:38	1.1	34
6 M	02:44	3.6	110	21 Tu	02:47	3.0	91
	10:42	-1.1	-34		10:30	-0.5	-15
	16:54	2.9	88		16:38	2.7	82
	22:09	1.4	43		22:16	1.0	30
7 Tu	03:27	3.5	107	22 W	03:22	3.0	91
	11:32	-0.8	-24		11:01	-0.5	-15
	17:41	2.6	79		17:15	2.7	82
	22:54	1.4	43		22:57	1.0	30
8 W	04:14	3.3	101	23 Th	04:00	2.9	88
	12:23	-0.5	-15		11:35	-0.4	-12
	18:30	2.4	73		17:53	2.7	82
	23:47	1.4	43		23:43	1.0	30
9 Th	05:08	2.9	88	24 F	04:45	2.8	85
	13:16	0.0	0		12:14	-0.2	-6
	19:23	2.3	70		18:34	2.6	79
10 F	00:57	1.3	40	25 Sa	00:38	1.0	30
	06:20	2.5	76		05:39	2.6	79
	14:13	0.4	12		12:59	0.0	0
	20:19	2.3	70		19:18	2.6	79
11 Sa	02:30	1.2	37	26 Su	01:44	0.9	27
	08:09	2.2	67		06:51	2.4	73
	15:14	0.7	21		13:52	0.3	9
◐	21:15	2.3	70		20:06	2.6	79
12 Su	04:09	0.9	27	27 M	02:59	0.6	18
	10:07	2.1	64		08:25	2.2	67
	16:16	1.0	30		14:53	0.6	18
	22:06	2.5	76	◐	20:57	2.6	79
13 M	05:25	0.5	15	28 Tu	04:15	0.2	6
	11:28	2.2	67		10:05	2.3	70
	17:11	1.2	37		16:00	0.9	27
	22:50	2.6	79		21:49	2.7	82
14 Tu	06:20	0.2	6	29 W	05:23	-0.2	-6
	12:25	2.4	73		11:30	2.5	76
	17:58	1.3	40		17:06	1.1	34
	23:29	2.7	82		22:40	2.9	88
15 W	07:04	-0.1	-3	30 Th	06:23	-0.7	-21
	13:09	2.5	76		12:38	2.7	82
	18:38	1.3	40		18:07	1.2	37
					23:30	3.0	91
				31 F	07:18	-1.1	-34
					13:35	2.9	88
					19:02	1.3	40

NOAA Tide Predictions

Apalachicola, FL, 2021

Times and Heights of High and Low Waters

January

Day	Time	ft	cm		Day	Time	ft	cm
1 F	03:32	1.4	43		16 Sa	04:44	1.2	37
	11:58	-0.8	-24			12:38	-0.6	-18
	19:36	1.1	34			19:15	1.0	30
	23:42	0.8	24					
2 Sa	04:25	1.4	43		17 Su	00:29	0.4	12
	12:32	-0.7	-21			05:37	1.1	34
	20:00	1.0	30			13:03	-0.4	-12
						19:33	0.9	27
3 Su	00:24	0.7	21		18 M	01:15	0.3	9
	05:19	1.3	40			06:32	0.9	27
	13:06	-0.6	-18			13:24	-0.2	-6
	20:20	1.0	30			19:53	1.0	30
4 M	01:14	0.5	15		19 Tu	02:12	0.1	3
	06:18	1.1	34			07:43	0.7	21
	13:43	-0.4	-12			13:45	0.0	0
	20:39	0.9	27			20:14	1.0	30
5 Tu	02:18	0.3	9		20 W ☽	03:20	0.0	0
	07:31	0.9	27			09:22	0.5	15
	14:23	-0.2	-6			14:07	0.2	6
	21:01	1.0	30			20:38	1.0	30
6 W ☽	03:36	0.1	3		21 Th	04:35	-0.2	-6
	09:11	0.7	21			11:15	0.5	15
	15:04	0.1	3			14:32	0.4	12
	21:25	1.0	30			21:04	1.0	30
7 Th	05:00	-0.2	-6		22 F	05:58	-0.3	-9
	11:08	0.6	18			21:33	1.0	30
	15:49	0.4	12					
	21:53	1.1	34					
8 F	06:20	-0.5	-15		23 Sa	07:01	-0.5	-15
	13:53	0.7	21			22:07	1.0	30
	16:46	0.7	21					
	22:25	1.1	34					
9 Sa	07:23	-0.7	-21		24 Su	07:48	-0.6	-18
	15:33	0.9	27			16:06	0.9	27
	18:27	0.9	27			18:47	0.9	27
	23:05	1.2	37			22:50	1.1	34
10 Su	08:16	-0.9	-27		25 M	08:30	-0.7	-21
	16:37	1.1	34			16:38	1.0	30
	19:40	1.0	30			19:50	0.9	27
	23:58	1.3	40			23:50	1.1	34
11 M	09:08	-1.0	-30		26 Tu	09:12	-0.8	-24
	17:17	1.1	34			17:08	1.1	34
	20:31	1.0	30			20:33	0.9	27
12 Tu	00:59	1.3	40		27 W	00:56	1.2	37
	10:00	-1.0	-30			09:54	-0.8	-24
	17:48	1.1	34			17:36	1.1	34
	21:24	1.0	30			21:15	0.9	27
13 W ●	01:57	1.4	43		28 Th ○	01:54	1.3	40
	10:49	-1.0	-30			10:33	-0.8	-24
	18:15	1.1	34			18:00	1.1	34
	22:19	0.9	27			22:00	0.8	24
14 Th	02:53	1.4	43		29 F	02:47	1.3	40
	11:32	-0.9	-27			11:10	-0.8	-24
	18:37	1.0	30			18:19	1.0	30
	23:06	0.8	24			22:45	0.7	21
15 F	03:49	1.3	40		30 Sa	03:40	1.3	40
	12:08	-0.7	-21			11:42	-0.7	-21
	18:57	1.0	30			18:32	1.0	30
	23:48	0.6	18			23:28	0.5	15
					31 Su	04:35	1.3	40
						12:13	-0.6	-18
						18:42	0.9	27

February

Day	Time	ft	cm		Day	Time	ft	cm
1 M	00:11	0.3	9		16 Tu	00:45	0.0	0
	05:32	1.2	37			06:34	0.9	27
	12:42	-0.4	-12			12:35	0.1	3
	18:55	0.9	27			18:30	1.1	34
2 Tu	00:58	0.1	3		17 W	01:25	-0.1	-3
	06:33	1.0	30			07:41	0.8	24
	13:10	-0.2	-6			12:54	0.2	6
	19:14	1.0	30			18:49	1.1	34
3 W	01:56	-0.1	-3		18 Th	02:13	-0.2	-6
	07:54	0.8	24			09:15	0.7	21
	13:37	0.1	3			13:16	0.4	12
	19:37	1.0	30			19:12	1.1	34
4 Th ◑	03:09	-0.3	-9		19 F ◑	03:14	-0.3	-9
	09:43	0.7	21			10:59	0.7	21
	14:02	0.4	12			13:38	0.6	18
	20:07	1.1	34			19:40	1.1	34
5 F	04:33	-0.5	-15		20 Sa	04:33	-0.3	-9
	20:45	1.1	34			20:18	1.1	34
6 Sa	06:03	-0.7	-21		21 Su	06:07	-0.4	-12
	21:31	1.2	37			21:12	1.1	34
7 Su	07:14	-0.8	-24		22 M	07:13	-0.5	-15
	22:28	1.2	37			15:29	1.0	30
						18:44	1.0	30
						22:16	1.1	34
8 M	08:11	-0.9	-27		23 Tu	08:02	-0.6	-18
	16:34	1.1	34			15:57	1.1	34
	19:51	1.0	30			19:43	0.9	27
	23:46	1.2	37			23:36	1.2	37
9 Tu	09:02	-0.9	-27		24 W	08:46	-0.6	-18
	16:50	1.1	34			16:25	1.1	34
	20:39	0.9	27			20:21	0.9	27
10 W	01:10	1.2	37		25 Th	00:57	1.3	40
	09:51	-0.9	-27			09:27	-0.6	-18
	17:08	1.0	30			16:47	1.1	34
	21:24	0.8	24			20:59	0.8	24
11 Th ●	02:15	1.3	40		26 F	02:00	1.4	43
	10:34	-0.7	-21			10:07	-0.6	-18
	17:23	1.0	30			17:03	1.1	34
	22:10	0.6	18			21:41	0.7	21
12 F	03:11	1.3	40		27 Sa ○	02:57	1.4	43
	11:11	-0.6	-18			10:44	-0.5	-15
	17:37	1.0	30			17:12	1.1	34
	22:53	0.5	15			22:27	0.5	15
13 Sa	04:04	1.2	37		28 Su	03:53	1.4	43
	11:39	-0.4	-12			11:17	-0.3	-9
	17:49	1.0	30			17:19	1.1	34
	23:32	0.3	9			23:12	0.2	6
14 Su	04:54	1.2	37					
	12:01	-0.2	-6					
	18:01	1.0	30					
15 M	00:08	0.2	6					
	05:42	1.0	30					
	12:18	-0.1	-3					
	18:14	1.1	34					

March

Day	Time	ft	cm		Day	Time	ft	cm
1 M	04:51	1.4	43		16 Tu	00:45	0.0	0
	11:47	-0.1	-3			06:52	1.2	37
	17:29	1.1	34			12:36	0.5	15
	23:57	0.0	0			18:05	1.4	43
2 Tu	05:51	1.3	40		17 W	01:15	-0.1	-3
	12:14	0.1	3			07:44	1.1	34
	17:45	1.2	37			12:57	0.6	18
						18:24	1.4	43
3 W	00:43	-0.2	-6		18 Th	01:46	-0.2	-6
	07:01	1.1	34			08:51	1.0	30
	12:38	0.4	12			13:21	0.7	21
	18:05	1.3	40			18:45	1.4	43
4 Th ◑	01:37	-0.3	-9		19 F	02:22	-0.2	-6
	08:38	1.0	30			10:18	1.0	30
	12:59	0.6	18			13:49	0.8	24
	18:30	1.3	40			19:09	1.4	43
5 F	02:47	-0.4	-12		20 Sa	03:10	-0.2	-6
	10:35	0.9	27			11:43	1.0	30
	13:06	0.8	24			14:22	0.9	27
	19:00	1.4	43			19:38	1.4	43
6 Sa ☽	04:12	-0.5	-15		21 Su ☽	04:19	-0.2	-6
	19:44	1.3	40			20:19	1.3	40
7 Su	05:45	-0.5	-15		22 M	05:53	-0.2	-6
	20:56	1.3	40			14:55	1.2	37
						17:13	1.1	34
						21:36	1.2	37
8 M	07:01	-0.6	-18		23 Tu	07:24	-0.2	-6
	15:31	1.1	34			15:30	1.2	37
	19:06	1.1	34			19:31	1.1	34
	22:24	1.2	37			23:03	1.2	37
9 Tu	07:58	-0.6	-18		24 W	08:23	-0.3	-9
	15:37	1.1	34			15:58	1.3	40
	19:56	0.9	27			20:25	1.0	30
10 W	00:12	1.2	37		25 Th	00:34	1.3	40
	08:46	-0.5	-15			09:08	-0.3	-9
	15:50	1.1	34			16:20	1.3	40
	20:36	0.7	21			21:03	0.8	24
11 Th	01:40	1.3	40		26 F	02:02	1.4	43
	09:29	-0.4	-12			09:49	-0.2	-6
	16:04	1.1	34			16:35	1.3	40
	21:16	0.6	18			21:41	0.7	21
12 F	02:40	1.3	40		27 Sa ○	03:09	1.5	46
	10:06	-0.2	-6			10:29	-0.1	-3
	16:17	1.2	37			16:44	1.3	40
	21:57	0.4	12			22:23	0.5	15
13 Sa ●	03:31	1.3	40		28 Su	04:10	1.6	49
	10:37	0.0	0			11:08	0.1	3
	16:28	1.2	37			16:51	1.3	40
	22:37	0.3	9			23:10	0.2	6
14 Su	05:19	1.3	40		29 M	05:12	1.6	49
	12:00	0.2	6			11:44	0.4	12
	17:38	1.3	40			17:03	1.4	43
						23:57	0.0	0
15 M	00:13	0.2	6		30 Tu	06:16	1.5	46
	06:06	1.3	40			12:17	0.6	18
	12:18	0.3	9			17:21	1.5	46
	17:50	1.3	40					
					31 W	00:43	-0.2	-6
						07:22	1.5	46
						12:46	0.9	27
						17:43	1.6	49

StationId: 8728690
Source: NOAA/NOS/CO-OPS
Station Type: Primary
Time Zone: LST_LDT
Datum: MLLW

NOAA Tide Predictions

Apalachicola, FL,2021

Times and Heights of High and Low Waters

April

Day	Time (h m)	Height ft	Height cm	Day	Time (h m)	Height ft	Height cm
1 Th	01:31	-0.4	-12	**16** F	01:17	-0.2	-6
	08:47	1.4	43		09:10	1.4	43
	13:11	1.1	34		13:01	1.1	34
	18:10	1.6	49		17:53	1.7	52
2	02:25	-0.4	-12	**17** Sa	01:50	-0.2	-6
	10:32	1.3	40		10:21	1.4	43
	13:32	1.2	37		13:38	1.2	37
	18:40	1.7	52		18:25	1.6	49
3 Sa	03:33	-0.4	-12	**18** Su	02:34	-0.2	-6
	19:16	1.6	49		11:23	1.3	40
					14:23	1.2	37
					19:02	1.5	46
4 Su	04:54	-0.4	-12	**19** M	03:36	-0.1	-3
	20:07	1.5	46		12:30	1.3	40
					15:38	1.3	40
					19:51	1.5	46
5	06:20	-0.3	-9	**20** Tu	04:55	-0.1	-3
	15:00	1.3	40		13:38	1.4	43
	18:29	1.2	37		17:18	1.2	37
	21:54	1.3	40		21:20	1.4	43
6	07:36	-0.2	-6	**21** W	06:17	0.0	0
	15:10	1.3	40		14:20	1.4	43
	20:03	1.0	30		19:03	1.1	34
	23:47	1.2	37		22:58	1.3	40
7	08:32	-0.1	-3	**22** Th	07:28	0.0	0
	15:25	1.3	40		14:45	1.4	43
	20:47	0.8	24		20:02	0.9	27
8	01:51	1.3	40	**23** F	00:33	1.3	40
	09:15	0.0	0		08:21	0.1	3
	15:39	1.3	40		15:01	1.4	43
	21:25	0.6	18		20:45	0.7	21
9	03:06	1.3	40	**24** Sa	02:08	1.4	43
	09:52	0.2	6		09:03	0.3	9
	15:52	1.3	40		15:11	1.4	43
	22:04	0.4	12		21:25	0.4	12
10	04:01	1.4	43	**25** Su	03:23	1.5	46
	10:23	0.4	12		09:43	0.5	15
	16:03	1.4	43		15:22	1.5	46
	22:43	0.3	9		22:08	0.2	6
11	04:51	1.4	43	**26** M	04:32	1.6	49
	10:48	0.6	18		10:23	0.8	24
	16:14	1.5	46		15:36	1.6	49
	23:20	0.1	3		22:55	-0.1	-3
12	05:39	1.4	43	**27** Tu	05:42	1.7	52
	11:09	0.8	24		11:04	1.0	30
	16:26	1.6	49		15:56	1.7	52
	23:53	0.0	0		23:45	-0.3	-9
13	06:25	1.4	43	**28** W	06:51	1.7	52
	11:30	0.9	27		11:44	1.3	40
	16:41	1.6	49		16:21	1.8	55
14	00:22	0.0	0	**29** Th	00:34	-0.4	-12
	07:11	1.4	43		08:06	1.6	49
	11:57	1.0	30		12:20	1.4	43
	17:01	1.7	52		16:52	1.9	58
15	00:48	-0.1	-3	**30** F	01:23	-0.5	-15
	08:03	1.4	43		09:38	1.6	49
	12:27	1.1	34		12:53	1.5	46
	17:25	1.7	52		17:29	1.9	58

May

Day	Time (h m)	Height ft	Height cm	Day	Time (h m)	Height ft	Height cm
1 Sa	02:17	-0.5	-15	**16** Su	01:35	-0.2	-6
	10:51	1.6	49		10:13	1.5	46
	13:26	1.5	46		13:32	1.4	43
	18:10	1.8	55		18:00	1.7	52
2 Su	03:21	-0.3	-9	**17** M	02:17	-0.2	-6
	11:45	1.5	46		10:56	1.5	46
	14:14	1.4	43		14:22	1.3	40
	18:59	1.7	52		18:46	1.6	49
3 M	04:31	-0.2	-6	**18** Tu	03:10	-0.1	-3
	12:34	1.4	43		11:36	1.5	46
	16:14	1.3	40		15:36	1.3	40
	20:08	1.5	46		19:45	1.5	46
4 Tu	05:42	0.0	0	**19** W	04:11	0.0	0
	13:14	1.4	43		12:14	1.5	46
	18:22	1.1	34		17:02	1.2	37
	22:12	1.3	40		21:15	1.4	43
5 W	06:51	0.1	3	**20** Th	05:14	0.1	3
	13:44	1.4	43		12:46	1.4	43
	19:42	0.9	27		18:30	1.0	30
					22:55	1.3	40
6 Th	00:11	1.2	37	**21** F	06:18	0.3	9
	07:47	0.3	9		13:10	1.5	46
	14:06	1.4	43		19:37	0.7	21
	20:30	0.6	18				
7 F	02:11	1.2	37	**22** Sa	00:37	1.3	40
	08:30	0.5	15		07:20	0.5	15
	14:24	1.4	43		13:29	1.5	46
	21:11	0.4	12		20:26	0.4	12
8 Sa	03:23	1.3	40	**23** Su	02:26	1.4	43
	09:02	0.7	21		08:12	0.7	21
	14:39	1.5	46		13:48	1.6	49
	21:49	0.2	6		21:11	0.1	3
9 Su	04:21	1.4	43	**24** M	03:49	1.5	46
	09:27	0.9	27		08:55	1.0	30
	14:52	1.6	49		14:10	1.7	52
	22:26	0.1	3		21:56	-0.2	-6
10 M	05:15	1.4	43	**25** Tu	05:07	1.6	49
	09:48	1.1	34		09:35	1.2	37
	15:05	1.7	52		14:35	1.8	55
	23:01	0.0	0		22:45	-0.4	-12
11 Tu	06:05	1.5	46	**26** W	06:20	1.7	52
	10:10	1.2	37		10:16	1.5	46
	15:21	1.8	55		15:05	1.9	58
	23:33	-0.1	-3		23:38	-0.5	-15
12 W	06:50	1.5	46	**27** Th	07:27	1.7	52
	10:40	1.3	40		11:05	1.6	49
	15:42	1.8	55		15:40	2.0	61
13 Th	00:02	-0.1	-3	**28** F	00:29	-0.6	-18
	07:35	1.5	46		08:38	1.7	52
	11:22	1.4	43		11:58	1.6	49
	16:07	1.8	55		16:21	2.0	61
14 F	00:31	-0.2	-6	**29** Sa	01:19	-0.5	-15
	08:25	1.6	49		09:46	1.7	52
	12:07	1.4	43		12:44	1.6	49
	16:39	1.8	55		17:10	2.0	61
15 Sa	01:01	-0.2	-6	**30** Su	02:09	-0.4	-12
	09:22	1.6	49		10:27	1.6	49
	12:49	1.4	43		13:31	1.5	46
	17:17	1.8	55		18:04	1.8	55
				31 M	03:02	-0.3	-9
					10:56	1.5	46
					14:35	1.3	40
					19:03	1.6	49

June

Day	Time (h m)	Height ft	Height cm	Day	Time (h m)	Height ft	Height cm
1 Tu	03:56	-0.1	-3	**16** W	02:44	-0.1	-3
	11:22	1.4	43		10:36	1.5	46
	16:13	1.2	37		15:17	1.1	34
	20:22	1.4	43		19:47	1.5	46
2 W	04:49	0.2	6	**17** Th	03:30	0.0	0
	11:46	1.4	43		10:57	1.5	46
	17:48	0.9	27		16:36	1.0	30
	22:20	1.2	37		21:17	1.3	40
3 Th	05:40	0.4	12	**18** F	04:19	0.2	6
	12:10	1.4	43		11:17	1.5	46
	19:11	0.7	21		17:57	0.7	21
					23:00	1.2	37
4 F	00:16	1.1	34	**19** Sa	05:10	0.5	15
	06:30	0.6	18		11:39	1.6	49
	12:34	1.5	46		19:12	0.4	12
	20:08	0.4	12				
5 Sa	02:22	1.1	34	**20** Su	01:00	1.2	37
	07:18	0.8	24		06:07	0.8	24
	12:57	1.6	49		12:04	1.6	49
	20:51	0.1	3		20:10	0.1	3
6 Su	03:40	1.2	37	**21** M	03:05	1.3	40
	07:57	1.0	30		07:13	1.1	34
	13:19	1.6	49		12:34	1.7	52
	21:30	0.0	0		21:00	-0.2	-6
7 M	04:44	1.4	43	**22** Tu	04:33	1.5	46
	08:28	1.2	37		08:11	1.3	40
	13:40	1.7	52		13:10	1.9	58
	22:06	-0.1	-3		21:49	-0.4	-12
8 Tu	05:40	1.5	46	**23** W	05:49	1.6	49
	08:56	1.3	40		08:56	1.5	46
	14:03	1.8	55		13:51	2.0	61
	22:42	-0.2	-6		22:41	-0.5	-15
9 W	06:25	1.5	46	**24** Th	06:47	1.7	52
	09:26	1.4	43		09:39	1.6	49
	14:29	1.8	55		14:36	2.0	61
	23:16	-0.2	-6		23:34	-0.6	-18
10 Th	07:05	1.6	49	**25** F	07:36	1.7	52
	10:04	1.5	46		10:32	1.7	52
	14:59	1.9	58		15:24	2.1	64
	23:50	-0.2	-6				
11 F	07:44	1.6	49	**26** Sa	00:24	-0.6	-18
	10:57	1.5	46		08:21	1.7	52
	15:35	1.9	58		11:40	1.6	49
					16:16	2.0	61
12 Sa	00:21	-0.2	-6	**27** Su	01:10	-0.5	-15
	08:26	1.6	49		08:59	1.6	49
	11:53	1.5	46		12:35	1.5	46
	16:15	1.9	58		17:13	1.9	58
13 Su	00:53	-0.2	-6	**28** M	01:52	-0.3	-9
	09:08	1.6	49		09:26	1.5	46
	12:38	1.5	46		13:25	1.3	40
	17:02	1.8	55		18:11	1.8	55
14 M	01:27	-0.2	-6	**29** Tu	02:31	-0.1	-3
	09:44	1.6	49		09:47	1.5	46
	13:21	1.4	43		14:23	1.1	34
	17:52	1.8	55		19:11	1.6	49
15 Tu	02:03	-0.2	-6	**30** W	03:08	0.1	3
	10:13	1.5	46		10:06	1.5	46
	14:11	1.3	40		15:40	0.9	27
	18:45	1.7	52		20:27	1.3	40

StationId: 8728690
Source: NOAA/NOS/CO-OPS
Station Type: Primary
Time Zone: LST_LDT
Datum: MLLW

NOAA Tide Predictions

Apalachicola, FL, 2021

Times and Heights of High and Low Waters

July

Day	Time (h m)	Height ft	Height cm	Day	Time (h m)	Height ft	Height cm
1 Th ☽	03:40	0.4	12	16 F	02:49	0.3	9
	10:26	1.5	46		09:33	1.6	49
	17:04	0.7	21		16:06	0.7	21
	22:17	1.1	34		21:31	1.3	40
2 F	04:09	0.6	18	17 Sa ☽	03:26	0.6	18
	10:46	1.5	46		09:58	1.6	49
	18:27	0.5	15		17:26	0.5	15
					23:23	1.2	37
3 Sa	00:11	1.0	30	18 Su	04:07	0.9	27
	04:38	0.8	24		10:27	1.7	52
	11:08	1.6	49		18:49	0.2	6
	19:36	0.3	9				
4 Su	02:36	1.1	34	19 M	02:09	1.2	37
	05:11	1.1	34		04:51	1.2	37
	11:33	1.6	49		11:01	1.8	55
	20:26	0.1	3		19:57	-0.1	-3
5 M	04:05	1.3	40	20 Tu	11:41	1.9	58
	06:06	1.2	37		20:53	-0.3	-9
	12:00	1.7	52				
	21:07	-0.1	-3				
6 Tu	05:05	1.4	43	21 W	05:19	1.6	49
	07:34	1.4	43		07:45	1.6	49
	12:32	1.7	52		12:32	2.0	61
	21:45	-0.2	-6		21:44	-0.4	-12
7 W	05:47	1.5	46	22 Th	06:02	1.7	52
	08:30	1.5	46		08:46	1.6	49
	13:12	1.8	55		13:33	2.0	61
	22:23	-0.2	-6		22:36	-0.5	-15
8 Th	06:22	1.6	49	23 F	06:34	1.7	52
	09:11	1.5	46		09:34	1.6	49
	13:56	1.8	55		14:35	2.1	64
	23:01	-0.2	-6		23:27	-0.4	-12
9 F	06:54	1.7	52	24 Sa ○	07:01	1.7	52
	09:53	1.6	49		10:27	1.6	49
	14:40	1.9	58		15:31	2.1	64
	23:37	-0.2	-6				
10 Sa ●	07:25	1.7	52	25 Su	00:12	-0.3	-9
	10:42	1.6	49		07:24	1.7	52
	15:25	1.9	58		11:27	1.4	43
					16:28	2.1	64
11 Su	00:11	-0.2	-6	26 M	00:51	-0.2	-6
	07:54	1.7	52		07:42	1.6	49
	11:35	1.5	46		12:20	1.3	40
	16:12	1.9	58		17:24	2.0	61
12 M	00:42	-0.2	-6	27 Tu	01:24	0.0	0
	08:20	1.6	49		07:57	1.6	49
	12:21	1.4	43		13:08	1.1	34
	17:03	1.9	58		18:19	1.8	55
13 Tu	01:12	-0.2	-6	28 W	01:51	0.3	9
	08:40	1.6	49		08:13	1.6	49
	13:05	1.3	40		13:57	0.9	27
	17:55	1.8	55		19:16	1.6	49
14 W	01:42	-0.1	-3	29 Th	02:12	0.5	15
	08:55	1.6	49		08:30	1.6	49
	13:52	1.1	34		14:56	0.8	24
	18:51	1.7	52		20:27	1.4	43
15 Th	02:14	0.1	3	30 F	02:30	0.7	21
	09:12	1.5	46		08:52	1.7	52
	14:51	0.9	27		16:08	0.6	18
	19:57	1.5	46		22:12	1.2	37
				31 Sa ☽	02:48	0.9	27
					09:17	1.7	52
					17:26	0.5	15

August

Day	Time (h m)	Height ft	Height cm	Day	Time (h m)	Height ft	Height cm
1 Su	00:05	1.2	37	16 M	00:21	1.4	43
	03:08	1.1	34		02:53	1.3	40
	09:46	1.7	52		09:20	1.9	58
	18:47	0.3	9		18:29	0.1	3
2 M	10:20	1.7	52	17 Tu	10:11	1.9	58
	19:52	0.2	6		19:46	0.0	0
3 Tu	10:58	1.8	55	18 W	11:10	2.0	61
	20:40	0.1	3		20:46	-0.2	-6
4 W	04:49	1.6	49	19 Th	05:05	1.8	55
	07:18	1.6	49		08:06	1.7	52
	11:44	1.8	55		12:24	2.0	61
	21:21	0.0	0		21:37	-0.2	-6
5 Th	05:18	1.7	52	20 F	05:25	1.8	55
	08:30	1.6	49		08:58	1.6	49
	12:43	1.8	55		13:46	2.1	64
	22:01	-0.1	-3		22:25	-0.2	-6
6 F	05:48	1.7	52	21 Sa	05:44	1.7	52
	09:10	1.6	49		09:41	1.5	46
	13:46	1.9	58		14:53	2.1	64
	22:40	-0.1	-3		23:10	0.0	0
7 Sa	06:16	1.7	52	22 Su ○	06:01	1.7	52
	09:47	1.6	49		10:27	1.4	43
	14:41	2.0	61		15:50	2.1	64
	23:16	-0.1	-3		23:50	0.1	3
8 Su ●	06:40	1.7	52	23 M	06:14	1.7	52
	10:27	1.5	46		11:17	1.2	37
	15:30	2.0	61		16:43	2.1	64
	23:50	0.0	0				
9 M	06:58	1.7	52	24 Tu	00:22	0.3	9
	11:14	1.4	43		06:25	1.7	52
	16:19	2.1	64		12:04	1.1	34
					17:35	2.0	61
10 Tu	00:20	0.1	3	25 W	00:46	0.5	15
	07:08	1.7	52		06:37	1.8	55
	12:01	1.3	40		12:47	0.9	27
	17:11	2.0	61		18:27	1.8	55
11 W	00:49	0.2	6	26 Th	01:05	0.7	21
	07:16	1.7	52		06:50	1.8	55
	12:46	1.1	34		13:27	0.8	24
	18:06	1.9	58		19:21	1.7	52
12 Th	01:16	0.3	9	27 F	01:21	0.9	27
	07:28	1.7	52		07:07	1.9	58
	13:32	0.9	27		14:11	0.7	21
	19:04	1.8	55		20:30	1.5	46
13 F	01:43	0.6	18	28 Sa	01:39	1.1	34
	07:45	1.7	52		07:45	1.9	58
	14:26	0.7	21		15:03	0.6	18
	20:17	1.6	49		22:11	1.4	43
14 Sa	02:10	0.8	24	29 Su	01:59	1.2	37
	08:09	1.8	55		07:50	1.9	58
	15:36	0.5	15		16:11	0.5	15
	22:06	1.4	43		23:54	1.4	43
15 Su ○	02:36	1.1	34	30 M ○	02:21	1.4	43
	08:40	1.9	58		08:20	1.9	58
	17:00	0.3	9		17:34	0.5	15
				31 Tu	09:04	1.8	55
					19:02	0.4	12

September

Day	Time (h m)	Height ft	Height cm	Day	Time (h m)	Height ft	Height cm
1 W	10:07	1.8	55	16 Th	03:55	1.8	55
	20:05	0.3	9		07:13	1.7	52
					11:07	1.9	58
					20:32	0.1	3
2 Th	03:57	1.7	52	17 F	04:06	1.8	55
	07:31	1.6	49		08:20	1.6	49
	11:16	1.8	55		12:46	1.9	58
	20:51	0.2	6		21:21	0.1	3
3 F	04:27	1.8	55	18 Sa	04:22	1.8	55
	08:26	1.6	49		09:02	1.4	43
	12:33	1.9	58		14:16	2.0	61
	21:31	0.2	6		22:04	0.2	6
4 Sa	04:55	1.8	55	19 Su	04:36	1.8	55
	09:01	1.5	46		09:42	1.2	37
	13:48	2.0	61		15:18	2.1	64
	22:08	0.2	6		22:42	0.4	12
5 Su	05:19	1.8	55	20 M ○	04:48	1.8	55
	09:35	1.4	43		10:23	1.0	30
	14:47	2.1	64		16:10	2.1	64
	22:44	0.2	6		23:15	0.6	18
6 M	05:35	1.8	55	21 Tu	04:59	1.8	55
	10:12	1.3	40		11:06	0.9	27
	15:38	2.1	64		17:01	2.0	61
	23:18	0.3	9		23:41	0.8	24
7 Tu ●	05:43	1.8	55	22 W	05:10	1.9	58
	10:55	1.2	37		11:48	0.8	24
	16:30	2.1	64		17:50	1.9	58
	23:49	0.5	15				
8 W	05:49	1.8	55	23 Th	00:01	1.0	30
	11:42	1.0	30		05:23	1.9	58
	17:26	2.1	64		12:25	0.6	18
					18:39	1.9	5
9 Th	00:19	0.7	21	24 F	05:40	2.0	6
	05:59	1.8	55		12:58	0.5	1
	12:28	0.8	24		19:32	1.8	5
	18:24	2.0	61				
10 F	00:46	0.9	27	25 Sa	00:40	1.3	4
	06:16	1.9	58		06:00	2.0	6
	13:15	0.6	18		13:32	0.5	1
	19:29	1.8	55		20:42	1.7	5
11 Sa	01:12	1.1	34	26 Su	01:05	1.4	4
	06:37	2.0	61		06:23	2.0	6
	14:07	0.4	12		14:09	0.4	1
	21:00	1.7	52		22:13	1.6	
12 Su	01:35	1.3	40	27 M	01:34	1.5	4
	07:03	2.0	61		06:48	2.0	6
	15:14	0.3	9		14:59	0.4	
	23:02	1.6	49		23:34	1.6	4
13 M ☽	01:52	1.5	46	28 Tu	02:11	1.6	4
	07:35	2.1	64		07:19	1.9	5
	16:40	0.2	6		16:15	0.5	
14 Tu	08:20	2.0	61	29 W ☽	01:07	1.7	
	18:12	0.2	6		03:19	1.6	
					08:01	1.8	
					17:49	0.4	
15 W	09:36	2.0	61	30 Th	02:22	1.7	
	19:32	0.1	3		05:16	1.6	
					09:26	1.8	
					19:12	0.4	

StationId: 8728690
Source: NOAA/NOS/CO-OPS
Station Type: Primary
Time Zone: LST_LDT
Datum: MLLW

NOAA Tide Predictions

Apalachicola, FL,2021

Times and Heights of High and Low Waters

October

Day	Time (h m)	Height (ft)	Height (cm)
1 F	03:00	1.8	55
	07:17	1.6	49
	10:59	1.7	52
	20:08	0.3	9
2 Sa	03:29	1.8	55
	08:09	1.5	46
	12:26	1.8	55
	20:51	0.3	9
3 Su	03:51	1.8	55
	08:45	1.3	40
	13:49	1.9	58
	21:27	0.4	12
4 M	04:05	1.8	55
	09:20	1.1	34
	14:53	2.0	61
	22:02	0.5	15
5 Tu	04:13	1.8	55
	09:57	0.9	27
	15:50	2.0	61
	22:37	0.7	21
6 W	04:20	1.8	55
	10:39	0.7	21
	16:48	2.1	64
	23:12	0.9	27
7 Th	04:32	1.9	58
	11:26	0.5	15
	17:50	2.0	61
	23:46	1.2	37
8 F	04:50	2.0	61
	12:14	0.3	9
	18:54	1.9	58
9 Sa	00:17	1.4	43
	05:14	2.1	64
	13:03	0.1	3
	20:12	1.8	55
10 Su ○	00:46	1.5	46
	05:43	2.1	64
	13:56	0.1	3
	22:02	1.8	55
11 M	01:11	1.6	49
	06:16	2.1	64
	15:02	0.1	3
12 Tu	06:55	2.1	64
	16:24	0.1	3
13 W	07:48	1.9	58
	17:49	0.1	3
14 Th	02:28	1.7	52
	05:17	1.6	49
	09:31	1.8	55
	19:07	0.2	6
15 F	02:43	1.7	52
	07:21	1.4	43
	11:25	1.7	52
	20:07	0.3	9
16 Sa	02:59	1.6	49
	08:16	1.2	37
	13:21	1.7	52
	20:53	0.4	12
17 Su	03:13	1.6	49
	08:57	0.9	27
	14:43	1.8	55
	21:31	0.6	18
18 M	03:25	1.7	52
	09:37	0.7	21
	15:41	1.8	55
	22:02	0.8	24
19 Tu	03:36	1.8	55
	10:16	0.6	18
	16:33	1.8	55
	22:28	1.0	30
20 W ○	03:47	1.8	55
	10:55	0.4	12
	17:24	1.8	55
	22:50	1.2	37
21 Th	04:01	1.9	58
	11:32	0.3	9
	18:12	1.8	55
	23:12	1.3	40
22 F	04:17	2.0	61
	12:05	0.3	9
	18:59	1.7	52
	23:38	1.4	43
23 Sa	04:38	2.0	61
	12:34	0.2	6
	19:50	1.7	52
24 Su	00:11	1.4	43
	05:04	2.0	61
	13:04	0.2	6
	20:55	1.7	52
25 M	00:47	1.5	46
	05:34	1.9	58
	13:37	0.2	6
	22:06	1.6	49
26 Tu	01:26	1.5	46
	06:07	1.9	58
	14:20	0.2	6
	23:05	1.6	49
27 W	02:13	1.5	46
	06:46	1.8	55
	15:21	0.2	6
28 Th ◐	00:02	1.6	49
	03:25	1.5	46
	07:35	1.7	52
	16:37	0.3	9
29 F	01:02	1.6	49
	05:02	1.4	43
	09:02	1.6	49
	17:55	0.3	9
30 Sa	01:48	1.6	49
	06:38	1.3	40
	10:54	1.5	46
	19:04	0.3	9
31 Su	02:17	1.6	49
	07:42	1.1	34
	12:16	1.5	46
	19:57	0.4	12

November

Day	Time (h m)	Height (ft)	Height (cm)
1 M	02:33	1.6	49
	08:25	0.8	24
	13:50	1.6	49
	20:39	0.5	15
2 Tu	02:44	1.6	49
	09:03	0.6	18
	15:04	1.7	52
	21:17	0.7	21
3 W	02:54	1.7	52
	09:43	0.3	9
	16:10	1.8	55
	21:53	0.9	27
4 Th ●	03:09	1.8	55
	10:27	0.1	3
	17:18	1.8	55
	22:31	1.2	37
5 F	03:29	1.9	58
	11:16	-0.1	-3
	18:25	1.8	55
	23:12	1.4	43
6 Sa	03:55	2.0	61
	12:07	-0.3	-9
	19:34	1.8	55
	23:52	1.5	46
7 Su	03:27	2.0	61
	11:58	-0.3	-9
	20:00	1.7	52
	23:30	1.6	49
8 M	04:06	2.0	61
	12:52	-0.3	-9
	21:24	1.7	52
9 Tu	00:06	1.6	49
	04:52	2.0	61
	13:53	-0.3	-9
	22:18	1.6	49
10 W	00:51	1.5	46
	05:43	1.8	55
	15:04	-0.1	-3
	23:02	1.5	46
11 Th ◐	02:20	1.4	43
	06:51	1.6	49
	16:14	0.0	0
	23:40	1.4	43
12 F	04:24	1.2	37
	08:45	1.4	43
	17:22	0.2	6
13 Sa	00:11	1.4	43
	06:00	0.9	27
	10:43	1.3	40
	18:23	0.3	9
14 Su	00:35	1.4	43
	07:01	0.6	18
	12:44	1.3	40
	19:10	0.5	15
15 M	00:55	1.4	43
	07:47	0.4	12
	14:05	1.3	40
	19:47	0.7	21
16 Tu	01:11	1.5	46
	08:27	0.1	3
	15:06	1.4	43
	20:15	0.9	27
17 W	01:27	1.6	49
	09:06	0.0	0
	16:02	1.5	46
	20:38	1.1	34
18 Th	01:43	1.7	52
	09:43	-0.1	-3
	16:52	1.5	46
	21:01	1.2	37
19 F ○	02:02	1.7	52
	10:18	-0.2	-6
	17:37	1.5	46
	21:30	1.3	40
20 Sa	02:25	1.7	52
	10:51	-0.2	-6
	18:19	1.5	46
	23:12	1.3	40
21 Su	02:52	1.7	52
	11:21	-0.2	-6
	19:03	1.5	46
	22:58	1.3	40
22 M	03:25	1.7	52
	11:50	-0.2	-6
	19:53	1.5	46
	23:40	1.3	40
23 Tu	04:04	1.7	52
	12:23	-0.2	-6
	20:44	1.4	43
24 W	00:21	1.2	37
	04:47	1.6	49
	13:01	-0.2	-6
	21:27	1.4	43
25 Th	01:07	1.2	37
	05:34	1.5	46
	13:48	-0.2	-6
	22:05	1.3	40
26 F ◑	02:10	1.1	34
	06:29	1.4	43
	14:43	-0.1	-3
	22:38	1.3	40
27 Sa ○	03:29	1.0	30
	10:47	1.2	37
	15:41	0.0	0
	23:07	1.3	40
28 Su	04:51	0.8	24
	09:31	1.1	34
	16:41	0.2	6
	23:31	1.3	40
29 M	06:07	0.5	15
	11:10	1.1	34
	17:45	0.4	12
	23:52	1.3	40
30 Tu	07:02	0.2	6
	13:03	1.1	34
	18:43	0.6	18

December

Day	Time (h m)	Height (ft)	Height (cm)
1 W	00:15	1.4	43
	07:47	-0.1	-3
	14:29	1.3	40
	19:31	0.8	24
2 Th	00:40	1.5	46
	08:31	-0.3	-9
	15:45	1.4	43
	20:13	1.0	30
3 F	01:09	1.6	49
	09:19	-0.6	-18
	16:56	1.5	46
	20:55	1.2	37
4 Sa ●	01:42	1.7	52
	10:12	-0.7	-21
	17:59	1.5	46
	21:42	1.3	40
5 Su	02:20	1.8	55
	11:06	-0.8	-24
	19:00	1.5	46
	22:37	1.4	43
6 M	03:04	1.8	55
	11:57	-0.8	-24
	20:04	1.4	43
	23:25	1.3	40
7 Tu	03:55	1.7	52
	12:47	-0.7	-21
	20:53	1.3	40
8 W	00:11	1.2	37
	04:52	1.6	49
	13:38	-0.6	-18
	21:26	1.2	37
9 Th	01:03	1.0	30
	05:52	1.4	43
	14:31	-0.4	-12
	21:50	1.1	34
10 F	02:21	0.8	24
	07:05	1.2	37
	15:24	-0.1	-3
	22:12	1.1	34
11 Sa ◑	03:54	0.6	18
	08:54	1.0	30
	16:13	0.1	3
	22:33	1.1	34
12 Su ○	05:24	0.3	9
	10:47	0.8	24
	17:04	0.3	9
	22:55	1.1	34
13 M	06:37	0.1	3
	13:02	0.8	24
	17:58	0.6	18
	23:19	1.2	37
14 Tu	07:29	-0.2	-6
	14:31	0.9	27
	18:47	0.7	21
	23:45	1.2	37
15 W	08:12	-0.4	-12
	15:37	1.0	30
	19:27	0.9	27
16 Th	00:13	1.3	40
	08:51	-0.5	-15
	16:30	1.1	34
	20:01	1.0	30
17 F	00:43	1.3	40
	09:30	-0.6	-18
	17:12	1.2	37
	20:35	1.1	34
18 Sa	01:15	1.4	43
	10:07	-0.6	-18
	17:47	1.3	40
	21:16	1.1	34
19 Su ○	01:50	1.4	43
	10:42	-0.6	-18
	18:20	1.3	40
	22:07	1.1	34
20 M	02:27	1.4	43
	11:14	-0.6	-18
	18:54	1.2	37
	22:54	1.0	30
21 Tu	03:09	1.4	43
	11:43	-0.6	-18
	19:28	1.2	37
	23:33	1.0	30
22 W	03:56	1.4	43
	12:13	-0.6	-18
	20:01	1.2	37
23 Th	00:11	0.9	27
	04:44	1.3	40
	12:44	-0.6	-18
	20:30	1.1	34
24 F	00:53	0.8	24
	05:35	1.2	37
	13:19	-0.5	-15
	20:53	1.1	34
25 Sa	01:45	0.6	18
	06:31	1.1	34
	13:58	-0.4	-12
	21:14	1.0	30
26 Su	02:52	0.5	15
	07:49	0.9	27
	14:42	-0.2	-6
	21:35	1.0	30
27 M ◑	04:07	0.2	6
	09:28	0.7	21
	15:29	0.1	3
	21:59	1.1	34
28 Tu	05:26	0.0	0
	11:18	0.7	21
	16:22	0.4	12
	22:25	1.1	34
29 W	06:37	-0.3	-9
	13:40	0.8	24
	17:29	0.6	18
	22:56	1.2	37
30 Th	07:33	-0.6	-18
	15:13	1.0	30
	18:47	0.9	27
	23:35	1.3	40
31 F	08:24	-0.8	-24
	16:26	1.2	37
	19:46	1.1	34

StationId: 8729840
Source: NOAA/NOS/CO-OPS
Station Type: Primary
Time Zone: LST_LDT
Datum: MLLW

NOAA Tide Predictions

Pensacola, FL, 2021

Times and Heights of High and Low Waters

January

Day	Time	ft	cm	Day	Time	ft	cm
1 F	10:41 / 23:59	-0.8 / 1.4	-24 / 43	16 Sa	00:09 / 10:52	1.1 / -0.6	34 / -18
2 Sa	11:12	-0.8	-24	17 Su	00:38 / 10:49	0.9 / -0.3	27 / -9
3 Su	00:40 / 11:35	1.2 / -0.6	37 / -18	18 M	00:53 / 10:24 / 19:43	0.6 / -0.2 / 0.4	18 / -6 / 12
4 M	01:21 / 11:46	1.0 / -0.4	30 / -12	19 Tu	09:28 / 17:44	0.0 / 0.5	0 / 15
5 Tu	02:05 / 11:34 / 19:37	0.6 / -0.1 / 0.4	18 / -3 / 12	20 W ◑	07:19 / 17:21	0.0 / 0.7	0 / 21
6 W ◐	10:23 / 18:14	0.1 / 0.6	3 / 18	21 Th	04:14 / 17:26	-0.2 / 0.8	-6 / 24
7 Th	03:26 / 18:03	-0.1 / 0.8	-3 / 24	22 F	04:27 / 17:50	-0.4 / 0.9	-12 / 27
8 F	04:19 / 18:25	-0.4 / 1.1	-12 / 34	23 Sa	05:04 / 18:28	-0.5 / 1.0	-15 / 30
9 Sa	05:17 / 19:07	-0.7 / 1.3	-21 / 40	24 Su	05:52 / 19:16	-0.6 / 1.1	-18 / 34
10 Su	06:19 / 19:59	-0.8 / 1.4	-24 / 43	25 M	06:43 / 20:09	-0.7 / 1.2	-21 / 37
11 M	07:23 / 20:57	-0.9 / 1.5	-27 / 46	26 Tu	07:34 / 21:01	-0.8 / 1.3	-24 / 40
12 Tu	08:25 / 21:55	-1.0 / 1.5	-30 / 46	27 W	08:20 / 21:50	-0.8 / 1.3	-24 / 40
13 W ●	09:21 / 22:47	-1.0 / 1.4	-30 / 43	28 Th ○	09:00 / 22:35	-0.9 / 1.3	-27 / 40
14 Th	10:05 / 23:32	-0.9 / 1.3	-27 / 40	29 F	09:33 / 23:19	-0.8 / 1.3	-24 / 40
15 F	10:37	-0.7	-21	30 Sa	09:59	-0.7	-21
				31 Su	00:05 / 10:17	1.1 / -0.5	34 / -15

February

Day	Time	ft	cm	Day	Time	ft	cm
1 M	00:57 / 10:18	0.8 / -0.2	24 / -6	16 Tu	01:47 / 07:24 / 14:53 / 23:40	0.3 / 0.2 / 0.6 / 0.1	9 / 6 / 18 / 3
2 Tu	02:07 / 09:45 / 16:13 / 23:07	0.5 / 0.1 / 0.3 / 0.1	15 / 3 / 9 / 3	17 W	14:54	0.7	21
3 W	05:06 / 07:13 / 15:47	0.2 / 0.2 / 0.6	6 / 6 / 18	18 Th	01:14 / 15:13	-0.1 / 0.9	-3 / 27
4 Th ◐	01:35 / 16:06	-0.2 / 0.9	-6 / 27	19 F ◐	02:23 / 15:48	-0.2 / 1.0	-6 / 30
5 F	03:04 / 16:48	-0.5 / 1.1	-15 / 34	20 Sa	03:29 / 16:38	-0.3 / 1.0	-9 / 30
6 Sa	04:18 / 17:47	-0.7 / 1.2	-21 / 37	21 Su	04:33 / 17:42	-0.4 / 1.1	-12 / 34
7 Su	05:28 / 18:56	-0.8 / 1.3	-24 / 40	22 M	05:32 / 18:51	-0.5 / 1.2	-15 / 37
8 M	06:33 / 20:05	-0.8 / 1.4	-24 / 43	23 Tu	06:23 / 19:54	-0.6 / 1.3	-18 / 40
9 Tu	07:31 / 21:08	-0.9 / 1.4	-27 / 43	24 W	07:06 / 20:51	-0.7 / 1.3	-21 / 40
10 W	08:19 / 22:02	-0.8 / 1.3	-24 / 40	25 Th	07:43 / 21:44	-0.7 / 1.3	-21 / 40
11 Th ●	08:55 / 22:48	-0.7 / 1.2	-21 / 37	26 F	08:13 / 22:37	-0.6 / 1.2	-18 / 37
12 F ○	09:16 / 23:28	-0.5 / 1.0	-15 / 30	27 Sa ○	08:37 / 23:37	-0.4 / 1.0	-12 / 30
13 Sa	09:21	-0.3	-9	28 Su	08:50	-0.1	-3
14 Su	00:06 / 09:07	0.8 / -0.1	24 / -3				
15 M	00:47 / 08:31 / 15:22 / 21:13	0.5 / 0.1 / 0.4 / 0.2	15 / 3 / 12 / 6				

March

Day	Time	ft	cm	Day	Time	ft	cm
1 M	00:52 / 08:36 / 13:40 / 19:27	0.8 / 0.2 / 0.3 / 0.1	24 / 6 / 9 / 3	16 Tu	13:34 / 22:38	0.9 / 0.0	27 / 0
2 Tu	02:47 / 07:22 / 13:11 / 21:39	0.5 / 0.4 / 0.6 / -0.1	15 / 12 / 18 / -3	17 W	13:46 / 23:43	1.0 / -0.1	30 / -3
3 W	13:26 / 23:32	0.9 / -0.2	27 / -6	18 Th	14:10	1.1	34
4 Th	14:04	1.1	34	19 F	00:56 / 14:46	-0.1 / 1.2	-3 / 37
5 F	01:18 / 14:58	-0.4 / 1.3	-12 / 40	20 Sa	02:22 / 15:37	-0.2 / 1.2	-6 / 37
6 Sa ◐	02:54 / 16:08	-0.5 / 1.3	-15 / 40	21 Su ◐	03:47 / 16:43	-0.2 / 1.3	-6 / 40
7 Su	04:16 / 17:30	-0.6 / 1.4	-18 / 43	22 M	04:55 / 17:58	-0.3 / 1.3	-9 / 40
8 M	05:24 / 18:53	-0.6 / 1.4	-18 / 43	23 Tu	05:48 / 19:14	-0.4 / 1.4	-12 / 43
9 Tu	06:20 / 20:06	-0.6 / 1.3	-18 / 40	24 W	06:31 / 20:24	-0.4 / 1.4	-12 / 43
10 W	07:02 / 21:07	-0.5 / 1.2	-15 / 37	25 Th	07:06 / 21:32	-0.3 / 1.3	-9 / 40
11 Th	07:29 / 22:00	-0.3 / 1.1	-9 / 34	26 F	07:34 / 22:44	-0.2 / 1.2	-6 / 37
12 F	07:40 / 22:50	-0.1 / 0.9	-3 / 27	27 Sa	07:53	0.0	
13 Sa ●	07:30 / 23:47	0.1 / 0.7	3 / 21	28 Su ○	00:09 / 07:53 / 12:52 / 18:35	1.0 / 0.3 / 0.5 / 0.3	30 / 9 / 15 / 9
14 Su	07:58 / 13:58 / 19:58	0.3 / 0.5 / 0.3	9 / 15 / 9	29 M	02:04 / 07:08 / 12:11 / 20:17	0.8 / 0.6 / 0.8 / 0.0	24 / 18 / 24 / 0
15 M	02:05 / 07:00 / 13:35 / 21:28	0.5 / 0.4 / 0.7 / 0.2	15 / 12 / 21 / 6	30 Tu	12:14 / 21:43	1.1 / -0.2	34 / -6
				31 W	12:42 / 23:09	1.3 / -0.3	40 / -9

StationId: 8729840
Source: NOAA/NOS/CO-OPS
Station Type: Primary
Time Zone: LST_LDT
Datum: MLLW

April

Day	Time	ft	cm	Day	Time	ft	cm
1 Th	13:26	1.5	46	16 F	13:16	1.4	43
2 F	00:42	-0.4	-12	17 Sa	00:40	-0.1	-3
	14:22	1.6	49		14:02	1.5	46
3 Sa	02:19	-0.4	-12	18 Su	02:00	-0.2	-6
	15:29	1.6	49		14:57	1.5	46
4 Su	03:46	-0.4	-12	19 M	03:07	-0.2	-6
	16:46	1.5	46		15:59	1.5	46
5 M	04:56	-0.4	-12	20 Tu	04:00	-0.3	-9
	18:10	1.4	43		17:06	1.5	46
6 Tu	05:48	-0.3	-9	21 W	04:40	-0.2	-6
	19:32	1.3	40		18:19	1.4	43
7 W	06:23	-0.2	-6	22 Th	05:12	-0.1	-3
	20:45	1.2	37		19:44	1.2	37
8	06:40	0.0	0	23 F	05:34	0.1	3
	21:55	1.0	30		21:28	1.0	30
9	06:34	0.2	6	24 Sa	05:42	0.3	9
	13:47	0.6	18		12:02	0.7	21
	16:54	0.6	18		17:03	0.5	15
	23:13	0.8	24		23:40	0.8	24
10	06:02	0.4	12	25 Su	05:15	0.6	18
	12:19	0.7	21		10:56	0.9	27
	18:59	0.4	12		18:39	0.2	6
11	01:01	0.6	18	26 M	10:40	1.2	37
	04:52	0.6	18		19:51	-0.1	-3
	11:52	0.9	27				
	20:08	0.2	6				
12	11:48	1.1	34	27 Tu	10:54	1.5	46
	20:57	0.1	3		20:59	-0.3	-9
13	11:56	1.3	40	28 W	11:28	1.7	52
	21:41	0.0	0		22:12	-0.4	-12
14	12:13	1.4	43	29 Th	12:13	1.8	55
	22:28	-0.1	-3		23:33	-0.5	-15
15	12:39	1.4	43	30 F	13:08	1.8	55
	23:26	-0.1	-3				

May

Day	Time	ft	cm	Day	Time	ft	cm
1 Sa	00:58	-0.5	-15	16 Su	00:42	-0.3	-9
	14:09	1.8	55		13:42	1.7	52
2 Su	02:17	-0.4	-12	17 M	01:36	-0.3	-9
	15:14	1.7	52		14:30	1.6	49
3 M	03:19	-0.4	-12	18 Tu	02:19	-0.3	-9
	16:19	1.5	46		15:18	1.6	49
4 Tu	04:04	-0.2	-6	19 W	02:52	-0.2	-6
	17:23	1.3	40		16:09	1.4	43
5 W	04:30	0.0	0	20 Th	03:17	-0.1	-3
	18:27	1.1	34		17:14	1.2	37
6 Th	04:32	0.2	6	21 F	03:29	0.1	3
	19:53	0.8	24		12:41	0.8	24
					15:04	0.8	24
					19:25	0.9	27
7 F	04:04	0.4	12	22 Sa	03:17	0.4	12
	11:22	0.9	27		10:16	0.9	27
	18:26	0.6	18		17:18	0.5	15
	22:29	0.6	18		23:27	0.6	18
8 Sa	02:48	0.5	15	23 Su	01:45	0.6	18
	10:38	1.0	30		09:33	1.1	34
	19:19	0.3	9		18:21	0.1	3
9 Su	10:26	1.2	37	24 M	09:29	1.4	43
	19:55	0.1	3		19:19	-0.2	-6
10 M	10:29	1.4	43	25 Tu	09:50	1.6	49
	20:28	0.0	0		20:21	-0.4	-12
11 Tu	10:43	1.5	46	26 W	10:28	1.8	55
	21:04	-0.1	-3		21:29	-0.5	-15
12 W	11:05	1.6	49	27 Th	11:16	1.9	58
	21:46	-0.2	-6		22:42	-0.6	-18
13 Th	11:35	1.6	49	28 F	12:11	2.0	61
	22:38	-0.2	-6		23:55	-0.6	-18
14 F	12:12	1.6	49	29 Sa	13:09	1.9	58
	23:40	-0.2	-6				
15 Sa	12:55	1.6	49	30 Su	01:00	-0.5	-15
					14:04	1.8	55
				31 M	01:51	-0.4	-12
					14:54	1.6	49

June

Day	Time	ft	cm	Day	Time	ft	cm
1 Tu	02:26	-0.2	-6	16 W	01:21	-0.3	-9
	15:33	1.4	43		14:44	1.4	43
2 W	02:40	0.0	0	17 Th	01:36	-0.1	-3
	15:45	1.1	34		15:20	1.1	34
3 Th	02:27	0.2	6	18 F	01:37	0.2	6
	11:33	0.9	27		10:31	0.8	24
4 F	01:39	0.4	12	19 Sa	01:03	0.4	12
	09:48	1.0	30		08:40	1.0	30
	22:53	0.4	12		17:03	0.4	12
5 Sa	09:14	1.2	37	20 Su	08:12	1.2	37
	19:08	0.2	6		17:48	0.1	3
6 Su	09:09	1.3	40	21 M	08:19	1.5	46
	19:26	0.0	0		18:42	-0.2	-6
7 M	09:19	1.5	46	22 Tu	08:49	1.7	52
	19:54	-0.1	-3		19:43	-0.4	-12
8 Tu	09:39	1.6	49	23 W	09:34	1.9	58
	20:30	-0.2	-6		20:50	-0.6	-18
9 W	10:08	1.6	49	24 Th	10:27	2.0	61
	21:14	-0.3	-9		21:57	-0.6	-18
10 Th	10:43	1.7	52	25 F	11:24	2.0	61
	22:05	-0.3	-9		23:01	-0.6	-18
11 F	11:24	1.7	52	26 Sa	12:20	2.0	61
	22:57	-0.3	-9		23:55	-0.6	-18
12 Sa	12:06	1.7	52	27 Su	13:10	1.8	55
	23:45	-0.4	-12				
13 Su	12:48	1.7	52	28 M	00:35	-0.4	-12
					13:53	1.6	49
14 M	00:25	-0.4	-12	29 Tu	01:00	-0.2	-6
	13:28	1.7	52		14:25	1.4	43
15 Tu	00:57	-0.4	-12	30 W	01:05	0.0	0
	14:07	1.6	49		14:34	1.1	34

StationId: 8729840
Source: NOAA/NOS/CO-OPS
Station Type: Primary
Time Zone: LST_LDT
Datum: MLLW

NOAA Tide Predictions

Pensacola, FL, 2021

Times and Heights of High and Low Waters

July

Day	Time (h m)	Height ft	Height cm	Day	Time (h m)	Height ft	Height cm
1 Th ☽	00:42	0.2	6	16 F	08:02	0.8	24
	09:57	0.9	27		13:35	0.7	21
	23:43	0.4	12		16:03	0.7	21
					23:00	0.5	15
2 F	08:09	1.0	30	17 Sa ☽	06:43	1.0	30
	21:00	0.4	12		15:49	0.4	12
3 Sa	07:43	1.2	37	18 Su	06:35	1.3	40
	18:21	0.2	6		16:51	0.1	3
4 Su	07:46	1.4	43	19 M	06:58	1.5	46
	18:34	0.0	0		17:53	-0.2	-6
5 M	08:04	1.5	46	20 Tu	07:42	1.7	52
	19:06	-0.1	-3		18:59	-0.3	-9
6 Tu	08:33	1.6	49	21 W	08:38	1.9	58
	19:48	-0.2	-6		20:06	-0.5	-15
7 W	09:12	1.6	49	22 Th	09:39	2.0	61
	20:36	-0.2	-6		21:10	-0.5	-15
8 Th	09:55	1.7	52	23 F	10:39	2.0	61
	21:26	-0.3	-9		22:06	-0.5	-15
9 F	10:40	1.8	55	24 Sa ○	11:34	2.0	61
	22:11	-0.4	-12		22:51	-0.4	-12
10 Sa ●	11:24	1.8	55	25 Su	12:23	1.8	55
	22:50	-0.4	-12		23:24	-0.2	-6
11 Su	12:04	1.8	55	26 M	13:05	1.6	49
	23:21	-0.4	-12		23:40	0.0	0
12 M	12:42	1.7	52	27 Tu	13:41	1.4	43
	23:46	-0.3	-9		23:36	0.2	6
13 Tu	13:20	1.6	49	28 W	14:11	1.1	34
					23:04	0.4	12
14 W	00:04	-0.1	-3	29 Th	07:07	0.9	27
	13:59	1.4	43		21:54	0.6	18
15 Th	00:11	0.1	3	30 F	05:52	1.0	30
	14:44	1.1	34		18:05	0.5	15
	23:59	0.3	9				
				31 Sa ☽	05:43	1.2	37
					16:31	0.3	9

August

Day	Time (h m)	Height ft	Height cm	Day	Time (h m)	Height ft	Height cm
1 Su	05:58	1.4	43	16 M	05:17	1.6	49
	17:07	0.2	6		16:43	0.0	0
2 M	06:28	1.5	46	17 Tu	06:19	1.8	55
	17:53	0.1	3		18:00	-0.1	-3
3 Tu	07:12	1.6	49	18 W	07:30	1.9	58
	18:46	0.0	0		19:09	-0.2	-6
4 W	08:04	1.7	52	19 Th	08:43	2.0	61
	19:39	-0.1	-3		20:09	-0.3	-9
5 Th	08:59	1.7	52	20 F	09:49	2.0	61
	20:28	-0.2	-6		21:00	-0.2	-6
6 F	09:50	1.8	55	21 Sa	10:46	1.9	58
	21:10	-0.2	-6		21:38	-0.1	-3
7 Sa	10:37	1.9	58	22 Su ○	11:37	1.8	55
	21:45	-0.2	-6		22:03	0.1	3
8 Su ●	11:19	1.8	55	23 M	12:23	1.6	49
	22:13	-0.2	-6		22:10	0.3	9
9 M	12:01	1.8	55	24 Tu	13:11	1.3	40
	22:34	0.0	0		21:51	0.6	18
10 Tu	12:46	1.6	49	25 W	14:08	1.1	34
	22:48	0.2	6		21:00	0.8	24
11 W	13:39	1.4	43	26 Th	03:16	1.0	30
	22:46	0.4	12		10:10	0.7	21
					15:51	0.9	27
					19:17	0.8	24
12 Th	14:53	1.1	34	27 F	03:04	1.2	37
	22:14	0.7	21		12:09	0.6	18
13 F	04:29	0.9	27	28 Sa	03:15	1.4	43
	11:19	0.7	21		13:38	0.5	15
	17:37	0.8	24				
	20:06	0.8	24				
14 Sa	04:11	1.2	37	29 Su	03:42	1.5	46
	13:40	0.4	12		14:54	0.4	12
15 Su ☽	04:32	1.4	43	30 M ☽	04:23	1.6	49
	15:20	0.2	6		16:08	0.3	9
				31 Tu	05:19	1.6	49
					17:17	0.2	6

September

Day	Time (h m)	Height ft	Height cm	Day	Time (h m)	Height ft	Height cm
1 W	06:27	1.7	52	16 Th	07:26	1.9	58
	18:16	0.1	3		18:51	0.0	0
2 Th	07:37	1.8	55	17 F	08:42	1.9	58
	19:06	0.1	3		19:35	0.1	3
3 F	08:39	1.8	55	18 Sa	09:48	1.8	55
	19:47	0.0	0		20:05	0.2	6
4 Sa	09:34	1.9	58	19 Su	10:47	1.6	49
	20:19	0.1	3		20:18	0.5	15
5 Su	10:25	1.8	55	20 M ○	11:46	1.4	43
	20:46	0.1	3		20:04	0.7	21
6 M	11:18	1.7	52	21 Tu	01:58	0.9	27
	21:05	0.3	9		05:53	0.9	27
					12:57	1.2	37
					19:19	0.9	27
7 Tu ●	12:18	1.5	46	22 W	00:57	1.1	34
	21:12	0.6	18		07:58	0.7	21
					14:52	1.0	30
					17:41	1.0	30
8 W	13:36	1.3	40	23 Th	00:46	1.3	40
	20:53	0.8	24		09:21	0.6	18
9 Th	01:50	1.0	30	24 F	00:54	1.5	46
	08:13	0.7	21		10:26	0.5	15
	15:42	1.1	34				
	19:33	1.0	30				
10 F	01:31	1.3	40	25 Sa	01:12	1.6	49
	10:08	0.5	15		11:30	0.4	12
11 Sa	01:49	1.5	46	26 Su	01:41	1.7	52
	11:52	0.3	9		12:42	0.3	9
12 Su	02:28	1.7	52	27 M	02:21	1.7	52
	13:36	0.2	6		14:06	0.3	9
13 M ☽	03:24	1.8	55	28 Tu	03:14	1.7	52
	15:15	0.1	3		15:27	0.3	9
14 Tu	04:36	1.9	58	29 W ☽	04:21	1.7	52
	16:42	0.0	0		16:32	0.2	6
15 W	06:00	1.9	58	30 Th	05:36	1.7	52
	17:53	0.0	0		17:23	0.2	6

StationId: 8729840
Source: NOAA/NOS/CO-OPS
Station Type: Primary
Time Zone: LST_LDT
Datum: MLLW

NOAA Tide Predictions

Pensacola, FL,2021

Times and Heights of High and Low Waters

October

Day	Time	ft	cm	Day	Time	ft	cm
1 F	06:51	1.8	55	16 Sa	08:23	1.5	46
	18:01	0.1	3		18:10	0.4	12
2 Sa	08:00	1.7	52	17 Su	09:42	1.3	40
	18:32	0.2	6		18:02	0.6	18
3 Su	09:08	1.6	49	18 M	00:39	1.0	30
	18:55	0.4	12		05:09	0.9	27
					11:14	1.1	34
					17:19	0.8	24
					23:31	1.1	34
4 M	10:22	1.5	46	19 Tu	06:53	0.6	18
	19:07	0.6	18		23:12	1.3	40
5 Tu	01:51	0.9	27	20 W ○	07:57	0.4	12
	04:06	0.9	27		23:15	1.5	46
	11:51	1.3	40				
	18:59	0.8	24				
6 W	00:06	1.0	30	21 Th	08:46	0.3	9
	06:31	0.7	21		23:28	1.6	49
	13:56	1.1	34				
	18:02	1.1	34				
	23:37	1.3	40				
7 Th	07:59	0.4	12	22 F	09:31	0.2	6
	23:43	1.5	46		23:49	1.7	52
8 F	09:18	0.2	6	23 Sa	10:19	0.1	3
9 Sa	00:11	1.8	55	24 Su	00:17	1.7	52
	10:39	0.1	3		11:19	0.1	3
10 Su	00:55	1.9	58	25 M	00:55	1.7	52
	12:10	0.0	0		12:31	0.1	3
11 M	01:51	2.0	61	26 Tu	01:40	1.7	52
	13:47	-0.1	-3		13:46	0.1	3
12 Tu	02:58	2.0	61	27 W	02:33	1.7	52
	15:14	-0.1	-3		14:47	0.0	0
13 W	04:16	1.9	58	28 Th ◐	03:31	1.7	52
	16:24	-0.1	-3		15:33	0.0	0
14 Th	05:41	1.8	55	29 F	04:32	1.6	49
	17:16	0.0	0		16:08	0.0	0
15 F	07:04	1.7	52	30 Sa	05:41	1.5	46
	17:53	0.2	6		16:35	0.1	3
				31 Su	07:06	1.3	40
					16:51	0.3	9

November

Day	Time	ft	cm	Day	Time	ft	cm
1 M	08:59	1.1	34	16 Tu	06:02	0.3	9
	16:51	0.5	15		20:56	1.3	40
	23:19	0.9	27				
2 Tu	05:10	0.7	21	17 W	06:40	0.0	0
	11:23	0.9	27		21:05	1.5	46
	16:15	0.8	24				
	22:27	1.1	34				
3 W	06:27	0.3	9	18 Th	07:15	-0.1	-3
	22:15	1.4	43		21:22	1.6	49
4 Th ●	07:31	0.1	3	19 F ○	07:53	-0.2	-6
	22:30	1.6	49		21:48	1.6	49
5 F	08:35	-0.2	-6	20 Sa	08:37	-0.2	-6
	23:03	1.8	55		22:19	1.6	49
6 Sa	09:47	-0.3	-9	21 Su	09:31	-0.2	-6
	23:49	1.9	58		22:57	1.6	49
7 Su	10:08	-0.4	-12	22 M	10:31	-0.3	-9
	23:44	2.0	61		23:39	1.6	49
8 M	11:34	-0.4	-12	23 Tu	11:29	-0.3	-9
9 Tu	00:45	1.9	58	24 W	00:22	1.6	49
	12:52	-0.4	-12		12:17	-0.3	-9
10 W	01:49	1.8	55	25 Th	01:04	1.5	46
	13:54	-0.3	-9		12:55	-0.3	-9
11 Th ◑	02:54	1.7	52	26 F	01:46	1.4	43
	14:39	-0.2	-6		13:23	-0.3	-9
12 F	03:57	1.4	43	27 Sa	02:26	1.3	40
	15:04	0.0	0		13:42	-0.1	-3
13 Sa ◐	05:05	1.2	37	28 Su	03:11	1.0	30
	15:06	0.3	9		13:49	0.1	3
	23:49	0.8	24		22:38	0.7	21
14 Su	03:10	0.8	24	29 M	03:12	0.7	21
	06:50	0.9	27		05:26	0.7	21
	14:33	0.5	15		13:33	0.3	9
	21:42	0.9	27		20:46	0.8	24
15 M	05:11	0.5	15	30 Tu	04:15	0.3	9
	10:08	0.6	18		20:08	1.0	30
	12:44	0.6	18				
	21:04	1.1	34				

December

Day	Time	ft	cm	Day	Time	ft	cm
1 W	05:04	0.0	0	16 Th	06:39	-0.4	-12
	20:06	1.3	40		20:22	1.3	40
2 Th	05:57	-0.3	-9	17 F	07:18	-0.5	-15
	20:29	1.5	46		20:55	1.4	43
3 F	06:57	-0.5	-15	18 Sa	08:03	-0.6	-18
	21:07	1.7	52		21:33	1.4	43
4 Sa ●	08:04	-0.7	-21	19 Su ○	08:54	-0.6	-18
	21:57	1.8	55		22:13	1.4	43
5 Su	09:19	-0.8	-24	20 M	09:44	-0.6	-18
	22:52	1.8	55		22:54	1.4	43
6 M	10:33	-0.8	-24	21 Tu	10:28	-0.6	-18
	23:50	1.8	55		23:33	1.4	43
7 Tu	11:38	-0.8	-24	22 W	11:03	-0.7	-21
8 W	00:46	1.7	52	23 Th	00:08	1.3	40
	12:31	-0.7	-21		11:31	-0.6	-18
9 Th	01:36	1.5	46	24 F	00:41	1.2	37
	13:07	-0.5	-15		11:51	-0.5	-15
10 F	02:18	1.2	37	25 Sa	01:12	1.0	30
	13:22	-0.2	-6		12:02	-0.3	-9
11 Sa ◑	02:36	0.8	24	26 Su	01:36	0.7	21
	13:08	0.0	0		11:58	-0.1	-3
	21:54	0.6	18		20:54	0.5	15
12 Su	12:07	0.2	6	27 M ◑	11:20	0.1	3
	20:11	0.7	21		19:08	0.6	18
13 M	05:39	0.2	6	28 Tu	03:50	0.0	0
	19:41	0.9	27		18:42	0.8	24
14 Tu	05:40	-0.1	-3	29 W	04:25	-0.3	-9
	19:42	1.1	34		18:52	1.1	34
15 W	06:06	-0.3	-9	30 Th	05:17	-0.6	-18
	19:57	1.3	40		19:25	1.3	40
				31 F	06:17	-0.8	-24
					20:08	1.5	46

StationId: 8735180
Source: NOAA/NOS/CO-OPS
Station Type: Primary
Time Zone: LST_LDT
Datum: MLLW

NOAA Tide Predictions

Dauphin Island, AL,2021

Times and Heights of High and Low Waters

January

Day	Time	ft	cm	Day	Time	ft	cm
1 F	10:53	-0.7	-21	16 Sa	11:50	-0.4	-12
	23:22	1.3	40				
2 Sa	11:31	-0.7	-21	17 Su	00:10	0.8	24
					11:47	-0.3	-9
3 Su	00:00	1.2	37	18 M	00:22	0.6	18
	12:00	-0.5	-15		10:57	-0.1	-3
					23:04	0.3	9
4 M	00:32	0.9	27	19 Tu	09:17	0.0	0
	12:12	-0.3	-9		18:06	0.4	12
5 Tu	00:42	0.7	21	20 W	06:42	0.0	0
	11:45	-0.1	-3		17:23	0.6	18
	21:36	0.4	12				
6 W	09:52	0.1	3	21 Th	04:46	-0.2	-6
	18:38	0.5	15		17:28	0.7	21
7 Th	05:22	-0.1	-3	22 F	04:45	-0.3	-9
	18:08	0.8	24		17:50	0.9	27
8 F	05:10	-0.4	-12	23 Sa	05:11	-0.5	-15
	18:25	1.0	30		18:22	1.0	30
9 Sa	05:49	-0.6	-18	24 Su	05:50	-0.6	-18
	19:00	1.2	37		19:00	1.1	34
10 Su	06:42	-0.7	-21	25 M	06:38	-0.6	-18
	19:45	1.4	43		19:43	1.2	37
11 M	07:43	-0.8	-24	26 Tu	07:31	-0.7	-21
	20:34	1.4	43		20:27	1.2	37
12 Tu	08:48	-0.8	-24	27 W	08:24	-0.8	-24
	21:25	1.4	43		21:12	1.2	37
13 W	09:50	-0.8	-24	28 Th	09:14	-0.8	-24
	22:15	1.3	40		21:56	1.2	37
14 Th	10:44	-0.7	-21	29 F	09:58	-0.7	-21
	23:00	1.2	37		22:38	1.2	37
15 F	11:25	-0.6	-18	30 Sa	10:36	-0.6	-18
	23:39	1.0	30		23:19	1.0	30
				31 Su	11:03	-0.5	-15
					23:57	0.8	24

February

Day	Time	ft	cm	Day	Time	ft	cm
1 M	11:06	-0.2	-6	16 Tu	00:15	0.3	9
					06:39	0.2	6
					14:38	0.4	12
2 Tu	00:25	0.5	15	17 W	02:20	0.0	0
	09:56	0.0	0		14:50	0.6	18
	17:53	0.2	6				
3 W	06:18	0.1	3	18 Th	02:13	-0.1	-3
	16:04	0.5	15		15:18	0.7	21
4 Th	03:13	-0.2	-6	19 F	02:47	-0.3	-9
	16:17	0.8	24		15:56	0.9	27
5 F	03:49	-0.4	-12	20 Sa	03:30	-0.4	-12
	16:56	1.0	30		16:41	1.0	30
6 Sa	04:43	-0.6	-18	21 Su	04:21	-0.4	-12
	17:46	1.2	37		17:32	1.0	30
7 Su	05:44	-0.7	-21	22 M	05:18	-0.5	-15
	18:42	1.2	37		18:26	1.1	34
8 M	06:51	-0.8	-24	23 Tu	06:16	-0.5	-15
	19:40	1.3	40		19:21	1.2	37
9 Tu	07:58	-0.7	-21	24 W	07:12	-0.6	-18
	20:37	1.2	37		20:13	1.2	37
10 W	09:00	-0.7	-21	25 Th	08:03	-0.6	-18
	21:29	1.2	37		21:03	1.2	37
11 Th	09:52	-0.6	-18	26 F	08:50	-0.5	-15
	22:16	1.1	34		21:53	1.1	34
12 F	10:33	-0.5	-15	27 Sa	09:32	-0.4	-12
	22:57	0.9	27		22:45	0.9	27
13 Sa	10:57	-0.3	-9	28 Su	10:07	-0.1	-3
	23:33	0.7	21		23:47	0.7	21
14 Su	10:40	-0.1	-3				
15 M	00:03	0.5	15				
	08:59	0.1	3				

March

Day	Time	ft	cm	Day	Time	ft	cm
1 M	09:47	0.1	3	16 Tu	12:50	0.7	21
	13:50	0.2	6		23:07	0.1	3
	16:19	0.2	6				
2 Tu	01:35	0.4	12	17 W	13:23	0.9	27
	06:19	0.3	9				
	12:33	0.5	15				
	22:19	0.1	3				
3 W	13:12	0.8	24	18 Th	00:25	-0.1	-3
					13:59	1.0	30
4 Th	00:38	-0.2	-6	19 F	01:26	-0.1	-3
	14:03	1.0	30		14:42	1.1	34
5 F	01:59	-0.4	-12	20 Sa	02:27	-0.2	-6
	15:03	1.1	34		15:33	1.1	34
6 Sa	03:13	-0.5	-15	21 Su	03:31	-0.2	-6
	16:09	1.2	37		16:33	1.1	34
7 Su	04:26	-0.5	-15	22 M	04:35	-0.3	-9
	17:19	1.3	40		17:39	1.2	37
8 M	05:39	-0.5	-15	23 Tu	05:36	-0.3	-9
	18:30	1.3	40		18:46	1.2	37
9 Tu	06:48	-0.5	-15	24 W	06:32	-0.3	-9
	19:37	1.2	37		19:50	1.2	37
10 W	07:51	-0.4	-12	25 Th	07:22	-0.3	-9
	20:37	1.1	34		20:53	1.2	37
11 Th	08:45	-0.3	-9	26 F	08:08	-0.1	
	21:31	1.0	30		21:58	1.0	
12 F	09:31	-0.1	-3	27 Sa	08:48	0.1	
	22:20	0.8	24		23:15	0.9	2
13 Sa	10:09	0.1	3	28 Su	08:57	0.3	
	23:14	0.6	18		11:36	0.3	
					16:27	0.3	
14 Su	08:39	0.3	9	29 M	01:22	0.6	
	11:47	0.3	9		06:15	0.6	
	17:52	0.2	6		10:52	0.6	
					19:53	0.1	
15 M	01:34	0.5	15	30 Tu	11:31	0.9	
	06:03	0.4	12		22:04	0.0	
	12:19	0.5	15	31 W	12:19	1.2	
	21:02	0.2	6		23:44	-0.2	

StationId: 8735180
Source: NOAA/NOS/CO-OPS
Station Type: Primary
Time Zone: LST_LDT
Datum: MLLW

NOAA Tide Predictions

Dauphin Island, AL, 2021

Times and Heights of High and Low Waters

April

Day	Time (h m)	ft	cm	Day	Time (h m)	ft	cm
1 Th	13:13	1.3	40	16 F	12:57	1.3	40
2	01:12	-0.3	-9	17 Sa	00:40	-0.1	-3
	14:13	1.4	43		13:41	1.3	40
3 Sa	02:35	-0.4	-12	18 Su	01:46	-0.2	-6
	15:21	1.4	43		14:34	1.3	40
4 Su	03:54	-0.4	-12	19 M	02:50	-0.2	-6
	16:35	1.4	43		15:34	1.3	40
5	05:08	-0.3	-9	20 Tu	03:48	-0.2	-6
	17:54	1.3	40		16:40	1.3	40
6	06:13	-0.2	-6	21 W	04:38	-0.2	-6
	19:11	1.2	37		17:50	1.2	37
7	07:07	-0.1	-3	22 Th	05:20	-0.1	-3
	20:23	1.1	34		19:05	1.1	34
8	07:46	0.1	3	23 F	05:51	0.1	3
	21:31	0.9	27		20:35	0.9	27
9	07:44	0.3	9	24 Sa	05:54	0.3	9
	22:45	0.7	21		12:36	0.5	15
					15:02	0.5	15
					22:50	0.7	21
10	06:04	0.5	15	25 Su	04:35	0.6	18
	10:21	0.6	18		10:04	0.7	21
	17:15	0.4	12		18:20	0.3	9
11	00:51	0.6	18	26 M	09:56	1.0	30
	03:26	0.6	18		19:58	0.0	0
	10:31	0.8	24				
	19:26	0.2	6				
12	10:54	1.0	30	27 Tu	10:24	1.3	40
	20:51	0.1	3		21:17	-0.2	-6
13	11:20	1.1	34	28 W	11:06	1.5	46
	21:52	0.0	0		22:33	-0.3	-9
14	11:48	1.2	37	29 Th	11:54	1.7	52
	22:45	-0.1	-3		23:51	-0.4	-12
15	12:20	1.3	40	30 F	12:49	1.7	52
	23:40	-0.1	-3				

May

Day	Time (h m)	ft	cm	Day	Time (h m)	ft	cm
1 Sa	01:10	-0.4	-12	16 Su	00:28	-0.2	-6
	13:49	1.6	49		13:09	1.5	46
2 Su	02:26	-0.3	-9	17 M	01:25	-0.2	-6
	14:53	1.5	46		13:56	1.4	43
3 M	03:33	-0.2	-6	18 Tu	02:14	-0.2	-6
	16:01	1.4	43		14:44	1.4	43
4 Tu	04:27	-0.1	-3	19 W	02:55	-0.1	-3
	17:11	1.2	37		15:34	1.2	37
5 W	05:02	0.1	3	20 Th	03:25	0.0	0
	18:22	1.0	30		16:24	1.0	30
6 Th	05:02	0.3	9	21 F	03:35	0.2	6
	19:45	0.8	24		17:25	0.8	24
7 F	04:01	0.5	15	22 Sa	03:01	0.4	12
	10:21	0.6	18		10:17	0.7	21
	16:39	0.5	15		17:49	0.5	15
	22:10	0.6	18				
8 Sa	01:42	0.6	18	23 Su	09:07	1.0	30
	09:31	0.9	27		18:44	0.2	6
	18:40	0.3	9				
9 Su	09:35	1.1	34	24 M	09:04	1.3	40
	19:41	0.1	3		19:39	-0.1	-3
10 M	09:53	1.2	37	25 Tu	09:29	1.5	46
	20:25	0.0	0		20:37	-0.3	-9
11 Tu	10:16	1.4	43	26 W	10:08	1.7	52
	21:05	-0.1	-3		21:42	-0.5	-15
12 W	10:42	1.5	46	27 Th	10:54	1.8	55
	21:47	-0.2	-6		22:53	-0.5	-15
13 Th	11:12	1.5	46	28 F	11:45	1.8	55
	22:35	-0.2	-6				
14 F	11:46	1.5	46	29 Sa	00:06	-0.5	-15
	23:29	-0.2	-6		12:39	1.7	52
15 Sa	12:26	1.5	46	30 Su	01:15	-0.4	-12
					13:34	1.6	49
				31 M	02:12	-0.3	-9
					14:27	1.4	43

June

Day	Time (h m)	ft	cm	Day	Time (h m)	ft	cm
1 Tu	02:54	-0.1	-3	16 W	01:31	-0.2	-6
	15:15	1.2	37		13:58	1.2	37
2 W	03:11	0.1	3	17 Th	01:49	0.0	0
	15:49	1.0	30		14:09	1.0	30
3 Th	02:46	0.3	9	18 F	01:41	0.2	6
	14:16	0.7	21		11:43	0.8	24
4 F	01:16	0.4	12	19 Sa	00:32	0.4	12
	09:14	0.8	24		08:50	0.8	24
	20:31	0.4	12		18:48	0.3	9
5 Sa	08:34	1.0	30	20 Su	08:01	1.1	34
	18:58	0.2	6		18:27	0.0	0
6 Su	08:36	1.2	37	21 M	08:05	1.3	40
	19:19	0.0	0		19:05	-0.2	-6
7 M	08:53	1.4	43	22 Tu	08:34	1.6	49
	19:49	-0.1	-3		19:58	-0.4	-12
8 Tu	09:17	1.5	46	23 W	09:14	1.7	52
	20:23	-0.2	-6		20:59	-0.5	-15
9 W	09:46	1.5	46	24 Th	10:02	1.8	55
	21:04	-0.3	-9		22:07	-0.6	-18
10 Th	10:18	1.6	49	25 F	10:53	1.8	55
	21:50	-0.3	-9		23:15	-0.5	-15
11 F	10:53	1.6	49	26 Sa	11:45	1.7	52
	22:41	-0.3	-9				
12 Sa	11:31	1.6	49	27 Su	00:17	-0.4	-12
	23:33	-0.3	-9		12:35	1.6	49
13 Su	12:10	1.6	49	28 M	01:07	-0.3	-9
					13:20	1.4	43
14 M	00:20	-0.3	-9	29 Tu	01:40	-0.1	-3
	12:49	1.5	46		13:56	1.2	37
15 Tu	01:00	-0.3	-9	30 W	01:46	0.1	3
	13:26	1.4	43		14:11	0.9	27

StationId: 8735180
Source: NOAA/NOS/CO-OPS
Station Type: Primary
Time Zone: LST_LDT
Datum: MLLW

NOAA Tide Predictions

Dauphin Island, AL, 2021

Times and Heights of High and Low Waters

July

Day	Time	ft	cm	Day	Time	ft	cm
1 Th ☽	01:02	0.3	9	16 F	09:39	0.7	21
	12:02	0.7	21		21:58	0.4	12
	23:11	0.4	12				
2 F	07:55	0.8	24	17 Sa �	06:58	0.9	27
	19:44	0.3	9		17:37	0.3	9
3 Sa	07:18	1.0	30	18 Su	06:32	1.1	34
	18:19	0.1	3		17:34	0.0	0
4 Su	07:24	1.2	37	19 M	06:51	1.4	43
	18:30	0.0	0		18:15	-0.2	-6
5 M	07:45	1.4	43	20 Tu	07:29	1.6	49
	18:58	-0.2	-6		19:10	-0.4	-12
6 Tu	08:14	1.5	46	21 W	08:17	1.7	52
	19:34	-0.2	-6		20:14	-0.4	-12
7 W	08:48	1.5	46	22 Th	09:10	1.8	55
	20:18	-0.3	-9		21:21	-0.5	-15
8 Th	09:25	1.6	49	23 F	10:04	1.8	55
	21:07	-0.3	-9		22:27	-0.4	-12
9 F	10:04	1.6	49	24 Sa ○	10:57	1.7	52
	21:57	-0.3	-9		23:24	-0.3	-9
10 Sa ●	10:44	1.6	49	25 Su	11:46	1.6	49
	22:44	-0.3	-9				
11 Su	11:23	1.6	49	26 M	00:10	-0.2	-6
	23:25	-0.3	-9		12:29	1.4	43
12 M	12:00	1.5	46	27 Tu	00:40	0.0	0
	23:58	-0.2	-6		13:05	1.2	37
13 Tu	12:34	1.4	43	28 W	00:38	0.2	6
					13:26	1.0	30
					23:24	0.5	15
14 W	00:22	-0.1	-3	29 Th	12:03	0.7	21
	13:01	1.2	37		21:00	0.5	15
15 Th	00:30	0.1	3	30 F	05:34	0.8	24
	13:06	1.0	30		17:27	0.4	12
	23:59	0.3	9				
				31 Sa ☽	05:23	1.1	34
					16:45	0.2	6

August

Day	Time	ft	cm	Day	Time	ft	cm
1 Su	05:44	1.2	37	16 M	05:13	1.5	46
	17:06	0.1	3		17:02	-0.1	-3
2 M	06:15	1.4	43	17 Tu	06:07	1.7	52
	17:42	0.0	0		18:06	-0.2	-6
3 Tu	06:54	1.5	46	18 W	07:08	1.8	55
	18:26	-0.1	-3		19:15	-0.2	-6
4 W	07:37	1.5	46	19 Th	08:10	1.8	55
	19:17	-0.1	-3		20:24	-0.2	-6
5 Th	08:23	1.6	49	20 F	09:11	1.8	55
	20:10	-0.1	-3		21:29	-0.1	-3
6 F	09:09	1.6	49	21 Sa	10:08	1.7	52
	21:01	-0.2	-6		22:26	0.0	0
7 Sa	09:54	1.6	49	22 Su ○	11:00	1.6	49
	21:46	-0.2	-6		23:13	0.1	3
8 Su ●	10:35	1.6	49	23 M	11:46	1.4	43
	22:25	-0.1	-3		23:47	0.4	12
9 M	11:15	1.5	46	24 Tu	12:31	1.2	37
	22:57	0.0	0		23:24	0.6	18
10 Tu	11:54	1.4	43	25 W	13:18	1.0	30
	23:18	0.2	6		20:39	0.8	24
11 W	12:31	1.2	37	26 Th	02:02	0.8	24
	23:11	0.4	12		09:27	0.7	21
12 Th	13:03	0.9	27	27 F	02:21	1.1	34
	21:48	0.6	18		13:13	0.5	15
13 F	05:07	0.8	24	28 Sa	02:53	1.2	37
	17:11	0.6	18		14:17	0.4	12
14 Sa	04:09	1.1	34	29 Su	03:31	1.4	43
	15:18	0.3	9		15:07	0.3	9
15 Su ☽	04:30	1.3	40	30 M ☽	04:14	1.5	46
	16:04	0.1	3		15:58	0.2	6
				31 Tu	05:05	1.5	46
					16:53	0.1	3

September

Day	Time	ft	cm	Day	Time	ft	cm
1 W	06:01	1.6	49	16 Th	06:52	1.8	55
	17:51	0.1	3		19:07	0.1	3
2 Th	06:59	1.6	49	17 F	08:03	1.8	55
	18:47	0.1	3		20:09	0.2	6
3 F	07:56	1.6	49	18 Sa	09:08	1.7	52
	19:38	0.1	3		21:03	0.3	9
4 Sa	08:48	1.7	52	19 Su	10:07	1.5	46
	20:24	0.1	3		21:48	0.5	15
5 Su	09:38	1.6	49	20 M ○	11:06	1.3	40
	21:03	0.2	6				
6 M	10:27	1.5	46	21 Tu	02:47	0.7	21
	21:35	0.3	9		12:17	1.1	34
					18:56	0.9	27
					23:13	1.0	30
7 Tu ●	11:20	1.4	43	22 W	06:54	0.7	21
	21:49	0.6	18		23:45	1.2	37
8 W	12:28	1.1	34	23 Th	09:20	0.6	18
	20:48	0.8	24				
9 Th	01:19	0.8	24	24 F	00:18	1.4	43
	07:28	0.7	21		10:55	0.5	15
10 F	01:00	1.1	34	25 Sa	00:51	1.5	46
	11:05	0.5	15		12:01	0.4	12
11 Sa	01:34	1.4	43	26 Su	01:28	1.6	49
	12:56	0.3	9		13:01	0.3	9
12 Su	02:22	1.6	49	27 M	02:10	1.6	49
	14:16	0.1	3		14:01	0.3	9
13 M ☽	03:20	1.7	52	28 Tu	03:00	1.6	49
	15:31	0.0	0		15:04	0.2	6
14 Tu	04:26	1.8	55	29 W ☽	03:58	1.6	49
	16:46	0.0	0		16:05	0.2	6
15 W	05:38	1.8	55	30 Th	05:02	1.6	49
	17:59	0.0	0		17:01	0.2	6

StationId: 8735180
Source: NOAA/NOS/CO-OPS
Station Type: Primary
Time Zone: LST_LDT
Datum: MLLW

October

Day	Time	ft	cm	Day	Time	ft	cm
1 F	06:08	1.6	49	16 Sa	07:40	1.5	46
	17:50	0.2	6		18:49	0.5	15
2 Sa	07:11	1.6	49	17 Su	08:54	1.3	40
	18:31	0.3	9		18:28	0.7	21
3 Su	08:13	1.5	46	18 M	10:23	1.0	30
	19:03	0.4	12		16:43	0.9	27
					22:13	1.0	30
4 M	09:20	1.4	43	19 Tu	05:59	0.7	21
	19:19	0.6	18		22:17	1.2	37
5 Tu	10:45	1.2	37	20 W	07:49	0.5	15
	18:44	0.8	24		22:37	1.4	43
	23:36	0.9	27				
6 W	05:50	0.8	24	21 Th	08:58	0.4	12
	13:40	1.0	30		23:03	1.6	49
	15:53	1.0	30				
	22:58	1.2	37				
7 Th	08:17	0.6	18	22 F	09:50	0.2	6
	23:18	1.5	46		23:31	1.7	52
8	09:57	0.3	9	23 Sa	10:39	0.2	6
	23:56	1.7	52				
9	11:21	0.1	3	24 Su	00:03	1.7	52
					11:30	0.1	3
10	00:45	1.9	58	25 M	00:39	1.7	52
	12:41	0.0	0		12:27	0.1	3
11	01:41	1.9	58	26 Tu	01:21	1.7	52
	14:01	0.0	0		13:27	0.1	3
12	02:45	1.9	58	27 W	02:08	1.6	49
	15:19	0.0	0		14:25	0.1	3
13	03:55	1.9	58	28 Th	03:00	1.6	49
	16:30	0.0	0		15:15	0.1	3
14	05:11	1.8	55	29 F	03:55	1.5	46
	17:31	0.1	3		15:57	0.1	3
15	06:27	1.6	49	30 Sa	04:53	1.4	43
	18:20	0.3	9		16:28	0.2	6
				31 Su	05:56	1.3	40
					16:45	0.4	12

November

Day	Time	ft	cm	Day	Time	ft	cm
1 M	07:21	1.1	34	16 Tu	06:06	0.4	12
	16:32	0.6	18		20:22	1.2	37
	23:43	0.9	27				
2 Tu	05:05	0.8	24	17 W	06:50	0.2	6
	10:04	0.8	24		20:40	1.4	43
	15:02	0.8	24				
	22:07	1.0	30				
3 W	06:55	0.5	15	18 Th	07:29	0.0	0
	21:53	1.3	40		21:03	1.5	46
4 Th	08:05	0.2	6	19 F ○	08:07	-0.1	-3
	22:13	1.6	49		21:31	1.6	49
5 F ○	09:10	0.0	0	20 Sa	08:48	-0.2	-6
	22:49	1.8	55		22:02	1.6	49
6 Sa	10:18	-0.2	-6	21 Su	09:34	-0.2	-6
	23:34	1.9	58		22:36	1.6	49
7 Su	10:32	-0.3	-9	22 M	10:25	-0.2	-6
	23:27	1.9	58		23:13	1.6	49
8 M	11:48	-0.3	-9	23 Tu	11:18	-0.2	-6
					23:53	1.5	46
9 Tu	00:24	1.9	58	24 W	12:06	-0.2	-6
	13:01	-0.3	-9				
10 W	01:25	1.8	55	25 Th	00:33	1.5	46
	14:05	-0.2	-6		12:47	-0.2	-6
11 Th ◐	02:28	1.6	49	26 F	01:11	1.4	43
	14:55	0.0	0		13:19	-0.1	-3
12 F	03:29	1.4	43	27 Sa ◑	01:45	1.2	37
	15:26	0.2	6		13:40	0.0	0
13 Sa	04:29	1.2	37	28 Su	02:03	1.0	30
	15:22	0.4	12		13:42	0.1	3
14 Su	05:34	0.9	27	29 M	00:08	0.8	24
	14:14	0.6	18		13:04	0.3	9
	21:13	0.8	24		21:06	0.8	24
15 M	04:44	0.6	18	30 Tu	07:23	0.4	12
	08:18	0.6	18		20:03	1.0	30
	11:32	0.6	18				
	20:20	1.0	30				

December

Day	Time	ft	cm	Day	Time	ft	cm
1 W	05:59	0.1	3	16 Th	06:50	-0.3	-9
	19:55	1.2	37		20:06	1.3	40
2 Th	06:37	-0.2	-6	17 F	07:25	-0.4	-12
	20:16	1.5	46		20:37	1.4	43
3 F	07:29	-0.4	-12	18 Sa	08:07	-0.5	-15
	20:52	1.7	52		21:11	1.4	43
4 Sa ●	08:31	-0.6	-18	19 Su ○	08:53	-0.5	-15
	21:37	1.8	55		21:47	1.4	43
5 Su	09:40	-0.6	-18	20 M	09:42	-0.5	-15
	22:29	1.8	55		22:23	1.3	40
6 M	10:51	-0.7	-21	21 Tu	10:27	-0.5	-15
	23:23	1.7	52		22:59	1.3	40
7 Tu	11:58	-0.6	-18	22 W	11:06	-0.5	-15
					23:33	1.2	37
8 W	00:17	1.6	49	23 Th	11:38	-0.5	-15
	12:54	-0.5	-15				
9 Th	01:08	1.4	43	24 F	00:03	1.1	34
	13:34	-0.3	-9		12:01	-0.4	-12
10 F	01:52	1.1	34	25 Sa	00:26	1.0	30
	13:51	-0.1	-3		12:13	-0.3	-9
11 Sa ◐	02:20	0.9	27	26 Su	00:23	0.8	24
	13:24	0.1	3		12:01	-0.1	-3
					22:12	0.5	15
12 Su	00:47	0.6	18	27 M ◑	10:56	0.1	3
	11:48	0.3	9		19:40	0.6	18
	20:01	0.6	18				
13 M	08:08	0.2	6	28 Tu	06:43	0.1	3
	19:17	0.8	24		18:49	0.8	24
14 Tu	06:06	0.0	0	29 W	05:26	-0.2	-6
	19:21	1.1	34		18:50	1.0	30
15 W	06:21	-0.2	-6	30 Th	05:55	-0.5	-15
	19:40	1.2	37		19:17	1.3	40
				31 F	06:45	-0.7	-21
					19:51	1.5	46

191

StationId: 8737048
Source: NOAA/NOS/CO-OPS
Station Type: Primary
Time Zone: LST_LDT
Datum: MLLW

NOAA Tide Predictions

Mobile State Docks, AL, 2021

Times and Heights of High and Low Waters

January

Day	Time	Height (ft)	Height (cm)
1 F	00:31	1.5	46
	11:51	-0.8	-24
2 Sa	01:14	1.4	43
	12:19	-0.7	-21
3 Su	01:57	1.3	40
	12:36	-0.6	-18
4 M	02:37	1.0	30
	12:38	-0.3	-9
5 Tu	03:07	0.7	21
	12:24	-0.1	-3
	20:26	0.6	18
6 W	11:35	0.1	3
	19:32	0.7	21
7 Th	06:56	-0.1	-3
	19:12	1.0	30
8 F	07:08	-0.4	-12
	19:30	1.3	40
9 Sa	07:46	-0.7	-21
	20:10	1.5	46
10 Su	08:31	-0.8	-24
	21:01	1.6	49
11 M	09:18	-1.0	-30
	21:57	1.6	49
12 Tu	10:06	-1.0	-30
	22:51	1.6	49
13 W	10:50	-0.9	-27
	23:42	1.5	46
14 Th	11:28	-0.8	-24
15 F	00:29	1.4	43
	11:52	-0.7	-21
16 Sa	01:12	1.2	37
	11:56	-0.5	-15
17 Su	01:50	1.0	30
	11:40	-0.3	-9
18 M	02:21	0.7	21
	11:17	-0.1	-3
	19:46	0.5	15
19 Tu	10:39	0.0	0
	18:38	0.7	21
20 W	08:48	0.0	0
	18:13	0.9	27
21 Th	07:04	-0.1	-3
	18:22	1.0	30
22 F	06:54	-0.3	-9
	18:48	1.2	37
23 Sa	07:19	-0.5	-15
	19:26	1.3	40
24 Su	07:53	-0.6	-18
	20:15	1.4	43
25 M	08:30	-0.7	-21
	21:10	1.4	43
26 Tu	09:07	-0.8	-24
	22:06	1.5	46
27 W	09:43	-0.8	-24
	22:58	1.5	46
28 Th	10:16	-0.8	-24
	23:47	1.5	46
29 F	10:45	-0.8	-24
30 Sa	00:33	1.4	43
	11:07	-0.6	-18
31 Su	01:21	1.2	37
	11:17	-0.4	-12

February

Day	Time	Height (ft)	Height (cm)
1 M	02:12	1.0	30
	11:07	-0.2	-6
	18:49	0.5	15
	21:26	0.4	12
2 Tu	03:10	0.6	18
	10:44	0.1	3
	18:01	0.6	18
3 W	00:02	0.3	9
	05:06	0.3	9
	09:42	0.2	6
	17:31	0.9	27
4 Th	04:55	0.0	0
	17:34	1.1	34
5 F	05:57	-0.3	-9
	18:03	1.4	43
6 Sa	06:52	-0.6	-18
	18:47	1.5	46
7 Su	07:42	-0.7	-21
	19:44	1.6	49
8 M	08:29	-0.8	-24
	20:51	1.6	49
9 Tu	09:11	-0.8	-24
	21:57	1.6	49
10 W	09:49	-0.7	-21
	22:55	1.5	46
11 Th	10:17	-0.6	-18
	23:45	1.4	43
12 F	10:32	-0.4	-12
13 Sa	00:30	1.2	37
	10:24	-0.2	-6
14 Su	01:14	1.0	30
	10:06	0.0	0
	18:09	0.6	18
	20:50	0.5	15
15 M	02:02	0.7	21
	09:49	0.1	3
	17:17	0.7	21
	22:26	0.4	12
16 Tu	03:06	0.5	15
	09:22	0.3	9
	16:33	0.8	24
17 W	00:41	0.3	9
	05:06	0.3	9
	07:52	0.3	9
	16:27	1.0	30
18 Th	03:24	0.1	3
	16:45	1.2	37
19 F	04:54	-0.1	-3
	17:14	1.3	40
20 Sa	05:57	-0.2	-6
	17:53	1.4	43
21 Su	06:46	-0.3	-9
	18:41	1.5	46
22 M	07:28	-0.5	-15
	19:41	1.5	46
23 Tu	08:05	-0.5	-15
	20:51	1.5	46
24 W	08:39	-0.6	-18
	21:58	1.6	49
25 Th	09:10	-0.6	-18
	22:59	1.5	46
26 F	09:36	-0.5	-15
	23:56	1.4	43
27 Sa	09:55	-0.3	-9
28 Su	00:59	1.2	37
	09:58	0.0	0
	17:23	0.6	18
	19:30	0.5	15

March

Day	Time	Height (ft)	Height (cm)
1 M	02:26	1.0	30
	09:43	0.3	9
	16:28	0.7	21
	21:08	0.4	12
2 Tu	04:31	0.7	21
	09:15	0.5	15
	15:45	0.9	27
	22:40	0.2	6
3 W	15:32	1.2	37
4 Th	01:52	0.1	3
	15:55	1.4	43
5 F	04:01	-0.1	-3
	16:34	1.6	49
6 Sa	05:27	-0.3	-9
	17:23	1.7	52
7 Su	06:33	-0.4	-12
	18:18	1.7	52
8 M	07:26	-0.5	-15
	19:24	1.7	52
9 Tu	08:09	-0.5	-15
	20:40	1.6	49
10 W	08:43	-0.4	-12
	21:56	1.5	46
11 Th	09:06	-0.2	-6
	23:00	1.4	43
12 F	09:10	0.0	0
	23:56	1.2	37
13 Sa	08:54	0.2	6
	16:27	0.7	21
	19:18	0.7	21
14 Su	00:58	1.0	30
	09:36	0.4	12
	16:41	0.8	24
	21:36	0.5	15
15 M	03:39	0.8	24
	09:21	0.5	15
	15:41	1.0	30
	22:37	0.4	12
16 Tu	05:57	0.7	21
	08:55	0.6	18
	15:24	1.2	37
	23:37	0.3	9
17 W	15:38	1.3	40
18 Th	00:55	0.2	6
	16:05	1.5	46
19 F	02:59	0.1	3
	16:40	1.6	49
20 Sa	04:40	0.1	3
	17:22	1.6	49
21 Su	06:00	0.0	0
	18:09	1.7	52
22 M	06:59	-0.1	-3
	19:02	1.7	52
23 Tu	07:45	-0.2	-6
	20:04	1.7	52
24 W	08:22	-0.2	-6
	21:21	1.6	49
25 Th	08:53	-0.2	-6
	22:50	1.6	49
26 F	09:20	-0.1	-3
27 Sa	00:15	1.4	43
	09:36	0.2	6
28 Su	01:48	1.2	37
	09:35	0.5	15
	15:47	0.8	24
	20:29	0.6	18
29 M	03:56	1.1	34
	09:13	0.7	21
	14:50	1.0	30
	21:45	0.4	12
30 Tu	06:16	1.0	30
	08:34	0.9	27
	14:22	1.3	40
	22:58	0.2	6
31 W	14:39	1.6	49

StationId: 8737048
Source: NOAA/NOS/CO-OPS
Station Type: Primary
Time Zone: LST_LDT
Datum: MLLW

NOAA Tide Predictions

Mobile State Docks, AL, 2021

Times and Heights of High and Low Waters

April

Day	Time (h m)	ft	cm
Th	00:41	0.0	0
	15:18	1.8	55
2	03:08	-0.1	-3
	16:07	1.9	58
3 Sa	04:40	-0.1	-3
	17:00	1.9	58
Su	05:58	-0.2	-6
	17:55	1.9	58
	07:02	-0.2	-6
	18:52	1.8	55
	07:52	-0.1	-3
	19:52	1.6	49
	08:27	0.0	0
	21:06	1.5	46
	08:46	0.2	6
	22:52	1.3	40
	08:39	0.4	12
	15:39	1.0	30
	18:40	0.9	27
00:38	1.1	34
08:07	0.6	18
14:54	1.0	30
20:22	0.7	21
02:40	1.0	30
07:43	0.8	24
13:58	1.2	37
21:22	0.5	15
13:32	1.3	40
22:08	0.4	12
13:41	1.5	46
22:51	0.3	9
14:04	1.7	52
23:39	0.2	6
14:35	1.8	55

Day	Time (h m)	ft	cm
16 F	00:50	0.2	6
	15:13	1.8	55
17 Sa	02:35	0.2	6
	15:57	1.9	58
18 Su	03:55	0.1	3
	16:44	1.9	58
19 M	04:59	0.0	0
	17:33	1.9	58
20 Tu ◐	05:53	0.0	0
	18:23	1.8	55
21 W	06:38	0.0	0
	19:18	1.7	52
22 Th	07:15	0.1	3
	20:32	1.5	46
23 F	07:44	0.3	9
	23:10	1.3	40
24 Sa	07:57	0.5	15
	14:25	1.0	30
	18:42	0.9	27
25 Su	01:40	1.2	37
	07:42	0.8	24
	13:30	1.1	34
	20:23	0.6	18
26 M	04:30	1.1	34
	06:56	1.1	34
	12:48	1.4	43
	21:30	0.3	9
27 Tu ○	12:47	1.7	52
	22:35	0.1	3
28 W	13:15	1.9	58
	23:56	-0.1	-3
29 Th	13:57	2.1	64
30 F	01:41	-0.1	-3
	14:48	2.1	64

May

Day	Time (h m)	ft	cm
1 Sa	03:07	-0.1	-3
	15:44	2.1	64
2 Su	04:16	-0.1	-3
	16:39	2.1	64
3 M ◐	05:16	0.0	0
	17:31	1.9	58
4 Tu	06:07	0.1	3
	18:18	1.7	52
5 W	06:43	0.3	9
	18:59	1.5	46
6 Th	06:49	0.5	15
	19:36	1.2	37
7 F	06:01	0.7	21
	13:39	1.1	34
	20:38	0.9	27
8 Sa	00:57	0.9	27
	05:15	0.8	24
	12:55	1.2	37
	20:49	0.7	21
9 Su	12:09	1.4	43
	21:21	0.4	12
10 M	12:04	1.6	49
	21:54	0.3	9
11 Tu ●	12:21	1.7	52
	22:29	0.2	6
12 W	12:49	1.9	58
	23:11	0.1	3
13 Th	13:23	1.9	58
14 F	00:05	0.1	3
	14:02	2.0	61
15 Sa	01:14	0.1	3
	14:46	2.0	61

Day	Time (h m)	ft	cm
16 Su	02:19	0.0	0
	15:32	2.0	61
17 M	03:11	0.0	0
	16:19	2.0	61
18 Tu	03:55	0.0	0
	17:03	1.9	58
19 W ◐	04:32	0.1	3
	17:46	1.7	52
20 Th	05:01	0.2	6
	18:28	1.5	46
21 F	05:17	0.4	12
	19:10	1.2	37
22 Sa	05:10	0.7	21
	12:33	1.1	34
	19:48	0.8	24
23 Su	01:38	1.0	30
	04:29	1.0	30
	11:41	1.3	40
	20:36	0.5	15
24 M	11:14	1.6	49
	21:25	0.2	6
25 Tu	11:29	1.8	55
	22:21	-0.1	-3
26 W ○	12:06	2.1	64
	23:26	-0.2	-6
27 Th	12:52	2.2	67
28 F	00:40	-0.3	-9
	13:44	2.2	67
29 Sa	01:50	-0.3	-9
	14:39	2.2	67
30 Su	02:49	-0.2	-6
	15:33	2.1	64
31 M	03:37	-0.1	-3
	16:23	1.9	58

June

Day	Time (h m)	ft	cm
1 Tu	04:12	0.1	3
	17:05	1.7	52
2 W ◐	04:24	0.3	9
	17:36	1.4	43
3 Th	03:55	0.6	18
	17:43	1.2	37
4 F	03:15	0.7	21
	12:02	1.2	37
	22:17	0.8	24
5 Sa	10:55	1.3	40
	21:17	0.6	18
6 Su	10:18	1.5	46
	21:17	0.3	9
7 M	10:33	1.7	52
	21:40	0.2	6
8 Tu	11:03	1.8	55
	22:12	0.1	3
9 W	11:40	1.9	58
	22:51	0.0	0
10 Th ●	12:20	2.0	61
	23:35	0.0	0
11 F	13:04	2.0	61
12 Sa	00:23	-0.1	-3
	13:49	2.0	61
13 Su	01:08	-0.1	-3
	14:34	2.0	61
14 M	01:47	-0.1	-3
	15:18	2.0	61
15 Tu	02:19	0.0	0
	16:02	1.9	58

Day	Time (h m)	ft	cm
16 W	02:44	0.1	3
	16:42	1.7	52
17 Th	02:58	0.3	9
	17:19	1.5	46
18 F ○	02:59	0.5	15
	17:40	1.1	34
19 Sa	02:40	0.7	21
	10:20	1.2	37
	20:38	0.7	21
20 Su	09:25	1.4	43
	20:31	0.4	12
21 M	09:29	1.7	52
	21:08	0.1	3
22 Tu	10:06	1.9	58
	21:56	-0.1	-3
23 W	10:57	2.1	64
	22:50	-0.3	-9
24 Th ○	11:53	2.2	67
	23:47	-0.3	-9
25 F	12:49	2.2	67
26 Sa	00:44	-0.3	-9
	13:44	2.2	67
27 Su	01:34	-0.2	-6
	14:38	2.1	64
28 M	02:13	-0.1	-3
	15:27	1.9	58
29 Tu	02:35	0.1	3
	16:10	1.7	52
30 W	02:26	0.4	12
	16:45	1.4	43

StationId: 8737048
Source: NOAA/NOS/CO-OPS
Station Type: Primary
Time Zone: LST_LDT
Datum: MLLW

NOAA Tide Predictions

Mobile State Docks, AL,2021

Times and Heights of High and Low Waters

July

Day	Time	ft	cm	Day	Time	ft	cm
1 Th ◑	01:51	0.6	18	16 F	01:06	0.6	18
	17:03	1.1	34		08:15	1.1	34
					12:25	1.0	30
					17:32	1.1	34
2 F	01:06	0.7	21	17 Sa ◐	00:32	0.8	24
	08:53	1.2	37		07:29	1.3	40
	22:02	0.8	24		19:24	0.8	24
3 Sa	08:00	1.4	43	18 Su	07:20	1.6	49
	20:46	0.6	18		19:40	0.5	15
4 Su	08:13	1.6	49	19 M	07:45	1.8	55
	20:43	0.4	12		20:26	0.2	6
5 M	08:45	1.7	52	20 Tu	08:33	2.0	61
	21:07	0.2	6		21:15	0.0	0
6 Tu	09:30	1.8	55	21 W	09:37	2.1	64
	21:39	0.1	3		22:05	-0.2	-6
7 W	10:22	1.9	58	22 Th	10:48	2.2	67
	22:17	0.0	0		22:54	-0.2	-6
8 Th	11:16	2.0	61	23 F	11:55	2.2	67
	22:55	0.0	0		23:42	-0.2	-6
9 F	12:09	2.0	61	24 Sa ○	12:55	2.2	67
	23:33	-0.1	-3				
10 Sa ●	12:58	2.1	64	25 Su	00:23	-0.1	-3
					13:50	2.1	64
11 Su	00:08	-0.1	-3	26 M	00:55	0.1	3
	13:44	2.1	64		14:41	1.9	58
12 M	00:37	-0.1	-3	27 Tu	01:05	0.3	9
	14:30	2.0	61		15:31	1.7	52
13 Tu	01:01	0.0	0	28 W	00:39	0.6	18
	15:16	1.9	58		16:20	1.4	43
14 W	01:15	0.2	6	29 Th	00:07	0.7	21
	16:03	1.7	52		07:13	1.1	34
					11:35	1.0	30
					17:09	1.2	37
					23:30	0.9	27
15 Th	01:17	0.4	12	30 F	06:16	1.3	40
	16:50	1.4	43		13:56	0.9	27
					17:57	0.9	27
					21:22	0.9	27
				31 Sa ◐	06:11	1.5	46
					18:30	0.7	21

August

Day	Time	ft	cm	Day	Time	ft	cm
1 Su	06:31	1.7	52	16 M	06:15	2.0	61
	19:21	0.5	15		19:11	0.3	9
2 M	07:03	1.8	55	17 Tu	07:03	2.1	64
	20:04	0.4	12		20:15	0.1	3
3 Tu	07:46	1.9	58	18 W	08:05	2.1	64
	20:46	0.3	9		21:08	0.0	0
4 W	08:43	1.9	58	19 Th	09:23	2.1	64
	21:25	0.2	6		21:55	0.0	0
5 Th	09:54	2.0	61	20 F	10:50	2.1	64
	22:01	0.1	3		22:37	0.1	3
6 F	11:04	2.0	61	21 Sa	12:04	2.1	64
	22:35	0.1	3		23:12	0.2	6
7 Sa	12:04	2.0	61	22 Su ○	13:06	2.0	61
	23:05	0.1	3		23:34	0.4	12
8 Su ●	12:57	2.0	61	23 M	14:05	1.8	55
	23:30	0.1	3		23:27	0.6	18
9 M	13:49	2.0	61	24 Tu	15:12	1.6	49
	23:48	0.3	9		22:57	0.8	24
10 Tu	14:44	1.9	58	25 W	05:45	1.2	37
	23:54	0.5	15		09:44	1.0	30
					16:37	1.4	43
					22:34	1.0	30
11 W	15:50	1.7	52	26 Th	04:37	1.3	40
	23:47	0.7	21		10:53	0.9	27
					18:14	1.2	37
					22:06	1.1	34
12 Th	06:33	1.1	34	27 F	04:10	1.5	46
	10:09	1.0	30		12:04	0.8	24
	17:12	1.4	43				
	23:29	0.9	27				
13 F	05:52	1.3	40	28 Sa	04:24	1.7	52
	11:37	0.8	24		13:34	0.7	21
	19:06	1.2	37				
	22:47	1.1	34				
14 Sa	05:29	1.5	46	29 Su	04:51	1.8	55
	13:34	0.7	21		15:41	0.6	18
15 Su ◑	05:41	1.8	55	30 M ◐	05:27	1.9	58
	17:29	0.5	15		17:52	0.6	18
				31 Tu	06:10	2.0	61
					19:15	0.5	15

September

Day	Time	ft	cm	Day	Time	ft	cm
1 W	07:01	2.0	61	16 Th	07:44	2.1	64
	20:08	0.4	12		20:43	0.2	6
2 Th	08:05	2.0	61	17 F	09:08	2.0	61
	20:49	0.3	9		21:23	0.3	9
3 F	09:25	2.0	61	18 Sa	10:52	1.9	58
	21:23	0.3	9		21:53	0.5	15
4 Sa	10:50	2.0	61	19 Su	12:20	1.7	52
	21:52	0.3	9		22:02	0.7	21
5 Su	12:01	1.9	58	20 M ○	13:42	1.6	49
	22:15	0.4	12		21:35	0.9	27
6 M	13:08	1.9	58	21 Tu	03:53	1.2	37
	22:30	0.6	18		08:21	1.0	30
					15:29	1.4	43
					21:06	1.1	33
7 Tu ●	14:24	1.7	52	22 W	02:34	1.3	40
	22:32	0.8	24		09:26	0.8	24
					17:29	1.3	40
					20:46	1.2	37
8 W	04:53	1.1	34	23 Th	01:59	1.5	46
	08:42	1.0	30		10:19	0.7	21
	16:05	1.6	49				
	22:19	1.0	30				
9 Th	04:02	1.3	40	24 F	02:12	1.7	52
	09:52	0.8	24		11:08	0.6	18
	17:57	1.4	43				
	21:55	1.2	37				
10 F	03:21	1.5	46	25 Sa	02:37	1.9	58
	10:59	0.6	18		12:01	0.5	15
11 Sa	03:26	1.8	55	26 Su	03:10	2.0	61
	12:20	0.5	15		13:16	0.5	15
12 Su	03:59	2.0	61	27 M	03:49	2.0	61
	14:55	0.4	12		15:09	0.5	
13 M ◐	04:44	2.1	64	28 Tu	04:35	2.0	61
	17:13	0.3	9		16:48	0.5	
14 Tu	05:37	2.2	67	29 W ◑	05:25	2.0	61
	18:45	0.2	6		18:06	0.4	
15 W	06:36	2.2	67	30 Th	06:20	1.9	58
	19:52	0.2	6		19:03	0.4	

NOAA Tide Predictions

Mobile State Docks, AL,2021

Times and Heights of High and Low Waters

October

Day	Time (h m)	Height (ft)	(cm)	Day	Time (h m)	Height (ft)	(cm)
1 F	07:22	1.9	58	16 Sa	08:25	1.5	46
	19:45	0.4	12		20:09	0.6	18
2 Sa	08:40	1.8	55	17 Su	11:09	1.3	40
	20:17	0.4	12		19:40	0.8	24
3 Su	10:31	1.7	52	18 M	02:08	1.2	37
	20:41	0.5	15		06:58	0.9	27
					13:41	1.1	34
4 M	12:19	1.6	49		18:45	1.0	30
	20:53	0.7	21	19 Tu	01:17	1.3	40
5 Tu	03:04	1.1	34		08:21	0.7	21
	07:11	1.0	30	20 W ○	00:29	1.5	46
	14:11	1.4	43		09:13	0.5	15
	20:48	1.0	30	21 Th	00:28	1.6	49
6 W	02:09	1.2	37		09:55	0.3	9
	08:31	0.8	24	22 F	00:47	1.8	55
	16:33	1.4	43		10:35	0.2	6
	20:24	1.2	37	23 Sa	01:14	1.9	58
7 Th	01:24	1.5	46		11:18	0.1	3
	09:32	0.5	15	24 Su	01:46	1.9	58
8	01:19	1.7	52		12:13	0.1	3
	10:31	0.3	9	25 M	02:23	1.9	58
9 Sa	01:44	2.0	61		13:33	0.1	3
	11:42	0.2	6	26 Tu	03:07	1.9	58
10 Su	02:24	2.1	64		14:53	0.1	3
	13:38	0.1	3	27 W	03:55	1.9	58
11	03:15	2.2	67		15:55	0.1	3
	15:30	0.1	3	28 Th ◐	04:46	1.8	55
12	04:12	2.2	67		16:44	0.1	3
	16:54	0.1	3	29 F	05:36	1.7	52
13	05:12	2.1	64		17:24	0.2	6
	18:06	0.1	3	30 Sa	06:27	1.6	49
14	06:12	2.0	61		17:54	0.3	9
	19:05	0.2	6	31 Su	07:29	1.3	40
15	07:13	1.8	55		18:11	0.5	15
	19:47	0.4	12				

November

Day	Time (h m)	Height (ft)	(cm)	Day	Time (h m)	Height (ft)	(cm)
1 M	01:54	1.1	34	16 Tu	07:49	0.3	9
	05:19	1.0	30		22:05	1.4	43
	10:53	1.1	34	17 W	08:12	0.1	3
	18:10	0.7	21		22:15	1.6	49
2 Tu	00:59	1.1	34	18 Th	08:42	-0.1	-3
	07:20	0.7	21		22:37	1.7	52
	14:03	1.0	30	19 F ○	09:17	-0.2	-6
	17:41	0.9	27		23:07	1.7	52
3 W	00:16	1.2	37	20 Sa	09:57	-0.3	-9
	08:24	0.4	12		23:41	1.8	55
	23:51	1.5	46	21 Su	10:46	-0.3	-9
4 Th ●	09:17	0.1	3	22 M	00:18	1.8	55
5 F	00:00	1.7	52		11:42	-0.3	-9
	10:14	-0.1	-3	23 Tu	00:59	1.7	52
6 Sa	00:30	1.9	58		12:37	-0.3	-9
	11:23	-0.3	-9	24 W	01:42	1.7	52
7 Su	01:11	2.1	64		13:22	-0.3	-9
	11:52	-0.3	-9	25 Th	02:26	1.6	49
8 M	01:00	2.1	64		13:56	-0.3	-9
	13:17	-0.4	-12	26 F	03:08	1.5	46
9 Tu	01:55	2.1	64		14:21	-0.2	-6
	14:24	-0.3	-9	27 Sa ◐	03:47	1.3	40
10 W	02:53	1.9	58		14:36	-0.1	-3
	15:20	-0.2	-6	28 Su	04:16	1.0	30
11 Th ◐	03:49	1.7	52		14:41	0.1	3
	16:03	0.0	0		23:15	0.9	27
12 F ◐	04:38	1.5	46	29 M	14:30	0.4	12
	16:24	0.2	6		22:21	0.9	27
13 Sa	05:18	1.2	37	30 Tu	07:16	0.3	9
	15:56	0.4	12		21:43	1.1	34
14 Su	00:06	1.0	30				
	15:12	0.6	18				
	23:24	1.0	30				
15 M	08:10	0.6	18				
	22:34	1.2	37				

December

Day	Time (h m)	Height (ft)	(cm)	Day	Time (h m)	Height (ft)	(cm)
1 W	07:27	0.0	0	16 Th	08:26	-0.5	-15
	21:32	1.4	43		21:28	1.5	46
2 Th	08:08	-0.3	-9	17 F	08:59	-0.6	-18
	21:51	1.6	49		22:04	1.5	46
3 F	08:59	-0.6	-18	18 Sa	09:37	-0.6	-18
	22:27	1.7	52		22:44	1.5	46
4 Sa ●	10:00	-0.7	-21	19 Su ○	10:18	-0.7	-21
	23:12	1.7	52		23:25	1.5	46
5 Su	11:08	-0.8	-24	20 M	11:00	-0.7	-21
6 M	00:01	1.9	58	21 Tu	00:06	1.5	46
	12:14	-0.8	-24		11:38	-0.7	-21
7 Tu	00:53	1.8	55	22 W	00:47	1.5	46
	13:11	-0.8	-24		12:08	-0.7	-21
8 W	01:47	1.7	52	23 Th	01:27	1.4	43
	13:55	-0.6	-18		12:31	-0.6	-18
9 Th	02:37	1.5	46	24 F	02:04	1.3	40
	14:22	-0.4	-12		12:45	-0.5	-15
10 F	03:20	1.2	37	25 Sa	02:38	1.1	34
	14:19	-0.1	-3		12:51	-0.3	-9
11 Sa ◐	03:47	0.9	27	26 Su	03:00	0.8	24
	13:43	0.1	3		12:49	-0.1	-3
	22:38	0.7	21		21:19	0.6	18
12 Su ◐	12:57	0.2	6	27 M ◐	12:27	0.1	3
	21:44	0.8	24		20:26	0.8	24
13 M	08:34	0.1	3	28 Tu	07:25	0.1	3
	20:45	1.0	30		20:00	1.0	30
14 Tu	07:56	-0.1	-3	29 W	07:10	-0.3	-9
	20:37	1.2	37		20:07	1.2	37
15 W	08:02	-0.3	-9	30 Th	07:44	-0.6	-18
	20:57	1.4	43		20:38	1.4	43
				31 F	08:31	-0.8	-24
					21:18	1.7	52

StationId: 8760551
Source: NOAA/NOS/CO-OPS
Station Type: Primary
Time Zone: LST_LDT
Datum: MLLW

NOAA Tide Predictions

South Pass, LA,2021

Times and Heights of High and Low Waters

January

Day	Time (h m)	Height (ft)	Height (cm)	Day	Time (h m)	Height (ft)	Height (cm)
1 F	08:03 / 21:38	-0.7 / 1.2	-21 / 37	16 Sa	08:43 / 22:24	-0.5 / 0.7	-15 / 21
2 Sa	08:43 / 22:18	-0.6 / 1.0	-18 / 30	17 Su	08:55 / 22:43	-0.3 / 0.5	-9 / 15
3 Su	09:18 / 22:54	-0.5 / 0.8	-15 / 24	18 M	08:35 / 22:04	-0.1 / 0.2	-3 / 6
4 M	09:43 / 23:19	-0.3 / 0.6	-9 / 18	19 Tu	07:15 / 15:53	0.0 / 0.2	0 / 6
5 Tu	09:40 / 19:18	-0.1 / 0.3	-3 / 9	20 W	04:07 / 15:07	-0.1 / 0.4	-3 / 12
6 W	07:55 / 16:33	0.1 / 0.4	3 / 12	21 Th	02:34 / 15:14	-0.2 / 0.5	-6 / 15
7 Th	02:20 / 16:06	-0.1 / 0.6	-3 / 18	22 F	02:43 / 15:42	-0.4 / 0.7	-12 / 21
8 F	02:46 / 16:25	-0.5 / 0.9	-15 / 27	23 Sa	03:11 / 16:22	-0.6 / 0.8	-18 / 24
9 Sa	03:29 / 17:04	-0.7 / 1.1	-21 / 34	24 Su	03:46 / 17:08	-0.7 / 0.9	-21 / 27
10 Su	04:17 / 17:52	-0.9 / 1.2	-27 / 37	25 M	04:24 / 17:57	-0.8 / 1.0	-24 / 30
11 M	05:08 / 18:44	-1.0 / 1.3	-30 / 40	26 Tu	05:04 / 18:46	-0.8 / 1.0	-24 / 30
12 Tu	05:58 / 19:36	-1.0 / 1.3	-30 / 40	27 W	05:44 / 19:33	-0.8 / 1.1	-24 / 34
13 W	06:48 / 20:26	-1.0 / 1.2	-30 / 37	28 Th	06:24 / 20:18	-0.8 / 1.0	-24 / 30
14 Th	07:34 / 21:11	-0.8 / 1.1	-24 / 34	29 F	07:02 / 21:03	-0.8 / 1.0	-24 / 30
15 F	08:14 / 21:51	-0.7 / 0.9	-21 / 27	30 Sa	07:37 / 21:48	-0.7 / 0.8	-21 / 24
				31 Su	08:06 / 22:34	-0.5 / 0.6	-15 / 18

February

Day	Time (h m)	Height (ft)	Height (cm)	Day	Time (h m)	Height (ft)	Height (cm)
1 M	08:18 / 23:23	-0.3 / 0.3	-9 / 9	16 Tu	05:16 / 12:17 / 21:37	0.1 / 0.3 / 0.0	3 / 9 / 0
2 Tu	07:42 / 14:29 / 21:47	0.0 / 0.1 / 0.0	0 / 3 / 0	17 W	12:23	0.5	15
3 W	13:41	0.4	12	18 Th	00:04 / 12:50	-0.1 / 0.6	-3 / 18
4 Th	00:41 / 13:59	-0.3 / 0.6	-9 / 18	19 F	00:53 / 13:30	-0.3 / 0.7	-9 / 21
5 F	01:36 / 14:43	-0.6 / 0.9	-18 / 27	20 Sa	01:39 / 14:23	-0.4 / 0.8	-12 / 24
6 Sa	02:28 / 15:39	-0.8 / 1.0	-24 / 30	21 Su	02:24 / 15:24	-0.5 / 0.9	-15 / 27
7 Su	03:20 / 16:41	-0.9 / 1.1	-27 / 34	22 M	03:09 / 16:30	-0.6 / 1.0	-18 / 30
8 M	04:11 / 17:45	-1.0 / 1.1	-30 / 34	23 Tu	03:53 / 17:34	-0.6 / 1.0	-18 / 30
9 Tu	05:01 / 18:46	-0.9 / 1.1	-27 / 34	24 W	04:35 / 18:34	-0.6 / 1.1	-18 / 34
10 W	05:47 / 19:42	-0.8 / 1.0	-24 / 30	25 Th	05:15 / 19:31	-0.6 / 1.0	-18 / 30
11 Th	06:28 / 20:32	-0.7 / 0.9	-21 / 27	26 F	05:53 / 20:27	-0.5 / 1.0	-15 / 30
12 F	07:00 / 21:16	-0.5 / 0.8	-15 / 24	27 Sa	06:27 / 21:26	-0.4 / 0.8	-12 / 24
13 Sa	07:20 / 21:57	-0.3 / 0.6	-9 / 18	28 Su	06:50 / 22:35	-0.1 / 0.6	-3 / 18
14 Su	07:18 / 22:37	-0.2 / 0.4	-6 / 12				
15 M	06:43 / 12:59 / 17:16 / 23:21	0.0 / 0.2 / 0.1 / 0.2	0 / 6 / 3 / 6				

March

Day	Time (h m)	Height (ft)	Height (cm)	Day	Time (h m)	Height (ft)	Height (cm)
1 M	06:45 / 11:35 / 16:49	0.1 / 0.2 / 0.1	3 / 6 / 3	16 Tu	11:07 / 20:22	0.7 / 0.1	21 / 3
2 Tu	00:27 / 05:14 / 10:58 / 19:48	0.4 / 0.3 / 0.5 / 0.0	12 / 9 / 15 / 0	17 W	11:24 / 21:52	0.8 / 0.0	24 / 0
3 W	11:15 / 22:14	0.7 / -0.3	21 / -9	18 Th	11:53 / 23:16	1.0 / -0.1	30 / -3
4 Th	11:55 / 23:50	1.0 / -0.5	30 / -15	19 F	12:30	1.1	34
5 F	12:49	1.1	34	20 Sa	00:29 / 13:18	-0.2 / 1.1	-6 / 34
6 Sa	01:02 / 13:52	-0.6 / 1.2	-18 / 37	21 Su	01:33 / 14:16	-0.2 / 1.2	-6 / 37
7 Su	02:05 / 15:05	-0.7 / 1.2	-21 / 37	22 M	02:29 / 15:26	-0.3 / 1.2	-9 / 37
8 M	03:02 / 16:24	-0.7 / 1.2	-21 / 37	23 Tu	03:20 / 16:44	-0.3 / 1.2	-9 / 37
9 Tu	03:53 / 17:41	-0.6 / 1.1	-18 / 34	24 W	04:06 / 18:04	-0.3 / 1.2	-9 / 37
10 W	04:38 / 18:51	-0.4 / 1.0	-12 / 30	25 Th	04:49 / 19:22	-0.2 / 1.1	-6 / 34
11 Th	05:14 / 19:52	-0.3 / 0.9	-9 / 27	26 F	05:27 / 20:40	-0.1 / 1.0	-3 / 30
12 F	05:37 / 20:49	-0.1 / 0.8	-3 / 24	27 Sa	05:58 / 22:07	0.1 / 0.9	3 / 27
13 Sa	05:43 / 21:47	0.1 / 0.6	3 / 18	28 Su	06:11 / 10:54 / 16:13	0.3 / 0.5 / 0.3	9 / 15 / 9
14 Su	06:20 / 11:35 / 17:03	0.3 / 0.4 / 0.3	9 / 12 / 9	29 M	00:03 / 05:30 / 10:01 / 18:13	0.7 / 0.6 / 0.7 / 0.1	21 / 18 / 21 / 3
15 M	00:01 / 05:18 / 11:06 / 18:49	0.5 / 0.4 / 0.5 / 0.2	15 / 12 / 15 / 6	30 Tu	10:05 / 19:56	1.0 / -0.1	30 / -3
				31 W	10:36 / 21:31	1.2 / -0.2	37 / -6

StationId: 8760551
Source: NOAA/NOS/CO-OPS
Station Type: Primary
Time Zone: LST_LDT
Datum: MLLW

NOAA Tide Predictions

South Pass, LA, 2021

Times and Heights of High and Low Waters

April

Day	Time	ft	cm	Day	Time	ft	cm
1 Th	11:20	1.4	43	16 F	11:03	1.4	43
	23:00	-0.3	-9		22:29	-0.1	-3
2	12:12	1.5	46	17 Sa	11:43	1.4	43
					23:33	-0.1	-3
3 Sa	00:20	-0.4	-12	18 Su	12:30	1.4	43
	13:10	1.5	46				
4 Su	01:32	-0.4	-12	19 M	00:34	-0.1	-3
	14:15	1.5	46		13:25	1.4	43
5	02:34	-0.3	-9	20 Tu	01:29	-0.1	-3
	15:30	1.4	43		14:28	1.4	43
6	03:28	-0.2	-6	21 W	02:19	0.0	0
	16:57	1.2	37		15:46	1.3	40
7	04:11	0.0	0	22 Th	03:02	0.1	3
	18:31	1.1	34		17:25	1.2	37
8	04:40	0.2	6	23 F	03:38	0.2	6
	20:02	0.9	27		19:27	1.0	30
9	04:49	0.4	12	24 Sa	04:00	0.4	12
	12:00	0.6	18		10:21	0.7	21
	14:32	0.6	18		14:52	0.6	18
	21:33	0.8	24		21:52	0.9	27
10	04:27	0.5	15	25 Su	03:45	0.7	21
	10:09	0.7	21		08:57	0.8	24
	16:38	0.5	15		16:40	0.3	9
	23:28	0.7	21				
11	03:14	0.6	18	26 M	08:34	1.1	34
	09:35	0.8	24		18:00	0.1	3
	17:49	0.3	9				
12	09:31	1.0	30	27 Tu	08:49	1.4	43
	18:47	0.2	6		19:13	-0.2	-6
13	09:42	1.1	34	28 W	09:23	1.6	49
	19:39	0.1	3		20:24	-0.3	-9
14	10:02	1.3	40	29 Th	10:07	1.8	55
	20:32	0.0	0		21:36	-0.4	-12
15	10:29	1.3	40	30 F	10:56	1.8	55
	21:28	0.0	0		22:47	-0.4	-12

May

Day	Time	ft	cm	Day	Time	ft	cm
1 Sa	11:49	1.8	55	16 Su	11:16	1.6	49
	23:55	-0.3	-9		22:55	-0.1	-3
2 Su	12:43	1.7	52	17 M	11:59	1.5	46
					23:44	-0.1	-3
3 M	00:57	-0.2	-6	18 Tu	12:45	1.4	43
	13:38	1.5	46				
4 Tu	01:49	0.0	0	19 W	00:29	0.0	0
	14:34	1.3	40		13:33	1.3	40
5 W	02:26	0.2	6	20 Th	01:06	0.1	3
	15:34	1.0	30		14:27	1.1	34
6 Th	02:42	0.4	12	21 F	01:33	0.3	9
	12:06	0.8	24		16:39	0.8	24
	15:14	0.8	24				
	18:03	0.8	24				
7 F	02:22	0.6	18	22 Sa	01:33	0.5	15
	09:28	0.8	24		08:36	0.8	24
	16:35	0.6	18		15:40	0.5	15
	22:19	0.7	21				
8 Sa	00:32	0.7	21	23 Su	07:37	1.0	30
	08:32	1.0	30		16:38	0.2	6
	17:18	0.4	12				
9 Su	08:17	1.1	34	24 M	07:27	1.3	40
	17:56	0.2	6		17:34	-0.1	-3
10 M	08:21	1.3	40	25 Tu	07:47	1.5	46
	18:31	0.1	3		18:31	-0.3	-9
11 Tu	08:36	1.4	43	26 W	08:23	1.7	52
	19:07	0.0	0		19:30	-0.5	-15
12 W	08:58	1.5	46	27 Th	09:08	1.9	58
	19:46	-0.1	-3		20:31	-0.6	-18
13 Th	09:26	1.5	46	28 F	09:56	1.9	58
	20:28	-0.1	-3		21:33	-0.5	-15
14 F	09:59	1.6	49	29 Sa	10:46	1.8	55
	21:14	-0.1	-3		22:33	-0.4	-12
15 Sa	10:36	1.6	49	30 Su	11:35	1.7	52
	22:04	-0.1	-3		23:27	-0.3	-9
				31 M	12:20	1.5	46

June

Day	Time	ft	cm	Day	Time	ft	cm
1 Tu	00:11	-0.1	-3	16 W	12:13	1.2	37
	12:53	1.2	37		23:24	0.0	0
2 W	00:38	0.1	3	17 Th	12:33	1.0	30
	12:49	1.0	30		23:34	0.2	6
3 Th	00:34	0.3	9	18 F	09:47	0.8	24
	10:05	0.8	24		22:58	0.4	12
	23:29	0.5	15				
4 F	08:01	0.9	27	19 Sa	07:06	0.8	24
	17:33	0.4	12		16:05	0.4	12
5 Sa	07:15	1.0	30	20 Su	06:20	1.0	30
	17:15	0.2	6		16:16	0.0	0
6 Su	07:07	1.2	37	21 M	06:21	1.3	40
	17:34	0.1	3		16:58	-0.3	-9
7 M	07:17	1.3	40	22 Tu	06:47	1.5	46
	18:01	-0.1	-3		17:47	-0.5	-15
8 Tu	07:37	1.4	43	23 W	07:27	1.7	52
	18:32	-0.2	-6		18:40	-0.7	-21
9 W	08:04	1.5	46	24 Th	08:15	1.8	55
	19:06	-0.3	-9		19:35	-0.7	-21
10 Th	08:35	1.5	46	25 F	09:05	1.8	55
	19:43	-0.3	-9		20:31	-0.7	-21
11 F	09:09	1.6	49	26 Sa	09:55	1.8	55
	20:22	-0.3	-9		21:23	-0.5	-15
12 Sa	09:46	1.6	49	27 Su	10:43	1.6	49
	21:03	-0.3	-9		22:10	-0.4	-12
13 Su	10:24	1.6	49	28 M	11:25	1.4	43
	21:43	-0.3	-9		22:46	-0.2	-6
14 M	11:02	1.5	46	29 Tu	11:56	1.2	37
	22:22	-0.2	-6		23:03	0.1	3
15 Tu	11:39	1.4	43	30 W	11:57	0.9	27
	22:57	-0.1	-3		22:45	0.3	9

StationId: 8760551
Source: NOAA/NOS/CO-OPS
Station Type: Primary
Time Zone: LST_LDT
Datum: MLLW

NOAA Tide Predictions

South Pass, LA, 2021

Times and Heights of High and Low Waters

July

Day	Time	Height (ft)	Height (cm)	Day	Time	Height (ft)	Height (cm)
1 Th ☾	09:17 / 21:15	0.7 / 0.4	21 / 12	16 F	07:53 / 20:32	0.7 / 0.4	21 / 12
2 F	06:32 / 17:30	0.8 / 0.3	24 / 9	17 Sa ☽	05:08 / 15:21	0.8 / 0.3	24 / 9
3 Sa	05:49 / 16:36	0.9 / 0.1	27 / 3	18 Su	04:43 / 15:28	1.1 / 0.0	34 / 0
4 Su	05:47 / 16:47	1.1 / 0.0	34 / 0	19 M	05:01 / 16:08	1.3 / -0.3	40 / -9
5 M	06:05 / 17:12	1.2 / -0.2	37 / -6	20 Tu	05:39 / 16:56	1.5 / -0.5	46 / -15
6 Tu	06:33 / 17:44	1.4 / -0.3	43 / -9	21 W	06:28 / 17:48	1.7 / -0.6	52 / -18
7 W	07:07 / 18:19	1.4 / -0.3	43 / -9	22 Th	07:22 / 18:40	1.8 / -0.6	55 / -18
8 Th	07:45 / 18:56	1.5 / -0.4	46 / -12	23 F	08:17 / 19:32	1.8 / -0.6	55 / -18
9 F	08:24 / 19:34	1.5 / -0.4	46 / -12	24 Sa ○	09:10 / 20:20	1.7 / -0.4	52 / -12
10 Sa ●	09:04 / 20:10	1.5 / -0.4	46 / -12	25 Su	09:59 / 21:02	1.6 / -0.2	49 / -6
11 Su	09:42 / 20:45	1.5 / -0.3	46 / -9	26 M	10:43 / 21:32	1.4 / 0.0	43 / 0
12 M	10:20 / 21:17	1.5 / -0.2	46 / -6	27 Tu	11:19 / 21:40	1.2 / 0.2	37 / 6
13 Tu	10:56 / 21:43	1.3 / -0.1	40 / -3	28 W	11:41 / 21:09	0.9 / 0.4	27 / 12
14 W	11:29 / 21:59	1.2 / 0.1	37 / 3	29 Th	10:36 / 19:31	0.7 / 0.5	21 / 15
15 Th	11:51 / 21:51	0.9 / 0.3	27 / 9	30 F	04:02 / 16:10	0.8 / 0.4	24 / 12
				31 Sa ◑	03:41 / 15:13	1.0 / 0.3	30 / 9

August

Day	Time	Height (ft)	Height (cm)	Day	Time	Height (ft)	Height (cm)
1 Su	03:56 / 15:30	1.1 / 0.1	34 / 3	16 M	03:16 / 14:58	1.5 / -0.1	46 / -3
2 M	04:27 / 16:02	1.3 / 0.0	40 / 0	17 Tu	04:11 / 15:52	1.7 / -0.3	52 / -9
3 Tu	05:09 / 16:38	1.4 / -0.1	43 / -3	18 W	05:14 / 16:46	1.8 / -0.3	55 / -9
4 W	05:56 / 17:18	1.5 / -0.2	46 / -6	19 Th	06:20 / 17:39	1.8 / -0.3	55 / -9
5 Th	06:45 / 17:57	1.5 / -0.2	46 / -6	20 F	07:24 / 18:29	1.8 / -0.2	55 / -6
6 F	07:33 / 18:36	1.6 / -0.2	49 / -6	21 Sa	08:24 / 19:13	1.7 / -0.1	52 / -3
7 Sa	08:19 / 19:12	1.6 / -0.2	49 / -6	22 Su ○	09:18 / 19:50	1.6 / 0.1	49 / 3
8 Su ●	09:03 / 19:45	1.6 / -0.1	49 / -3	23 M	10:08 / 20:12	1.4 / 0.4	43 / 12
9 M	09:44 / 20:14	1.5 / 0.0	46 / 0	24 Tu	10:54 / 20:06	1.2 / 0.6	37 / 18
10 Tu	10:26 / 20:35	1.4 / 0.2	43 / 6	25 W	11:42 / 19:14	1.0 / 0.7	30 / 21
11 W	11:10 / 20:40	1.2 / 0.4	37 / 12	26 Th	01:03 / 07:02 / 12:52 / 17:08	0.9 / 0.8 / 0.8 / 0.8	27 / 24 / 24 / 24
12 Th	11:59 / 20:06	1.0 / 0.6	30 / 18	27 F	00:45 / 10:43	1.1 / 0.6	34 / 18
13 F	02:56 / 09:39 / 13:34 / 17:17	0.8 / 0.7 / 0.7 / 0.7	24 / 21 / 21 / 21	28 Sa	01:00 / 12:36	1.2 / 0.5	37 / 15
14 Sa	02:18 / 13:03	1.0 / 0.4	30 / 12	29 Su	01:31 / 13:32	1.4 / 0.4	43 / 12
15 Su ◑	02:35 / 14:03	1.3 / 0.1	40 / 3	30 M ☾	02:14 / 14:22	1.5 / 0.2	46 / 6
				31 Tu	03:08 / 15:09	1.5 / 0.2	46 / 6

September

Day	Time	Height (ft)	Height (cm)	Day	Time	Height (ft)	Height (cm)
1 W	04:11 / 15:56	1.6 / 0.1	49 / 3	16 Th	04:56 / 16:26	1.9 / 0.1	58 / 3
2 Th	05:18 / 16:40	1.7 / 0.1	52 / 3	17 F	06:16 / 17:15	1.8 / 0.2	55 / 6
3 F	06:22 / 17:21	1.7 / 0.1	52 / 3	18 Sa	07:30 / 17:55	1.7 / 0.4	52 / 12
4 Sa	07:20 / 17:59	1.7 / 0.2	52 / 6	19 Su	08:37 / 18:21	1.6 / 0.6	49 / 18
5 Su	08:14 / 18:32	1.7 / 0.3	52 / 9	20 M ○	09:41 / 18:25	1.4 / 0.8	43 / 24
6 M	09:08 / 18:59	1.6 / 0.4	49 / 12	21 Tu	00:23 / 02:40 / 10:49 / 17:48 / 22:45	0.9 / 0.9 / 1.3 / 1.0 / 1.1	27 / 27 / 40 / 30 / 34
7 Tu ●	10:05 / 19:14	1.5 / 0.6	46 / 18	22 W	05:16 / 12:28 / 16:11 / 22:29	0.9 / 1.1 / 1.1 / 1.3	27 / 34 / 34 / 40
8 W	11:13 / 19:00 / 23:56	1.3 / 0.8 / 0.9	40 / 24 / 27	23 Th	06:57 / 22:39	0.8 / 1.4	24 / 43
9 Th	05:39 / 13:04 / 17:30 / 23:31	0.8 / 1.1 / 1.0 / 1.2	24 / 34 / 30 / 37	24 F	08:26 / 23:01	0.7 / 1.6	21 / 49
10 F	08:19 / 23:49	0.7 / 1.4	21 / 43	25 Sa	09:49 / 23:32	0.6 / 1.7	18 / 52
11 Sa	10:35	0.5	15	26 Su	11:06	0.5	15
12 Su	00:28 / 12:12	1.6 / 0.3	49 / 9	27 M	00:10 / 12:15	1.7 / 0.4	52 / 12
13 M ◑	01:20 / 13:27	1.8 / 0.1	55 / 3	28 Tu ◑	00:59 / 13:18	1.8 / 0.4	55 / 12
14 Tu	02:23 / 14:32	1.9 / 0.0	58 / 0	29 W ☽	01:58 / 14:13	1.8 / 0.4	55 / 12
15 W	03:36 / 15:32	1.9 / 0.0	58 / 0	30 Th	03:09 / 15:03	1.8 / 0.4	55 / 12

StationId: 8760551
Source: NOAA/NOS/CO-OPS
Station Type: Primary
Time Zone: LST_LDT
Datum: MLLW

NOAA Tide Predictions

South Pass, LA,2021

Times and Heights of High and Low Waters

October

Day	Time (h m)	Height (ft)	Height (cm)	Day	Time (h m)	Height (ft)	Height (cm)
1 F	04:28 / 15:47	1.7 / 0.4	52 / 12	16 Sa	06:10 / 16:18	1.6 / 0.6	49 / 18
2 Sa	05:47 / 16:25	1.7 / 0.5	52 / 15	17 Su	07:48 / 16:26 / 23:03	1.4 / 0.8 / 1.1	43 / 24 / 34
3 Su	07:03 / 16:57	1.7 / 0.6	52 / 18	18 M	02:46 / 09:31 / 15:54 / 21:30	1.0 / 1.2 / 1.0 / 1.2	30 / 37 / 30 / 37
4 M	08:20 / 17:20	1.6 / 0.8	49 / 24	19 Tu	04:37 / 21:04	0.9 / 1.3	27 / 40
5 Tu	09:45 / 17:21 / 22:11	1.4 / 1.0 / 1.1	43 / 30 / 34	20 W ○	05:47 / 21:07	0.7 / 1.5	21 / 46
6 W	04:09 / 11:44 / 16:28 / 21:36	0.9 / 1.3 / 1.2 / 1.3	27 / 40 / 37 / 40	21 Th	06:43 / 21:21	0.6 / 1.6	18 / 49
7 Th	05:56 / 21:42	0.7 / 1.6	21 / 49	22 F	07:34 / 21:43	0.5 / 1.7	15 / 52
8	07:31 / 22:12	0.5 / 1.8	15 / 55	23 Sa	08:25 / 22:11	0.4 / 1.8	12 / 55
9	09:02 / 22:54	0.3 / 2.0	9 / 61	24 Su	09:20 / 22:45	0.4 / 1.8	12 / 55
10	10:29 / 23:44	0.2 / 2.1	6 / 64	25 M	10:20 / 23:25	0.3 / 1.8	9 / 55
11	11:49	0.1	3	26 Tu	11:22	0.3	9
12	00:42 / 13:02	2.1 / 0.1	64 / 3	27 W	00:11 / 12:21	1.8 / 0.3	55 / 9
13	01:48 / 14:06	2.0 / 0.1	61 / 3	28 Th ☽	01:03 / 13:14	1.8 / 0.3	55 / 9
14	03:04 / 15:02	1.9 / 0.3	58 / 9	29 F	02:04 / 13:59	1.7 / 0.4	52 / 12
15	04:32 / 15:47	1.7 / 0.4	52 / 12	30 Sa	03:18 / 14:36	1.6 / 0.4	49 / 12
				31 Su	04:56 / 15:05	1.4 / 0.6	43 / 18

November

Day	Time (h m)	Height (ft)	Height (cm)	Day	Time (h m)	Height (ft)	Height (cm)
1 M	07:03 / 15:17 / 21:38	1.3 / 0.8 / 1.0	40 / 24 / 30	16 Tu	04:06 / 18:54	0.5 / 1.3	15 / 40
2 Tu	02:57 / 09:33 / 14:51 / 20:32	0.9 / 1.1 / 1.0 / 1.2	27 / 34 / 30 / 37	17 W	04:45 / 19:03	0.3 / 1.4	9 / 43
3 W	04:28 / 20:15	0.6 / 1.4	18 / 43	18 Th	05:21 / 19:21	0.2 / 1.5	6 / 46
4 Th ●	05:40 / 20:30	0.4 / 1.7	12 / 52	19 F ○	05:57 / 19:45	0.1 / 1.6	3 / 49
5 F	06:48 / 21:03	0.1 / 1.9	3 / 58	20 Sa	06:35 / 20:13	0.0 / 1.6	0 / 49
6 Sa	07:58 / 21:45	-0.1 / 2.0	-3 / 61	21 Su	07:17 / 20:46	0.0 / 1.6	0 / 49
7 Su	08:09 / 21:34	-0.2 / 2.1	-6 / 64	22 M	08:03 / 21:23	-0.1 / 1.6	-3 / 49
8 M	09:21 / 22:27	-0.2 / 2.0	-6 / 61	23 Tu	08:53 / 22:02	-0.1 / 1.6	-3 / 49
9 Tu	10:31 / 23:22	-0.2 / 1.9	-6 / 58	24 W	09:42 / 22:42	-0.1 / 1.5	-3 / 46
10 W	11:36	0.0	0	25 Th	10:29 / 23:24	0.0 / 1.4	0 / 43
11 Th ☽	00:19 / 12:30	1.7 / 0.1	52 / 3	26 F	11:10	0.0	0
12 F	01:17 / 13:10	1.5 / 0.3	46 / 9	27 Sa ☾	00:05 / 11:43	1.3 / 0.1	40 / 3
13 Sa	02:22 / 13:28 / 22:30	1.2 / 0.5 / 1.0	37 / 15 / 30	28 Su	00:43 / 12:03 / 21:57	1.1 / 0.3 / 0.8	34 / 9 / 24
14 Su	02:01 / 05:14 / 13:05 / 19:57	1.0 / 1.0 / 0.7 / 1.0	30 / 30 / 21 / 30	29 M	11:56 / 19:09	0.5 / 0.8	15 / 24
15 M	03:20 / 19:05	0.7 / 1.1	21 / 34	30 Tu	02:35 / 18:16	0.5 / 1.0	15 / 30

December

Day	Time (h m)	Height (ft)	Height (cm)	Day	Time (h m)	Height (ft)	Height (cm)
1 W	03:20 / 18:08	0.2 / 1.2	6 / 37	16 Th	04:46 / 18:23	-0.3 / 1.2	-9 / 37
2 Th	04:11 / 18:28	-0.1 / 1.5	-3 / 46	17 F	05:17 / 18:52	-0.4 / 1.3	-12 / 40
3 F	05:05 / 19:04	-0.4 / 1.7	-12 / 52	18 Sa	05:51 / 19:25	-0.5 / 1.3	-15 / 40
4 Sa ●	06:04 / 19:49	-0.6 / 1.8	-18 / 55	19 Su ○	06:28 / 20:01	-0.5 / 1.3	-15 / 40
5 Su	07:05 / 20:39	-0.7 / 1.8	-21 / 55	20 M	07:08 / 20:37	-0.5 / 1.3	-15 / 40
6 M	08:09 / 21:30	-0.7 / 1.8	-21 / 55	21 Tu	07:48 / 21:14	-0.5 / 1.2	-15 / 37
7 Tu	09:12 / 22:21	-0.6 / 1.6	-18 / 49	22 W	08:27 / 21:50	-0.5 / 1.2	-15 / 37
8 W	10:10 / 23:09	-0.4 / 1.4	-12 / 43	23 Th	09:03 / 22:24	-0.4 / 1.1	-12 / 34
9 Th	11:00 / 23:47	-0.2 / 1.1	-6 / 34	24 F	09:34 / 22:55	-0.3 / 0.9	-9 / 27
10 F	11:32 / 23:51	0.0 / 0.8	0 / 24	25 Sa	09:56 / 23:13	-0.2 / 0.7	-6 / 21
11 Sa ☾	11:31 / 20:45	0.2 / 0.6	6 / 18	26 Su	10:01 / 20:43	0.0 / 0.5	0 / 15
12 Su	10:04 / 18:28	0.4 / 0.7	12 / 21	27 M ☾	09:16 / 17:34	0.1 / 0.5	3 / 15
13 M	03:47 / 17:46	0.2 / 0.8	6 / 24	28 Tu	02:51 / 16:49	0.1 / 0.7	3 / 21
14 Tu	03:52 / 17:44	0.0 / 1.0	0 / 30	29 W	02:52 / 16:53	-0.3 / 0.9	-9 / 27
15 W	04:17 / 17:59	-0.2 / 1.1	-6 / 34	30 Th	03:31 / 17:22	-0.6 / 1.1	-18 / 34
				31 F	04:19 / 18:00	-0.8 / 1.4	-24 / 43

StationId: 8761724
Source: NOAA/NOS/CO-OPS
Station Type: Primary
Time Zone: LST_LDT
Datum: MLLW

NOAA Tide Predictions

Grand Isle, LA,2021

Times and Heights of High and Low Waters

January

Day	Time	Height ft	Height cm	Day	Time	Height ft	Height cm
1 F	09:36 / 22:59	-0.6 / 1.0	-18 / 30	16 Sa	10:27 / 23:48	-0.4 / 0.6	-12 / 18
2 Sa	10:12 / 23:39	-0.6 / 0.8	-18 / 24	17 Su	10:40	-0.3	-9
3 Su	10:44	-0.4	-12	18 M	00:03 / 10:21 / 22:49	0.4 / -0.1 / 0.2	12 / -3 / 6
4 M	00:15 / 11:03	0.7 / -0.3	21 / -9	19 Tu	08:54 / 17:37	0.0 / 0.2	0 / 6
5 Tu	00:37 / 10:52 / 19:43	0.4 / -0.1 / 0.2	12 / -3 / 6	20 W	05:08 / 16:38	0.0 / 0.3	0 / 9
6 W	08:38 / 17:38	0.1 / 0.4	3 / 12	21 Th	03:52 / 16:38	-0.2 / 0.5	-6 / 15
7 Th	03:34 / 17:18	-0.2 / 0.6	-6 / 18	22 F	04:05 / 17:02	-0.3 / 0.6	-9 / 18
8 F	04:06 / 17:39	-0.4 / 0.7	-12 / 21	23 Sa	04:35 / 17:40	-0.5 / 0.7	-15 / 21
9 Sa	04:52 / 18:20	-0.6 / 0.9	-18 / 27	24 Su	05:13 / 18:25	-0.5 / 0.8	-15 / 24
10 Su	05:44 / 19:11	-0.8 / 1.0	-24 / 30	25 M	05:54 / 19:14	-0.6 / 0.8	-18 / 24
11 M	06:38 / 20:06	-0.8 / 1.0	-24 / 30	26 Tu	06:37 / 20:03	-0.7 / 0.9	-21 / 27
12 Tu	07:33 / 21:01	-0.8 / 1.0	-24 / 30	27 W	07:19 / 20:51	-0.7 / 0.9	-21 / 27
13 W	08:26 / 21:52	-0.8 / 1.0	-24 / 30	28 Th	08:00 / 21:37	-0.7 / 0.9	-21 / 27
14 Th	09:15 / 22:38	-0.7 / 0.9	-21 / 27	29 F	08:38 / 22:22	-0.6 / 0.8	-18 / 24
15 F	09:56 / 23:17	-0.6 / 0.7	-18 / 21	30 Sa	09:12 / 23:08	-0.5 / 0.7	-15 / 21
				31 Su	09:40 / 23:58	-0.4 / 0.5	-12 / 15

February

Day	Time	Height ft	Height cm	Day	Time	Height ft	Height cm
1 M	09:50	-0.2	-6	16 Tu	01:09 / 06:46 / 13:48 / 23:27	0.2 / 0.1 / 0.3 / 0.0	6 / 3 / 9 / 0
2 Tu	01:00 / 09:10 / 15:46 / 23:36	0.3 / 0.0 / 0.2 / 0.0	9 / 0 / 6 / 0	17 W	13:47	0.4	12
3 W	15:01	0.4	12	18 Th	01:10 / 14:13	-0.1 / 0.5	-3 / 15
4 Th	01:44 / 15:19	-0.2 / 0.6	-6 / 18	19 F	02:05 / 14:54	-0.2 / 0.6	-6 / 18
5 F	02:48 / 16:03	-0.5 / 0.7	-15 / 21	20 Sa	02:56 / 15:47	-0.3 / 0.7	-9 / 21
6 Sa	03:47 / 17:01	-0.6 / 0.9	-18 / 27	21 Su	03:46 / 16:48	-0.4 / 0.8	-12 / 24
7 Su	04:45 / 18:05	-0.7 / 0.9	-21 / 27	22 M	04:36 / 17:52	-0.4 / 0.9	-12 / 27
8 M	05:42 / 19:11	-0.8 / 1.0	-24 / 30	23 Tu	05:23 / 18:54	-0.5 / 0.9	-15 / 27
9 Tu	06:37 / 20:13	-0.7 / 0.9	-21 / 27	24 W	06:09 / 19:53	-0.5 / 0.9	-15 / 27
10 W	07:29 / 21:09	-0.7 / 0.9	-21 / 27	25 Th	06:51 / 20:49	-0.5 / 0.9	-15 / 27
11 Th	08:14 / 21:59	-0.6 / 0.8	-18 / 24	26 F	07:30 / 21:47	-0.4 / 0.8	-12 / 24
12 F	08:51 / 22:43	-0.4 / 0.7	-12 / 21	27 Sa	08:06 / 22:51	-0.3 / 0.7	-9 / 21
13 Sa	09:17 / 23:25	-0.3 / 0.5	-9 / 15	28 Su	08:33	-0.1	-3
14 Su	09:22	-0.1	-3				
15 M	00:08 / 08:45 / 15:14 / 18:39	0.4 / 0.0 / 0.1 / 0.1	12 / 0 / 3 / 3				

March

Day	Time	Height ft	Height cm	Day	Time	Height ft	Height cm
1 M	00:13 / 08:31 / 12:48 / 18:33	0.5 / 0.2 / 0.2 / 0.1	15 / 6 / 6 / 3	16 Tu	12:08 / 21:55	0.6 / 0.1	18 / 3
2 Tu	02:54 / 06:31 / 12:04 / 21:25	0.4 / 0.3 / 0.4 / 0.0	12 / 9 / 12 / 0	17 W	12:30 / 23:15	0.7 / 0.0	21 / 0
3 W	12:25 / 23:29	0.6 / -0.2	18 / -6	18 Th	13:03	0.8	24
4 Th	13:10	0.8	24	19 F	00:30 / 13:45	0.0 / 0.9	0 / 27
5 F	01:00 / 14:08	-0.3 / 0.9	-9 / 27	20 Sa	01:42 / 14:38	-0.1 / 0.9	-3 / 27
6 Sa	02:17 / 15:17	-0.4 / 1.0	-12 / 30	21 Su	02:49 / 15:41	-0.1 / 1.0	-3 / 30
7 Su	03:27 / 16:34	-0.5 / 1.0	-15 / 30	22 M	03:51 / 16:53	-0.2 / 1.0	-6 / 30
8 M	04:30 / 17:56	-0.5 / 1.0	-15 / 30	23 Tu	04:46 / 18:08	-0.2 / 1.0	-6 / 30
9 Tu	05:28 / 19:12	-0.4 / 1.0	-12 / 30	24 W	05:35 / 19:24	-0.2 / 1.0	-6 / 30
10 W	06:20 / 20:20	-0.3 / 0.9	-9 / 27	25 Th	06:19 / 20:41	-0.1 / 1.0	-3 / 30
11 Th	07:03 / 21:21	-0.2 / 0.8	-6 / 24	26 F	07:00 / 22:04	0.0 / 0.9	0 / 27
12 F	07:36 / 22:21	0.0 / 0.7	0 / 21	27 Sa	07:34 / 23:43	0.1 / 0.8	3 / 24
13 Sa	07:52 / 23:28	0.1 / 0.6	3 / 18	28 Su	07:52 / 11:48 / 17:46	0.4 / 0.4 / 0.3	12 / 12 / 9
14 Su	08:32 / 12:53 / 18:21	0.3 / 0.3 / 0.2	9 / 9 / 6	29 M	02:11 / 06:56 / 10:50 / 19:46	0.6 / 0.6 / 0.6 / 0.1	18 / 18 / 18 / 3
15 M	02:08 / 06:56 / 12:04 / 20:23	0.5 / 0.4 / 0.5 / 0.2	15 / 12 / 15 / 6	30 Tu	11:01 / 21:22	0.9 / -0.1	27 / -3
				31 W	11:40 / 22:50	1.1 / -0.2	

StationId: 8761724
Source: NOAA/NOS/CO-OPS
Station Type: Primary
Time Zone: LST_LDT
Datum: MLLW

April

Day	Time	ft	cm	Day	Time	ft	cm
Th	12:29	1.2	37	16 F	12:12 / 23:46	1.2 / 0.0	37 / 0
	00:15 / 13:26	-0.3 / 1.3	-9 / 40	17 Sa	12:58	1.2	37
Sa	01:36 / 14:30	-0.3 / 1.3	-9 / 40	18 Su	00:50 / 13:49	0.0 / 1.2	0 / 37
u	02:52 / 15:42	-0.3 / 1.2	-9 / 37	19 M	01:53 / 14:47	0.0 / 1.2	0 / 37
	04:00 / 17:03	-0.2 / 1.1	-6 / 34	20 Tu	02:50 / 15:52	0.0 / 1.2	0 / 37
	05:00 / 18:32	-0.1 / 1.0	-3 / 30	21 W	03:40 / 17:07	0.0 / 1.1	0 / 34
	05:49 / 20:04	0.0 / 0.9	0 / 27	22 Th	04:23 / 18:44	0.1 / 1.0	3 / 30
	06:26 / 21:38	0.2 / 0.8	6 / 24	23 F	04:59 / 20:57	0.2 / 0.8	6 / 24
	06:45 / 23:23	0.3 / 0.7	9 / 21	24 Sa	05:18 / 11:11 / 16:31 / 23:57	0.4 / 0.6 / 0.5 / 0.7	12 / 18 / 15 / 21
	06:25 / 11:19 / 18:04	0.5 / 0.6 / 0.4	15 / 18 / 12	25 Su	04:49 / 09:48 / 18:11	0.6 / 0.7 / 0.3	18 / 21 / 9
	10:28 / 19:19	0.7 / 0.3	21 / 9	26 M	09:29 / 19:26	1.0 / 0.0	30 / 0
	10:24 / 20:15	0.8 / 0.2	24 / 6	27 Tu	09:50 / 20:34	1.2 / -0.1	37 / -3
	10:39 / 21:04	1.0 / 0.1	30 / 3	28 W	10:29 / 21:43	1.4 / -0.3	43 / -9
	11:03 / 21:53	1.1 / 0.0	34 / 0	29 Th	11:16 / 22:54	1.5 / -0.3	46 / -9
	11:34 / 22:46	1.1 / 0.0	34 / 0	30 F	12:09	1.5	46

May

Day	Time	ft	cm	Day	Time	ft	cm
1 Sa	00:06 / 13:06	-0.3 / 1.5	-9 / 46	16 Su	12:33	1.3	40
2 Su	01:17 / 14:04	-0.2 / 1.4	-6 / 43	17 M	00:16 / 13:17	-0.1 / 1.3	-3 / 40
3 M	02:22 / 15:03	-0.1 / 1.2	-3 / 37	18 Tu	01:03 / 14:03	-0.1 / 1.2	-3 / 37
4 Tu	03:17 / 16:00	0.0 / 1.1	0 / 34	19 W	01:46 / 14:48	0.0 / 1.1	0 / 34
5 W	03:59 / 17:00	0.2 / 0.9	6 / 27	20 Th	02:20 / 15:32	0.1 / 0.9	3 / 27
6 Th	04:20 / 13:33 / 17:04 / 20:02	0.3 / 0.7 / 0.7 / 0.7	9 / 21 / 21 / 21	21 F	02:41 / 12:04	0.3 / 0.7	9 / 21
7 F	04:01 / 10:50 / 18:07	0.5 / 0.7 / 0.5	15 / 21 / 15	22 Sa	02:25 / 09:27 / 17:15	0.5 / 0.7 / 0.4	15 / 21 / 12
8 Sa	09:39 / 18:47	0.8 / 0.3	24 / 9	23 Su	08:34 / 18:04	0.9 / 0.1	27 / 3
9 Su	09:17 / 19:22	0.9 / 0.2	27 / 6	24 M	08:30 / 18:56	1.1 / -0.1	34 / -3
10 M	09:21 / 19:55	1.1 / 0.1	34 / 3	25 Tu	08:54 / 19:51	1.3 / -0.3	40 / -9
11 Tu	09:38 / 20:29	1.2 / 0.0	37 / 0	26 W	09:33 / 20:50	1.5 / -0.4	46 / -12
12 W	10:02 / 21:06	1.2 / 0.0	37 / 0	27 Th	10:20 / 21:52	1.6 / -0.4	49 / -12
13 Th	10:33 / 21:48	1.3 / -0.1	40 / -3	28 F	11:12 / 22:55	1.6 / -0.4	49 / -12
14 F	11:09 / 22:35	1.3 / -0.1	40 / -3	29 Sa	12:05 / 23:56	1.5 / -0.3	46 / -9
15 Sa	11:49 / 23:25	1.3 / -0.1	40 / -3	30 Su	12:55	1.4	43
				31 M	00:52 / 13:39	-0.2 / 1.3	-6 / 40

June

Day	Time	ft	cm	Day	Time	ft	cm
1 Tu	01:37 / 14:09	0.0 / 1.1	0 / 34	16 W	00:14 / 13:25	-0.1 / 1.1	-3 / 34
2 W	02:06 / 13:49	0.2 / 0.9	6 / 27	17 Th	00:35 / 13:31	0.1 / 0.9	3 / 27
3 Th	02:04 / 11:19	0.3 / 0.7	9 / 21	18 F	00:35 / 10:09 / 23:26	0.3 / 0.7 / 0.4	9 / 21 / 12
4 F	00:35 / 09:21 / 18:42	0.5 / 0.8 / 0.4	15 / 24 / 12	19 Sa	07:59 / 17:21	0.8 / 0.3	24 / 9
5 Sa	08:27 / 18:37	0.9 / 0.2	27 / 6	20 Su	07:21 / 17:37	1.0 / 0.0	30 / 0
6 Su	08:14 / 18:56	1.0 / 0.1	30 / 3	21 M	07:27 / 18:18	1.2 / -0.2	37 / -6
7 M	08:23 / 19:22	1.1 / 0.0	34 / 0	22 Tu	07:58 / 19:08	1.4 / -0.4	43 / -12
8 Tu	08:44 / 19:53	1.2 / -0.1	37 / -3	23 W	08:41 / 20:02	1.5 / -0.5	46 / -15
9 W	09:12 / 20:27	1.3 / -0.2	40 / -6	24 Th	09:32 / 20:59	1.6 / -0.5	49 / -15
10 Th	09:45 / 21:05	1.3 / -0.2	40 / -6	25 F	10:24 / 21:56	1.6 / -0.5	49 / -15
11 F	10:22 / 21:45	1.4 / -0.2	43 / -6	26 Sa	11:16 / 22:50	1.5 / -0.4	46 / -12
12 Sa	11:00 / 22:26	1.4 / -0.2	43 / -6	27 Su	12:04 / 23:37	1.4 / -0.2	43 / -6
13 Su	11:39 / 23:06	1.4 / -0.2	43 / -6	28 M	12:44	1.2	37
14 M	12:17 / 23:43	1.3 / -0.1	40 / -3	29 Tu	00:14 / 13:10	-0.1 / 1.0	-3 / 30
15 Tu	12:54	1.2	37	30 W	00:31 / 12:55	0.1 / 0.8	3 / 24

StationId: 8761724
Source: NOAA/NOS/CO-OPS
Station Type: Primary
Time Zone: LST_LDT
Datum: MLLW

NOAA Tide Predictions

Grand Isle, LA,2021

Times and Heights of High and Low Waters

July

Day	Time	ft	cm	Day	Time	ft	cm
1 Th ◐	00:11	0.3	9	16 F	07:57	0.7	21
	10:15	0.7	21		20:55	0.5	15
	22:13	0.4	12				
2 F	07:55	0.7	21	17 Sa ◑	06:04	0.8	24
	18:23	0.3	9		16:25	0.3	9
3 Sa	07:05	0.9	27	18 Su	05:48	1.0	30
	17:54	0.2	6		16:44	0.0	0
4 Su	06:59	1.0	30	19 M	06:10	1.2	37
	18:08	0.0	0		17:28	-0.2	-6
5 M	07:16	1.1	34	20 Tu	06:52	1.4	43
	18:35	-0.1	-3		18:18	-0.3	-9
6 Tu	07:44	1.2	37	21 W	07:45	1.5	46
	19:07	-0.1	-3		19:12	-0.4	-12
7 W	08:20	1.3	40	22 Th	08:42	1.6	49
	19:43	-0.2	-6		20:07	-0.4	-12
8 Th	08:59	1.3	40	23 F	09:39	1.6	49
	20:22	-0.2	-6		21:01	-0.4	-12
9 F	09:39	1.4	43	24 Sa ○	10:33	1.5	46
	21:00	-0.2	-6		21:50	-0.3	-9
10 Sa ●	10:19	1.4	43	25 Su	11:21	1.4	43
	21:36	-0.2	-6		22:32	-0.1	-3
11 Su	10:57	1.4	43	26 M	12:03	1.2	37
	22:10	-0.2	-6		23:03	0.1	3
12 M	11:34	1.3	40	27 Tu	12:36	1.1	34
	22:39	-0.1	-3		23:13	0.3	9
13 Tu	12:10	1.2	37	28 W	12:50	0.9	27
	23:02	0.0	0		22:40	0.4	12
14 W	12:41	1.0	30	29 Th	09:24	0.7	21
	23:12	0.2	6		20:37	0.5	15
15 Th	12:55	0.8	24	30 F	05:31	0.8	24
	22:53	0.3	9		16:57	0.4	12
				31 Sa ◑	05:00	0.9	27
					16:31	0.3	9

August

Day	Time	ft	cm	Day	Time	ft	cm
1 Su	05:12	1.0	30	16 M	04:30	1.4	43
	16:52	0.2	6		16:16	0.0	0
2 M	05:42	1.2	37	17 Tu	05:27	1.5	46
	17:26	0.1	3		17:16	-0.1	-3
3 Tu	06:24	1.2	37	18 W	06:33	1.6	49
	18:04	0.0	0		18:14	-0.2	-6
4 W	07:11	1.3	40	19 Th	07:42	1.6	49
	18:45	-0.1	-3		19:10	-0.2	-6
5 Th	08:01	1.4	43	20 F	08:47	1.6	49
	19:26	-0.1	-3		20:02	-0.1	-3
6 F	08:49	1.4	43	21 Sa	09:47	1.5	46
	20:05	-0.1	-3		20:49	0.0	0
7 Sa	09:34	1.4	43	22 Su ○	10:42	1.4	43
	20:41	-0.1	-3		21:27	0.2	6
8 Su ●	10:17	1.4	43	23 M	11:32	1.3	40
	21:13	0.0	0		21:53	0.4	12
9 M	10:59	1.4	43	24 Tu	12:20	1.1	34
	21:40	0.1	3		21:52	0.6	18
10 Tu	11:42	1.2	37	25 W	13:15	0.9	27
	21:58	0.2	6		20:55	0.7	21
11 W	12:28	1.1	34	26 Th	02:46	0.8	24
	21:58	0.4	12		09:11	0.7	21
					15:18	0.8	24
					17:44	0.8	24
12 Th	13:26	0.9	27	27 F	02:10	1.0	30
	21:11	0.6	18		12:27	0.6	18
13 F	03:58	0.8	24	28 Sa	02:22	1.1	34
	11:56	0.6	18		13:54	0.5	15
14 Sa	03:28	1.0	30	29 Su	02:52	1.2	37
	14:12	0.4	12		14:52	0.4	12
15 Su ◐	03:47	1.2	37	30 M ◐	03:35	1.3	40
	15:17	0.2	6		15:45	0.3	9
				31 Tu	04:28	1.4	43
					16:36	0.2	6

September

Day	Time	ft	cm	Day	Time	ft	cm
1 W	05:30	1.4	43	16 Th	06:19	1.6	49
	17:25	0.2	6		17:59	0.1	3
2 Th	06:34	1.4	43	17 F	07:38	1.6	49
	18:11	0.2	6		18:51	0.2	6
3 F	07:36	1.5	46	18 Sa	08:52	1.5	46
	18:53	0.2	6		19:35	0.4	12
4 Sa	08:32	1.5	46	19 Su	10:01	1.4	43
	19:30	0.2	6		20:08	0.5	15
5 Su	09:27	1.5	46	20 M ○	11:10	1.2	3.
	20:03	0.3	9		20:22	0.7	2.
6 M	10:23	1.4	43	21 Tu	12:33	1.1	3.
	20:30	0.4	12		19:47	0.9	2
7 Tu ●	11:25	1.3	40	22 W	00:14	0.9	2
	20:45	0.6	18		07:02	0.8	2
					23:43	1.1	3
8 W	12:48	1.1	34	23 Th	08:45	0.7	2
	20:26	0.8	24		23:53	1.2	3
9 Th	01:12	0.9	27	24 F	10:05	0.6	1
	07:35	0.7	21				
	15:35	0.9	27				
	18:15	0.9	27				
10 F	00:45	1.1	34	25 Sa	00:18	1.3	4
	10:01	0.6	18		11:16	0.5	1
11 Sa	01:04	1.3	40	26 Su	00:51	1.4	4
	11:54	0.4	12		12:26	0.4	
12 Su	01:45	1.4	43	27 M	01:33	1.4	
	13:25	0.2	6		13:34	0.4	
13 M ◐	02:39	1.6	49	28 Tu	02:23	1.5	
	14:43	0.1	3		14:40	0.4	
14 Tu	03:44	1.6	49	29 W ◐	03:23	1.5	
	15:55	0.1	3		15:39	0.3	
15 W	04:59	1.7	52	30 Th	04:30	1.5	
	17:00	0.1	3		16:30	0.3	

StationId: 8761724
Source: NOAA/NOS/CO-OPS
Station Type: Primary
Time Zone: LST_LDT
Datum: MLLW

NOAA Tide Predictions

Grand Isle, LA, 2021

Times and Heights of High and Low Waters

October

Day	Time (h m)	ft	cm	Day	Time (h m)	ft	cm
1 F	05:41	1.5	46	16 Sa	07:24	1.3	40
	17:15	0.3	9		17:58	0.5	15
2 Sa	06:54	1.4	43	17 Su	09:09	1.1	34
	17:54	0.4	12		18:15	0.7	21
3 Su	08:10	1.4	43	18 M	01:19	0.9	27
	18:27	0.5	15		04:14	0.9	27
					11:18	1.0	30
					17:45	0.9	27
					22:58	0.9	27
4 M	09:34	1.3	40	19 Tu	06:24	0.7	21
	18:50	0.7	21		22:14	1.1	34
5 Tu	11:18	1.2	37	20 W ○	07:31	0.6	18
	18:49	0.8	24		22:13	1.2	37
	23:24	0.9	27				
6 W	05:53	0.7	21	21 Th	08:23	0.5	15
	14:03	1.0	30		22:30	1.3	40
	17:28	1.0	30				
	22:42	1.1	34				
7 Th	07:38	0.5	15	22 F	09:09	0.4	12
	22:51	1.3	40		22:56	1.4	43
8	09:04	0.4	12	23 Sa	09:56	0.3	9
	23:25	1.5	46		23:28	1.4	43
9 Sa	10:25	0.2	6	24 Su	10:47	0.3	9
10 Su	00:11	1.6	49	25 M	00:06	1.5	46
	11:46	0.1	3		11:44	0.2	6
11 M	01:05	1.7	52	26 Tu	00:49	1.5	46
	13:06	0.1	3		12:44	0.2	6
12 Tu	02:06	1.7	52	27 W	01:38	1.5	46
	14:21	0.1	3		13:43	0.2	6
13 W	03:14	1.7	52	28 Th ◐	02:30	1.4	43
	15:30	0.1	3		14:34	0.2	6
14 Th	04:29	1.6	49	29 F	03:26	1.4	43
	16:31	0.2	6		15:19	0.3	9
15 F	05:52	1.4	43	30 Sa	04:29	1.3	40
	17:21	0.3	9		15:55	0.3	9
				31 Su	05:51	1.1	34
					16:22	0.5	15

November

Day	Time (h m)	ft	cm	Day	Time (h m)	ft	cm
1 M	08:08	1.0	30	16 Tu	05:47	0.3	9
	16:29	0.6	18		20:03	1.0	30
	22:47	0.8	24				
2 Tu	04:41	0.7	21	17 W	06:22	0.2	6
	11:35	0.9	27		20:10	1.1	34
	15:37	0.8	24				
	21:34	1.0	30				
3 W	06:07	0.4	12	18 Th	06:55	0.1	3
	21:19	1.2	37		20:30	1.2	37
4 Th ●	07:13	0.2	6	19 F ○	07:30	0.0	0
	21:38	1.4	43		20:57	1.3	40
5 F	08:17	0.0	0	20 Sa	08:07	-0.1	-3
	22:15	1.5	46		21:29	1.3	40
6 Sa	09:23	-0.1	-3	21 Su	08:49	-0.1	-3
	23:02	1.6	49		22:06	1.3	40
7 Su	09:32	-0.2	-6	22 M	09:34	-0.1	-3
	22:55	1.7	52		22:45	1.3	40
8 M	10:43	-0.2	-6	23 Tu	10:22	-0.1	-3
	23:51	1.6	49		23:26	1.3	40
9 Tu	11:53	-0.2	-6	24 W	11:08	-0.1	-3
10 W	00:49	1.5	46	25 Th	00:07	1.2	37
	12:58	-0.1	-3		11:51	-0.1	-3
11 Th ◐	01:46	1.4	43	26 F	00:47	1.1	34
	13:54	0.0	0		12:27	0.0	0
12 F ◑	02:41	1.2	37	27 Sa	01:25	1.0	30
	14:37	0.2	6		12:54	0.1	3
13 Sa	03:28	1.0	30	28 Su	01:55	0.8	24
	14:59	0.4	12		13:06	0.2	6
					22:56	0.6	18
14 Su	00:21	0.8	24	29 M	12:41	0.4	12
	14:37	0.6	18		20:07	0.6	18
	21:33	0.8	24				
15 M	05:11	0.5	15	30 Tu	04:15	0.3	9
	20:22	0.9	27		19:16	0.8	24

December

Day	Time (h m)	ft	cm	Day	Time (h m)	ft	cm
1 W	04:51	0.1	3	16 Th	06:16	-0.3	-9
	19:13	1.0	30		19:35	0.9	27
2 Th	05:39	-0.2	-6	17 F	06:49	-0.4	-12
	19:38	1.2	37		20:07	1.0	30
3 F	06:32	-0.4	-12	18 Sa	07:26	-0.4	-12
	20:18	1.3	40		20:42	1.0	30
4 Sa ●	07:31	-0.5	-15	19 Su ○	08:04	-0.5	-15
	21:07	1.4	43		21:20	1.0	30
5 Su	08:32	-0.6	-18	20 M	08:44	-0.5	-15
	22:00	1.4	43		21:58	1.0	30
6 M	09:36	-0.6	-18	21 Tu	09:24	-0.5	-15
	22:54	1.4	43		22:35	1.0	30
7 Tu	10:39	-0.5	-15	22 W	10:00	-0.5	-15
	23:47	1.3	40		23:11	1.0	30
8 W	11:36	-0.4	-12	23 Th	10:32	-0.4	-12
					23:45	0.9	27
9 Th	00:35	1.1	34	24 F	10:58	-0.3	-9
	12:24	-0.3	-9				
10 F	01:11	0.9	27	25 Sa	00:15	0.7	21
	12:56	-0.1	-3		11:13	-0.2	-6
11 Sa ◐	01:08	0.6	18	26 Su	00:29	0.5	15
	12:58	0.1	3		11:09	-0.1	-3
	22:14	0.5	15		21:11	0.3	9
12 Su ◑	11:25	0.3	9	27 M ◑	10:04	0.1	3
	19:57	0.5	15		18:29	0.4	12
13 M	05:19	0.1	3	28 Tu	04:07	0.0	0
	19:03	0.6	18		17:53	0.6	18
14 Tu	05:23	0.0	0	29 W	04:13	-0.3	-9
	18:55	0.6	18		18:02	0.8	24
15 W	05:47	-0.2	-6	30 Th	04:54	-0.5	-15
	19:10	0.9	27		18:35	0.9	27
				31 F	05:45	-0.7	-21
					19:16	1.1	34

StationId: 8771416
Source: NOAA/NOS/CO-OPS
Station Type: Primary
Time Zone: LST_LDT
Datum: MLLW

NOAA Tide Predictions

Galveston Bay Entrance, South Jetty, TX,2021

Times and Heights of High and Low Waters

January

Day	Time	ft	cm	Day	Time	ft	cm
1 F	09:57	-0.7	-21	16 Sa	00:50	1.0	30
	18:37	2.0	61		03:40	1.1	34
					11:04	-0.5	-15
					19:05	1.5	46
2 Sa	10:41	-0.6	-18	17 Su	01:35	0.9	27
	19:17	1.9	58		04:54	1.0	30
					11:51	-0.1	-3
					19:36	1.4	43
3 Su	11:32	-0.4	-12	18 M	02:19	0.6	18
	19:57	1.8	55		06:30	0.9	27
					12:45	0.2	6
					20:01	1.2	37
4 M	12:33	-0.1	-3	19 Tu	02:59	0.4	12
	20:34	1.6	49		08:45	0.9	27
					13:52	0.5	15
					20:20	1.1	34
5 Tu	03:39	0.7	21	20 W	03:35	0.2	6
	07:39	0.9	27		11:00	1.0	30
	13:43	0.2	6		15:42	0.8	24
	21:06	1.4	43		20:27	1.0	30
6 W	03:45	0.4	12	21 Th	04:08	-0.1	-3
	10:02	1.1	34		12:21	1.2	37
	15:06	0.6	18		17:50	1.0	30
	21:33	1.3	40		20:16	1.0	30
7 Th	04:11	0.0	0	22 F	04:41	-0.3	-9
	11:38	1.4	43		13:20	1.4	43
	17:12	0.9	27				
	21:53	1.2	37				
8 F	04:49	-0.4	-12	23 Sa	05:17	-0.4	-12
	12:52	1.8	55		14:10	1.6	49
	19:18	1.0	30				
	22:07	1.1	34				
9 Sa	05:35	-0.7	-21	24 Su	05:55	-0.6	-18
	13:57	2.0	61		14:53	1.7	52
10 Su	06:25	-1.0	-30	25 M	06:34	-0.7	-21
	14:54	2.2	67		15:30	1.8	55
11 M	07:15	-1.1	-34	26 Tu	07:13	-0.8	-24
	15:46	2.2	67		16:02	1.8	55
12 Tu	08:04	-1.2	-37	27 W	07:52	-0.9	-27
	16:33	2.2	67		16:30	1.8	55
13 W	08:51	-1.1	-34	28 Th	08:30	-0.9	-27
	17:16	2.1	64		16:58	1.8	55
14 Th	09:35	-1.0	-30	29 F	09:10	-0.9	-27
	17:55	1.9	58		17:26	1.8	55
					23:46	1.1	34
15 F	00:11	1.2	37	30 Sa	02:26	1.1	34
	02:34	1.2	37		09:51	-0.8	-24
	10:19	-0.7	-21		17:55	1.7	52
	18:32	1.7	52		23:33	0.9	27
				31 Su	03:39	1.1	34
					10:37	-0.6	-18
					18:25	1.5	46

February

Day	Time	ft	cm	Day	Time	ft	cm
1 M	00:02	0.7	21	16 Tu	00:14	0.3	9
	04:59	1.1	34		06:47	1.1	34
	11:29	-0.3	-9		12:22	0.5	15
	18:53	1.4	43		18:26	1.1	34
2 Tu	00:46	0.4	12	17 W	00:59	0.1	3
	06:33	1.1	34		08:26	1.1	34
	12:32	0.1	3		13:37	0.8	24
	19:19	1.2	37		18:28	1.0	30
3 W	01:35	0.1	3	18 Th	01:45	0.0	0
	08:25	1.1	34		10:27	1.2	37
	13:49	0.5	15		16:04	1.0	30
	19:40	1.1	34		18:26	1.0	30
4 Th	02:25	-0.2	-6	19 F	02:32	-0.2	-6
	10:17	1.4	43		11:49	1.4	43
	15:53	0.8	24				
	19:54	1.0	30				
5 F	03:17	-0.5	-15	20 Sa	03:19	-0.3	-9
	11:46	1.6	49		12:47	1.5	46
6 Sa	04:13	-0.7	-21	21 Su	04:09	-0.4	-12
	12:56	1.8	55		13:37	1.6	49
7 Su	05:14	-0.9	-27	22 M	05:02	-0.4	-12
	13:58	1.9	58		14:20	1.7	52
8 M	06:16	-1.0	-30	23 Tu	05:56	-0.5	-15
	14:52	2.0	61		14:56	1.8	55
9 Tu	07:15	-1.0	-30	24 W	06:47	-0.6	-18
	15:39	1.9	58		15:26	1.8	55
10 W	08:08	-0.9	-27	25 Th	07:34	-0.7	-21
	16:19	1.8	55		15:51	1.8	55
	22:19	1.1	34		21:57	1.1	34
11 Th	01:12	1.2	37	26 F	00:52	1.2	37
	08:54	-0.8	-24		08:18	-0.7	-21
	16:51	1.7	52		16:15	1.8	55
	22:36	1.0	30		21:44	1.0	30
12 F	02:21	1.2	37	27 Sa	02:06	1.3	40
	09:34	-0.7	-21		09:02	-0.6	-18
	17:18	1.6	49		16:39	1.7	52
	22:50	0.8	24		21:50	0.8	24
13 Sa	03:25	1.2	37	28 Su	03:17	1.4	43
	10:12	-0.4	-12		09:48	-0.4	-12
	17:41	1.4	43		17:03	1.6	49
	23:06	0.7	21		22:19	0.5	15
14 Su	04:27	1.2	37				
	10:50	-0.1	-3				
	18:01	1.3	40				
	23:34	0.5	15				
15 M	05:32	1.1	34				
	11:32	0.2	6				
	18:17	1.2	37				

March

Day	Time	ft	cm	Day	Time	ft	cm
1 M	04:29	1.5	46	16 Tu	06:47	1.6	49
	10:38	-0.1	-3		12:29	0.8	24
	17:25	1.4	43		17:55	1.3	40
	22:58	0.3	9				
2 Tu	05:43	1.5	46	17 W	00:07	0.2	6
	11:36	0.3	9		07:48	1.6	49
	17:45	1.3	40		13:40	1.0	30
	23:45	0.0	0		17:58	1.3	40
3 W	07:05	1.6	49	18 Th	00:47	0.1	3
	12:53	0.7	21		09:03	1.6	49
	18:01	1.2	37		15:53	1.2	37
					18:00	1.2	37
4 Th	00:39	-0.2	-6	19 F	01:32	0.0	0
	08:39	1.7	52		10:39	1.7	52
	15:03	1.0	30				
	18:12	1.2	37				
5 F	01:38	-0.4	-12	20 Sa	02:22	0.0	0
	10:18	1.8	55		12:02	1.8	55
6 Sa	02:41	-0.5	-15	21 Su	03:16	0.0	0
	11:40	2.0	61		13:01	1.9	58
7 Su	03:49	-0.6	-18	22 M	04:13	-0.1	-3
	12:46	2.0	61		13:48	1.9	58
8 M	05:03	-0.6	-18	23 Tu	05:13	-0.1	-3
	13:43	2.0	61		14:27	1.9	58
9 Tu	06:18	-0.5	-15	24 W	06:15	-0.1	-3
	14:32	1.9	58		15:00	2.0	61
	20:58	1.2	37				
	23:35	1.2	37				
10 W	07:23	-0.4	-12	25 Th	07:17	-0.1	-3
	15:12	1.8	55		15:28	1.9	58
	21:11	1.1	34		21:42	1.2	37
11 Th	00:56	1.3	40	26 F	01:10	1.5	46
	08:15	-0.3	-9		08:14	-0.1	-3
	15:43	1.7	52		15:53	1.9	58
	21:28	1.0	30		21:29	1.1	34
12 F	02:03	1.4	43	27 Sa	02:29	1.6	49
	08:58	-0.2	-6		09:07	0.0	0
	16:06	1.6	49		16:16	1.8	55
	21:41	0.8	24		21:36	0.8	24
13 Sa	03:03	1.5	46	28 Su	03:41	1.8	55
	09:35	0.0	0		09:59	0.2	6
	16:24	1.5	46		16:38	1.7	52
	21:50	0.6	18		22:03	0.5	15
14 Su	04:58	1.5	46	29 M	04:48	2.0	61
	11:09	0.3	9		10:51	0.4	12
	17:39	1.4	43		16:58	1.6	49
	23:07	0.5	15		22:38	0.2	6
15 M	05:52	1.5	46	30 Tu	05:54	2.2	67
	11:45	0.5	15		11:51	0.8	24
	17:50	1.3	40		17:16	1.5	46
	23:34	0.3	9		23:19	-0.1	-3
				31 W	07:02	2.3	70
					13:13	1.1	34
					17:31	1.4	43

StationId: 8771416
Source: NOAA/NOS/CO-OPS
Station Type: Primary
Time Zone: LST_LDT
Datum: MLLW

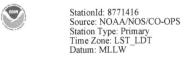

Galveston Bay Entrance, South Jetty, TX, 2021

Times and Heights of High and Low Waters

April

Day	Time	ft	cm	Day	Time	ft	cm
Th	00:07	-0.3	-9	16 F	08:41	2.1	64
	08:15	2.3	70				
	15:14	1.3	40				
	17:41	1.4	43				
	01:02	-0.4	-12	17 Sa	00:38	0.1	3
	09:40	2.3	70		09:54	2.1	64
Sa	02:06	-0.3	-9	18 Su	01:28	0.2	6
	11:08	2.3	70		11:10	2.2	67
u	03:17	-0.3	-9	19 M	02:26	0.2	6
	12:22	2.3	70		12:07	2.2	67
	04:35	-0.1	-3	20 Tu ☽	03:28	0.2	6
	13:21	2.2	67		12:49	2.2	67
	06:00	0.0	0	21 W	04:31	0.2	6
	14:09	2.1	64		13:23	2.2	67
	20:47	1.3	40				
	00:02	1.4	43	22 Th	05:38	0.3	9
	07:19	0.1	3		13:51	2.1	64
	14:49	2.0	61		20:33	1.3	40
	21:02	1.2	37				
	01:24	1.5	46	23 F	00:17	1.6	49
	08:23	0.3	9		06:47	0.4	12
	15:20	1.9	58		14:17	2.0	61
	21:22	1.0	30		20:18	1.1	34
	02:33	1.7	52	24 Sa	01:41	1.8	55
	09:15	0.5	15		07:57	0.5	15
	15:42	1.7	52		14:41	1.9	58
	21:40	0.9	27		20:25	0.8	24
	03:34	1.8	55	25 Su	02:54	2.1	64
	10:00	0.6	18		09:03	0.7	21
	15:59	1.6	49		15:03	1.8	55
	21:52	0.7	21		20:52	0.4	12
	04:29	1.9	58	26 M	04:01	2.4	73
	10:40	0.8	24		10:06	0.9	27
	16:12	1.6	49		15:23	1.7	52
	22:04	0.5	15		21:27	0.1	3
	05:18	2.0	61	27 Tu ○	05:04	2.6	79
	11:21	1.0	30		11:13	1.2	37
	16:20	1.5	46		15:40	1.7	52
	22:24	0.3	9		22:07	-0.2	-6
	06:05	2.1	64	28 W	06:06	2.7	82
	12:10	1.2	37		12:36	1.5	46
	16:23	1.5	46		15:55	1.6	49
	22:50	0.2	6		22:51	-0.4	-12
	06:51	2.1	64	29 Th	07:08	2.8	85
	13:27	1.4	43		23:41	-0.5	-15
	16:25	1.5	46				
	23:21	0.1	3				
	07:41	2.1	64	30 F	08:15	2.7	82
	23:56	0.1	3				

May

Day	Time	ft	cm	Day	Time	ft	cm
1 Sa	00:37	-0.4	-12	16 Su	00:01	0.1	3
	09:31	2.6	79		09:18	2.3	70
2 Su	01:43	-0.2	-6	17 M	00:50	0.1	3
	10:48	2.5	76		10:19	2.3	70
3 M ☽	02:59	0.1	3	18 Tu	01:48	0.2	6
	11:52	2.4	73		11:09	2.3	70
4 Tu	04:22	0.3	9	19 W ☽	02:52	0.3	9
	12:41	2.2	67		11:47	2.3	70
	19:27	1.4	43				
	22:57	1.5	46				
5 W	05:48	0.5	15	20 Th	03:57	0.4	12
	13:18	2.1	64		12:16	2.2	67
	19:47	1.2	37		19:23	1.3	40
					23:10	1.5	46
6 Th	00:36	1.6	49	21 F	05:07	0.6	18
	07:07	0.7	21		12:42	2.0	61
	13:46	1.9	58		19:06	1.0	30
	20:11	1.0	30				
7 F	01:53	1.8	55	22 Sa	00:47	1.7	52
	08:14	0.9	27		06:26	0.8	24
	14:07	1.8	55		13:04	1.9	58
	20:34	0.8	24		19:11	0.7	21
8 Sa	02:59	1.9	58	23 Su	02:02	2.0	61
	09:11	1.1	34		07:55	1.1	34
	14:23	1.7	52		13:24	1.8	55
	20:53	0.6	18		19:41	0.3	9
9 Su	03:56	2.1	64	24 M	03:10	2.4	73
	10:03	1.3	40		09:20	1.3	40
	14:34	1.7	52		13:42	1.7	52
	21:07	0.4	12		20:19	-0.1	-3
10 M	04:46	2.2	67	25 Tu	04:13	2.7	82
	10:54	1.4	43		10:37	1.5	46
	14:37	1.6	49		13:58	1.7	52
	21:24	0.2	6		21:01	-0.4	-12
11 Tu ●	05:28	2.3	70	26 W ○	05:12	2.9	88
	11:49	1.5	46		11:53	1.6	49
	14:35	1.6	49		14:15	1.7	52
	21:47	0.1	3		21:45	-0.6	-18
12 W	06:08	2.4	73	27 Th	06:09	2.9	88
	22:15	0.0	0		22:32	-0.7	-21
13 Th	06:47	2.4	73	28 F	07:06	2.9	88
	22:46	0.0	0		23:23	-0.6	-18
14 F	07:30	2.4	73	29 Sa	08:06	2.7	82
	23:21	0.0	0				
15 Sa	08:19	2.4	73	30 Su	00:20	-0.4	-12
					09:11	2.5	76
				31 M	01:25	-0.1	-3
					10:14	2.4	73

June

Day	Time	ft	cm	Day	Time	ft	cm
1 Tu	02:40	0.2	6	16 W	01:20	0.1	3
	11:07	2.2	67		10:07	2.2	67
	17:55	1.4	43				
	21:00	1.4	43				
2 W ☽	04:01	0.5	15	17 Th	02:25	0.3	9
	11:46	2.0	61		10:41	2.0	61
	18:23	1.1	34		18:01	1.1	34
	23:24	1.5	46		21:39	1.3	40
3 Th	05:25	0.8	24	18 F ☽	03:35	0.6	18
	12:13	1.9	58		11:09	1.9	58
	18:52	0.9	27		17:47	0.8	24
					23:45	1.5	46
4 F	00:58	1.7	52	19 Sa	04:52	0.9	27
	06:48	1.1	34		11:31	1.8	55
	12:33	1.7	52		17:56	0.5	15
	19:20	0.6	18				
5 Sa	02:10	1.8	55	20 Su	01:08	1.8	55
	08:04	1.3	40		06:32	1.2	37
	12:46	1.7	52		11:49	1.6	49
	19:45	0.4	12		18:28	0.1	3
6 Su	03:12	2.0	61	21 M	02:17	2.2	67
	09:12	1.4	43		08:33	1.4	43
	12:52	1.6	49		12:05	1.6	49
	20:07	0.2	6		19:09	-0.3	-9
7 M	04:04	2.2	67	22 Tu	03:21	2.5	76
	10:14	1.5	46		09:57	1.5	46
	12:46	1.6	49		12:21	1.6	49
	20:27	0.0	0		19:56	-0.6	-18
8 Tu	04:49	2.3	70	23 W	04:19	2.7	82
	20:51	-0.1	-3		20:44	-0.8	-24
9 W	05:27	2.4	73	24 Th ○	05:14	2.8	85
	21:19	-0.2	-6		21:32	-0.9	-27
10 Th ●	06:02	2.4	73	25 F	06:05	2.7	82
	21:49	-0.2	-6		22:22	-0.8	-24
11 F	06:36	2.4	73	26 Sa	06:55	2.6	79
	22:22	-0.2	-6		23:13	-0.6	-18
12 Sa	07:13	2.4	73	27 Su	07:45	2.4	73
	22:57	-0.2	-6				
13 Su	07:54	2.3	70	28 M	00:06	-0.3	-9
	23:37	-0.1	-3		08:34	2.2	67
14 M	08:39	2.3	70	29 Tu	01:05	0.0	0
					09:20	2.0	61
					16:06	1.3	40
					19:02	1.4	43
15 Tu	00:24	0.0	0	30 W	02:12	0.4	12
	09:25	2.2	67		10:00	1.8	55
					16:44	1.0	30
					21:27	1.3	40

StationId: 8771416
Source: NOAA/NOS/CO-OPS
Station Type: Primary
Time Zone: LST_LDT
Datum: MLLW

NOAA Tide Predictions

Galveston Bay Entrance, South Jetty, TX,2021

Times and Heights of High and Low Waters

July

Day	Time	ft	cm	Day	Time	ft	cm
1 Th ☽	03:30	0.7	21	16 F	02:09	0.5	15
	10:31	1.7	52		09:26	1.7	52
	17:20	0.7	21		16:02	0.7	21
	23:39	1.4	43		22:25	1.4	43
2 F	05:02	1.0	30	17 Sa ◖	03:28	0.9	27
	10:53	1.6	49		09:50	1.6	49
	17:53	0.5	15		16:30	0.3	9
3 Sa	01:07	1.6	49	18 Su	00:06	1.7	52
	06:38	1.2	37		05:15	1.2	37
	11:07	1.5	46		10:08	1.5	46
	18:24	0.2	6		17:10	0.0	0
4 Su	02:13	1.9	58	19 M	01:21	2.0	61
	08:08	1.4	43		07:48	1.4	43
	11:07	1.5	46		10:23	1.5	46
	18:54	0.1	3		17:57	-0.3	-9
5 M	03:08	2.0	61	20 Tu	02:25	2.3	70
	19:23	-0.1	-3		18:50	-0.6	-18
6 Tu	03:56	2.1	64	21 W	03:24	2.5	76
	19:53	-0.2	-6		19:44	-0.8	-24
7 W	04:37	2.2	67	22 Th	04:18	2.6	79
	20:25	-0.3	-9		20:37	-0.8	-24
8 Th	05:12	2.3	70	23 F	05:07	2.6	79
	20:57	-0.4	-12		21:29	-0.8	-24
9 F	05:44	2.3	70	24 Sa ○	05:51	2.4	73
	21:31	-0.4	-12		11:57	1.6	49
					14:23	1.7	52
					22:17	-0.7	-21
10 Sa ●	06:14	2.3	70	25 Su	06:30	2.3	70
	22:05	-0.4	-12		12:21	1.5	46
					15:32	1.7	52
					23:04	-0.4	-12
11 Su	06:44	2.2	67	26 M	07:06	2.1	64
	22:41	-0.3	-9		12:51	1.4	43
					16:43	1.6	49
					23:50	-0.1	-3
12 M	07:16	2.2	67	27 Tu	07:38	1.9	58
	23:21	-0.2	-6		13:33	1.2	37
					17:59	1.5	46
13 Tu	07:50	2.1	64	28 W	00:40	0.3	9
					08:07	1.7	52
					14:24	1.0	30
					19:30	1.4	43
14 W	00:07	0.0	0	29 Th	01:38	0.6	18
	08:24	2.0	61		08:31	1.6	49
					15:13	0.8	24
					21:29	1.4	43
15 Th	01:02	0.2	6	30 F	03:03	1.0	30
	08:57	1.9	58		08:49	1.5	46
	16:02	1.0	30		15:57	0.5	15
	20:06	1.2	37		23:40	1.5	46
				31 Sa ☽	05:04	1.2	37
					08:51	1.4	43
					16:37	0.3	9

August

Day	Time	ft	cm	Day	Time	ft	cm
1 Su	01:01	1.8	55	16 M	00:16	2.1	64
	17:17	0.1	3		16:36	-0.2	-6
2 M	02:00	1.9	58	17 Tu	01:25	2.4	73
	17:59	0.0	0		17:38	-0.3	-9
3 Tu	02:49	2.1	64	18 W	02:24	2.5	76
	18:41	-0.1	-3		18:43	-0.5	-15
4 W	03:33	2.2	67	19 Th	03:18	2.5	76
	19:23	-0.2	-6		19:46	-0.5	-15
5 Th	04:11	2.2	67	20 F	04:05	2.5	76
	20:03	-0.2	-6		10:23	1.6	49
					12:51	1.7	52
					20:42	-0.5	-15
6 F	04:44	2.2	67	21 Sa	04:46	2.4	73
	20:40	-0.3	-9		10:39	1.6	49
					14:04	1.8	55
					21:31	-0.3	-9
7 Sa	05:12	2.2	67	22 Su ○	05:19	2.2	67
	21:16	-0.3	-9		10:51	1.5	46
					15:11	1.8	55
					22:15	-0.1	-3
8 Su ●	05:36	2.2	67	23 M	05:47	2.1	64
	12:00	1.5	46		11:01	1.3	40
	14:19	1.6	49		16:15	1.8	55
	21:52	-0.3	-9		22:55	0.1	3
9 M	06:01	2.2	67	24 Tu	06:10	1.9	58
	11:58	1.4	43		11:19	1.1	34
	15:18	1.6	49		17:17	1.8	55
	22:29	-0.2	-6		23:34	0.5	15
10 Tu	06:26	2.1	64	25 W	06:29	1.8	55
	11:49	1.3	40		11:49	0.9	27
	16:24	1.6	49		18:22	1.8	55
	23:10	0.0	0				
11 W	06:51	2.0	61	26 Th	00:16	0.8	24
	12:18	1.1	34		06:42	1.7	52
	17:37	1.5	46		12:29	0.7	21
	23:57	0.3	9		19:36	1.7	52
12 Th	07:16	1.8	55	27 F	01:10	1.1	34
	13:00	0.9	27		06:47	1.6	49
	19:04	1.5	46		13:16	0.6	18
					21:16	1.7	52
13 F	00:55	0.7	21	28 Sa	03:28	1.4	43
	07:38	1.7	52		06:40	1.5	46
	13:50	0.6	18		14:09	0.5	15
	20:50	1.6	49		23:21	1.9	58
14 Sa	02:12	1.0	30	29 Su	15:05	0.4	12
	07:56	1.6	49				
	14:43	0.3	9				
	22:44	1.8	55				
15 Su ◖	04:33	1.4	43	30 M ◐	00:39	2.0	61
	08:08	1.5	46		16:02	0.3	9
	15:38	0.1	3				
				31 Tu	01:33	2.2	67
					17:00	0.2	6

September

Day	Time	ft	cm	Day	Time	ft	cm
1 W	02:18	2.3	70	16 Th	02:11	2.7	82
	17:58	0.2	6		18:49	0.0	0
2 Th	02:58	2.3	70	17 F	02:57	2.6	79
	18:52	0.1	3		09:25	1.7	52
					12:32	1.8	55
					19:55	0.1	3
3 F	03:32	2.3	70	18 Sa	03:35	2.5	76
	19:40	0.1	3		09:38	1.6	49
					13:45	1.9	58
					20:50	0.2	6
4 Sa	04:00	2.3	70	19 Su	04:06	2.3	70
	10:22	1.6	49		09:53	1.4	43
	12:55	1.7	52		14:49	2.0	61
	20:22	0.1	3		21:35	0.4	12
5 Su	04:22	2.3	70	20 M ○	04:30	2.2	67
	10:28	1.5	46		10:04	1.2	37
	13:59	1.7	52		15:48	2.1	64
	21:01	0.1	3		22:14	0.6	18
6 M	04:44	2.2	67	21 Tu	04:48	2.0	61
	10:19	1.4	43		10:15	1.0	30
	15:00	1.8	55		16:43	2.2	67
	21:39	0.2	6		22:49	0.9	27
7 Tu ●	05:04	2.2	67	22 W	05:02	1.9	58
	10:23	1.2	37		10:34	0.8	24
	16:01	1.9	58		17:36	2.2	67
	22:20	0.3	9		23:23	1.1	34
8 W	05:25	2.1	64	23 Th	05:09	1.8	55
	10:47	1.0	30		11:01	0.7	21
	17:06	2.0	61		18:31	2.2	67
	23:04	0.6	18				
9 Th	05:44	2.0	61	24 F	00:04	1.4	43
	11:21	0.7	21		05:08	1.8	55
	18:14	2.1	64		11:33	0.5	15
	23:55	1.0	30		19:32	2.2	67
10 F	05:59	1.8	55	25 Sa	01:32	1.7	52
	12:03	0.5	15		05:03	1.8	55
	19:32	2.2	67		12:11	0.5	15
					20:51	2.2	
11 Sa	01:03	1.3	40	26 Su	12:56	0.5	15
	06:12	1.7	52		22:42	2.3	
	12:53	0.3	9				
	21:04	2.3	70				
12 Su	03:56	1.6	49	27 M	13:51	0.5	
	06:16	1.7	52				
	13:53	0.1	3				
	22:49	2.4	73				
13 M ◖	15:01	0.0	0	28 Tu	00:05	2.4	
					14:54	0.5	
14 Tu	00:15	2.6	79	29 W ◐	00:58	2.4	
	16:14	0.0	0		16:01	0.5	
15 W	01:18	2.6	79	30 Th	01:39	2.5	
	17:32	0.0	0		17:09	0.5	

StationId: 8771416
Source: NOAA/NOS/CO-OPS
Station Type: Primary
Time Zone: LST_LDT
Datum: MLLW

NOAA Tide Predictions

Galveston Bay Entrance, South Jetty, TX,2021

Times and Heights of High and Low Waters

October

Day	Time	ft	cm
1 F	02:12	2.5	76
	18:12	0.5	15
2 Sa	02:39	2.5	76
	09:26	1.6	49
	12:12	1.7	52
	19:09	0.5	15
3 Su	03:01	2.4	73
	09:26	1.5	46
	13:24	1.9	58
	20:00	0.5	15
4 M	03:21	2.4	73
	09:19	1.4	43
	14:27	2.0	61
	20:46	0.6	18
5 Tu	03:40	2.3	70
	09:19	1.1	34
	15:27	2.2	67
	21:31	0.8	24
6 W	03:59	2.2	67
	09:39	0.8	24
	16:27	2.4	73
	22:18	1.0	30
7 Th	04:15	2.1	64
	10:09	0.5	15
	17:28	2.6	79
	23:08	1.3	40
8 F	04:29	2.0	61
	10:46	0.2	6
	18:31	2.7	82
9 Sa	00:10	1.6	49
	04:40	1.9	58
	11:28	0.1	3
	19:41	2.7	82
10 Su	12:19	0.0	0
	21:05	2.7	82
11 M	13:21	0.0	0
	22:41	2.8	85
12 Tu	14:35	0.1	3
13 W	00:01	2.8	85
	16:00	0.3	9
14 Th	00:58	2.7	82
	17:32	0.4	12
15 F	01:43	2.6	79
	08:31	1.6	49
	11:53	1.8	55
	18:54	0.5	15
16 Sa	02:19	2.5	76
	08:40	1.5	46
	13:14	2.0	61
	20:00	0.6	18
17 Su	02:48	2.3	70
	08:58	1.3	40
	14:20	2.1	64
	20:53	0.8	24
18 M	03:09	2.2	67
	09:15	1.1	34
	15:19	2.2	67
	21:39	1.0	30
19 Tu	03:26	2.1	64
	09:28	0.9	27
	16:13	2.4	73
	22:19	1.2	37
20 W ○	03:37	2.0	61
	09:41	0.6	18
	17:02	2.4	73
	22:58	1.5	46
21 Th	03:42	1.9	58
	10:00	0.5	15
	17:47	2.5	76
	23:40	1.6	49
22 F	03:39	1.9	58
	10:25	0.3	9
	18:33	2.5	76
23 Sa	00:54	1.8	55
	03:36	1.9	58
	10:55	0.3	9
	19:23	2.5	76
24 Su	11:28	0.3	9
	20:24	2.5	76
25 M	12:07	0.4	12
	21:49	2.4	73
26 Tu	12:55	0.4	12
	23:17	2.5	76
27 W	13:56	0.5	15
28 Th	00:12	2.5	76
	15:06	0.6	18
29 F	00:47	2.5	76
	16:16	0.7	21
30 Sa	01:13	2.4	73
	17:25	0.7	21
31 Su	01:34	2.4	73
	08:31	1.4	43
	12:33	1.7	52
	18:33	0.8	24

November

Day	Time	ft	cm
1 M	01:54	2.3	70
	08:23	1.2	37
	13:42	2.0	61
	19:39	0.9	27
2 Tu	02:13	2.2	67
	08:18	0.9	27
	14:44	2.2	67
	20:39	1.1	34
3 W	02:30	2.1	64
	08:36	0.6	18
	15:43	2.5	76
	21:35	1.2	37
4 Th ●	02:46	2.0	61
	09:02	0.2	6
	16:41	2.8	85
	22:31	1.5	46
5 F ○	03:01	1.9	58
	09:41	-0.2	-6
	17:38	2.9	88
	23:35	1.7	52
6 Sa	03:15	1.9	58
	10:22	-0.4	-12
	18:37	3.0	91
7 Su	10:07	-0.4	-12
	18:42	2.9	88
8 M	11:00	-0.3	-9
	19:57	2.8	85
9 Tu	12:02	-0.1	-3
	21:20	2.7	82
10 W	13:17	0.1	3
	22:31	2.6	79
11 Th ☽	14:48	0.4	12
	23:21	2.4	73
12 F	06:31	1.5	46
	09:31	1.6	49
	16:24	0.6	18
	23:58	2.3	70
13 Sa	06:35	1.3	40
	11:25	1.7	52
	17:47	0.8	24
14 Su	00:25	2.1	64
	06:56	1.0	30
	12:42	1.9	58
	18:56	1.0	30
15 M	00:46	2.0	61
	07:19	0.8	24
	13:46	2.1	64
	19:54	1.2	37
16 Tu	01:01	1.9	58
	07:38	0.5	15
	14:42	2.2	67
	20:46	1.4	43
17 W	01:12	1.8	55
	07:54	0.3	9
	15:30	2.4	73
	21:34	1.5	46
18 Th	01:14	1.7	52
	08:11	0.1	3
	16:13	2.5	76
	22:24	1.6	49
19 F ○	01:11	1.7	52
	08:32	0.0	0
	16:52	2.5	76
20 Sa	08:58	-0.1	-3
	17:30	2.5	76
21 Su	09:28	-0.1	-3
	18:12	2.4	73
22 M	10:00	-0.1	-3
	19:00	2.4	73
23 Tu	10:37	0.0	0
	20:01	2.3	70
24 W	11:21	0.1	3
	21:09	2.3	70
25 Th	12:14	0.3	9
	22:02	2.2	67
26 F	13:18	0.4	12
	22:37	2.2	67
27 Sa ☽	14:28	0.5	15
	23:02	2.1	64
28 Su	06:32	1.1	34
	10:14	1.3	40
	15:41	0.7	21
	23:23	2.0	61
29 M	06:18	0.9	27
	11:46	1.6	49
	17:01	0.9	27
	23:42	1.9	58
30 Tu	06:10	0.6	18
	12:54	1.9	58
	18:31	1.1	34
	23:59	1.8	55

December

Day	Time	ft	cm
1 W	06:28	0.2	6
	13:55	2.2	67
	19:54	1.2	37
2 Th	00:14	1.7	52
	07:00	-0.2	-6
	14:53	2.5	76
	21:04	1.4	43
3 F	00:31	1.7	52
	07:39	-0.6	-18
	15:48	2.7	82
	22:10	1.6	49
4 Sa ●	00:51	1.7	52
	08:22	-0.8	-24
	16:42	2.8	85
5 Su	09:07	-0.9	-27
	17:37	2.8	85
6 M	09:56	-0.9	-27
	18:35	2.6	79
7 Tu	10:50	-0.7	-21
	19:37	2.4	73
8 W	11:51	-0.4	-12
	20:42	2.2	67
9 Th	13:02	0.0	0
	21:40	2.0	61
10 F	04:41	1.2	37
	06:44	1.3	40
	14:27	0.3	9
	22:23	1.9	58
11 Sa ☽	05:07	1.0	30
	09:58	1.3	40
	16:02	0.6	18
	22:53	1.7	52
12 Su	05:37	0.7	21
	11:44	1.5	46
	17:32	0.9	27
	23:15	1.6	49
13 M	06:07	0.4	12
	12:59	1.7	52
	18:52	1.1	34
	23:31	1.5	46
14 Tu	06:34	0.1	3
	14:00	1.9	58
	20:01	1.2	37
	23:41	1.4	43
15 W	06:59	-0.1	-3
	14:52	2.0	61
	21:02	1.3	40
	23:38	1.4	43
16 Th	07:21	-0.3	-9
	15:36	2.1	64
17 F	07:44	-0.4	-12
	16:14	2.2	67
18 Sa	08:10	-0.5	-15
	16:49	2.2	67
19 Su ○	08:40	-0.5	-15
	17:22	2.2	67
20 M	09:11	-0.5	-15
	17:57	2.1	64
21 Tu	09:44	-0.5	-15
	18:34	2.0	61
22 W	10:20	-0.4	-12
	19:15	2.0	61
23 Th	11:00	-0.3	-9
	19:58	1.9	58
24 F	11:48	-0.1	-3
	20:38	1.8	55
25 Sa	12:46	0.1	3
	21:12	1.7	52
26 Su	05:00	0.8	24
	07:43	0.9	27
	13:55	0.4	12
	21:39	1.6	49
27 M ☽	04:45	0.6	18
	10:28	1.1	34
	15:12	0.7	21
	22:00	1.4	43
28 Tu	04:40	0.2	6
	11:53	1.4	43
	16:49	0.9	27
	22:18	1.3	40
29 W	05:07	-0.2	-6
	13:00	1.8	55
	19:09	1.1	34
	22:34	1.3	40
30 Th	05:47	-0.6	-18
	14:01	2.1	64
	20:35	1.2	37
	22:54	1.3	40
31 F	06:33	-0.9	-27
	14:58	2.3	70

StationId: 8773701
Source: NOAA/NOS/CO-OPS
Station Type: Primary
Time Zone: LST_LDT
Datum: MLLW

NOAA Tide Predictions

Port O'Connor, TX, 2021

Times and Heights of High and Low Waters

January

Day	Time	ft	cm	Day	Time	ft	cm
1 F	01:28	0.9	27	16 Sa	02:22	0.8	24
	13:07	-0.3	-9		13:58	-0.1	-3
2 Sa	02:10	0.9	27	17 Su	01:06	0.7	21
	13:48	-0.2	-6		14:30	0.0	0
					23:57	0.6	18
3 Su	02:38	0.8	24	18 M	14:46	0.2	6
	14:30	-0.1	-3		22:47	0.5	15
4 M	02:20	0.7	21	19 Tu	06:39	0.4	12
	15:10	0.0	0		08:59	0.4	12
					13:11	0.3	9
					21:49	0.5	15
5 Tu	01:17	0.6	18	20 W	06:34	0.2	6
	15:46	0.2	6		21:03	0.6	18
	23:35	0.5	15				
6 W	06:24	0.4	12	21 Th	06:59	0.1	3
	21:46	0.5	15		20:14	0.7	21
7 Th	06:46	0.2	6	22 F	07:31	0.1	3
	21:03	0.6	18		19:57	0.7	21
8 F	07:26	0.0	0	23 Sa	08:08	0.0	0
	20:41	0.8	24		20:18	0.8	24
9 Sa	08:16	-0.1	-3	24 Su	08:50	0.0	0
	20:53	0.9	27		20:53	0.8	24
10 Su	09:12	-0.2	-6	25 M	09:34	-0.1	-3
	21:35	0.9	27		21:35	0.8	24
11 M	10:09	-0.3	-9	26 Tu	10:18	-0.1	-3
	22:32	0.9	27		22:23	0.9	27
12 Tu	11:04	-0.3	-9	27 W	11:00	-0.2	-6
	23:45	0.9	27		23:21	0.9	27
13 W	11:54	-0.3	-9	28 Th	11:40	-0.2	-6
14 Th	00:59	0.9	27	29 F	00:35	0.9	27
	12:39	-0.3	-9		12:19	-0.2	-6
15 F	01:53	0.9	27	30 Sa	01:50	0.9	27
	13:21	-0.2	-6		12:57	-0.2	-6
				31 Su	03:00	0.8	24
					13:36	-0.1	-3

February

Day	Time	ft	cm	Day	Time	ft	cm
1 M	04:22	0.6	18	16 Tu	02:49	0.3	9
	14:13	0.1	3		09:20	0.4	12
	22:53	0.5	15		13:27	0.4	12
					19:38	0.5	15
2 Tu	02:13	0.5	15	17 W	03:46	0.2	6
	06:50	0.5	15		18:33	0.6	18
	14:46	0.3	9				
	20:58	0.4	12				
3 W	03:38	0.3	9	18 Th	04:39	0.1	3
	11:16	0.5	15		17:44	0.6	18
	14:11	0.5	15				
	19:39	0.5	15				
4 Th	04:49	0.1	3	19 F	05:29	0.1	3
	19:04	0.6	18		17:59	0.7	21
5 F	05:53	0.0	0	20 Sa	06:20	0.1	3
	19:04	0.8	24		18:36	0.7	21
6 Sa	06:57	-0.1	-3	21 Su	07:13	0.0	0
	19:45	0.8	24		19:22	0.8	24
7 Su	08:03	-0.1	-3	22 M	08:09	0.0	0
	20:39	0.9	27		20:11	0.8	24
8 M	09:10	-0.2	-6	23 Tu	09:05	-0.1	-3
	21:37	0.9	27		20:59	0.8	24
9 Tu	10:12	-0.2	-6	24 W	09:55	-0.1	-3
	22:41	0.9	27		21:51	0.8	24
10 W	11:04	-0.2	-6	25 Th	10:41	-0.2	-6
					23:10	0.8	24
11 Th	00:06	0.8	24	26 F	11:24	-0.1	-3
	11:49	-0.2	-6				
12 F	01:35	0.8	24	27 Sa	01:35	0.8	24
	12:27	-0.1	-3		12:06	-0.1	-3
13 Sa	02:47	0.7	21	28 Su	03:17	0.7	21
	13:01	0.0	0		12:47	0.0	0
	22:32	0.6	18		21:41	0.5	15
					23:49	0.5	15
14 Su	00:46	0.6	18				
	04:04	0.6	18				
	13:29	0.1	3				
	21:43	0.5	15				
15 M	01:50	0.4	12				
	06:12	0.5	15				
	13:48	0.3	9				
	20:38	0.5	15				

March

Day	Time	ft	cm	Day	Time	ft	cm
1 M	05:07	0.6	18	16 Tu	02:00	0.2	6
	13:29	0.2	6		10:41	0.5	15
	20:16	0.4	12		14:15	0.5	15
					17:12	0.5	15
2 Tu	00:43	0.3	9	17 W	02:33	0.1	3
	08:03	0.6	18		16:35	0.6	18
	14:11	0.4	12				
	17:29	0.4	12				
3 W	01:37	0.2	6	18 Th	03:08	0.1	3
	10:47	0.6	18		16:41	0.7	21
4 Th	02:40	0.0	0	19 F	03:49	0.1	3
	16:01	0.7	21		17:07	0.7	21
5 F	03:57	0.0	0	20 Sa	04:48	0.1	3
	16:51	0.8	24		17:43	0.7	21
6 Sa	05:20	-0.1	-3	21 Su	06:04	0.0	0
	17:54	0.8	24		18:25	0.8	24
7 Su	06:40	-0.1	-3	22 M	07:17	0.0	0
	19:04	0.8	24		19:13	0.8	24
8 M	07:55	-0.1	-3	23 Tu	08:22	0.0	0
	20:11	0.8	24		20:03	0.8	24
9 Tu	09:04	-0.1	-3	24 W	09:23	-0.1	
	21:10	0.8	24		20:51	0.8	
10 W	10:03	-0.1	-3	25 Th	10:20	-0.1	
	22:10	0.7	21		21:30	0.7	
11 Th	10:52	-0.1	-3	26 F	11:15	0.0	
12 F	01:18	0.7	21	27 Sa	02:19	0.6	
	11:33	0.0	0		12:07	0.1	
	20:55	0.5	15		20:59	0.5	
	23:14	0.5	15		23:21	0.5	
13 Sa	03:09	0.6	18	28 Su	04:38	0.6	
	12:09	0.1	3		19:39	0.4	
	20:17	0.5	15		23:59	0.3	
	23:52	0.4	12				
14 Su	06:04	0.5	15	29 M	07:15	0.6	
	13:41	0.3	9		13:54	0.4	
	19:40	0.4	12		16:37	0.4	
15 M	01:27	0.3	9	30 Tu	00:41	0.1	
	08:50	0.5	15		09:32	0.7	
	14:06	0.4	12				
	18:04	0.5	15				
				31 W	01:26	0.0	
					11:17	0.7	

StationId: 8773701
Source: NOAA/NOS/CO-OPS
Station Type: Primary
Time Zone: LST_LDT
Datum: MLLW

NOAA Tide Predictions

Port O'Connor, TX, 2021

Times and Heights of High and Low Waters

April

Day	Time	ft	cm
1 (Th)	02:15	-0.1	-3
	14:01	0.8	24
2	03:15	-0.1	-3
	16:12	0.8	24
3	04:31	-0.1	-3
	17:14	0.8	24
4	06:01	-0.1	-3
	18:10	0.8	24
5	07:23	-0.1	-3
	19:01	0.8	24
6	08:34	0.0	0
	19:39	0.7	21
7	09:38	0.0	0
	19:51	0.7	21
8	10:36	0.1	3
	19:43	0.6	18
	23:31	0.5	15
9	02:21	0.5	15
	11:27	0.2	6
	19:14	0.5	15
	23:38	0.4	12
10	05:41	0.5	15
	12:15	0.3	9
	17:20	0.4	12
11	00:03	0.2	6
	08:04	0.6	18
	13:02	0.4	12
	16:01	0.5	15
12	00:29	0.1	3
	09:38	0.6	18
13	00:55	0.0	0
	10:55	0.7	21
14	01:21	0.0	0
	12:25	0.7	21
15	01:48	0.0	0
	14:51	0.7	21
16 (F)	02:18	0.0	0
	15:36	0.7	21
17 (Sa)	02:56	0.0	0
	16:14	0.8	24
18 (Su)	03:49	0.0	0
	16:50	0.8	24
19 (M)	05:04	0.0	0
	17:24	0.8	24
20 (Tu)	06:22	0.0	0
	17:57	0.8	24
21 (W)	07:29	0.0	0
	18:24	0.7	21
22 (Th)	08:32	0.0	0
	18:39	0.7	21
23 (F)	09:36	0.1	3
	18:34	0.5	15
	22:44	0.5	15
24 (Sa)	02:03	0.5	15
	10:46	0.2	6
	17:44	0.4	12
	22:38	0.3	9
25 (Su)	05:41	0.6	18
	12:05	0.4	12
	15:18	0.4	12
	23:07	0.1	3
26 (M)	07:56	0.7	21
	23:44	0.0	0
27 (Tu)	09:30	0.8	24
28 (W)	00:27	-0.1	-3
	10:51	0.8	24
29 (Th)	01:14	-0.2	-6
	12:27	0.9	27
30 (F)	02:06	-0.2	-6
	14:45	0.9	27

May

Day	Time	ft	cm
1 (Sa)	03:07	-0.2	-6
	15:58	0.9	27
2 (Su)	04:21	-0.2	-6
	16:45	0.9	27
3 (M)	05:41	-0.1	-3
	17:18	0.8	24
4 (Tu)	06:53	0.0	0
	17:35	0.7	21
5 (W)	07:54	0.1	3
	17:37	0.6	18
6 (Th)	08:51	0.2	6
	17:21	0.5	15
	23:02	0.4	12
7 (F)	04:37	0.4	12
	09:50	0.3	9
	16:18	0.5	15
	22:50	0.3	9
8 (Sa)	06:54	0.5	15
	11:02	0.5	15
	14:24	0.5	15
	23:10	0.1	3
9 (Su)	08:39	0.6	18
	23:35	0.0	0
10 (M)	09:54	0.7	21
11 (Tu)	00:00	-0.1	-3
	10:52	0.8	24
12 (W)	00:26	-0.1	-3
	11:47	0.8	24
13 (Th)	00:53	-0.1	-3
	12:53	0.8	24
14 (F)	01:23	-0.1	-3
	14:07	0.8	24
15 (Sa)	01:57	-0.1	-3
	14:58	0.8	24
16 (Su)	02:37	-0.1	-3
	15:36	0.8	24
17 (M)	03:27	-0.1	-3
	16:05	0.8	24
18 (Tu)	04:26	-0.1	-3
	16:26	0.8	24
19 (W)	05:30	0.0	0
	16:39	0.8	24
20 (Th)	06:33	0.0	0
	16:40	0.7	21
21 (F)	07:35	0.2	6
	16:19	0.5	15
	22:02	0.4	12
22 (Sa)	03:18	0.4	12
	08:45	0.3	9
	14:32	0.5	15
	21:43	0.2	6
23 (Su)	06:25	0.6	18
	22:09	0.0	0
24 (M)	08:08	0.7	21
	22:48	-0.1	-3
25 (Tu)	09:24	0.8	24
	23:33	-0.2	-6
26 (W)	10:32	0.9	27
27 (Th)	00:22	-0.3	-9
	11:46	0.9	27
28 (F)	01:13	-0.3	-9
	13:30	1.0	30
29 (Sa)	02:08	-0.3	-9
	14:56	0.9	27
30 (Su)	03:06	-0.2	-6
	15:43	0.9	27
31 (M)	04:07	-0.2	-6
	16:05	0.8	24

June

Day	Time	ft	cm
1 (Tu)	05:08	-0.1	-3
	16:07	0.7	21
2 (W)	06:05	0.1	3
	15:56	0.6	18
3 (Th)	06:55	0.2	6
	15:21	0.5	15
	22:03	0.3	9
4 (F)	05:03	0.4	12
	07:39	0.4	12
	13:24	0.5	15
	21:47	0.2	6
5 (Sa)	11:59	0.6	18
	22:08	0.1	3
6 (Su)	09:12	0.7	21
	22:35	0.0	0
7 (M)	09:47	0.8	24
	23:05	-0.1	-3
8 (Tu)	10:26	0.8	24
	23:36	-0.1	-3
9 (W)	11:07	0.9	27
10 (Th)	00:07	-0.2	-6
	11:54	0.9	27
11 (F)	00:39	-0.2	-6
	12:49	0.9	27
12 (Sa)	01:13	-0.2	-6
	13:47	0.9	27
13 (Su)	01:49	-0.2	-6
	14:32	0.9	27
14 (M)	02:28	-0.2	-6
	15:01	0.9	27
15 (Tu)	03:10	-0.1	-3
	15:14	0.8	24
16 (W)	03:55	-0.1	-3
	15:12	0.7	21
17 (Th)	04:42	0.0	0
	14:56	0.6	18
18 (F)	05:31	0.2	6
	13:58	0.5	15
	20:41	0.4	12
19 (Sa)	11:50	0.5	15
	20:34	0.2	6
20 (Su)	10:42	0.6	18
	21:04	0.0	0
21 (M)	08:42	0.7	21
	21:47	-0.1	-3
22 (Tu)	09:24	0.9	27
	22:37	-0.2	-6
23 (W)	10:18	0.9	27
	23:31	-0.3	-9
24 (Th)	11:20	1.0	30
25 (F)	00:25	-0.3	-9
	12:39	1.0	30
26 (Sa)	01:17	-0.3	-9
	14:05	0.9	27
27 (Su)	02:07	-0.3	-9
	14:58	0.9	27
28 (M)	02:55	-0.2	-6
	15:13	0.8	24
29 (Tu)	03:41	-0.1	-3
	14:45	0.7	21
30 (W)	04:22	0.1	3
	14:06	0.6	18

StationId: 8773701
Source: NOAA/NOS/CO-OPS
Station Type: Primary
Time Zone: LST_LDT
Datum: MLLW

Port O'Connor, TX, 2021

Times and Heights of High and Low Waters

July

Day	Time	ft	cm	Day	Time	ft	cm
1 Th ☽	04:55	0.2	6	16 F	03:54	0.2	6
	12:46	0.5	15		11:19	0.5	15
	20:23	0.3	9		18:37	0.3	9
2 F	11:25	0.5	15	17 Sa ☽	09:59	0.5	15
	20:25	0.2	6		19:04	0.2	6
3 Sa	10:30	0.6	18	18 Su	09:12	0.6	18
	20:51	0.1	3		19:46	0.0	0
4 Su	09:10	0.7	21	19 M	08:39	0.8	24
	21:24	0.0	0		20:38	-0.1	-3
5 M	09:07	0.8	24	20 Tu	09:02	0.9	27
	22:01	-0.1	-3		21:36	-0.2	-6
6 Tu	09:39	0.8	24	21 W	09:50	0.9	27
	22:40	-0.1	-3		22:37	-0.3	-9
7 W	10:17	0.9	27	22 Th	10:46	1.0	30
	23:18	-0.1	-3		23:36	-0.3	-9
8 Th	10:59	0.9	27	23 F	11:50	0.9	27
	23:56	-0.2	-6				
9 F	11:44	0.9	27	24 Sa ○	00:28	-0.3	-9
					13:11	0.9	27
10 Sa ●	00:31	-0.2	-6	25 Su	01:15	-0.3	-9
	12:33	0.9	27		14:29	0.8	24
11 Su	01:06	-0.2	-6	26 M	01:56	-0.2	-6
	13:23	0.9	27		15:24	0.8	24
12 M	01:40	-0.2	-6	27 Tu	02:34	-0.1	-3
	14:03	0.8	24		12:35	0.6	18
13 Tu	02:16	-0.2	-6	28 W	03:06	0.1	3
	14:03	0.8	24		11:46	0.6	18
14 W	02:51	-0.1	-3	29 Th	03:26	0.3	9
	13:23	0.7	21		10:39	0.5	15
					17:59	0.3	9
15 Th	03:26	0.1	3	30 F	09:44	0.5	15
	12:44	0.6	18		18:34	0.2	6
				31 Sa ☽	08:49	0.6	18
					19:12	0.1	3

August

Day	Time	ft	cm	Day	Time	ft	cm
1 Su	07:35	0.7	21	16 M	07:02	0.8	24
	19:54	0.0	0		19:16	-0.1	-3
2 M	07:49	0.8	24	17 Tu	07:52	0.9	27
	20:39	0.0	0		20:24	-0.2	-6
3 Tu	08:27	0.8	24	18 W	08:51	0.9	27
	21:27	-0.1	-3		21:33	-0.2	-6
4 W	09:10	0.8	24	19 Th	09:49	0.9	27
	22:15	-0.1	-3		22:38	-0.2	-6
5 Th	09:53	0.8	24	20 F	10:44	0.9	27
	23:00	-0.1	-3		23:34	-0.2	-6
6 F	10:35	0.9	27	21 Sa	11:41	0.8	24
	23:40	-0.1	-3				
7 Sa	11:15	0.9	27	22 Su ○	00:20	-0.2	-6
					14:01	0.8	24
8 Su ●	00:16	-0.2	-6	23 M	01:00	-0.1	-3
	11:51	0.8	24		15:44	0.7	21
9 M	00:51	-0.2	-6	24 Tu	01:36	0.0	0
	12:12	0.8	24		10:31	0.5	15
					13:43	0.5	15
					17:23	0.6	18
10 Tu	01:26	-0.1	-3	25 W	02:07	0.2	6
	15:29	0.7	21		09:38	0.5	15
					14:29	0.4	12
					20:19	0.5	15
11 W	02:01	0.0	0	26 Th	02:30	0.3	9
	11:22	0.6	18		08:14	0.5	15
	14:15	0.6	18		15:15	0.2	6
	17:15	0.6	18		23:22	0.5	15
12 Th	02:35	0.1	3	27 F	02:13	0.5	15
	10:37	0.5	15		07:09	0.5	15
	15:03	0.4	12		16:05	0.1	3
	20:11	0.5	15				
13 F	03:04	0.3	9	28 Sa	05:53	0.6	18
	08:52	0.5	15		16:58	0.1	3
	16:00	0.2	6				
14 Sa	07:41	0.5	15	29 Su	05:40	0.7	21
	17:03	0.1	3		17:55	0.0	0
15 Su ☽	06:56	0.7	21	30 M ☽	06:09	0.8	24
	18:09	0.0	0		18:53	0.0	0
				31 Tu	06:50	0.8	24
					19:50	0.0	0

September

Day	Time	ft	cm	Day	Time	ft	cm
1 W	07:37	0.8	24	16 Th	08:19	0.9	27
	20:47	0.0	0		21:23	-0.1	-3
2 Th	08:24	0.8	24	17 F	09:08	0.8	24
	21:40	-0.1	-3		22:24	-0.1	-3
3 F	09:07	0.8	24	18 Sa	09:29	0.7	21
	22:27	-0.1	-3		23:15	0.0	
4 Sa	09:42	0.8	24	19 Su	09:17	0.6	18
	23:11	-0.1	-3				
5 Su	10:06	0.8	24	20 M ○	00:00	0.1	
	23:52	-0.1	-3		08:56	0.5	
					12:19	0.5	
					16:02	0.5	
6 M	10:10	0.7	21	21 Tu	00:39	0.2	
					08:08	0.5	
					12:47	0.3	
					18:43	0.5	
7 Tu ●	00:32	0.0	0	22 W	01:14	0.3	
	09:55	0.6	18		06:02	0.5	
	12:39	0.6	18		13:17	0.5	
	16:02	0.6	18		21:31	0.5	
8 W	01:12	0.1	3	23 Th	01:46	0.5	
	09:24	0.5	15		05:09	0.5	
	13:02	0.4	12		13:49	0.1	
	18:12	0.6	18		23:19	0.6	
9 Th	01:52	0.3	9	24 F	02:01	0.6	
	07:14	0.4	12		04:26	0.6	
	13:38	0.2	6		14:22	0.0	
	21:29	0.6	18				
10 F	02:32	0.4	12	25 Sa	03:52	0.7	
	05:43	0.5	15		14:58	0.0	
	14:21	0.1	3				
	23:54	0.6	18				
11 Sa	02:56	0.6	18	26 Su	04:09	0.7	
	04:58	0.6	18		15:41	0.0	
	15:13	0.0	0				
12 Su	04:43	0.7	21	27 M	04:42	0.8	
	16:19	-0.1	-3		16:37	0.0	
13 M ☽	05:23	0.8	24	28 Tu	05:18	0.8	
	17:39	-0.1	-3		17:46	0.0	
14 Tu ☽	06:17	0.9	27	29 W	05:56	0.8	
	19:00	-0.1	-3		18:53	0.0	
15 W	07:18	0.9	27	30 Th	06:35	0.8	
	20:15	-0.1	-3		19:52	0.0	

StationId: 8773701
Source: NOAA/NOS/CO-OPS
Station Type: Primary
Time Zone: LST_LDT
Datum: MLLW

NOAA Tide Predictions

Port O'Connor, TX,2021

Times and Heights of High and Low Waters

October

Day	Time	ft	cm
1 F	07:10	0.8	24
	20:45	0.0	0
2 Sa	07:39	0.8	24
	21:37	0.0	0
3 Su	07:56	0.7	21
	22:30	0.0	0
4 M	07:56	0.6	18
	23:23	0.1	3
5 Tu	07:34	0.5	15
	11:47	0.4	12
	16:38	0.5	15
6 W	00:17	0.3	9
	05:44	0.4	12
	12:03	0.3	9
	19:42	0.6	18
7 Th	01:13	0.4	12
	04:10	0.5	15
	12:35	0.1	3
	21:43	0.7	21
8 F	13:13	-0.1	-3
	23:22	0.8	24
9 Sa	13:59	-0.1	-3
10 Su	02:36	0.8	24
	14:54	-0.2	-6
11 M	04:03	0.9	27
	16:03	-0.2	-6
12 Tu	04:58	0.9	27
	17:25	-0.2	-6
13 W	05:47	0.9	27
	18:45	-0.1	-3
14 Th	06:30	0.9	27
	19:53	-0.1	-3
15 F	06:57	0.8	24
	20:53	0.0	0
16 Sa	07:04	0.7	21
	21:48	0.1	3
17 Su	06:55	0.6	18
	22:41	0.2	6
18 M	06:19	0.5	15
	11:36	0.4	12
	18:04	0.5	15
	23:32	0.3	9
19 Tu	04:29	0.5	15
	11:55	0.2	6
	20:25	0.6	18
20 W ○	00:24	0.5	15
	03:28	0.5	15
	12:21	0.1	3
	21:59	0.6	18
21 Th	12:48	0.0	0
	23:20	0.7	21
22 F	13:17	-0.1	-3
23 Sa	01:17	0.8	24
	13:48	-0.1	-3
24 Su	02:41	0.8	24
	14:21	-0.1	-3
25 M	03:26	0.8	24
	14:59	-0.1	-3
26 Tu	04:04	0.8	24
	15:47	-0.1	-3
27 W	04:36	0.8	24
	16:46	0.0	0
28 Th ◗	05:03	0.8	24
	17:49	0.0	0
29 F	05:25	0.8	24
	18:47	0.0	0
30 Sa	05:41	0.8	24
	19:41	0.0	0
31 Su	05:47	0.7	21
	20:37	0.1	3

November

Day	Time	ft	cm
1 M	05:38	0.6	18
	21:41	0.3	9
2 Tu	04:50	0.5	15
	10:52	0.3	9
	17:57	0.5	15
	23:01	0.4	12
3 W	03:01	0.5	15
	11:05	0.1	3
	20:09	0.6	18
4 Th ●	11:36	0.0	0
	21:39	0.8	24
5 F	12:16	-0.2	-6
	22:59	0.9	27
6 Sa	13:02	-0.3	-9
7 Su	00:47	0.9	27
	12:54	-0.3	-9
8 M	01:55	0.9	27
	13:52	-0.3	-9
9 Tu	02:56	1.0	30
	14:59	-0.2	-6
10 W	03:40	0.9	27
	16:10	-0.2	-6
11 Th ◗	04:08	0.9	27
	17:17	-0.1	-3
12 F	04:19	0.8	24
	18:14	0.0	0
13 Sa	04:14	0.7	21
	19:04	0.2	6
14 Su	03:55	0.6	18
	19:52	0.3	9
15 M	02:50	0.5	15
	09:42	0.2	6
	18:00	0.5	15
	20:47	0.5	15
16 Tu	01:01	0.5	15
	09:59	0.1	3
	20:01	0.6	18
17 W	10:25	0.0	0
	21:13	0.7	21
18 Th	10:55	-0.1	-3
	22:08	0.8	24
19 F ○	11:25	-0.1	-3
	23:07	0.8	24
20 Sa	11:57	-0.2	-6
21 Su	00:16	0.8	24
	12:29	-0.2	-6
22 M	01:17	0.9	27
	13:03	-0.1	-3
23 Tu	02:01	0.9	27
	13:39	-0.1	-3
24 W	02:32	0.9	27
	14:19	-0.1	-3
25 Th	02:54	0.9	27
	15:03	-0.1	-3
26 F	03:07	0.8	24
	15:52	-0.1	-3
27 Sa ◖	03:11	0.8	24
	16:42	0.0	0
28 Su	03:07	0.7	21
	17:34	0.2	6
29 M	02:46	0.6	18
	18:28	0.3	9
30 Tu	01:22	0.5	15
	08:46	0.2	6
	23:38	0.5	15

December

Day	Time	ft	cm
1 W	09:01	0.1	3
	19:34	0.7	21
2 Th	09:36	-0.1	-3
	20:41	0.8	24
3 F	10:21	-0.2	-6
	21:47	0.9	27
4 Sa ●	11:11	-0.3	-9
	23:12	1.0	30
5 Su	12:03	-0.3	-9
6 M	01:00	1.0	30
	12:57	-0.3	-9
7 Tu	02:08	1.0	30
	13:53	-0.3	-9
8 W	02:52	1.0	30
	14:49	-0.2	-6
9 Th	03:15	0.9	27
	15:44	-0.1	-3
10 F	03:09	0.8	24
	16:34	0.0	0
11 Sa ◖	02:47	0.7	21
	17:19	0.2	6
12 Su ◗	02:08	0.6	18
	12:22	0.3	9
	15:32	0.4	12
	17:51	0.4	12
13 M	00:10	0.5	15
	08:30	0.2	6
	22:57	0.6	18
14 Tu	08:52	0.1	3
	21:42	0.7	21
15 W	09:23	-0.1	-3
	21:01	0.8	24
16 Th	09:59	-0.1	-3
	21:33	0.8	24
17 F	10:36	-0.2	-6
	22:17	0.9	27
18 Sa	11:13	-0.2	-6
	23:10	0.9	27
19 Su ○	11:48	-0.2	-6
20 M	00:09	0.9	27
	12:20	-0.2	-6
21 Tu	01:00	0.9	27
	12:52	-0.2	-6
22 W	01:37	0.9	27
	13:23	-0.2	-6
23 Th	02:00	0.9	27
	13:56	-0.1	-3
24 F	02:06	0.8	24
	14:30	-0.1	-3
25 Sa	01:53	0.8	24
	15:06	0.0	0
26 Su	01:31	0.7	21
	15:41	0.2	6
27 M ◗	00:41	0.6	18
	14:06	0.3	9
	22:54	0.5	15
28 Tu	07:23	0.2	6
	21:52	0.6	18
29 W	07:48	0.1	3
	21:03	0.7	21
30 Th	08:31	-0.1	-3
	20:51	0.8	24
31 F	09:23	-0.2	-6
	21:33	1.0	30

StationId: 8779750
Source: NOAA/NOS/CO-OPS
Station Type: Primary
Time Zone: LST_LDT
Datum: MLLW

NOAA Tide Predictions

South Padre Island, Brazos Santiago Pass, TX, 2021

Times and Heights of High and Low Waters

January

Day	Time	ft	cm	Day	Time	ft	cm
1 F	09:48	-0.6	-18	16 Sa	10:57	-0.4	-12
	19:49	1.7	52		19:46	1.2	37
2 Sa	10:30	-0.5	-15	17 Su	11:38	0.0	0
	20:14	1.6	49		19:48	1.1	34
3 Su	11:15	-0.3	-9	18 M	01:41	0.8	24
	20:27	1.5	46		04:48	0.9	27
					12:16	0.3	9
					19:42	1.0	30
4 M	12:03	0.0	0	19 Tu	02:17	0.6	18
	20:29	1.3	40		07:24	0.8	24
					12:53	0.6	18
					19:28	1.0	30
5 Tu	12:57	0.3	9	20 W ◑	02:56	0.3	9
	20:21	1.1	34		10:44	0.8	24
					13:28	0.8	24
					18:59	0.9	27
6 W ◑	03:21	0.5	15	21 Th	03:35	0.1	3
	09:25	0.8	24		17:30	1.0	30
	14:05	0.7	21				
	20:02	1.0	30				
7 Th	03:49	0.0	0	22 F	04:14	-0.1	-3
	12:19	1.0	30		14:36	1.1	34
	16:05	1.0	30				
	19:18	1.0	30				
8 F	04:29	-0.4	-12	23 Sa	04:54	-0.3	-9
	14:01	1.3	40		15:11	1.2	37
9 Sa	05:15	-0.8	-24	24 Su	05:35	-0.5	-15
	15:08	1.5	46		15:46	1.3	40
10 Su	06:04	-1.0	-30	25 M	06:15	-0.6	-18
	16:06	1.6	49		16:21	1.3	40
11 M	06:56	-1.2	-37	26 Tu	06:56	-0.7	-21
	17:00	1.6	49		16:57	1.4	43
12 Tu	07:48	-1.2	-37	27 W	07:37	-0.8	-24
	17:51	1.6	49		17:32	1.5	46
13 W ●	08:38	-1.1	-34	28 Th ○	08:18	-0.8	-24
	18:36	1.5	46		18:03	1.5	46
14 Th	09:27	-0.9	-27	29 F	09:00	-0.7	-21
	19:12	1.5	46		18:27	1.4	43
15 F	10:14	-0.7	-21	30 Sa	09:42	-0.6	-18
	19:35	1.4	43		18:43	1.3	40
				31 Su	10:27	-0.4	-12
					18:48	1.2	37

February

Day	Time	ft	cm	Day	Time	ft	cm
1 M	00:08	0.9	27	16 Tu	06:05	0.9	27
	03:12	0.9	27		12:00	0.6	18
	11:14	-0.1	-3		17:31	0.8	24
	18:45	1.0	30				
2 Tu	00:33	0.6	18	17 W	00:29	0.3	9
	05:31	0.8	24		08:06	0.9	27
	12:05	0.2	6		12:44	0.8	24
	18:32	0.9	27		16:55	0.9	27
3 W	01:12	0.2	6	18 Th	01:14	0.1	3
	08:07	0.8	24		10:53	0.9	27
	13:07	0.6	18				
	18:06	0.8	24				
4 Th ◐	02:01	-0.2	-6	19 F ◑	02:04	0.0	0
	10:59	1.0	30		13:03	1.1	34
5 F	02:55	-0.5	-15	20 Sa	02:58	-0.2	-6
	13:05	1.2	37		13:52	1.2	37
6 Sa	03:54	-0.8	-24	21 Su	03:54	-0.3	-9
	14:17	1.4	43		14:31	1.3	40
7 Su	04:54	-1.0	-30	22 M	04:50	-0.4	-12
	15:14	1.5	46		15:07	1.4	43
8 M	05:54	-1.1	-34	23 Tu	05:42	-0.4	-12
	16:04	1.5	46		15:40	1.4	43
9 Tu	06:52	-1.0	-30	24 W	06:31	-0.5	-15
	16:48	1.5	46		16:09	1.5	46
10 W	07:46	-0.9	-27	25 Th	07:18	-0.5	-15
	17:24	1.4	43		16:33	1.5	46
11 Th ●	08:35	-0.7	-21	26 F	08:05	-0.5	-15
	17:48	1.3	40		16:50	1.4	43
	21:55	1.2	37		21:30	1.2	37
12 F ○	00:03	1.2	37	27 Sa ○	00:09	1.2	37
	09:21	-0.5	-15		08:52	-0.3	-9
	18:01	1.2	37		16:58	1.2	37
	22:04	1.0	30		21:35	1.0	30
13 Sa	01:38	1.1	34	28 Su	01:52	1.2	37
	10:04	-0.2	-6		09:41	-0.1	-3
	18:05	1.1	34		16:58	1.0	30
	22:33	0.9	27		22:00	0.7	21
14 Su	03:02	1.1	34				
	10:43	0.1	3				
	18:02	1.0	30				
	23:09	0.7	21				
15 M	04:28	1.0	30				
	11:22	0.3	9				
	17:51	0.9	27				
	23:48	0.5	15				

March

Day	Time	ft	cm	Day	Time	ft	cm
1 M	03:30	1.1	34	16 Tu	06:26	1.2	37
	10:33	0.2	6		12:35	0.8	24
	16:50	0.9	27		16:18	0.9	27
	22:35	0.3	9		23:37	0.2	6
2 Tu	05:12	1.1	34	17 W	07:47	1.2	37
	11:32	0.5	15				
	16:33	0.8	24				
	23:20	0.0	0				
3 W	07:06	1.1	34	18 Th	00:12	0.1	3
	12:51	0.8	24		09:21	1.2	37
	15:56	0.8	24				
4 Th ◐	00:11	-0.3	-9	19 F	00:52	0.0	0
	09:15	1.2	37		11:12	1.3	40
5 F	01:10	-0.6	-18	20 Sa	01:42	0.0	0
	11:22	1.4	43		12:45	1.3	40
6 Sa ◑	02:17	-0.7	-21	21 Su ◑	02:42	-0.1	-3
	12:53	1.5	46		13:45	1.4	43
7 Su	03:27	-0.7	-21	22 M	03:50	-0.1	-3
	13:56	1.6	49		14:29	1.5	46
8 M	04:38	-0.7	-21	23 Tu	04:58	-0.1	-3
	14:46	1.6	49		15:03	1.6	49
9 Tu	05:45	-0.6	-18	24 W	06:02	-0.1	-3
	15:24	1.5	46		15:30	1.6	49
10 W	06:46	-0.5	-15	25 Th	07:01	-0.1	-3
	15:51	1.4	43		15:49	1.6	49
11 Th	07:40	-0.3	-9	26 F	07:57	0.0	0
	16:06	1.3	40		16:01	1.4	43
	20:25	1.1	34		21:00	1.1	34
12 F	00:23	1.3	40	27 Sa	01:12	1.3	40
	08:29	0.0	0		08:53	0.1	3
	16:13	1.2	37		16:04	1.2	37
	20:42	1.0	30		21:11	0.8	24
13 Sa ●	01:46	1.3	40	28 Su ○	02:49	1.4	43
	09:15	0.2	6		09:51	0.3	9
	16:12	1.1	34		16:00	1.1	34
	21:07	0.8	24		21:36	0.5	15
14 Su	04:00	1.3	40	29 M	04:17	1.4	43
	10:59	0.4	12		10:54	0.6	18
	17:04	1.0	30		15:47	0.9	27
	22:36	0.6	18		22:11	0.1	3
15 M	05:12	1.2	37	30 Tu	05:45	1.5	46
	11:44	0.6	18		12:11	0.8	24
	16:47	0.9	27		15:20	0.9	27
	23:05	0.4	12		22:53	-0.2	-6
				31 W	07:17	1.5	46
					23:41	-0.5	-15

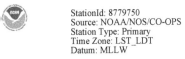

StationId: 8779750
Source: NOAA/NOS/CO-OPS
Station Type: Primary
Time Zone: LST_LDT
Datum: MLLW

NOAA Tide Predictions

South Padre Island, Brazos Santiago Pass, TX,2021

Times and Heights of High and Low Waters

April

Day	Time (h m)	ft	cm
1 Th	08:55	1.6	49
2	00:36	-0.6	-18
	10:37	1.7	52
3	01:38	-0.7	-21
	12:09	1.7	52
4	02:48	-0.6	-18
	13:19	1.7	52
5	04:04	-0.4	-12
	14:10	1.7	52
6	05:19	-0.2	-6
	14:44	1.6	49
7	06:29	0.0	0
	15:05	1.5	46
	20:29	1.2	37
	23:27	1.3	40
8	07:33	0.2	6
	15:15	1.4	43
	20:26	1.0	30
9	01:20	1.3	40
	08:30	0.4	12
	15:17	1.3	40
	20:43	0.8	24
10	02:45	1.4	43
	09:25	0.7	21
	15:12	1.2	37
	21:06	0.6	18
11	03:57	1.4	43
	10:21	0.8	24
	14:58	1.1	34
	21:30	0.4	12
12	05:03	1.5	46
	11:25	1.0	30
	14:29	1.0	30
	21:55	0.2	6
13	06:05	1.5	46
	22:21	0.1	3
14	07:06	1.5	46
	22:49	0.0	0
15	08:11	1.5	46
	23:22	-0.1	-3
16 F	09:23	1.5	46
17 Sa	00:01	-0.1	-3
	10:39	1.5	46
18 Su	00:49	-0.1	-3
	11:48	1.6	49
19 M	01:47	0.0	0
	12:40	1.7	52
20 Tu ◐	02:54	0.0	0
	13:17	1.7	52
21 W	04:05	0.1	3
	13:43	1.7	52
22 Th	05:17	0.2	6
	14:00	1.6	49
23 F	06:27	0.3	9
	14:08	1.5	46
	19:56	1.0	30
24 Sa	00:48	1.3	40
	07:38	0.5	15
	14:07	1.3	40
	20:04	0.6	18
25 Su	02:29	1.4	43
	08:52	0.7	21
	13:58	1.1	34
	20:29	0.2	6
26 M	03:55	1.5	46
	10:15	0.9	27
	13:36	1.0	30
	21:03	-0.2	-6
27 Tu ○	05:16	1.7	52
	21:43	-0.6	-18
28 W	06:35	1.8	55
	22:29	-0.8	-24
29 Th	07:55	1.8	55
	23:20	-0.9	-27
30 F	09:17	1.8	55

May

Day	Time (h m)	ft	cm
1 Sa	00:16	-0.8	-24
	10:35	1.8	55
2 Su	01:18	-0.7	-21
	11:41	1.8	55
3 M ◐	02:24	-0.4	-12
	12:30	1.7	52
4 Tu	03:36	-0.1	-3
	13:00	1.6	49
5 W	04:49	0.2	6
	13:17	1.5	46
	19:37	1.1	34
	22:41	1.1	34
6 Th	06:01	0.5	15
	13:23	1.4	43
	19:30	0.9	27
7 F	01:00	1.2	37
	07:12	0.7	21
	13:22	1.3	40
	19:48	0.6	18
8 Sa	02:34	1.3	40
	08:23	0.9	27
	13:11	1.2	37
	20:11	0.4	12
9 Su	03:49	1.4	43
	09:44	1.0	30
	12:45	1.1	34
	20:35	0.1	3
10 M	04:52	1.5	46
	21:00	-0.1	-3
11 Tu ●	05:47	1.5	46
	21:25	-0.2	-6
12 W	06:39	1.5	46
	21:51	-0.3	-9
13 Th	07:30	1.5	46
	22:21	-0.4	-12
14 F	08:24	1.5	46
	22:55	-0.4	-12
15 Sa	09:20	1.6	49
	23:34	-0.3	-9
16 Su	10:15	1.6	49
17 M	00:20	-0.3	-9
	11:02	1.7	52
18 Tu	01:11	-0.2	-6
	11:37	1.7	52
19 W ◐	02:10	0.0	0
	12:01	1.7	52
20 Th	03:17	0.2	6
	12:14	1.5	46
21 F	04:33	0.4	12
	12:17	1.4	43
	18:56	0.7	21
22 Sa	00:06	1.0	30
	05:59	0.6	18
	12:11	1.2	37
	19:00	0.3	9
23 Su	02:04	1.2	37
	07:36	0.8	24
	11:54	1.0	30
	19:25	-0.1	-3
24 M	03:32	1.4	43
	19:59	-0.6	-18
25 Tu	04:48	1.6	49
	20:41	-0.9	-27
26 W ○	05:58	1.7	52
	21:27	-1.2	-37
27 Th	07:07	1.8	55
	22:17	-1.2	-37
28 F	08:15	1.8	55
	23:09	-1.2	-37
29 Sa	09:20	1.8	55
30 Su	00:04	-0.9	-27
	10:16	1.7	52
31 M	01:01	-0.6	-18
	10:57	1.6	49

June

Day	Time (h m)	ft	cm
1 Tu	01:59	-0.3	-9
	11:21	1.5	46
2 W ◑	02:59	0.1	3
	11:33	1.4	43
	18:40	0.9	27
	20:52	0.9	27
3 Th	04:05	0.4	12
	11:36	1.2	37
	18:25	0.6	18
4 F	00:09	0.9	27
	05:20	0.7	21
	11:30	1.1	34
	18:45	0.4	12
5 Sa	02:11	1.1	34
	06:53	0.9	27
	11:13	1.1	34
	19:10	0.1	3
6 Su	03:34	1.2	37
	19:38	-0.2	-6
7 M	04:35	1.3	40
	20:05	-0.4	-12
8 Tu	05:25	1.4	43
	20:33	-0.5	-15
9 W	06:11	1.4	43
	21:03	-0.6	-18
10 Th ●	06:55	1.4	43
	21:33	-0.6	-18
11 F	07:39	1.5	46
	22:06	-0.6	-18
12 Sa	08:24	1.5	46
	22:42	-0.6	-18
13 Su	09:06	1.6	49
	23:20	-0.5	-15
14 M	09:43	1.6	49
15 Tu	00:02	-0.4	-12
	10:10	1.6	49
16 W	00:48	-0.3	-9
	10:27	1.5	46
17 Th	01:39	0.0	0
	10:34	1.3	40
18 F ◐	02:40	0.2	6
	10:31	1.2	37
	17:39	0.5	15
	23:01	0.7	21
19 Sa	03:59	0.5	15
	10:19	1.0	30
	17:47	0.1	3
20 Su	01:34	1.0	30
	05:57	0.8	24
	09:50	0.9	27
	18:16	-0.4	-12
21 M	03:09	1.2	37
	18:55	-0.8	-24
22 Tu	04:20	1.5	46
	19:40	-1.1	-34
23 W	05:24	1.6	49
	20:29	-1.3	-40
24 Th ○	06:24	1.7	52
	21:19	-1.4	-43
25 F	07:23	1.7	52
	22:11	-1.3	-40
26 Sa	08:17	1.6	49
	23:03	-1.1	-34
27 Su	09:02	1.5	46
	23:54	-0.8	-24
28 M	09:32	1.4	43
29 Tu	00:43	-0.5	-15
	09:49	1.3	40
30 W	01:31	-0.1	-3
	09:55	1.2	37
	16:34	0.8	24
	18:54	0.8	24

StationId: 8779750
Source: NOAA/NOS/CO-OPS
Station Type: Primary
Time Zone: LST_LDT
Datum: MLLW

NOAA Tide Predictions

South Padre Island, Brazos Santiago Pass, TX,2021

Times and Heights of High and Low Waters

July

Day	Time (h m)	Height (ft)	Height (cm)
1 Th ◐	02:20	0.3	9
	09:53	1.1	34
	16:49	0.5	15
	22:23	0.8	24
2 F	03:14	0.6	18
	09:43	1.0	30
	17:19	0.2	6
3 Sa	01:21	0.9	27
	04:36	0.9	27
	09:19	1.0	30
	17:53	0.0	0
4 Su	03:08	1.1	34
	18:28	-0.2	-6
5 M	04:06	1.2	37
	19:02	-0.4	-12
6 Tu	04:51	1.3	40
	19:37	-0.6	-18
7 W	05:32	1.3	40
	20:12	-0.6	-18
8 Th	06:12	1.4	43
	20:46	-0.7	-21
9 F	06:51	1.4	43
	21:21	-0.7	-21
10 Sa ●	07:27	1.4	43
	21:56	-0.7	-21
11 Su	08:00	1.5	46
	22:33	-0.6	-18
12 M	08:27	1.5	46
	23:11	-0.5	-15
13 Tu	08:45	1.4	43
	23:52	-0.3	-9
14 W	08:55	1.3	40
15 Th	00:35	-0.1	-3
	08:55	1.2	37
	15:41	0.7	21
	18:00	0.8	24
16 F	01:24	0.2	6
	08:47	1.0	30
	15:41	0.4	12
	21:36	0.7	21
17 Sa ◑	02:25	0.6	18
	08:28	0.9	27
	16:12	0.0	0
18 Su	00:44	0.9	27
	04:11	0.9	27
	07:44	0.9	27
	16:54	-0.4	-12
19 M	02:38	1.2	37
	17:43	-0.8	-24
20 Tu	03:46	1.4	43
	18:35	-1.0	-30
21 W	04:44	1.6	49
	19:29	-1.2	-37
22 Th	05:39	1.6	49
	20:24	-1.2	-37
23 F	06:30	1.6	49
	21:17	-1.2	-37
24 Sa ○	07:14	1.6	49
	22:08	-1.0	-30
25 Su	07:47	1.5	46
	22:56	-0.7	-21
26 M	08:06	1.4	43
	23:42	-0.4	-12
27 Tu	08:14	1.2	37
	12:57	1.0	30
	16:13	1.1	34
28 W	00:26	0.0	0
	08:14	1.1	34
	13:40	0.8	24
	18:05	1.0	30
29 Th	01:08	0.3	9
	08:08	1.1	34
	14:27	0.6	18
	20:20	0.9	27
30 F	01:51	0.6	18
	07:54	1.0	30
	15:14	0.3	9
	23:12	1.0	30
31 Sa ◑	02:43	0.9	27
	07:24	1.0	30
	16:02	0.1	3

August

Day	Time (h m)	Height (ft)	Height (cm)
1 Su	02:03	1.1	34
	16:50	0.0	0
2 M	03:13	1.2	37
	17:37	-0.2	-6
3 Tu	03:57	1.3	40
	18:23	-0.3	-9
4 W	04:36	1.4	43
	19:07	-0.4	-12
5 Th	05:13	1.5	46
	19:49	-0.4	-12
6 F	05:47	1.5	46
	20:29	-0.4	-12
7 Sa	06:17	1.6	49
	21:07	-0.4	-12
8 Su ●	06:41	1.6	49
	21:45	-0.4	-12
9 M	06:59	1.6	49
	22:25	-0.2	-6
10 Tu	07:10	1.5	46
	23:06	-0.1	-3
11 W	07:13	1.3	40
	12:23	1.1	34
	16:10	1.2	37
	23:51	0.2	6
12 Th	07:09	1.2	37
	12:50	0.8	24
	18:09	1.1	34
13 F	00:41	0.5	15
	06:56	1.1	34
	13:29	0.4	12
	20:27	1.1	34
14 Sa	01:42	0.8	24
	06:30	1.0	30
	14:17	0.1	3
	23:07	1.2	37
15 Su ◑	15:13	-0.2	-6
16 M	01:25	1.4	43
	16:14	-0.5	-15
17 Tu	02:46	1.6	49
	17:18	-0.7	-21
18 W	03:46	1.8	55
	18:22	-0.7	-21
19 Th	04:38	1.8	55
	19:23	-0.7	-21
20 F	05:22	1.8	55
	20:21	-0.6	-18
21 Sa	05:56	1.7	52
	21:14	-0.4	-12
22 Su ○	06:17	1.6	49
	10:12	1.5	46
	13:09	1.5	46
	22:03	-0.2	-6
23 M ●	06:26	1.5	46
	10:27	1.3	40
	14:45	1.5	46
	22:49	0.1	3
24 Tu	06:28	1.4	43
	10:59	1.1	34
	16:10	1.5	46
	23:33	0.4	12
25 W	06:24	1.3	40
	11:36	0.9	27
	17:35	1.4	43
26 Th	00:18	0.7	21
	06:13	1.2	37
	12:17	0.7	21
	19:09	1.3	40
27 F	01:05	1.0	30
	05:53	1.2	37
	12:59	0.5	15
	20:59	1.3	40
28 Sa	02:10	1.2	37
	05:10	1.2	37
	13:45	0.4	12
	23:17	1.4	43
29 Su	14:37	0.3	9
30 M ○	01:20	1.5	46
	15:35	0.2	6
31 Tu	02:27	1.6	49
	16:36	0.2	6

September

Day	Time (h m)	Height (ft)	Height (cm)
1 W	03:14	1.7	52
	17:36	0.2	6
2 Th	03:51	1.7	52
	18:30	0.1	3
3 F	04:22	1.8	55
	19:19	0.1	3
4 Sa	04:46	1.8	55
	20:04	0.1	3
5 Su	05:04	1.8	55
	20:49	0.2	6
6 M	05:16	1.8	55
	10:02	1.5	46
	13:19	1.6	49
	21:34	0.3	9
7 Tu ●	05:21	1.6	49
	10:10	1.3	40
	14:52	1.6	49
	22:21	0.5	15
8 W	05:20	1.5	46
	10:33	1.1	34
	16:21	1.6	49
	23:13	0.7	21
9 Th	05:12	1.3	40
	11:05	0.8	24
	17:55	1.6	49
10 F	00:14	1.0	30
	04:54	1.3	40
	11:45	0.4	12
	19:38	1.7	52
11 Sa	01:38	1.3	40
	04:12	1.3	40
	12:33	0.1	3
	21:35	1.8	55
12 Su	13:29	-0.1	-3
	23:36	1.9	58
13 M ◑	14:34	-0.2	-6
14 Tu	01:13	2.0	61
	15:45	-0.2	-6
15 W	02:22	2.1	64
	16:59	-0.2	-6
16 Th	03:14	2.1	64
	18:10	-0.1	-3
17 F	03:53	2.0	61
	19:15	0.1	3
18 Sa	04:18	1.9	58
	20:14	0.3	9
19 Su	04:31	1.8	55
	09:00	1.6	49
	13:15	1.8	55
	21:08	0.5	15
20 M ○	04:35	1.7	52
	09:17	1.4	43
	14:44	1.8	55
	21:59	0.8	24
21 Tu	04:32	1.6	49
	09:44	1.2	37
	16:02	1.8	55
	22:49	1.0	30
22 W	04:24	1.5	46
	10:15	0.9	27
	17:16	1.8	55
	23:43	1.2	37
23 Th	04:07	1.4	43
	10:46	0.8	24
	18:30	1.8	55
24 F	00:50	1.4	43
	03:31	1.4	43
	11:19	0.6	18
	19:47	1.8	55
25 Sa	11:54	0.5	15
	21:14	1.8	55
26 Su	12:34	0.5	15
	22:51	1.9	58
27 M	13:22	0.5	15
28 Tu	00:20	1.9	58
	14:21	0.5	15
29 W ◑	01:23	2.0	61
	15:28	0.6	18
30 Th	02:07	2.1	64
	16:36	0.6	18

StationId: 8779750
Source: NOAA/NOS/CO-OPS
Station Type: Primary
Time Zone: LST_LDT
Datum: MLLW

October

Time	ft	cm		Time	ft	cm
h m	ft	cm		h m	ft	cm
02:38	2.1	64	**16** 02:30	2.1	64
17:40	0.6	18	08:16	1.7	52
F			Sa 10:56	1.8	55
			19:00	0.8	24
2 03:00	2.1	64	**17** 02:39	1.9	58
18:39	0.7	21	08:05	1.5	46
Sa			Su 13:07	1.8	55
			20:04	1.0	30
3 03:15	2.1	64	**18** 02:39	1.8	55
09:10	1.7	52	08:22	1.3	40
Su 11:11	1.8	55	M 14:39	1.9	58
19:35	0.7	21	21:06	1.3	40
4 03:23	1.9	58	**19** 02:33	1.7	52
08:44	1.6	49	08:47	1.0	30
13:14	1.8	55	Tu 15:55	2.0	61
20:31	0.9	27	22:10	1.4	43
5 03:25	1.8	55	**20** 02:17	1.6	49
08:53	1.3	40	09:14	0.8	24
14:45	1.9	58	W 17:03	2.0	61
21:30	1.0	30	○ 23:32	1.6	49
6 03:21	1.6	49	**21** 01:40	1.6	49
09:16	1.0	30	09:41	0.6	18
16:08	2.0	61	Th 18:06	2.1	64
22:36	1.2	37			
7 03:07	1.5	46	**22** 10:09	0.5	15
09:47	0.6	18	19:07	2.1	64
17:31	2.1	64	F		
8 00:00	1.4	43	**23** 10:39	0.4	12
02:35	1.5	46	20:09	2.1	64
10:26	0.3	9	Sa		
18:56	2.1	64			
9 11:11	0.0	0	**24** 11:11	0.3	9
20:26	2.2	67	21:16	2.1	64
			Su		
10 12:03	-0.2	-6	**25** 11:49	0.4	12
22:02	2.3	70	22:27	2.1	64
			M		
11 13:02	-0.2	-6	**26** 12:33	0.4	12
23:32	2.3	70	23:30	2.1	64
			Tu		
12 14:09	-0.1	-3	**27** 13:25	0.5	15
			W		
13 00:44	2.3	70	**28** 00:17	2.2	67
15:22	0.1	3	14:26	0.6	18
			Th		
14 01:37	2.3	70	**29** 00:50	2.2	67
16:38	0.3	9	15:33	0.7	21
			F		
15 02:11	2.2	67	**30** 01:11	2.2	67
17:52	0.5	15	16:43	0.8	24
			Sa		
			31 01:24	2.1	64
			17:55	1.0	30
			Su		

November

Time	ft	cm		Time	ft	cm
h m	ft	cm		h m	ft	cm
1 01:30	1.9	58	**16** 06:52	0.7	21
07:43	1.4	43	14:45	1.9	58
M 12:43	1.7	52	Tu 20:36	1.5	46
19:08	1.1	34	23:01	1.6	49
2 01:28	1.8	55	**17** 07:19	0.4	12
07:48	1.1	34	15:50	1.9	58
Tu 14:23	1.8	55	W		
20:26	1.3	40			
3 01:18	1.6	49	**18** 07:47	0.2	6
08:09	0.7	21	16:46	2.0	61
W 15:46	2.0	61	Th		
21:58	1.4	43			
4 00:53	1.5	46	**19** 08:15	0.1	3
08:41	0.3	9	17:38	2.0	61
Th 17:03	2.2	67	F		
●			○		
5 09:20	-0.1	-3	**20** 08:44	0.0	0
18:17	2.3	70	18:29	2.0	61
F			Sa		
6 10:04	-0.4	-12	**21** 09:14	0.0	0
19:33	2.3	70	19:21	2.0	61
Sa			Su		
7 09:54	-0.5	-15	**22** 09:47	0.0	0
19:50	2.4	73	20:13	2.0	61
Su			M		
8 10:48	-0.5	-15	**23** 10:24	0.1	3
21:05	2.4	73	21:03	2.0	61
M			Tu		
9 11:47	-0.3	-9	**24** 11:04	0.2	6
22:11	2.3	70	21:43	2.0	61
Tu			W		
10 12:51	-0.1	-3	**25** 11:49	0.3	9
22:59	2.2	67	22:11	2.0	61
W			Th		
11 13:58	0.2	6	**26** 12:40	0.4	12
23:28	2.1	64	22:29	2.0	61
Th ☾			F		
12 15:09	0.6	18	**27** 13:39	0.6	18
23:43	2.0	61	22:38	1.9	58
F			Sa		
13 06:22	1.5	46	**28** 14:49	0.8	24
08:58	1.5	46	22:40	1.7	52
Sa 16:23	0.9	27	Su		
23:48	1.8	55			
14 06:08	1.2	37	**29** 05:41	1.0	30
11:41	1.6	49	10:51	1.3	40
Su 17:38	1.2	37	M 16:15	1.0	30
23:45	1.7	52	22:33	1.5	46
15 06:26	1.0	30	**30** 05:41	0.7	21
13:26	1.7	52	12:54	1.5	46
M 18:59	1.4	43	Tu 18:01	1.2	37
23:33	1.6	49	22:15	1.4	43

December

Time	ft	cm		Time	ft	cm
h m	ft	cm		h m	ft	cm
1 06:04	0.2	6	**16** 06:53	-0.2	-6
14:21	1.7	52	16:20	1.6	49
W			Th		
2 06:37	-0.2	-6	**17** 07:25	-0.3	-9
15:33	1.9	58	17:06	1.7	52
Th			F		
3 07:18	-0.6	-18	**18** 07:56	-0.4	-12
16:41	2.1	64	17:51	1.7	52
F			Sa		
4 08:04	-0.9	-27	**19** 08:28	-0.4	-12
17:47	2.1	64	18:35	1.7	52
Sa ●			Su ○		
5 08:53	-1.0	-30	**20** 09:01	-0.4	-12
18:53	2.1	64	19:18	1.7	52
Su			M		
6 09:46	-0.9	-27	**21** 09:34	-0.4	-12
19:56	2.1	64	19:55	1.7	52
M			Tu		
7 10:40	-0.8	-24	**22** 10:09	-0.3	-9
20:50	2.0	61	20:24	1.7	52
Tu			W		
8 11:36	-0.5	-15	**23** 10:45	-0.2	-6
21:29	1.9	58	20:44	1.7	52
W			Th		
9 12:32	-0.1	-3	**24** 11:25	0.0	0
21:52	1.8	55	20:56	1.6	49
Th			F		
10 13:30	0.3	9	**25** 12:10	0.2	6
22:01	1.6	49	20:59	1.5	46
F			Sa		
11 05:02	1.1	34	**26** 13:01	0.4	12
07:10	1.2	37	20:55	1.3	40
Sa 14:31	0.6	18	Su		
☽ 22:02	1.5	46			
12 04:54	0.8	24	**27** 04:13	0.7	21
10:41	1.2	37	09:25	0.9	27
Su 15:45	1.0	30	M 14:11	0.7	21
21:55	1.4	43	☽ 20:43	1.2	37
13 05:18	0.5	15	**28** 04:21	0.3	9
12:58	1.3	40	12:16	1.1	34
M 17:23	1.2	37	Tu 16:06	1.0	30
21:36	1.3	40	20:13	1.1	34
14 05:49	0.2	6	**29** 04:50	-0.2	-6
14:26	1.5	46	13:54	1.3	40
Tu			W		
15 06:21	0.0	0	**30** 05:29	-0.6	-18
15:29	1.6	49	15:03	1.6	49
W			Th		
			31 06:15	-1.0	-30
			16:04	1.7	52
			F		

215

TABLE 2. — TIDAL DIFFERENCES AND OTHER CONSTANTS

EXPLANATION OF TABLE

The publication of full daily predictions is necessarily limited to a comparatively small number of stations. Tide predictions for many other places, however, can be obtained by applying certain differences to the predictions for the reference stations in Table 1. The following pages list the places called "subordinate stations" for which such predictions can be made, and the differences or ratios to be used. These differences or ratios are to be applied to the predictions for the proper reference station which is listed in Table 2 in boldface type above the differences for the subordinate station. The stations in this table are arranged in geographical order. The index to stations at the end of this volume will assist in locating a particular station.

Caution.— The time and height differences listed in Table 2 are average difference derived from comparisons of simultaneous tide observations at the subordinate location and its reference station. Because these figures are constant, they may not always provide for the daily variations of the actual tide, especially if the subordinate station is some distance from the reference station. Therefore, although the application of the time and height differences will generally provide reasonable accurate approximations, they cannot result in predictions as accurate as those listed for the reference stations which are based upon much larger periods of analyses and which do provide for daily variations.

Time differences.—To determine the time of high water or low water at any station listed in this table there is given in the columns headed "Differences, Time" the hours and minutes to be added to or subtracted from the time of high or low water at some reference station. A plus (+) sign indicates that the tide at the subordinate station is later than at the reference station and the difference should be added; a minus (–) sign indicates that it is earlier and should be subtracted.

To obtain the tide at a subordinate station on any date, apply the difference to the tide at the reference station for that same date. In some cases, however, to obtain an a.m. tide it may be necessary to use the preceding day's p.m. tide at the reference station (or to obtain a p.m. tide it may be necessary to use the following day's a.m. tide). For example, if a high water at a reference station occurs at 0200 on July 17, and the tide at the subordinate station occurs 5 hour earlier, the high water at the subordinate station will occur at 2100 on July 16. For the second case, if a high water occurs at a reference station at 2200 on July 2, and the tide at the subordinate station occurs 3 hours later, then high water will occur at 0100 on July 3 at the subordinate station. The necessary allowance for change in date when the international date line is crossed is included in the time difference. In such cases use the same date at the reference station as desired for the subordinate station as explained above.

The results obtained by the application of the time differences will be in the kind of time indicated by the time meridian shown above the name of the subordinate station. Differences in time meridians between a subordinate station and its reference station have been accounted for and no further adjustment by the reader is necessary. Summer or daylight-saving time is not used in the tide tables.

Height differences.—The height of the tide, referred to the datum of charts, is obtained by means of the height differences or ratios. A plus (+) sign indicates that the difference should be added to the height at the reference station, and a minus (–) sign indicates that it should be subtracted. All height differences, ranges, and levels in Table 2 are in feet but may be converted to centimeters by the use of Table 7.

Ratio.— For some stations, use of predicted height difference would give unsatisfactory predictions. In such cases they have been omitted and one or two ratios are given (*). Where two ratios are given, one in the "height of high water" column and one in the "height of low water" column, the high waters and low waters at the reference station should be multiplied by these respective ratios. Where only one is given, the omitted ratio is either unreliable or unknown.

TABLE 2. — TIDAL DIFFERENCES AND OTHER CONSTANTS

For some subordinate stations there is given in parentheses a ratio as well as a correction in feet. In those instances, each predicted high and low water at the reference station should first be multiplied by the ratio and then the correction in feet is added to or subtracted from each product as indicated.

As an example, at Port of Spain, Trinidad, the values in the time and height difference columns in Table 2 are given as -0 44, -1 12, and (*0.31 + 1.4) as referred to the reference station at Punta Gorda, Venezuela. If we assume that the tide predictions in column (1) below are those of Ketchikan on a particular day, application of the time and height correction in columns (2) and (3) would result in the tide predictions for Treadwell Bay in column (4).

(1)		(2)	(3)	(4)		
Time h.m.	Height ft.	Time Corrections	Height Corrections	Time h.m.	ft.	Height centimeters
0326	0.6	$-1^h\ 12^m$	x0.31 + 1.4	0214	1.6	49
0900	5.1	$-0^h\ 44^m$	x0.31 + 1.4	0816	3.0	91
1608	-0.3	$-1^h\ 12^m$	x0.31 + 1.4	1456	1.3	40
2148	5.4	$-0^h\ 44^m$	x0.31 + 1.4	2104	3.1	94

Range. —The mean range is the difference in height between mean high water (MHW) and mean low water (MLW). The *spring range* is the average semidiurnal range occurring semimonthly as a result of the Moon being new or full. It is larger than the mean range where the type of tide is either semidiurnal or mixed, and is of not practical significance where the type of tide is diurnal. Where the tide is chiefly of the diurnal type the table gives the *diurnal range*, which is the difference in height between mean higher high water and mean lower low water.

Datum. — The datum of the predictions obtained through the height differences or ratios is also the datum of the largest scale chart for the locality. To obtain the depth at the time of high or low water, the predicted height should be added to the depth on the chart unless such height is negative (–), when it should be subtracted. To find the height at times between high and low water see Table 3. On some charts the depths are given in meters or centimeters and in such cases the heights of the tide can be converted to other units by the use of Table 7. Chart datums for the portion of the world covered by these tables are approximately as follows: *Mean lower low water* for the Pacific coast of the United States, Alaska, and the Hawaiian Islands, mean low water springs for Central American and Mexico. For the rest of the area covered by these tables the datums generally used are approximately *mean low water springs, Indian spring low water*, or the *lowest possible low water*.

Mean Tide Level (Half-Tide Level). — The mean tide level is a plane midway between mean low water and mean high water. Tabular values are reckoned from chart depth.

Observations Supporting Predictions.– All tidal predictions made by the National Ocean Service are based upon observations taken at the location in question. For most reference stations these observations often are of a continuing nature. As such, they are used to quality control the predictions and to update the harmonic constants used in generating annual predictions. For subordinate stations, the age and duration of their observations vary from a few days of observation taken decades ago to the most recent survey data.

The precision with which the position, ranges and mean tide level are reported in Table 2 is an indication of the age and analytical history of the supporting observation. Stations whose position is reported to the nearest tenth minute of latitude and longitude and whose ranges and mean tide level are reported to the nearest hundredth foot are supported by the most recent observations, analyzed with regard to current chart datums and the 1983-2001 National Tidal Datum Epoch. Stations whose position is reported to the nearest tenth minute but whose ranges and mean tide level are reported to the nearest tenth foot are typically supported by observations taken in the 1960's and 1970's with analysis based upon the previous National Tidal Datum Epochs. Finally, stations whose positions are reported to the nearest minute and whose ranges and mean tide level are reported to the nearest tenth foot indicated either older supporting observations or simply data not yet reviewed and entered into the Tables with full published precision. NOS is in the continuous process of updating the Tables with all available data.

TABLE 2. — TIDAL DIFFERENCES AND OTHER CONSTANTS

Old observations are not in and of themselves an indication of poor present predictions. Certain coastal areas do not undergo much human or natural modification while other coastal areas are subject to nearly constant modification by both agents. Local knowledge of conditions is still very important to the wise use of these astronomical predictions.

NOTE. — Dashes are entered in the place of data which are unknown, unreliable, or not applicable.

TABLE 2. – TIDAL DIFFERENCES AND OTHER CONSTANTS

No.	PLACE	POSITION		DIFFERENCES				RANGES		Mean Tide Level
				Time		Height				
		Latitude	Longitude	High Water	Low Water	High Water	Low Water	Mean	Spring	
		North	West	h m	h m	ft	ft	ft	ft	ft
	ARCTIC ARCHIPELAGO Time meridian, local			on Hampton Roads,						
1	Princess Royal Islands	72° 45'	117° 45'	+3 14	+3 32	0.0	+0.2	2.3	3.0	1.4
3	Mercy Bay, Banks Island	74° 07'	118° 15'	+4 05	+4 05	-0.8	+0.1	1.6	2.0	1.0
5	Winter Harbour, Melville Island	74° 47'	110° 48'	+4 44	+4 40	+0.2	+0.2	2.5	3.2	1.6
7	Bridport Inlet, Melville Island	74° 56'	108° 49'	+4 33	+4 33	+1.3	+1.0	2.8	4.1	2.5
9	Byam Martin Island	75° 10'	103° 34'	+3 42	+3 42	+1.8	+1.5	2.8	3.7	3.0
11	Cambridge Bay, Dease Strait	69° 07'	105° 07'	+2 35	+2 30	-0.4	+1.2	1.0	1.3	1.7
	Time meridian, 75° W			on Harrington Harbour,						
13	Igloolik, Fury and Hecla Strait	69° 21'	81° 37'	+9 12	+9 12	+1.6	+0.8	4.6	6.0	4.7
15	Hall Beach, Foxe Basin	68° 45'	81° 13'	+9 45	+10 15	(*0.45+0.5)		1.7	2.0	2.1
	Time meridian, local									
17	Port Kennedy, Bellot Strait	72° 01'	94° 12'	+1 35	+1 44	+0.5	+0.8	3.5	4.5	4.2
19	Port Bowen, Prince Regent Inlet	73° 14'	88° 55'	+1 01	+1 06	+0.9	+1.3	3.4	4.5	4.6
21	Port Leopold, Prince Regent Inlet	73° 48'	90° 15'	+0 50	+0 45	+0.9	+0.1	4.6	5.9	4.0
23	Beechy Island, Barrow Strait	74° 43'	91° 54'	+1 30	+1 35	+1.0	-0.1	4.9	6.4	4.0
25	Assistance Bay, Barrow Strait	74° 37'	94° 15'	+1 56	+1 57	-0.1	+0.6	3.1	4.1	3.8
27	Griffith Island, Barrow Strait	74° 35'	95° 30'	+2 12	+2 13	-0.3	+0.5	3.0	3.9	3.6
29	Refuge Cove, Wellington Channel	75° 31'	92° 10'	+1 23	+1 38	+0.6	+0.2	4.2	5.5	3.9
31	Penny Strait	76° 52'	97° 00'	+1 53	+2 03	*0.39	*0.38	1.5	1.9	1.4
				on Hampton Roads,						
33	Cape Columbia, Lincoln Sea	83° 14'	69° 55'	-0 55	-0 55	-1.8	0.0	0.8	1.1	0.5
35	Alert, Lincoln Sea	82° 30'	62° 20'	+1 26	+1 17	-0.4	+0.6	1.6	2.2	1.5
37	Cape Sheridan, Lincoln Sea	82° 29'	61° 30'	+1 37	+1 28	-0.5	+0.2	1.8	2.5	1.2
39	Cape Bryant, North Greenland	82° 21'	55° 30'	+3 33	+3 35	-1.4	+0.2	1.1	1.5	0.7
41	Cape Morris Jesup, North Greenland	83° 40'	34° 15'	+1 51	+1 43	-2.0	0.0	0.4	0.6	0.3
	GREENLAND East Coast			on Harrington Harbour,						
43	Danmarks Havn	76° 46'	18° 46'	-12 41	-12 32	-0.8	-0.6	3.6	4.7	2.8
45	Cape Borgen	75° 26'	18° 05'	-11 04	-11 03	*0.80	*0.81	3.0	3.9	2.8
47	Lille Pendulum	74° 37'	18° 29'	-11 40	-11 39	*0.80	*0.81	3.0	4.0	2.8
49	Finsch Islands	73° 59'	21° 08'	-12 18	-12 18	*0.81	*0.75	3.2	4.3	2.8
51	Myggbukta, Foster Bay	73° 28'	21° 33'	-11 57	-12 00	-0.9	-0.5	3.4	4.4	2.8
53	Blomsterbugten	73° 21'	25° 17'	-12 15	-12 27	-0.4	-0.3	3.7	4.8	3.2
	Time meridian, 30° W									
55	Danmarks Island, Scoresby Sound	70° 27'	26° 12'	-11 45	-11 45	*0.63	*0.62	2.4	3.3	2.2
	Time meridian, 45° W									
57	Angmagssalik (Kulusuk)	65° 36'	37° 09'	-7 00	-6 50	(*1.71-0.8)		6.5	8.8	5.2
				on Argentia,						
59	Finnsbu	63° 24'	41° 17'	-4 09	-3 42	+0.8	-0.4	6.1	8.1	4.6
61	Kap Farvel	59° 45'	43° 53'	-2 21	-1 53	+0.2	-0.9	6.0	8.0	4.0
	West Coast									
63	Frederiksdal	60° 00'	44° 40'	-2 10	-1 41	+1.5	-0.7	7.1	9.5	4.7
65	Nanortalik	60° 07'	45° 15'	-2 43	-2 16	+0.5	-0.9	6.3	8.4	4.2
67	Julianehaab	60° 43'	46° 01'	-2 09	-1 46	+0.3	-0.9	6.1	8.0	4.0
69	Narsarssuaq	61° 08'	45° 25'	-2 15	-1 46	+1.8	+0.1	6.6	8.6	5.3
71	Ivigtut, Arsuk Fjord	61° 12'	48° 11'	-1 49	-1 24	+0.7	-0.9	6.5	8.6	4.3
73	Frederikshaab	62° 00'	49° 43'	-1 22	-1 00	+3.0	-0.6	8.5	11.1	5.6
75	Godthaab	64° 10'	51° 44'	-1 21	-0 46	(*2.00-2.1)		9.8	13.0	6.5
77	Fishmaster's Harbour, Sondre Stromfjord	66° 01'	53° 29'	-1 41	-1 16	+3.6	-0.1	8.6	10.2	6.1
79	Camp Lloyd, Sondre Stromfjord	66° 58'	50° 57'	+2 21	+2 51	+1.7	-1.1	7.7	9.4	4.7
81	Holsteinsborg	66° 56'	53° 42'	-1 29	-1 00	+2.0	-0.8	7.7	10.0	5.0
83	Camp Michigan, Maligiak Fjord	66° 56'	52° 37'	-0 22	+0 10	+2.2	-0.8	7.9	10.2	5.1
				on Harrington Harbour,						
85	Aningaq, Rifkol	67° 55'	53° 50'	-1 42	-1 42	+1.0	-0.8	5.6	7.4	3.6
87	Nunarssuaq, Kronprinsens Ejlanden	68° 59'	53° 21'	-0 48	-0 52	-0.5	-0.9	4.2	5.7	2.8
89	Godhavn, Disko Island	69° 15'	53° 33'	-1 37	-1 32	-0.4	-0.9	4.3	5.7	2.9
91	Ingnerit, Umanak Fjord	71° 00'	51° 00'	+0 00	+0 00	-1.6	-1.1	3.3	4.3	2.2
	Time meridian, local									
93	North Star Bay, Wolstenholme Fjord	76° 32'	68° 50'	+0 30	+0 32	*1.33	*1.12	5.4	7.0	4.5
95	Port Foulke	78° 18'	72° 45'	+0 28	+0 26	(*2.08-0.8)		7.9	10.7	6.5
97	Rensselaer Bugt	78° 37'	70° 53'	+1 05	+0 58	(*2.08-1.1)		7.9	10.8	6.2
99	Thank God Harbor, Polaris Bugt	81° 36'	61° 40'	+1 34	+1 31	-0.3	-0.4	3.9	5.4	3.2

Endnotes can be found at the end of table 2.

TABLE 2. – TIDAL DIFFERENCES AND OTHER CONSTANTS

No.	PLACE	POSITION		DIFFERENCES				RANGES		Mean Tide Level
				Time		Height				
		Latitude	Longitude	High Water	Low Water	High Water	Low Water	Mean	Spring	
		North	West	h m	h m	ft	ft	ft	ft	ft
	NORTHERN CANADA Baffin Bay, etc., West Side Time meridian, local			on Halifax,						
101	Fort Conger, Discovery Harbor	81° 44'	64° 44'	+3 48	+3 25	-1.4	-1.3	4.3	5.9	3.0
103	Cape Lawrence	80° 21'	69° 15'	+3 46	+3 40	-0.2	-1.3	5.5	7.2	3.6
105	Payer Harbour, Cape Sabine	78° 43'	74° 25'	+3 36	+3 30	+1.7	-0.9	7.0	9.4	4.7
107	Cape Adair	71° 33'	71° 30'	+3 06	+3 06	+0.4	-1.2	6.0	7.8	3.9
109	Cape Hewett	70° 16'	67° 47'	+2 56	+2 56	+0.6	-0.5	5.5	7.2	4.4
	Davis Strait, West Side Time meridian, 60° W			on Pictou,						
111	Cape Hooper, Baffin Island	68° 23'	66° 45'	-5 52	-5 41	*0.47	*0.43	1.6	1.9	1.8
113	Kivitoo, Baffin Island	67° 56'	64° 56'	-5 17	-5 10	*0.51	*0.43	1.8	2.4	1.9
				on Saint John, N. B.,						
115	Cape Dyer, Baffin Island	66° 34'	61° 40'	-6 19	-6 21	*0.31	*0.45	5.8	7.3	4.7
117	Clearwater Fiord, Cumberland Sound	66° 36'	67° 20'	-5 36	-5 38	-5.5	-0.6	15.9	20.6	11.4
119	Frobisher Bay	63° 29'	68° 02'	-4 13	-4 15	+5.5	+3.3	23.0	29.8	18.8
	Hudson Strait and Bay									
121	Pikyulik Island, Payne River	60° 00'	69° 55'	-2 15	-1 54	+3.7	+3.2	21.3	26.8	17.9
	Time meridian, 75° W									
123	Sorry Harbor, Resolution Island	61° 37'	64° 44'	-5 30	-5 30	-8.3	-0.9	13.4	17.6	9.8
125	Lower Savage Islands	61° 46'	65° 51'	-4 46	-4 55	-1.2	+2.0	17.6	25.4	14.8
127	Ashe Inlet, Big Island	62° 33'	70° 35'	-3 46	-3 43	+4.2	+2.2	22.8	30.9	17.6
129	Schooner Harbour, Baffin Island	64° 24'	77° 52'	-0 49	-0 44	-6.2	+0.4	14.2	18.9	11.5
131	Winter Island, Foxe Basin	66° 11'	83° 10'	+1 02	+1 10	-12.1	-0.8	9.5	12.4	8.0
	Time meridian, 90° W									
133	Coral Harbour, Southampton Island	64° 08'	83° 10'	-0 25	+0 04	-14.4	-1.5	7.9	10.3	6.5
135	Chesterfield Inlet	63° 20'	90° 42'	-8 17	-8 20	-12.4	-0.8	9.2	11.8	7.8
137	Churchill	58° 47'	94° 12'	-4 25	-4 36	-11.5	-1.4	10.7	13.4	7.9
				on Quebec,						
139	Port Nelson, Nelson River entrance	57° 05'	92° 36'	+3 56	+4 35	-3.1	-0.9	11.5	12.9	6.4
	Time meridian, 75° W									
141	Moosonee, James Bay	51° 17'	80° 38'	+9 29	+9 32	*0.48	*1.81	4.5	5.4	5.2
143	Moose Factory, James Bay	51° 16'	80° 35'	+9 33	+10 37	*0.42	*1.56	4.0	5.4	4.5
145	Charlton Island, James Bay	51° 57'	79° 16'	+8 00	+6 38	*0.39	*1.06	4.3	5.3	3.9
				on Saint John, N. B.,						
147	Digges Harbour	62° 30'	77° 42'	-2 11	-2 05	*0.39	*0.62	7.1	9.3	6.1
149	Port de Boucherville, Nottingham Island	63° 12'	77° 28'	-2 07	-2 02	-11.6	-1.2	10.4	14.0	8.0
151	Wakeham Bay	61° 43'	71° 57'	-3 52	-3 55	-0.4	+2.2	18.2	27.0	15.3
153	Stupart Bay	61° 35'	71° 32'	-4 10	-4 17	0.0	+2.4	18.4	27.2	15.6
155	Diana Bay	60° 52'	70° 04'	-4 00	-4 03	+2.8	+3.1	20.5	26.8	17.4
157	Hopes Advance Bay, Ungava Bay	59° 21'	69° 38'	-3 59	-4 00	*1.44	*2.20	27.0	34.4	22.3
159	Leaf Bay, Ungava Bay	58° 55'	69° 00'	-4 00	-4 00	*1.49	*2.25	28.0	36.0	23.0
161	Leaf Lake, Ungava Bay	58° 45'	69° 40'	-3 00	-3 00	(*1.54+5.8)		32.0	40.0	28.0
163	Koksoak River entrance	58° 32'	68° 11'	-3 50	-3 53	*1.47	*2.00	28.5	36.4	22.3
165	Port Burwell, Ungava Bay	60° 25'	64° 52'	-4 13	-4 13	-6.5	-0.9	15.2	19.9	10.7
	LABRADOR Time meridian, 52° 30' W									
167	Button Islands	60° 37'	64° 44'	-2 38	-2 38	-9.5	-0.3	11.6	15.4	9.5
169	Williams Harbour	60° 00'	64° 19'	-3 07	-3 27	*0.32	*0.30	6.8	8.2	4.6
				on Halifax,						
171	Eclipse Harbour	59° 48'	64° 09'	+0 25	+0 02	-2.4	-1.0	3.0	3.7	2.6
173	Kangalaksiorvik Fiord	59° 23'	63° 47'	+1 00	+0 42	-2.6	-1.5	3.3	4.1	2.2
175	Nachvak Bay	59° 03'	63° 35'	+0 04	-0 20	-1.5	-1.1	4.0	5.0	3.0
177	Port Manvers	56° 57'	61° 25'	-0 55	-0 55	-2.3	-1.2	3.3	4.2	2.6
179	Hebron, Hebron Fjord	58° 12'	62° 38'	-0 49	-1 05	-1.4	-0.9	3.9	4.7	3.2
181	Nain	56° 33'	61° 41'	-0 32	-0 54	+0.3	-0.5	5.2	6.5	4.2
183	Hopedale Harbour	55° 27'	60° 13'	-0 46	-1 09	-0.4	-0.3	4.3	5.6	4.0
185	Webeck Harbour	54° 54'	58° 02'	-1 07	-1 38	-1.3	-0.8	3.9	5.0	3.3
	Hamilton Inlet and Lake Melville									
187	Indian Harbour	54° 27'	57° 12'	-0 37	-1 33	-1.0	-0.9	4.3	5.7	3.4
189	Ticoralak Island	54° 17'	58° 12'	-0 35	-0 35	-0.9	-0.5	4.0	4.9	3.7
191	Rigolet	54° 11'	58° 25'	-0 02	-0 17	-1.9	-1.0	3.5	4.5	2.8
193	Goose Bay	53° 21'	60° 24'	+4 22	+4 24	(*0.27+0.4)		1.2	1.7	1.6
195	Cartwright Harbour	53° 42'	57° 02'	-0 03	-0 34	-1.3	-0.6	3.7	4.9	3.4
197	Curlew Harbour	53° 45'	56° 33'	-0 07	-0 38	-1.6	-0.9	3.7	4.9	3.1
199	Comfort Bight	53° 09'	55° 46'	-0 32	-1 03	-1.9	-1.0	3.5	4.6	2.9

TABLE 2. – TIDAL DIFFERENCES AND OTHER CONSTANTS

No.	PLACE	POSITION Latitude	POSITION Longitude	DIFFERENCES Time High Water	DIFFERENCES Time Low Water	DIFFERENCES Height High Water	DIFFERENCES Height Low Water	RANGES Mean	RANGES Spring	Mean Tide Level
		North	West	h m	h m	ft	ft	ft	ft	ft
	LABRADOR Time meridian, 52° 30' W			on Halifax,						
201	Square Island Harbour	52° 44'	55° 49'	-0 34	-1 05	-2.0	-1.1	3.5	4.7	2.8
203	Port Marnham	52° 23'	55° 44'	-0 43	-1 14	-2.7	-1.0	2.7	3.6	2.5
205	Battle Harbour	52° 16'	55° 36'	-1 03	-1 30	-2.1	-0.3	2.6	3.8	3.1
				on Harrington Harbour,						
	Strait of Bell Isle									
207	Chateau Bay	52° 00'	55° 50'	-3 08	-3 19	*0.69	*0.81	2.4	3.1	2.5
209	Red Bay	51° 43'	56° 25'	-2 00	-1 55	*0.56	*0.56	2.1	2.6	2.0
211	Forteau Bay	51° 27'	56° 53'	-0 26	-0 17	*0.78	*0.81	2.9	3.7	2.8
	NEWFOUNDLAND East Coast			on Halifax,						
213	Pistolet Bay	51° 30'	55° 44'	-0 14	-0 28	*0.46	*0.29	2.4	3.1	1.8
215	Ariege Bay	51° 10'	56° 00'	-0 34	-0 34	-2.6	-1.5	3.3	4.3	2.3
217	Wild Cove	50° 42'	56° 10'	-0 49	-1 01	-2.0	-1.1	3.5	4.7	2.8
219	Sops Island, White Bay	49° 50'	56° 46'	-0 49	-1 24	*0.46	*0.29	2.4	3.4	1.8
221	Exploits Lower Harbour	49° 32'	55° 04'	-0 34	-1 09	-3.1	-1.3	2.6	3.5	2.1
223	Fogo Harbour	49° 43'	54° 16'	-0 34	-0 42	-2.6	-1.3	3.1	4.2	2.4
225	Valleyfield	49° 10'	53° 37'	-0 46	-1 13	*0.45	*0.33	2.2	2.9	1.8
227	Port Union	48° 30'	53° 05'	-0 53	-1 15	*0.49	*0.48	2.2	3.0	2.1
229	Random Head Harbour, Trinity Bay	48° 06'	53° 34'	-0 53	-1 05	*0.48	*0.33	2.4	3.2	1.9
231	Harbour Grace, Conception Bay	47° 41'	53° 12'	-0 28	-0 46	*0.51	*0.33	2.6	3.5	2.0
233	St. John's	47° 34'	52° 42'	-0 34	-0 46	*0.52	*0.38	2.6	3.5	2.1
	South Coast			on Argentia,						
235	Trepassey Harbour	46° 43'	53° 23'	-0 19	-0 11	-1.2	-0.5	4.2	5.6	3.5
237	St. Mary Harbour, St. Mary Bay	46° 55'	53° 35'	-0 14	-0 06	-1.2	-0.5	4.2	5.6	3.5
	Placentia Bay									
239	ARGENTIA	47° 18'	53° 59'	*Daily predictions*				4.9	6.3	4.4
241	Woody Island	47° 47'	54° 10'	+0 09	+0 09	-0.5	-0.3	4.7	6.0	4.0
243	Mortier Bay	47° 10'	55° 09'	+0 15	+0 26	-1.0	-0.8	4.7	6.0	3.5
245	Great St. Lawrence Harbour	46° 55'	55° 22'	+0 28	+0 55	-0.7	+0.3	3.9	5.0	4.2
	Time meridian, 60° W									
247	St. Pierre Harbor, St. Pierre Island	46° 47'	56° 10'	-0 09	+0 13	-0.8	+0.2	3.9	5.0	4.1
	Time meridian, 52° 30' W *Fortune Bay*									
249	Grande le Pierre Harbour	47° 40'	54° 47'	+1 09	+1 09	-1.0	+0.2	3.7	4.8	4.0
251	Belleoram	47° 32'	55° 25'	+0 57	+0 57	(*0.67+0.8)		3.3	4.3	3.8
253	Ship Cove, Bay d'Espoir	47° 52'	55° 50'	+0 45	+0 53	-0.4	0.0	4.5	5.5	4.2
255	Great Jervis Harbour, Bay d'Espoir	47° 39'	56° 11'	+0 38	+1 05	-1.1	+0.1	3.7	4.8	3.9
257	Hare Bay	47° 37'	56° 32'	+0 41	+1 08	(*0.67+0.6)		3.3	4.3	3.6
259	Grey River	47° 34'	57° 07'	+0 45	+1 12	(*0.63+0.7)		3.1	4.0	3.5
261	Connoire Bay	47° 40'	57° 54'	+0 50	+0 50	(*0.59+0.7)		2.9	3.8	3.3
263	La Poile Bay	47° 40'	58° 24'	+1 15	+1 15	(*0.63+0.6)		3.1	4.0	3.4
				on Harrington Harbour,						
265	Port Aux Basques	47° 35'	59° 09'	-1 24	-1 28	*0.80	*0.75	3.1	4.0	2.8
267	Codroy Road	47° 53'	59° 24'	-1 22	-1 27	*0.74	*0.75	2.8	3.7	2.6
	West Coast									
269	St. Georges Harbour	48° 27'	58° 30'	-0 28	-0 38	*0.78	*0.88	2.8	3.5	2.8
271	Port-au-Port	48° 33'	58° 45'	+0 05	+0 10	-1.3	-1.0	3.5	4.5	2.4
273	Frenchman's Cove, Bay of Islands	49° 04'	58° 10'	+0 10	+0 10	-0.5	0.0	3.3	4.2	3.3
275	Norris Cove, Bonne Bay	49° 31'	57° 52'	+0 10	+0 10	-0.7	-0.4	3.5	4.4	3.0
277	Portland Cove	50° 11'	57° 36'	+0 19	+0 19	-0.6	-0.4	3.6	4.6	3.0
279	Port Saunders	50° 39'	57° 18'	+0 07	+0 03	-0.3	-0.3	3.8	4.9	3.2
281	Castors Harbour, St. John Bay	50° 55'	56° 59'	+0 10	+0 10	*0.78	*0.75	3.0	4.1	2.7
283	St. Barbe Bay	51° 12'	56° 46'	+0 00	+0 00	*0.78	*0.56	3.3	4.4	2.6
	QUEBEC Gulf of St. Lawrence Time meridian, 60° W									
285	Bradore Bay	51° 28'	57° 15'	-0 35	-0 30	-0.6	-0.1	3.3	4.4	3.1
287	Mistanoque Harbour	51° 16'	58° 12'	-0 15	-0 15	-0.4	-0.1	3.5	4.6	3.3
289	HARRINGTON HARBOUR	50° 30'	59° 28'	*Daily predictions*				3.8	4.9	3.5
291	Wapitagun Harbour	50° 12'	60° 01'	+0 15	+0 15	-0.3	+0.1	3.4	4.4	3.4
293	Kegaska	50° 12'	61° 14'	+0 40	+0 40	-0.9	-0.2	3.1	4.0	3.0
295	Natashquan	50° 12'	61° 50'	+1 00	+1 10	-0.8	-0.1	3.1	4.0	3.1
297	Betchewun Harbour	50° 14'	63° 11'	+2 09	+2 13	-0.7	-0.4	3.5	4.6	3.0
299	Havre St. Pierre	50° 14'	63° 36'	+2 23	+2 32	0.0	-0.1	3.9	4.8	3.5
301	Mingan	50° 18'	64° 03'	+2 35	+2 40	+0.9	0.0	4.7	5.8	3.9

Endnotes can be found at the end of table 2.

TABLE 2. – TIDAL DIFFERENCES AND OTHER CONSTANTS

No.	PLACE	POSITION		DIFFERENCES				RANGES		Mean Tide Level
				Time		Height				
		Latitude	Longitude	High Water	Low Water	High Water	Low Water	Mean	Spring	
		North	West	h m	h m	ft	ft	ft	ft	ft
	QUEBEC Gulf of St. Lawrence-cont. Time meridian, 60° W				on Harrington Harbour,						
	Anticosti Island									
303	Heath Point	49° 05'	61° 42'	+0 51	+0 52	(*0.61+0.3)		2.3	3.0	2.4
305	Southwest Point	49° 24'	63° 36'	+3 21	+3 26	-0.3	0.0	3.5	4.4	3.4
307	Ellis Bay	49° 48'	64° 22'	+3 37	+3 38	+0.3	-0.5	4.6	5.7	3.4
309	Moisie Bay	50° 12'	66° 05'	+3 43	+3 49	+2.3	+0.5	5.6	7.2	4.9
311	Sept Iles	50° 13'	66° 24'	+3 54	+3 58	+2.7	-0.1	6.6	8.6	4.8
313	Cawee Islands	49° 50'	67° 00'	+4 01	+4 07	+3.0	+0.6	6.2	8.0	5.3
	St. Lawrence River Time meridian, 75° W									
315	Ste. Anne des Monts	49° 08'	66° 29'	+3 17	+3 19	+3.4	+0.6	6.6	8.6	5.5
317	Cap Chat	49° 06'	66° 45'	+3 17	+3 21	+4.2	+1.0	7.0	9.0	6.1
319	Pointe des Monts	49° 20'	67° 22'	+3 10	+3 16	+4.3	+0.8	7.3	9.6	6.1
321	Matane	48° 51'	67° 32'	+3 18	+3 22	+4.7	+0.9	7.6	9.9	6.3
323	Metis-sur-Mer	48° 41'	68° 02'	+3 24	+3 28	+5.4	+1.1	8.1	10.6	6.8
					on Quebec,					
325	Betsiamites River	48° 53'	68° 39'	-4 20	-5 08	-3.8	+1.4	8.5	11.2	7.3
327	Father Point	48° 31'	68° 28'	-4 22	-5 29	-3.4	+1.4	8.9	11.7	7.5
329	Old Bic Harbour	48° 22'	68° 44'	-4 12	-5 14	-3.3	+1.4	9.0	11.8	7.5
331	Tadoussac, Saguenay River . . .	48° 08'	69° 43'	-3 47	-4 54	-1.8	+0.8	11.1	14.0	8.0
333	Chicoutimi, Saguenay River . . .	48° 26'	71° 03'	-3 28	-3 40	-1.4	+1.3	11.0	14.4	8.4
335	Brandypot Islands	47° 52'	69° 41'	-3 36	-4 40	-0.5	+2.2	11.0	14.5	9.3
337	Murray Bay	47° 39'	70° 08'	-3 20	-4 22	+0.4	+2.3	11.8	15.3	9.8
339	Pointe aux Orignaux	47° 29'	70° 01'	-2 47	-3 41	-0.3	+2.2	11.2	14.7	9.4
341	Ile aux Coudres	47° 26'	70° 19'	-2 10	-3 21	+1.2	+2.0	12.9	15.8	10.1
343	L' Islet	47° 08'	70° 22'	-1 17	-2 05	0.0	+0.9	12.8	15.3	9.0
345	Beaujeu Channel	47° 05'	70° 29'	-1 10	-1 43	+0.6	+0.5	13.8	15.7	9.0
347	Grosse Ile	47° 02'	70° 40'	-0 57	-1 19	+1.3	0.0	15.0	17.1	9.1
349	Berthier	46° 56'	70° 44'	-0 47	-1 08	+1.3	0.0	15.0	16.9	9.1
351	St. Laurent d' Orleans	46° 52'	71° 00'	-0 20	-0 30	+0.3	+0.2	13.8	15.6	8.7
353	QUEBEC	46° 49'	71° 11'	*Daily predictions*				13.7	15.5	8.5
355	St. Nicolas	46° 43'	71° 24'	+0 35	+0 32	-0.7	- - -	12.6	14.3	- -
357	St. Augustin	46° 43'	71° 28'	+0 54	+0 53	-1.6	- - -	11.8	13.3	- -
359	Ste. Croix <1>	46° 37'	71° 45'	+1 31	+2 00	- - -	- - -	11.8	13.3	- -
361	Pointe Platon <1>	46° 40'	71° 51'	+1 43	+2 11	- - -	- - -	11.4	12.9	- -
363	Grondines <1>	46° 36'	72° 04'	+2 14	+3 18	- - -	- - -	6.7	8.1	- -
365	Cap a la Roche <1>	46° 33'	72° 10'	+2 37	+3 48	- - -	- - -	5.4	6.7	- -
367	Batiscan <1>	46° 31'	72° 15'	+3 32	+4 49	- - -	- - -	2.3	3.3	- -
369	Champlain <1>	46° 26'	72° 21'	+4 08	+5 30	- - -	- - -	1.8	2.8	- -
371	Trois Rivieres <1>	46° 20'	72° 33'	+4 45	+6 15	- - -	- - -	0.7	1.0	- -
	QUEBEC and NEW BRUNSWICK Gulf of St. Lawrence Time meridian, 60° W				on Pictou,						
373	GaspÖ Bay	48° 50'	64° 29'	+4 43	+4 58	-1.1	-0.5	2.6	3.3	3.1
375	Point St. Peter	48° 38'	64° 10'	+4 59	+5 11	*0.67	*0.52	2.5	3.2	2.5
	Chaleur Bay									
377	Port Daniel	48° 10'	64° 57'	+5 27	+5 42	-0.7	-0.6	3.1	3.8	3.3
379	Paspebiac	48° 01'	65° 14'	+5 22	+5 34	-0.4	-1.0	3.8	4.6	3.2
381	Carleton Point	48° 05'	66° 07'	+5 31	+5 36	+0.8	-0.7	4.7	6.2	4.0
383	Campbellton	48° 01'	66° 40'	+6 04	+6 40	+3.5	+0.9	5.8	7.2	6.1
385	Dalhousie	48° 04'	66° 22'	+5 42	+5 52	+2.2	-0.2	5.6	7.1	4.9
387	Bathurst	47° 37'	65° 39'	+6 04	+6 50	-0.3	-1.1	4.0	4.8	3.2
389	Caraquet Harbour	47° 48'	64° 56'	+5 49	+5 50	-1.0	-1.1	3.3	4.0	2.9
391	Miscou Harbour	47° 54'	64° 35'	+5 45	+5 57	-0.5	-1.1	3.8	5.0	3.1
393	Old Tracadie Gully entrance . . .	47° 31'	64° 52'	+6 25	+6 36	-1.6	-1.2	2.8	3.5	2.5
395	Tracadie	47° 31'	64° 55'	+6 55	+7 06	*0.55	*0.35	2.2	2.8	1.9
								Mean Diurnal		
397	Portage Island, Miramichi Bay #	47° 09'	65° 03'	-5 11	-4 59	-1.7	-0.8	- -	3.3	2.2
399	Newcastle, Miramichi River # . .	47° 00'	65° 34'	-3 53	-3 13	-0.7	-0.5	- -	4.0	- -
401	Richibucto River entrance # . . .	46° 43'	64° 48'	-4 45	- - -	-2.7	-0.8	- -	2.3	1.8
403	Shediac Bay #	46° 15'	64° 32'	- - -	+0 18	-1.9	-0.5	- -	2.8	2.8
								Mean Spring		
405	Cape Tormentine	46° 08'	63° 47'	+0 41	+1 03	+1.5	-0.1	4.8	5.7	4.6
407	Tidnish Head, Baie Verte	46° 01'	64° 01'	+0 33	+0 54	+1.7	-0.2	5.1	6.3	4.7
	PRINCE EDWARD ISLAND							Mean Diurnal		
409	Tignish #	46° 58'	64° 00'	-4 59	-5 27	-2.5	-0.8	- -	2.5	1.7
411	Alberton #	46° 49'	64° 03'	-4 27	-4 10	-2.8	-0.7	- -	2.1	1.7
413	Malpeque Bay #	46° 35'	63° 40'	-3 29	-3 13	-2.5	-0.8	- -	2.5	1.8
415	North Rustico #	46° 28'	63° 17'	-4 10	-4 04	-2.7	-1.0	- -	2.5	1.6
417	St. Peters Bay #	46° 26'	62° 44'	-3 52	-3 37	-3.3	-1.0	- -	1.9	1.5
419	Naufrage #	46° 28'	62° 25'	-3 09	-3 27	-2.6	-0.8	- -	2.4	2.0

Endnotes can be found at the end of table 2.

TABLE 2. – TIDAL DIFFERENCES AND OTHER CONSTANTS

No.	PLACE	POSITION Latitude	POSITION Longitude	DIFFERENCES Time High Water	DIFFERENCES Time Low Water	DIFFERENCES Height High Water	DIFFERENCES Height Low Water	RANGES Mean	RANGES Spring	Mean Tide Level
		North	West	h m	h m	ft	ft	ft	ft	ft
	PRINCE EDWARD ISLAND Time meridian, 60° W			**on Pictou,**						
421	Souris Head	46° 20'	62° 17'	-1 23	-1 25	-0.6	-0.2	2.8	3.5	3.5
423	Georgetown Harbour	46° 11'	62° 32'	-1 03	-1 00	-0.5	-0.1	2.8	3.5	3.6
425	Cape Bear	46° 00'	62° 27'	-0 42	-0 40	-0.6	-0.5	3.1	4.0	3.4
427	Charlottetown	46° 13'	63° 08'	+0 33	+0 42	+2.5	+0.5	5.2	6.4	5.4
429	Summerside Harbour	46° 24'	63° 47'	+0 57	+1 19	+0.9	+0.3	3.8	4.5	4.5
	NOVA SCOTIA Gulf of St. Lawrence									
431	St. Paul Island	47° 12'	60° 09'	-1 25	-1 22	*0.64	*0.57	2.2	2.8	2.4
433	Amherst Harbour, Magdalen Islands	47° 14'	61° 07'	-1 05	-1 07	*0.53	*0.57	1.6	2.0	2.1
435	Pugwash	45° 51'	63° 40'	+1 00	+1 03	+1.8	0.0	5.0	6.0	4.8
437	PICTOU	45° 41'	62° 42'	*Daily predictions*				3.2	3.9	3.9
439	Merigomish Harbour	45° 39'	62° 27'	-0 13	-0 01	-0.3	0.0	2.9	3.4	3.8
441	Cape George	45° 53'	61° 53'	-0 54	-0 51	-1.6	-0.8	2.4	3.2	2.7
443	Antigonish Harbour	45° 40'	61° 53'	+0 09	+0 17	-1.7	-0.5	2.0	2.5	2.8
445	Cape Jack	45° 42'	61° 33'	-1 11	-1 18	-1.8	-0.7	2.1	2.6	2.7
447	Auld Cove	45° 39'	61° 26'	-0 27	-0 33	(*0.62+1.3)		2.0	2.6	3.7
	Cape Breton Island									
449	Port Hood	46° 01'	61° 32'	-0 46	-0 45	-1.6	-0.9	2.5	3.2	2.7
451	Mabou River entrance	46° 06'	61° 28'	-0 53	-1 04	*0.66	*0.61	2.2	2.9	2.5
453	Cheticamp	46° 37'	61° 02'	-1 23	-1 20	*0.56	*0.74	1.4	1.8	2.4
	Outer Coast									
	Cape Breton Island-cont.									
455	Neil Harbour	46° 48'	60° 20'	-1 44	-1 45	*0.69	*0.65	2.4	3.1	2.7
457	Ingonish Island	46° 40'	60° 23'	-1 40	-1 33	-1.5	-0.9	2.6	3.2	2.7
459	St. Anns Harbour	46° 15'	60° 34'	-1 37	-1 40	-1.4	-1.0	2.8	3.5	2.7
461	North Sydney	46° 13'	60° 15'	-1 54	-1 49	*0.73	*0.61	2.6	3.2	2.7
463	Glace Bay	46° 12'	59° 55'	-1 59	-1 54	-1.6	-0.9	2.5	3.2	2.7
				on Halifax,						
465	Louisburg Harbour	45° 54'	59° 59'	-0 08	-0 14	-1.6	-0.7	3.5	4.2	3.2
467	Gabarus Cove	45° 51'	60° 10'	+0 08	+0 10	-1.4	-0.7	3.7	4.4	3.3
469	St. Peter Bay	45° 38'	60° 52'	-0 12	-0 07	-0.6	-0.4	4.2	5.1	3.8
471	Arichat	45° 31'	61° 02'	-0 25	-0 14	-0.9	-0.5	4.0	4.8	3.6
473	Port Hastings, Strait of Canso	45° 39'	61° 24'	-0 16	-0 12	0.0	+0.2	4.2	5.1	4.4
475	Guysborough	45° 23'	61° 29'	+0 06	+0 18	-1.1	-0.5	3.8	4.6	3.5
477	Canso Harbour	45° 21'	61° 00'	-0 05	-0 04	-1.1	-0.6	3.9	4.7	3.5
479	Whitehaven Harbour	45° 14'	61° 12'	-0 10	-0 02	-1.1	-0.4	3.7	4.7	3.6
481	Isaacs Harbour	45° 11'	61° 40'	-0 03	+0 04	-0.6	-0.1	3.9	4.6	4.0
483	Sonora, St. Mary River	45° 03'	61° 55'	-0 02	+0 09	-0.7	-0.6	4.3	5.2	3.7
485	Liscomb Harbour	45° 00'	62° 02'	-0 11	-0 05	-0.6	-0.4	4.2	5.0	3.8
487	Sheet Harbour	44° 54'	62° 30'	-0 08	-0 04	-1.1	-0.9	4.2	5.0	3.3
489	Ship Harbour	44° 47'	62° 49'	-0 07	-0 04	-0.6	-0.4	4.2	5.1	3.8
491	Jeddore Harbour	44° 45'	63° 01'	-0 06	-0 03	-0.5	-0.4	4.3	5.2	3.9
493	HALIFAX	44° 40'	63° 34'	*Daily predictions*				4.4	5.3	4.3
495	Sable Island, north side	43° 57'	60° 06'	-0 06	-0 12	-2.7	-0.9	2.6	3.2	2.5
497	Sable Island, south side	43° 56'	59° 54'	-0 02	-0 06	-2.1	-1.6	3.9	4.8	2.5
499	St. Margarets Bay	44° 31'	63° 56'	+0 08	+0 07	-0.5	-0.3	4.2	4.9	3.9
501	Chester, Mahone Bay	44° 34'	64° 18'	+0 01	-0 04	-0.2	-0.2	4.4	5.3	4.1
503	Mahone Harbour, Mahone Bay	44° 27'	64° 22'	+0 03	-0 01	-0.1	-0.2	4.5	5.5	4.2
505	Lunenburg	44° 22'	64° 19'	+0 07	+0 07	-0.1	+0.1	4.2	4.9	4.3
507	Riverport, La Have River	44° 17'	64° 20'	+0 12	+0 05	-0.3	-0.4	4.5	5.3	4.0
509	Bridgewater, La Have River	44° 23'	64° 31'	+0 09	+0 06	-0.2	-0.3	4.5	5.5	4.1
511	Liverpool Bay	44° 02'	64° 41'	+0 14	+0 04	-0.5	-0.4	4.3	5.1	3.9
513	Lockeport	43° 44'	65° 05'	+0 27	+0 02	-0.2	-0.4	4.6	5.4	4.0
515	Shelburne	43° 45'	65° 18'	+0 30	+0 35	+0.1	-0.3	4.8	5.8	4.2
517	Barrington Passage	43° 32'	65° 36'	+0 51	+0 30	+1.6	+0.6	5.4	6.2	5.4
519	Swim Point	43° 26'	65° 38'	+1 41	+1 03	+2.9	+0.1	7.2	8.4	5.8
	NOVA SCOTIA and NEW BRUNSWICK Bay of Fundy			**on Saint John, N. B.,**						
521	Lower East Pubnico	43° 38'	65° 46'	-1 52	-2 07	*0.43	*0.48	8.7	10.0	6.3
523	Yarmouth Harbour	43° 48'	66° 08'	-1 07	-1 15	*0.53	*0.42	11.5	13.4	7.5
525	Westport, St. Mary Bay	44° 16'	66° 21'	-0 35	-0 30	*0.72	*0.72	15.0	16.7	10.4
527	Tiverton, St. Mary Bay	44° 24'	66° 13'	-0 38	-0 30	-5.6	-0.7	15.9	18.3	11.3
529	Weymouth, St. Mary Bay	44° 27'	66° 01'	-0 26	-0 22	-6.5	-0.7	15.0	17.0	10.8
531	Digby, Annapolis Basin	44° 38'	65° 45'	-0 09	-0 07	+0.7	+0.3	21.2	24.6	14.9
533	Annapolis Royal, Annapolis River	44° 45'	65° 30'	+0 06	+0 10	+2.2	+0.4	22.6	25.7	15.7
535	Port George	45° 01'	65° 10'	-0 06	-0 06	+6.7	+0.8	26.7	30.5	18.2
537	Ile Haute	45° 15'	65° 00'	-0 02	-0 02	+7.4	+0.7	27.5	31.5	18.5
539	Spencer Island	45° 20'	64° 42'	+0 17	+0 21	*1.47	*1.50	30.5	35.0	21.2
	Minas Basin									
541	Parrsboro (Partridge Island) <2>	45° 22'	64° 20'	+0 51	+0 49	+14.7	- - -	34.4	39.0	22.3
543	Horton Bluff, Avon River	45° 06'	64° 13'	+0 58	+1 02	*1.76	*1.38	38.1	43.6	24.6
545	Windsor <2>	45° 00'	64° 08'	+1 03	- - -	+19.5	- - -	- -	- -	- -
547	Burntcoat Head	45° 18'	63° 49'	+1 06	+1 12	*1.90	*2.18	38.4	43.5	27.9
549	Truro <2>	45° 22'	63° 20'	+1 43	- - -	+26.1	- - -	- -	- -	- -
551	Spicer Cove, Chignecto Bay	45° 26'	64° 54'	+0 12	+0 16	+7.0	+0.8	27.0	30.0	18.3
553	Joggins <2>	45° 41'	64° 28'	+0 14	+0 26	+14.2	+1.8	33.2	37.0	22.4
555	Amherst Point, Cumberland Basin	45° 50'	64° 17'	+0 33	+0 45	*1.69	*1.55	35.6	40.5	24.0

TABLE 2. – TIDAL DIFFERENCES AND OTHER CONSTANTS

No.	PLACE	POSITION		DIFFERENCES				RANGES		Mean Tide Level
				Time		Height				
		Latitude	Longitude	High Water	Low Water	High Water	Low Water	Mean	Spring	
		North	West	h m	h m	ft	ft	ft	ft	ft
	NOVA SCOTIA and NEW BRUNSWICK Bay of Fundy-cont. Time meridian, 60° W			on Saint John, N. B.,						
	Petitcodiac River <3>									
557	Grindstone Island	45° 43'	64° 37'	+0 21	+0 28	*1.49	*1.45	31.1	35.6	21.4
559	Hopewell Cape	45° 52'	64° 35'	+0 14	+0 39	*1.64	*1.85	33.2	38.0	24.0
561	Moncton <2> <3>	46° 05'	64° 46'	+0 46	- - -	+17.2	- - -	--	--	--
563	Salisbury	46° 01'	65° 03'	+1 31	- - -	+18.2	- - -	--	--	--
565	Herring Cove	45° 35'	64° 58'	+0 22	+0 20	+8.4	+0.9	28.3	32.4	19.1
567	Quaco Bay	45° 20'	65° 32'	+0 11	+0 12	+2.0	-0.3	23.1	26.3	15.3
569	SAINT JOHN <4>	45° 15'	66° 04'	*Daily predictions*				20.8	23.7	14.4
571	Indiantown, St. John River	45° 16'	66° 05'	+1 30	+2 25	- - -	- - -	1.2	1.4	2.4
573	Lepreau Harbour	45° 07'	66° 29'	-0 01	+0 03	-2.3	-0.5	19.0	21.7	13.0
575	L' Etang Harbour	45° 02'	66° 49'	+0 01	+0 05	-3.2	-0.8	18.4	21.0	12.4
577	North Head, Grand Manan Island	44° 46'	66° 45'	-0 05	-0 05	-4.5	-0.9	17.2	19.3	11.7
579	Seal Cove, Grand Manan Island	44° 37'	66° 51'	-0 15	-0 17	*0.68	*0.65	14.3	16.3	9.8
581	Outer Wood Island <5>	44° 36'	66° 48'	-0 25	-0 27	-7.8	-0.8	13.8	16.2	10.1
583	Machias Seal Island <5>	44° 30'	67° 06'	-0 01	- - -	-9.6	-1.7	12.9	14.5	8.8
585	Welshpool, Campobello Island <5>	44° 53'	66° 57'	-0 01	+0 06	-3.5	-1.0	18.3	21.2	12.1
587	Wilsons Beach, Campobello Island <5>	44° 56'	66° 56'	+0 00	+0 01	-3.7	+0.1	17.0	19.4	12.6
589	Back Bay, Letite Harbour <5>	45° 03'	66° 52'	+0 00	-0 03	-3.5	0.0	17.3	20.1	12.6
591	Midjik Bluff, Passamaquoddy Bay <5>	45° 07'	66° 54'	+0 12	+0 17	-2.0	-0.5	19.3	22.0	13.1
593	St. Andrews, Passamaquoddy Bay <5>	45° 04'	67° 03'	+0 14	+0 20	-2.3	0.0	18.5	21.2	13.2
	MAINE Time meridian, 75° W			on Eastport,						
595	Pettegrove Point, Dochet Island	45° 07.7'	67° 08.6'	+0 08	+0 12	*1.07	*1.00	19.57	22.12	10.24
597	EASTPORT	44° 54.2'	66° 59.1'	*Daily predictions*				18.35	21.18	9.6
	Cobscook Bay									
599	Garnet Point, Pennamquan River	44° 55.4'	67° 07.8'	+0 11	+0 14	*1.04	*1.00	19.17	22.05	10.04
601	Coffins Point	44° 52.2'	67° 06.5'	+0 31	+0 33	*0.94	*0.77	17.3	19.7	9.0
603	Birch Islands, Whiting Bay	44° 52.5'	67° 09.5'	+0 59	+1 13	*0.94	*0.75	17.4	19.8	9.0
605	Gravelly Point, Whiting Bay	44° 49.4'	67° 09.1'	+1 07	+1 18	*0.97	*0.73	17.90	19.06	9.28
607	Cutler, Little River	44° 39.4'	67° 12.6'	-0 10	-0 19	*0.74	*0.74	13.5	15.4	7.1
609	Cutler, Naval Radio Station	44° 38.5'	67° 17.8'	-0 07	-0 14	*0.70	*0.84	12.78	14.67	6.76
611	Stone Island, Machias Bay	44° 36.2'	67° 22.1'	-0 11	-0 28	*0.68	*0.68	12.4	14.1	6.5
613	Machiasport, Machias River	44° 41.9'	67° 23.6'	+0 01	-0 09	*0.69	*0.69	12.6	14.4	6.6
615	Shoppee Point, Englishman Bay	44° 36.9'	67° 29.8'	-0 05	-0 13	*0.66	*0.66	12.1	13.8	6.2
				on Portland,						
617	Steele Harbor Island	44° 29.6'	67° 32.6'	-0 28	-0 20	*1.27	*1.27	11.6	13.3	6.2
619	Millbridge, Narraguagus River, Maine	44° 32.4'	67° 52.5'	-0 15	+0 05	*1.23	*1.09	11.31	12.89	6.03
621	Green Island, Petit Manan Bar	44° 22.3'	67° 52.2'	-0 28	-0 24	*1.16	*1.16	10.6	12.2	5.7
623	Prospect Harbor	44° 24'	68° 01'	-0 24	-0 15	*1.15	*1.15	10.5	12.1	5.7
				on Bar Harbor,						
625	Winter Harbor, Frenchman Bay	44° 23.3'	68° 05.2'	-0 01	+0 10	*0.95	*0.95	10.1	11.6	5.4
	Mount Desert Island									
627	BAR HARBOR	44° 23.5'	68° 12.3'	*Daily Predictions*				10.56	12.25	5.66
629	Southwest Harbor	44° 16.5'	68° 18.8'	+0 00	-0 27	*0.96	*0.95	10.2	11.7	5.5
631	Bass Harbor	44° 14.5'	68° 21.2'	+0 04	-0 27	*0.93	*0.93	9.9	11.3	5.4
	Blue Hill Bay									
633	Blue Hill Harbor	44° 24.5'	68° 33.8'	+0 09	+0 11	*0.95	*0.95	10.1	11.6	5.4
635	Mackerel Cove	44° 10.2'	68° 26.1'	+0 02	-0 27	*0.94	*0.93	10.0	11.5	5.4
637	Ellsworth, Union River	44° 32.1'	68° 25.3'	+0 15	+0 16	*1.00	*0.97	10.59	12.07	5.67
639	Burnt Coat Harbor, Swans Island	44° 08.7'	68° 27.0'	-0 01	+0 06	*0.89	*0.88	9.5	10.8	5.1
	Penobscot Bay									
	Eggemoggin Reach									
641	Center Harbor	44° 15.8'	68° 35.2'	+0 09	+0 12	*0.95	*0.95	10.1	11.5	5.4
643	Little Deer Isle	44° 17.5'	68° 41.6'	+0 16	+0 14	*0.94	*0.93	10.0	11.5	5.4
645	Isle Au Haut	44° 04.4'	68° 38.2'	-0 01	-0 27	*0.87	*0.88	9.3	10.7	5.0
647	Oceanville, Deer Isle	44° 11.5'	68° 37.2'	+0 08	+0 05	*0.93	*0.95	9.86	11.62	5.29
649	Stonington, Deer Isle	44° 09.2'	68° 39.7'	+0 08	+0 06	*0.91	*0.90	9.7	11.2	5.2
651	Matinicus Harbor, Wheaton Island	43° 51.7'	68° 52.9'	+0 05	-0 27	*0.85	*0.85	9.0	10.4	4.8
653	Vinalhaven, Vinalhaven Island	44° 02.6'	68° 50.4'	+0 09	+0 10	*0.87	*0.88	9.3	10.7	5.0
655	North Haven	44° 07.6'	68° 52.4'	+0 13	+0 10	*0.91	*0.90	9.7	11.2	5.3
657	Pulpit Harbor, North Haven Island	44° 09.4'	68° 53.2'	+0 12	+0 10	*0.93	*0.97	9.85	11.43	5.30
659	Castine	44° 23.2'	68° 47.8'	+0 15	+0 11	*0.95	*1.00	10.1	11.6	5.4
	Penobscot River									
661	Fort Point	44° 28.3'	68° 44.80'	+0 09	+0 06	*0.98	*0.95	10.39	11.67	5.55
663	Gross Point, Eastern Channel	44° 32.2'	68° 45.5'	-0 06	+0 10	*0.99	*0.98	10.4	12.0	5.6
665	Bucksport	44° 34.3'	68° 48.1'	-0 04	+0 11	*1.01	*1.00	10.8	12.4	5.8
667	Winterport	44° 38.2'	68° 50.5'	-0 09	+0 04	*1.11	*0.92	11.76	13.64	6.22
669	Sandy Point	44° 40.3'	68° 48.3'	-0 06	+0 08	*0.99	*0.98	10.5	12.1	5.6
671	Bangor	44° 47.7'	68° 46.3'	-0 06	+0 18	*1.25	*0.87	13.40	14.97	7.03
673	Belfast	44° 25.6'	69° 00.3'	+0 09	+0 04	*0.97	*1.03	10.23	11.66	5.51
675	Rockland	44° 06.3'	69° 06.1'	+0 09	+0 06	*0.93	*1.03	9.78	11.15	5.28

Endnotes can be found at the end of table 2.

TABLE 2. – TIDAL DIFFERENCES AND OTHER CONSTANTS

No.	PLACE	POSITION		DIFFERENCES				RANGES		Mean Tide Level
				Time		Height				
		Latitude	Longitude	High Water	Low Water	High Water	Low Water	Mean	Spring	
		North	West	h m	h m	ft	ft	ft	ft	ft
	MAINE Outer Coast Time meridian, 75° W			on Portland,						
677	Tenants Harbor	43° 57.9'	69° 13.0'	-0 11	-0 11	*1.02	*1.02	9.3	10.6	5.0
679	Monhegan Island	43° 45.9'	69° 19.3'	-0 13	-0 09	*0.97	*0.97	8.8	10.1	4.7
681	Burnt Island, Georges Islands	43° 52.3'	69° 17.7'	-0 13	-0 12	*0.98	*0.98	8.9	10.2	4.8
	St. George River									
683	Port Clyde	43° 55.5'	69° 15.6'	-0 11	-0 07	*0.98	*0.98	8.9	10.2	4.8
685	Otis Cove	43° 59.2'	69° 14.2'	-0 15	-0 14	*1.00	*1.00	9.1	10.5	4.9
687	Thomaston	44° 04.3'	69° 10.9'	-0 04	-0 03	*1.03	*1.03	9.4	10.8	5.0
689	New Harbor, Muscongus Bay	43° 52.5'	69° 29.4'	-0 10	-0 08	*0.97	*0.97	8.8	10.1	4.7
691	Muscongus Harbor, Muscongus Sound	43° 58.0'	69° 26.5'	-0 09	-0 03	*0.99	*0.99	9.0	10.4	4.8
693	Friendship Harbor	43° 58.2'	69° 20.5'	-0 18	-0 11	*0.99	*0.99	9.0	10.4	4.8
	Medomak River									
695	Jones Neck	44° 00.2'	69° 22.8'	-0 10	-0 05	*1.00	*1.00	9.1	10.5	4.9
697	Waldoboro	44° 05.6'	69° 22.6'	-0 16	-0 04	*1.04	*1.04	9.5	10.9	5.1
699	Pemaquid Harbor, Johns Bay	43° 52.6'	69° 31.5'	-0 05	-0 04	*0.97	*0.97	8.8	10.1	4.7
	Damariscotta River									
701	East Boothbay	43° 51.9'	69° 35.0'	-0 02	+0 01	*0.98	*0.98	8.9	10.2	4.8
703	Walpole	43° 56.0'	69° 34.8'	+0 06	+0 14	*1.03	*1.06	9.35	10.66	5.05
705	Newcastle	44° 02.0'	69° 32.2'	+0 16	+0 25	*1.02	*1.02	9.3	10.7	5.0
707	Damariscove Harbor, Damariscove Island	43° 45.5'	69° 36.9'	-0 09	-0 10	*0.97	*0.97	8.8	10.1	4.7
709	Boothbay Harbor	43° 51.1'	69° 37.7'	-0 06	-0 08	*0.97	*0.97	8.8	10.1	4.7
711	Southport, Townsend Gut	43° 50.8'	69° 39.7'	+0 01	+0 01	*0.98	*0.98	8.9	10.2	4.8
	Sheepscot River									
713	Isle of Springs	43° 51.6'	69° 41.2'	-0 02	-0 04	*0.98	*0.98	8.9	10.3	4.8
715	Cross River entrance	43° 55.5'	69° 40.2'	+0 07	+0 04	*1.00	*1.00	9.1	10.5	4.8
717	Wiscasset	44° 00.0'	69° 40.0'	+0 16	+0 04	*1.03	*1.03	9.4	10.8	5.0
719	Sheepscot (below rapids)	44° 03.0'	69° 37.1'	+0 20	+0 20	*1.05	*1.05	9.6	11.0	5.2
721	Back River	43° 57.5'	69° 41.1'	+0 34	+0 31	*1.00	*1.00	9.1	10.5	4.9
723	Robinhood, Sasanoa River	43° 51.2'	69° 44.0'	+0 14	+0 14	*0.97	*0.97	8.8	10.1	4.7
725	Mill Point, Sasanoa River	43° 53.2'	69° 45.8'	+0 35	+0 43	*0.97	*0.97	8.8	10.1	4.7
	Kennebec River									
727	Fort Popham, Hunniwell Point	43° 45.3'	69° 47.3'	+0 09	+0 04	*0.92	*0.92	8.4	9.7	4.5
729	Phippsburg	43° 49.1'	69° 48.6'	+0 26	+0 28	*0.88	*0.88	8.0	9.2	4.3
731	Bath	43° 55.1'	69° 48.8'	+1 01	+1 17	*0.70	*0.70	6.4	7.4	3.4
733	Sturgeon Island, Merrymeeting Bay	43° 58.9'	69° 50.1'	+2 00	+2 04	*0.58	*0.58	5.3	6.1	2.8
735	Androscoggin River entrance	43° 57.0'	69° 53.3'	+2 24	+3 26	*0.52	*0.52	4.7	5.4	2.5
737	Brunswick, Androscoggin River	43° 55.3'	69° 57.8'	+2 35	+4 36	*0.42	*0.42	3.8	4.4	2.0
739	Bowdoinham, Cathance River	44° 00.5'	69° 53.7'	+2 34	+2 42	*0.63	*0.63	5.7	6.6	3.1
	Casco Bay									
741	Cundy Harbor, New Meadows River	43° 47.3'	69° 53.6'	-0 01	-0 02	*0.98	*0.98	8.9	10.2	4.8
743	Howard Point, New Meadows River	43° 53.4'	69° 53.0'	-0 05	+0 01	*0.99	*0.99	9.0	10.3	4.8
745	South Harpswell, Potts Harbor	43° 44.3'	70° 01.4'	+0 02	+0 01	*0.98	*0.98	8.9	10.2	4.8
747	Wilson Cove, Middle Bay	43° 49.5'	69° 58.6'	+0 02	+0 02	*1.00	*1.00	9.1	10.5	4.9
749	South Freeport	43° 49.2'	70° 06.2'	+0 12	+0 10	*0.99	*0.99	9.0	10.3	4.8
751	Prince Point	43° 45.7'	70° 10.4'	+0 00	+0 01	*1.00	*0.99	9.19	10.57	4.90
753	Doyle Point	43° 45.1'	70° 08.4'	-0 02	-0 03	*1.00	*0.88	9.2	10.5	4.9
755	Falmouth Foreside	43° 43.9'	70° 12.3'	+0 01	+0 01	*1.00	*0.97	9.16	10.53	4.91
757	Great Chebeague Island	43° 43.3'	70° 08.5'	+0 02	+0 02	*1.00	*1.03	9.11	10.48	4.91
759	Cliff Island, Luckse Sound	43° 41.7'	70° 06.6'	-0 02	-0 02	*1.00	*1.00	9.1	10.4	4.9
761	Vaill Island	43° 40.6'	70° 09.3'	+0 05	+0 01	*0.98	*1.03	9.0	10.3	4.8
763	Long Island	43° 41.4'	70° 10.2'	-0 01	-0 01	*1.00	*1.00	9.09	10.45	4.89
765	Cow Island	43° 41.4'	70° 11.4'	-0 01	+0 00	*1.00	*1.00	9.11	10.48	4.89
767	Presumpscot River Bridge	43° 41.4'	70° 14.8'	+0 01	+0 04	*1.01	*1.06	9.2	10.6	5.0
769	Back Cove	43° 41'	70° 15'	+0 02	+0 06	*0.97	*0.97	9.1	10.5	4.9
771	Great Diamond Island	43° 40.2'	70° 12.0'	+0 00	+0 00	*1.00	*1.03	9.08	10.44	4.89
773	Peak Island	43° 39.3'	70° 12.0'	-0 04	-0 08	*0.99	*0.99	9.0	10.4	4.8
775	Cushing Island	43° 38.7'	70° 11.9'	+0 01		*0.99	*1.03	9.02	10.37	4.87
777	PORTLAND	43° 39.6'	70° 14.8'	Daily predictions				9.12	10.53	4.91
779	Fore River	43° 38.5'	70° 17.1'	+0 02	+0 02	*1.00	*1.03	9.16	10.53	4.93
781	Portland Head Light	43° 37.4'	70° 12.4'	-0 02	-0 01	*0.97	*1.00	8.89	10.13	4.78
	Outer Coast									
783	Pine Point, Scarborough River	43° 32.7'	70° 20.0'	+0 06	+0 16	*0.96	*0.97	8.77	9.72	4.71
785	Old Orchard Beach	43° 31'	70° 22'	+0 00	-0 06	*0.97	*0.97	8.8	10.1	4.7
787	Camp Ellis, Saco River Entrance	43° 27.7'	70° 22.9'	+0 03	+0 10	*0.97	*1.00	8.92	10.17	4.79
789	Biddeford, Saco River	43° 29.5'	70° 26.8'	+0 12	+0 26	*0.99	*0.97	9.06	10.33	4.86
791	Cape Porpoise	43° 22.0'	70° 25.9'	+0 12	+0 14	*0.95	*0.95	8.7	9.9	4.7
793	Kennebunkport	43° 21.5'	70° 28.6'	+0 07	+0 05	*0.97	*1.00	8.84	10.08	4.76
795	Wells, Webhannet River	43° 19.2'	70° 33.8'	+0 06	+0 02	*0.96	*1.00	8.77	10.09	4.72
797	Cape Neddick	43° 10.0'	70° 35.6'	+0 02	+0 08	*0.95	*1.00	8.69	9.99	4.68
799	York Harbor	43° 07.9'	70° 38.5'	+0 03	+0 13	*0.95	*0.95	8.6	9.9	4.6
801	Fort Point, York Harbor	43° 07.8'	70° 38.3'	-0 04	+0 10	*0.95	*0.94	8.69	9.99	4.66
803	Seapoint, Cutts Island	43° 05.1'	70° 39.7'	+0 01	-0 04	*0.96	*0.96	8.8	10.1	4.7

Endnotes can be found at the end of table 2.

TABLE 2. – TIDAL DIFFERENCES AND OTHER CONSTANTS

No.	PLACE	POSITION		DIFFERENCES				RANGES		Mean Tide Level
				Time		Height				
		Latitude	Longitude	High Water	Low Water	High Water	Low Water	Mean	Spring	
		North	West	h m	h m	ft	ft	ft	ft	ft
	MAINE and NEW HAMPSHIRE Time meridian, 75° W			on Portland,						
	Portsmouth Harbor									
805	Jaffrey Point	43° 03.4'	70° 43.9'	-0 03	-0 05	*0.95	*0.95	8.7	10.0	4.7
807	Gerrish Island	43° 04.0'	70° 41.7'	-0 02	-0 03	*0.95	*0.95	8.7	10.0	4.7
809	Fort Point	43° 04.3'	70° 42.7'	+0 09	+0 05	*0.95	*1.00	8.63	9.92	4.65
811	Kittery Point	43° 04.9'	70° 42.2'	-0 07	+0 01	*0.96	*0.96	8.7	10.0	4.7
813	Seavey Island	43° 05'	70° 45'	+0 20	+0 18	*0.89	*0.89	8.1	9.4	4.4
815	Portsmouth	43° 04.7'	70° 45.1'	+0 22	+0 17	*0.86	*0.86	7.8	9.0	4.2
	Piscataqua River									
817	Atlantic Heights	43° 05.4'	70° 46.0'	+0 37	+0 28	*0.82	*0.82	7.5	8.6	4.0
819	Dover Point	43° 07'	70° 50'	+1 33	+1 27	*0.70	*0.70	6.4	7.4	3.4
821	Dover, Cocheco River	43° 11.9'	70° 52.1'	+1 45	+1 39	*0.77	*0.76	7.04	8.03	3.78
823	Salmon Falls River	43° 11.4'	70° 49.5'	+1 35	+1 52	*0.75	*0.75	6.8	7.8	3.6
825	Squamscott River RR. Bridge	43° 03.2'	70° 54.8'	+2 19	+2 41	*0.75	*0.75	6.8	7.8	3.6
827	Gosport Harbor, Isles of Shoals	42° 58.7'	70° 36.9'	+0 02	-0 02	*0.93	*0.93	8.5	9.8	4.5
829	Hampton Harbor	42° 54'	70° 49'	+0 14	+0 32	*0.91	*0.91	8.3	9.5	4.5
	MASSACHUSETTS									
	Merrimack River									
831	Plum Island, Merrimack River Entrance	42° 49.0'	70° 49.2'	+0 06	+0 29	*0.88	*0.88	8.00	9.12	4.30
833	Newburyport	42° 48.7'	70° 51.9'	+0 31	+1 11	*0.86	*0.86	7.8	9.0	4.2
835	Salisbury Point	42° 50.3'	70° 54.5'	+0 55	+1 18	*0.83	*0.56	7.64	8.71	4.01
837	Merrimacport	42° 49.5'	70° 59.3'	+1 26	+2 08	*0.76	*0.50	7.05	8.04	3.70
839	Riverside	42° 45.8'	71° 04.6'	+1 56	+3 30	*0.62	*0.35	5.72	6.52	2.80
841	Plum Island Sound (south end)	42° 42.6'	70° 47.3'	+0 12	+0 37	*0.94	*0.94	8.6	9.9	4.6
843	Essex	42° 37.9'	70° 46.6'	+0 22	+0 31	*1.00	*0.94	9.18	10.47	4.90
845	Annisquam, Lobster Cove	42° 39.3'	70° 40.6'	+0 11	+0 03	*0.97	*0.97	8.81	10.04	4.74
847	Rockport	42° 39.5'	70° 36.9'	+0 06	+0 06	*0.95	*0.97	8.70	9.92	4.71
				on Boston,						
849	Gloucester Harbor	42° 36.6'	70° 39.6'	+0 00	-0 04	*0.93	*0.97	8.80	10.03	4.73
851	Salem, Salem Harbor	42° 31.4'	70° 52.6'	-0 02	-0 05	*0.94	*0.97	8.93	10.18	4.79
853	Lynn, Lynn Harbor	42° 27.5'	70° 56.6'	+0 01	-0 03	*0.97	*1.00	9.16	10.44	4.92
	Boston Harbor									
855	Boston Light	42° 19.7'	70° 53.5'	-0 01	-0 02	*0.95	*0.97	9.05	10.03	4.85
857	Deer Island (south end)	42° 20.7'	70° 57.5'	+0 01	+0 00	*0.97	*0.97	9.3	10.8	4.9
859	BOSTON	42° 21.3'	71° 03.2'	Daily predictions				9.49	11.07	5.09
861	Charlestown, Charles River entrance	42° 22.5'	71° 03.0'	+0 00	+0 01	*1.00	*1.00	9.5	11.0	5.0
863	Amelia Earhart Dam, Mystic River	42° 23.7'	71° 04.6'	+0 01	+0 02	*1.01	*0.97	9.56	10.89	5.11
865	Chelsea St. Bridge, Chelsea River	42° 23.2'	71° 01.4'	+0 01	+0 06	*1.01	*1.01	9.6	11.1	5.1
867	Neponset, Neponset River	42° 17.1'	71° 02.4'	-0 02	+0 03	*1.00	*1.00	9.5	11.0	5.0
869	Moon Head	42° 18.5'	70° 59.3'	+0 01	+0 04	*0.99	*0.99	9.4	10.9	5.0
	Hingham Bay									
871	Nut Island, Quincy Bay	42° 16.8'	70° 57.3'	+0 01	+0 01	*0.99	*1.00	9.42	10.74	5.05
873	Weymouth Fore River Bridge	42° 14.7'	70° 58.1'	+0 09	+0 06	*1.00	*1.00	9.5	11.0	5.0
875	Crow Point, Hingham Harbor entrance	42° 15.7'	70° 53.6'	+0 02	+0 05	*0.99	*0.99	9.4	10.9	5.0
877	Hingham	42° 14.8'	70° 53.1'	+0 09	+0 08	*1.00	*1.00	9.5	11.0	5.0
879	Nantasket Beach, Weir River	42° 16.2'	70° 51.6'	+0 06	+0 07	*0.99	*0.99	9.4	10.9	5.0
881	Hull	42° 18.2'	70° 55.2'	+0 05	+0 07	*0.97	*0.97	9.3	10.8	5.0
	Cohasset Harbor to Davis Bank									
883	Cohasset Harbor (White Head)	42° 14.9'	70° 47.0'	+0 04	-0 02	*0.92	*0.92	8.8	10.2	4.7
885	Scituate, Scituate Harbor	42° 12.1'	70° 43.6'	+0 03	-0 01	*0.95	*1.03	8.94	10.19	4.83
887	Damons Point, North River	42° 09.6'	70° 44.0'	+0 20	+0 36	*0.89	*0.89	8.5	9.9	4.5
889	Brant Rock, Green Harbor River	42° 05.0'	70° 38.8'	+0 05	+0 03	*0.96	*1.03	9.08	10.35	4.89
	Cape Cod Bay									
891	Duxbury, Duxbury Harbor	42° 02.3'	70° 40.2'	+0 06	+0 33	*1.04	*1.03	9.89	11.27	5.30
893	Plymouth	41° 57.6'	70° 39.7'	+0 04	+0 18	*1.03	*1.00	9.76	11.13	5.22
895	Cape Cod Canal, east entrance	41° 46.3'	70° 30.4'	-0 01	-0 03	*0.91	*0.68	8.74	9.96	4.59
897	Cape Cod Canal, Sagamore (Sta. 115)	41° 46.5'	70° 32.1'	-0 15	-0 06	*0.83	*0.88	7.90	9.01	4.25
899	Cape Cod Canal, Bournedale (Sta. 200)	41° 46.2'	70° 33.7'	-0 29	-0 21	*0.66	*0.79	6.18	7.05	3.37
901	Cape Cod Canal, Bourne Bridge (Sta. 320)	41° 44.7'	70° 35.6'	-1 13	-0 24	*0.46	*0.79	4.29	4.89	2.42
903	Barnstable Harbor, Beach Point	41° 43.3'	70° 17.1'	+0 11	+0 30	*1.00	*1.00	9.5	11.0	5.0
905	Sesuit Harbor, East Dennis	41° 45.1'	70° 09.3'	+0 02	-0 01	*1.02	*0.82	9.73	11.09	5.1
907	Wellfleet	41° 55.8'	70° 02.5'	+0 14	+0 30	*1.05	*1.05	10.0	11.6	5.4
909	Provincetown	42° 03'	70° 11'	+0 16	+0 18	*0.95	*0.95	9.1	10.6	4.8
	Cape Cod									
911	Chatham, Stage Harbor	41° 40.0'	69° 58.0'	+0 46	+0 19	*0.43	*0.43	3.95	4.50	2.2
913	Chatham Harbor, Aunt Lydias Cove	41° 41.6'	69° 57.0'	+0 56	+1 10	*0.61	*0.71	5.77	6.58	3.1
915	Pleasant Bay	41° 44.2'	69° 58.9'	+2 28	+3 27	*0.34	*0.34	3.2	3.7	1.7
917	Georges Shoal, Texas Tower	41° 41.3'	67° 45.6'	-0 47	-0 43	*0.44	*0.44	4.2	4.8	2.2
	Nantucket Sound, north side									
919	Saquatucket Harbor	41° 40.1'	70° 03.4'	+0 46	+0 16	*0.41	*0.41	3.72	4.24	2.1
921	Wychmere Harbor	41° 39.9'	70° 03.9'	+0 52	+0 25	*0.39	*0.39	3.7	4.3	1.9
923	Dennisport	41° 39.5'	70° 06.9'	+1 03	+0 38	*0.36	*0.36	3.4	4.1	1.8
925	South Yarmouth, Bass River	41° 39.9'	70° 11.0'	+1 48	+1 46	*0.29	*0.29	2.8	3.4	1.5
927	Hyannis Port	41° 37.9'	70° 18.0'	+1 00	+0 26	*0.35	*0.76	3.20	3.80	1.8

226

TABLE 2. – TIDAL DIFFERENCES AND OTHER CONSTANTS

No.	PLACE	POSITION		DIFFERENCES				RANGES		Mean Tide Level
				Time		Height				
		Latitude	Longitude	High Water	Low Water	High Water	Low Water	Mean	Spring	
		North	West	h m	h m	ft	ft	ft	ft	ft
	MASSACHUSETTS Nantucket Sound, north side-cont. Time meridian, 75° W				on Boston,					
929	Cotuit Highlands	41° 36.5'	70° 26.2'	+1 17	+0 47	*0.26	*0.26	2.5	3.0	1.3
931	Poponesset Island, Poponesset Bay	41° 35.2'	70° 27.8'	+2 03	+1 52	*0.24	*0.24	2.3	2.8	1.2
933	Falmouth Heights	41° 32.7'	70° 35.9'	-0 16	-0 09	*0.14	*0.14	1.3	1.6	0.6
	Nantucket Island									
935	Great Point	41° 23.2'	70° 02.8'	+0 43	+0 28	*0.32	*0.32	3.1	3.7	1.6
937	NANTUCKET	41° 17.1'	70° 05.8'		Daily predictions,			3.0	3.36	1.7
939	Eel Point	41° 17.5'	70° 12.5'	+0 39	+0 07	*0.24	*0.24	2.3	2.7	1.2
941	Muskeget Island, north side	41° 20.2'	70° 18.3'	+0 25	+0 15	*0.21	*0.21	2.0	2.4	1.1
	Martha's Vineyard				on Newport,					
943	Vineyard Haven	41° 27.5'	70° 36.0'	+3 39	+3 27	*0.48	*1.14	1.58	1.69	0.95
945	Oak Bluffs	41° 27.5'	70° 33.3'	+3 59	+3 47	*0.50	*0.71	1.7	2.0	0.9
947	Edgartown	41° 23.3'	70° 30.7'	+4 26	+4 16	*0.65	*1.64	2.13	2.68	1.29
949	Wasque Point, Chappaquiddick Island	41° 21.8'	70° 27.0'	+2 02	+3 20	*0.31	*0.31	1.1	1.4	0.6
951	Southshore (buoy)	41° 19.6'	70° 35.4'	-0 28	-0 03	*0.80	*0.86	2.78	3.38	1.51
953	Squibnocket Point	41° 18.7'	70° 46.1'	-0 45	-0 02	*0.82	*0.82	2.9	3.7	1.6
955	Nomans Land	41° 15.7'	70° 49.0'	-0 19	+0 18	*0.85	*0.85	3.0	3.6	1.6
957	Gay Head	41° 21.2'	70° 49.8'	-0 06	+0 45	*0.82	*0.82	2.9	3.5	1.5
959	Cedar Tree Neck	41° 26.1'	70° 41.8'	+0 10	+1 32	*0.62	*0.62	2.2	2.8	1.2
	Vineyard Sound									
	Woods Hole									
961	Little Harbor	41° 31.2'	70° 39.9'	+0 32	+2 21	*0.40	*0.40	1.4	1.8	0.8
963	OCEANOGRAPHIC INSTITUTION	41° 31.4'	70° 40.3'		Daily predictions,			1.8	2.33	1.0
965	Uncatena Island (south side)	41° 30.9'	70° 42.2'	+0 12	+0 22	*1.02	*1.02	3.6	4.5	1.9
967	Quicks Hole, North side	41° 26.9'	70° 51.4'	-0 08	-0 08	*0.99	*0.99	3.5	4.4	1.8
969	Cuttyhunk	41° 25.5'	70° 55.0'	+1 20	+1 15	*0.97	*0.93	3.37	4.25	1.81
	Buzzards Bay									
971	Penikese Island	41° 27.0'	70° 55.3'	+0 02	+0 12	*0.98	*0.96	3.42	4.30	1.84
973	Chappaquoit Point, West Falmouth Harbor	41° 36.3'	70° 39.1'	+0 06	+0 08	*1.11	*1.14	3.82	4.70	2.07
975	Monument Beach	41° 42.9'	70° 37.0'	+0 16	+0 30	*1.15	*1.15	3.97	5.00	2.17
977	Gray Gables	41° 44.1'	70° 37.4'	+0 37	+1 16	*1.05	*1.21	3.62	4.45	1.98
979	Cape Cod Canal, RR. bridge <6>	41° 44.5'	70° 37.0'	+1 17	+2 50	*1.01	*1.01	3.43	4.22	1.93
981	Onset Beach, Onset Bay	41° 44.5'	70° 39.5'	+0 41	+1 25	*1.03	*1.03	3.50	4.41	1.97
983	Great Hill	41° 42.7'	70° 42.9'	+0 12	+0 12	*1.14	*1.21	3.96	4.99	2.15
985	Marion, Sippican Harbor	41° 43.2'	70° 45.6'	+0 10	+0 12	*1.13	*1.29	4.0	4.9	2.2
987	Piney Point	41° 41.7'	70° 43.2'	+0 10	+0 10	*1.13	*1.21	3.91	4.81	2.13
989	Mattapoisett, Mattapoisett Harbor	41° 39'	70° 49'	+0 11	+0 20	*1.09	*1.00	3.9	4.8	2.1
991	Clarks Point	41° 35.6'	70° 54.0'	+0 14	+0 23	*1.03	*1.07	3.56	4.49	1.93
993	New Bedford	41° 38.4'	70° 55.1'	+0 07	+0 07	*1.05	*1.05	3.7	4.6	1.9
995	Round Hill Point	41° 32.3'	70° 55.7'	+0 14	+0 22	*0.99	*1.00	3.43	4.32	1.85
	Westport River									
997	Westport Harbor	41° 31'	71° 05'	+0 09	+0 33	*0.85	*0.85	3.0	3.7	1.6
999	Hix Bridge, East Branch	41° 34.2'	71° 04.4'	+1 40	+2 30	*0.77	*0.77	2.7	3.4	1.4
	RHODE ISLAND, and MASSACHUSETTS Narragansett Bay									
	Sakonnet River									
1001	Sakonnet	41° 27.9'	71° 11.6'	-0 09	+0 13	*0.91	*0.86	3.17	3.99	1.70
1003	Sachuest, Flint Point	41° 29.2'	71° 14.3'	-0 05	+0 15	*0.90	*0.93	3.13	3.94	1.69
1005	The Glen	41° 33.5'	71° 14.2'	-0 13	-0 03	*0.98	*1.00	3.40	4.28	1.84
1007	Nannaquaket Neck	41° 37.1'	71° 12.2'	-0 12	-0 13	*1.01	*1.01	3.50	4.41	1.91
1009	Anthony Point	41° 38.3'	71° 12.7'	+0 00	-0 01	*1.09	*1.09	3.75	4.73	2.05
1011	North End, Bay Oil pier	41° 39.1'	71° 12.6'	+0 20	+0 01	*1.20	*1.07	4.17	5.25	2.27
1013	Castle Hill	41° 27.8'	71° 21.7'	-0 05	+0 13	*0.94	*1.00	3.25	4.10	1.77
1015	NEWPORT	41° 30.3'	71° 19.6'		Daily predictions			3.47	4.38	1.87
	Conanicut Island									
1017	Beavertail Point	41° 27.1'	71° 24.1'	-0 05	+0 04	*0.98	*0.98	3.34	4.21	1.86
1019	West Jamestown, Dutch Island Harbor	41° 29.8'	71° 23.2'	+0 05	+0 04	*1.00	*1.00	3.46	4.36	1.87
1021	Conanicut Point	41° 34.4'	71° 22.3'	+0 07	-0 06	*1.07	*1.07	3.8	4.7	2.0
1023	Prudence Island, (south end)	41° 34.8'	71° 19.3'	+0 08	-0 03	*1.08	*1.14	3.74	4.71	2.03
1025	Bristol Ferry	41° 38.2'	71° 15.3'	+0 15	+0 00	*1.17	*1.14	4.08	5.14	2.20
1027	Bristol, Bristol Harbor	41° 40.1'	71° 16.7'	+0 13	+0 00	*1.16	*1.14	4.1	5.1	2.2
1029	Bristol Highlands	41° 41.8'	71° 17.6'	+0 11	-0 04	*1.19	*1.21	4.13	5.03	2.23
1031	Kickamuit River	41° 42.5'	71° 14.5'	+0 22	+0 14	*1.24	*1.29	4.30	5.41	2.33
1033	Fall River, Massachusetts	41° 42.3'	71° 09.8'	+0 18	+0 03	*1.25	*1.21	4.36	5.41	2.35
1035	Steep Brook, Taunton River	41° 44.4'	71° 07.9'	+0 26	+0 05	*1.30	*1.29	4.51	5.68	2.44
1037	Conimicut Light	41° 43.0'	71° 20.6'	+0 11	-0 02	*1.20	*1.19	4.17	5.25	2.25
1039	Bay Spring, Bullock Cove	41° 45.1'	71° 21.1'	+0 12	+0 01	*1.22	*1.21	4.25	5.23	2.30
1041	Pawtuxet, Pawtuxet Cove	41° 45.7'	71° 23.3'	+0 06	-0 11	*1.25	*1.29	4.35	5.35	2.35
1043	Providence, State Pier no.1	41° 48.4'	71° 24.1'	+0 13	+0 00	*1.27	*1.29	4.41	5.63	2.40
1045	Rumford, Seekonk River	41° 50.4'	71° 22.4'	+0 12	+0 06	*1.34	*1.29	4.66	5.73	2.51
1047	Pawtucket, Seekonk River	41° 52.1'	71° 22.8'	+0 18	+0 09	*1.31	*1.29	4.6	5.8	2.5
1049	Quonset Point	41° 35.2'	71° 24.7'	+0 06	-0 01	*1.07	*1.10	3.70	4.66	2.01
1051	East Greenwich	41° 39.9'	71° 26.7'	+0 12	+0 03	*1.18	*1.21	4.06	4.93	2.20

227

CAUTION

Cape Cod Canal, Railroad Bridge

Predictions of the times of low water must be used with caution because of the peculiarities in the behavior of the tide. Since the tide may be practically at a stand for as much as two hours before or after the predicted times of low water, the levels at other than high and low water times cannot be obtained in the usual way as in Table 3 (Height of Tide at Any Time). The peculiar behavior of the tide near low water, which is prevalent at this place, is illustrated by the first three curves; however there are brief periods each month when the behavior is as depicted by the fourth curve.

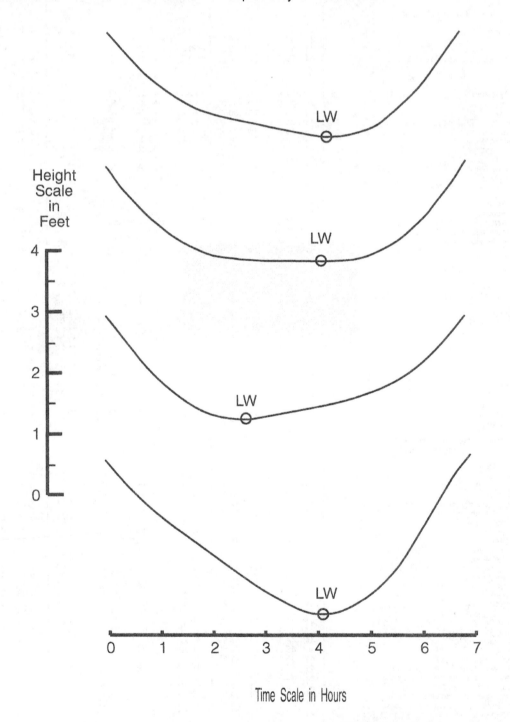

Time Scale in Hours

TABLE 2. – TIDAL DIFFERENCES AND OTHER CONSTANTS

No.	PLACE	POSITION Latitude	Longitude	DIFFERENCES Time High Water	Low Water	Height High Water	Low Water	RANGES Mean	Spring	Mean Tide Level
		North	West	h m	h m	ft	ft	ft	ft	ft
	RHODE ISLAND, and MASSACHUSETTS Narragansett Bay-cont. Time meridian, 75° W			on Newport,						
1053	Wickford	41° 34.3'	71° 26.7'	+0 03	-0 06	*1.07	*1.07	3.71	4.56	2.01
1055	Watson Pier, Boston Neck	41° 27.6'	71° 25.7'	-0 03	+0 16	*0.96	*0.93	3.32	4.18	1.79
1057	Narragansett Pier	41° 25.3'	71° 27.3'	-0 11	+0 11	*0.91	*0.93	3.2	4.0	1.7
	RHODE ISLAND, Outer Coast									
1059	Point Judith, Harbor of Refuge	41° 21.8'	71° 29.4'	+0 00	+0 33	*0.87	*0.93	3.00	3.13	1.63
1061	Block Island (Old Harbor)	41° 10.4'	71° 33.4'	-0 13	+0 15	*0.82	*0.86	2.85	3.51	1.54
1063	Southwest Point, Block Island	41° 09.8'	71° 36.6'	+0 05	+0 42	*0.75	*0.79	2.60	3.20	1.41
1065	Weekapaug Point, Block Island Sound	41° 19.7'	71° 45.7'	+0 41	+1 06	*0.74	*0.93	2.53	3.11	1.39
1067	Watch Hill Point	41° 18.3'	71° 51.6'	+0 41	+1 16	*0.74	*0.71	2.6	3.2	1.4
				on New London,						
1069	Westerly, Pawcatuck River	41° 22.9'	71° 49.9'	-0 21	+0 03	*1.02	*1.00	2.6	3.1	1.5
	CONNECTICUT Long Island Sound									
1071	West Mystic, Mystic River	41° 20.6'	71° 58.5'	-0 20	-0 16	*0.97	*1.00	2.50	2.97	1.44
1073	Silver Eel Pond, Fishers Island, N.Y.	41° 15.4'	72° 01.8'	-0 04	-0 04	*0.91	*1.00	2.33	2.83	1.37
	Thames River									
1075	NEW LONDON, State Pier	41° 21.6'	72° 05.5'	Daily predictions				2.56	3.09	1.47
1077	Yale boathouse	41° 25.8'	72° 05.6'	+0 14	+0 10	*1.07	*1.11	2.73	3.22	1.57
1079	Norwich	41° 31.4'	72° 04.7'	+0 24	+0 19	*1.18	*1.21	3.03	3.57	1.75
1081	Niantic, Niantic River	41° 19.5'	72° 11.2'	+0 52	+0 57	*0.99	*0.84	2.58	3.04	1.44
	Connecticut River									
1083	Saybrook Jetty	41° 15.8'	72° 20.6'	+1 11	+0 45	*1.36	*1.35	3.5	4.2	2.0
1085	Saybrook Point	41° 17.0'	72° 21.0'	+1 11	+0 53	*1.24	*1.25	3.2	3.8	1.8
1087	Lyme, highway bridge	41° 19.3'	72° 21.0'	+1 36	+1 09	*1.26	*0.95	3.31	3.91	1.83
1089	Essex <7>	41° 20.9'	72° 23.1'	+1 39	+1 38	*1.16	*1.15	3.0	3.6	1.7
1091	Hadlyme <7>	41° 25.2'	72° 25.7'	+2 19	+2 23	*1.05	*1.05	2.7	3.2	1.5
1093	Tylerville <7>	41° 27.1'	72° 27.9'	+2 38	+2 51	*1.02	*1.02	2.71	3.20	1.46
1095	Haddam <7>	41° 28.9'	72° 30.4'	+2 48	+3 08	*0.97	*0.95	2.5	3.0	1.4
1097	Higganum Creek <7>	41° 30.2'	72° 33.2'	+3 08	+3 40	*0.91	*0.91	2.40	2.83	1.30
1099	Maromas <7>	41° 32.5'	72° 33.1'	+3 25	+4 01	*0.91	*0.91	2.41	2.84	1.31
1101	Middletown <7>	41° 33.6'	72° 38.7'	+3 54	+4 39	*0.83	*0.83	2.17	2.56	1.19
1103	Rocky Hill <7>	41° 39.8'	72° 37.8'	+4 30	+5 36	*0.72	*0.63	1.88	2.22	1.07
1105	South Hartford <7>	41° 45.3'	72° 39.5'	+5 24	+6 54	*0.74	*0.58	1.94	2.29	1.07
				on Bridgeport,						
1107	Westbrook, Duck Island Roads	41° 16.4'	72° 28.5'	-0 24	-0 32	*0.61	*0.60	4.1	4.7	2.2
1109	Clinton, Clinton Harbor	41° 16.1'	72° 31.9'	-0 11	-0 16	*0.67	*1.00	4.55	5.27	2.51
1111	Madison	41° 16.2'	72° 36.2'	-0 21	-0 30	*0.73	*0.72	4.9	5.6	2.6
1113	Guilford Harbor	41° 16.3'	72° 40.0'	-0 11	-0 21	*0.77	*0.96	5.19	5.92	2.83
1115	Sachem Head	41° 14.7'	72° 42.5'	-0 11	-0 15	*0.80	*0.80	5.4	6.2	2.9
1117	Branford, Branford River	41° 15.7'	72° 49.1'	-0 05	-0 13	*0.87	*0.96	5.85	6.67	3.15
1119	Lighthouse Point, New Haven Harbor	41° 15.1'	72° 54.3'	-0 04	-0 07	*0.91	*0.96	6.12	6.98	3.29
1121	New Haven Harbor, New Haven Reach	41° 17.0'	72° 54.5'	-0 01	-0 06	*0.92	*1.00	6.15	7.11	3.32
1123	Gulf Beach	41° 12.3'	73° 02.5'	-0 05	-0 08	*0.94	*1.04	6.29	7.17	3.40
1125	Milford Harbor	41° 13.1'	73° 03.3'	-0 02	-0 03	*0.94	*1.04	6.32	7.20	3.41
	Housatonic River									
1127	Sniffens Point	41° 11.2'	73° 06.8'	+0 10	+0 09	*0.96	*1.00	6.43	7.33	3.46
1129	Stratford, I-95 bridge	41° 12.2'	73° 06.7'	+0 23	+0 23	*0.98	*1.00	6.58	7.50	3.53
1131	Long Hill	41° 16.5'	73° 05.3'	+0 43	+1 13	*1.02	*1.04	6.85	7.81	3.67
1133	Shelton	41° 18.1'	73° 04.3'	+0 46	+1 19	*1.04	*0.96	7.01	7.99	3.74
1135	BRIDGEPORT	41° 10.4'	73° 10.9'	Daily predictions				6.74	7.80	3.61
1137	Black Rock Harbor	41° 09.4'	73° 12.8'	+0 00	+0 01	*1.00	*1.04	6.75	7.75	3.63
1139	Southport, Southport Harbor	41° 08.0'	73° 17.0'	-0 02	+0 02	*1.01	*1.00	6.84	8.18	3.66
1141	Saugatuck, Saugatuck River	41° 07.2'	73° 22.1'	+0 01	+0 09	*1.04	*1.00	6.99	8.14	3.74
1143	South Norwalk	41° 05.9'	73° 24.9'	+0 09	+0 15	*1.05	*1.04	7.1	8.2	3.8
1145	Rowayton, Fivemile River	41° 03.9'	73° 26.7'	+0 00	+0 05	*1.05	*1.08	7.09	8.08	3.80
1147	Long Neck Point	41° 02.3'	73° 28.8'	-0 09	+0 01	*1.06	*0.96	7.17	8.17	3.82
1149	Stamford	41° 02.3'	73° 32.8'	+0 03	+0 08	*1.07	*1.08	7.2	8.3	3.9
1151	Cos Cob Harbor	41° 01.0'	73° 35.8'	+0 05	+0 11	*1.07	*1.08	7.2	8.3	3.9
	NEW YORK Long Island Sound, north side			on Kings Point,						
1153	Rye Beach	40° 57.7'	73° 40.3'	-0 20	-0 27	*1.00	*0.86	7.29	7.89	3.88
1155	New Rochelle	40° 53.6'	73° 46.9'	-0 16	-0 18	*1.01	*0.93	7.29	8.46	3.90
1157	Throgs Neck, Fort Schuyler	40° 48.3'	73° 47.7'	+0 01	+0 04	*1.00	*1.00	7.13	8.62	3.84
	East River									
1159	Whitestone	40° 47.9'	73° 48.8'	+0 07	+0 09	*1.00	*1.04	7.1	8.3	3.8
1161	College Point, Flushing Bay	40° 47.0'	73° 51.4'	+0 17	+0 16	*0.95	*1.04	6.8	7.9	3.7
1163	Worlds Fair Marina, Flushing Bay	40° 45.7'	73° 51.0'	+0 10	+0 16	*0.94	*1.00	6.75	8.10	3.65
1165	Hunts Point	40° 48.0'	73° 52.4'	+0 12	+0 10	*0.97	*1.07	6.92	7.57	3.75
1167	North Brother Island	40° 48.1'	73° 54.0'	+0 18	+0 18	*0.93	*1.11	6.6	7.8	3.6
1169	Port Morris (Stony Point)	40° 48.1'	73° 54.4'	+0 07	+0 10	*0.87	*0.96	6.24	6.85	3.39

TABLE 2. – TIDAL DIFFERENCES AND OTHER CONSTANTS

No.	PLACE	Latitude	Longitude	High Water h m	Low Water h m	High Water ft	Low Water ft	Mean ft	Spring ft	Mean Tide Level ft
		POSITION		**DIFFERENCES**				**RANGES**		
				Time		Height				
		North	**West**							
	NEW YORK East River–cont. Time meridian, 75° W			on New York,						
1171	Hell Gate, Wards Island	40° 47.2'	73° 55.3'	+2 58	+3 45	*1.33	*1.59	6.0	7.3	3.4
1173	Horns Hook, East 90th Street	40° 46.6'	73° 56.5'	+1 54	+1 34	*1.03	*0.90	4.68	5.18	2.53
1175	Queensboro Bridge	40° 45.5'	73° 57.5'	+1 23	+0 57	*0.96	*1.00	4.33	5.24	2.38
1177	East 41st Street, New York City	40° 44.8'	73° 58.1'	+1 03	+0 46	*0.95	*1.09	4.31	4.89	2.40
1179	Hunters Point, Newtown Creek	40° 44.4'	73° 57.7'	+1 22	+0 56	*0.89	*0.90	4.1	4.9	2.2
1181	Williamsburg Bridge	40° 42.7'	73° 58.1'	+0 45	+0 28	*0.93	*0.95	4.22	5.11	2.31
1183	Wallabout Bay, Brooklyn Navy Yard	40° 42.4'	73° 58.5'	+0 32	+0 22	*0.94	*1.05	4.3	5.2	2.4
1185	Brooklyn Bridge	40° 42.2'	73° 59.3'	+0 24	–0 04	*0.99	*1.00	4.53	5.13	2.48
1187	Harlem River, Randalls Island	40° 48.0'	73° 55.6'	+1 55	+1 30	*1.00	*0.86	4.56	5.31	2.46
	Long Island, Long Island Sound			on Kings Point,						
1189	Willets Point	40° 47.6'	73° 46.9'	–0 01	+0 00	*1.00	*1.04	7.15	8.21	3.88
1191	KINGS POINT	40° 48.6'	73° 45.9'	Daily predictions				7.16	8.46	3.86
1193	Port Washington, Manhasset Bay	40° 49.9'	73° 42.2'	–0 12	–0 12	*1.02	*0.96	7.29	8.46	3.92
1195	Glen Cove, Hempstead Harbor	40° 51.8'	73° 39.3'	–0 22	–0 26	*1.01	*0.82	7.27	7.87	3.87
1197	Harry Tappen Marina, Hempstead Harbor	40° 50.1'	73° 39.1'	–0 20	–0 23	*1.01	*0.82	7.29	8.87	3.88
				on Bridgeport,						
	Oyster Bay									
1199	Oyster Bay Harbor	40° 53'	73° 32'	+0 07	+0 13	*1.08	*1.08	7.3	8.4	3.9
1201	Bayville Bridge	40° 54.2'	73° 33.0'	–0 06	+0 04	*1.09	*1.04	7.37	7.99	3.94
1203	Cold Spring Harbor	40° 52.4'	73° 28.2'	–0 07	+0 02	*1.07	*0.92	7.27	7.86	3.86
1205	Eatons Neck Point	40° 57.2'	73° 24.0'	+0 02	+0 08	*1.05	*1.04	7.1	8.2	3.9
1207	Lloyd Harbor, Huntington Bay	40° 54.6'	73° 25.9'	–0 01	+0 07	*1.04	*0.88	7.02	7.60	3.73
1209	Northport, Northport Bay	40° 54.0'	73° 21.2'	–0 05	+0 04	*1.07	*0.92	7.25	7.84	3.86
1211	Port Jefferson Harbor entrance	40° 58'	73° 05'	+0 02	+0 01	*0.98	*0.98	6.6	7.6	3.5
1213	Port Jefferson	40° 57.0'	73° 04.6'	+0 04	+0 05	*0.98	*0.92	6.61	7.70	3.53
1215	Cedar Beach	40° 57.9'	73° 02.6'	+0 07	+0 05	*0.96	*1.00	6.43	7.01	3.46
1217	Mount Sinai Harbor	40° 57.8'	73° 02.4'	+0 04	+0 18	*0.89	*0.88	6.0	6.9	3.2
1219	Northville	40° 58.9'	72° 38.7'	+0 05	–0 03	*0.80	*0.92	5.35	6.10	2.89
1221	Mattituck Inlet	41° 00.9'	72° 33.7'	+0 11	+0 02	*0.76	*0.85	5.08	5.79	2.75
1223	Hashamomuck Beach	41° 05.7'	72° 23.9'	+0 03	–0 13	*0.64	*0.64	4.2	4.8	2.3
				on New London,						
1225	Plum Gut Harbor, Plum Island	41° 10.3'	72° 12.3'	+0 33	+0 24	*1.01	*1.04	2.60	3.07	1.50
1227	Little Gull Island	41° 12.4'	72° 06.1'	+0 13	–0 22	*0.85	*0.85	2.2	2.6	1.3
	Shelter Island Sound									
1229	Orient	41° 08'	72° 18'	+0 37	+0 36	*0.97	*0.97	2.5	3.0	1.4
1231	Greenport	41° 06.1'	72° 21.7'	+1 12	+0 48	*0.95	*0.95	2.44	2.81	1.40
1233	Southold	41° 04'	72° 25'	+1 44	+1 33	*0.89	*0.89	2.3	2.7	1.3
1235	Noyack Bay	41° 00'	72° 20'	+2 06	+1 44	*0.89	*0.89	2.3	2.7	1.3
1237	Sag Harbor	41° 00.2'	72° 17.8'	+1 00	+0 48	*0.93	*0.89	2.41	2.78	1.37
	Peconic Bays									
1239	New Suffolk	41° 00'	72° 28'	+2 27	+2 11	*1.01	*1.00	2.6	3.1	1.5
1241	South Jamesport	40° 56.1'	72° 34.9'	+2 34	+2 43	*1.07	*0.95	2.79	3.29	1.57
1243	Threemile Harbor entrance, Gardiners Bay	41° 02.1'	72° 11.4'	+0 39	+0 19	*0.96	*1.00	2.48	2.98	1.44
1245	Lake Montauk	41° 04.4'	71° 56.1'	–0 26	–0 22	*0.77	*0.89	2.01	2.37	1.18
1247	Montauk Harbor entrance	41° 04.5'	71° 56.2'	–0 24	–0 16	*0.74	*0.75	1.9	2.3	1.0
1249	MONTAUK, FORT POND BAY	41° 02.9'	71° 57.6'	Daily Predictions,				2.07	2.66	1.21
	Long Island, south shore			on Sandy Hook,						
1251	Shinnecock Inlet (ocean)	40° 50.2'	72° 28.8'	–0 16	–1 11	*0.66	*0.68	3.08	3.68	1.67
	Shinnecock Bay									
1253	Shinnecock Bay entrance	40° 49.2'	72° 33.7'	+1 12	+1 51	*0.51	*0.37	2.41	2.89	1.27
1255	Ponquogue Point	40° 51.0'	72° 30.2'	–0 06	+0 03	*0.60	*0.65	2.81	3.20	1.53
1257	Shinnecock Yacht Club, Penniman Creek	40° 49.1'	72° 33.2'	+1 01	+1 45	*0.55	*0.55	2.56	2.93	1.39
1259	Moriches Inlet	40° 45.8'	72° 45.3'	–0 10	–1 08	*0.61	*0.79	2.83	3.40	1.56
1261	Moriches Inlet Coast Guard Station	40° 47.2'	72° 45.0'	+0 42	+0 48	*0.46	*0.63	2.15	2.51	1.19
1263	Smith Point Bridge, Narrow Bay	40° 44.3'	72° 52.1'	+1 58	+2 34	*0.27	*0.60	1.19	1.47	0.71
1265	Democrat Point, Fire Island Inlet	40° 38'	73° 18'	–0 39	–0 27	*0.56	*0.55	2.6	3.1	1.4
	Great South Bay									
1267	Fire Island Coast Guard Station	40° 37.6'	73° 15.6'	–0 04	–0 01	*0.42	*0.74	1.89	2.19	1.08
1269	Fire Island Light	40° 38.1'	73° 13.2'	+0 46	+1 22	*0.15	*0.15	0.7	0.8	0.3
1271	West Fire Island	40° 39.4'	73° 12.3'	+2 10	+2 18	*0.13	*0.13	0.6	0.7	0.3
1273	Seaview Ferry Dock	40° 38.9'	73° 09.0'	+2 20	+2 23	*0.27	*0.68	1.18	1.31	0.72
1275	Patchogue	40° 45.0'	73° 00.0'	+3 14	+3 33	*0.25	*0.53	1.11	1.33	0.66
1277	Great River, Connetquot River	40° 43.4'	73° 09.1'	+3 19	+3 32	*0.15	*0.15	0.7	0.8	0.3
1279	Bay Shore, Watchogue Creek Entrance	40° 43.0'	73° 14.4'	+2 15	+2 27	*0.22	*0.37	0.99	1.19	0.5
1281	Oak Beach	40° 38.5'	73° 17.2'	+2 23	+2 58	*0.15	*0.15	0.7	0.8	0.3
1283	Babylon	40° 41.1'	73° 18.9'	+2 11	+2 41	*0.13	*0.15	0.6	0.7	0.3
1285	Gilgo Heading	40° 37.2'	73° 23.7'	+2 22	+2 58	*0.24	*0.25	1.1	1.3	0.5
1287	Amityville	40° 39.3'	73° 25.1'	+2 20	+3 05	*0.26	*0.25	1.2	1.4	0.7
1289	Biltmore Shores, South Oyster Bay	40° 40'	73° 28'	+2 04	+2 32	*0.30	*0.30	1.4	1.7	0.8
1291	Point Lookout, Jones Inlet	40° 35.2'	73° 34.7'	–0 20	–0 25	*0.77	*0.75	3.6	4.3	2.0
1293	Point Lookout (marina), Jones Inlet	40° 35.6'	73° 35.0'	–0 02	–0 15	*0.89	*0.75	4.14	4.86	2.2
	Hempstead Bay									
1295	Deep Creek Meadow	40° 36.2'	73° 31.5'	+1 01	+1 11	*0.51	*0.50	2.4	2.9	1.3
1297	Green Island Drawbridge	40° 37.4'	73° 30.1'	+0 33	+0 31	*0.67	*0.89	3.11	3.56	1.7
1299	Cuba Island	40° 37.2'	73° 31.4'	+1 07	+1 22	*0.49	*0.50	2.3	2.8	1.2
1301	Bellmore, Bellmore Creek	40° 39.8'	73° 31.2'	+1 28	+1 58	*0.43	*0.45	2.0	2.4	1.1
1303	Neds Creek	40° 37.4'	73° 33.3'	+0 49	+0 54	*0.58	*0.60	2.7	3.3	1.4

TABLE 2. – TIDAL DIFFERENCES AND OTHER CONSTANTS

No.	PLACE	POSITION Latitude	POSITION Longitude	DIFFERENCES Time High Water	DIFFERENCES Time Low Water	DIFFERENCES Height High Water	DIFFERENCES Height Low Water	RANGES Mean	RANGES Spring	Mean Tide Level
		North	West	h m	h m	ft	ft	ft	ft	ft
	NEW YORK Long Island, south shore-cont. Time meridian, 75° W				on Sandy Hook,					
	Hempstead Bay-cont.									
1305	Freeport, Baldwin Bay	40° 38.0'	73° 35.2'	+0 37	+0 55	*0.64	*0.65	3.0	3.6	1.6
1307	Baldwin, Parsonage Cove	40° 38.0'	73° 37.0'	+0 10	+0 20	*0.93	*0.95	4.35	5.08	2.36
1309	Long Beach (Inside)	40° 36'	73° 39'	+0 18	+0 02	*0.84	*0.85	3.9	4.7	2.1
1311	Long Beach, Bridgewater Yacht Club	40° 35.7'	73° 39.3'	+0 06	+0 08	*0.94	*0.89	4.43	5.14	2.39
1313	Bay Park, Hewlett Bay	40° 37.7'	73° 40.1'	+0 20	+0 25	*0.99	*1.00	4.63	5.33	2.51
1315	Woodmere, Brosewere Bay	40° 37'	73° 42'	+0 34	+0 50	*0.84	*0.85	3.9	4.7	2.1
1317	East Rockaway Inlet, Atlantic Beach	40° 35.6'	73° 44.4'	-0 05	-0 21	*0.93	*1.00	4.37	5.16	2.38
	Jamaica Bay									
1319	Kingsborough, Sheepshead Bay	40° 34.9'	73° 56.0'	+0 05	-0 03	*1.05	*1.11	4.92	5.82	2.67
1321	Plumb Beach Channel	40° 35.1'	73° 55.5'	+0 02	-0 03	*1.05	*1.05	4.9	5.9	2.6
1323	Barren Island, Rockaway Inlet	40° 34.7'	73° 53.3'	-0 01	-0 04	*1.07	*1.05	5.0	6.0	2.7
1325	Beach Channel (bridge)	40° 35'	73° 49'	+0 37	+0 24	*1.09	*1.10	5.1	6.2	2.7
1327	Motts Basin	40° 37.0'	73° 45.5'	+0 39	+0 48	*1.16	*1.15	5.4	6.5	2.9
1329	Norton Point, Hook Creek	40° 38.1'	73° 44.8'	+0 38	+0 45	*1.16	*1.16	5.4	6.5	2.9
1331	J.F.K. International Airport	40° 37.4'	73° 47.0'	+0 25	+0 45	*1.14	*1.15	5.3	6.4	2.8
1333	North Channel Bridge, Grassy Bay	40° 38.7'	73° 50.2'	+0 21	+0 27	*1.18	*1.16	5.56	6.42	3.01
1335	Canarsie	40° 37.8'	73° 53.1'	+0 27	+0 08	*1.12	*1.10	5.2	6.3	2.8
1337	Mill Basin	40° 37'	73° 55'	+0 28	+0 04	*1.12	*1.10	5.2	6.3	2.8
	NEW YORK and NEW JERSEY New York Harbor									
1339	Coney Island	40° 34'	73° 59'	-0 04	-0 17	*1.01	*1.00	4.7	5.7	2.5
1341	Norton Point, Gravesend Bay	40° 35.4'	73° 59.9'	-0 01	+0 03	*1.02	*1.15	4.7	5.7	2.6
1343	Fort Wadsworth, The Narrows	40° 36.4'	74° 03.3'	+0 06	+0 06	*0.98	*1.05	4.8	5.4	2.5
1345	Fort Hamilton, The Narrows	40° 36.5'	74° 02.1'	+0 02	+0 07	*1.01	*1.00	4.7	5.7	2.5
1347	U.S. Coast Guard Station, Staten Island	40° 36.7'	74° 03.6'	+0 12	+0 11	*0.96	*1.05	4.47	5.35	2.43
				on New York,						
1349	St. George, Staten Island	40° 38.6'	74° 04.4'	-0 17	-0 15	*0.99	*0.99	4.5	5.4	2.4
1351	Gowanus Bay	40° 39.9'	74° 00.8'	-0 18	-0 12	*1.03	*0.95	4.7	5.7	2.6
1353	NEW YORK (The Battery)	40° 42.0'	74° 00.9'	*Daily Predictions*				4.53	5.50	2.47
	Hudson River <8>									
1355	Weehawken, Union City, N.J.	40° 45.9'	74° 01.1'	+0 13	+0 15	*0.96	*0.96	4.37	5.29	2.41
1357	Edgewater, N.J.	40° 48.8'	73° 58.7'	+0 31	+0 28	*0.93	*0.93	4.24	5.13	2.33
1359	Dyckman Street, Ferry Slip, N.Y.	40° 52.0'	73° 56.0'	+0 51	+0 44	*0.88	*0.81	3.98	4.66	2.16
1361	Spuyten Duyvil Creek ent., N.Y.	40° 52.7'	73° 55.5'	+0 52	+0 48	*0.84	*0.84	3.85	4.66	2.20
1363	Riverdale, N.Y.	40° 54.2'	73° 54.9'	+0 48	+0 49	*0.85	*0.85	3.86	4.67	2.13
1365	Alpine, N.J.	40° 56.7'	73° 55.1'	+1 05	+1 02	*0.83	*0.90	3.75	4.54	2.06
1367	Tarrytown	41° 04.7'	73° 52.2'	+1 49	+1 57	*0.70	*0.70	3.2	3.7	1.8
1369	Haverstraw	41° 13.1'	73° 57.8'	+2 15	+2 42	*0.72	*0.81	3.23	3.91	1.78
1371	Peekskill	41° 17'	73° 56'	+2 28	+3 03	*0.64	*0.64	2.9	3.4	1.8
1373	Newburgh	41° 30.0'	74° 00.4'	+3 46	+4 03	*0.62	*0.64	2.8	3.2	1.5
1375	Beacon	41° 30.3'	73° 58.2'	+3 37	+3 49	*0.70	*0.90	3.13	3.68	1.75
1377	New Hamburg	41° 35'	73° 57'	+4 04	+4 28	*0.64	*0.64	2.9	3.3	1.6
1379	Poughkeepsie	41° 42'	73° 57'	+4 34	+4 46	*0.68	*0.68	3.1	3.5	1.7
1381	Hyde Park	41° 47.2'	73° 57.8'	+5 00	+5 12	*0.70	*0.68	3.2	3.6	1.8
1383	Kingston	41° 55'	73° 59'	+5 20	+5 34	*0.81	*0.82	3.7	4.2	2.0
1385	Turkey Point	42° 00.8'	73° 56.3'	+5 29	+5 47	*0.87	*1.00	3.90	4.50	2.17
1387	Tivoli	42° 04'	73° 56'	+5 50	+6 04	*0.86	*0.86	3.9	4.4	1.9
1389	Hudson	42° 15'	73° 48'	+6 58	+7 12	*0.88	*0.86	4.0	4.4	2.2
				on Albany,						
1391	Castleton	42° 32'	73° 46'	-0 17	-0 29	-0.2	+0.1	4.3	4.7	2.2
1393	ALBANY	42° 39.0'	73° 44.8'	*Daily predictions*				4.6	5.0	2.5
1395	Troy	42° 44'	73° 42'	+0 08	+0 10	*1.00	*1.00	4.7	5.1	2.3
	The Kills and Newark Bay				on New York,					
	Kill Van Kull									
1397	Constable Hook	40° 39.3'	74° 05.2'	-0 18	-0 08	*1.02	*1.02	4.63	5.60	2.54
1399	BAYONNE BRIDGE, STATEN ISLAND	40° 38.4'	74° 08.8'	*Daily predictions,*				4.98	5.52	2.70
1401	Port Elizabeth	40° 40.4'	74° 08.4'	-0 02	+0 13	*1.11	*0.95	5.05	6.11	2.73
1403	Port Newark Terminal	40° 41'	74° 08'	+0 03	+0 21	*1.12	*1.12	5.1	6.1	2.7
	Passaic River									
1405	Point No Point	40° 43.9'	74° 07.0'	+0 00	+0 22	*1.15	*1.04	5.21	6.30	2.83
1407	Belleville	40° 47.2'	74° 08.8'	+0 09	+0 49	*1.23	*1.19	5.60	6.78	3.08
1409	East Rutherford	40° 50.8'	74° 07.2'	+0 09	+1 06	*1.29	*1.29	5.87	7.10	3.20
1411	Garfield	40° 52.1'	74° 06.7'	+0 08	---	---	---	--	--	--
	Hackensack River									
1413	Kearny Point	40° 43.7'	74° 06.2'	+0 11	+0 22	*1.15	*1.14	5.21	6.30	2.85
1415	Amtrak RR. swing bridge	40° 45.1'	74° 05.8'	+0 33	+0 39	*1.16	*1.10	5.27	6.38	2.87
1417	Fish Creek, Berrys Creek	40° 47.6'	74° 05.5'	+1 02	+1 00	*1.16	*1.00	5.31	6.43	2.86
1419	Carlstadt, Garretts Reach	40° 48.4'	74° 03.6'	+0 59	+0 45	*1.26	*1.29	5.71	6.29	3.12
1421	North Secaucus, Garretts Reach	40° 48.4'	74° 02.6'	+0 57	+0 57	*1.23	*1.23	5.61	6.79	3.06
1423	Mill Creek, 0.8 n.mi. above entrance	40° 47.9'	74° 03.0'	+1 34	---	---	---	--	--	--
1425	Cromakill Creek, N.J. Turnpike	40° 48.2'	74° 02.0'	+1 00	---	---	---	--	--	--

TABLE 2. – TIDAL DIFFERENCES AND OTHER CONSTANTS

No.	PLACE	POSITION		DIFFERENCES				RANGES		Mean Tide Level
				Time		Height				
		Latitude	Longitude	High Water	Low Water	High Water	Low Water	Mean	Spring	
		North	West	h m	h m	ft	ft	ft	ft	ft

NEW YORK and NEW JERSEY
The Kills and Newark Bay-cont.
Time meridian, 75° W

on New York,

Hackensack River-cont.

1427	Ridgefield Park	40° 51.0'	74° 01.8'	+1 00	+1 00	*1.26	*1.26	5.73	6.93	- -
1429	Hackensack	40° 52.8'	74° 02.4'	+1 06	+1 00	*1.33	*1.38	6.01	7.27	3.29
1431	New Millford	40° 56.1'	74° 01.8'	+1 17	+2 49	*1.02	*1.02	4.76	5.76	2.44

on Sandy Hook,

Arthur Kill

1433	Port Ivory, Howland Hook, N.Y.	40° 38.7'	74° 10.8'	+0 27	+0 39	*1.09	*1.09	5.10	6.12	2.78
1435	Rahway River, RR. Bridge	40° 35.9'	74° 13.9'	+0 17	+0 30	*1.14	*1.16	5.36	6.49	2.91
1437	Chelsea	40° 36'	74° 12'	+0 23	+0 37	*1.07	*1.05	5.0	6.0	2.7
1439	Carteret	40° 35.2'	74° 12.6'	+0 22	+0 33	*1.09	*1.09	5.1	6.2	2.8
1441	Rossville, N.Y.	40° 33.3'	74° 13.4'	+0 20	+0 29	*1.12	*1.12	5.22	5.84	2.89
1443	Port Reading	40° 33.3'	74° 14.7'	+0 14	+0 24	*1.13	*1.32	5.29	6.24	2.89
1445	Woodbridge Creek, 0.8 n.mi. above entrance	40° 32.7'	74° 15.9'	+0 09	+0 21	*1.10	*1.00	5.20	6.29	2.79

Lower New York Bay, Raritan Bay, etc.

| 1447 | Great Kills Harbor | 40° 32.6' | 74° 08.4' | -0 01 | +0 04 | *1.05 | *1.16 | 4.91 | 5.79 | 2.67 |
| 1449 | Princes Bay | 40° 30.7' | 74° 12.0' | +0 00 | +0 06 | *1.05 | *1.05 | 4.9 | 5.9 | 2.6 |

Raritan River

1451	South Amboy	40° 29.5'	74° 16.9'	-0 04	+0 08	*1.09	*1.09	5.09	6.11	2.77
1453	Keasbey	40° 30.5'	74° 18.7'	+0 06	+0 18	*1.10	*1.00	5.21	6.25	2.85
1455	Sayreville	40° 28.7'	74° 21.4'	+0 11	+0 25	*1.14	*1.21	5.43	6.57	2.95
1457	Old Bridge, South River	40° 25.0'	74° 21.8'	+0 48	+0 59	*1.18	*1.16	5.58	6.75	3.01
1459	New Brunswick	40° 29.3'	74° 26.1'	+0 32	+0 48	*1.21	*1.16	5.71	6.91	3.08
1461	Cheesequake Creek, Garden State Parkway	40° 27.2'	74° 16.4'	+0 12	+0 13	*1.09	*1.05	5.12	6.20	2.77
1463	Keyport	40° 26.4'	74° 11.9'	-0 04	+0 06	*1.08	*1.10	5.05	6.06	2.74
1465	Matawan Creek, Route 35 bridge	40° 26.0'	74° 13.1'	-0 01	+0 07	*1.08	*1.08	5.06	6.12	2.77
1467	Waackaack Creek	40° 26.9'	74° 08.6'	-0 06	+0 21	*0.99	*0.99	4.62	5.54	2.47

NEW JERSEY
Sandy Hook Bay

1469	Pews Creek	40° 26.5'	74° 06.3'	-0 08	- - -	- - -	- - -	- -	- -	- -
1471	Compton Creek	40° 25.9'	74° 05.1'	+0 13						
1473	Atlantic Highlands	40° 25.1'	74° 02.1'	-0 10	-0 10	*1.01	*1.01	4.71	5.65	2.55
1475	SANDY HOOK (Fort Hancock)	40° 28.0'	74° 00.6'		*Daily predictions*			4.70	5.71	2.54

Shrewsbury River

1477	Highlands, Route 36 bridge	40° 23.8'	73° 58.9'	+0 17	+0 14	*0.90	*0.90	4.19	5.03	2.27
1479	Oceanic Bridge, Navesink River	40° 22.6'	74° 00.9'	+1 13	+1 45	*0.72	*0.63	3.41	4.13	1.82
1481	Red Bank, Navesink River	40° 21.3'	74° 03.9'	+1 17	+1 57	*0.74	*0.63	3.51	4.25	1.87
1483	Sea Bright	40° 21.9'	73° 58.5'	+1 15	+1 07	*0.68	*0.68	3.15	3.78	1.74
1485	Gooseneck Point, bridge	40° 19.6'	74° 01.0'	+2 18	+2 41	*0.55	*0.55	2.57	3.08	1.44
1487	Long Branch Reach	40° 19.5'	73° 59.8'	+2 18	+2 41	*0.56	*0.63	2.60	3.15	1.42

Outer Coast

| 1489 | Long Branch (fishing pier) | 40° 18.2' | 73° 58.6' | -0 26 | -0 36 | *0.94 | *1.00 | 4.40 | 5.28 | 2.39 |

Shark River

1491	Shark River Island, fixed RR. bridge	40° 11.2'	74° 01.6'	-0 13	-0 08	*0.93	*0.93	4.32	5.18	2.32
1493	Shark River Hills	40° 11.6'	74° 02.3'	-0 13	-0 09	*0.94	*0.94	4.40	5.28	2.38
1495	New Bedford	40° 10.7'	74° 02.8'	-0 13	-0 07	*0.95	*0.95	4.41	5.29	2.40
1497	Belmar, Atlantic Ocean	40° 11.1'	74° 00.5'	-0 35	-0 45	*0.95	*0.95	4.43	5.32	2.38
1499	Manasquan Inlet, USCG Station	40° 06.1'	74° 02.1'	-0 12	-0 24	*0.86	*0.95	4.02	4.82	2.19

Manasquan River

| 1501 | Brielle, Route 35 bridge | 40° 06.3' | 74° 03.3' | -0 06 | -0 20 | *0.83 | *0.83 | 3.86 | 4.63 | 2.10 |
| 1503 | Riviera Beach | 40° 05.8' | 74° 05.2' | +0 08 | +0 38 | *0.73 | *0.73 | 3.39 | 4.07 | 1.83 |

Metedeconk River

1505	Beaverdam Creek entrance	40° 03.7'	74° 03.7'	+2 41	+2 40	*0.07	*0.37	0.30	0.36	0.22
1507	Beaverdam Creek, inside	40° 03.7'	74° 04.4'	+2 49	+2 47	*0.06	*0.06	0.29	0.35	0.25
1509	Forge Pond	40° 03.9'	74° 08.1'	+2 17	+2 07	*0.07	*0.07	0.31	0.37	0.23
1511	Tall Pines Camp	40° 03.5'	74° 07.0'	+2 23	+2 24	*0.06	*0.06	0.30	0.36	0.23
1513	Seaside Heights, ocean	39° 56.5'	74° 04.1'	-0 30	-0 32	*0.92	*0.92	4.29	5.15	2.33

Barnegat Bay

1515	Mantoloking	40° 02.2'	74° 03.2'	+4 28	+4 39	*0.07	*0.07	0.33	0.40	0.25
1517	Kettle Creek, Green Island	40° 00.8'	74° 06.8'	+4 23	+4 41	*0.08	*0.08	0.38	0.46	0.28
1519	Ocean Beach	39° 59.3'	74° 04.1'	+4 17	+4 36	*0.08	*0.08	0.37	0.44	0.27
1521	Silver Bay, Silver Bay Marina	39° 59.8'	74° 08.9'	+4 26	+4 39	*0.08	*0.08	0.37	0.44	0.27
1523	Goose Creek entrance	39° 57.8'	74° 06.9'	+4 06	+4 29	*0.08	*0.08	0.35	0.42	0.25
1525	Coates Point	39° 56.9'	74° 06.9'	+4 00	+4 21	*0.08	*0.08	0.37	0.44	0.25
1527	Toms River (town), Toms River	39° 57.0'	74° 11.9'	+3 33	+3 48	*0.18	*0.47	0.78	0.83	0.48
1529	Seaside Park	39° 55.3'	74° 05.0'	+3 40	+4 05	*0.08	*0.08	0.38	0.46	0.25
1531	Barnegat Pier	39° 55.1'	74° 06.6'	+3 35	+3 55	*0.08	*0.08	0.36	0.43	0.23
1533	Sloop Creek	39° 54.3'	74° 08.0'	+3 38	+4 01	*0.08	*0.08	0.35	0.42	0.22
1535	Cedar Creek	39° 52.2'	74° 09.3'	+3 23	+3 45	*0.08	*0.08	0.35	0.42	0.23
1537	Island Beach	39° 51.1'	74° 05.4'	+3 04	+3 28	*0.08	*0.08	0.35	0.42	0.24
1539	Stouts Creek	39° 50.7'	74° 09.1'	+3 16	+3 33	*0.06	*0.06	0.30	0.36	0.20
1541	Forked River	39° 49.5'	74° 10.4'	+3 08	+3 20	*0.07	*0.07	0.32	0.38	0.24
1543	Oyster Creek	39° 48.5'	74° 11.3'	+3 30	+3 36	*0.06	*0.06	0.29	0.35	0.20
1545	Island Beach, Sedge Islands	39° 47.3'	74° 05.9'	+3 00	+3 56	*0.07	*0.07	0.34	0.41	0.24
1547	Waretown	39° 47.5'	74° 10.9'	+2 43	+3 00	*0.07	*0.07	0.34	0.41	0.24
1549	Barnegat Inlet, USCG Station	39° 45.7'	74° 06.7'	-0 12	+0 02	*0.47	*0.63	2.16	2.59	1.20

TABLE 2. – TIDAL DIFFERENCES AND OTHER CONSTANTS

No.	PLACE	POSITION		DIFFERENCES				RANGES		Mean Tide Level
		Latitude	Longitude	Time High Water	Time Low Water	Height High Water	Height Low Water	Mean	Spring	
		North	West	h m	h m	ft	ft	ft	ft	ft
	NEW JERSEY Outer Coast-cont. Time meridian, 75° W			on Sandy Hook,						
	Barnegat Bay-cont.									
1551	High Bar	39° 45.4'	74° 07.7'	+1 04	+1 55	*0.12	*0.12	0.54	0.65	0.39
1553	Double Creek	39° 44.7'	74° 12.1'	+3 03	+3 33	*0.07	*0.07	0.31	0.37	0.19
1555	Loveladies Harbor	39° 43.5'	74° 08.2'	+3 02	+3 39	*0.10	*0.10	0.46	0.55	0.30
	Manahawkin Bay									
1557	Flat Creek	39° 42.4'	74° 11.5'	+3 33	+4 35	*0.18	*0.18	0.84	1.01	0.49
1559	North Beach	39° 40.5'	74° 09.6'	+3 02	+4 07	*0.22	*0.22	1.02	1.22	0.58
1561	Manahawkin Creek	39° 40.0'	74° 12.9'	+2 50	+3 51	*0.27	*0.27	1.25	1.50	0.69
1563	Manahawkin Drawbridge	39° 39.2'	74° 11.1'	+2 47	+3 39	*0.27	*0.27	1.26	1.51	0.70
	Little Egg Harbor									
1565	Mill Creek, 1 n.mi. above entrance	39° 39.9'	74° 13.9'	+2 32	+3 33	*0.35	*0.35	1.61	1.93	0.87
1567	Cedar Run	39° 39.2'	74° 15.4'	+2 10	+2 56	*0.40	*0.40	1.86	2.23	1.01
1569	Dinner Point Creek, upper end	39° 39.4'	74° 16.2'	+2 41	+3 17	*0.40	*0.40	1.88	2.26	1.03
1571	Beach Haven Crest	39° 36.8'	74° 12.6'	+2 13	+2 59	*0.38	*0.32	1.81	2.19	0.96
1573	Westecunk Creek entrance, Long Point	39° 36.8'	74° 15.8'	+2 00	+2 40	*0.42	*0.47	1.97	2.38	1.07
1575	West Creek, Westecunk Creek	39° 37.9'	74° 17.8'	+2 10	+2 40	*0.44	*0.47	2.08	2.52	1.13
1577	Parker Run, upper end	39° 37.0'	74° 18.6'	+2 05	+2 39	*0.45	*0.47	2.09	2.53	1.13
1579	Tuckerton Creek entrance	39° 34.6'	74° 19.9'	+1 32	+1 59	*0.45	*0.45	2.11	2.53	1.15
1581	Tuckerton, Tuckerton Creek	39° 36.1'	74° 20.5'	+1 45	+2 15	*0.45	*0.47	2.11	2.55	1.14
1583	Beach Haven Coast Guard Station	39° 32.9'	74° 15.4'	+1 18	+1 23	*0.46	*0.58	2.15	2.60	1.19
	Great Bay									
1585	Shooting Thorofare, Little Egg Inlet	39° 30.5'	74° 19.5'	+0 38	+0 21	*0.62	*0.79	2.88	3.24	1.59
1587	Little Sheepshead Creek	39° 31.1'	74° 19.2'	+0 35	+0 44	*0.66	*0.68	3.10	3.75	1.68
1589	Seven Island, Newmans Thorofare	39° 31.0'	74° 20.2'	+0 32	+0 28	*0.73	*0.73	3.4	4.1	1.8
1591	Graveling Point	39° 32.4'	74° 23.2'	+0 44	+1 14	*0.68	*0.68	3.18	3.82	1.72
	Mullica River									
1593	Nacote Creek, U.S. Highway 9 bridge	39° 32.1'	74° 27.8'	+1 34	+1 55	*0.66	*0.68	3.09	3.74	1.68
1595	Chestnut Neck Boat Yard	39° 32.9'	74° 27.7'	+1 27	+2 01	*0.63	*0.79	2.94	3.53	1.74
1597	New Gretna, Bass River	39° 35.5'	74° 26.5'	+1 52	+2 06	*0.66	*0.74	3.10	3.75	1.69
1599	Wading River (town), Wading River	39° 37.1'	74° 29.8'	+2 48	+2 44	*0.64	*0.79	2.98	3.61	1.64
1601	Green Bank	39° 36.7'	74° 35.4'	+2 59	+3 16	*0.66	*0.66	3.07	3.68	1.70
1603	Sweetwater, Mullica River Marina	39° 37.5'	74° 38.5'	+3 23	+4 21	*0.56	*0.56	2.42	3.14	1.42
				on Atlantic City,						
1605	Main Marsh Thorofare	39° 28.7'	74° 23.0'	+1 10	+1 52	*0.80	*0.76	3.21	3.92	1.74
1607	Brigantine Channel, Hoffman Thorofare	39° 26.1'	74° 21.8'	+0 59	+0 58	*0.90	*0.88	3.63	4.43	1.97
1609	Reed Bay, Turtle Cove	39° 27.2'	74° 25.6'	+1 07	- - -	- - -	- - -	- -	- -	- -
1611	Absecon, Absecon Creek, U.S. Hwy. 30 bridge	39° 25.4'	74° 30.0'	+1 28	+1 37	*0.96	*0.94	3.87	4.72	2.09
1613	Absecon Channel, State Route 87 bridge	39° 23.1'	74° 25.5'	+0 38	+0 26	*0.96	*1.13	3.90	4.68	2.13
1615	ATLANTIC CITY, OCEAN	39° 21.3'	74° 25.1'	Daily predictions				4.02	4.90	2.18
1617	Ventnor City, ocean pier	39° 20.1'	74° 28.6'	-0 02	-0 02	*1.00	*1.00	4.04	4.92	2.19
1619	Longport (inside), Great Egg Harbor Inlet	39° 18.5'	74° 32.0'	+0 26	+0 32	*0.94	*0.88	3.78	4.61	2.04
1621	Dock Thorofare, Risley Channel	39° 21.1'	74° 32.4'	+0 55	+1 00	*0.98	*0.94	3.92	4.78	2.12
1623	Pleasantville, Lakes Bay, Great Egg Harbor Inlet	39° 22.9'	74° 31.1'	+1 00	+1 37	*0.98	*0.82	3.96	4.83	2.12
	Great Egg Harbor Bay									
1625	Beesleys Point	39° 17.3'	74° 37.7'	+0 55	+1 32	*0.87	*1.00	3.55	4.26	1.93
1627	Steelmanville, Patcong Ck., 2.5 nm above ent.	39° 20.1'	74° 35.8'	+1 28	+1 50	*0.92	*0.94	3.70	4.51	2.01
1629	Tuckahoe, Tuckahoe River	39° 17.7'	74° 44.9'	+2 12	+2 40	*0.86	*1.25	3.47	4.16	1.93
1631	Cedar Swamp Creek, Tuckahoe River	39° 14.8'	74° 43.1'	+3 14	+3 03	*0.78	*1.53	2.99	3.65	1.75
1633	River Bend Marina, Great Egg Harbor River	39° 22.1'	74° 43.0'	+2 12	+2 25	*0.87	*1.00	3.47	4.23	1.90
1635	Mays Landing, Great Egg Harbor River	39° 26.9'	74° 43.7'	+2 50	+3 10	*1.01	*1.12	4.06	4.95	2.22
	Corson Inlet									
1637	Strathmere, Strathmere Bay	39° 12.0'	74° 39.4'	+0 31	+0 38	*0.95	*1.00	3.81	4.65	2.07
1639	Middle Thorofare, Ocean Drive bridge	39° 12.9'	74° 38.9'	+0 31	+0 30	*0.95	*0.94	3.80	4.64	2.06
1641	Ludlam Bay, west side	39° 10.6'	74° 42.6'	+0 56	+1 12	*0.98	*0.94	3.94	4.81	2.13
	Townsends Inlet									
1643	Ocean Drive bridge	39° 07.3'	74° 43.0'	+0 29	+0 21	*0.99	*1.06	3.96	4.62	2.16
1645	Townsend Sound	39° 08.8'	74° 45.0'	+1 08	+1 39	*0.90	*0.59	3.69	4.50	1.95
1647	Stites Sound	39° 07.2'	74° 45.3'	+0 49	+1 04	*0.97	*1.00	3.98	4.78	2.15
1649	Ingram Thorofare	39° 06.6'	74° 44.4'	+0 44	+0 50	*0.96	*1.00	3.93	4.72	2.12
1651	Long Reach, Ingram Thorofare	39° 06.1'	74° 45.3'	+1 06	+1 11	*0.98	*1.06	4.00	4.80	2.17
	Hereford Inlet									
1653	Great Sound, west side	39° 06.1'	74° 47.3'	+0 56	- - -	- - -	- - -	- -	- -	- -
1655	Stone Harbor, Great Channel	39° 03.4'	74° 45.9'	+0 56	+0 57	*1.04	*0.94	4.19	4.72	2.26
1657	Jenkins Sound	39° 03.9'	74° 48.5'	+0 52	- - -	- - -	- - -	- -	- -	- -
1659	Nummy Island, Grassy Sound Channel	39° 01.7'	74° 48.1'	+0 32	+0 45	*1.00	*1.00	4.09	4.91	2.21
1661	West Wildwood, Grassy Sound	39° 00.3'	74° 49.6'	+0 57	+1 11	*1.04	*1.00	4.27	5.12	2.30
1663	Old Turtle Thorofare, RR. bridge	39° 01.1'	74° 50.5'	+0 56	+1 10	*1.06	*1.00	4.33	5.20	2.33
1665	Wildwood Crest, ocean pier	38° 58.5'	74° 49.4'	+0 03	+0 03	*1.07	*1.06	4.31	5.15	2.34
	Cape May Inlet									
1667	Swain Channel, Taylor Sound	38° 58.8'	74° 51.8'	+0 55	+0 40	*1.09	*1.06	4.46	5.35	2.40
1669	Wildwood Crest, Sunset Lake	38° 58.7'	74° 50.2'	+0 52	+0 47	*1.10	*1.06	4.50	5.40	2.42
1671	Cape May Harbor	38° 56.9'	74° 53.5'	+0 33	+0 19	*1.10	*1.06	4.49	5.39	2.42
1673	Cape Island Creek, Cape May	38° 56.8'	74° 54.8'	+0 40	+0 20	*1.11	*1.19	4.51	5.41	2.44
1675	Cape May, Atlantic Ocean	38° 55.8'	74° 56.1'	+0 34	+0 21	*1.12	*1.06	4.59	5.51	2.46
	Delaware Bay, Eastern Shore			on Breakwater Harbor,						
1677	Brandywine Shoal Light	38° 59.2'	75° 06.8'	+0 12	+0 17	*1.19	*1.06	4.89	5.77	2.61
1679	Cape May Point, Sunset Beach	38° 56.8'	74° 58.3'	-0 05	-0 08	*1.16	*1.16	4.80	5.66	2.56
1681	Cape May, ferry terminal	38° 58.1'	74° 57.5'	-0 06	-0 05	*1.18	*1.00	4.85	5.73	2.58
1683	North Highlands Beach	39° 01.1'	74° 57.2'	+0 04	+0 14	*1.26	*1.26	5.24	6.18	2.78
1685	Dias Creek, Route 47 bridge	39° 05.0'	74° 53.2'	+1 09	+3 18	*0.46	*0.46	1.89	2.23	1.04

TABLE 2. – TIDAL DIFFERENCES AND OTHER CONSTANTS

No.	PLACE	POSITION Latitude	POSITION Longitude	DIFFERENCES Time High Water	DIFFERENCES Time Low Water	DIFFERENCES Height High Water	DIFFERENCES Height Low Water	RANGES Mean	RANGES Spring	Mean Tide Level
		North	West	h m	h m	ft	ft	ft	ft	ft
	NEW JERSEY Delaware Bay, Eastern Shore-cont. Time meridian, 75° W			on Breakwater Harbor,						
1687	Bidwell Creek entrance	39° 07.7'	74° 53.5'	+0 15	+0 46	*1.39	*1.19	5.67	6.69	3.03
1689	Bidwell Creek, Route 47 bridge	39° 07.1'	74° 52.1'	+0 36	+0 48	*1.36	*1.36	5.66	6.68	3.01
1691	Dennis Creek, 2.5 n.mi. above entrance	39° 10.7'	74° 51.1'	+0 55	+1 17	*1.26	*1.26	5.23	6.17	2.88
1693	Sluice Creek, Route 47 bridge, Dennis Creek	39° 09.7'	74° 49.9'	+1 49	+1 36	*1.22	*1.22	5.05	5.96	2.82
1695	Dennis Creek, Route 47 bridge	39° 11.0'	74° 49.3'	+2 01	+1 30	*1.20	*1.20	4.96	5.85	2.79
1697	East Creek, Route 47 bridge	39° 12.5'	74° 54.1'	+1 46	+2 24	*0.94	*0.94	3.92	4.63	2.20
1699	West Creek, 0.7 n.mi. above entrance	39° 11.3'	74° 54.9'	+0 20	+1 31	*1.15	*1.15	4.76	5.33	2.55
1701	West Creek, Route 47 bridge	39° 13.0'	74° 55.5'	+2 20	+3 17	*0.58	*0.58	2.40	2.83	1.51
1703	Riggins Ditch, 0.5 n.mi. above entrance	39° 12.0'	74° 58.2'	+0 29	+1 29	*1.24	*1.24	5.14	6.07	2.79
1705	Riggins Ditch, Heislerville	39° 13.1'	74° 58.8'	+1 36	+1 40	*1.12	*1.12	4.65	5.49	2.55
1707	East Point, Maurice River Cove	39° 12.0'	75° 01.2'	+0 40	+1 08	*1.39	*1.39	5.75	6.78	3.08
	Maurice River									
1709	Bivalve	39° 13.9'	75° 02.0'	+0 35	+1 11	*1.38	*1.19	5.66	6.26	3.02
1711	Mauricetown	39° 17.1'	74° 59.5'	+2 17	+2 30	*1.05	*1.05	4.36	5.14	2.42
1713	Port Elizabeth, Manumuskin River	39° 18.8'	74° 59.1'	+2 52	+2 58	*1.05	*1.05	4.34	5.12	2.42
1715	Menantico Creek entrance	39° 20.6'	75° 00.5'	+3 06	+3 09	*1.10	*1.10	4.58	5.40	2.52
1717	Millville	39° 23.5'	75° 02.5'	+3 33	+3 36	*1.21	*1.21	5.01	5.91	2.75
1719	Dividing Creek entrance	39° 13.0'	75° 06.4'	+0 29	+1 05	*1.35	*1.35	5.62	6.63	2.99
1721	Weir Creek bridge, Dividing Creek	39° 15.0'	75° 07.7'	+1 38	+2 33	*0.71	*0.71	2.96	3.49	1.69
1723	Dividing Creek (town), Dividing Creek	39° 16.0'	75° 05.7'	+3 07	---	---	---	--	--	--
				on Reedy Point,						
1725	Fishing Creek entrance	39° 12.9'	75° 09.6'	-1 51	-2 10	*1.02	*1.02	5.63	6.14	3.00
1727	Fortescue Creek	39° 14.3'	75° 10.5'	-1 57	-2 13	*1.09	*0.94	5.85	7.06	3.10
1729	Hollywood Beach, The Glades	39° 16.5'	75° 08.5'	+1 45	+1 13	*0.21	*0.21	1.16	1.26	0.71
1731	Money Island, Nantuxent Creek entrance	39° 17.1'	75° 14.3'	-1 43	-1 58	*1.10	*1.10	6.07	6.62	3.21
1733	Newport Landing, Nantuxent Creek	39° 17.5'	75° 11.9'	-0 03	-0 28	*0.74	*0.74	4.06	4.43	2.38
1735	Cedar Creek entrance, Nantuxent Cove	39° 17.9'	75° 14.8'	-1 37	-1 51	*1.08	*1.08	5.96	6.50	3.17
1737	Cedarville, Cedar Creek, Nantuxent Cove	39° 19.8'	75° 12.7'	-0 37	---	---	---	--	--	--
1739	Back Creek entrance, Nantuxent Cove	39° 18.3'	75° 16.7'	-1 29	-1 34	*1.07	*1.07	5.91	6.44	3.11
1741	Husted Landing, Ogden Creek, Back Creek	39° 21.1'	75° 15.1'	-0 47	---	---	---	--	--	--
1743	Greenwich Pier, Cohansey River	39° 23.0'	75° 21.0'	-0 42	-0 54	*0.99	*0.99	5.47	5.96	2.94
1745	Tindalls Wharf, Cohansey River	39° 22.7'	75° 14.1'	+1 01	-0 02	*1.09	*1.09	5.98	6.52	3.20
	DELAWARE Delaware Bay, Western Shore			on Breakwater Harbor,						
1747	LEWES (BREAKWATER HARBOR)	38° 46.9'	75° 07.2'	Daily predictions				4.08	4.94	2.19
1749	Mispillion River entrance	38° 56.9'	75° 18.9'	+0 22	+0 50	*1.13	*1.00	4.63	5.46	2.48
1751	Murderkill River entrance	39° 03.5'	75° 23.8'	+0 39	+1 11	*1.25	*0.94	5.12	6.04	2.71
1753	Mahon River entrance	39° 11.1'	75° 24.0'	+0 58	+1 29	*1.30	*1.13	5.33	6.29	2.84
1755	Leipsic, Leipsic River	39° 14.6'	75° 31.1'	+3 35	+3 49	*0.85	*0.63	3.50	4.13	1.80
	DELAWARE and NEW JERSEY Delaware River			on Reedy Point,						
1757	Stathems Neck, Stow Creek, N.J.	39° 24.4'	75° 24.3'	-0 22	-0 37	*0.88	*0.88	4.85	5.29	2.65
1759	Woodland Beach, Del.	39° 20.2'	75° 28.3'	-1 07	-1 10	*1.11	*1.11	5.90	6.80	3.00
1761	Raccoon Ditch, Newport Meadows, Stow Creek, N.J.	39° 25.3'	75° 22.9'	+1 08	+0 33	*0.76	*0.76	4.17	4.55	2.30
1763	Canton, Stow Creek, N.J.	39° 27.7'	75° 24.2'	+1 36	+0 45	*0.80	*0.80	4.42	4.82	2.49
	Mad Horse Creek									
1765	1 n.mi. above entrance, N.J.	39° 25.9'	75° 26.8'	-0 20	-0 47	*1.07	*1.07	5.86	6.39	3.12
1767	Pine Island, Malapartis Creek, N.J.	39° 25.3'	75° 25.7'	+0 21	-0 18	*0.92	*0.92	5.08	5.54	2.76
1769	Silver Lake Fork, N.J.	39° 27.2'	75° 27.4'	+0 04	---	---	---	--	--	--
1771	Hope Creek, 0.6 n.mi. above entrance, N.J.	39° 27.5'	75° 29.7'	-0 25	-0 36	*1.05	*1.05	5.78	6.30	3.07
1773	Hope Creek, upper end, N.J.	39° 29.1'	75° 29.6'	+0 49	---	---	---	--	--	--
1775	Taylors Bridge, Blackbird Creek, Del.	39° 24.0'	75° 36.0'	+1 53	+0 57	*0.54	*0.56	2.90	3.30	1.50
1777	Artificial Island, Salem Nuclear Plant, N.J.	39° 27.7'	75° 31.9'	-0 35	-0 33	*1.08	*1.08	5.93	6.46	3.16
	Alloway Creek, New Jersey									
1779	0.8 n.mi. above entrance	39° 29.8'	75° 31.0'	+0 21	-0 10	*0.99	*0.99	5.44	5.93	3.18
1781	Abbots Meadow	39° 30.7'	75° 29.6'	+0 44	+0 12	*0.94	*0.94	5.15	5.61	2.76
1783	2.5 n.mi. above entrance	39° 30.3'	75° 29.0'	+0 51	+0 15	*0.90	*0.90	4.95	5.40	2.6
1785	Coopers Creek bridge	39° 30.8'	75° 26.8'	+1 51	+1 00	*0.78	*0.78	4.30	4.69	2.3
1787	Quinton	39° 32.9'	75° 24.9'	+2 24	+1 30	*0.69	*0.69	3.79	4.13	2.1
1789	Alloway	39° 33.9'	75° 21.8'	+3 37	---	---	---	--	--	--
1791	Mill Creek, Elsinboro, N.J.	39° 32.1'	75° 30.7'	-0 04	---	---	---	--	--	--
	Salem River, New Jersey									
1793	Sinnickson Landing	39° 34.2'	75° 29.9'	+0 04	+0 19	*0.97	*0.97	5.32	5.80	2.8
1795	Salem	39° 34.6'	75° 28.6'	+0 49	+0 41	*0.76	*0.76	4.19	4.57	2.2
1797	Kates Creek Meadow	39° 37.5'	75° 27.2'	+1 54	---	---	---	--	--	--
1799	Winslow Farms	39° 37.7'	75° 28.9'	+2 09	---	---	---	--	--	--
1801	Beaver Dam	39° 39.0'	75° 29.2'	+2 32	---	---	---	--	--	--
1803	REEDY POINT	39° 33.5'	75° 34.4'	Daily predictions				5.34	5.81	2.8
	Chesapeake and Delaware Canal									
1805	St. Georges, Delaware	39° 33.3'	75° 38.9'	-0 16	-0 17	*0.83	*1.00	4.41	4.81	2.3
1807	Summit Bridge, Delaware	39° 32.0'	75° 44.0'	-0 28	-0 52	*0.65	*0.56	3.50	3.90	1.8
1809	Chesapeake City, Maryland	39° 31.6'	75° 48.6'	-0 45	-1 12	*0.56	*1.28	2.86	3.14	1.6
1811	Delaware City Branch Channel bridge	39° 34.2'	75° 35.4'	+0 00	+0 05	*1.02	*0.89	5.45	5.94	2.8
1813	Delaware City	39° 34.9'	75° 35.3'	+0 11	+0 14	*1.02	*1.00	5.44	5.93	2.9
1815	Pea Patch Island, Bulkhead Shoal Channel, Del.	39° 35.1'	75° 34.4'	+0 03	+0 00	*1.05	*1.00	5.62	6.13	2.9
1817	Mill Creek, Penns Neck, N.J.	39° 36.6'	75° 31.2'	+0 08	---	---	---	--	--	--
1819	New Castle, Delaware	39° 39.4'	75° 33.7'	+0 29	+0 40	*0.98	*1.00	5.21	5.68	2.7
1821	Salem Canal entrance, N.J.	39° 41.0'	75° 30.6'	+0 36	+0 52	*1.00	*1.00	5.52	6.02	2.9

TABLE 2. – TIDAL DIFFERENCES AND OTHER CONSTANTS

No.	PLACE	POSITION Latitude	POSITION Longitude	DIFFERENCES Time High Water	DIFFERENCES Time Low Water	DIFFERENCES Height High Water	DIFFERENCES Height Low Water	RANGES Mean	RANGES Spring	Mean Tide Level
		North	West	h m	h m	ft	ft	ft	ft	ft
	DELAWARE and NEW JERSEY Delaware River-cont. Time meridian, 75° W					on Reedy Point,				
	Christina River, Delaware									
1823	Wilmington Marine Terminal	39° 43.1'	75° 31.2'	+0 50	+1 06	*0.99	*1.11	5.27	5.74	2.83
1825	Millside, RR. bridge	39° 43.5'	75° 33.6'	+1 08	+1 19	*0.99	*1.06	5.30	5.78	2.84
1827	Edgemoor, Del.	39° 45.0'	75° 29.6'	+0 52	+1 11	*1.02	*1.17	5.52	6.02	2.97
1829	Pedricktown, Oldmans Creek, N.J.	39° 45.7'	75° 24.2'	+2 11	+2 07	*0.75	*0.75	4.13	4.50	2.32
1831	Auburn, Oldmans Creek, N.J.	39° 42.9'	75° 21.6'	+4 12	+3 30	*0.55	*0.55	2.74	2.99	1.65
	NEW JERSEY and PENNSYLVANIA Delaware River					on Philadelphia,				
1833	Marcus Hook, Pa.	39° 48.7'	75° 24.7'	-1 23	-1 07	*0.92	*0.95	5.53	5.86	2.96
1835	Bridgeport, Raccoon Creek, N.J.	39° 48.4'	75° 21.3'	-1 11	-0 50	*0.91	*1.00	5.42	5.66	2.91
1837	Swedesboro, Raccoon Creek, N.J.	39° 45.1'	75° 18.4'	+0 40	- - -	- - -	- - -	- -	- -	- -
	Darby Creek, Pennsylvania									
1839	Wanamaker Bridge	39° 52.6'	75° 18.3'	-0 46	-0 34	*0.95	*0.95	5.71	6.05	3.05
1841	Norwood City	39° 52.8'	75° 17.4'	-0 42	-0 35	*0.97	*1.00	5.79	6.13	3.09
1843	Tinicum National Wildlife Refuge	39° 52.7'	75° 16.6'	-0 22	-0 08	*0.91	*0.90	5.47	5.80	2.91
1845	Tinicum National Wildlife Refuge	39° 53.2'	75° 15.9'	-0 24	+0 27	*0.74	*0.74	4.51	4.78	2.33
1847	Tinicum Nat. Wildlife Refuge, Visitor Center . . .	39° 53.5'	75° 15.5'	-0 10	- - -	- - -	- - -	- -	- -	- -
1849	Billingsport, N.J.	39° 51.0'	75° 15.0'	-0 35	-0 28	*0.93	*0.95	5.59	5.93	2.99
1851	Paulsboro, Mantua Creek, N.J.	39° 50.1'	75° 14.3'	-0 24	-0 19	*0.94	*0.90	5.64	5.88	3.01
1853	Mantua, Mantua Creek, N.J.	39° 47.8'	75° 10.6'	+1 28	+0 56	*0.71	*0.71	4.19	4.37	2.31
1855	Woodbury Creek, N.J.	39° 51.6'	75° 11.2'	-0 13	-0 14	*0.96	*0.95	5.75	6.10	3.07
	Schuylkill River, Pennsylvania									
1857	Penrose Avenue Bridge	39° 53.9'	75° 12.7'	-0 22	-0 11	*0.96	*0.85	5.79	6.14	3.07
1859	Market Street Bridge	39° 57.3'	75° 10.8'	-0 20	+0 00	*0.99	*0.80	5.94	6.30	3.13
1861	Westville, Rt. 47 bridge, Big Timber Creek, N.J. . .	39° 52.5'	75° 07.4'	+0 02	+0 03	*0.97	*1.00	5.80	6.15	3.10
1863	Sunset Beach, Big Timber Creek, N.J.	39° 48.9'	75° 05.3'	+1 32	- - -	- - -	- - -	- -	- -	- -
1865	Philadelphia, Municipal Pier 11, Pa.	39° 57.2'	75° 08.3'	+0 02	+0 05	*1.04	*0.95	6.24	6.61	3.32
1867	PHILADELPHIA, US Coast Guard Station, Pa. . . .	39° 56.0'	75° 08.5'		Daily predictions			5.99	6.32	3.30
1869	Pavonia, Cooper River, RR. bridge, N.J.	39° 56.8'	75° 06.3'	+0 14	+0 23	*1.04	*1.00	6.24	6.61	3.32
1871	Bridesburg, Philadelphia, Pa.	39° 59.0'	75° 04.5'	+0 12	+0 15	*1.06	*0.90	6.39	6.50	3.38
1873	Palmyra, Pennsauken Creek, Route 73 bridge, N.J.	39° 59.6'	75° 01.7'	+0 51	+1 03	*0.89	*0.89	5.25	5.48	2.86
1875	Cinnaminson, Pennsauken Ck., Rt. 130 bridge, N.J.	39° 59.1'	75° 00.9'	+1 37	- - -	- - -	- - -	- -	- -	- -
1877	Tacony-Palmyra Bridge	40° 00.7'	75° 02.6'	+0 24	+0 25	*1.10	*0.95	6.60	7.00	3.49
1879	Pompeston Creek, N.J.	40° 00.8'	75° 00.5'	+0 21	+0 43	*1.05	*1.05	6.39	6.68	3.30
	Rancocas Creek, New Jersey									
1881	Bridgeboro	40° 01.7'	74° 55.9'	+1 15	+1 18	*1.06	*1.00	6.35	6.73	3.38
1883	North Branch	39° 59.9'	74° 49.1'	+2 58	+3 29	*0.48	*0.60	2.86	3.03	1.55
1885	Hainesport, South Branch	39° 58.7'	74° 49.4'	+2 58	+3 05	*0.62	*0.62	3.63	3.85	2.05
1887	Cornwells Heights, Pa.	40° 04.1'	74° 56.3'	+0 46	+0 58	*1.17	*1.00	7.02	7.44	3.71
1889	Burlington, N.J.	40° 04.8'	74° 52.5'	+0 53	+1 07	*1.20	*1.00	7.24	7.63	3.83
1891	Assiscunk Creek, Route 130 bridge, N.J.	40° 04.4'	74° 50.9'	+1 04	+1 31	*1.12	*0.85	6.75	7.16	3.54
1893	Edgely, Pa.	40° 07.7'	74° 49.4'	+1 08	+1 28	*1.27	*1.15	7.64	8.10	4.05
1895	Fieldsboro, N.J.	40° 08.2'	74° 44.2'	+1 07	+1 39	*1.29	*1.10	7.78	8.25	4.11
1897	Newbold, Pa.	40° 08.2'	74° 45.1'	+1 10	+1 31	*1.30	*1.00	7.86	8.33	4.13
1899	Blacks Creek, Route 130 bridge, N.J.	40° 08.3'	74° 42.7'	+1 13	- - -	- - -	- - -	- -	- -	- -
1901	Sylvan Glen, Crosswicks Ck., Rt. 206 bridge, N.J.	40° 10.9'	74° 42.3'	+2 03	- - -	- - -	- - -	- -	- -	- -
1903	Crosswicks Creek, Route 130 bridge, N.J. . . .	40° 10.4'	74° 40.8'	+3 07	- - -	- - -	- - -	- -	- -	- -
1905	Trenton, N.J.	40° 11.3'	74° 45.3'	+1 13	+1 54	*1.35	*1.00	8.18	8.47	4.29
	DELAWARE and MARYLAND Outer Coast					on Ocean City,				
1907	Rehoboth Beach	38° 43.2'	75° 04.6'	+0 15	+0 08	*1.13	*1.33	3.9	4.7	2.1
1909	Indian River Inlet (Coast Guard Station)	38° 36.6'	75° 04.2'	+1 14	+0 45	*0.76	*1.00	2.51	2.94	1.41
1911	OCEAN CITY (FISHING PIER)	38° 19.6'	75° 05.0'		Daily predictions			3.36	4.00	1.84
1913	Ocean City Inlet	38° 19.7'	75° 05.5'	+0 28	+0 14	*0.65	*1.00	2.13	2.62	1.23
1915	Ocean City (Isle of Wight Bay)	38° 19.9'	75° 05.4'	+0 25	+0 23	*0.67	*0.94	2.20	2.61	1.25
1917	Keydash, Isle of Wight Bay	38° 20.5'	75° 05.1'	-0 57	+0 54	*0.47	*0.81	1.53	1.82	0.89
	MARYLAND and VIRGINIA Chincoteague Bay									
1919	Assateague Beach, Toms Cove	37° 52.0'	75° 22.0'	+0 35	+0 48	*1.08	*1.25	3.60	4.28	2.00
1921	Harbor of Refuge	37° 54.2'	75° 24.4'	+0 31	+0 35	*0.73	*0.88	2.43	2.89	1.35
1923	Chincoteague Channel (south end)	37° 54.4'	75° 24.3'	+0 39	+0 47	*0.64	*0.69	2.16	2.57	1.19
1925	Wishart Point, Bogues Bay	37° 52.9'	75° 29.5'	+0 52	+1 13	*0.77	*0.63	2.60	3.09	1.40
1927	Chincoteague Island, USCG Station	37° 55.9'	75° 23.0'	+0 56	+1 11	*0.48	*0.56	1.59	1.89	0.89
1929	Chincoteague Island, Lewis Creek	37° 56.3'	75° 22.4'	+1 17	+1 38	*0.40	*0.63	1.32	1.57	0.76
1931	Chincoteague Island, Oyster Bay	37° 56.5'	75° 20.8'	+1 44	+2 05	*0.46	*0.56	1.54	1.83	0.86
1933	Chincoteague Island, Blake Cove	37° 57.1'	75° 21.3'	+1 51	+2 32	*0.28	*0.56	0.89	1.06	0.53
1935	Jesters Island	37° 58.9'	75° 18.1'	+2 32	+3 24	*0.24	*0.24	0.76	0.90	0.48
1937	Franklin City	38° 00.4'	75° 23.0'	+2 20	+3 00	*0.22	*0.63	0.66	0.79	0.43
1939	Public Landing	38° 08.9'	75° 17.1'	+4 41	+5 21	*0.18	*0.18	0.53	0.63	0.36
1941	Buntings Bridge	38° 08.3'	75° 11.0'	+4 25	+4 56	*0.20	*0.69	0.61	0.82	0.41
1943	South Point, Sinepuxent Neck	38° 12.9'	75° 11.5'	+5 16	+5 02	*0.16	*0.16	0.46	0.54	0.33
	VIRGINIA Outer Coast									
1945	Wallops Island	37° 50.5'	75° 28.7'	+0 04	-0 04	*1.06	*0.31	3.67	4.37	1.89
1947	Gargathy Neck	37° 46.6'	75° 33.7'	+1 31	+1 27	*0.88	*0.63	3.01	3.58	1.60
1949	Metompkin Inlet	37° 40.3'	75° 35.7'	+1 01	+0 44	*1.08	*1.25	3.60	4.28	2.00

TABLE 2. – TIDAL DIFFERENCES AND OTHER CONSTANTS

No.	PLACE	POSITION		DIFFERENCES				RANGES		Mean Tide Level
				Time		Height				
		Latitude	Longitude	High Water	Low Water	High Water	Low Water	Mean	Spring	
		North	West	h m	h m	ft	ft	ft	ft	ft
	VIRGINIA Outer Coast-cont. Time meridian, 75° W					on Ocean City,				
1951	Folly Creek, Metompkin Inlet	37° 41.8'	75° 38.1'	+1 24	+1 12	*0.97	*0.63	3.30	3.93	1.80
1953	Wachapreague, Wachapreague Channel	37° 36.4'	75° 41.2'	+1 10	+0 56	*1.19	*1.06	4.02	4.85	2.18
1955	Revel Creek, Revel Island	37° 29.8'	75° 41.0'	+0 35	+0 27	*1.19	*1.00	4.04	4.81	2.18
1957	Great Machipongo Inlet (inside)	37° 23.6'	75° 42.8'	+1 05	+0 56	*1.16	*1.25	3.86	4.59	2.10
1959	Upshur Neck, south end	37° 28.0'	75° 48.0'	+1 09	+1 14	*1.31	*1.25	4.40	5.24	2.40
1961	Sand Shoal Inlet (Coast Guard Station)	37° 18.1'	75° 46.7'	+0 32	+0 17	*1.18	*1.00	4.00	4.76	2.16
1963	Oyster Harbor	37° 17.3'	75° 55.5'	+1 00	+0 36	*1.34	*1.13	4.52	5.38	2.40
1965	Smith Island (Coast Guard Station)	37° 07.4'	75° 54.7'	+0 52	+1 29	*1.05	*1.25	3.50	4.17	1.90
	Chesapeake Bay, Eastern Shore				on Ches. Bay Bridge Tunnel,					
1967	Fishermans Island	37° 05.8'	75° 58.9'	+0 02	+0 11	*1.19	*1.25	3.02	3.62	1.71
1969	Kiptopeke Beach	37° 10.0'	75° 59.3'	+0 23	+0 32	*1.01	*0.92	2.60	3.09	1.41
1971	Old Plantation Light	37° 14'	76° 03'	+0 33	+0 52	*0.92	*0.83	2.4	2.9	1.3
1973	Cape Charles Harbor	37° 15.8'	76° 00.9'	+0 45	+1 03	*0.90	*0.92	2.3	2.8	1.3
1975	Gaskins Point, Occohannock Creek	37° 33.3'	75° 55.2'	+2 35	+3 13	*0.66	*0.83	1.70	2.00	0.94
1977	Harborton, Pungoteague Creek	37° 40.0'	75° 50.0'	+3 11	+3 33	*0.70	*0.83	1.76	2.11	0.98
1979	Onancock, Onancock Creek	37° 42.7'	75° 45.4'	+3 55	+4 19	*0.71	*0.83	1.80	2.16	1.00
1981	Chesconessex Creek, Schooner Bay	37° 45.8'	75° 46.4'	+3 41	+3 59	*0.78	*1.25	1.94	2.33	1.12
1983	Watts Island	37° 47.9'	75° 53.8'	+4 02	+4 12	*0.64	*0.83	1.60	1.92	0.90
1985	Tangier Island	37° 49.7'	75° 59.6'	+3 58	+4 16	*0.60	*0.75	1.41	1.69	0.80
1987	Muddy Creek Entrance	37° 51.3'	75° 40.5'	+4 14	+4 51	*0.86	*0.83	2.20	2.64	1.20
1989	Guard Shore	37° 51.0'	75° 42.0'	+4 06	+4 47	*0.90	*0.83	2.30	2.76	1.27
1991	Saxis, Starling Creek, Pocomoke Sound	37° 55.3'	75° 43.7'	+3 52	+4 36	*0.89	*1.17	2.24	2.69	1.26
	MARYLAND Chesapeake Bay, Eastern Shore									
1993	Ape Hole Creek, Pocomoke Sound	37° 57.7'	75° 49.3'	+4 27	+4 58	*0.90	*0.83	2.30	2.80	1.20
	Pocomoke River									
1995	Shelltown	37° 58.8'	75° 38.3'	+4 32	+5 16	*0.94	*1.00	2.40	2.90	1.30
1997	Snow Hill, city park	38° 10.7'	75° 23.8'	+7 26	+7 36	*0.70	*1.33	1.62	1.96	0.98
1999	Crisfield, Little Annemessex River	37° 58.6'	75° 51.8'	+4 34	+4 51	*0.75	*1.00	1.86	2.23	1.05
2001	Colburn Creek, Big Annemessex River	38° 02.9'	75° 48.2'	+4 59	+5 30	*0.78	*1.17	1.94	2.33	1.11
2003	Long Point, Big Annemessex River	38° 03.4'	75° 48.2'	+5 19	+5 47	*0.82	*0.83	2.10	2.50	1.10
2005	Teague Creek, Manokin River	38° 06.5'	75° 50.3'	+5 38	+6 05	*0.82	*0.83	2.10	2.50	1.10
2007	Ewell, Smith Island	37° 59.7'	76° 01.9'	+4 56	+5 19	*0.61	*1.00	1.53	1.84	0.88
2009	Holland Island Bar Light	38° 04.1'	76° 05.8'	+5 16	+5 30	*0.56	*0.58	1.40	1.70	0.80
2011	Chance	38° 10.2'	75° 56.8'	+5 29	+5 57	*0.78	*1.17	1.94	2.33	1.11
2013	Sharkfin Shoal Light	38° 12.1'	75° 59.2'	+5 46	+6 06	*0.86	*0.92	2.20	2.64	1.20
2015	Great Shoals Light, Monie Bay	38° 13.0'	75° 53.0'	+6 00	+6 22	*0.90	*0.92	2.30	2.80	1.30
	Wicomico River									
2017	Whitehaven	38° 16.0'	75° 47.0'	+6 26	+6 46	*0.94	*1.00	2.40	2.90	1.30
2019	Salisbury	38° 22.0'	75° 36.0'	+7 21	+7 24	*1.20	*1.25	3.00	3.60	1.70
	Nanticoke River									
2021	Roaring Point	38° 15.7'	75° 55.2'	+6 00	+6 35	*0.90	*0.92	2.30	2.76	1.30
2023	Vienna	38° 29.0'	75° 49.1'	+8 25	+8 32	*0.79	*1.33	1.94	2.33	1.13
2025	Sharptown	38° 32.5'	75° 43.4'	+9 19	+9 28	*0.97	*1.00	2.50	3.00	1.40
2027	McCreedy's Creek, Fishing Bay	38° 18.0'	76° 00.4'	+5 49	+6 22	*0.82	*1.17	2.05	2.46	1.16
2029	Hooper Strait Light	38° 13.6'	76° 04.6'	+5 26	+5 51	*0.61	*1.17	1.48	1.77	0.88
2031	Bishops Head, Hooper Strait	38° 13.2'	76° 02.3'	+5 32	+6 04	*0.70	*1.08	1.73	2.08	0.99
					on Baltimore,					
2033	Middle Hooper Island	38° 17.8'	76° 12.3'	-4 40	-4 39	*1.32	*1.50	1.51	1.71	1.09
2035	Barren Island	38° 20.5'	76° 15.9'	-4 45	-4 56	*1.01	*0.68	1.22	1.38	0.77
	Little Choptank River									
2037	Smithville Road Bridge, Beaverdam Creek	38° 25.7'	76° 14.2'	-2 26	-2 49	*1.01	*0.82	1.19	1.34	0.78
2039	Taylors Island, Slaughter Creek	38° 28.0'	76° 17.7'	-3 15	-3 00	*1.10	*1.18	1.30	1.47	0.88
2041	Woolford, Church Creek	38° 30.4'	76° 10.4'	-3 11	-2 55	*1.25	*1.41	1.40	1.58	1.00
2043	Cherry Island, Beckwiths Creek	38° 33.7'	76° 12.5'	-3 07	-2 57	*1.18	*1.27	1.34	1.51	0.90
	Choptank River									
2045	Cambridge	38° 34.4'	76° 04.1'	-2 42	-2 28	*1.23	*0.95	1.62	1.83	1.02
2047	Dover Bridge	38° 45.4'	75° 59.9'	-0 18	-0 41	*1.54	*1.68	1.70	1.92	1.24
2049	Hillsboro, Tuckahoe Creek	38° 55.0'	75° 56.7'	+1 29	+1 19	*1.82	*0.86	2.29	2.59	1.33
	Tred Avon River									
2051	Oxford	38° 42.0'	76° 10.4'	-2 50	-2 45	*1.25	*1.41	1.40	1.58	1.00
2053	Easton Point	38° 46.1'	76° 05.9'	-2 45	-2 35	*1.47	*1.59	1.60	1.81	1.20
2055	Deep Neck Point, Broad Creek	38° 43.9'	76° 16.1'	-2 57	-2 47	*1.25	*1.41	1.40	1.58	1.00
2057	St. Michaels, San Domingo Creek	38° 46.5'	76° 14.0'	-2 55	-2 52	*1.25	*1.41	1.40	1.58	1.00
2059	Avalon, Dogwood Harbor	38° 42.5'	76° 19.8'	-2 54	-2 48	*1.18	*1.36	1.30	1.47	0.90
2061	Tilghman Island, Ferry Cove, Eastern Bay	38° 45.9'	76° 19.7'	-2 33	-2 42	*0.98	*1.00	1.10	1.24	0.78
2063	Poplar Island	38° 45.5'	76° 22.6'	-2 33	-2 41	*0.97	*0.95	1.10	1.54	0.77
2065	Claiborne, Eastern Bay	38° 50.2'	76° 16.8'	-2 26	-2 28	*0.96	*1.09	1.10	1.24	0.70
2067	St. Michaels, Miles River	38° 47.2'	76° 13.3'	-2 12	-2 12	*1.22	*1.18	1.40	1.58	0.96
2069	Kent Island Narrows	38° 58.0'	76° 14.6'	-1 30	-1 23	*1.10	*1.18	1.20	1.36	0.90
2071	Matapeake, Kent Island	38° 57.4'	76° 21.3'	-1 30	-1 49	*0.90	*0.95	1.02	1.15	0.72
2073	Kent Point Marina	38° 50.2'	76° 22.4'	-2 21	-2 29	*0.97	*0.95	1.11	1.25	0.78
	Chester River									
2075	Love Point	39° 01.9'	76° 18.1'	-0 25	-0 41	*1.03	*0.95	1.19	1.34	0.84
2077	Queenstown	38° 59.8'	76° 09.5'	+0 05	-0 08	*1.18	*1.27	1.30	1.47	0.90
2079	Centreville Landing, Corsica River	39° 03.2'	76° 04.5'	+0 20	+0 14	*1.47	*1.89	1.60	1.81	1.20
2081	Cliffs Point	39° 06.4'	76° 08.5'	+0 12	-0 02	*1.32	*1.50	1.50	1.70	1.00
2083	Cliffs Wharf	39° 06.7'	76° 08.3'	+0 09	-0 08	*1.33	*1.27	1.53	1.73	1.05

TABLE 2. – TIDAL DIFFERENCES AND OTHER CONSTANTS

No.	PLACE	POSITION Latitude	POSITION Longitude	DIFFERENCES Time High Water	DIFFERENCES Time Low Water	DIFFERENCES Height High Water	DIFFERENCES Height Low Water	RANGES Mean	RANGES Spring	Mean Tide Level
		North	West	h m	h m	ft	ft	ft	ft	ft
	MARYLAND Chesapeake Bay, Eastern Shore-cont. Time meridian, 75° W					on Baltimore,				
	Chester River-cont.									
2085	Chestertown	39° 12.4'	76° 03.8'	+1 03	+0 36	*1.62	*1.77	1.80	2.03	1.31
2087	Crumpton	39° 14.7'	75° 55.5'	+1 10	+1 04	*1.82	*0.91	2.28	2.58	1.34
2089	Deep Landing, Swan Creek	39° 08.7'	76° 15.6'	+0 02	-0 04	*0.96	*1.09	1.13	1.28	0.70
2091	Tolchester Beach	39° 12.8'	76° 14.7'	+0 18	+0 11	*1.04	*0.95	1.21	1.35	0.81
2093	Worton Creek entrance	39° 17.8'	76° 10.3'	+1 22	+1 19	*1.18	*1.27	1.30	1.47	0.90
2095	Sassafras River, Betterton	39° 22.3'	76° 03.8'	+2 35	+2 15	*1.34	*1.00	1.60	1.81	1.02
	Elk River									
2097	Town Point Wharf	39° 30.2'	75° 55.0'	+3 18	+2 59	*1.74	*0.86	2.17	2.45	1.28
	C & D Canal (see Delaware River)	- - -	- - -	- - -	- - -	- - -	- - -	- -	- -	- -
	Chesapeake City, Maryland (see C & D Canal) .	- - -	- - -	- - -	- - -	- - -	- - -	- -	- -	- -
2099	Old Frenchtown Wharf	39° 34.5'	75° 50.6'	+3 13	+3 00	*2.06	*2.27	2.30	2.60	1.60
2101	Charlestown, Northeast River	39° 34.4'	75° 58.2'	+3 52	+4 03	*1.69	*1.86	1.90	2.15	1.30
	Chesapeake Bay, western shore									
	Susquehanna River									
2103	Havre de Grace	39° 32.2'	76° 05.4'	+3 13	+3 27	*1.55	*0.95	1.90	2.15	1.16
2105	Port Deposit	39° 36.0'	76° 06.8'	+3 24	+3 49	*1.51	*1.14	1.81	2.04	1.16
2107	Pond Point, Bush River	39° 23.3'	76° 15.3'	+1 52	+1 31	*1.06	*0.86	1.25	1.41	0.81
	Patapsco River									
2109	North Point	39° 11.8'	76° 26.8'	+0 12	+0 04	*0.93	*1.09	1.03	1.16	0.75
2111	Stony Creek	39° 09.8'	76° 31.6'	+0 03	-0 05	*0.95	*0.91	1.09	1.23	0.75
2113	Hawkins Point	39° 12.5'	76° 32.0'	+0 00	+0 06	*1.03	*0.95	1.19	1.34	0.80
2115	Curtis Creek, US Coast Guard Station	39° 11.7'	76° 34.6'	+0 12	+0 08	*0.96	*1.14	1.06	1.20	0.78
2117	BALTIMORE, Fort McHenry	39° 16.0'	76° 34.7'		Daily predictions			1.14	1.25	0.79
2119	Fort McHenry Marsh	39° 15.7'	76° 35.1'	-0 01	-0 01	*1.00	*1.00	1.14	1.29	0.78
2121	Mountain Point, Gibson Is., Magothy River . . .	39° 03.7'	76° 26.0'	-0 04	-0 04	*0.74	*0.77	0.80	0.90	0.60
2123	Cornfield Creek, Magothy River	39° 06.0'	76° 26.7'	-0 29	-0 38	*0.89	*0.95	0.99	1.12	0.71
	Severn River									
2125	Brewer Point	39° 01.6'	76° 32.0'	-0 45	-0 54	*0.74	*0.91	0.80	0.90	0.60
2127	Annapolis (US Naval Academy)	38° 59.0'	76° 28.8'	-1 30	-1 44	*0.88	*1.00	0.97	1.12	0.71
2129	Thomas Point Shoal Light	38° 54.0'	76° 26.0'	-1 56	-2 11	*0.81	*0.91	0.90	1.02	0.60
2131	Edgewater, South River	38° 57.0'	76° 33.0'	-1 51	-2 07	*0.81	*0.91	0.90	1.02	0.60
2133	Gingerville Creek, South River	38° 57.5'	76° 33.3'	-2 01	-2 06	*0.92	*1.00	1.03	1.16	0.74
2135	Rhode River (County Wharf)	38° 53.2'	76° 32.4'	-2 07	-2 17	*0.88	*1.00	0.98	1.10	0.70
2137	Galesville, West River	38° 50.0'	76° 32.0'	-1 39	-1 34	*0.81	*0.91	0.90	1.01	0.60
2139	Rose Haven, Herring Bay	38° 43.5'	76° 32.5'	-2 37	-2 44	*0.81	*0.91	0.90	1.01	0.60
2141	Chesapeake Beach	38° 41.0'	76° 32.0'	-2 47	-3 05	*0.88	*1.00	1.00	1.13	0.70
2143	Long Beach	38° 27.9'	76° 28.4'	-3 47	-4 04	*0.87	*0.77	1.01	1.14	0.67
2145	Cove Point	38° 23.5'	76° 23.9'	-4 10	-4 25	*0.83	*0.83	1.04	1.18	0.61
	Patuxent River									
2147	Solomons Island	38° 19.0'	76° 27.1'	-4 38	-4 46	*0.98	*0.73	1.17	1.34	0.74
2149	Broomes Island	38° 24.9'	76° 32.7'	-4 13	-4 19	*1.18	*1.36	1.30	1.47	0.94
2151	Benedict	38° 30.8'	76° 40.2'	-3 54	-3 54	*1.47	*1.82	1.60	1.81	0.81
2153	Lower Marlboro	38° 39.3'	76° 41.0'	-2 46	-2 54	*1.47	*0.77	1.82	2.06	1.09
2155	Point Lookout	38° 02.4'	76° 1.4'	-5 28	-5 37	*1.02	*0.77	1.22	1.38	0.78
	MD., VA. and DISTRICT OF COLUMBIA Potomac River					on Washington,				
2157	Cornfield Harbor, Md.	38° 03.7'	76° 21.5'	-6 16	-7 35	*0.48	*0.53	1.30	1.43	0.76
2159	Lewisetta, Va.	37° 59.7'	76° 27.9'	-6 19	-7 31	*0.46	*0.80	1.25	1.42	0.74
2161	Travis Point, Coan River, Va.	37° 59.8'	76° 28.0'	-6 00	-7 05	*0.44	*0.67	1.20	1.32	0.70
2163	Kinsale, Yeocomico River, Va.	38° 01.9'	76° 34.6'	-5 46	-6 53	*0.44	*0.67	1.20	1.32	0.70
2165	Piney Point, Md.	38° 08.0'	76° 32.0'	-5 54	-7 16	*0.51	*0.60	1.40	1.54	0.80
2167	Ragged Point, Coles Neck, Va.	38° 08.5'	76° 36.8'	-5 35	-7 03	*0.54	*0.67	1.50	1.65	0.85
2169	Mount Holly, Nomini Creek, Va.	38° 05.9'	76° 44.1'	-4 51	-6 14	*0.54	*0.67	1.50	1.65	0.80
2171	Colton Point, Md.	38° 13.2'	76° 45.0'	-5 18	-6 43	*0.65	*0.73	1.80	1.98	1.03
2173	Mills Point (south of), Wicomico Riv., Md. . .	38° 19.6'	76° 50.0'	-5 05	-6 05	*0.65	*0.73	1.80	1.98	1.00
2175	Colonial Beach, Va.	38° 15.1'	76° 57.6'	-5 08	-6 13	*0.61	*0.93	1.63	1.79	0.96
2177	Dahlgren, Upper Machodoc Creek, Va.	38° 19.2'	77° 02.2'	-4 53	-5 59	*0.56	*0.93	1.58	1.87	0.93
2179	Lower Cedar Point, Md.	38° 20.5'	76° 58.6'	-4 48	-5 56	*0.54	*0.60	1.50	1.65	0.80
2181	Mathias Point, Va.	38° 23.9'	77° 03.2'	-4 00	-4 56	*0.44	*0.67	1.20	1.32	0.70
2183	Goose Creek, Port Tobacco River, Md. . . .	38° 27.2'	77° 03.3'	-4 08	-5 07	*0.54	*0.60	1.46	1.61	0.82
2185	Riverside, Md.	38° 23.2'	77° 08.7'	-3 23	-4 24	*0.48	*0.53	1.28	1.41	0.78
2187	Aquia Creek, Va.	38° 25.1'	77° 21.2'	-1 28	-2 32	*0.48	*0.67	1.26	1.39	0.71
2189	Clifton Beach, Smith Point, Md.	38° 24.8'	77° 16.0'	-1 42	-2 46	*0.41	*0.67	1.10	1.21	0.60
2191	Liverpool Point, Md.	38° 27.6'	77° 16.2'	-0 39	-1 58	*0.44	*0.67	1.20	1.32	0.70
2193	Quantico, Va.	38° 31.2'	77° 17.2'	-0 52	-2 04	*0.51	*0.67	1.40	1.54	0.80
2195	Indian Head, Md.	38° 36.1'	77° 11.1'	-0 14	-1 33	*0.65	*0.73	1.80	1.98	1.03
2197	Marshall Hall, Md.	38° 41.2'	77° 06.1'	+0 10	-0 55	*0.82	*0.93	2.30	2.53	1.27
2199	Alexandria, Va.	38° 48.3'	77° 02.3'	+0 18	-0 11	*0.96	*1.33	2.62	2.88	1.51
2201	Bellevue, D.C.	38° 49.6'	77° 01.6'	+0 34	-0 11	*1.02	*1.33	2.80	3.08	1.60
2203	WASHINGTON, Washington Channel, D.C.	38° 52.3'	77° 01.2'		Daily predictions			2.77	3.07	1.55
	Anacostia River									
2205	Washington Naval Yard	38° 52.3'	76° 59.7'	+0 18	-0 06	*1.01	*1.20	2.80	3.08	1.57
2207	Kingman Lake	38° 53.7'	76° 58.1'	+0 22	+0 04	*1.03	*1.20	2.84	3.12	1.60
2209	Kenilworth Aquatic Garden	38° 54.6'	76° 57.3'	+0 29	+0 10	*1.05	*1.07	2.92	3.21	1.62
2211	Bladensburg, Md.	38° 56.0'	76° 56.3'	+0 31	+0 25	*1.06	*1.13	2.95	3.25	1.64

Endnotes can be found at the end of table 2.

TABLE 2. – TIDAL DIFFERENCES AND OTHER CONSTANTS

No.	PLACE	POSITION		DIFFERENCES				RANGES		Mean Tide Level
		Latitude	Longitude	Time		Height		Mean	Spring	
				High Water	Low Water	High Water	Low Water			
		North	West	h m	h m	ft	ft	ft	ft	ft

VIRGINIA
Chesapeake Bay, western shore
Time meridian, 75° W

on Ches. Bay Bridge Tunnel,

No.	PLACE	Latitude	Longitude	High Water	Low Water	High Water	Low Water	Mean	Spring	Mean Tide Level
2213	Sunnybank, Little Wicomico River	37° 53.2'	76° 16.0'	+6 41	+6 45	*0.30	*0.30	0.80	0.96	0.40
2215	Great Wicomico River Light	37° 48.3'	76° 16.1'	+3 58	+4 11	*0.41	*0.41	1.10	1.32	0.50
2217	Fleeton Point	37° 48.8'	76° 16.5'	+3 58	+4 14	*0.41	*0.41	1.10	1.32	0.59
2219	Glebe Point, Great Wicomico River	37° 50.8'	76° 22.1'	+4 15	+4 37	*0.49	*0.83	1.20	1.44	0.70
2221	Windmill Point Light	37° 35.8'	76° 14.2'	+2 48	+3 12	*0.41	*0.41	1.10	1.32	0.50

on Hampton Roads,

No.	PLACE	Latitude	Longitude	High Water	Low Water	High Water	Low Water	Mean	Spring	Mean Tide Level
	Rappahannock River									
2223	Windmill Point	37° 36.9'	76° 17.4'	+1 55	+2 14	*0.49	*0.83	1.16	1.40	0.68
2225	Mill Creek (Grey Point)	37° 35.0'	76° 25.1'	+2 28	+2 42	*0.55	*0.83	1.30	1.57	0.69
2227	Millenbeck, Corrotoman River	37° 40.1'	76° 29.2'	+2 37	+3 05	*0.55	*0.83	1.30	1.57	0.70
2229	Urbanna	37° 39.0'	76° 34.5'	+2 50	+3 09	*0.59	*0.83	1.40	1.69	0.79
2231	Bayport	37° 45.3'	76° 40.4'	+3 22	+3 51	*0.67	*0.83	1.60	1.94	0.90
2233	Wares Wharf	37° 52.4'	76° 47.0'	+4 04	+4 34	*0.75	*0.33	1.88	2.27	0.98
2235	Tappahannock	37° 55.8'	76° 51.4'	+4 40	+5 18	*0.71	*0.83	1.74	2.11	0.95

on Washington,

No.	PLACE	Latitude	Longitude	High Water	Low Water	High Water	Low Water	Mean	Spring	Mean Tide Level
2237	Saunders Wharf	38° 05.4'	77° 02.0'	-3 53	-4 41	*0.54	*0.66	1.50	1.65	0.85
2239	Port Royal	38° 10.4'	77° 11.4'	-2 19	-3 02	*0.68	*0.67	1.90	2.09	1.10
2241	Park Turn	38° 12.8'	77° 14.6'	-1 35	-2 30	*0.73	*0.20	2.13	2.34	1.09
2243	Hopyard Landing	38° 14.6'	77° 13.6'	-1 07	-1 57	*0.75	*0.67	2.10	2.31	1.19
2245	Massaponax Sand & Gravel	38° 15.3'	77° 24.6'	-0 39	-0 41	*0.88	*1.33	2.50	2.75	1.39

on Hampton Roads,

No.	PLACE	Latitude	Longitude	High Water	Low Water	High Water	Low Water	Mean	Spring	Mean Tide Level
	Piankatank River									
2247	Jackson Creek, Deltaville	37° 32.9'	76° 19.9'	+1 36	+2 04	*0.51	*0.83	1.20	1.45	0.70
2249	Dixie	37° 30.5'	76° 25.0'	+1 34	+2 14	*0.55	*0.83	1.30	1.57	0.72
2251	Wolf Trap Light	37° 23.4'	76° 11.4'	-0 02	+0 32	*0.67	*0.83	1.60	1.94	0.90
	Mobjack Bay									
2253	Mobjack, East River	37° 22.4'	76° 20.8'	-0 17	+0 02	*0.98	*0.83	2.40	2.90	1.30
2255	Belleville	37° 24.7'	76° 26.3'	-0 06	+0 00	*1.02	*0.83	2.48	3.00	1.36
2257	Browns Bay	37° 18.1'	76° 24.2'	-0 11	-0 03	*0.98	*1.58	2.32	2.81	1.35

York River

No.	PLACE	Latitude	Longitude	High Water	Low Water	High Water	Low Water	Mean	Spring	Mean Tide Level
2259	Tue Marshes Light	37° 14.1'	76° 23.1'	+0 03	+0 03	*0.90	*0.83	2.17	2.63	1.19
2261	Yorktown, Goodwin Neck	37° 13.4'	76° 26.4'	+0 18	+0 15	*0.90	*0.83	2.20	2.66	1.23
2263	Yorktown, USCG Training Center	37° 13.6'	76° 28.7'	+0 10	+0 15	*0.95	*1.08	2.29	2.77	1.28
2265	Gloucester Point	37° 14.8'	76° 30.0'	+0 10	+0 11	*0.98	*1.00	2.38	2.93	1.30
2267	Cheatham Annex	37° 17.5'	76° 35.2'	+0 48	+0 40	*1.02	*0.83	2.50	3.03	1.34
2269	Roane Point	37° 26.9'	76° 42.4'	+1 47	+1 50	*1.14	*0.83	2.81	3.40	1.54
2271	West Point	37° 32.1'	76° 47.6'	+2 12	+2 38	*1.14	*0.83	2.80	3.39	1.50
2273	Wakema (Fraziers Ferry), Mattaponi River	37° 39.0'	76° 54.0'	+3 34	+3 57	*1.41	*1.67	3.42	4.14	1.90
	Pamunkey River									
2275	Lester Manor	37° 35.0'	76° 59.4'	+4 45	+5 00	*1.05	*0.83	2.80	3.39	1.50
2277	Northbury	37° 37.5'	77° 07.3'	+6 03	+6 18	*1.37	*1.67	3.30	4.01	1.80

Chesapeake Bay, western shore

No.	PLACE	Latitude	Longitude	High Water	Low Water	High Water	Low Water	Mean	Spring	Mean Tide Level
2279	Messick Point, Back River	37° 06.5'	76° 19.1'	-0 07	+0 02	*0.97	*0.97	2.30	2.78	1.33
	Hampton Roads									
2281	Old Point Comfort	37° 00.2'	76° 18.9'	+0 01	+0 09	*1.02	*0.83	2.52	3.05	1.38
2283	HAMPTON ROADS (Sewells Point)	36° 56.8'	76° 19.8'		*Daily predictions*			2.43	2.95	1.34
	Elizabeth River									
2285	Craney Island Light	36° 53.5'	76° 20.3'	+0 18	+0 04	*1.06	*0.83	2.60	3.15	1.40
2287	Lafayette River	36° 53.0'	76° 16.5'	+0 06	+0 10	*1.10	*1.17	2.67	3.14	1.47
2289	Western Branch, Rt 337 bridge	36° 49.3'	76° 23.9'	+0 11	+0 13	*1.14	*1.17	2.77	3.26	1.53
2291	Norfolk	36° 51.1'	76° 17.9'	+0 23	+0 20	*1.14	*0.83	2.82	3.41	1.50
2293	Portsmouth, Naval Shipyard	36° 49.3'	76° 17.6'	+0 08	+0 10	*1.13	*1.17	2.76	3.26	1.52
2295	Money Point	36° 46.7'	76° 18.1'	+0 15	+0 12	*1.18	*1.17	2.86	3.46	1.52
2297	Deep Creek Entrance	36° 45.3'	76° 17.6'	+0 22	+0 18	*1.21	*1.25	2.92	3.53	1.6
	Nansemond River									
2299	Pig Point	36° 55.0'	76° 26.1'	+0 42	+0 40	*1.05	*0.83	2.80	3.39	1.56
2301	Town Point	36° 53.0'	76° 30.5'	+0 37	+0 44	*1.22	*0.83	3.00	3.63	1.6
2303	Hollidays Point (Kings Highway bridge)	36° 50.3'	76° 33.0'	+0 56	+1 03	*1.25	*1.67	3.00	3.63	1.6

James River

No.	PLACE	Latitude	Longitude	High Water	Low Water	High Water	Low Water	Mean	Spring	Mean Tide Level
2305	Newport News	36° 58.4'	76° 26.0'	+0 29	+0 28	*1.08	*0.83	2.60	3.15	1.4
2307	Huntington Park	37° 00.8'	76° 27.5'	+0 38	+0 39	*1.07	*0.92	2.62	3.17	1.4
2309	Menchville	37° 04.9'	76° 31.5'	+1 03	+1 19	*1.06	*0.83	2.60	3.15	1.4
2311	Smithfield, Pagan River	36° 59.1'	76° 37.8'	+1 34	+1 38	*1.14	*0.83	2.78	3.36	1.5
2313	Burwell Bay	37° 03.4'	76° 40.1'	+1 17	+1 39	*1.00	*1.17	2.42	2.93	1.3
2315	Fort Eustis	37° 08.2'	76° 37.3'	+1 44	+1 51	*0.92	*1.25	2.19	2.52	1.2
2317	Kingsmill	37° 13.2'	76° 39.8'	+2 05	+2 26	*0.94	*1.33	2.26	2.73	1.2
2319	Scotland	37° 11.1'	76° 47.0'	+2 44	+3 13	*0.78	*1.08	1.84	2.22	1.0
2321	Jamestown Wharf	37° 13.2'	76° 47.4'	+2 59	+3 15	*0.78	*1.42	1.81	2.09	1.0
	Chickahominy River									
2323	Ferry Point (bridge)	37° 15.8'	76° 52.7'	+4 01	+4 26	*0.78	*0.83	1.90	2.30	1.0
2325	Wright Island Landing	37° 20.7'	76° 52.5'	+4 44	+5 03	*0.90	*0.83	2.20	2.66	1.2
2327	Lanexa	37° 24.2'	76° 54.7'	+5 00	+4 51	*1.05	*1.08	2.56	2.77	1.4
2329	Claremont	37° 13.9'	76° 56.9'	+3 51	+4 25	*0.76	*1.17	1.79	2.11	1.0
2331	Tettington	37° 14.4'	76° 56.6'	+3 52	+4 17	*0.79	*1.13	1.87	2.26	1.0

TABLE 2. – TIDAL DIFFERENCES AND OTHER CONSTANTS

No.	PLACE	POSITION		DIFFERENCES				RANGES		Mean Tide Level
		Latitude	Longitude	Time		Height		Mean	Spring	
				High Water	Low Water	High Water	Low Water			
		North	West	h m	h m	ft	ft	ft	ft	ft
	VIRGINIA James River-cont. Time meridian, 75° W			**on Hampton Roads,**						
2333	Sturgeon Point	37° 18.4'	77° 00.4'	+4 37	+5 09	*0.86	*0.83	2.10	2.54	1.10
2335	Willcox Wharf, Charles City	37° 19.0'	77° 05.9'	+5 30	+5 33	*0.89	*1.33	2.12	2.52	1.22
2337	Jordan Point	37° 18.8'	77° 13.4'	+6 16	+6 39	*1.02	*0.83	2.50	3.02	1.40
				on Washington,						
2339	City Point, Hopewell	37° 18.8'	77° 16.2'	-4 31	-5 36	*0.87	*0.80	2.45	2.58	1.35
2341	Puddledock, Appomattox River	37° 16.0'	77° 22.3'	-3 49	-4 32	*1.00	*1.07	2.80	3.08	1.55
2343	Haxall	37° 22.4'	77° 14.6'	-4 10	-4 53	*0.99	*1.33	2.70	2.97	1.60
2345	Chester	37° 23.0'	77° 22.7'	-3 39	-3 59	*1.02	*0.67	2.90	3.19	1.60
2347	Meadowville	37° 22.7'	77° 19.4'	-3 46	-4 17	*1.05	*1.33	2.90	3.19	1.60
2349	Richmond Deepwater Terminal	37° 27.5'	77° 25.2'	-3 39	-3 51	*1.08	*0.93	3.05	3.25	1.66
2351	Richmond (river locks)	37° 31.5'	77° 25.2'	-3 16	-3 26	*1.16	*1.33	3.20	3.52	1.80
	Chesapeake Bay, southern shore			**on Ches. Bay Bridge Tunnel,**						
2353	Little Creek, NAB	36° 54.7'	76° 10.5'	+0 08	+0 09	*1.01	*1.17	2.57	3.08	1.42
2355	CHESAPEAKE BAY BRIDGE TUNNEL	36° 58.0'	76° 06.8'	*Daily predictions*				2.55	3.07	1.40
2357	Lynnhaven Inlet, Virginia Pilots Dock	36° 54.4'	76° 05.4'	+0 40	+0 38	*0.88	*1.08	2.22	2.66	1.24
	Lynnhaven Bay									
2359	Bayville	36° 53.6'	76° 06.3'	+1 52	+2 48	*0.67	*0.83	1.70	2.04	1.00
2361	Buchanan Creek entrance	36° 51.7'	76° 06.9'	+2 02	+2 56	*0.75	*0.83	1.90	2.28	1.00
2363	Brown Cove	36° 52.5'	76° 03.7'	+2 05	+2 43	*0.65	*0.83	1.64	1.96	0.92
2365	Broad Bay Canal	36° 54.1'	76° 03.7'	+2 05	+2 00	*0.56	*0.92	1.38	1.66	0.80
2367	Long Creek	36° 54.2'	76° 04.2'	+1 15	+1 15	*0.68	*1.08	1.68	2.02	0.97
	Outer Coast			**on Duck Pier,**						
2369	Cape Henry	36° 55.8'	76° 00.4'	+0 31	+0 36	*0.96	*0.93	3.12	3.71	1.68
2371	Virginia Beach	36° 50.6'	75° 58.3'	+0 15	+0 16	*1.07	*1.07	3.34	3.97	1.85
2373	Rudee Inlet entrance	36° 49.9'	75° 58.1'	+0 02	+0 02	*1.01	*0.86	3.28	3.90	1.77
2375	Rudee Inlet, interior channel	36° 49.9'	75° 58.4'	+0 17	+0 17	*1.02	*0.94	3.29	3.92	1.78
2377	Rudee Heights, Lake Wesley	36° 49.5'	75° 58.5'	+0 18	+0 16	*1.03	*1.00	3.32	3.95	1.81
2379	Lake Rudee, south end	36° 49.5'	75° 58.9'	+0 20	+0 19	*1.05	*1.07	3.39	4.03	1.85
2381	Sandbridge	36° 41.5'	75° 55.2'	+0 07	+0 07	*1.04	*1.04	3.35	3.99	1.85
	NORTH CAROLINA									
2383	DUCK PIER	36° 11.0'	75° 44.8'	*Daily predictions*				3.22	3.96	1.75
2385	Albemarle and Pamlico Sounds <9>	- - -	- - -	- - -	- - -		- - -		- -	- -
2387	Kitty Hawk (ocean)	36° 06.1'	75° 42.6'	-0 01	+0 02	*1.01	*1.43	3.19	3.80	1.80
2389	Jennettes Pier, Nags Head (ocean)	35° 54.6'	75° 35.5'	-0 05	+0 01	*1.04	*1.43	3.26	3.88	1.80
				on Oregon Inlet,						
2391	Roanoke Sound Channel	35° 48'	75° 35'	+1 37	+1 17	*0.47	*0.14	0.5	0.6	0.3
2393	OREGON INLET MARINA	35° 47.7'	75° 32.9'	*Daily predictions*				0.89	1.08	0.58
2395	Oregon Inlet	35° 46'	75° 31'	-0 03	-0 27	*1.98	*0.71	2.0	2.4	1.1
2397	Oregon Inlet (USCG Station)	35° 46.1'	75° 31.6'	-0 22	-0 51	*2.00	*0.69	1.97	2.30	1.07
2399	Oregon Inlet Bridge	35° 46.4'	75° 32.3'	-0 17	-0 55	*1.89	*0.64	1.9	2.3	1.1
2401	Oregon Inlet Channel	35° 46.5'	75° 33.5'	-0 09	-0 34	*1.23	*0.43	1.2	1.4	0.7
2403	Old House Channel	35° 46.5'	75° 34.9'	+0 34	+0 28	*0.66	*0.21	0.7	0.8	0.4
2405	Davis Slough	35° 44.9'	75° 33.2'	+0 09	-0 01	*0.85	*0.29	0.9	1.1	0.5
2407	Rodanthe, Pamlico Sound	35° 35.7'	75° 28.3'	+2 03	+1 36	*0.79	*0.69	0.72	0.84	0.45
2409	Roanoke Marshes Light, Croatan Sound	35° 48.7'	75° 42.0'	+2 10	+2 04	*0.50	*0.85	0.40	0.59	0.31
2411	Oyster Creek, Croatan Sound	35° 50.7'	75° 39.3'	+2 12	+2 06	*0.51	*0.77	0.41	0.60	0.31
2413	Manns Harbor, Croatan Sound	35° 54.2'	75° 46.2'	+2 31	+2 26	*0.37	*0.54	0.37	0.40	0.23
				on Cape Hatteras,						
2415	Cape Hatteras	35° 14'	75° 31'	+0 01	+0 01	*1.00	*1.08	3.6	4.3	2.0
2417	CAPE HATTERAS FISHING PIER	35° 13.4'	75° 38.1'	*Daily predictions*				2.99	3.60	1.61
2419	Peters Ditch, Avon, Pamlco Sound	35° 21.0'	75° 30.7'	+3 20	+3 40	*0.17	*0.17	0.43	0.61	0.30
2421	Hatteras, Pamlico Sound	35° 12.3'	75° 42.2'	+1 16	+1 25	*0.17	*1.08	0.41	0.49	0.33
2423	Hatteras Inlet	35° 12'	75° 44'	+0 08	+0 13	*0.66	*0.83	2.0	2.4	1.1
2425	Ocracoke Inlet	35° 04'	76° 01'	+0 09	+0 11	*0.63	*0.83	1.9	2.3	1.0
2427	Ocracoke, Ocracoke Island	35° 06.9'	75° 59.3'	+0 15	+0 47	*0.34	*0.50	0.99	1.19	0.56
2429	Cape Lookout Bight	34° 36.8'	76° 32.3'	-0 17	-0 12	*1.35	*1.33	4.05	4.86	2.19
2431	Cape Lookout (ocean)	34° 36.5'	76° 31.7'	-0 22	-0 22	*1.15	*1.25	3.44	4.13	1.87
2433	Shell Point, Harkers Island	34° 41'	76° 32'	+1 52	+2 34	*0.54	*0.83	1.6	1.8	0.9
2435	Harkers Island Bridge	34° 43'	76° 35'	+2 08	+2 31	*0.52	*0.67	1.6	1.7	0.9
2437	Davis, Core Sound	34° 47.8'	76° 27.3'	+3 13	+3 39	*0.38	*0.75	1.08	1.23	0.64
2439	Channel Marker Lt. 59	34° 42'	76° 37'	+1 25	+1 27	*0.66	*0.83	2.0	2.3	1.1
2441	Lenoxville Point	34° 42.5'	76° 37.2'	+1 18	+1 11	*0.80	*1.00	2.37	2.84	1.31
2443	North River Bridge	34° 47'	76° 37'	+2 25	+3 08	*0.59	*0.67	1.8	2.0	1.0
2445	Beaufort Inlet Channel Range	34° 42'	76° 40'	+0 07	+0 11	*1.07	*1.67	3.2	3.8	1.6
2447	Beaufort, Taylor Creek	34° 42.7'	76° 38.7'	+0 52	+0 48	*0.95	*1.17	2.82	3.38	1.55
2449	Beaufort, Duke Marine Lab	34° 43.2'	76° 40.2'	+0 39	+0 36	*1.05	*1.17	3.11	3.58	1.70
2451	Gallant Channel	34° 44'	76° 40'	+0 49	+0 44	*1.01	*1.25	3.0	3.5	1.7
2453	Newport River (Yacht Club)	34° 46.1'	76° 40.3'	+1 03	+1 13	*1.03	*1.00	3.08	3.70	1.66
2455	Core Creek Bridge	34° 50'	76° 42'	+1 26	+1 46	*0.68	*0.83	2.1	2.3	1.1
2457	Fort Macon, USCG Station	34° 42'	76° 41'	+0 17	+0 18	*1.03	*1.25	3.1	3.7	1.7
2459	Morehead City	34° 43'	76° 42'	+0 26	+0 27	*1.04	*1.25	3.1	3.7	1.7
2461	Morehead City Harbor	34° 43.2'	76° 43.7'	+0 35	+0 37	*1.04	*1.17	3.08	3.70	1.68

TABLE 2. – TIDAL DIFFERENCES AND OTHER CONSTANTS

No.	PLACE	POSITION Latitude	POSITION Longitude	DIFFERENCES Time High Water	DIFFERENCES Time Low Water	DIFFERENCES Height High Water	DIFFERENCES Height Low Water	RANGES Mean	RANGES Spring	Mean Tide Level
		North	West	h m	h m	ft	ft	ft	ft	ft
	NORTH CAROLINA Time meridian, 75° W			on Cape Hatteras,						
2463	Atlantic Beach	34° 41.6'	76° 42.7'	-0 02	+0 01	*1.23	*1.25	3.65	4.38	1.98
2465	Triple S Marina, Bogue Sd.	34° 41.7'	76° 42.7'	+0 35	+0 28	*0.93	*1.17	2.8	3.3	1.5
2467	Atlantic Beach Bridge	34° 43'	76° 44'	+0 48	+1 02	*0.79	*0.83	2.4	2.8	1.2
2469	N.C. State Fisheries	34° 43'	76° 45'	+1 05	+1 32	*0.66	*0.83	2.0	2.3	1.1
2471	Coral Bay, Atlantic Beach	34° 42'	76° 46'	+1 47	+2 14	*0.53	*0.83	1.6	1.8	0.9
2473	Spooner Creek	34° 43.5'	76° 48.2'	+2 06	+2 20	*0.56	*1.08	1.27	1.85	0.94
2475	Bogue Inlet	34° 39'	77° 06'	+0 13	+0 15	*0.73	*0.83	2.2	2.6	1.2
2477	New River Inlet	34° 32'	77° 20'	+0 16	+0 17	*0.98	*0.83	3.0	3.6	1.6
2479	Ocean City Beach (fishing pier)	34° 27.1'	77° 29.7'	+0 03	-0 01	*1.40	*1.33	4.20	5.04	2.25
2481	Wrightsville Beach	34° 12.8'	77° 47.2'	+0 18	+0 23	*1.27	*1.25	3.80	4.56	2.05
2483	Wilmington Beach	34° 01.9'	77° 53.6'	+0 18	+0 10	*1.40	*1.25	4.21	5.05	2.26
2485	Cape Fear	33° 51'	77° 58'	+0 04	+0 07	*1.47	*1.33	4.5	5.1	2.3
	Cape Fear River			on Wilmington,						
2487	Bald Head	33° 52.8'	78° 00.1'	-2 06	-2 43	*1.05	*1.13	4.49	4.89	2.41
2489	Fort Caswell	33° 54'	78° 01'	-2 02	-2 45	*1.03	*1.25	4.2	4.8	2.3
2491	Southport	33° 54.9'	78° 01.1'	-1 49	-2 22	*0.99	*1.00	4.24	4.62	2.28
2493	Zekes Island	33° 57.0'	77° 57.1'	-1 12	-1 43	*0.96	*1.07	4.09	4.46	2.20
2495	Federal Point	33° 57.7'	77° 56.4'	-1 17	-1 52	*0.94	*0.93	4.04	4.40	2.16
2497	Sunny Point Army Base, Wharf no.1	33° 59.4'	77° 57.4'	-1 03	-1 45	*0.95	*0.93	4.06	4.43	2.17
2499	Reaves Point	34° 00.2'	77° 57.3'	-0 54	-1 18	*0.96	*1.07	4.09	4.46	2.21
2501	Sunny Point Army Base, Wharf no.3	34° 01.4'	77° 56.8'	-0 57	-1 15	*0.97	*1.07	4.15	4.52	2.24
2503	Orton Point	34° 03.4'	77° 56.4'	-0 36	-0 58	*0.98	*1.00	4.17	4.55	2.24
2505	WILMINGTON	34° 13.6'	77° 57.2'	Daily predictions				4.28	4.70	2.29
2507	Castle Hayne, Northeast River	34° 21'	77° 56'	+2 44	+2 54	*0.42	*0.42	1.7	1.9	0.9
2509	Bannermans Branch, Northeast River	34° 35'	77° 46'	+5 58	+6 08	*0.32	*0.31	1.3	1.4	0.6
				on Myrtle Beach,						
2511	Oak Island	33° 54.1'	78° 04.9'	-0 05	-0 05	*0.94	*0.84	4.72	5.57	2.53
2513	Lockwoods Folly Inlet	33° 55'	78° 14'	+0 04	+0 15	*0.84	*1.00	4.2	4.8	2.3
2515	Shallotte Inlet (Bowen Point)	33° 55'	78° 22'	+0 43	+0 55	*0.91	*1.00	4.6	5.4	2.5
2517	Sunset Beach Pier	33° 51.9'	78° 30.4'	+0 02	-0 03	*0.97	*1.11	4.82	5.78	2.62
2519	Sunset Beach Bridge	33° 52.9'	78° 30.6'	+0 34	+0 56	*0.94	*0.84	4.72	5.57	2.52
	SOUTH CAROLINA									
2521	Dunn Sound, Little River Inlet	33° 51.5'	78° 34.2'	+0 15	+0 41	*0.91	*0.80	4.64	5.52	2.48
2523	Dunn Sound, north end	33° 51.6'	78° 34.8'	+0 25	+0 40	*0.93	*0.84	4.67	5.51	2.50
2525	Dunn Sound, west end	33° 51.1'	78° 35.3'	+0 29	+0 36	*0.96	*1.00	4.85	5.58	2.63
2527	Little River Neck, north end	33° 52.2'	78° 34.4'	+0 32	+0 46	*0.92	*0.84	4.63	5.56	2.47
2529	Cherry Grove (inside)	33° 50.1'	78° 38.0'	+0 40	+0 44	*0.92	*0.74	4.67	5.51	2.47
2531	Hog Inlet Pier	33° 50.2'	78° 36.4'	-0 06	-0 07	*0.99	*0.90	5.0	5.7	2.7
2533	MYRTLE BEACH, SPRINGMAID PIER	33° 39.3'	78° 55.1'	Daily predictions				5.02	6.00	2.70
2535	Garden City Pier (ocean)	33° 34.5'	78° 59.8'	+0 00	+0 00	*1.00	*1.00	5.07	5.88	2.74
	Murrells Inlet									
2537	Garden City Bridge, Main Creek	33° 34.7'	79° 00.2'	+1 19	+2 09	*0.84	*0.68	4.26	5.03	2.25
2539	Divine's Dock	33° 32.5'	79° 01.7'	+0 40	+1 18	*0.84	*0.84	4.22	5.06	2.27
2541	Smith's Dock	33° 32.7'	79° 02.7'	+1 01	+1 36	*0.86	*0.95	4.29	5.06	2.32
2543	Captain Alex's Marina, Parsonage Creek	33° 33.1'	79° 02.2'	+0 57	+1 28	*0.85	*0.68	4.30	5.16	2.28
2545	Oaks Creek, 0.5 mi. above entrance	33° 31.8'	79° 02.6'	+0 38	+1 03	*0.85	*0.95	4.27	5.12	2.32
2547	Allston Creek	33° 31.9'	79° 03.2'	+0 52	+1 32	*0.84	*0.95	4.24	4.92	2.31
2549	Oaks Creek, upper end	33° 30.7'	79° 04.1'	+1 10	+1 43	*0.87	*1.05	4.35	5.22	2.37
2551	Litchfield Beach bridge	33° 28.3'	79° 06.1'	+1 10	+3 02	*0.58	*0.75	2.89	3.35	1.59
2553	Midway Inlet North, Pawleys Island	33° 26.9'	79° 06.7'	+0 16	+0 42	*0.87	*1.00	4.40	5.10	2.40
2555	Bennet's Dock, Pawleys Island Creek	33° 26.1'	79° 07.6'	+0 55	+1 35	*0.78	*1.21	3.84	4.61	2.15
2557	Pawleys Island Pier (ocean)	33° 25.9'	79° 07.0'	+0 06	+0 06	*0.98	*0.95	4.92	5.81	2.65
2559	Ward's Dock, Pawleys Inlet	33° 24.7'	79° 08.1'	+0 35	+2 07	*0.67	*0.95	3.32	3.98	1.84
2561	Oyster Landing, Crab Haul Creek, North Inlet	33° 21.1'	79° 11.2'	+1 08	+0 52	*0.92	*1.00	4.58	5.50	2.48
2563	Clambank Creek, Goat Island, North Inlet	33° 20.0'	79° 11.6'	+1 01	+0 36	*0.94	*1.00	4.69	5.53	2.54
	Intracoastal Waterway Little River Inlet to Winyah Bay			on Charleston,						
2565	Little River (town)	33° 52.2'	78° 36.5'	+0 13	+0 39	*0.84	*0.79	4.41	5.07	2.35
2567	Nixon Crossroads	33° 51.3'	78° 38.9'	+0 27	+0 51	*0.78	*0.68	4.10	4.55	2.18
2569	Myrtle Beach Airport	33° 49.2'	78° 43.1'	+1 09	+1 47	*0.56	*0.84	2.88	3.34	1.60
2571	North Myrtle Beach	33° 46.0'	78° 48.9'	+2 15	+3 12	*0.36	*0.84	1.78	2.10	1.25
2573	Myrtle Beach, Combination Bridge	33° 42.8'	78° 55.3'	+2 56	+4 18	*0.35	*0.89	1.71	2.02	1.03
2575	Socastee Bridge	33° 41.2'	79° 00.3'	+3 27	+4 41	*0.41	*0.74	2.08	2.45	1.18
	Winyah Bay									
2577	Winyah Bay Entrance (South Jetty)	33° 11'	79° 09'	-0 21	-0 24	*0.87	*0.89	4.6	5.4	2.5
2579	Georgetown Lighthouse	33° 13.4'	79° 11.1'	+0 26	+0 25	*0.75	*1.05	3.89	4.51	2.15
2581	South Island Plantation (C.G. Station)	33° 14.1'	79° 12.2'	+0 35	+0 36	*0.74	*0.84	3.81	4.38	2.07
2583	South Island Ferry, Intracoastal Waterway	33° 15.1'	79° 16.1'	+0 54	+1 25	*0.71	*0.74	3.69	4.24	1.99
2585	Frazier Point	33° 19'	79° 17'	+1 26	+2 07	*0.66	*0.68	3.5	4.1	1.8
	Sampit River									
2587	Georgetown	33° 21.7'	79° 16.8'	+1 25	+2 09	*0.71	*0.79	3.72	4.32	2.07
2589	Jacobs Wharf	33° 21.8'	79° 21.3'	+2 15	+2 22	*0.73	*0.74	3.84	4.45	2.06
2591	Cumberland	33° 22.2'	79° 26.0'	+2 42	+2 29	*0.77	*0.74	4.02	4.74	2.15

TABLE 2. – TIDAL DIFFERENCES AND OTHER CONSTANTS

No.	PLACE	POSITION		DIFFERENCES				RANGES		Mean Tide Level
				Time		Height				
		Latitude	Longitude	High Water	Low Water	High Water	Low Water	Mean	Spring	
		North	West	h m	h m	ft	ft	ft	ft	ft

	SOUTH CAROLINA Winyah Bay-cont. Time meridian, 75° W			on Charleston,						
	Great Pee Dee River									
2593	Windsor Plantation, Black River	33° 24.9'	79° 15.0'	+2 00	+2 45	*0.66	*0.74	3.45	3.97	1.86
2595	Black River (south of Dunbar)	33° 30.7'	79° 20.5'	+3 29	+4 09	*0.47	*0.89	2.42	2.81	1.38
2597	Winea Plantation, Black River	33° 32.1'	79° 23.3'	+4 23	+4 39	*0.47	*0.84	2.37	2.73	1.34
2599	Mt. Pleasant Plantation, Black River	33° 29.7'	79° 27.7'	+5 38	+6 04	*0.37	*1.05	1.82	2.11	1.11
2601	Rhems, Black Mingo Creek, Black River	33° 36.2'	79° 25.6'	+6 00	+6 13	*0.36	*1.05	1.75	2.03	1.08
2603	Weymouth Plantation	33° 27.3'	79° 12.3'	+2 16	+3 02	*0.68	*0.89	3.56	4.13	1.95
2605	Carr Creek, 1 mile above entrance	33° 27.9'	79° 11.2'	+2 13	+3 00	*0.69	*0.84	3.62	4.20	1.97
2607	South of Sam Worth Game Management Area	33° 28.1'	79° 11.3'	+2 21	+3 06	*0.69	*0.68	3.66	4.25	1.96
2609	Arundel Plantation	33° 29.0'	79° 10.7'	+2 38	+3 39	*0.53	*0.79	2.75	3.19	1.53
2611	Holly Grove Plantation	33° 33.1'	79° 10.6'	+3 20	+4 12	*0.50	*0.68	2.59	3.00	1.43
2613	Lower Topsaw Landing	33° 36.5'	79° 09.1'	+4 48	+5 20	*0.20	*0.53	0.96	1.13	0.58
2615	Yauhannah Bridge	33° 39.6'	79° 09.3'	+4 33	+5 24	*0.33	*0.68	1.66	1.91	0.96
	Waccamaw River									
2617	Entrance	33° 22.0'	79° 15.3'	+1 19	+2 11	*0.69	*0.58	3.60	4.14	1.91
2619	Hagley Landing	33° 26.1'	79° 10.9'	+1 58	+2 53	*0.67	*0.79	3.47	3.99	1.88
2621	Thoroughfare Creek entrance	33° 30.4'	79° 08.8'	+2 32	+3 15	*0.64	*0.89	3.34	3.94	1.84
2623	Wachesaw Landing	33° 33.6'	79° 05.1'	+3 11	+4 00	*0.53	*0.84	2.74	3.18	1.53
2625	Bull Creek entrance	33° 35.8'	79° 05.9'	+3 36	+4 22	*0.48	*0.79	2.46	2.85	1.38
2627	Little Bull Creek entrance, Bull Creek	33° 36.1'	79° 07.1'	+3 59	+4 43	*0.46	*0.84	2.35	2.73	1.33
2629	Bucksport	33° 38.8'	79° 05.7'	+4 23	+4 53	*0.43	*0.89	2.16	2.48	1.25
2631	Enterprise Landing	33° 40'	79° 04'	+5 01	+5 35	*0.38	*0.37	2.0	2.4	1.1
2633	Keysfield	33° 44.7'	79° 03.9'	+6 09	+6 20	*0.28	*0.89	1.37	1.59	0.85
2635	Pitch Landing	33° 48.0'	79° 03.3'	+7 25	+7 30	*0.20	*0.74	0.94	1.09	0.61
2637	Conway, RR. bridge	33° 50.1'	79° 02.5'	+7 19	+7 28	*0.25	*0.74	1.24	1.44	0.76
2639	Grahamville	33° 49.8'	78° 57.2'	+8 17	+8 32	*0.20	*0.58	0.97	1.13	0.60
2641	North Santee River Inlet	33° 08'	79° 15'	-0 09	+0 04	*0.85	*0.84	4.5	5.3	2.3
2643	Cedar Island, North Santee Bay	33° 08.4'	79° 14.7'	-0 03	+0 17	*0.80	*0.95	4.19	4.86	2.28
2645	Minim Creek ent., ICWW, North Santee Bay	33° 11.7'	79° 16.5'	+0 16	+1 00	*0.77	*0.95	3.98	4.70	2.18
2647	North Santee Bridge	33° 12.6'	79° 23.1'	+1 09	+1 54	*0.72	*0.74	3.8	4.2	2.0
2649	Cedar Island Point, South Santee River	33° 07.2'	79° 16.2'	-0 16	+0 08	*0.78	*0.79	4.1	4.8	2.1
2651	Brown Island, South Santee River	33° 09'	79° 20'	+0 27	+1 31	*0.78	*0.79	4.1	4.8	2.1
2653	U.S. Highway 17 bridge, South Santee River	33° 11.1'	79° 24.4'	+0 43	+1 43	*0.78	*0.95	4.07	4.68	2.20
2655	Pleasant Hill Landing, Santee River	33° 14.7'	79° 31.3'	+2 28	+3 47	*0.45	*0.74	2.30	2.71	1.29
2657	Jamestown Bridge, Santee River	33° 18.3'	79° 40.7'	+4 15	+6 30	*0.22	*0.37	1.12	1.29	0.63
2659	Cape Romain	33° 01'	79° 21'	-0 22	-0 17	*0.89	*0.89	4.7	5.5	2.5
2661	Cape Romain, 46 miles east of	33° 06'	78° 26'	-1 05	-1 13	*0.78	*0.79	4.1	4.8	2.1
2663	Casino Creek, ICWW	33° 06.5'	79° 23.6'	+0 40	+0 53	*0.87	*0.79	4.55	5.37	2.42
	Bulls Bay									
2665	Five Fathom Creek entrance	33° 00'	79° 30'	-0 06	-0 07	*0.93	*0.95	4.9	5.8	2.6
2667	McClellanville, Jeremy Creek	33° 04.7'	79° 27.6'	+0 31	+0 24	*0.93	*0.89	4.86	5.59	2.60
2669	Harbor River entrance	33° 02.0'	79° 32.1'	+0 03	+0 36	*0.93	*0.95	4.9	5.8	2.6
2671	Buck Hall, Awendaw Creek	33° 02.4'	79° 33.6'	+0 22	+0 37	*0.95	*1.00	4.97	5.77	2.67
2673	Jack Creek entrance	32° 56'	79° 35'	-0 14	-0 15	*0.95	*0.95	5.0	5.9	2.7
2675	Wharf Creek entrance	32° 55'	79° 37'	+0 12	-0 08	*0.97	*0.95	5.1	6.0	2.7
2677	Moores Landing, ICWW, Sewee Bay	32° 56.2'	79° 39.3'	+0 11	+0 08	*0.96	*1.00	5.04	5.85	2.71
2679	Price Creek, North Capers Island	32° 52.9'	79° 39.5'	-0 01	-0 21	*0.92	*0.89	4.80	5.52	2.57
2681	Old Capers Landing, Santee Pass, Capers Island	32° 52.2'	79° 41.2'	+0 21	-0 09	*0.94	*0.84	4.93	5.67	2.62
2683	North Dewees Island, Capers Inlet	32° 51.0'	79° 42.2'	-0 02	-0 11	*0.91	*0.95	4.76	5.62	2.56
2685	Capers Creek, South Capers Island	32° 51.4'	79° 42.4'	+0 04	-0 15	*0.94	*0.95	4.89	5.62	2.63
2687	South Dewees Island, Dewees Inlet	32° 50.0'	79° 43.6'	-0 01	-0 17	*0.94	*0.89	4.93	5.67	2.63
2689	Hamlin Sound	32° 49.6'	79° 47.2'	+0 13	-0 13	*0.99	*1.00	5.19	5.97	2.78
2691	Isle of Palms Pier	32° 47.0'	79° 47.1'	-0 25	-0 28	*0.95	*0.89	4.94	5.68	2.65
2693	Hamlin Creek, Isle of Palms	32° 47.2'	79° 47.5'	+0 06	-0 12	*0.97	*1.00	5.04	5.80	2.71
2695	Breach Inlet, Isle of Palms	32° 46.6'	79° 48.7'	-0 05	-0 14	*0.95	*1.05	4.94	5.68	2.66
2697	Sullivans Island (outer coast)	32° 46'	79° 50'	-0 08	-0 12	*0.99	*1.00	5.2	6.1	2.8
2699	Ben Sawyer Bridge, ICWW	32° 46.4'	79° 50.5'	+0 06	-0 12	*0.97	*1.00	5.05	5.81	2.71
	Charleston Harbor									
2701	Fort Sumter	32° 45.2'	79° 52.6'	+0 02	-0 01	*0.97	*0.95	5.09	5.90	2.72
2703	The Cove, Fort Moultrie	32° 45.8'	79° 51.4'	-0 01	-0 10	*0.97	*0.95	5.08	5.84	2.72
2705	Fort Johnson	32° 45.1'	79° 53.9'	-0 05	-0 02	*0.97	*1.00	5.09	5.90	2.74
2707	Shem Creek	32° 47.6'	79° 52.9'	-0 02	-0 03	*0.99	*1.00	5.20	6.03	2.79
2709	CHARLESTON (Customhouse Wharf)	32° 46.9'	79° 55.5'	*Daily predictions*				5.22	6.15	2.80
2711	Shipyard Creek, 0.8 mile above entrance	32° 50'	79° 57'	+0 34	+0 20	*1.01	*1.00	5.3	6.1	2.8
	Cooper River									
2713	Clouter Creek, south entrance	32° 51.6'	79° 56.3'	+0 25	+0 19	*1.02	*1.00	5.35	6.31	2.87
2715	Goose Creek entrance	32° 54.6'	79° 57.1'	+0 42	+0 33	*1.04	*1.00	5.41	6.22	2.90
2717	Yeamans Hall, Goose Creek	32° 55.5'	79° 59.2'	+2 06	+1 31	*1.00	*1.37	5.14	6.07	2.84
2719	Hanahan, Turkey Creek, Goose Creek	32° 55.1'	80° 00.7'	+2 51	+2 13	*0.90	*0.79	4.70	5.55	2.50
2721	Clouter Creek, north entrance	32° 54.4'	79° 56.1'	+0 45	+0 33	*1.04	*1.00	5.43	6.41	2.91
2723	Snow Point, 0.4 mi. North of	32° 56.9'	79° 55.9'	+0 59	+0 45	*1.02	*1.05	5.31	6.10	2.86
2725	General Dynamics Pier	33° 00.5'	79° 55.4'	+1 40	+1 24	*0.84	*1.11	4.35	5.03	2.39
2727	Dupont, Dean Hall	33° 03.5'	79° 56.2'	+2 21	+2 07	*0.68	*1.58	3.43	3.98	2.01
2729	Bonneau Ferry, East Branch	33° 04.3'	79° 53.0'	+3 14	+2 49	*0.63	*1.79	3.11	3.61	1.90
2731	Blessing Plantation, East Branch	33° 03.3'	79° 52.8'	+3 24	+3 20	*0.56	*1.32	2.79	3.29	1.64
2733	Richmond Plantation, East Branch	33° 04.6'	79° 51.3'	+3 43	+3 43	*0.54	*1.37	2.67	3.07	1.59
2735	Quinby Creek bridge, East Branch	33° 05.7'	79° 48.5'	+4 37	+4 12	*0.56	*1.42	2.75	3.25	1.65
2737	Huger Landing, East Branch	33° 07.8'	79° 48.7'	+4 46	- - -	- - -	- - -	- -	- -	- -
2739	Old Rice Mill, West Branch	33° 04.7'	79° 55.5'	+2 56	+2 51	*0.53	*1.63	2.60	3.02	1.61
2741	Back River Reservoir, West Branch	32° 59.7'	79° 56.2'	+5 44	+5 57	*0.17	*0.79	0.78	0.90	0.54
2743	Pimlico, West Branch	33° 05.7'	79° 57.2'	+3 19	+3 53	*0.34	*0.89	1.69	1.94	1.01

TABLE 2. – TIDAL DIFFERENCES AND OTHER CONSTANTS

No.	PLACE	POSITION Latitude	POSITION Longitude	DIFFERENCES Time High Water	DIFFERENCES Time Low Water	DIFFERENCES Height High Water	DIFFERENCES Height Low Water	RANGES Mean	RANGES Spring	Mean Tide Level
		North	West	h m	h m	ft	ft	ft	ft	ft
	SOUTH CAROLINA Charleston Harbor-cont. Time meridian, 75° W			**on Charleston,**						
	Wando River									
2745	Hobcaw Point	32° 49.3'	79° 54.0'	+0 19	+0 13	*1.03	*0.95	5.39	6.20	2.88
2747	Parker Island, Horlbeck Creek	32° 53.1'	79° 50.7'	+0 43	+0 27	*1.09	*1.11	5.70	6.73	3.06
2749	Nowell Creek	32° 54.0'	79° 54.0'	+0 47	+0 23	*1.13	*1.05	5.91	6.80	3.16
2751	Cainhoy	32° 55.6'	79° 49.8'	+0 49	+0 31	*1.15	*1.00	6.02	6.92	3.20
2753	Big Paradise Island	32° 54.9'	79° 44.8'	+1 24	+0 52	*1.24	*1.11	6.48	7.45	3.45
2755	Woodville	32° 55.2'	79° 44.0'	+2 07	+1 22	*1.19	*1.19	6.3	7.3	3.4
	Ashley River									
2757	James Island Creek, 1 mi. above ent.	32° 44.7'	79° 56.9'	+0 17	+0 07	*1.02	*1.05	5.36	6.22	2.88
2759	Wappoo Creek, highway bridge	32° 46.0'	79° 58.4'	+0 22	+0 22	*0.99	*0.99	5.2	6.0	2.8
2761	South Ashley Bridge	32° 47.0'	79° 57.4'	+0 04	+0 07	*1.01	*1.05	5.34	6.19	2.87
2763	Duck Island	32° 49.8'	79° 58.0'	+0 23	+0 17	*1.06	*1.06	5.6	6.5	3.0
2765	Cosgrove Bridge	32° 50.1'	79° 59.2'	+0 25	+0 17	*1.07	*1.05	5.57	6.57	2.99
2767	I-526 bridge	32° 50.2'	80° 01.3'	+0 30	+0 29	*1.08	*1.11	5.68	6.53	3.05
2769	Drayton, Bee's Ferry	32° 50.9'	80° 03.1'	+0 41	+0 39	*1.09	*1.05	5.69	6.54	3.05
2771	Magnolia Gardens	32° 52.6'	80° 04.9'	+1 02	+0 54	*1.10	*1.05	5.79	6.72	3.10
2773	Greggs Landing, Mateeba Gardens	32° 55.7'	80° 09.3'	+2 06	+1 42	*1.15	*1.16	6.06	7.03	3.25
2775	Bacon Bridge	32° 57.5'	80° 12.2'	+2 45	+3 41	*0.39	*0.16	2.10	2.48	1.08
	Outer Coast									
2777	Secessionville, Secessionville Creek	32° 42.4'	79° 56.2'	+0 22	- - -	- - -	- - -	- -	- -	- -
2779	Folly Island (outer coast)	32° 39'	79° 56'	-0 08	-0 14	*0.98	*1.00	5.2	6.1	2.8
2781	Folly River Bridge, Folly Island	32° 39.7'	79° 56.7'	+0 21	-0 03	*1.01	*0.95	5.27	6.06	2.22
2783	Folly Creek, Hwy. 171 bridge	32° 40.5'	79° 57.1'	+0 25	-0 06	*1.04	*1.00	5.41	6.22	2.89
2785	Folly River, north, Folly Island	32° 40.2'	79° 55.0'	+0 24	-0 05	*1.03	*0.95	5.38	6.19	2.87
	Stono River									
2787	Snake Island	32° 38.4'	80° 00.9'	+0 01	-0 12	*1.01	*1.00	5.27	6.06	2.83
2789	Abbapoola Creek entrance	32° 40.6'	80° 00.4'	+0 17	+0 02	*1.01	*0.95	5.36	6.22	2.86
2791	Elliott Cut entrance	32° 45.8'	80° 00.1'	+0 48	+0 52	*0.99	*1.16	5.14	5.91	2.79
2793	Pennys Creek, west entrance	32° 46.1'	80° 04.2'	+1 23	+1 20	*1.03	*1.32	5.32	6.12	2.91
2795	Sandblasters, Pennys Creek	32° 46.2'	80° 03.8'	+1 30	+1 18	*1.02	*1.02	5.26	6.21	2.91
2797	Limehouse Bridge	32° 47.2'	80° 06.3'	+1 43	+1 34	*1.08	*1.08	5.58	6.58	3.04
2799	Church Flats	32° 44.8'	80° 09.9'	+1 51	+1 14	*1.22	*1.16	6.37	7.33	3.41
2801	Kiawah River Bridge	32° 36.2'	80° 07.9'	+0 14	+0 06	*1.07	*0.89	5.60	6.44	2.97
	North Edisto River									
2803	Ocella Creek, 2 mi. above entrance	32° 33.7'	80° 14.3'	+0 32	+0 09	*1.08	*1.08	5.7	6.6	3.0
2805	Rockville, Bohicket Creek	32° 35.9'	80° 11.7'	+0 19	+0 07	*1.09	*1.11	5.76	6.68	3.09
2807	Ho-Non-Wah Boy Scout Camp, Bohicket Creek	32° 37.5'	80° 10.0'	+0 49	+0 30	*1.13	*1.11	5.93	6.82	3.17
2809	Oak Branch, Bohicket Creek	32° 41.0'	80° 05.8'	+1 39	+0 57	*1.26	*1.16	6.66	7.73	3.55
2811	Point of Pines	32° 35.1'	80° 13.7'	+0 15	+0 11	*1.08	*1.05	5.66	6.51	3.04
2813	Leadenwah Creek, 3 mi. above entrance	32° 38.2'	80° 12.1'	+0 54	+0 23	*1.15	*1.11	5.99	6.89	3.21
2815	Steamboat Landing, Steamboat Creek	32° 36.2'	80° 17.2'	+0 45	+0 25	*1.15	*1.11	6.02	6.92	3.22
2817	Windsor Plantation, Russel Creek	32° 35.9'	80° 20.7'	+1 16	+0 35	*1.21	*1.11	6.40	7.42	3.41
2819	Dawho Bridge, Dawho River	32° 38.2'	80° 20.5'	+0 56	+0 47	*1.18	*1.11	6.17	7.10	3.29
2821	Park Island, Tom Point Creek	32° 39.9'	80° 19.0'	+1 19	+0 34	*1.21	*1.21	6.40	7.42	3.43
2823	Toogoodoo Creek, 2 mi. above entrance	32° 40.1'	80° 17.6'	+1 06	+0 38	*1.21	*1.05	6.36	7.31	3.38
2825	Lower Toogoodoo Creek, 2 mi. above entrance	32° 42.2'	80° 16.7'	+1 26	+0 47	*1.29	*1.26	6.73	7.94	3.61
	Wadmalaw River									
2827	Bluff Point	32° 38.8'	80° 15.4'	+0 58	+0 31	*1.17	*1.11	6.13	7.05	3.28
2829	Yonges Island	32° 41.7'	80° 13.4'	+1 22	+0 45	*1.24	*1.16	6.50	7.48	3.47
2831	Johns Island, Church Creek	32° 42.4'	80° 09.4'	+1 43	+1 00	*1.30	*1.16	6.85	7.88	3.64
2833	Church Creek bridge	32° 42.9'	80° 05.5'	+1 58	+0 58	*1.30	*1.00	6.93	8.04	3.66
				on Savannah River Ent.,						
2835	Edisto Beach, Edisto Island	32° 30.1'	80° 17.8'	-0 21	-0 29	*0.84	*0.95	5.75	6.61	3.08
	South Edisto River									
2837	Edisto Marina, Big Bay Creek entrance	32° 29.6'	80° 20.4'	-0 06	-0 13	*0.86	*0.91	5.96	6.85	3.1
2839	Carters Dock, Big Bay Creek	32° 29.6'	80° 19.6'	+0 08	-0 07	*0.87	*0.91	5.97	6.87	3.1
2841	Scott Creek, 0.5 mi. above ent., Big Bay Creek	32° 30.1'	80° 19.1'	+0 29	- - -	- - -	- - -	- -	- -	- -
2843	Peters Point, St. Pierre Creek	32° 32.4'	80° 20.4'	+0 22	+0 09	*0.88	*0.95	6.09	7.00	3.2
2845	Fenwick Island	32° 33.6'	80° 25.1'	+0 15	+0 25	*0.90	*1.09	6.19	7.12	3.3
2847	Pine Landing	32° 36.2'	80° 23.3'	+0 29	+0 45	*0.92	*0.95	6.29	7.30	3.3
2849	Dawho River	32° 39.4'	80° 23.5'	+1 07	+1 31	*0.89	*0.95	6.15	7.07	3.2
2851	Willtown Bluff, Edisto River	32° 40.9'	80° 25.0'	+1 34	+2 03	*0.83	*1.00	5.69	6.54	3.0
2853	Hope Creek, Edisto River	32° 42.0'	80° 25.6'	+1 46	+2 13	*0.82	*1.05	5.62	6.46	3.0
2855	Penny Creek, south of, Edisto River	32° 42.9'	80° 26.2'	+2 10	+2 43	*0.73	*1.18	4.97	5.72	2.7
2857	Jacksonboro Camp	32° 45.2'	80° 27.0'	+2 46	+3 34	*0.59	*0.86	4.04	4.65	2.2
2859	Canaday Landing, south of, Edisto River	32° 48.8'	80° 24.4'	+4 20	+5 34	*0.13	*0.32	0.84	0.97	0.4
2861	Hart Bluff, Edisto River <24>	32° 55.6'	80° 23.9'	- - -	- - -	- - -	- - -	- -	- -	-
	St. Helena Sound									
2863	Otter Island	32° 28.6'	80° 25.2'	+0 04	+0 07	*0.87	*0.95	6.01	6.91	3.2
2865	Johnson Creek Bridge, Hunting Island	32° 23.5'	80° 26.3'	+0 03	+0 03	*0.85	*0.86	5.88	6.76	3.1
2867	Harbor River Bridge	32° 24.2'	80° 27.2'	+0 03	-0 06	*0.88	*0.95	6.09	7.00	3.2
	Ashepoo River									
2869	Seabrook	32° 31.4'	80° 24.4'	+0 11	+0 18	*0.90	*0.91	6.2	7.3	3.3
2871	Ashepoo-Coosaw Cutoff, ICWW	32° 31.5'	80° 27.1'	+0 15	+0 23	*0.90	*0.91	6.20	7.19	3.3
2873	Musselboro Island, Mosquito Creek	32° 34.7'	80° 26.9'	+1 21	+0 57	*0.90	*0.91	6.22	7.15	3.3
2875	Hutchinson Island	32° 33.1'	80° 28.9'	+0 31	+0 44	*0.87	*0.91	6.01	6.97	3.2
2877	Bluff Islands	32° 34.7'	80° 29.6'	+0 46	+1 04	*0.84	*0.91	5.79	6.72	3.1

TABLE 2. – TIDAL DIFFERENCES AND OTHER CONSTANTS

No.	PLACE	POSITION Latitude	POSITION Longitude	DIFFERENCES Time High Water	DIFFERENCES Time Low Water	DIFFERENCES Height High Water	DIFFERENCES Height Low Water	RANGES Mean	RANGES Spring	Mean Tide Level
		North	West	h m	h m	ft	ft	ft	ft	ft
	SOUTH CAROLINA St. Helena Sound-cont. Time meridian, 75° W			on Savannah River Ent.,						
	Ashepoo River-cont.									
2879	Brickyard Ferry, swing bridge	32° 36.8'	80° 28.9'	+1 27	+1 34	*0.71	*0.86	4.82	5.59	2.60
2881	Airy Hall Plantation	32° 37.9'	80° 28.3'	+1 57	+1 59	*0.60	*1.00	4.16	4.71	2.25
2883	Ashepoo	32° 44.6'	80° 33.4'	+4 18	+4 00	*0.34	*1.05	2.18	2.53	1.32
	Morgan River									
2885	Village Creek Entrance	32° 26.7'	80° 30.2'	+0 17	+0 07	*0.93	*1.00	6.35	7.37	3.40
2887	Village Creek Cemetery	32° 25.0'	80° 31.2'	+0 36	+0 15	*0.94	*0.95	6.45	7.48	3.43
2889	Edding Point, Edding Creek	32° 26.8'	80° 32.0'	+0 31	+0 14	*0.93	*0.95	6.41	7.37	3.42
2891	Jenkins Creek, 1 mi. above entrance	32° 26.4'	80° 33.2'	+0 41	+0 17	*0.98	*0.95	6.80	7.82	3.61
2893	Jenkins Creek, Polawana Island	32° 25.2'	80° 34.6'	+0 55	+0 27	*1.01	*1.05	6.91	8.02	3.69
2895	Lucy Point Creek entrance	32° 27.1'	80° 36.6'	+0 53	+0 33	*0.90	*0.88	6.32	7.33	3.21
	Combahee River									
2897	Bowles Island, New Chehaw River	32° 33.9'	80° 31.0'	+1 02	+0 42	*0.96	*1.00	6.59	7.64	3.51
2899	Wiggins, Chehaw River	32° 36.1'	80° 32.5'	+1 45	+1 20	*0.88	*1.18	6.03	6.93	3.28
2901	Fields Point	32° 34.0'	80° 33.7'	+0 42	+0 52	*0.91	*0.91	6.2	7.3	3.3
2903	Railroad Bridge	32° 35.4'	80° 37.8'	+1 37	- - -	- - -	- - -	- -	- -	- -
2905	U.S. 17 Bridge	32° 39.1'	80° 41.0'	+3 00	+2 29	*0.71	*1.14	4.83	5.55	2.66
2907	Bluff Plantation	32° 41.0'	80° 44.3'	+4 17	+3 51	*0.50	*1.59	3.12	3.59	1.95
2909	Cuckolds Creek	32° 42.8'	80° 41.7'	+4 45	+4 12	*0.51	*1.73	3.26	3.81	2.01
	Coosaw River									
2911	Summerhouse Point, Bull River	32° 31.6'	80° 34.4'	+0 55	+0 37	*0.96	*0.95	6.58	7.63	3.50
2913	Briars Creek ent., Wimbee Creek, Bull River . . .	32° 34.7'	80° 40.2'	+2 06	+1 24	*0.93	*0.95	6.39	7.35	3.41
2915	Sams Point, Lucy Point Creek	32° 29.0'	80° 35.9'	+0 55	+0 45	*0.97	*0.91	6.71	7.78	3.55
2917	Brickyard Point, Brickyard Creek	32° 29.6'	80° 41.1'	+1 27	+1 19	*1.08	*0.95	7.45	8.64	3.94
2919	Whale Branch entrance	32° 31.5'	80° 40.5'	+1 27	+1 20	*1.06	*0.95	7.32	8.49	3.87
2921	Lobeco, Whale Branch	32° 34.4'	80° 44.7'	+1 40	+1 28	*1.11	*0.95	7.75	8.91	4.08
2923	Sheldon, Huspa Creek, Whale Branch	32° 35.0'	80° 47.0'	+2 11	+1 52	*1.16	*0.77	8.07	9.28	4.21
2925	Fripps Inlet, Hunting Island Bridge	32° 20.4'	80° 27.9'	-0 10	-0 22	*0.88	*0.91	6.10	7.02	3.25
	Port Royal Sound									
2927	Capers Island, Trenchards Inlet	32° 16.4'	80° 35.1'	-0 01	-0 18	*0.93	*0.95	6.37	7.39	3.39
2929	Club Bridge Creek ent., Trenchards Inlet	32° 20.1'	80° 32.5'	+0 15	-0 24	*0.99	*1.00	6.78	7.86	3.61
2931	Port Royal Plantation, Hilton Head Island . . .	32° 13.2'	80° 40.1'	+0 01	-0 11	*0.88	*1.00	6.10	7.02	3.27
2933	The Folly, Hilton Head Island	32° 11.4'	80° 42.1'	+0 03	- - -	- - -	- - -	- -	- -	- -
2935	Station Creek, west end	32° 16.8'	80° 38.3'	+0 16	+0 13	*0.96	*0.91	6.62	7.68	3.51
2937	Station Creek, County Landing	32° 19.5'	80° 36.1'	+0 27	-0 16	*0.99	*1.00	6.84	7.87	3.64
	Beaufort River									
2939	Fort Fremont	32° 18.4'	80° 38.7'	+0 19	+0 17	*0.95	*0.64	6.63	7.69	3.45
2941	Parris Island, Marine Corps Recruit Depot	32° 21.0'	80° 40.1'	+0 37	+0 26	*1.02	*0.91	7.02	8.14	3.71
2943	Distant Island, Cowen Creek	32° 22.7'	80° 38.0'	+0 43	+0 27	*1.06	*1.05	7.29	8.46	3.87
2945	Distant Island Creek, upper end, Cowen Creek .	32° 24.1'	80° 39.2'	+1 00	+1 08	*0.98	*0.36	6.92	7.96	3.54
2947	Capers Creek, Cowen Creek, St. Helena Island	32° 22.3'	80° 36.3'	+0 58	+0 34	*1.08	*0.95	7.44	8.63	3.93
2949	Cowen Creek, Rt. 21 bridge	32° 23.9'	80° 37.0'	+0 55	+0 58	*1.00	*0.55	6.97	8.09	3.61
2951	Battery Creek, 4 mi. above entrance	32° 24.8'	80° 42.0'	+1 14	+0 37	*1.10	*0.91	7.64	8.79	4.02
2953	Beaufort	32° 25.8'	80° 40.5'	+1 09	+0 51	*1.07	*0.95	7.39	8.17	3.90
2955	Marine Corps Air Station, Brickyard Creek	32° 27.9'	80° 41.5'	+1 27	+1 11	*1.10	*0.95	7.62	8.84	4.02
2957	Albergottie Creek, Rt. 21 bridge	32° 27.0'	80° 43.9'	+1 48	+2 02	*0.98	*0.45	6.83	7.92	3.52
2959	Skull Creek, north entrance, Hilton Head Island . .	32° 16.0'	80° 44.2'	+0 15	+0 16	*0.99	*0.91	6.83	7.85	3.62
2961	Skull Creek, south entrance, Hilton Head Island	32° 13.4'	80° 46.3'	+0 34	+0 23	*1.05	*1.05	7.28	8.37	3.87
2963	Pinckney Island, Mackay Creek, Chechessee River	32° 15.6'	80° 46.0'	+0 36	+0 25	*1.04	*0.91	7.21	8.36	3.80
2965	Colleton River Entrance	32° 19.3'	80° 47.5'	+0 49	+0 37	*1.05	*1.05	7.2	8.4	3.8
2967	Callawassie Creek, Colleton River	32° 19.0'	80° 50.5'	+1 15	+0 53	*1.13	*1.14	7.8	9.1	4.1
2969	Callawassie Island, south, Colleton River	32° 18.8'	80° 51.6'	+1 09	+0 40	*1.19	*1.11	7.7	9.0	4.1
2971	Callawassie Island Bridge, Colleton River	32° 20.5'	80° 51.1'	+1 12	+0 49	*1.13	*1.14	7.8	9.1	4.2
2973	Baileys Landing, Okatee River, Colleton River . . .	32° 20.8'	80° 53.4'	+1 25	+0 57	*1.17	*1.05	8.09	9.30	4.28
2975	Chechessee Bluff, Chechessee River	32° 22.4'	80° 50.2'	+1 06	+0 48	*1.10	*1.00	7.62	8.84	4.03
	Broad River									
2977	Hwy. 170 bridge	32° 23.2'	80° 46.6'	+0 51	+0 45	*1.06	*0.91	7.35	8.45	3.88
2979	Broughton Point, Hazzard Creek	32° 24.6'	80° 53.1'	+1 34	+1 30	*1.10	*0.82	7.61	8.83	3.99
2981	Euhaw Creek, 2.5 mi. above entrance	32° 26.1'	80° 51.1'	+1 33	+1 09	*1.14	*0.91	7.92	9.19	4.16
2983	Salvesbarg Landing, West Branch Boyds Creek	32° 28.5'	80° 51.0'	+1 29	- - -	- - -	- - -	- -	- -	- -
2985	Pilot Island, West Branch Boyds Creek	32° 30.3'	80° 51.8'	+1 50	+1 24	*1.15	*0.91	7.98	9.26	4.19
2987	Corning Landing, Whale Branch	32° 30.0'	80° 47.1'	+1 37	+1 25	*1.15	*0.77	8.00	9.28	4.17
2989	RR. Bridge, Hall Island	32° 31.3'	80° 50.3'	+1 39	+1 24	*1.17	*1.05	8.08	9.37	4.27
2991	Pocotaligo River, 4 mi. above entrance	32° 35.7'	80° 49.9'	+2 21	+1 48	- - -	- - -	- -	- -	- -
2993	North Dawson Landing, Coosawhatchie River . . .	32° 33.7'	80° 54.6'	+2 34	+2 10	*1.12	*1.14	7.71	8.94	4.10
2995	Tulifiny River, I-95 bridge	32° 36.1'	80° 54.2'	+3 24	+3 31	*0.73	*0.73	5.01	5.81	2.66
	Calibogue Sound									
2997	Braddock Point, Hilton Head Island	32° 06.8'	80° 49.8'	+0 05	-0 02	*0.98	*1.00	6.74	7.82	3.59
2999	Calibogue Cay, Broad Creek, Hilton Head Island .	32° 09.2'	80° 47.7'	+0 20	+0 09	*1.04	*1.00	7.13	8.27	3.79
3001	Broad Creek, Hilton Head Island	32° 11.1'	80° 45.2'	+0 33	+0 17	*1.08	*1.05	7.48	8.60	3.97
3003	Haig Point, Daufuskie Island, Cooper River	32° 08.8'	80° 50.2'	+0 20	+0 10	*1.02	*1.00	7.05	8.18	3.74
3005	Bull Creek, Bull Island South, Cooper River . . .	32° 09.9'	80° 51.4'	+0 28	+0 12	*1.05	*1.05	7.23	8.39	3.84
3007	Pine Island, Ramshorn Creek, Cooper River . . .	32° 07.3'	80° 53.9'	+0 34	+0 28	*1.03	*0.91	7.17	8.25	3.78
3009	Savage I., Savage Creek, Bull Creek	32° 11.1'	80° 51.6'	+0 46	+0 19	*1.10	*1.00	7.56	8.77	4.00
	May River									
3011	Moreland Cemetery	32° 10.5'	80° 53.5'	+0 49	+0 23	*1.11	*0.77	7.73	8.97	4.04
3013	Bull Island North	32° 12.0'	80° 48.9'	+0 40	+0 25	*1.09	*1.05	7.52	8.72	3.99
3015	Bluffton	32° 13.8'	80° 51.7'	+1 00	+0 37	*1.16	*1.05	8.01	9.29	4.23
3017	Rose Dew Creek	32° 13.2'	80° 55.2'	+1 19	- - -	- - -	- - -	- -	- -	- -

TABLE 2. – TIDAL DIFFERENCES AND OTHER CONSTANTS

No.	PLACE	POSITION Latitude	POSITION Longitude	DIFFERENCES Time High Water	DIFFERENCES Time Low Water	DIFFERENCES Height High Water	DIFFERENCES Height Low Water	RANGES Mean	RANGES Spring	Mean Tide Level
		North	West	h m	h m	ft	ft	ft	ft	ft
	SOUTH CAROLINA Calibogue Sound-cont. Time meridian, 75° W				on Savannah River Ent.,					
	New River									
3019	Bloody Point, Daufuskie Island	32° 04.9'	80° 52.7'	+0 01	+0 19	*0.98	*0.91	6.77	7.79	3.59
3021	Hargray Pier, Daufuskie Island	32° 05.9'	80° 53.9'	+0 19	+0 27	*1.01	*1.05	6.96	8.07	3.71
3023	Daufuskie Landing, Daufuskie Island	32° 06.2'	80° 53.7'	+0 30	+0 33	*1.01	*0.95	7.02	8.07	3.72
3025	Doughboy Island	32° 08.3'	80° 55.9'	+1 04	+1 06	*1.01	*1.05	6.96	8.07	3.71
3027	Good Hope Landing, south of	32° 10.6'	80° 58.0'	+2 19	+2 06	*0.85	*1.55	5.71	6.62	3.20
3029	Cook Landing Cemetery	32° 11.7'	81° 00.0'	+3 09	+3 00	*0.69	*1.41	4.58	5.31	2.60
3031	Rt. 170 bridge	32° 14.2'	81° 00.7'	+4 12	+3 53	*0.51	*0.51	3.33	3.83	2.01
3033	Fields Cut, Wright River	32° 05.2'	80° 56.0'	+0 16	+0 29	*1.02	*1.05	6.98	8.10	3.72
3035	Turnbridge Landing, Salt Water Creek	32° 07.7'	81° 00.7'	+1 41	+0 59	*1.06	*1.09	7.27	8.43	3.87
	GEORGIA Savannah River									
3037	Tybee Light	32° 02'	80° 51'	-0 10	-0 12	*0.99	*0.99	6.8	8.0	3.6
3039	SAVANNAH RIVER ENTRANCE, FORT PULASKI	32° 02.0'	80° 54.1'	Daily predictions				6.92	8.03	3.67
3041	Fort Jackson	32° 04.9'	81° 02.2'	+0 29	+0 42	*1.09	*1.09	7.50	8.70	4.04
3043	Savannah, Bull Street	32° 05'	81° 05'	+0 44	+0 33	*1.14	*1.14	7.9	8.8	4.2
3045	Port Wentworth	32° 08.6'	81° 08.5'	+0 44	+0 41	*1.17	*0.95	8.14	9.12	4.28
3047	Little Back River, Hwy. 17, Back River, S.C.	32° 09.9'	81° 07.8'	+1 28	+1 41	*1.10	*1.14	7.63	8.55	4.06
3049	S.C.L. RR. bridge	32° 14'	81° 09'	+1 51	+3 08	*0.90	*0.91	6.2	7.2	3.3
3051	Purrysburg Landing, S.C.	32° 18.2'	81° 07.3'	+2 14	+3 38	*0.44	*0.41	3.03	3.48	1.60
	Tybee Creek and Wassaw Sound									
3053	Tybee Creek entrance	31° 59'	80° 51'	-0 09	+0 05	*0.99	*1.00	6.8	8.0	3.6
3055	Beach Hammock	31° 57'	80° 56'	-0 01	-0 07	*1.00	*1.00	6.9	8.1	3.7
3057	Romerly Marsh Creek	31° 56'	81° 00'	+0 08	-0 03	*1.03	*1.03	7.1	8.3	3.7
	Wilmington River									
3059	Savannah Sheraton Resort Hotel	32° 00'	81° 00'	+0 14	+0 06	*1.13	*1.14	7.8	9.1	4.2
3061	Thunderbolt	32° 02'	81° 03'	+0 32	+0 12	*1.15	*1.14	7.9	9.2	4.2
3063	North entrance	32° 04'	81° 00'	+0 40	+0 44	*1.10	*1.09	7.6	8.9	4.0
3065	Isle of Hope, Skidaway River	31° 59'	81° 03'	+0 50	+0 28	*1.13	*1.13	7.8	9.1	4.1
	Ossabaw Sound									
3067	Egg Islands	31° 50'	81° 05'	+0 04	+0 10	*1.04	*1.04	7.2	8.4	3.8
3069	Vernon View, Burnside River	31° 56'	81° 06'	+0 40	+0 31	*1.09	*1.09	7.5	8.8	4.0
3071	Coffee Bluff, Forest River	31° 56'	81° 09'	+1 05	+0 42	*1.09	*1.09	7.5	8.8	3.9
3073	Fort McAllister, Ogeechee River	31° 53'	81° 13'	+0 48	+1 16	*1.00	*1.00	6.9	8.1	3.6
3075	Highway bridge, Ogeechee River	31° 59'	81° 17'	+3 19	+4 25	*0.15	*0.14	1.0	1.2	0.5
3077	Florida Passage, Ogeechee River	31° 51'	81° 09'	+0 34	+0 46	*1.05	*0.91	7.3	8.5	3.8
3079	Florida Passage, Bear River	31° 49'	81° 10'	+0 46	+0 49	*1.09	*0.95	7.6	8.8	4.0
3081	Cane Patch Creek entrance	31° 49'	81° 09'	+0 55	+0 43	*1.05	*1.05	7.2	8.4	3.8
3083	Bradley Point, Bradley River	31° 49'	81° 03'	+0 04	+0 13	*1.02	*0.95	7.0	8.2	3.7
	St. Catherines and Sapelo Sounds									
3085	Walburg Creek entrance	31° 42'	81° 09'	+0 16	+0 21	*1.03	*1.00	7.1	8.3	3.8
3087	Kilkenny Club, Kilkenny Creek	31° 47'	81° 12'	+0 48	+0 37	*1.09	*0.91	7.5	8.8	4.0
3089	Bear River, (Range 'A' Light)	31° 47.6'	81° 10.9'	+0 42	+0 29	*1.06	*0.95	7.36	8.46	3.89
3091	Bear River Entrance	31° 43.3'	81° 08.5'	+0 10	+0 13	*1.00	*0.86	6.97	8.12	3.67
3093	Sunbury, Medway River	31° 46.0'	81° 16.7'	+0 55	+0 49	*1.05	*1.00	7.28	8.27	3.87
3095	Belfast, Belfast River	31° 49'	81° 18'	+1 23	+1 10	*1.13	*1.14	7.8	9.1	4.2
3097	North Newport River (Daymark 119)	31° 41'	81° 12'	+0 35	+0 31	*1.05	*1.00	7.2	8.4	3.8
3099	North Newport River	31° 40'	81° 16'	+0 56	+0 36	*1.10	*1.09	7.6	8.9	4.0
3101	South Newport Cut, N. Newport River	31° 40'	81° 16'	+1 01	+0 54	*1.08	*1.04	7.5	8.7	4.0
3103	Halfmoon, Timmons River	31° 41.7'	81° 16.3'	+1 21	+1 09	*1.06	*1.05	7.35	8.45	3.90
3105	Eagle Neck, South Newport River	31° 39'	81° 18'	+1 16	+1 06	*1.09	*1.00	7.5	8.8	4.0
3107	Thomas Landing, S. Newport River	31° 39'	81° 15'	+0 57	+0 46	*1.06	*0.95	7.4	8.6	3.9
3109	South Newport River (Daymark 135)	31° 34.5'	81° 11.4'	+0 22	+0 13	*1.00	*0.95	7.11	7.99	3.66
3111	Dallas Bluff, Julienton River	31° 35'	81° 19'	+0 48	+1 04	*1.10	*1.09	7.6	8.9	4.0
3113	Harris Neck, Barbour Island River	31° 37'	81° 16'	+0 54	+0 32	*1.08	*1.00	7.5	8.8	4.0
3115	Barbour Island, Barbour Island River	31° 35'	81° 14'	+0 36	+0 24	*1.06	*1.00	7.3	8.5	3.9
3117	Blackbeard Island	31° 32'	81° 12'	+0 18	+0 22	*1.00	*1.00	6.9	8.1	3.6
3119	Dog Hammock, Sapelo River	31° 32'	81° 16'	+0 33	+0 22	*1.04	*0.91	7.2	8.4	3.8
3121	Bellville Point, Sapelo River	31° 32'	81° 22'	+1 12	+1 02	*1.08	*0.86	7.5	8.8	3.9
3123	Pine Harbor, Sapelo River	31° 33'	81° 22'	+1 03	+1 04	*1.05	*1.05	7.2	8.4	3.8
3125	Eagle Creek, Mud River	31° 31'	81° 17'	+0 21	+0 19	*1.05	*1.05	7.2	8.4	3.8
3127	Creighton Narrows Entrance, Crescent River .	31° 29'	81° 20'	+0 49	+0 37	*1.08	*1.09	7.4	8.6	4.0
3129	Mud River, Old Teakettle Cr.(Daymark 156)	31° 29.2'	81° 19.2'	+0 46	+0 33	*1.08	*1.00	7.50	8.43	3.97
	Doboy and Altamaha Sounds									
3131	Old Tea Kettle Creek (Daymark 173)	31° 26'	81° 18'	+0 39	+0 39	*0.96	*0.82	6.7	7.8	3.5
3133	Blackbeard Creek, Blackbeard Island	31° 29'	81° 13'	+0 19	+0 47	*0.94	*0.95	6.5	7.6	3.5
3135	Old Tower, Sapelo Island	31° 23.4'	81° 17.3'	+0 15	+0 14	*0.99	*0.95	6.82	7.84	3.62
3137	Hudson Creek entrance	31° 27'	81° 21'	+0 37	+0 31	*1.05	*1.05	7.2	8.4	3.8
3139	Threemile Cut entrance, Darien River	31° 21'	81° 23'	+0 44	+0 55	*1.03	*1.05	7.1	8.3	3.7
3141	Darien, Darien River	31° 22'	81° 26'	+1 08	+1 15	*1.06	*1.05	7.3	8.5	3.9
3143	Rockdedundy River (Daymark 185)	31° 22.4'	81° 20.0'	+0 25	+0 26	*1.00	*1.00	6.86	8.03	3.62
3145	Wolf Island, south end	31° 20'	81° 19'	+0 25	+0 45	*0.97	*1.09	6.7	7.8	3.6

TABLE 2. – TIDAL DIFFERENCES AND OTHER CONSTANTS

No.	PLACE	Latitude	Longitude	High Water h m	Low Water h m	High Water ft	Low Water ft	Mean ft	Spring ft	Mean Tide Level ft
		North	**West**							
	GEORGIA Doboy and Altamaha Sounds-cont. Time meridian, 75° W				**on Savannah River Ent.,**					
3147	Champney Island, South Altamaha River	31° 20'	81° 28'	+1 10	+2 33	*0.76	*0.77	5.2	6.1	2.8
3149	Hampton River entrance	31° 13'	81° 19'	+0 16	+0 04	*0.96	*0.95	6.6	7.8	3.5
3151	Jones Creek entrance, Hampton River	31° 18'	81° 20'	+1 03	+0 13	*1.05	*1.05	7.2	8.5	3.8
	St. Simons Sound									
3153	St. Simons Sound Bar	31° 06'	81° 19'	-0 01	-0 02	*0.95	*0.95	6.5	7.6	3.4
3155	St. Simons Light	31° 07.9'	81° 23.8'	+0 14	+0 16	*0.95	*0.91	6.60	7.72	3.50
3157	Frederick River Bridge	31° 10'	81° 25'	+0 43	+0 45	*1.00	*1.09	6.9	8.0	3.7
3159	Frederica River	31° 13'	81° 24'	+0 48	+0 56	*1.05	*1.05	7.2	8.4	3.8
3161	Mackay River (Daymark 239)	31° 13'	81° 26'	+0 58	+0 56	*1.03	*1.09	7.1	8.3	3.8
3163	Mackay River (ICWW), Buttermilk Sound	31° 17.1'	81° 23.1'	+0 58	+1 23	*1.00	*1.09	6.87	7.90	3.68
3165	Brunswick, East River, Howe Street Pier	31° 08.6'	81° 29.8'	+0 44	+0 35	*1.03	*1.00	7.13	8.27	3.78
	Turtle River									
3167	Crispen Island	31° 13'	81° 33'	+1 33	+0 55	*1.15	*1.05	7.9	9.3	4.2
3169	Allied Chemical Corp. docks	31° 11'	81° 31'	+1 03	+0 42	*1.10	*1.09	7.6	8.9	4.0
3171	Dillard Creek	31° 14'	81° 34'	+1 32	+1 02	*1.16	*1.18	8.0	9.4	4.3
3173	Buffalo River entrance	31° 13'	81° 35'	+1 37	+0 58	*1.16	*1.18	8.0	9.4	4.3
3175	Highway bridge, South Brunswick River	31° 09'	81° 34'	+1 07	+0 49	*1.10	*1.09	7.6	8.9	4.0
	St. Andrew Sound				**on Fernandina Beach,**					
3177	Raccoon Key Spit	31° 00.8'	81° 27.3'	-0 19	+0 09	*1.09	*1.11	6.56	7.63	3.49
3179	Jekyll Island Marina, Jekyll Creek	31° 03.4'	81° 25.4'	+0 03	+0 36	*1.13	*1.16	6.83	7.85	3.63
3181	Jointer Island, Jointer Creek	31° 06'	81° 30'	+0 11	+0 31	*1.18	*1.18	7.2	8.4	3.8
	Little Satilla River									
3183	2.5 miles above mouth	31° 04'	81° 30'	-0 04	+0 31	*1.12	*1.12	6.8	7.9	3.6
3185	8 miles above mouth	31° 06'	81° 34'	+0 24	+1 02	*1.20	*1.20	7.3	8.5	3.8
3187	Below Spring Bluff	31° 10'	81° 37'	+1 09	+1 31	*1.23	*1.23	7.5	8.7	3.9
3189	Dover Bluff, Dover Creek	31° 01'	81° 32'	+0 06	+0 31	*1.15	*1.15	7.0	8.1	3.7
	Satilla River									
3191	Todd Creek entrance	30° 58'	81° 31'	-0 08	+0 41	*1.10	*1.10	6.7	7.8	3.5
3193	Bailey Cut, 0.8 mile west of	30° 59.1'	81° 35.5'	+0 28	+1 12	*1.13	*1.21	6.80	7.39	3.62
3195	Ceylon	30° 58'	81° 39'	+0 34	+1 35	*1.09	*1.09	6.6	7.7	3.5
3197	Burnt Fort	30° 57'	81° 54'	+3 55	+5 05	*0.53	*0.53	3.2	3.7	1.7
3199	Cumberland Wharf, Cumberland River	30° 55.8'	81° 26.8'	+0 00	+0 26	*1.12	*1.12	6.8	7.9	3.6
3201	Floyd Creek, 2.8 miles above entrance	30° 56'	81° 30'	+0 08	+0 21	*1.17	*1.17	7.1	8.2	3.7
	GEORGIA and FLORIDA Cumberland Sound									
3203	St. Marys Entrance, North Jetty	30° 43'	81° 26'	-0 36	-0 03	*0.96	*0.96	5.8	6.7	3.1
3205	Kings Bay, Navy Base	30° 48.1'	81° 30.9'	+0 12	+0 10	*1.09	*1.05	6.43	7.39	3.42
3207	Beach Creek ent., Cumberland Island	30° 43.6'	81° 28.6'	+0 00	-0 04	*0.98	*0.95	5.92	6.81	3.14
3209	Seacamp Dock, Cumberland Island	30° 45.8'	81° 28.3'	+0 12	+0 16	*1.04	*1.05	6.23	7.16	3.31
3211	Crooked River, Cumberland Dividings	30° 50.6'	81° 29.2'	+0 44	+0 56	*1.12	*1.12	6.8	7.9	3.6
3213	Harrietts Bluff, Crooked River	30° 52.2'	81° 35.1'	+1 29	+1 56	*1.05	*1.05	6.4	7.4	3.4
	St. Marys River									
3215	St. Marys	30° 43.2'	81° 32.9'	+0 38	+0 45	*0.98	*1.05	5.86	6.74	3.13
3217	Crandall	30° 43.3'	81° 37.3'	+1 06	+1 25	*0.81	*1.00	4.84	5.57	2.61
3219	U.S. Highway 17	30° 44.5'	81° 41.3'	+2 30	- - -	- - -	- - -	- -	- -	- -
3221	Little St. Marys River	30° 43.9'	81° 43.6'	+2 49	+2 36	*0.71	*0.79	4.27	4.91	2.29
3223	Kings Ferry	30° 47.2'	81° 50.4'	+4 05	+4 09	*0.49	*1.16	2.83	3.25	1.63
3225	Chester, Bells River	30° 41.0'	81° 32.0'	+0 27	+0 19	*1.04	*1.11	6.27	7.21	3.34
3227	Roses Bluff, Bells River	30° 42.2'	81° 34.6'	+0 35	+0 35	*1.03	*0.95	6.18	7.11	3.28
3229	Lofton, Lanceford Creek	30° 38.6'	81° 31.4'	+0 18	-0 01	*1.05	*1.05	6.33	7.28	3.36
3231	FERNANDINA BEACH, Amelia River	30° 40.5'	81° 27.9'		*Daily Predictions*			6.02	7.07	3.20
3233	Kingsley Creek, RR. bridge	30° 37.9'	81° 28.6'	+0 27	+0 25	*0.99	*1.00	5.97	6.87	3.18
	FLORIDA Nassau Sound and Fort George River									
3235	Amelia City, South Amelia River	30° 35.2'	81° 27.8'	+0 21	+0 42	*0.89	*0.89	5.39	6.20	2.86
	Nassau River									
3237	entrance	30° 31.1'	81° 27.2'	-0 18	+0 41	*0.86	*1.00	5.16	5.93	2.77
3239	Nassauville	30° 34.1'	81° 30.9'	+0 24	+1 09	*0.80	*1.00	4.75	5.46	2.56
3241	Tiger Point, Pumpkin Hill Creek	30° 30.1'	81° 29.7'	+1 22	+1 46	*0.82	*0.95	4.89	5.62	2.63
3243	Edwards Creek, 1 mi. above entrance	30° 30.1'	81° 32.5'	+1 24	+1 51	*0.77	*0.85	4.62	5.36	2.48
3245	Cuno, Lofton Creek	30° 34.6'	81° 34.3'	+2 14	+2 48	*0.60	*1.05	3.55	4.12	1.98
3247	Mink Creek entrance	30° 32.2'	81° 34.9'	+1 13	+2 05	*0.72	*1.05	4.26	4.90	2.33
3249	Halfmoon Island, highway bridge	30° 34.6'	81° 36.5'	+2 00	+2 39	*0.70	*1.05	4.16	4.78	2.28
3251	Boggy Creek, 2 mi. above entrance	30° 35.3'	81° 39.8'	+3 29	+3 50	*0.49	*0.89	2.90	3.34	1.62
3253	Sawpit Creek entrance, bridge	30° 30.8'	81° 27.4'	-0 14	+0 21	*0.84	*1.00	5.05	5.81	2.71
3255	Sawpit Creek, 1 mi. above entrance	30° 30.2'	81° 28.3'	+0 05	+0 31	*0.84	*0.74	5.08	5.84	2.68
3257	Simpson Creek, A1A highway bridge	30° 27.9'	81° 25.9'	+0 04	+0 17	*0.84	*0.63	5.08	5.84	2.66
3259	Little Talbot Island, ocean	30° 25.8'	81° 24.3'	-0 36	-0 13	*0.91	*1.00	5.45	6.27	2.91
3261	Fort George Island, Fort George River	30° 26.4'	81° 26.3'	+0 10	+0 33	*0.79	*0.74	4.78	5.50	2.53
	St. Johns River				**on Mayport,**					
3263	Mayport Naval Station, Degausing Structure	30° 23.8'	81° 23.7'	-0 21	-0 04	*1.07	*1.13	4.87	5.36	2.61
3265	Mayport Naval Station, Water Treatment Dock ...	30° 24.0'	81° 24.8'	-0 12	-0 06	*1.03	*1.00	4.72	5.17	2.51
3267	MAYPORT (BAR PILOT DOCK)	30° 23.8'	81° 25.8'		*Daily predictions*			4.57	5.32	2.44
3269	Pablo Creek entrance	30° 22.6'	81° 26.9'	+0 29	+0 33	*0.85	*0.73	3.89	4.24	2.05

245

TABLE 2. – TIDAL DIFFERENCES AND OTHER CONSTANTS

No.	PLACE	POSITION Latitude	POSITION Longitude	DIFFERENCES Time High Water	DIFFERENCES Time Low Water	DIFFERENCES Height High Water	DIFFERENCES Height Low Water	RANGES Mean	RANGES Spring	Mean Tide Level
		North	West	h m	h m	ft	ft	ft	ft	ft
	FLORIDA St. Johns River-cont. Time meridian, 75° W				on Mayport,					
3271	Pablo Creek, ICWW bridge	30° 19.4'	81° 26.3'	+1 14	+1 20	*0.84	*1.00	3.82	4.16	2.06
3273	Sisters Creek	30° 25.0'	81° 27.2'	+0 32	+0 50	*0.95	*0.93	4.34	4.70	2.31
3275	Clapboard Creek, Pelotes Island	30° 24.4'	81° 30.6'	+0 32	+0 56	*0.79	*0.80	3.64	3.94	1.94
3277	Fulton	30° 23.4'	81° 30.4'	+0 24	+0 40	*0.80	*0.73	3.66	3.97	1.94
3279	Blount Island Bridge	30° 24.8'	81° 32.7'	+0 42	+1 05	*0.77	*0.73	3.51	3.80	1.87
3281	Dame Point	30° 23.2'	81° 33.5'	+0 42	+1 12	*0.70	*0.67	3.19	3.44	1.70
3283	Mill Cove	30° 22.2'	81° 33.5'	+0 51	- - -	- - -	- - -			
3285	Cedar Heights, Broward River	30° 26.2'	81° 38.5'	+1 08	+1 53	*0.65	*0.53	2.99	3.47	1.58
3287	Jacksonville, Navy Fuel Depot	30° 24.0'	81° 37.6'	+1 14	+1 48	*0.56	*0.53	2.60	2.81	1.37
	Trout River									
3289	Moncrief Creek entrance	30° 23.5'	81° 39.7'	+1 11	+1 53	*0.55	*0.53	2.51	2.91	1.34
3291	Lake Forest, Ribault River	30° 23.9'	81° 41.9'	+1 13	+2 10	*0.58	*0.60	2.64	2.82	1.41
3293	Sherwood Forest	30° 25.2'	81° 43.7'	+1 42	+2 13	*0.58	*0.67	2.65	2.88	1.43
3295	Phoenix Park	30° 23.0'	81° 38.2'	+1 02	+1 47	*0.56	*0.60	2.54	2.75	1.36
3297	Jacksonville, Long Branch	30° 21.6'	81° 37.2'	+1 15	+1 54	*0.55	*0.73	2.49	2.89	1.35
3299	Little Pottsburg Creek	30° 18.6'	81° 36.6'	+1 31	+2 09	*0.44	*0.53	2.02	2.34	1.09
3301	Jacksonville, Main Street Bridge	30° 19.2'	81° 39.5'	+1 42	+2 13	*0.41	*0.73	1.83	2.03	1.03
3303	Ortega River entrance	30° 16.7'	81° 42.3'	+2 09	+2 47	*0.25	*0.47	1.11	1.26	0.63
3305	Piney Point	30° 13.7'	81° 39.8'	+2 39	+3 36	*0.20	*0.40	0.87	1.01	0.49
3307	I-295 bridge (west end)	30° 11.5'	81° 41.5'	+2 56	+3 43	*0.21	*0.21	0.91	1.06	0.55
3309	Orange Park Landing, Orange Park	30° 10.1'	81° 41.7'	+3 24	+4 44	*0.17	*0.17	0.74	0.87	0.45
3311	Peoria Point, Doctors Lake	30° 07.2'	81° 45.5'	+3 36	+4 56	*0.18	*0.18	0.80	0.93	0.45
3313	Julington Creek	30° 08.1'	81° 37.8'	+3 58	+5 13	*0.16	*0.16	0.71	0.83	0.43
3315	Black Creek, S.C.L. RR. bridge	30° 04.8'	81° 45.7'	+4 46	+5 52	*0.18	*0.18	0.82	0.92	0.46
3317	Green Cove Springs	29° 59.4'	81° 39.8'	+4 57	+5 55	*0.17	*0.27	0.78	0.90	0.43
3319	Tocoi	29° 51.5'	81° 33.2'	+6 02	+7 03	*0.21	*0.27	0.95	1.10	0.51
3321	Palmetto Bluff	29° 45.8'	81° 33.7'	+6 35	+7 36	*0.23	*0.47	1.04	1.18	0.59
3323	Palatka	29° 38.6'	81° 37.9'	+7 11	+8 38	*0.25	*0.53	1.09	1.22	0.63
3325	Sutherlands Still, Dunns Creek	29° 34.3'	81° 36.4'	+7 35	+9 05	*0.18	*0.20	0.84	0.97	0.45
3327	Buffalo Bluff	29° 35.7'	81° 40.9'	+7 27	+8 58	*0.21	*0.40	0.93	1.03	0.52
3329	Welaka	29° 28.6'	81° 40.5'	+7 16	+8 07	*0.10	*0.27	0.43	0.50	0.25
3331	Georgetown <24>	29° 23.1'	81° 38.2'	- - -	- - -	- - -	- - -			
	Atlantic Coast				on Fernandina Beach,					
3333	Atlantic Beach	30° 20.1'	81° 23.7'	-0 41	-0 23	*0.86	*0.86	5.2	6.0	2.8
3335	Jacksonville Beach	30° 17.0'	81° 23.2'	-0 50	-0 27	*0.84	*0.84	5.07	5.83	2.70
3337	Oak Landing, ICWW	30° 15.2'	81° 25.8'	+2 15	+2 03	*0.68	*0.80	4.07	4.72	2.20
3339	Palm Valley, ICWW	30° 08.0'	81° 23.2'	+2 00	+1 49	*0.79	*0.75	4.79	5.56	2.55
3341	Vilano Beach, Tolomato River	29° 55.0'	81° 18.0'	-0 20	-0 05	*0.74	*0.90	4.48	5.20	2.42
3343	St. Augustine, city dock	29° 53.5'	81° 18.6'	-0 20	+0 01	*0.75	*0.89	4.48	5.15	2.41
3345	St. Augustine Beach	29° 51.4'	81° 15.8'	-0 51	-0 32	*0.77	*0.84	4.61	5.48	2.47
	Matanzas River, ICWW									
3347	State Road 312	29° 52.0'	81° 18.4'	-0 03	+0 15	*0.72	*1.00	4.31	5.04	2.34
3349	Crescent Beach	29° 46.1'	81° 15.5'	+0 39	+1 14	*0.69	*0.95	4.09	4.79	2.23
3351	Fort Matanzas	29° 42.9'	81° 14.3'	+0 03	+0 49	*0.65	*0.95	3.86	4.44	2.11
3353	Matanzas Inlet, A1A bridge	29° 42.3'	81° 13.7'	-0 26	+0 00	*0.61	*0.84	3.64	4.21	2.05
3355	Bing Landing	29° 36.9'	81° 12.3'	+2 15	+2 52	*0.26	*0.68	1.46	1.71	0.86
3357	Smith Creek, Flagler Beach	29° 28.7'	81° 08.2'	+4 33	+5 00	*0.15	*0.30	0.86	1.00	0.49
3359	Ormond Beach, Halifax River	29° 17.1'	81° 03.2'	+3 17	+4 31	*0.11	*0.45	0.60	0.70	0.39
3361	Daytona Beach Shores, Sunglow Pier	29° 08.8'	80° 57.8'	-0 56	-0 42	*0.65	*0.84	3.90	4.49	2.11
					on Miami, Government Cut,					
3363	Ponce de Leon Inlet	29° 03.8'	80° 54.9'	-0 11	+0 19	*1.17	*0.92	2.76	3.37	1.4
3365	Ponce Inlet, Halifax River	29° 04.9'	80° 56.2'	+0 05	+0 33	*1.18	*1.00	2.75	3.36	1.5
	Mosquito Lagoon									
3367	New Smyrna Beach	29° 01.4'	80° 55.1'	+0 19	+0 40	*1.04	*1.00	2.43	2.77	1.3
3369	Packwood Place	28° 56.4'	80° 52.2'	+1 43	+2 40	*0.44	*0.44	1.06	1.24	0.5
3371	Turtle Mound	28° 55.6'	80° 49.5'	+3 01	+4 30	*0.17	*0.17	0.45	0.51	0.2
3373	Oak Hill <21>	28° 52'	80° 50'	- - -	- - -	- - -	- - -	- -	- -	-
3375	Cape Canaveral	28° 26'	80° 34'	-1 06	-0 44	*1.50	*1.42	3.5	4.1	2.0
3377	PORT CANAVERAL (TRIDENT PIER)	28° 24.9'	80° 35.6'	*Daily predictions, p.160*				3.47	4.13	1.8
3379	Cocoa Beach	28° 22.1'	80° 36.0'	-1 01	-0 38	*1.47	*1.14	3.46	4.22	1.8
3381	Patrick Air Force Base	28° 14.7'	80° 36.0'	-1 04	-0 38	*1.50	*1.43	3.50	4.20	1.9
	Banana River									
3383	Kennedy Pkwy., Banana Creek, Merritt I. <22>	28° 35.4'	80° 39.5'	- - -	- - -	- - -	- - -	- -	- -	-
3385	VAB Turning Basin, Merritt Island <22>	28° 35.1'	80° 38.6'	- - -	- - -	- - -	- - -	- -	- -	-
3387	Orsino Causeway <22>	28° 30.8'	80° 36.7'	- - -	- - -	- - -	- - -	- -	- -	-
3389	Port Canaveral locks <22>	28° 24.5'	80° 38.3'	- - -	- - -	- - -	- - -	- -	- -	-
3391	Sykes Creek <22>	28° 24.3'	80° 41.8'	- - -	- - -	- - -	- - -	- -	- -	-
3393	Carter's Cut, Merritt Island <22>	28° 09.5'	80° 36.7'	- - -	- - -	- - -	- - -	- -	- -	-
	Indian River									
3395	Titusville <22>	28° 37.2'	80° 48.0'	- - -	- - -	- - -	- - -	- -	- -	-
3397	Williams Point <22>	28° 27.4'	80° 45.6'	- - -	- - -	- - -	- - -	- -	- -	-
3399	Pineda <22>	28° 12.7'	80° 39.8'	- - -	- - -	- - -	- - -	- -	- -	-
3401	Canova Beach	28° 08.3'	80° 34.7'	-0 53	-0 26	*1.49	*1.50	3.45	4.14	1.9
	Indian River - cont.									
3403	Eau Gallie <22>	28° 08.0'	80° 37.5'	- - -	- - -	- - -	- - -	- -	- -	-
3405	Melbourne <22>	28° 06.0'	80° 36.7'	- - -	- - -	- - -	- - -	- -	- -	-
3407	Palm Bay <22>	28° 02.5'	80° 34.9'	- - -	- - -	- - -	- - -	- -	- -	-
3409	Micco	27° 52.4'	80° 29.8'	+1 14	+2 19	*0.14	*0.57	0.26	0.31	0.2
3411	Sebastian Inlet bridge	27° 51.6'	80° 26.9'	-0 48	-0 24	*0.93	*1.00	2.16	2.64	1.2

TABLE 2. – TIDAL DIFFERENCES AND OTHER CONSTANTS

No.	PLACE	POSITION		DIFFERENCES				RANGES		Mean Tide Level
				Time		Height				
		Latitude	Longitude	High Water	Low Water	High Water	Low Water	Mean	Spring	
		North	West	h m	h m	ft	ft	ft	ft	ft
	FLORIDA Atlantic Coast-cont. Time meridian, 75° W			on Miami, Government Cut,						
	Indian River - cont.									
3413	Sebastian	27° 48.7'	80° 27.8'	+1 32	+2 36	*0.15	*0.50	0.30	0.36	0.22
3415	Wabasso	27° 45.3'	80° 25.6'	+2 20	+3 24	*0.17	*0.42	0.37	0.44	0.25
3417	Vero Beach	27° 38.0'	80° 22.5'	+2 56	+3 41	*0.37	*0.79	0.80	0.96	0.51
3419	Oslo	27° 35.6'	80° 21.4'	+3 00	+3 59	*0.34	*0.50	0.77	0.92	0.46
3421	St. Lucie	27° 28.7'	80° 20.0'	+0 41	+1 46	*0.48	*1.00	1.05	1.26	0.66
3423	Vero Beach (ocean)	27° 40.2'	80° 21.6'	-0 55	-0 35	*1.45	*1.36	3.39	4.03	1.88
3425	Fort Pierce Inlet, south jetty	27° 28.2'	80° 17.3'	-0 31	-0 18	*1.14	*1.50	2.61	3.13	1.52
3427	Fort Pierce Inlet, Binney dock	27° 28.1'	80° 17.8'	-0 14	-0 01	*0.82	*1.28	1.85	2.22	1.11
	Indian River - cont.									
3429	Fort Pierce, North Beach Causeway	27° 28.3'	80° 19.5'	+0 21	+0 45	*0.67	*1.14	1.50	1.79	0.91
3431	Fort Pierce, South Beach Causeway	27° 27.4'	80° 19.6'	+0 35	+0 44	*0.64	*1.00	1.43	1.64	0.85
3433	Ankona	27° 21.3'	80° 16.5'	+2 16	+3 03	*0.52	*0.85	1.10	1.32	0.67
3435	Eden, Nettles Island	27° 17.2'	80° 13.6'	+2 35	+3 31	*0.45	*0.92	0.98	1.18	0.62
3437	Jensen Beach	27° 14.1'	80° 12.6'	+2 17	+3 04	*0.48	*0.92	1.05	1.26	0.65
	St. Lucie River									
3439	North Fork	27° 14.6'	80° 18.8'	+2 28	+3 28	*0.46	*0.92	0.99	1.19	0.63
3441	Stuart	27° 12.0'	80° 15.5'	+2 13	+3 30	*0.40	*0.86	0.88	1.06	0.56
3443	South Fork	27° 09.9'	80° 15.3'	+2 35	+3 32	*0.43	*0.92	0.93	1.12	0.59
3445	Sewall Point	27° 10.5'	80° 11.3'	+1 13	+2 10	*0.43	*0.93	0.93	1.11	0.59
3447	Port Salerno, Manatee Pocket	27° 09.1'	80° 11.7'	+0 51	+1 46	*0.42	*0.92	0.90	1.08	0.58
3449	Seminole Shores	27° 11.0'	80° 09.5'	-0 59	-0 35	*1.29	*1.28	3.00	3.60	1.68
3451	Great Pocket	27° 09.1'	80° 10.3'	+0 55	+1 42	*0.50	*1.00	1.08	1.30	0.68
3453	Peck Lake, ICWW	27° 06.8'	80° 08.7'	+1 13	+2 10	*0.58	*1.00	1.28	1.54	0.78
3455	Gomez, South Jupiter Narrows	27° 05.7'	80° 08.2'	+1 33	+2 37	*0.60	*1.07	1.32	1.58	0.81
3457	Hobe Sound bridge	27° 03.8'	80° 07.4'	+1 28	+2 25	*0.68	*1.00	1.53	1.84	0.90
3459	Hobe Sound, Jupiter Island	27° 02.2'	80° 06.4'	+1 16	+2 12	*0.75	*1.00	1.72	2.06	1.00
3461	Conch Bar, Jupiter Sound	26° 59.3'	80° 05.6'	+0 56	+1 34	*0.74	*1.07	1.68	2.02	0.99
3463	Jupiter Sound, south end	26° 57.1'	80° 04.7'	+0 22	+0 45	*0.88	*1.36	1.98	2.38	1.18
3465	Jupiter Inlet, south jetty	26° 56.6'	80° 04.4'	-0 10	-0 09	*1.08	*1.42	2.46	2.95	1.43
3467	Jupiter Inlet, U.S. Highway 1 Bridge	26° 56.9'	80° 05.1'	+0 28	+1 05	*0.86	*1.14	1.96	2.35	1.14
	Loxahatchee River									
3469	A1A highway bridge	26° 56.8'	80° 05.4'	+0 34	+0 54	*0.87	*1.14	2.00	2.40	1.16
3471	Tequesta	26° 57.0'	80° 06.1'	+0 59	+1 58	*0.80	*1.14	1.83	2.20	1.08
3473	Tequesta, North Fork entrance	26° 57.1'	80° 06.1'	+0 51	+1 42	*0.78	*0.92	1.80	2.16	1.03
3475	Tequesta, North Fork	26° 57.6'	80° 06.3'	+1 14	+2 13	*0.75	*1.00	1.72	2.06	1.00
3477	North Fork, 2 miles above entrance	26° 58.6'	80° 06.9'	+1 04	+1 55	*0.86	*1.14	1.95	2.34	1.14
3479	3 miles above A1A highway bridge	26° 58.2'	80° 07.5'	+0 56	+1 49	*0.86	*1.14	1.98	2.38	1.15
3481	Boy Scout Dock	26° 59.2'	80° 08.5'	+1 01	+1 57	*0.92	*1.36	2.09	2.51	1.23
3483	Southwest Fork, 0.5 mile above entrance	26° 56.6'	80° 07.2'	+0 41	+1 35	*0.89	*1.42	2.00	2.40	1.20
3485	Southwest Fork (spillway)	26° 56.1'	80° 08.6'	+0 52	+1 45	*0.86	*1.28	1.94	2.33	1.15
3487	Jupiter, Lake Worth Creek, ICWW	26° 56.1'	80° 05.1'	+0 34	+1 12	*0.91	*1.28	2.06	2.47	1.21
3489	Lake Worth Creek, Day Beacon 19, ICWW	26° 54.7'	80° 04.8'	+0 29	+1 08	*0.92	*1.21	2.10	2.52	1.22
3491	Donald Ross Bridge, ICWW	26° 52.9'	80° 04.2'	+0 20	+0 50	*1.00	*1.21	2.31	2.77	1.32
3493	PGA Boulevard Bridge, ICWW	26° 50.6'	80° 04.0'	-0 02	+0 31	*1.16	*1.36	2.68	3.22	1.53
	Lake Worth									
3495	North Palm Beach	26° 49.6'	80° 03.3'	-0 17	+0 15	*1.22	*1.29	2.81	3.34	1.59
3497	Port of Palm Beach	26° 46.2'	80° 03.1'	-0 21	+0 04	*1.18	*1.36	2.72	3.26	1.55
3499	Palm Beach	26° 44.0'	80° 02.5'	-0 11	+0 16	*1.17	*1.29	2.69	3.20	1.54
3501	Palm Beach, Highway 704 bridge	26° 42.3'	80° 02.7'	+0 18	+0 40	*1.10	*1.07	2.57	3.06	1.44
3503	West Palm Beach Canal	26° 38.7'	80° 02.7'	+0 48	+1 35	*1.07	*1.14	2.46	2.92	1.40
3505	Rt. 802 bridge	26° 36.8'	80° 02.8'	+0 42	+1 26	*1.18	*1.07	2.75	3.27	1.52
3507	Boynton Beach	26° 32.9'	80° 03.2'	+1 05	+2 07	*1.06	*1.07	2.47	2.94	1.38
3509	Lake Worth Pier (ocean)	26° 36.7'	80° 02.0'	-0 45	-0 19	*1.16	*1.00	2.73	3.25	1.50
3511	Ocean Ridge, ICWW	26° 31.6'	80° 03.2'	+1 16	+2 10	*1.10	*1.21	2.54	3.05	1.44
3513	Delray Beach, ICWW	26° 28.4'	80° 03.7'	+1 24	+2 07	*1.07	*1.14	2.47	2.94	1.40
3515	South Delray Beach, ICWW	26° 26.8'	80° 03.9'	+1 28	+2 03	*1.03	*1.10	2.37	2.82	1.34
3517	Yamato, ICWW	26° 24.2'	80° 04.2'	+1 22	+1 57	*1.02	*1.14	2.35	2.81	1.34
3519	Lake Wyman, ICWW	26° 22.2'	80° 04.2'	+1 24	+1 54	*0.93	*1.06	2.14	2.55	1.22
3521	Boca Raton, Lake Boca Raton	26° 20.6'	80° 04.6'	+0 23	+1 07	*0.97	*1.14	2.23	2.68	1.27
3523	Deerfield Beach, Hillsboro River	26° 18.8'	80° 04.9'	+0 28	+1 03	*1.02	*1.07	2.36	2.83	1.33
3525	Hillsboro Beach, ICWW	26° 16.5'	80° 04.8'	+0 02	+0 34	*1.06	*1.07	2.47	2.96	1.39
3527	Hillsboro Inlet, Coast Guard Light Station	26° 15.5'	80° 04.8'	-0 16	+0 03	*1.08	*1.14	2.49	2.96	1.41
3529	Hillsboro Inlet Marina	26° 15.6'	80° 05.1'	-0 06	+0 24	*1.06	*1.14	2.45	2.94	1.38
3531	Hillsboro Inlet (ocean)	26° 15.4'	80° 04.8'	-0 23	+0 00	*1.12	*1.21	2.60	3.12	1.47
3533	Lauderdale-by-the-Sea, Anglin Fishing Pier	26° 11.3'	80° 05.6'	-0 34	-0 13	*1.14	*1.28	2.64	3.17	1.50
	Fort Lauderdale									
3535	Bahia Mar Yacht Club	26° 06.8'	80° 06.5'	-0 05	+0 33	*1.05	*1.21	2.42	2.90	1.38
3537	Andrews Avenue bridge, New River	26° 07.1'	80° 08.7'	+0 15	+0 51	*0.92	*1.07	2.13	2.56	1.22
3539	Mayan Lake	26° 06.0'	80° 06.5'	+0 20	+1 02	*0.91	*1.00	2.11	2.53	1.19
3541	Port Everglades, Turning Basin	26° 05.5'	80° 07.4'	-0 29	-0 09	*1.09	*1.14	2.53	3.01	1.43
3543	South Port Everglades, ICWW	26° 04.9'	80° 07.0'	-0 23	-0 03	*1.10	*1.42	2.52	3.02	1.46
3545	Whiskey Creek, north end	26° 04.8'	80° 06.7'	-0 23	-0 06	*1.10	*1.28	2.52	3.02	1.44
3547	Port Laudania, Dania cut-off Canal	26° 03.6'	80° 07.8'	+0 01	+0 11	*1.00	*1.21	2.30	2.76	1.32
3549	Whiskey Creek, south entrance, ICWW	26° 03.3'	80° 06.8'	+0 04	+0 31	*0.96	*1.14	2.21	2.63	1.27
3551	Hollywood Beach, West Lake, north end	26° 02.6'	80° 07.6'	+1 08	+1 42	*0.85	*1.07	1.94	2.33	1.12
3553	Hollywood Beach, West Lake, south end	26° 02.0'	80° 07.4'	+1 02	+1 45	*0.88	*1.14	2.02	2.42	1.17
3555	Hollywood Beach	26° 02.4'	80° 06.9'	+0 37	+1 41	*0.91	*1.14	2.08	2.50	1.20
3557	Golden Beach, ICWW	25° 58.0'	80° 07.4'	+1 13	+1 57	*0.91	*1.07	2.10	2.52	1.20
3559	Dumfoundling Bay	25° 56.5'	80° 07.5'	+1 17	+2 07	*0.88	*1.00	2.02	2.40	1.15
3561	Sunny Isles, Biscayne Creek	25° 55.9'	80° 07.8'	+2 00	+2 24	*0.77	*0.71	1.8	2.2	1.0
3563	Biscayne Creek, ICWW	25° 52.8'	80° 09.8'	+0 47	+1 39	*0.93	*1.00	2.15	2.56	1.21
3565	North Miami Beach, Newport Fishing Pier	25° 55.8'	80° 07.2'	-0 22	+0 00	*1.08	*1.21	2.49	2.96	1.41
3567	Haulover Pier, N. Miami Beach	25° 54.2'	80° 07.2'	-0 29	-0 06	*1.06	*1.00	2.48	2.95	1.37

TABLE 2. – TIDAL DIFFERENCES AND OTHER CONSTANTS

No.	PLACE	POSITION Latitude	POSITION Longitude	DIFFERENCES Time High Water	DIFFERENCES Time Low Water	DIFFERENCES Height High Water	DIFFERENCES Height Low Water	RANGES Mean	RANGES Spring	Mean Tide Level
		North	West	h m	h m	ft	ft	ft	ft	ft
	FLORIDA Atlantic Coast-cont. Time meridian, 75° W			on Miami, Government Cut,						
3569	Bakers Haulover Inlet (inside)	25° 54.2'	80° 07.5'	+0 57	+1 37	*0.87	*0.92	2.01	2.20	1.13
3571	Indian Creek Golf Club, ICWW	25° 52.5'	80° 08.6'	+1 13	+1 46	*0.92	*0.92	2.13	2.56	1.20
3573	Miami Harbor Entrance	25° 46.1'	80° 07.9'	-0 22	-0 02	*1.07	*1.14	2.46	2.93	1.39
3575	GOVERNMENT CUT, MIAMI HARBOR ENTRANCE	25° 45.8'	80° 07.8'	Daily predictions				2.32	2.83	1.32
	Biscayne Bay									
3577	San Marino Island	25° 47.6'	80° 09.8'	+0 37	+0 58	*0.92	*1.00	2.14	2.57	1.21
3579	Miami, Miamarina	25° 46.7'	80° 11.1'	+0 20	+0 49	*0.94	*0.92	2.18	2.59	1.22
3581	Dodge Island, Fishermans Channel	25° 46.2'	80° 10.1'	+0 34	+1 10	*0.91	*1.00	2.10	2.52	1.19
3583	Dinner Key Marina	25° 43.6'	80° 14.2'	+0 54	+1 48	*0.84	*0.92	1.94	2.33	1.10
	Florida Keys									
3585	Bear Cut, Virginia Key	25° 43.9'	80° 09.7'	+0 28	+0 51	*0.88	*0.86	2.05	2.44	1.15
3587	Key Biscayne Yacht Club, Biscayne Bay	25° 41.9'	80° 10.2'	+0 44	+1 31	*0.86	*0.92	2.00	2.40	1.13
3589	Coral Shoal, Biscayne Channel	25° 39.1'	80° 09.4'	+0 11	+0 37	*0.88	*0.92	2.05	2.46	1.15
3591	Cutler, Biscayne Bay	25° 36.9'	80° 18.3'	+1 01	+1 58	*0.84	*0.92	1.94	2.22	1.10
3593	Soldier Key	25° 35'	80° 10'	+0 30	+1 16	*0.81	*0.71	1.9	2.3	1.0
3595	Ragged Keys, Biscayne Bay	25° 32.0'	80° 10.3'	+0 43	+1 18	*0.73	*1.00	1.65	1.96	0.96
3597	Boca Chita Key, Biscayne Bay	25° 31.4'	80° 10.6'	+1 01	+1 39	*0.70	*1.14	1.57	1.88	0.94
3599	Sands Key, northwest point, Biscayne Bay	25° 30.3'	80° 11.3'	+1 25	+2 26	*0.63	*0.64	1.46	1.64	0.82
3601	Coon Point, Elliott Key, Biscayne Bay	25° 28.7'	80° 11.4'	+1 55	+2 56	*0.63	*0.71	1.44	1.63	0.82
3603	Elliott Key Harbor, Elliott Key, Biscayne Bay	25° 27.2'	80° 11.8'	+1 56	+3 00	*0.64	*0.64	1.48	1.67	0.83
3605	Turkey Point, Biscayne Bay	25° 26.2'	80° 19.7'	+2 11	+3 21	*0.70	*0.79	1.61	1.71	0.92
3607	Billys Point, south of, Elliott Key, Biscayne Bay	25° 24.9'	80° 12.6'	+2 08	+3 20	*0.63	*0.64	1.46	1.65	0.82
3609	Sea Grape Point, Elliott Key	25° 28.6'	80° 10.8'	-0 25	-0 05	*1.03	*1.03	2.30	2.74	1.39
3611	Christmas Point, Elliott Key	25° 23.5'	80° 13.8'	+0 13	+0 37	*0.80	*1.07	1.82	2.13	1.06
3613	Adams Key, south end, Biscayne Bay	25° 23.8'	80° 14.0'	+1 01	+1 08	*0.67	*1.00	1.52	1.75	0.90
3615	Totten Key, west side, Biscayne Bay	25° 22.7'	80° 15.4'	+2 19	+3 21	*0.54	*0.57	1.26	1.41	0.71
3617	East Arsenicker, Card Sound	25° 22.4'	80° 17.5'	+2 26	+3 09	*0.40	*0.64	0.91	1.04	0.54
3619	Card Sound, western side	25° 20.7'	80° 19.9'	+2 51	+3 40	*0.30	*0.43	0.68	0.77	0.40
3621	Pumpkin Key, south end, Card Sound	25° 19.5'	80° 17.6'	+2 35	+2 52	*0.30	*0.78	0.63	0.71	0.43
3623	Wednesday Point, Key Largo, Card Sound	25° 18.6'	80° 17.9'	+2 38	+3 30	*0.34	*0.57	0.77	0.88	0.46
3625	Cormorant Point, Key Largo, Card Sound	25° 17.4'	80° 20.3'	+2 45	+3 01	*0.32	*0.50	0.73	0.82	0.43
3627	Little Card Sound bridge	25° 17.3'	80° 22.2'	+3 30	+4 03	*0.24	*0.43	0.53	0.63	0.33
3629	Ocean Reef Harbor, Key Largo	25° 18.6'	80° 16.8'	-0 08	+0 17	*1.02	*1.50	2.30	2.74	1.36
3631	Main Key, Barnes Sound	25° 14.4'	80° 24.0'	+5 04	+6 16	*0.19	*0.36	0.41	0.46	0.26
3633	Manatee Creek, Manatee Bay, Barnes Sound	25° 14.1'	80° 25.8'	+5 14	+6 20	*0.18	*0.36	0.39	0.44	0.25
3635	Manatee Creek, Hwy. 1 bridge, Long Sound <26>	25° 14.1'	80° 26.1'	- - -	- - -	- - -	- - -	- -	- -	- -
3637	Carysfort Reef	25° 13.3'	80° 12.7'	+0 19	+0 39	*1.03	*1.36	2.34	2.60	1.36
3639	Jewfish Creek entrance, Blackwater Sound <26>	25° 11.0'	80° 23.2'	- - -	- - -	- - -	- - -	- -	- -	- -
3641	Deep Six Marina, Blackwater Sound <26>	25° 08.4'	80° 24.2'	- - -	- - -	- - -	- - -	- -	- -	- -
3643	Garden Cove, Key Largo	25° 10.3'	80° 22.0'	-0 01	+0 25	*0.94	*1.14	2.16	2.53	1.24
3645	Largo Sound, Key Largo	25° 08.4'	80° 23.7'	+2 13	+3 03	*0.35	*0.50	0.80	0.96	0.47
3647	Key Largo, South Sound, Key Largo	25° 06.8'	80° 25.0'	+0 23	+1 49	*0.66	*0.64	1.55	1.86	0.85
3649	Point Charles, Key Largo	25° 04.9'	80° 27.0'	+0 25	+1 53	*0.77	*0.64	1.80	2.14	0.99
3651	Rock Harbor, Key Largo	25° 04.9'	80° 26.8'	+0 22	+0 36	*0.94	*1.21	2.14	2.57	1.24
3653	Sunset Cove, Key Largo, Buttonwood Sound <26>	25° 05.7'	80° 26.6'	- - -	- - -	- - -	- - -	- -	- -	- -
3655	Hammer Point, Key Largo, Florida Bay <26>	25° 02.1'	80° 30.3'	- - -	- - -	- - -	- - -	- -	- -	- -
3657	Tavernier, Key Largo, Florida Bay <26>	25° 00.9'	80° 30.9'	- - -	- - -	- - -	- - -	- -	- -	- -
3659	Tavernier Harbor, Hawk Channel	25° 00.3'	80° 31.0'	+0 07	+0 26	*0.90	*1.36	2.04	2.43	1.21
3661	Tavernier Creek, Hwy. 1 bridge, Hawk Channel	25° 00.2'	80° 31.8'	+0 25	+0 52	*0.60	*1.07	1.32	1.58	0.81
3663	Plantation Key, northern end, Florida Bay <26>	25° 00.1'	80° 32.6'	- - -	- - -	- - -	- - -	- -	- -	- -
3665	Crane Keys, north side, Florida Bay	25° 00.3'	80° 37.1'	+2 52	+4 35	*0.17	*0.21	0.39	0.46	0.22
3667	East Key, southern end, Florida Bay	24° 59.8'	80° 36.6'	+2 43	+4 06	*0.22	*0.14	0.52	0.62	0.28
3669	Plantation Key, Hawk Channel	24° 58.4'	80° 33.0'	+0 05	+0 12	*0.96	*1.21	2.20	2.64	1.27
3671	Yacht Harbor, Cowpens Anchorage, Plantation Key	24° 57.9'	80° 34.1'	+2 45	+4 00	*0.23	*0.29	0.53	0.64	0.31
3673	Snake Creek, Hwy. 1 bridge, Windley Key	24° 57.1'	80° 35.3'	+0 49	+0 56	*0.46	*0.50	1.07	1.28	0.61
3675	Snake Creek, USCG Station, Plantation Key	24° 57.2'	80° 35.2'	+1 08	+1 56	*0.36	*0.50	0.82	0.98	0.48
3677	Whale Harbor, Windley Key, Hawk Channel	24° 56.4'	80° 36.5'	+0 07	+0 51	*0.65	*0.36	1.56	1.87	0.83
3679	Whale Harbor Channel, Hwy. 1 bridge, Windley Key	24° 56.3'	80° 36.6'	+0 16	+1 00	*0.59	*0.71	1.36	1.63	0.78
3681	Upper Matecumbe Key, Hawk Channel	24° 54.9'	80° 37.9'	+0 34	+0 49	*0.87	*1.21	1.98	2.38	1.16
3683	Alligator Reef, Hawk Channel	24° 51.0'	80° 37.1'	+0 08	+0 24	*0.86	*1.36	1.93	2.37	1.15
				on Key West,						
3685	Flamingo, Florida Bay	25° 08.5'	80° 55.4'	+5 28	+7 20	*1.47	*1.08	2.02	2.52	1.27
3687	Upper Matecumbe Key, west end, Hawk Channel	24° 53.8'	80° 39.5'	-1 00	+0 14	*0.98	*0.33	1.44	1.80	0.80
3689	Indian Key, Hawk Channel	24° 52.6'	80° 40.6'	-0 58	-0 35	*1.30	*0.71	1.84	2.30	1.09
3691	Shell Key Channel, Florida Bay	24° 54.8'	80° 39.6'	-0 20	+0 45	*0.78	*0.78	1.02	1.28	0.58
3693	Lignumvitae Key, NE side, Florida Bay	24° 54.2'	80° 41.7'	+0 09	+1 31	*0.52	*0.52	0.68	0.85	0.37
3695	Lignumvitae Key, west side, Florida Bay	24° 54.0'	80° 42.3'	+0 32	+1 54	*0.47	*0.47	0.62	0.74	0.3
3697	Little Basin, Upper Matecumbe Key, Florida Bay	24° 54.9'	80° 38.4'	+0 08	+1 15	*0.61	*0.61	0.80	1.00	0.4
3699	Shell Key, northwest side, Lignumvitae Basin	24° 55.4'	80° 40.3'	+0 31	+1 57	*0.46	*0.46	0.60	0.75	0.3
3701	Islamorada, Upper Matecumbe Key, Florida Bay	24° 55.5'	80° 37.9'	+0 39	+2 07	*0.37	*0.37	0.49	0.57	0.36
3703	Indian Key Anchorage, Lower Matecumbe Key	24° 52.1'	80° 42.2'	-1 25	-0 54	*1.38	*0.88	1.89	2.34	1.1
3705	Matecumbe Bight, Lower Matecumbe Key, Fla. Bay	24° 51.9'	80° 43.0'	-0 18	+0 33	*0.55	*0.38	0.75	0.93	0.4
3707	Matecumbe Harbor, Lower Matecumbe Key, Fla. Bay	24° 51.1'	80° 44.4'	-0 25	+0 23	*0.59	*0.33	0.83	1.04	0.5
3709	Channel Two, east, Lower Matecumbe Key, Fla. Bay	24° 50.7'	80° 44.9'	-0 49	-0 42	*0.85	*0.54	1.18	1.48	0.7
3711	Channel Two, west side, Hawk Channel	24° 50.5'	80° 45.2'	-1 06	-0 54	*1.12	*0.75	1.55	1.94	0.9
3713	Channel Five, east side, Hawk Channel	24° 50.2'	80° 46.0'	-0 54	-0 42	*0.90	*0.58	1.25	1.56	0.7
3715	Channel Five, west side, Hawk Channel	24° 50.4'	80° 46.8'	-0 58	-0 41	*1.00	*0.67	1.39	1.74	0.8
3717	Jewfish Hole, Long Key, Florida Bay	24° 50.3'	80° 47.9'	-0 11	+1 32	*0.42	*0.38	0.56	0.70	0.3
3719	Long Key Bight, Long Key	24° 49.7'	80° 48.5'	-0 59	-0 43	*1.03	*0.62	1.44	1.80	0.8
3721	Long Key Lake, Long Key	24° 49.2'	80° 49.0'	+0 33	+0 57	*0.62	*0.46	0.85	1.06	0.5

TABLE 2. – TIDAL DIFFERENCES AND OTHER CONSTANTS

No.	PLACE	POSITION		DIFFERENCES				RANGES		Mean Tide Level
		Latitude	Longitude	Time		Height		Mean	Spring	
				High Water	Low Water	High Water	Low Water			
		North	West	h m	h m	ft	ft	ft	ft	ft
	FLORIDA Florida Keys-cont. Time meridian, 75° W			on Key West,						
3723	Long Key, western end	24° 48.1'	80° 51.0'	-1 01	-0 54	*0.82	*0.33	1.19	1.49	0.67
3725	Conch Key, eastern end	24° 47.5'	80° 53.0'	-1 09	-0 45	*0.85	*0.54	1.18	1.48	0.72
3727	Toms Harbor Cut	24° 47.0'	80° 54.4'	-1 19	-0 30	*0.37	*0.38	0.48	0.60	0.33
3729	Toms Harbor, Duck Key <26>	24° 46.4'	80° 54.9'	- - -	- - -	- - -	- - -	--	--	--
3731	Duck Key, Hawk Channel	24° 45.9'	80° 54.8'	-1 11	-0 40	*0.97	*0.55	1.34	1.66	0.80
3733	Toms Harbor Channel, Hwy. 1 bridge	24° 46.6'	80° 55.4'	+5 07	+4 49	*0.38	*0.38	0.50	0.62	0.45
3735	Grassy Key, north side, Florida Bay	24° 46.3'	80° 56.4'	+5 40	+6 48	*0.73	*1.04	0.86	1.07	0.68
3737	Grassy Key, south side, Hawk Channel	24° 45.3'	80° 57.5'	-0 52	-0 26	*1.22	*0.71	1.72	2.15	1.03
3739	Fat Deer Key, Florida Bay	24° 44.0'	81° 01.1'	+5 09	+6 26	*0.87	*0.87	1.14	1.42	0.82
3741	Vaca Key-Fat Deer Key bridge	24° 43.8'	81° 01.8'	-1 11	-0 36	*0.95	*0.71	1.31	1.64	0.83
3743	Key Colony Beach	24° 43.1'	81° 01.0'	-1 17	-0 53	*1.22	*0.83	1.66	2.06	1.03
3745	VACA KEY, USCG STATION, FLORIDA BAY ...	24° 42.7'	81° 06.3'	Daily predictions,				0.72	0.97	0.51
3747	Boot Key Harbor bridge, Boot Key	24° 42.2'	81° 06.3'	-1 03	-0 37	*1.13	*0.75	1.57	1.96	0.96
3749	Sombrero Key, Hawk Channel	24° 37.6'	81° 06.7'	-1 03	-0 39	*1.18	*0.79	1.64	2.02	1.01
3751	Knight Key Channel, Knight Key, Florida Bay	24° 42.4'	81° 07.5'	-0 02	-0 18	*0.54	*0.50	0.72	0.90	0.48
3753	Pigeon Key, south side, Hawk Channel	24° 42.2'	81° 09.3'	-0 55	-0 26	*0.81	*0.50	1.14	1.42	0.69
3755	Pigeon Key, north side, Florida Bay	24° 42.3'	81° 09.4'	-0 10	+0 45	*0.46	*0.46	0.60	0.75	0.44
3757	Molasses Key Channel, Molasses Keys	24° 41.0'	81° 11.5'	-0 56	-0 16	*0.79	*0.50	1.10	1.38	0.67
3759	Money Key	24° 41.0'	81° 12.9'	+0 03	+1 17	*0.58	*0.58	0.76	0.95	0.54
3761	Little Duck Key, east end, Hawk Channel	24° 40.9'	81° 13.7'	-0 49	+0 05	*0.67	*0.67	0.88	1.10	0.60
3763	East Bahia Honda Key, south end, Florida Bay	24° 46.5'	81° 13.6'	+4 04	+2 49	*0.69	*0.69	0.90	1.12	0.77
3765	Cocoanut Key, Florida Bay	24° 44.7'	81° 14.2'	+3 52	+2 50	*0.55	*0.55	0.72	0.90	0.66
3767	West Bahia Honda Key	24° 46.8'	81° 16.3'	+3 59	+4 01	*0.97	*1.00	1.27	1.59	0.88
3769	Horseshoe Keys, south end	24° 46.0'	81° 17.0'	+3 54	+3 09	*0.86	*1.00	1.09	1.36	0.79
3771	Johnson Keys, south end	24° 44.6'	81° 18.0'	+3 36	+2 33	*0.72	*0.96	0.88	1.10	0.67
3773	Johnson Keys, north end	24° 46.0'	81° 19.4'	+3 35	+4 22	*1.31	*1.38	1.70	2.12	1.18
3775	Missouri Key-Little Duck Key Channel	24° 40.8'	81° 14.1'	-0 52	+0 36	*0.70	*0.46	0.98	1.22	0.60
3777	Missouri Key-Ohio Key Channel, west side ..	24° 40.4'	81° 14.6'	-0 47	-0 22	*0.77	*0.50	1.08	1.35	0.66
3779	Ohio Key-Bahia Honda Key Channel, west side ..	24° 40.2'	81° 15.1'	-0 57	-0 14	*0.81	*0.62	1.10	1.38	0.70
3781	Bahia Honda Key, Bahia Honda Channel	24° 39.3'	81° 16.9'	-0 46	-0 28	*0.86	*0.63	1.16	1.44	0.73
3783	Big Pine Key, Spanish Harbor	24° 38.9'	81° 19.8'	-0 44	-0 03	*0.75	*0.42	1.07	1.34	0.64
3785	Big Pine Key, Doctors Arm, Bogie Channel ..	24° 41.4'	81° 21.4'	+0 41	+1 47	*0.63	*0.71	0.80	1.00	0.57
3787	Big Pine Key, Bogie Channel Bridge	24° 41.9'	81° 20.9'	+2 10	+2 11	*0.65	*0.83	0.80	1.00	0.60
3789	No Name Key, east side, Bahia Honda Channel ..	24° 41.9'	81° 19.1'	+1 35	+1 33	*0.58	*0.83	0.70	0.88	0.55
3791	Little Pine Key, south end	24° 42.8'	81° 18.2'	+1 07	+1 07	*0.56	*0.79	0.68	0.85	0.53
3793	Porpoise Key, Big Spanish Channel	24° 43.1'	81° 21.1'	+3 23	+2 29	*0.72	*1.00	0.88	1.10	0.68
3795	Water Key, west end, Big Spanish Channel ..	24° 44.4'	81° 20.5'	+3 23	+2 37	*0.81	*1.04	1.00	1.25	0.75
3797	Mayo Key, Big Spanish Channel	24° 44.0'	81° 21.7'	+3 35	+3 01	*0.92	*1.08	1.17	1.46	0.85
3799	Little Pine Key, north end	24° 45.0'	81° 19.7'	+3 38	+3 28	*1.05	*1.21	1.33	1.66	0.96
3801	Big Pine Key, northeast shore	24° 43.7'	81° 23.2'	+3 19	+2 30	*0.86	*1.08	1.08	1.35	0.80
3803	Crawl Key, Big Spanish Channel	24° 45.4'	81° 21.5'	+3 34	+4 13	*1.33	*1.33	1.74	2.18	1.19
3805	Big Pine Key, north end	24° 44.7'	81° 23.7'	+4 24	+5 56	*0.96	*0.83	1.29	1.61	0.85
3807	Annette Key, north end, Big Spanish Channel	24° 45.5'	81° 23.4'	+3 30	+4 33	*1.44	*1.29	1.92	2.40	1.27
3809	Little Spanish Key, Spanish Banks	24° 46.5'	81° 22.2'	+3 25	+4 30	*1.74	*1.62	2.30	2.88	1.54
3811	Big Spanish Key	24° 47.3'	81° 24.7'	+3 19	+4 29	*1.97	*1.50	2.69	3.36	1.71
3813	Munson Island, Newfound Harbor Channel	24° 37.4'	81° 24.2'	-0 40	-0 12	*0.98	*0.67	1.36	1.70	0.84
3815	Ramrod Key, Newfound Harbor	24° 39.0'	81° 24.2'	-0 41	+0 05	*0.90	*0.50	1.28	1.60	0.76
3817	Middle Torch Key, Torch Ramrod Channel ...	24° 39.7'	81° 24.1'	-0 16	+1 29	*0.69	*0.38	0.98	1.22	0.58
3819	Little Torch Key, Torch Channel	24° 39.9'	81° 23.7'	+0 11	+1 45	*0.57	*0.33	0.80	1.00	0.48
3821	Big Pine Key, Newfound Harbor Channel	24° 39.1'	81° 22.5'	-0 09	+0 44	*0.82	*0.46	1.16	1.45	0.69
3823	Big Pine Key, Coupon Bight	24° 39.1'	81° 21.0'	-0 20	+0 49	*0.87	*0.50	1.19	1.48	0.72
3825	Little Torch Key, Pine Channel Bridge, south side .	24° 39.9'	81° 23.3'	-0 15	+0 57	*0.68	*0.33	0.97	1.21	0.56
3827	Big Pine Key, Pine Channel Bridge, south side ...	24° 40.1'	81° 22.3'	-0 13	+1 03	*0.67	*0.33	0.96	1.20	0.56
3829	Big Pine Key, Pine Channel Bridge, north side ...	24° 40.2'	81° 22.1'	+0 03	+1 43	*0.57	*0.33	0.79	0.98	0.47
3831	Big Pine Key, west side, Pine Channel	24° 41.4'	81° 23.0'	+0 21	+1 52	*0.52	*0.42	0.71	0.89	0.45
3833	Howe Key, south end, Harbor Channel	24° 43.5'	81° 24.4'	+4 43	+4 49	*0.72	*0.62	0.96	1.20	0.63
3835	Big Torch Key, Harbor Channel	24° 44.3'	81° 26.6'	+3 47	+5 51	*1.58	*1.29	2.14	2.68	1.38
3837	Water Keys, south end, Harbor Channel	24° 44.8'	81° 27.0'	+3 42	+5 41	*1.52	*1.00	2.11	2.64	1.29
3839	Howe Key, northwest end	24° 45.5'	81° 25.7'	+3 29	+5 22	*1.68	*1.33	2.28	2.85	1.46
3841	Summerland Key, Niles Channel South	24° 39.1'	81° 26.1'	-0 36	+0 11	*0.85	*0.71	1.14	1.42	0.74
3843	Summerland Key, Niles Channel Bridge	24° 39.6'	81° 26.2'	-0 10	+0 56	*0.67	*0.58	0.90	1.12	0.59
3845	Ramrod Key, Niles Channel Bridge	24° 39.6'	81° 25.4'	-0 13	+1 12	*0.67	*0.46	0.93	1.16	0.58
3847	Big Torch Key, Niles Channel	24° 42.3'	81° 26.0'	+3 15	+2 05	*0.61	*0.71	0.77	0.96	0.56
3849	Knockemdown Key, north end	24° 42.9'	81° 28.7'	+3 30	+4 54	*1.35	*1.21	1.80	2.25	1.19
3851	Raccoon Key, east side	24° 44.5'	81° 29.0'	+3 20	+5 09	*1.50	*1.21	2.04	2.55	1.31
3853	Content Keys, Content Passage	24° 47.4'	81° 29.0'	+2 46	+3 49	*2.13	*1.83	2.79	3.46	1.84
3855	Key Lois, southeast end	24° 36.4'	81° 28.2'	-1 15	-0 45	*1.06	*0.75	1.46	1.82	0.91
3857	Sugarloaf Key, east side, Tarpon Creek	24° 37.7'	81° 30.6'	-0 41	+0 15	*0.89	*0.58	1.24	1.55	0.76
3859	Gopher Key, Cudjoe Bay	24° 38.5'	81° 29.1'	-0 46	+0 17	*0.90	*0.71	1.22	1.52	0.78
3861	Sugarloaf Key, Pirates Cove	24° 39.2'	81° 30.9'	-0 48	+1 41	*0.59	*0.75	0.74	0.92	0.55
3863	Cudjoe Key, Cudjoe Bay	24° 39.6'	81° 29.5'	-0 38	+0 41	*0.87	*0.71	1.18	1.48	0.76
3865	Summerland Key, southwest side, Kemp Channel	24° 39.0'	81° 26.8'	-0 26	+0 50	*0.81	*0.54	1.12	1.40	0.69
3867	Kemp Channel Viaduct, Hwy A1A bridge	24° 39.1'	81° 28.1'	+0 47	+2 04	*0.58	*0.46	0.77	0.95	0.50
3869	Cudjoe Key, Kemp Channel Bridge	24° 39.7'	81° 28.1'	- - -	- - -	*0.59	*0.50	0.79	0.99	0.52
3871	Cudjoe Key, northeast side, Kemp Channel ..	24° 41.2'	81° 29.0'	+3 45	- - -	- - -	- - -	--	--	--
3873	Cudjoe Key, north end, Kemp Channel	24° 42.0'	81° 30.3'	+3 33	+4 40	*1.61	*1.46	2.10	2.60	1.41
3875	Sugarloaf Key, northeast side, Bow Channel	24° 40.3'	81° 32.0'	+3 47	+3 24	*1.01	*0.71	1.40	1.75	0.87
3877	Cudjoe Key, Pirates Cove	24° 39.7'	81° 30.9'	+3 50	+2 54	*0.77	*0.79	0.98	1.21	0.68
3879	Sugarloaf Key, north end, Bow Channel	24° 41.6'	81° 33.3'	+3 37	+5 20	*1.29	*0.75	1.82	2.28	1.09
3881	Pumpkin Key, Bow Channel	24° 43.0'	81° 33.7'	+3 17	+4 39	*1.56	*1.17	2.14	2.68	1.35
3883	Sawyer Key, outside, Cudjoe Channel	24° 45.5'	81° 33.7'	+2 45	+5 24	*1.57	*0.50	2.32	2.90	1.28
3885	Sawyer Key, inside, Cudjoe Channel	24° 45.5'	81° 33.7'	+2 37	+5 19	*1.43	*0.50	2.10	2.62	1.17
3887	Johnston Key, southwest end, Turkey Basin	24° 42.6'	81° 35.6'	+3 26	+5 38	*1.10	*0.50	1.59	1.99	0.92

TABLE 2. – TIDAL DIFFERENCES AND OTHER CONSTANTS

No.	PLACE	POSITION Latitude	POSITION Longitude	DIFFERENCES Time High Water	DIFFERENCES Time Low Water	DIFFERENCES Height High Water	DIFFERENCES Height Low Water	RANGES Mean	RANGES Spring	Mean Tide Level
		North	West	h m	h m	ft	ft	ft	ft	ft
	FLORIDA Florida Keys-cont. Time meridian, 75° W			*on Key West,*						
	Upper Sugarloaf Sound									
3889	Perky	24° 38.9'	81° 34.2'	+5 37	+8 25	*0.28	*0.08	0.42	0.52	0.23
3891	Park Channel Bridge	24° 39.3'	81° 32.4'	+5 47	+8 33	*0.26	*0.29	0.34	0.42	0.24
3893	North Harris Channel	24° 39.0'	81° 33.2'	+5 32	+8 04	*0.25	*0.25	0.33	0.41	0.22
3895	Sugarloaf Shores East <26>	24° 38.6'	81° 33.6'	- - -	- - -	- - -	- - -	- -	- -	- -
3897	Tarpon Creek	24° 37.8'	81° 31.0'	-0 29	+0 17	*0.35	*0.38	0.46	0.58	0.32
	Lower Sugarloaf Sound <27>									
3899	Sugarloaf Shores <27>	24° 38.0'	81° 33.1'	- - -	- - -	- - -	- - -	- -	- -	- -
3901	Sugarloaf Beach <27>	24° 36.4'	81° 34.0'	- - -	- - -	- - -	- - -	- -	- -	- -
3903	Sugarloaf Shores North <27>	24° 38.4'	81° 34.2'	- - -	- - -	- - -	- - -	- -	- -	- -
3905	Saddlebunch Keys, south end <27>	24° 36.1'	81° 34.9'	- - -	- - -	- - -	- - -	- -	- -	- -
3907	Lower Sugarloaf Channel Bridge <27>	24° 38.0'	81° 35.2'	- - -	- - -	- - -	- - -	- -	- -	- -
3909	Saddlebunch Keys, Channel No. 2 <27>	24° 37.6'	81° 35.9'	- - -	- - -	- - -	- - -	- -	- -	- -
3911	Saddlebunch Keys <27>	24° 37.1'	81° 36.1'	- - -	- - -	- - -	- - -	- -	- -	- -
3913	Snipe Keys, southeast end, Inner Narrows	24° 39.5'	81° 36.5'	+3 25	+5 39	*1.28	*0.83	1.79	2.24	1.10
3915	Snipe Keys, Middle Narrows	24° 40.0'	81° 37.8'	+3 44	+5 54	*1.02	*0.67	1.42	1.78	0.87
3917	Snipe Keys, Snipe Point	24° 41.5'	81° 40.4'	+2 15	+3 33	*1.69	*1.29	2.31	2.89	1.47
3919	Waltz Key, Waltz Key Basin	24° 38.8'	81° 39.2'	+3 53	+5 33	*1.03	*0.96	1.36	1.70	0.91
3921	Duck Key Point, Duck Key, Waltz Key Basin	24° 37.4'	81° 41.1'	+3 27	+4 57	*1.19	*0.96	1.61	2.01	1.03
3923	O'Hara Key, north end, Waltz Key Basin	24° 37.0'	81° 38.7'	+3 53	+5 39	*1.03	*0.83	1.40	1.75	0.90
3925	Saddlebunch Keys, Channel No. 5	24° 36.7'	81° 37.5'	+4 32	+6 58	*0.66	*1.12	0.76	0.95	0.65
3927	Saddlebunch Keys, Channel No. 4	24° 36.9'	81° 37.0'	+4 35	+5 36	*0.54	*0.29	0.76	0.95	0.45
3929	Saddlebunch Keys, Channel No. 3	24° 37.4'	81° 36.2'	+1 44	-0 10	*0.43	*0.21	0.62	0.78	0.36
3931	Bird Key, Similar Sound	24° 35.3'	81° 38.3'	-0 21	+1 03	*0.59	*0.42	0.82	1.02	0.51
3933	Shark Key, southeast end, Similar Sound	24° 36.2'	81° 38.7'	+0 18	+1 51	*0.52	*0.46	0.70	0.88	0.46
3935	Saddlebunch Keys, Similar Sound	24° 36.0'	81° 37.3'	+0 39	+2 41	*0.37	*0.21	0.52	0.65	0.31
3937	Geiger Key, inside <26>	24° 35.0'	81° 39.3'	- - -	- - -	- - -	- - -	- -	- -	- -
3939	Big Coppitt Key, northeast side, Waltz Key Basin	24° 36.1'	81° 39.3'	+4 21	+6 54	*0.84	*0.33	1.22	1.52	0.69
3941	Rockland Key, Rockland Channel Bridge	24° 35.5'	81° 40.1'	+5 02	+6 06	*0.76	*0.88	0.97	1.21	0.69
3943	Boca Chica Key, Long Point	24° 36.2'	81° 41.9'	+3 54	+5 22	*0.94	*0.71	1.28	1.60	0.81
3945	Channel Key, west side	24° 36.2'	81° 43.5'	+3 09	+3 07	*0.70	*0.71	0.91	1.14	0.62
3947	Boca Chica Marina	24° 34.5'	81° 42.5'	+0 20	+1 11	*0.66	*0.71	0.83	1.03	0.58
3949	Boca Chica Key, Southwest end	24° 33.8'	81° 42.8'	-0 14	+0 16	*0.66	*0.63	0.87	1.08	0.58
3951	Boca Chica Channel Bridge	24° 34.6'	81° 43.2'	+1 23	+1 29	*0.57	*0.67	0.72	0.90	0.52
3953	Key Haven - Stock Island Channel	24° 34.8'	81° 44.3'	+2 25	+2 57	*0.73	*0.79	0.94	1.18	0.66
3955	Cow Key Channel	24° 34.2'	81° 45.0'	+1 55	+2 05	*0.65	*0.71	0.82	1.01	0.58
3957	Sigsbee Park, Garrison Bight Channel	24° 35.1'	81° 46.5'	+1 59	+2 06	*0.81	*0.88	1.04	1.30	0.73
3959	Fleming Key, north end	24° 35.5'	81° 47.7'	+1 38	+1 54	*0.79	*0.79	1.01	1.25	0.69
3961	Riveria Canal, Key West	24° 33.9'	81° 45.1'	-0 12	+1 00	*0.65	*0.63	0.84	1.04	0.57
3963	Key West, south side, White Street Pier	24° 32.7'	81° 47.0'	-0 53	-0 31	*1.07	*0.92	1.41	1.75	0.92
3965	KEY WEST	24° 33.2'	81° 48.5'	*Daily predictions*				1.28	1.65	0.88
3967	Sand Key Lighthouse, Sand Key Channel	24° 27.2'	81° 52.6'	-0 43	-0 32	*0.95	*0.88	1.23	1.53	0.83
3969	Garden Key, Dry Tortugas	24° 37.6'	82° 52.3'	+0 29	+0 33	*0.94	*1.33	1.14	1.42	0.89
3971	Loggerhead Key, Dry Tortugas	24° 37.9'	82° 55.2'	+0 19	+0 24	*0.91	*1.13	1.12	1.38	0.83
3973	Smith Shoal Light	24° 43.1'	81° 55.2'	+1 43	+2 20	*2.10	*2.37	2.63	3.44	1.88
	Southern Gulf Coast			*on Naples,*				Mean	Diurnal	
3975	Cape Sable, East Cape	25° 07'	81° 05'	+1 33	+1 50	*1.30	*0.98	2.9	3.8	2.0
3977	Shark River entrance	25° 21'	81° 08'	+0 57	+1 45	*1.43	*0.98	3.6	4.5	2.4
3979	Whitewater Bay	25° 19'	81° 02'	+3 53	+4 38	*0.26	*0.33	0.5	0.8	0.4
3981	Lostmans River entrance	25° 33'	81° 13'	+1 09	+1 59	*1.33	*0.98	3.0	3.9	2.1
3983	Onion Key, Lostmans River	25° 37'	81° 08'	+3 09	+4 53	*0.26	*0.16	0.6	0.9	0.4
3985	Chatham River entrance	25° 41'	81° 17'	+0 59	+1 53	*1.43	*0.66	3.3	4.2	2.1
3987	Chokoloskee	25° 48.8'	81° 21.8'	+2 15	+3 14	*1.11	*0.62	2.53	3.18	1.62
3989	Everglades City, Barron River	25° 51.5'	81° 23.2'	+2 25	+3 26	*0.99	*0.57	2.26	2.84	1.47
3991	Indian Key	25° 48'	81° 28'	+0 55	+1 19	*1.48	*0.98	3.4	4.3	2.3
3993	Round Key	25° 50'	81° 32'	+0 54	+1 12	*1.48	*0.98	3.4	4.3	2.3
3995	Pumpkin Bay	25° 55'	81° 33'	+2 39	+3 07	*0.89	*0.49	2.1	2.7	1.3
3997	Marco Island, Caxambas Pass	25° 54.5'	81° 43.7'	+0 25	+0 18	*1.07	*0.98	2.22	3.05	1.7
3999	Coon Key	25° 53.8'	81° 38.2'	+1 06	+1 25	*1.34	*1.03	2.90	3.86	2.0
4001	Cape Romano	25° 51'	81° 41'	+0 43	+1 04	*1.19	*0.98	2.6	3.5	1.9
4003	Marco, Big Marco River	25° 58.3'	81° 43.7'	+1 00	+0 46	*0.98	*0.85	2.04	2.78	1.5
4005	McIlvanine Bay	25° 59.1'	81° 42.1'	+1 39	+1 55	*0.90	*0.75	1.92	2.61	1.4
4007	Keewaydin Island (inside)	26° 01.5'	81° 46.1'	+0 58	+0 55	*0.90	*0.78	1.90	2.61	1.4
4009	Naples, Naples Bay, north end	26° 08.2'	81° 47.3'	+0 43	+0 56	*0.97	*0.90	2.06	2.85	1.5
4011	NAPLES (outer coast)	26° 07.8'	81° 48.4'	*Daily Predictions*				2.01	2.87	1.6
4013	Wiggins Pass, Cocohatchee River	26° 17.4'	81° 49.1'	+0 44	+0 59	*0.77	*0.73	1.59	2.26	1.2
4015	Cocohatchee River, U.S. 41 bridge	26° 16.9'	81° 48.1'	+1 10	+1 28	*0.74	*0.65	1.54	2.18	1.1
	Estero Bay			*on St. Petersburg,*						
4017	Little Hickory Island	26° 21'	81° 51'	-0 58	-1 05	*1.09	*1.09	- -	2.5	1.3
4019	Coconut Point	26° 24.0'	81° 50.6'	-1 21	-0 44	*1.12	*1.21	1.75	2.48	1.3
4021	Carlos Point	26° 24'	81° 53'	-1 08	-1 28	*1.17	*1.17	- -	2.7	1.4
4023	Estero River	26° 25.8'	81° 51.4'	-0 45	-0 10	*1.09	*1.11	1.74	2.45	1.2
4025	Hendry Creek	26° 28.2'	81° 52.6'	-0 25	+0 28	*0.89	*0.68	1.51	2.06	1.0
4027	Estero Island	26° 26.3'	81° 55.1'	-1 08	-0 43	*1.14	*1.30	1.77	2.52	1.3
4029	Matanzas Pass (fixed bridge) Estero Island	26° 27'	81° 57'	-1 10	-1 34	*1.22	*1.22	- -	2.8	1.4
4031	Point Ybel, San Carlos Bay entrance	26° 27'	82° 01'	-1 50	-1 12	*1.21	*1.21	- -	2.6	1.4
4033	Punta Rassa, San Carlos Bay	26° 29.3'	82° 00.8'	-1 06	-0 59	*1.02	*1.26	1.54	2.26	1.2

Endnotes can be found at the end of table 2.

TABLE 2. – TIDAL DIFFERENCES AND OTHER CONSTANTS

No.	PLACE	POSITION Latitude	POSITION Longitude	DIFFERENCES Time High Water	DIFFERENCES Time Low Water	DIFFERENCES Height High Water	DIFFERENCES Height Low Water	RANGES Mean	RANGES Diurnal	Mean Tide Level
		North	West	h m	h m	ft	ft	ft	ft	ft
	FLORIDA Southern Gulf Coast-cont. Time meridian, 75° W			on St. Petersburg,						
	Caloosahatchee River									
4035	Iona Shores	26° 31'	81° 58'	+1 08	+1 40	*0.43	*0.43	- -	1.0	0.5
4037	Cape Coral Bridge	26° 34'	81° 56'	+1 15	+2 02	*0.43	*0.43	- -	1.0	0.5
4039	Fort Myers	26° 38.8'	81° 52.3'	+1 56	+2 23	*0.56	*0.39	0.95	1.32	0.63
4041	Tarpon Bay, Sanibel Island	26° 26.6'	82° 04.9'	-0 46	-0 18	*1.02	*1.18	1.57	2.27	1.23
4043	St. James City, Pine Island	26° 30'	82° 05'	-0 30	-0 44	*1.04	*1.04	- -	2.4	1.2
4045	Galt Island, Pine Island Sound	26° 31'	82° 06'	-0 25	+0 16	*0.91	*0.91	- -	2.1	1.1
4047	Captiva Island (outside)	26° 29'	82° 11'	-2 20	-2 28	*1.13	*1.13	- -	2.6	1.3
4049	Captiva Island, Pine Island Sound	26° 31'	82° 11'	-0 46	-0 20	*0.91	*0.91	- -	2.1	1.1
4051	North Captiva Island	26° 36.3'	82° 12.1'	-1 42	-1 17	*0.92	*0.71	1.54	2.02	1.05
4053	Redfish Pass, Captiva Island (north end)	26° 33'	82° 12'	-0 55	-1 14	*0.91	*0.91	- -	2.1	1.0
4055	Tropical Homesites Landing, Pine Island	26° 33'	82° 05'	-0 08	+0 22	*0.87	*0.87	- -	2.0	1.0
4057	Matlacha Pass (bascule bridge)	26° 38'	82° 04'	+0 43	+1 28	*0.83	*0.83	- -	1.9	1.0
4059	Pineland, Pine Island	26° 40'	82° 09'	-0 19	+0 26	*0.83	*0.83	- -	1.9	0.9
	Charlotte Harbor									
4061	Port Boca Grande	26° 43.1'	82° 15.5'	-0 50	-1 42	*0.67	*1.03	0.93	1.56	0.86
4063	Bokeelia	26° 42.4'	82° 09.8'	-0 35	-0 09	*0.80	*0.63	1.34	1.73	0.91
4065	Turtle Bay	26° 47.8'	82° 11.0'	+0 51	+0 35	*0.69	*0.95	1.02	1.56	0.86
4067	Punta Gorda	26° 56'	82° 04'	+1 06	+1 27	*0.83	*0.83	- -	1.9	1.0
4069	Shell Point (Harbor Heights), Peace River	26° 59.3'	81° 59.6'	+1 42	+2 10	*0.89	*0.89	1.32	2.02	1.10
4071	Locust Point, Hog Islan	26° 55.8'	82° 08.2'	+1 15	+1 27	*0.82	*0.82	1.22	1.95	1.03
4073	El Jobean, Myakka River	26° 58'	82° 13'	+1 38	+1 56	*0.83	*0.83	- -	1.9	1.0
4075	Myakka River, US 41 bridge	27° 02.7'	82° 17.6'	+2 48	+3 01	*0.83	*0.97	1.31	1.90	1.00
4077	Placida, Gasparilla Sound	26° 50.0'	82° 15.9'	-0 43	-0 56	*0.59	*0.94	0.82	1.41	0.77
4079	Don Pedro Island State Park, Cutoff (south)	26° 51.3'	82° 18.2'	-0 54	-0 53	*0.63	*0.84	0.91	1.49	0.78
4081	Englewood, Lemon Bay	26° 56.0'	82° 21.2'	-0 17	-0 17	*0.66	*0.82	1.00	1.57	0.81
4083	Manasota, Lemon Bay	27° 00.7'	82° 24.6'	-0 24	-0 11	*0.70	*0.89	1.05	1.68	0.86
4085	Venice Municipal Airport	27° 04.3'	82° 27.2'	-2 33	-2 43	*0.97	*0.97	1.56	2.20	1.15
4087	Venice Inlet (inside)	27° 07'	82° 28'	-2 02	-1 38	*0.91	*0.91	- -	2.1	1.1
4089	Sarasota, Sarasota Bay	27° 20'	82° 33'	-1 38	-0 58	*0.91	*0.91	- -	2.1	1.1
4091	Cortez, Sarasota Bay	27° 28'	82° 41'	-2 00	-1 25	*0.96	*0.96	- -	2.2	1.1
	Tampa Bay									
4093	Egmont Key, Egmont Channel	27° 36.1'	82° 45.6'	-2 15	-3 20	*0.96	*1.00	- -	2.16	1.14
4095	Anna Maria Key, Bradenton Beach	27° 29.8'	82° 42.8'	-2 27	-3 32	*0.99	*1.00	1.58	2.25	1.17
4097	Anna Maria Key, city pier	27° 32.0'	82° 43.8'	-2 10	-2 19	*0.99	*0.99	- -	2.22	1.11
4099	Bradenton, Manatee River	27° 30'	82° 34'	-1 24	-0 55	*0.97	*0.95	- -	2.3	1.2
4101	Redfish Point, Manatee River	27° 32'	82° 29'	-0 30	+0 14	*0.92	*1.00	- -	2.2	1.1
4103	Mullet Key Channel (Skyway)	27° 36.9'	82° 43.6'	-2 03	-2 01	*0.92	*0.92	1.48	2.08	1.09
4105	Port Manatee	27° 38.2'	82° 33.8'	-1 00	-0 48	*0.97	*0.95	1.56	2.19	1.14
4107	Shell Point	27° 43'	82° 29'	+0 08	+0 17	*0.91	*0.91	- -	2.3	1.2
4109	Little Manatee River, US 41 Bridge	27° 42.3'	82° 26.9'	+0 51	+1 15	*0.91	*0.68	1.55	1.99	1.03
4111	Point Pinellas	27° 42'	82° 38'	-0 22	-0 29	*0.86	*0.86	- -	2.0	1.0
4113	ST. PETERSBURG	27° 46.4'	82° 37.3'	Daily predictions				1.59	2.26	1.18
4115	Apollo Beach	27° 47.2'	82° 25.6'	-0 53	-0 32	*1.10	*1.18	1.72	2.46	1.31
4117	Newman Branch	27° 47.0'	82° 24.4'	-0 02	+0 12	*1.17	*1.11	1.89	2.61	1.37
4119	Ballast Point	27° 53.4'	82° 28.8'	+0 20	+0 23	*1.22	*1.16	1.98	2.73	1.43
4121	Pendola Point, Hillsborough Bay	27° 53.9'	82° 25.6'	+0 21	+0 05	*1.14	*1.18	1.81	2.61	1.36
4123	Davis Island, Hillsborough Bay	27° 54.5'	82° 27.1'	+0 03	+0 32	*1.16	*1.24	1.82	2.63	1.38
4125	McKay Bay entrance	27° 54.8'	82° 25.5'	+0 02	+0 28	*1.19	*1.26	1.89	2.69	1.42
4127	Old Port Tampa	27° 51.5'	82° 33.2'	+0 25	+0 39	*1.10	*1.18	1.73	2.48	1.31
4129	Gandy Bridge, Old Tampa Bay	27° 53.6'	82° 32.3'	+0 59	+0 57	*1.12	*1.24	1.75	2.55	1.35
4131	Bay Aristocrat Village, Old Tampa Bay	27° 56.5'	82° 43.2'	+1 01	+1 32	*1.24	*1.37	1.95	2.81	1.49
4133	Safety Harbor, Old Tampa Bay	27° 59.3'	82° 41.1'	+1 32	+1 34	*1.23	*1.39	1.91	2.79	1.48
4135	Mobbly Bayou	28° 01.3'	82° 39.3'	+2 38	+2 54	*0.71	*0.45	1.24	1.77	0.79
	Boca Ciega Bay									
4137	Pass-a-Grille Beach	27° 41'	82° 44'	-1 34	-1 30	*0.87	*0.87	- -	2.1	1.0
4139	Gulfport	27° 44'	82° 42'	-1 32	-1 05	*0.96	*0.96	- -	2.3	1.2
4141	Long Key, 0.5mi N. of Corey Causeway	27° 44.7'	82° 44.8'	-1 18	-0 44	*0.92	*1.00	- -	2.2	1.1
4143	Johns Pass	27° 47'	82° 47'	-2 14	-2 04	*0.97	*1.02	- -	2.3	1.2
4145	Madeira Beach Causeway	27° 48.5'	82° 47.7'	-1 32	-1 45	*1.08	*1.18	- -	2.42	1.29
	Northern Gulf Coast				on Cedar Key,					
4147	Indian Rocks Beach (inside)	27° 52'	82° 51'	-0 57	-0 53	*0.65	*0.63	1.8	2.6	1.3
4149	Clearwater	27° 57'	82° 48'	-1 48	-1 35	*0.65	*0.63	1.8	2.6	1.3
4151	Clearwater Beach	27° 58.7'	82° 49.9'	-2 07	-2 19	*0.69	*0.84	1.87	2.74	1.46
4153	Dunedin, St. Joseph Sound	28° 01'	82° 48'	-1 50	-1 45	*0.70	*0.79	1.9	2.8	1.4
4155	Anclote Key, southern end	28° 09.9'	82° 50.6'	-2 16	-2 11	*0.88	*0.60	2.65	3.32	1.71
4157	Anclote, Anclote River	28° 10.3'	82° 47.1'	-1 28	-1 24	*0.78	*0.87	2.16	3.07	1.63
4159	Tarpon Springs, Anclote River	28° 09.6'	82° 46.1'	-1 16	-1 03	*0.77	*0.83	2.10	3.00	1.57
4161	North Anclote Key	28° 12.6'	82° 50.4'	-1 55	-1 38	*0.80	*0.86	2.20	3.11	1.64
4163	Gulf Harbors	28° 14.6'	82° 45.8'	-1 15	-0 52	*0.84	*0.90	2.30	3.26	1.72
4165	Hwy. 19 bridge, Pithlachascotee River	28° 16.1'	82° 43.6'	-1 16	-0 40	*0.85	*0.84	2.36	3.27	1.71
4167	New Port Richey, Pithlachascotee River	28° 14.9'	82° 43.4'	-0 58	-0 11	*0.88	*0.87	2.44	3.40	1.77
4169	Hudson, Hudson Creek	28° 21.7'	82° 42.6'	-1 12	-1 02	*0.91	*0.89	2.53	3.48	1.82
4171	Aripeka, Hammock Creek	28° 26.0'	82° 40.1'	-0 37	+0 23	*0.81	*0.63	2.37	3.15	1.58
4173	Hernando Beach, Rocky Creek, Little Pine I. Bay	28° 29.2'	82° 39.7'	-0 20	+0 58	*0.83	*0.83	2.16	- -	- -
4175	Bayport	28° 32.0'	82° 39.0'	-0 01	+0 43	*0.80	*0.71	2.33	3.16	1.61
4177	Johns Island, Chassahowitzka Bay	28° 41.5'	82° 38.3'	+1 09	+2 14	*0.62	*0.49	1.81	2.53	1.22
4179	Chassahowitzka, Chassahowitzka River	28° 42.9'	82° 34.6'	+3 59	+5 45	*0.14	*0.16	0.39	0.60	0.30
4181	Mason Creek, Homosassa Bay	28° 45.7'	82° 38.3'	+3 09	+4 44	*0.32	*0.25	0.96	1.35	0.64
4183	Tuckers Island, Homosassa River	28° 46.3'	82° 41.7'	+1 26	+2 23	*0.47	*0.33	1.38	1.92	0.90

251

TABLE 2. – TIDAL DIFFERENCES AND OTHER CONSTANTS

No.	PLACE	POSITION Latitude	POSITION Longitude	DIFFERENCES Time High Water	DIFFERENCES Time Low Water	DIFFERENCES Height High Water	DIFFERENCES Height Low Water	RANGES Mean	RANGES Diurnal	Mean Tide Level
		North	West	h m	h m	ft	ft	ft	ft	ft
	FLORIDA Northern Gulf Coast-cont. Time meridian, 75° W					*on Cedar Key,*				
4185	Halls River bridge, Homosassa River	28° 48.0'	82° 36.2'	+4 30	+5 41	*0.16	*0.13	0.45	0.72	0.30
4187	Ozello, St. Martins River	28° 49.5'	82° 39.5'	+4 25	+5 21	*0.17	*0.14	0.49	0.74	0.33
4189	Mangrove Pt., Crystal Bay	28° 52.2'	82° 43.4'	+0 22	+0 41	*0.95	*0.76	2.82	3.65	1.89
4191	Ozello north, Crystal Bay	28° 51.8'	82° 40.0'	+1 25	+3 17	*0.50	*0.25	1.53	2.03	0.93
4193	Dixie Bay, Salt River, Crystal Bay	28° 52.9'	82° 38.1'	+2 00	+3 06	*0.55	*0.33	1.66	2.15	1.04
	Crystal River									
4195	Florida Power	28° 57.6'	82° 43.5'	-0 03	+0 30	*1.04	*0.89	3.00	3.90	2.06
4197	Shell Island, north end	28° 55.4'	82° 41.5'	+0 36	+1 30	*0.79	*0.59	2.32	3.01	1.53
4199	Twin Rivers Marina	28° 54.3'	82° 38.3'	+1 46	+2 30	*0.64	*0.49	1.90	2.53	1.26
4201	Kings Bay	28° 53.9'	82° 35.9'	+2 20	+3 07	*0.59	*0.41	1.76	2.31	1.14
4203	Withlacoochee River entrance	29° 00'	82° 46'	+0 07	+0 55	*0.91	*0.95	2.5	3.5	1.8
4205	CEDAR KEY	29° 08.1'	83° 01.9'		*Daily predictions*			2.83	3.80	2.05
4207	Suwannee River entrance	29° 17'	83° 09'	+0 06	+0 18	*0.88	*0.95	2.4	3.4	1.8
4209	Suwannee, Salt Creek	29° 19.7'	83° 09.1'	-0 07	+0 24	*0.91	*0.83	2.65	3.47	1.84
4211	Horseshoe Point	29° 26.2'	83° 17.6'	-0 21	+0 08	*0.95	*0.94	2.69	3.58	1.94
4213	Pepperfish Keys	29° 30'	83° 22'	+0 12	+0 24	*0.88	*0.95	2.4	3.4	1.8
4215	Steinhatchee River ent., Deadman Bay	29° 40.3'	83° 23.4'	+0 02	+0 00	*1.03	*1.08	2.87	3.83	2.12
						on St. Marks River Ent.,				
4217	Fishermans Rest	29° 44'	83° 32'	-0 14	-0 02	*0.93	*0.86	2.4	3.4	1.8
4219	Spring Warrior Creek	29° 55.2'	83° 40.3'	-0 25	-0 06	*0.98	*0.84	2.68	3.46	1.86
4221	Rock Islands	29° 58'	83° 50'	-0 03	+0 04	*0.93	*0.91	2.4	3.3	1.8
	Apalachee Bay									
4223	Mandalay, Aucilla River	30° 07.6'	83° 58.5'	+0 25	+0 57	*0.69	*0.55	1.92	2.47	1.30
4225	ST. MARKS RIVER ENTRANCE	30° 04.7'	84° 10.7'		*Daily predictions*			2.63	3.49	1.94
4227	St. Marks, St. Marks River	30° 09'	84° 12'	+0 36	+1 04	*0.93	*0.91	2.4	3.3	1.8
4229	Shell Point, Walker Creek	30° 03.6'	84° 17.4'	-0 03	-0 03	*1.02	*1.08	2.65	3.56	2.00
4231	Bald Point, Ochlockonee Bay	29° 56.9'	84° 20.5'	+0 33	+0 19	*0.85	*0.70	2.28	3.07	1.60
4233	Panacea, Dickerson Bay	30° 01.7'	84° 23.2'	+0 16	+0 20	*1.01	*0.82	2.73	3.66	1.90
4235	Alligator Point, St. James Island	29° 54.2'	84° 24.8'	-0 08	+0 11	*0.75	*0.73	1.95	2.82	1.45
4237	Turkey Point, St. James Island	29° 54.9'	84° 30.7'	-0 16	-0 21	*0.78	*0.98	1.92	2.74	1.57
						on Apalachicola,				
	St. George Sound									
4239	Dog Island, east end	29° 48.6'	84° 35.1'	-1 43	-2 00	*1.50	*1.40	1.70	2.46	1.41
4241	Dog Island, west end	29° 47'	84° 40'	-1 53	-2 38	*1.73	*1.40	--	2.6	1.3
4243	Lanark	29° 52.7'	84° 35.7'	-1 38	-1 48	*1.60	*1.53	1.81	2.62	1.51
4245	Carrabelle, Carrabelle River	29° 51'	84° 40'	-1 25	-2 13	*1.60	*1.60	--	2.6	1.3
4247	South Carabelle Beach	29° 48.1'	84° 44.2'	-1 16	-1 21	*1.50	*1.53	1.66	2.46	1.44
4249	St. George Island, Northeast End	29° 46.0'	84° 42.0'	+0 13	+0 05	*1.36	*1.25	1.56	2.20	1.28
4251	St. George Island, East End	29° 41.2'	84° 47.2'	-2 02	-2 48	*1.13	*1.00	--	1.9	1.1
4253	St. George Island, Rattlesnake Cove	29° 41.5'	84° 47.5'	-1 00	-1 35	*1.33	*1.20	--	2.2	1.3
4255	St. George Island, 12th St. W (Bayside)	29° 39'	84° 54'	-0 55	-1 08	*1.26	*1.26	--	2.2	1.1
4257	St. George Island, Sikes Cut	29° 36.8'	84° 57.5'	+0 07	+0 07	*1.15	*1.30	1.22	1.97	1.13
	Apalachicola Bay									
4259	Cat Point	29° 43'	84° 53'	-0 40	-1 17	*1.07	*0.60	--	2.2	1.1
4261	White Beach, East Bay	29° 47.1'	84° 53.9'	-0 11	+0 10	*1.21	*1.40	1.27	1.98	1.19
4263	APALACHICOLA	29° 43.6'	84° 58.9'		*Daily predictions*			1.11	1.61	0.96
4265	Apalachicola River (A&N RR bridge)	29° 45.8'	85° 02.0'	+0 28	+0 35	*0.85	*0.83	0.97	1.39	0.81
4267	Huckleberry Landing, Jackson River	29° 46.2'	85° 05.1'	+2 07	+1 52	*0.73	*0.95	0.72	1.21	0.74
4269	Lower Anchorage	29° 36'	85° 03'	-0 17	-0 35	*0.93	*1.00	--	1.5	0.8
4271	West Pass, St. Vincent Island	29° 38'	85° 06'	-0 27	-0 27	*0.87	*1.00	--	1.4	0.7
4273	Eleven Mile, St. Vincent Sound	29° 42.4'	85° 09.2'	+1 44	+1 31	*1.02	*1.03	1.12	1.67	0.97
						on Pensacola,				
	St. Joseph Bay									
4275	Port Saint Joe #	29° 48.9'	85° 18.8'	-1 06	-1 45	*1.11	*1.11	1.15	1.65	0.78
4277	St. Joseph Point #	29° 52.4'	85° 23.4'	-2 17	-2 48	*1.02	*1.02	1.17	1.56	0.67
4279	White City, ICWW #	29° 52.8'	85° 13.3'	-0 40	+1 31	*0.77	*0.77	0.86	1.01	0.52
	Time meridian, 90° W									
	St. Andrew Bay									
4281	Channel entrance #	30° 07.5'	85° 43.8'	-1 39	-1 50	*1.02	*1.02	1.20	1.29	0.67
4283	Panama City #	30° 09.1'	85° 40.0'	-0 57	-1 11	*1.05	*1.66	1.25	1.34	0.7
4285	Panama City Beach (outside) #	30° 12.8'	85° 52.7'	-2 17	-2 44	*1.05	*1.05	1.22	1.37	0.68
4287	Parker #	30° 08'	85° 37'	-0 05	+0 22	*1.20	*1.20	--	1.5	0.7
4289	Laird Bayou, East Bay #	30° 07.3'	85° 32.7'	-0 28	-1 05	*1.13	*1.13	1.28	1.47	0.75
4291	Farmdale, East Bay #	30° 01.0'	85° 28.2'	-0 16	-0 59	*1.17	*1.17	1.31	1.56	0.78
4293	Allanton, East Bay #	30° 01.8'	85° 27.9'	-0 16	-1 01	*1.15	*1.15	1.30	1.53	0.76
4295	Wetappo Creek, East Bay #	30° 02'	85° 24'	+1 01	+1 40	*1.10	*1.10	--	1.4	0.7
4297	Overstreet, East Bay #	29° 59.8'	85° 22.2'	+0 17	+0 04	*1.20	*1.20	1.34	1.58	0.82
4299	Alligator Bayou #	30° 10.2'	85° 45.3'	-0 47	-1 10	*1.07	*1.07	1.25	1.37	0.68
4301	Lynn Haven, North Bay #	30° 15.3'	85° 38.9'	-0 31	-1 01	*1.10	*1.10	1.25	1.47	0.73
4303	West Bay Creek, West Bay #	30° 17.6'	85° 51.5'	-0 10	-0 47	*1.13	*1.13	1.30	1.46	0.74
	Choctawhatchee Bay <11>									
4305	East Pass (Destin)	30° 23.7'	86° 30.8'	-0 33	-0 34	*0.49	*0.33	0.59	0.61	0.3
4307	Shalimar, Garnier Bayou #	30° 26.1'	86° 35.2'	+3 33	+3 03	*0.32	*0.32	0.36	0.41	0.2
4309	Harris, The Narrows#	30° 24'	86° 44'	+1 37	+2 51	*1.10	*1.10	--	1.4	0.7
4311	Navarre Beach	30° 22.6'	86° 51.9'	-2 07	-2 26	*1.07	*1.67	1.26	1.38	0.6
4313	Fishing Bend, Santa Rosa Sound #	30° 20'	87° 08'	+0 41	+0 51	*1.10	*1.10	--	1.4	0.7

TABLE 2. – TIDAL DIFFERENCES AND OTHER CONSTANTS

No.	PLACE	POSITION Latitude	POSITION Longitude	DIFFERENCES Time High Water	DIFFERENCES Time Low Water	DIFFERENCES Height High Water	DIFFERENCES Height Low Water	RANGES Mean	RANGES Diurnal	Mean Tide Level
		North	West	h m	h m	ft	ft	ft	ft	ft
	FLORIDA Northern Gulf Coast-cont. Time meridian, 90° W			on Pensacola,						
	Pensacola Bay									
4315	Entrance #	30° 20'	87° 19'	-1 23	-0 34	*0.80	*0.80	- -	1.1	0.5
4317	Warrington, 2 miles south of #	30° 21'	87° 16'	-0 27	-0 30	*1.00	*1.00	- -	1.3	0.6
4319	PENSACOLA #	30° 24.2'	87° 13.8'	Daily predictions				1.20	1.26	0.63
4321	Hernandez Point, Escambia Bay #	30° 27.3'	87° 06.0'	+0 52	+0 51	*1.02	*1.02	1.16	1.30	0.65
4323	Lora Point, Escambia Bay #	30° 30.9'	87° 09.7'	+0 20	+0 02	*1.10	*1.10	1.30	1.41	0.70
4325	Floridatown, Escambia Bay #	30° 34.9'	87° 10.8'	+0 45	+0 34	*1.13	*1.13	1.29	1.45	0.75
4327	Holley, East Bay #	30° 27.0'	86° 55.1'	+0 19	-0 11	*1.15	*1.15	1.37	1.50	0.74
4329	Bay Point, Blackwater River #	30° 34'	87° 00'	+1 23	+1 27	*1.20	*1.20	- -	1.6	0.8
4331	Sheild Point, Blackwater River #	30° 34.9'	87° 00.9'	+0 42	+0 10	*1.21	*1.21	1.39	1.59	0.79
4333	Milton, Blackwater River #	30° 37'	87° 02'	+1 40	+1 47	*1.20	*1.20	- -	1.6	0.8
4335	Hawkins Rec. Park, Blackwater River #	30° 38.2'	87° 01.7'	+0 59	+0 22	*1.24	*1.24	1.41	1.66	0.83
4337	Woodlawn Beach, Santa Rosa Sound #	30° 23.2'	86° 59.5'	+0 49	+0 58	*1.07	*0.67	1.29	1.36	0.67
4339	Big Lagoon #	30° 19.6'	87° 21.4'	-0 25	+0 09	*0.84	*0.84	0.99	1.02	0.53
	Perdido Bay									
4341	Blue Angels Park #	30° 23.2'	87° 25.7'	+2 36	+4 00	*0.58	*0.58	0.71	0.73	0.35
4343	Nix Point #	30° 23.6'	87° 25.5'	+2 29	+3 37	*0.57	*0.33	0.69	0.71	0.35
4345	Millview #	30° 25.1'	87° 21.4'	+2 33	+4 33	*0.67	*0.67	0.82	0.85	0.41
4347	Alabama Point, Perdido Pass, Alabama	30° 16.7'	87° 33.3'	-1 26	-1 24	*0.67	*0.67	0.78	0.86	0.42
	ALABAMA			on Mobile,						
4349	Mobile Point (Fort Morgan) #	30° 14'	88° 01'	-1 46	-1 32	*0.80	*0.80	- -	1.2	0.6
4351	DAUPHIN ISLAND #	30° 15.0'	88° 04.5'	Daily predictions,				1.18	1.20	0.60
4353	Gulf Shores, ICWW #	30° 16.8'	87° 41.1'	-0 41	-0 16	*0.75	*0.90	1.03	1.15	0.60
4355	Bon Secour, Bon Secour River #	30° 18'	87° 44'	-1 13	-1 17	*1.07	*1.07	- -	1.6	0.8
4357	East Fowl River, Hwy 193 bridge, Mobile Bay #	30° 26.6'	88° 06.8'	-0 53	-0 58	*0.88	*0.30	1.28	1.36	0.68
4359	West Fowl River, Hwy 188 bridge #	30° 22.6'	88° 09.5'	-2 00	-2 01	*0.94	*1.48	1.33	1.61	0.79
4361	Point Clear, Mobile Bay #	30° 29.2'	87° 56.1'	-1 03	-0 34	*1.00	*1.00	1.50	1.52	0.77
4363	Dog River, Hwy 163 bridge, Mobile Bay #	30° 33.9'	88° 05.2'	-0 38	-0 47	*0.93	*0.60	1.39	1.44	0.72
4365	Meaher State Park, Mobile Bay #	30° 40.0'	87° 56.1'	-0 38	+0 25	*1.03	*0.50	1.48	1.54	0.79
4367	Coast Guard Station, Mobile Bay #	30° 38.9'	88° 03.5'	-0 38	-0 38	*1.03	*0.90	1.45	1.63	0.82
4369	MOBILE, Mobile River (State Dock) #	30° 42.3'	88° 02.4'	Daily predictions				1.38	1.61	0.80
4371	William Brooks Park, Chickasaw Creek #	30° 46.9'	88° 04.4'	-0 05	-0 07	*0.99	*1.00	1.39	1.56	0.79
4373	Lower Hall Landing, Tensaw River #	30° 49'	87° 55'	+2 16	+3 05	*0.87	*0.87	- -	1.3	0.6
				on South Pass,						
4375	Bayou La Batre, Mississippi Sound #	30° 22'	88° 16'	+1 52	+1 14	*1.23	*1.23	- -	1.5	0.8
4377	Bayou La Batre, Hwy 188 Bridge #	30° 24.3'	88° 14.8'	+1 29	+0 56	*1.28	*1.28	1.46	1.60	0.82
	MISSISSIPPI									
4379	Grand Bay NERR #	30° 24.8'	88° 24.2'	+1 38	+0 54	*1.25	*1.25	1.37	1.59	0.81
4381	Point of Pines, Bayou Cumbest #	30° 23.2'	88° 26.4'	+1 49	+1 09	*1.25	*1.25	1.37	1.62	0.81
4383	Hollingsworth Point, Davis Bayou #	30° 23.2'	88° 46.4'	+2 24	+1 52	*1.42	*1.42	1.59	1.80	0.91
4385	Petit Bois Island, Mississippi Sound #	30° 12.2'	88° 26.5'	+1 14	+0 41	*1.18	*1.18	1.37	1.47	0.73
4387	Horn Island, Mississippi Sound #	30° 14.3'	88° 40.0'	+1 34	+0 59	*1.25	*1.25	1.38	1.60	0.81
4389	Ship Island, Mississippi Sound #	30° 12.8'	88° 58.3'	+1 48	+1 05	*1.32	*1.32	1.49	1.60	0.83
4391	Port of Pascagoula, Dock E #	30° 20.8'	88° 30.3'	+1 08	+0 44	*1.22	*1.22	1.37	1.55	0.78
4393	Pascagoula, Mississippi Sound #	30° 20.4'	88° 32.0'	+1 20	+0 48	*1.21	*1.21	1.37	1.53	0.86
4395	Graveline Bayou Entrance #	30° 21.7'	88° 39.8'	+1 43	+1 04	*1.29	*1.29	1.44	1.63	0.82
4397	Gulfport Harbor, Mississippi Sound #	30° 21.6'	89° 04.9'	+2 09	+1 09	*1.29	*1.29	1.38	1.64	0.86
4399	Biloxi (Cadet Point), Biloxi Bay #	30° 23.4'	88° 51.4'	+2 04	+1 30	*1.38	*1.38	1.55	1.76	0.88
4401	Turkey Creek, Bernard Bayou #	30° 25.6'	89° 03.2'	+3 23	+2 27	*1.54	*1.54	1.65	2.00	1.02
4403	Handsboro Bridge, Bernard Bayou #	30° 24.4'	89° 01.6'	+3 40	+2 06	*1.53	*1.53	1.64	1.98	1.01
4405	Cat Island #	30° 13.9'	89° 07.0'	+2 13	+2 00	*1.23	*1.23	1.39	1.57	0.78
4407	Pass Christian Yacht Club, Mississippi Sound #	30° 18.6'	89° 14.7'	+2 36	+2 04	*1.37	*1.37	1.53	1.73	0.87
4409	Wolf River, Henderson Avenue bridge #	30° 21.5'	89° 16.4'	+3 18	+2 51	*1.36	*1.36	1.47	1.80	0.90
4411	St. Louis Bay entrance #	30° 19.5'	89° 19.5'	+3 17	+2 57	*1.36	*1.36	1.52	1.73	0.87
4413	Waveland #	30° 16.9'	89° 22.0'	+3 09	+2 49	*1.28	*1.28	1.44	1.60	0.81
4415	Pearlington, Pearl River #	30° 14.4'	89° 36.9'	+5 51	+5 31	*0.99	*0.99	1.15	1.23	0.62
	LOUISIANA									
4417	The Rigolets #	30° 09.9'	89° 44.4'	+6 22	+5 35	*0.64	*0.50	0.76	0.79	0.39
4419	Bayou BonFouca, Route 433 #	30° 16.3'	89° 47.6'	+11 12	+11 31	*0.43	*0.43	0.53	0.53	0.26
4421	Tchefuncta River, Lake Pontchartrain	30° 22.7'	90° 09.6'	+11 36	+12 21	*0.48	*0.48	0.57	0.57	0.28
4423	New Canal USCG station, Lake Pontchartrain	30° 01.6'	90° 06.8'	+11 47	+12 09	*0.43	*0.43	0.51	0.52	0.26
4425	Chef Menteur, Chef Menteur Pass #	30° 03.9'	89° 48.0'	+6 25	+6 27	*0.88	*0.88	0.97	1.06	0.56
4427	Michoud Substation, ICWW #	30° 00.4'	89° 56.2'	+6 37	+6 22	*1.09	*1.09	1.23	1.39	0.70
4429	Shell Beach, Lake Borgne #	29° 52.0'	89° 40.3'	+5 34	+5 13	*1.17	*1.17	1.35	1.45	0.73
4431	Grand Pass #	30° 07.6'	89° 13.3'	+3 01	+2 36	*1.18	*1.18	1.14	1.47	0.73
4433	Chandeleur Light #	30° 03'	88° 52'	+1 50	+1 54	*0.98	*0.98	- -	1.2	0.6
4435	Comfort Island #	29° 49.4'	89° 16.2'	+2 47	+2 14	*1.28	*1.28	1.45	1.57	0.80
4437	Bay Gardene #	29° 35.9'	89° 37.1'	+4 04	+4 04	*1.16	*1.16	1.34	1.44	0.75
4439	Breton Islands #	29° 29.6'	89° 10.4'	+2 07	+2 08	*1.14	*1.14	1.37	1.37	0.69
4441	Jack Bay #	29° 22.0'	89° 20.7'	+3 12	+2 48	*1.00	*1.00	- -	1.2	0.6
4443	Grand Bay #	29° 23.1'	89° 22.8'	+2 54	+2 56	*1.08	*1.08	1.25	1.34	0.67
4445	Lonesome Bayou (Thomasin) #	29° 14'	89° 03'	+0 34	-0 29	*0.90	*0.90	- -	1.1	0.5
	Mississippi River									
4447	North Pass, Pass a Loutre #	29° 12.3'	89° 02.2'	+0 42	+0 43	*0.91	*0.91	1.08	1.10	0.55
4449	Venice, Grand Pass #	29° 16.4'	89° 21.1'	+2 38	+2 54	*0.82	*0.82	0.98	0.98	0.50
4451	Pilottown #	29° 10.7'	89° 15.5'	+1 59	+2 15	*0.82	*1.00	0.96	1.06	0.50

TABLE 2. – TIDAL DIFFERENCES AND OTHER CONSTANTS

No.	PLACE	POSITION		DIFFERENCES				RANGES		Mean Tide Level
				Time		Height				
		Latitude	Longitude	High Water	Low Water	High Water	Low Water	Mean	Diurnal	
		North	West	h m	h m	ft	ft	ft	ft	ft
	LOUISIANA Time meridian, 90° W			on South Pass,						
	Mississippi River-cont.									
4453	Southeast Pass #	29° 07.0'	89° 02.7'	+0 37	-0 28	*0.98	*0.98	--	1.2	0.6
4455	SOUTH PASS #	28° 59.4'	89° 08.4'	Daily predictions				1.18	1.22	0.61
4457	Port Eads, South Pass #	29° 00.9'	89° 09.6'	+0 56	-0 17	*0.90	*0.90	--	1.1	0.5
4459	Southwest Pass #	28° 55.9'	89° 25.7'	+0 35	-0 13	*1.07	*1.07	--	1.3	0.6
4461	Joseph Bayou #	29° 03.5'	89° 16.3'	+0 37	-0 17	*1.15	*1.15	--	1.4	0.7
4463	New Orleans <12> #	29° 55'	90° 04'	- - -		- - -	- - -	--	--	--
				on Grand Isle,						
4465	Paris Road Bridge (ICWW) #	30° 00'	89° 56'	+5 53	+5 58	*1.04	*1.04	--	1.1	0.6
4467	Empire Jetty #	29° 15.0'	89° 36.5'	-1 03	-1 45	*1.23	*1.23	--	1.3	0.7
4469	Bastian Island #	29° 17.2'	89° 39.8'	+0 41	+0 12	*1.13	*1.13	--	1.2	0.6
4471	Quatre Bayous Pass #	29° 18.6'	89° 51.2'	+2 18	+0 17	*1.23	*1.23	--	1.3	0.6
4473	Barataria Pass #	29° 16'	89° 57'	+1 00	-0 10	*1.13	*1.13	--	1.2	0.6
	Barataria Bay									
4475	EAST POINT, GRAND ISLE	29° 15.8'	89° 57.4'	Daily predictions				1.04	1.06	0.53
4477	Bayou Rigaud, Grand Isle #	29° 16'	89° 58'	+1 32	+0 46	*0.94	*0.94	--	1.0	0.5
4479	Independence Island #	29° 18.6'	89° 56.3'	+2 29	+1 59	*0.85	*0.85	--	0.9	0.4
4481	Mendicant Island #	29° 19.1'	89° 58.8'	+0 51	+1 16	*0.94	*1.00	0.98	1.00	0.50
4483	Manilla #	29° 25.6'	89° 58.6'	+2 32	+3 13	*0.94	*0.94	--	1.0	0.5
4485	Caminada Pass (bridge) #	29° 12.6'	90° 02.4'	+0 20	+0 12	*0.94	*0.94	0.99	0.99	0.50
4487	Port Fourchon, Belle Pass #	29° 06.8'	90° 11.9'	-0 27	-0 29	*1.16	*1.16	1.21	1.23	0.62
4489	Leeville, Bayou Lafourche #	29° 14.9'	90° 12.7'	+3 00	+3 00	*0.83	*0.83	0.85	0.88	0.44
4491	East Timbalier Island, Timbalier Bay#	29° 04.6'	90° 17.1'	+0 07	+0 53	*1.22	*1.22	1.25	1.32	0.66
4493	Timbalier Island, Timbalier Bay #	29° 05'	90° 32'	+0 19	+0 23	*1.13	*1.13	--	1.2	0.6
4495	Pelican Islands, Timbalier Bay #	29° 07.7'	90° 25.4'	+2 26	+2 26	*1.13	*1.13	--	1.2	0.6
4497	Wine Island, Terrebonne Bay #	29° 04.7'	90° 37.1'	+1 08	+1 02	*1.23	*1.23	--	1.3	0.6
4499	Cocodrie, Terrebonne Bay #	29° 14.7'	90° 39.7'	+1 22	+1 33	*0.98	*0.98	1.01	1.05	0.53
4501	East Isle Dernieres, Lake Pelto #	29° 04.3'	90° 38.40'	-0 55	-0 43	*1.19	*1.19	1.22	1.28	0.7
4503	Caillou Boca #	29° 03.8'	90° 48.4'	+0 40	+0 48	*1.32	*1.32	--	1.4	0.7
4505	Raccoon Point, Caillou Bay #	29° 03.5'	90° 57.7'	-0 03	-0 20	*1.60	*1.60	--	1.7	0.8
4507	Texas Gas Platform, Caillou Bay #	29° 10.4'	90° 58.5'	-0 49	-0 20	*1.35	*1.35	1.22	1.51	0.81
4509	Ship Shoal Light #	28° 55'	91° 04'	-1 54	-1 50	*1.51	*1.51	--	1.6	0.8
				on Galveston,						
	Atchafalaya Bay									
4511	Eugene Island, north of	29° 22.4'	91° 23.0'	-1 48	-1 51	*1.34	*1.23	1.39	1.96	1.07
4513	Point Au Fer #	29° 20'	91° 21'	-0 21	-2 26	*1.40	*1.40	--	2.0	1.0
4515	Shell Island #	29° 28'	91° 18'	+0 54	-0 39	*1.07	*1.07	--	1.5	0.7
4517	Stouts Pass, Six Mile Lake #	29° 44.6'	91° 13.8'	+2 09	+2 32	*0.61	*0.23	0.74	0.89	0.44
4519	Point Chevreuil #	29° 31'	91° 33'	+1 02	-0 54	*1.07	*1.07	--	1.5	0.8
4521	Rabbit Island, 5 miles south of #	29° 25'	91° 36'	-0 13	-2 00	*1.40	*1.40	--	2.0	1.0
4523	South Point, Marsh Island #	29° 29'	91° 46'	-0 19	-1 57	*1.30	*1.30	--	1.8	0.9
4525	Lighthouse Point #	29° 31'	92° 03'	-1 16	-2 17	*1.40	*1.40	--	2.0	1.0
4527	Cote Blanche Island, West Cote Blanche Bay #	29° 44'	91° 43'	+2 19	+2 16	*1.00	*1.00	--	1.4	0.7
4529	Southwest Pass, Vermilion Bay #	29° 35'	92° 02'	-0 32	-0 33	*1.14	*1.14	--	1.6	0.8
4531	Cypremort Point, Vermilion Bay #	29° 42.8'	91° 52.8'	+2 18	+1 52	*1.18	*0.80	1.32	1.70	0.90
4533	Weeks Bay, Vermilion Bay #	29° 50.2'	91° 50.3'	+3 47	+2 30	*1.15	*0.83	1.27	1.61	0.88
4535	Freshwater Canal Locks #	29° 33.3'	92° 18.3'	-2 32	-2 17	*1.52	*1.73	1.48	2.16	1.26
4537	Mermentau River entrance #	29° 45'	93° 06'	-1 54	-0 59	*1.79	*1.79	--	2.5	1.2
4539	Calcasieu Pass, East Jetty #	29° 46.1'	93° 20.6'	-2 27	-1 23	*1.38	*1.80	1.28	1.93	1.13
4541	Calcasieu Ship Channel, Bulk Terminal #	30° 11.4'	93° 18.0'	+3 48	+3 59	*0.94	*0.91	1.03	1.33	0.73
4543	Lake Charles, Calcasieu River #	30° 13.4'	93° 13.3'	+3 03	+3 54	*0.99	*0.81	1.06	1.40	0.73
	TEXAS									
4545	Sabine Pass, Texas Point #	29° 40.6'	93° 50.2'	-1 51	-1 03	*1.41	*1.66	1.36	1.98	1.13
4547	Sabine Pass #	29° 43.8'	93° 52.2'	-1 18	-0 38	*1.14	*1.14	1.09	1.60	0.93
4549	Port Arthur, Sabine Naches Canal #	29° 52.0'	93° 55.8'	+1 08	+1 08	*0.75	*0.53	0.83	1.04	0.5
4551	Rainbow Bridge, Neches River #	29° 58.8'	93° 52.9'	+4 04	+3 23	*0.75	*0.33	0.90	1.06	0.5
4553	High Island, ICWW #	29° 35.7'	94° 23.4'	+3 33	+3 55	*1.00	*0.73	1.09	1.41	0.7
4555	Galveston Bay Entrance, north jetty #	29° 21.2'	94° 43.4'	-1 06	-0 42	*1.20	*1.17	1.23	1.70	0.9
4557	GALVESTON, Galveston Channel #	29° 18.6'	94° 47.6'	Daily predictions				1.02	1.41	0.8
	Galveston Bay									
4559	Port Bolivar #	29° 21.9'	94° 46.8'	+0 57	+0 09	*1.00	*0.63	1.13	1.40	0.8
4561	Texas City, Turning Basin #	29° 23'	94° 53'	+0 33	+0 41	*1.00	*1.00	--	1.4	0.7
4563	Eagle Point <20> #	29° 28.8'	94° 55.1'	+5 34	+2 38	*0.80	*0.80	1.01	1.09	0.6
4565	Clear Lake <20> #	29° 33.8'	95° 04.0'	+6 57	+5 19	*0.83	*0.83	1.05	1.16	0.6
4567	Morgans Point, Barbours Cut <20> #	29° 40.9'	94° 59.1'	+5 11	+4 17	*0.95	*0.40	1.14	1.31	0.7
4569	Lynchburg Landing, San Jacinto River <20> #	29° 45.9'	95° 04.7'	+4 55	+4 51	*1.06	*0.67	1.20	1.50	0.8
4571	Annie's Landing, San Jacinto River <20> #	29° 49.1'	95° 04.7'	+5 20	+5 16	*1.14	*0.83	1.26	1.59	0.8
4573	Manchester, Houston Ship Channel <20> #	29° 43.1'	95° 15.1'	+4 55	+5 05	*1.15	*0.83	1.27	1.64	0.9
4575	Round Point, Trinity Bay <20> #	29° 44'	94° 42'	+10 39	+5 15	*0.71	*0.71	--	1.0	0.5
4577	Umbrella Point, Trinity Bay <20> #	29° 40.8'	94° 52.1'	+4 41	+3 39	*0.93	*0.33	1.14	1.27	0.6
4579	Point Barrow, Trinity Bay #	29° 44'	94° 50'	+5 48	+4 43	*0.79	*0.79	--	1.1	0.5
4581	Rollover Pass, East Bay #	29° 30.9'	94° 30.8'	+4 25	+3 16	*0.95	*0.53	1.10	1.35	0.6
4583	Gilchrist, East Bay #	29° 31'	94° 29'	+3 16	+4 18	*0.86	*0.86	--	1.2	0.6
4585	Galveston Railroad Bridge #	29° 18.1'	94° 53.8'	+2 10	+0 58	*0.88	*0.67	0.97	1.25	0.6
4587	Jamaica Beach, West Bay #	29° 12'	94° 59'	+2 38	+3 31	*0.71	*0.71	--	1.0	0.5
4589	Alligator Point, West Bay #	29° 10'	95° 08'	+2 39	+2 33	*0.64	*0.64	--	0.9	0.4
4591	Christmas Bay #	29° 02.5'	95° 10.5'	+4 47	+2 37	*0.58	*0.23	0.71	0.82	0.4
4593	Galveston Pleasure Pier #	29° 17.1'	94° 47.3'	-1 33	-1 03	*1.40	*1.30	1.46	2.04	1.1
4595	San Luis Pass #	29° 05.7'	95° 06.8'	+0 10	+0 11	*1.06	*0.80	1.16	1.50	0.8
4597	Freeport SPIP (ocean) #	29° 56.14'	95° 17.65'	-1 20	-1 07	*1.26	*0.83	1.42	1.80	0.5

254

TABLE 2. – TIDAL DIFFERENCES AND OTHER CONSTANTS

No.	PLACE	POSITION		DIFFERENCES				RANGES		Mean Tide Level
				Time		Height				
		Latitude	Longitude	High Water	Low Water	High Water	Low Water	Mean	Diurnal	
		North	West	h m	h m	ft	ft	ft	ft	ft

TEXAS
Time meridian, 90° W
on Galveston,

4599	Freeport, US Coast Guard Station #	28° 56.6'	95° 18.1'	-1 18	-1 08	*1.25	*0.87	1.39	1.80	0.95
4601	Sargent, ICWW #	28° 46.3'	95° 37.0'	+3 04	+0 17	*0.51	*0.13	0.64	0.72	0.36
4603	Matagorda City, ICWW #	28° 46.2'	95° 54.8'	+3 13	+0 51	*0.41	*0.17	0.49	0.54	0.30
4605	Matagorda Bay Entrance Channel #	28° 25.6'	96° 19.7'	-2 48	-2 48	*0.91	*0.37	1.09	1.23	0.65
4607	PORT O'CONNOR, MATAGORDA BAY #	28° 27'	96° 24'	Daily predictions,				--	0.5	0.2
4609	Port Lavaca, Matagorda Bay #	28° 37'	96° 37'	- - -	- - -	- - -	- - -	--	0.7	0.3
4611	Rockport, Aransas Bay #	28° 01.3'	97° 02.8'	- - -	- - -	- - -	- - -	0.36	0.36	0.18
4613	Aransas, Aransas Pass #	27° 50.2'	97° 02.3'	-1 12	-1 17	*0.99	*0.63	1.11	1.37	0.75
4615	Corpus Christi #	27° 34.8'	97° 13.0'	-1 09	-1 30	*1.17	*0.73	1.31	1.63	0.93
4617	Riviera Beach, Baffin Bay #	27° 17'	97° 40'	- - -	- - -	- - -	- - -	--	0.3	0.1

on Padre Island,

4619	South Padre Island, Brazos Santiago Pass #	26° 04.1'	97° 09.3'	-0 04	-0 02	*0.96	*0.88	1.22	1.43	0.75
4621	PADRE ISLAND (south end) #	26° 04.1'	97° 09.4'	Daily predictions				1.25	1.47	0.87
4623	Queen Isabella Causeway (east end) #	26° 04.7'	97° 10.2'	+0 24	+0 21	*0.87	*0.75	1.11	1.28	0.68
4625	Queen Isabella Causeway (west end) #	26° 04.3'	97° 11.5'	+0 52	+0 30	*0.81	*0.63	1.05	1.19	0.62
4627	Port Isabel #	26° 03.6'	97° 12.9'	+0 10	+0 26	*0.92	*1.00	1.15	1.37	0.74
4629	South Bay entrance #	26° 03.1'	97° 10.9'	+0 14	+0 21	*0.91	*0.94	1.14	1.35	0.72

MEXICO <13>
Gulf of Mexico
on Tampico Harbor,

4631	Matamoros #	25° 53'	97° 31'	+0 55	+0 40	*1.00	*1.00	--	1.4	0.7
4633	TAMPICO HARBOR (Madero) #	22° 13'	97° 51'	Daily predictions				--	1.4	0.7
4635	Tuxpan #	21° 00'	97° 20'	+0 02	+0 04	*1.21	*1.21	--	1.7	0.8
4637	Veracruz #	19° 12'	96° 08'	-0 19	-0 12	*1.21	*1.21	--	1.7	0.8
4639	Alvarado #	18° 46'	95° 46'	+0 51	+0 27	*0.93	*0.93	--	1.3	0.6
4641	Coatzcoalcos #	18° 09'	94° 25'	-0 40	+0 05	*1.07	*1.07	--	1.5	0.7
4643	Frontera #	18° 32'	92° 39'	-0 18	-0 27	*1.14	*1.14	--	1.6	0.8
4645	Progreso #	21° 18'	89° 40'	+1 19	+0 23	*1.29	*1.29	--	1.8	0.9

BELIZE
on Key West,

4647	Belize City	17° 30'	88° 11'	+0 14	+0 47	*0.46	*0.46	0.6	0.7	0.4
4649	Punta Gorda	16° 06'	88° 49'	-0 27	+0 30	*0.46	*0.46	0.6	0.8	0.4

GUATEMALA <13>

4651	Rio Dulce entrance	15° 50'	88° 49'	-1 25	-1 35	*0.92	*0.92	1.2	1.5	0.7

HONDURAS <13>

4653	Puerto Cortes	15° 50'	87° 57'	-0 43	-0 02	*0.38	*0.38	0.5	0.6	0.2
4655	Port Royal, Isla de Roatan	16° 24'	86° 20'	-2 41	-2 35	*0.92	*0.92	1.2	1.4	0.6
4657	Puerto Castilla	16° 00'	86° 02'	-0 48	-0 13	*0.46	*0.46	0.6	0.8	0.4
4659	Isla de Guanaja	16° 29'	85° 54'	-1 26	-1 42	*0.72	*0.72	1.0	1.3	0.6
4661	Harbor Bay, Great Swan Island	17° 24'	83° 56'	-1 18	-0 33	*0.51	*0.51	0.7	0.9	0.4

NICARAGUA <13>
on Hampton Roads,

4663	Cabo Gracias a Dios	15° 00'	83° 10'	+0 23	-0 32	*0.57	*0.57	1.2	1.6	0.8
4665	Puerto Cabezas	14° 01'	83° 23'	+3 05	+3 11	*0.56	*0.56	1.4	1.9	0.9
4667	Cayos de Perlas	12° 25'	83° 25'	+4 53	+4 33	*0.46	*0.46	0.9	1.3	0.6
4669	Isla del Maiz Grande	12° 10'	83° 03'	+4 38	+4 13	*0.46	*0.46	0.9	1.3	0.3
4671	Bluefields Lagoon entrance	12° 00'	83° 42'	+3 54	+3 27	*0.28	*0.28	0.7	1.0	0.4
4673	San Juan del Norte (Greytown)	10° 55'	83° 42'	+4 03	+4 03	*0.28	*0.28	0.7	1.1	0.5

COSTA RICA <13>
on Cristobal,

4675	Limon	10° 00'	83° 02'	-0 32	-0 29	*1.00	*1.00	0.7	1.2	0.5

PANAMA <13>
Time meridian, 75° W

4677	Bocas del Toro, Almirante Bay	9° 21'	82° 15'	+0 21	+0 24	*1.14	*1.14	0.8	1.2	0.6
4679	CRISTOBAL (COLON)	9° 21'	79° 55'	Daily Predictions				0.7	1.1	0.4
4681	Bahia de Caledonia	8° 54'	77° 41'	+0 12	+0 00	*1.00	*1.00	0.7	1.1	0.4

BERMUDA ISLANDS
Time meridian, 60° W
on St. Georges Island,

								Mean	Spring	
4683	Ireland Island	32° 19'	64° 50'	+0 11	+0 13	*1.07	*1.23	2.6	3.1	1.6
4685	Ferry Reach (Biological Station)	32° 22.2'	64° 41.7'	-0 04	+0 03	*0.93	*1.00	2.4	2.9	1.3
4687	ST. GEORGES ISLAND	32° 22.4'	64° 42.2'	Daily Predictions				2.5	3.0	1.3

BAHAMAS
Time meridian, 75° W
on Settlement Point,

4689	Guinchos Cay	22° 45'	78° 07'	+0 06	+0 16	*0.79	*1.11	2.1	2.6	1.2
4691	Elbow Cay, Cay Sal Bank	23° 57'	80° 28'	+1 18	+1 28	*0.79	*1.11	2.1	2.6	1.2
4693	Fresh Creek, Andros Island	24° 44'	77° 48'	+0 05	-0 08	*0.97	*1.11	2.4	2.9	1.3
4695	North Cat Cay	25° 33'	79° 17'	+0 22	+0 32	*0.86	*1.11	2.3	2.8	1.3
4697	North Bimini	25° 44'	79° 18'	+0 05	+0 22	*0.90	*1.11	2.4	2.9	1.3
4699	Memory Rock	26° 57'	79° 07'	+0 16	+0 26	*0.86	*1.11	2.3	2.7	1.3

TABLE 2. – TIDAL DIFFERENCES AND OTHER CONSTANTS

No.	PLACE	POSITION Latitude	Longitude	DIFFERENCES Time High Water (h m)	Low Water (h m)	Height High Water (ft)	Low Water (ft)	RANGES Mean (ft)	Spring (ft)	Mean Tide Level (ft)
		North	**West**							
	BAHAMAS Time meridian, 75° W			*on Settlement Point,*						
4701	SETTLEMENT POINT, GRAND BAHAMAS ISLAND	26° 42.6'	78° 59.8'	*Daily predictions*				2.7	3.1	1.4
4703	Pelican Harbor	26° 23'	76° 58'	+0 18	+0 28	*0.97	*1.11	2.6	3.1	1.4
4705	Nassau, New Providence Island	25° 05'	77° 21'	-0 08	-0 03	*0.98	*1.44	2.6	3.1	1.9
4707	Eleuthera Island, west coast	25° 15'	76° 19'	+2 09	+2 33	*0.94	*1.11	2.4	2.9	1.3
4709	Eleuthera Island, east coast	24° 56'	76° 09'	+0 11	+0 23	*0.82	*1.11	2.2	2.6	1.2
4711	The Bight, Cat Island	24° 19'	75° 26'	-0 37	-0 27	*0.97	*1.11	2.6	3.1	1.4
4713	San Salvador	24° 03'	74° 33'	-0 08	-0 06	*0.86	*1.11	2.3	2.8	1.3
4715	Clarence Harbor, Long Island	23° 06'	74° 59'	+0 41	+0 51	*0.97	*1.11	2.6	3.1	1.4
4717	Nurse Channel	22° 31'	75° 51'	+0 00	+0 10	*0.79	*1.11	2.1	2.6	1.1
4719	Datum Bay, Acklin Island	22° 10'	74° 18'	-0 21	-0 11	*0.75	*1.11	2.0	2.6	1.1
4721	Mathew Town, Great Inagua Island	20° 57'	73° 41'	+0 08	+0 28	*0.79	*1.11	2.1	2.6	1.2
4723	Abraham Bay, Mayaguana Island	22° 22'	73° 00'	+0 02	-0 10	*0.79	*1.11	2.0	2.5	1.1
4725	Hawks Nest Anchorage, Turks Islands	21° 26'	71° 07'	-0 27	-0 17	*0.79	*1.11	2.1	2.6	1.1
	CUBA			*on Hampton Roads,*						
4727	La Isabela	22° 56'	80° 00'	+0 20	+0 16	*0.64	*0.64	1.6	2.0	0.9
4729	Bahia de Nuevitas entrance	21° 38'	77° 07'	-0 05	-0 46	*0.52	*0.52	1.3	1.5	0.7
4731	Nuevitas, Bahia de Nuevitas	21° 35'	77° 15'	+1 32	+1 33	*0.56	*0.56	1.4	1.6	0.7
4733	Puerto Padre	21° 14'	76° 33'	-0 05	-0 10	*0.84	*0.84	2.1	2.4	1.1
4735	Puerto de Gibara	21° 07'	76° 07'	-1 06	-1 03	*0.76	*0.76	1.9	2.2	1.0
4737	Bahia de Nipe entrance	20° 47'	75° 34'	-0 55	-1 01	*0.81	*0.81	2.0	2.3	1.1
4739	Antilla, Bahia de Nipe	20° 50'	75° 44'	-0 37	-0 44	*0.89	*0.89	2.2	2.5	1.2
4741	Bahia de Levisa entrance	20° 45'	75° 28'	-1 03	-1 07	*0.77	*0.77	1.9	2.2	1.0
4743	Sagua de Tanamo, Bahia de	20° 43'	75° 19'	-1 00	-1 08	*0.76	*0.76	1.9	2.2	1.0
4745	MOA, HOLGUIN	20° 39.2'	74° 54.6'	*Daily predictions,*				1.74	--	--
4747	Baracoa	20° 21'	74° 30'	-1 14	-1 18	*0.68	*0.68	1.7	2.0	0.9
4749	Punta Maisi	20° 15'	74° 08'	-1 16	-1 20	*0.88	*0.88	2.2	2.8	1.2
				on San Juan,				**Mean Diurnal**		
4751	Guantanamo Bay	19° 54'	75° 09'	-0 17	-0 23	*0.89	*0.89	--	1.4	0.7
4753	SANTIAGO DE CUBA	19° 59.1'	75° 52.5'	*Daily predictions,*				1.01	--	--
4755	Puerto de Pilon	19° 54'	77° 19'	+0 11	+0 13	*0.72	*0.72	--	1.2	0.6
4757	Manzanillo, Golfo de Guacanayabo	20° 21'	77° 07'	+1 41	+1 38	+1.39	+1.39	--	2.2	1.1
4759	Casilda	21° 45'	79° 59'	+1 04	+0 52	*0.65	*0.65	--	1.0	0.5
	Bahia de Cienfuegos									
4761	Punta Pasacaballos	22° 04'	80° 27'	+0 49	+0 58	*0.80	*0.80	--	1.3	0.6
4763	CIENFUEGOS	22° 09.1'	80° 27.3'	*Daily predictions,*				0.89	--	--
4765	Carapachibey, Isla de Pinos	21° 27'	82° 55'	+0 43	+0 52	*0.54	*0.54	--	0.9	0.4
4767	La Coloma	22° 14'	83° 34'	+2 04	+2 23	*0.54	*0.54	--	0.9	0.4
4769	Cabo San Antonio	21° 52'	84° 58'	-0 50	-0 07	*0.92	*0.92	1.2	1.5	0.8
				on Key West,				**Mean Spring**		
4771	Bahia Honda	22° 58'	83° 13'	-1 04	-0 23	*0.76	*0.76	1.0	1.4	0.7
4773	HAVANA	23° 08.9'	82° 20.2'	*Daily predictions, p. 248*				0.95	--	--
4775	Matanzas	23° 04'	81° 32'	-0 59	-0 59	*0.92	*0.92	1.2	1.5	0.8
4777	Cardenas	23° 04'	81° 12'	-0 11	+0 34	*1.08	*1.08	1.4	1.8	1.0
	JAMAICA			*on Galveston,*				**Mean Diurnal**		
4779	Port Morant	17° 53'	76° 20'	-7 45	-7 45	*0.57	*0.57	--	0.8	0.4
4781	Port Royal #	17° 56'	76° 51'	-7 07	-8 14	*0.50	*0.50	--	0.7	0.3
4783	Galleon Harbour	17° 54'	77° 04'	---	---	---	---	--	0.8	0.4
4785	South Negril Point #	18° 18'	78° 24'	-2 47	-2 47	*1.21	*1.21	--	1.7	0.8
4787	Montego Bay	18° 28'	77° 55'	-6 44	-6 40	*0.71	*0.71	--	1.0	0.5
4789	St. Anns Bay	18° 25'	77° 14'	-7 17	-7 17	*0.57	*0.57	--	0.8	0.4
4791	Grand Cayman #	19° 20'	81° 20'	-8 01	-8 01	*0.93	*0.93	--	1.3	0.6
	HAITI and DOMINICAN REPUBLIC			*on San Juan,*						
4793	Port-au-Prince	18° 33'	72° 21'	-0 35	-0 38	*0.99	*0.99	--	1.6	0.8
4795	Massacre, Riviere du entrance	19° 43'	71° 46'	-1 04	-1 07	*1.44	*1.44	--	2.3	1.2
4797	Puerto Plata	19° 49'	70° 42'	-1 12	-1 20	*1.44	*1.44	--	2.3	1.2
4799	Santa Barbara de Samana	19° 12'	69° 20'	-0 54	-0 53	*1.25	*1.25	--	2.0	1.0
4801	Sanchez	19° 13'	69° 36'	-0 40	-0 43	*2.05	*2.05	--	3.3	1.6
				on Galveston,						
4803	Saona, Isla #	18° 10'	68° 40'	---	---	---	---	--	0.6	0.3
4805	La Romana #	18° 25'	68° 57'	---	---	---	---	--	0.6	--
4807	Santo Domingo #	18° 27'	69° 53'	-6 28	-11 01	*0.57	*0.57	--	0.8	0.4
4809	Barahona #	18° 12'	71° 05'	---	---	---	---	--	0.7	0.3
4811	Jacmel #	18° 13'	72° 34'	-10 00	-10 00	*1.43	*1.43	--	2.0	1.0
	PUERTO RICO Time meridian, 60° W			*on Magueyes,*						
4813	MAGUEYES ISLAND #	17° 58.3'	67° 02.8'	*Daily predictions*				0.65	0.67	0.3
4815	Guanica #	17° 58'	66° 55'	-1 22	+0 18	*1.00	*1.00	--	0.7	0.3
4817	Playa de Ponce #	17° 58'	66° 37'	-0 39	-0 13	*1.14	*1.14	--	0.8	0.4
4819	Playa Cortada #	17° 59'	66° 27'	+0 16	-0 37	*1.14	*1.14	--	0.8	0.4
4821	Arroyo #	17° 58'	66° 04'	+0 52	+0 13	*1.14	*1.14	--	0.8	0.4

TABLE 2. – TIDAL DIFFERENCES AND OTHER CONSTANTS

No.	PLACE	POSITION		DIFFERENCES				RANGES		Mean Tide Level
				Time		Height				
		Latitude	Longitude	High Water	Low Water	High Water	Low Water	Mean	Diurnal	
		North	West	h m	h m	ft	ft	ft	ft	ft

No.	PLACE	Latitude	Longitude	High Water	Low Water	High Water	Low Water	Mean	Diurnal	Mean Tide Level
	PUERTO RICO Time meridian, 60° W					*on Magueyes,*				
4823	Puerto Maunabo #	18° 00'	65° 53'	-0 56	+1 13	*1.00	*1.00	--	0.7	0.4
4825	Culebrita, Isla #	18° 19'	65° 14'	-2 34	+2 40	*1.57	*1.57	--	1.1	0.6
4827	Puerto Ferro, Isla de Vieques #	18° 06'	65° 26'	-2 26	+3 01	*1.14	*1.14	--	0.8	0.4
						on San Juan,				
4829	Punta Mulas, Isla de Vieques	18° 09'	65° 26'	-0 14	-0 17	*0.72	*0.72	--	1.2	0.6
4831	Roosevelt Roads	18° 14'	65° 37'	+0 02	+0 20	*0.63	*0.63	--	1.0	0.5
4833	Ensenada Honda, Culebra Island	18° 18'	65° 17'	-0 34	-0 15	*0.63	*0.63	--	1.0	0.5
4835	Culebra	18° 18.05'	65° 18.15'	-0 19	+0 08	*0.72	*0.73	0.78	1.14	0.55
4837	Playa de Fajardo	18° 20'	65° 38'	-0 10	-0 13	*0.99	*0.99	--	1.6	0.8
4839	SAN JUAN	18° 27.5'	66° 07.0'			*Daily predictions*		1.10	1.58	0.76
4841	Mayaguez	18° 13.2'	67° 09.6'	-0 09	-0 11	*0.93	*0.76	1.06	1.40	0.69
4843	Puerto Real	18° 05'	67° 11'	-0 33	-0 26	*0.72	*0.72	--	1.2	0.6
	LESSER ANTILLES & VIRGIN ISLANDS					*on Charlotte Amalie,*				
	St. Thomas Island									
4845	Botany Bay #	18° 21.8'	65° 02.1'	+0 01	-0 17	*1.39	*1.39	0.90	1.28	0.58
4847	Dorothea Bay, Ruy Point #	18° 22.2'	64° 57.8'	+0 03	-0 17	*1.41	*1.41	0.93	1.29	0.58
4849	Magens Bay #	18° 22'	64° 55'	-0 06	-0 17	*1.59	*1.59	1.0	1.4	0.7
4851	Water Bay #	18° 20.9'	64° 51.8'	-0 11	-0 14	*1.30	*1.30	0.81	1.19	0.56
4853	Redhook Bay #	18° 19.1'	64° 51.1'	-0 46	+0 44	*1.28	*1.28	0.82	1.09	0.54
4855	CHARLOTTE AMALIE #	18° 20.1'	64° 55.2'			*Daily predictions*		0.70	0.79	0.40
4857	Dog Island #	18° 17.8'	64° 49.0'	-0 09	+0 06	*0.97	*0.97	0.63	0.80	0.40
	St. Johns Island									
4859	Lovango Cay #	18° 21.6'	64° 48.2'	-0 27	-0 31	*1.13	*1.13	0.61	1.06	0.49
4861	Leinster Point #	18° 22.0'	64° 43.2'	-0 12	-0 20	*1.22	*1.22	0.90	1.12	0.51
4863	Coral Harbor #	18° 20.9'	64° 43.0'	-0 13	-0 13	*1.08	*1.08	0.72	0.90	0:44
4865	Lameshur Bay #	18° 19.0'	64° 43.4'	-0 04	-0 06	*1.04	*1.14	0.72	0.82	0.41
	St. Croix Island					*on Lime Tree Bay,*				
4867	Christiansted Harbor #	17° 45.0'	64° 42.3'	-1 37	+0 23	*1.03	*1.03	0.69	0.73	0.37
4869	LIME TREE BAY, ST.CROIX ISLAND #	17° 41.8'	64° 45.2'			*Daily predictions*		0.69	0.71	0.36
4871	Fredericksted #	17° 42.8'	64° 53.0'	-0 14	+0 59	*1.01	*1.00	0.70	0.73	0.36
4873	St. Barthelemy #	17° 54'	62° 51'	-3 26	-1 11	*1.87	*1.00	--	1.4	0.7
4875	Pointe-a-Pitre, Guadeloupe	16° 14'	61° 32'	-4 28	-0 33	*3.24	*1.80	--	1.0	0.5
						on Key West,				
4877	Roseau, Dominica	15° 18'	61° 24'	-6 29	-6 05	*0.65	*0.65	0.7	1.2	0.6
4879	Fort-de-France, Martinique	14° 35'	61° 03'	-6 55	-6 18	*0.38	*0.38	0.5	--	0.5
4881	Castries, St. Lucia	14° 01'	61° 00'	-7 09	-7 05	*0.62	*0.62	0.8	1.2	0.6
4883	Vieux Fort Bay, St. Lucia	13° 44'	60° 58'	-6 02	-5 38	*0.69	*0.69	0.9	--	0.7
4885	Kingstown, St. Vincent <15>	13° 10'	61° 13'	-7 09	-6 38	*1.53	*1.53	2.0	2.7	1.4
4887	Bridgetown, Barbados	13° 06'	59° 38'	-6 28	-5 47	*1.30	*1.30	1.7	2.1	1.0
4889	Grenada	12° 04'	61° 45'	-7 26	-6 51	*0.92	*0.92	1.2	1.5	0.8
4891	Scarborough, Tobago	11° 11'	60° 44'	-6 40	-6 22	*1.60	*1.60	2.1	2.7	1.4
						on Cristobal,				
4893	Schottegat, Curacao #	12° 07'	68° 56'	+0 25	+1 09	*0.82	*0.82	--	0.9	0.5
4895	St. Nicolaas Bay, Aruba #	12° 26'	69° 54'	---	---	---	---	--	0.8	0.4
	COLOMBIA <13> Time meridian, 75° W					*on Hampton Roads,*				
4897	Isla de Providencia	13° 20'	81° 23'	+7 53	+7 53	*0.28	*0.28	0.7	1.1	0.4
						on Cristobal,				
4899	Turbo	8° 10'	76° 45'	-0 49	-0 30	*1.43	*1.43	1.0	1.4	0.6
4901	Covenas	9° 20'	75° 40'	-1 06	-0 46	*1.14	*1.14	0.8	1.2	0.5
4903	Cartagena, Bahia de Cartagena	10° 24'	75° 33'	-1 16	-0 48	*1.00	*1.00	0.7	1.1	0.4
4905	Puerto Colombia	11° 00'	74° 58'	-0 52	-1 08	*1.29	*1.29	0.9	1.3	0.5
4907	Santa Marta	11° 18'	74° 12'	-1 19	-1 08	*1.00	*1.00	0.7	1.1	0.4
4909	Riohacha	11° 33'	72° 55'	-1 54	-1 09	*1.00	*1.00	0.7	1.1	0.4
	VENEZUELA Time meridian, 60° 30' W					*on Isla Zapara,*		Mean	Spring	
4911	ISLA ZAPARA, Lake Maracaibo	11° 00'	71° 35'			*Daily predictions*		2.8	3.0	2.7
4913	Bahia de Tablazos, Lake Maracaibo	10° 53'	71° 35'	+0 30	+0 11	*0.61	*0.31	2.1	2.3	1.5
4915	Punta de Palmas	10° 48'	71° 37'	+0 35	+0 16	*0.49	*0.31	1.6	1.8	1.2
						on Amuay,		Mean	Diurnal	
4917	AMUAY	11° 45'	70° 13'			*Daily predictions*		--	1.2	0.6
4919	La Guaira #	10° 36'	66° 56'	-2 29	-1 59	+0.8	+1.0	--	1.0	1.5
4921	Carenero #	10° 32'	66° 07'	-1 51	-1 59	+0.8	+1.0	--	1.0	1.5
4923	Cumana #	10° 28'	64° 11'	-2 37	-1 02	-0.1	0.0	--	1.1	0.5
4925	Porlamar, Isla de Margarita #	10° 57'	63° 51'	-1 19	-0 59	+0.6	0.0	--	1.8	0.9
4927	Carupano #	10° 40'	63° 15'	-1 17	-0 42	+0.2	0.0	--	1.4	0.7

TABLE 2. – TIDAL DIFFERENCES AND OTHER CONSTANTS

No.	PLACE	POSITION Latitude	POSITION Longitude	DIFFERENCES Time High Water	DIFFERENCES Time Low Water	DIFFERENCES Height High Water	DIFFERENCES Height Low Water	RANGES Mean	RANGES Spring	Mean Tide Level
		North	West	h m	h m	ft	ft	ft	ft	ft
	VENEZUELA Time meridian, 60° 30' W				**on Punta Gorda,**					
	Gulf of Paria									
4929	Macuro	10° 39'	61° 56'	-1 15	-2 05	*0.38	*0.38	2.2	2.7	1.4
4931	Puerto de Hierro	10° 37'	62° 05'	-0 46	-1 19	*0.59	*0.59	3.3	4.2	2.0
4933	Barra de Maturin, channel entrance	10° 18'	62° 31'	-0 22	-0 45	-1.0	+0.2	4.6	5.7	2.8
4935	PUNTA GORDA, Rio San Juan	10° 10'	62° 38'		*Daily predictions*			5.8	7.1	3.2
4937	Boca Pedernales entrance	10° 01'	62° 12'	-0 03	-0 34	-1.3	+0.2	4.3	5.4	2.6
4939	Rio Orinoco entrance, Isla Ramon Isidro	8° 39'	60° 35'	+0 07	-0 12	+0.2	+1.0	5.0	6.7	3.8
	TRINIDAD Time meridian, 60° W				**on Suriname Rivier,**					
4941	Staubles Bay	10° 41'	61° 39'	-0 37	-1 32	(*0.33+1.7)		1.9	2.5	2.8
4943	Carenage Bay	10° 41'	61° 36'	-0 28	-1 10	(*0.34+1.6)		2.0	2.6	2.7
4945	Port of Spain	10° 39'	61° 31'	-0 14	-0 42	(*0.31+1.4)		1.8	2.3	2.4
4947	Bonasse pier	10° 05'	61° 52'	-0 13	-0 45	-1.0	+1.4	3.4	4.4	3.4
4949	Erin Bay	10° 04'	61° 39'	-0 20	-1 11	-0.3	+1.2	4.3	5.6	3.6
4951	Guayaguayare Bay	10° 09'	61° 01'	-1 02	-1 39	(*0.53+1.3)		3.1	3.8	3.0
4953	Nariva River	10° 24'	61° 02'	-0 36	-1 46	(*0.41+1.3)		2.4	3.1	2.5
	GUYANA Time meridian, 56° 15' W				**on Suriname Rivier,**					
4955	Parika, Essequibo River	6° 52'	58° 25'	+0 07	+0 31	+1.6	+1.0	6.6	8.3	5.6
4957	Georgetown	6° 48'	58° 10'	-0 13	-0 29	+0.9	+1.1	5.8	8.0	5.3
	SURINAM Time meridian, 45° W									
4959	Nickerie River	5° 57'	56° 59'	+0 09	+0 21	+1.1	0.0	7.1	9.2	4.9
4961	SURINAME RIVIER ENTRANCE	6° 00'	55° 14'		*Daily predictions*			6.0	7.6	4.3
4963	Paramaribo, Suriname Rivier	5° 49'	55° 09'	+1 09	+1 42	0.0	0.0	6.0	7.3	4.3
	FRENCH GUIANA Time meridian, 60° W									
4965	Rio Maroni entrance	5° 45'	53° 58'	+0 18	+0 24	+0.7	+1.2	5.5	7.2	5.2
4967	Iles du Salut	5° 17'	52° 35'	-0 07	-0 07	+1.7	+2.2	5.5	7.2	6.2
4969	Cayenne	4° 56'	52° 20'	+0 15	+0 15	+2.4	+1.8	6.6	7.8	6.4
	BRAZIL <16> Time meridian, 45° W									
4971	Cape Cassipore	3° 49'	51° 01'	+1 24	+1 19	+1.5	+0.3	7.2	9.5	5.2
4973	Rio Cunani entrance	2° 50'	50° 53'	+2 10	+2 24	(*2.42-0.2)		14.5	19.0	10.1
		South	West							
4975	Ilha de Maraca anchorage	2° 09'	50° 30'	+1 40	+1 52	(*2.42-0.2)		14.5	19.0	10.1
4977	Ilha do Brigue, Amazon River	0° 55'	50° 05'	+7 09	+7 40	+8.3	+1.1	13.2	15.7	9.0
4979	Ponta Pedreira, Amazon River	0° 11'	50° 43'	+6 31	+6 43	*2.08	*2.23	12.3	16.2	9.0
4981	Macapa, Amazon River	0° 03'	51° 11'	+10 57	+12 13	+2.8	+0.4	8.4	9.5	5.9
4983	Canal de Braganca, Rio Para entrance	0° 23'	47° 55'	+6 09	+6 09	+1.8	-0.1	7.9	10.4	5.1
4985	Salinopolis	0° 39'	47° 23'	+2 38	+2 52	*1.99	*1.54	12.5	15.9	8.3
4987	Belem (Para)	1° 27'	48° 30'	+6 34	+7 37	+2.9	+0.7	8.2	10.1	6.1
4989	Ilhas de Sao Joao	1° 17'	44° 55'	+1 31	+1 31	*1.70	*1.31	10.7	14.1	7.0
4991	Sao Luiz	2° 32'	44° 18'	+2 28	+2 25	(*2.35-0.7)		14.1	17.1	9.3
4993	Santana, Recifes de	2° 16'	43° 36'	+0 46	+0 45	*1.58	*1.15	10.0	13.1	6.5
4995	Tutoia, Baia da	2° 46'	42° 14'	+0 11	+0 10	+2.4	+0.4	8.0	10.0	5.7
4997	Luis Correia	2° 53'	41° 40'	+0 01	+0 13	+1.8	+0.4	7.4	9.4	5.4
4999	Camocim	2° 53'	40° 52'	+1 07	+1 06	+2.0	+0.4	7.6	9.7	5.5
5001	Rio Ceara (bar)	3° 41'	38° 37'	-0 13	-0 21	+0.2	-0.1	6.3	8.3	4.3
5003	Fortaleza	3° 43'	38° 29'	-0 08	-0 12	+0.2	-0.3	6.5	8.5	4.2
	Time meridian, 30° W				**on Recife,**					
5005	Fernando de Noronha	3° 50'	32° 25'	+1 32	+1 33	-1.2	-0.5	4.5	6.0	2.9
5007	Rocas, Atol das	3° 51'	33° 49'	+1 43	+1 44	+2.3	0.0	7.5	10.0	4.9
	Time meridian, 45° W									
5009	Macau, Rio Acu	5° 06'	36° 41'	+1 29	+1 58	+0.6	-0.1	5.9	7.6	4.1
5011	Natal	5° 47'	35° 12'	+0 28	+0 30	+0.1	-0.2	5.5	7.3	3.7
5013	Cabedelo	6° 58'	34° 50'	+0 36	+0 37	+0.1	-0.2	5.5	7.2	3.7
5015	Tambau	7° 06'	34° 50'	-0 04	-0 03	+0.7	-0.1	6.0	7.6	4.1
5017	RECIFE	8° 03'	34° 52'		*Daily predictions*			5.3	7.1	3.8
5019	Maceio	9° 40'	35° 43'	+0 10	+0 14	-0.3	-0.2	5.1	6.8	3.6
5021	Rio Sao Francisco (bar)	10° 31'	36° 24'	+0 06	+0 14	-0.7	0.0	4.5	6.0	3.5
5023	Aracaju	10° 56'	37° 03'	+0 33	+0 48	-0.8	-0.3	4.7	6.1	3.
5025	Salvador	12° 58'	38° 31'	-0 02	-0 08	+0.6	+0.4	5.5	7.4	4.3
5027	Ponta da Areia	12° 47'	38° 30'	+0 10	+0 06	+0.6	-0.1	5.9	7.6	4.0
5029	Morro de Sao Paulo	13° 21'	38° 54'	-0 11	-0 13	-0.6	0.0	4.6	6.0	3.
5031	Camamu	13° 54'	38° 58'	-0 08	-0 04	-0.2	+0.1	4.9	6.5	3.
5033	Ilheus	14° 48'	39° 02'	-0 33	-0 32	-0.9	-0.3	4.6	5.8	3.
5035	Canavieiras	15° 40'	38° 56'	+0 16	+0 22	-1.0	-0.2	4.5	5.8	3.
5037	Santa Cruz Cabralia	16° 17'	39° 02'	-0 35	-0 35	-1.2	-0.5	4.5	6.0	2.9
5039	Cumuruxatiba	17° 06'	39° 11'	-0 23	-0 09	+0.4	+0.3	5.3	7.2	4.
5041	Caravelas	17° 43'	39° 09'	-0 50	-0 49	-0.8	-0.5	4.9	6.4	3.

TABLE 2. – TIDAL DIFFERENCES AND OTHER CONSTANTS

No.	PLACE	Latitude	Longitude	Time High Water	Time Low Water	Height High Water	Height Low Water	Mean	Spring	Mean Tide Level
		South	**West**	h m	h m	ft	ft	ft	ft	ft
	BRAZIL <16> Time meridian, 45° W			*on Recife,*						
5043	Abrolhos Anchorage	17° 58'	38° 42'	-0 01	+0 04	+0.6	+0.1	5.7	7.6	4.2
5045	Vitoria	20° 19'	40° 19'	-0 34	-0 35	*0.66	*0.75	3.3	4.6	2.6
5047	Guarapari	20° 40'	40° 30'	+0 12	+0 17	*0.62	*0.75	3.1	4.2	2.5
				on Rio de Janeiro,						
5049	Sao Joao da Barra	21° 38'	41° 03'	+0 34	-0 42	-0.1	-0.2	2.6	3.6	2.1
5051	Macae (Imbitiba Bay)	22° 23'	41° 46'	-0 23	-1 08	0.0	-0.2	2.7	3.6	2.1
5053	Armacao dos Buzios	22° 45'	41° 53'	-0 01	-0 55	-0.1	-0.1	2.5	3.4	2.1
5055	Cabo Frio	23° 00'	42° 03'	-0 03	-0 05	*0.91	*0.90	2.3	3.2	2.0
5057	RIO DE JANEIRO	22° 54'	43° 10'	*Daily predictions*				2.5	3.5	2.2
5059	Itacurussa	22° 56'	43° 55'	+0 50	-0 26	0.0	-0.1	2.6	3.3	2.2
5061	Angra dos Reis	23° 01'	44° 19'	-0 35	-0 40	*0.86	*0.86	2.1	3.0	1.9
5063	Parati	23° 14'	44° 43'	-0 09	-1 25	-0.1	0.0	2.4	3.4	2.2
5065	Sao Sebastiao	23° 49'	45° 24'	-0 28	-1 24	*0.94	*1.00	2.3	3.3	2.2
5067	SANTOS	23° 57'	46° 19'	*Daily predictions,*				2.6	3.8	2.4
5069	Cananeia	25° 01'	47° 56'	+1 09	-1 09	+0.4	+0.2	2.7	4.1	2.6
5071	Paranagua	25° 31'	48° 27'	+1 51	-1 32	+1.8	+0.2	4.1	6.0	3.2
5073	Sao Francisco do Sul	26° 15'	48° 38'	+0 38	- - -	+0.8	-0.1	3.4	4.8	2.6
5075	Itajai	26° 54'	48° 39'	-0 08	-0 16	(*0.76+0.4)		1.9	2.8	2.1
5077	Porto Belo	27° 09'	48° 33'	-0 38	-0 28	*0.74	*0.74	1.8	2.5	1.7
5079	Florianopolis	27° 36'	48° 34'	-0 14	+0 15	*0.69	*0.70	1.7	2.4	1.6
5081	Imbituba	28° 14'	48° 39'	-0 17	-1 10	*0.54	*0.50	1.4	2.0	1.2
5083	Laguna	28° 30'	48° 47'	+1 10	-1 31	(*0.32+0.4)		0.8	1.2	1.1
5085	Barra do Rio Grande <18> #	32° 10'	52° 05'	- - -	- - -	- - -	- - -	- -	0.8	0.3
	URUGUAY			*on Buenos Aires,*						
5087	Montevideo	34° 55'	56° 13'	-5 10	-7 11	(*0.52+1.6)		1.1	1.4	3.0
5089	Colonia, Rio de la Plata	34° 28'	57° 51'	+0 17	-0 33	(*0.52+1.2)		1.1	1.3	2.6
	ARGENTINA									
	Rio de la Plata									
5091	BUENOS AIRES	34° 34'	58° 23'	*Daily predictions*				2.1	2.5	2.6
5093	La Plata	34° 50'	57° 53'	-1 50	-2 04	+0.2	+0.6	1.7	2.0	3.0
5095	Banco Chico	34° 50'	57° 30'	-3 00	-3 24	+0.8	+0.8	2.1	2.5	3.4
5097	Banco Cuirassier	35° 06'	57° 08'	-5 25	-5 39	+0.8	+0.8	2.1	2.5	3.4
5099	Punta Piedras	35° 26'	57° 07'	-7 10	-7 23	+2.2	+1.1	3.2	3.8	4.2
5101	Punta Norte del Cabo San Antonio <17>	36° 18'	56° 47'	-8 50	-9 26	+1.2	+0.3	3.0	3.7	3.3
5103	Mar del Plata <17>	38° 03'	57° 33'	-0 02	+0 14	+0.7	+0.2	2.6	3.0	3.0
5105	Quequen <17>	38° 35'	58° 42'	-0 18	-0 22	+1.5	-0.3	3.9	4.2	3.2
				on Puerto Ingeniero White,						
5107	Faro Recalada	39° 00'	61° 16'	-0 48	-0 28	-4.9	-1.3	6.5	7.1	5.3
5109	Monte Hermoso	38° 59'	61° 41'	-0 46	-0 40	-3.4	-1.2	7.9	9.1	6.2
	Bahia Blanca									
5111	Punta Ancla	38° 57'	62° 00'	-0 57	-0 21	-1.9	-0.9	9.1	9.9	7.1
5113	Puerto Rosales	38° 55'	62° 04'	-0 28	-0 06	-0.5	-0.5	10.1	11.0	8.0
5115	Puerto Belgrano	38° 53'	62° 06'	-0 22	-0 07	-0.5	-0.3	9.9	11.0	8.0
5117	PUERTO INGENIERO WHITE	38° 47'	62° 16'	*Daily Predictions*				10.1	11.6	8.5
5119	General Daniel Cerri	38° 45'	62° 24'	+0 16	+0 20	+1.8	+0.1	11.8	12.9	9.4
5121	Canal del Sur, Isla Bermejo	39° 01'	61° 58'	-0 55	-0 24	-2.2	-0.9	8.8	9.6	6.9
5123	Canal Bermejo, Isla Trinidad	39° 05'	61° 58'	-0 57	-0 26	-2.7	-1.0	8.4	9.2	6.6
5125	Punta Lobos, Isla Trinidad	39° 11'	61° 52'	-0 58	-0 41	-3.3	-1.2	8.0	8.8	6.2
5127	El Chara (Punta Laberinto)	39° 26'	62° 03'	-1 19	-0 51	-2.9	-1.0	8.3	9.2	6.5
5129	Bahia Anegada, Islote NW	40° 01'	62° 10'	-2 07	-2 00	(*0.63-0.6)		6.4	7.1	4.8
5131	Bahia San Blas	40° 33'	62° 14'	-3 47	-3 41	*0.50	+0.35	5.6	6.0	4.0
5133	Faro Segunda Barranca	40° 47'	62° 17'	-4 51	-4 40	(*0.53-0.5)		5.4	5.9	4.0
5135	Punta Redonda, Rio Negro entrance	41° 02'	62° 46'	-6 16	-6 10	-1.6	-1.4	9.9	11.2	7.0
				on Comodoro Rivadavia,						
	Golfo San Matias									
5137	Caleta de los Loros	41° 02'	64° 06'	+7 14	+7 08	*1.45	*1.39	20.3	24.0	14.8
5139	Puerto San Antonio	40° 48'	64° 52'	+7 30	+7 23	(*1.57-1.6)		21.9	25.6	14.6
	Golfo San Jose									
5141	San Roman	42° 15'	64° 14'	+7 15	+7 18	(*1.42-1.1)		19.8	23.4	13.5
5143	Pueyrredon (Fondeadero)	42° 24'	64° 09'	+7 46	+7 40	(*1.52-2.2)		21.2	24.6	13.5
5145	La Argentina (Fondeadero)	42° 23'	64° 31'	+7 04	+6 58	*1.31	*1.36	18.0	23.3	13.5
5147	Punta Norte	42° 05'	63° 46'	+6 50	+6 44	-0.8	-1.4	14.5	17.0	9.5
5149	Caleta Valdes	42° 31'	63° 36'	+5 04	+4 58	-5.2	-1.9	10.6	12.4	6.7
5151	Punta Delgada	42° 46'	63° 38'	+4 08	+4 02	-5.8	-2.0	10.1	11.7	6.4
	Golfo Nuevo									
5153	Punta Ninfas (Fondeadero)	42° 57'	64° 25'	+2 48	+3 31	-2.3	-1.0	12.6	15.4	8.6
5155	Puerto Piramides	42° 35'	64° 17'	+2 56	+3 33	-2.7	-1.3	12.5	15.0	8.3
5157	Puerto Madryn	42° 46'	65° 02'	+3 08	+3 42	-0.8	-0.1	13.2	16.0	9.8
5159	Bahia Engano	43° 20'	65° 04'	+2 06	+2 00	-2.7	-1.3	12.5	15.2	8.2
5161	Isla Escondida	43° 40'	65° 17'	+2 10	+2 05	-3.3	-0.3	10.9	13.1	8.5
5163	Bahia Janssen	44° 02'	65° 14'	+1 48	+2 03	-4.1	-1.9	11.7	13.9	7.3
5165	Cabo Raso	44° 20'	65° 14'	+1 41	+1 26	-4.8	-1.6	10.7	14.4	7.0
5167	Bahia Cruz	44° 27'	65° 19'	+2 13	+2 07	-6.1	-2.1	9.9	11.5	6.2
5169	Santa Elena, Puerto	44° 31'	65° 22'	+1 45	+1 40	-3.1	-0.4	11.2	13.6	8.5
5171	Bahia Camarones	44° 54'	65° 36'	+1 10	+1 14	-2.3	+0.1	11.5	13.7	9.2

TABLE 2. – TIDAL DIFFERENCES AND OTHER CONSTANTS

No.	PLACE	POSITION		DIFFERENCES				RANGES		Mean Tide Level
				Time		Height				
		Latitude	Longitude	High Water	Low Water	High Water	Low Water	Mean	Spring	
		South	West	h m	h m	ft	ft	ft	ft	ft
	ARGENTINA Time meridian, 45° W			on Comodoro Rivadavia,						
	Golfo San Jorge									
5173	Caleta Leones	45° 03'	65° 37'	+1 11	+1 05	-0.7	-0.2	13.4	14.7	9.8
5175	Bahia Gil (Caleta Horno)	45° 02'	65° 41'	+0 42	+0 36	-1.7	+0.3	11.9	14.1	9.6
5177	Puerto Melo	45° 01'	65° 50'	+0 27	+0 24	-1.5	+0.1	12.3	14.6	9.6
5179	Isla Tova	45° 06'	65° 59'	+0 27	+0 24	-1.5	+0.1	12.3	14.6	9.6
5181	Bahia Bustamante	45° 07'	66° 32'	+0 28	+0 23	-0.8	+0.7	12.4	14.7	10.2
5183	COMODORO RIVADAVIA	45° 52'	67° 29'	*Daily predictions*				14.0	16.3	10.3
5185	Cabo Blanco	47° 12'	65° 45'	-1 15	-1 20	-2.3	-0.3	11.9	13.2	9.0
5187	Puerto Deseado	47° 45'	65° 55'	-2 52	-2 44	-0.6	+1.0	12.4	14.5	10.5
5189	Bahia Oso Marino	47° 56'	65° 48'	-3 35	-3 40	-1.2	+1.2	11.5	14.1	10.3
5191	Bahia de los Nodales	48° 01'	65° 57'	-3 01	-3 06	-1.2	+0.1	12.6	15.3	9.7
5193	Bahia Laura	48° 23'	66° 29'	-5 28	-5 28	+6.7	-1.9	22.5	25.4	12.7
5195	Bahia San Julian (Punta Pena)	49° 15'	67° 40'	-4 58	-5 04	(*1.40-1.4)		19.5	23.6	13.0
				on Punta Loyola,						
5197	Santa Cruz (Punta Quilla)	50° 07'	68° 25'	+0 43	+0 44	+0.2	+0.1	26.0	32.4	20.4
5199	Ria Coig	50° 57'	69° 10'	-0 05	-0 04	0.0	-0.7	26.6	32.2	19.9
5201	PUNTA LOYOLA	51° 36'	69° 01'	*Daily predictions*				25.9	32.4	20.3
5203	Rio Gallegos (Reduccion Beacon)	51° 37'	69° 13'	+0 21	+0 30	+4.2	+1.1	29.0	36.2	22.9
5205	Cabo Virgenes	52° 21'	68° 22'	-0 36	-0 55	-2.1	0.0	23.8	29.8	19.2
	Tierra del Fuego <19>			on Comodoro Rivadavia,						
5207	Bahia San Sebastian	53° 10'	68° 30'	-7 50	-7 55	*1.69	*1.91	22.8	28.6	17.7
5209	Rio Grande (Muelle)	53° 48'	67° 41'	-7 50	-7 55	*1.15	*1.18	15.8	19.2	11.8
5211	Cabo San Pablo	54° 17'	66° 42'	-8 48	-8 53	*1.17	*1.27	16.0	19.3	12.2
				on Puerto Ingeniero White,						
5213	Bahia Thetis	54° 38'	65° 15'	+1 00	+1 07	-2.0	-0.6	8.7	10.6	7.2
	SOUTH ATLANTIC OCEAN ISLANDS Time meridian, 60° W			on Pictou,						
	Falkland Islands									
5215	Port Louis (Berkeley Sound)	51° 33'	58° 09'	+7 50	+7 47	-0.9	-1.0	3.3	4.2	3.0
5217	Stanley Harbor	51° 42'	57° 51'	+7 51	+7 48	-1.0	-1.0	3.2	4.2	2.9
	South Georgia									
5219	Royal Bay (Moltke Harbor)	54° 31'	36° 01'	+9 58	+10 19	*0.36	*0.13	1.7	2.3	1.2
5221	Leith Harbor	54° 08'	36° 41'	+9 15	+9 35	*0.64	*0.65	2.0	2.7	2.5
	Time meridian, local									
	South Orkneys									
5223	Scotia Bay, Laurie Island	60° 44'	44° 39'	+8 21	+8 32	-0.3	-0.6	3.5	5.0	3.5
	South Shetlands									
5225	Port Foster, Deception Island	62° 58'	60° 34'	+8 26	+8 38	0.0	-0.1	3.3	4.3	3.9
	Time meridian, 45° W									
5227	Admiralty Bay	62° 03'	58° 24'	+9 49	+10 05	-0.5	-0.4	3.1	4.4	3.5

Endnotes can be found at the end of table 2.

ENDNOTES

* RATIO. If the ratio is accompanied by a correction factor multiply the heights of the high and low waters at the reference station by the ratio and then apply the correction factor.

  #   The tide at this location is chiefly diurnal. SEE CAUTION NOTE.

<1>   Neap low water falls lower than spring low water.

<2>   Wharves are dry at low water.

<3>   There is a bore in the Petitcodiac River. It arrives at Moncton about 1h 38m before high water at St. John: its height is about 3 to 3 1/2 feet on average spring tides, but it sometimes exceeds 5 feet on highest tides. On small tides it is not much more than a large ripple.

<4>   The Reversing Falls at St. John—The most turbulence in the gorge occurs on days when the tides are largest. On largest tides the outward fall is between 15 and 16 1/2 feet and is accompanied by a greater turbulence than the inward fall which is between 11 and 12 1/2 feet. The outward fall is at its greatest between 2 hours before and 1 hour after low water at St John: the inward fall is greater just before the time of high water.

<5>   For Eastern Standard, time subtract one hour from the predictions obtained using these differences.

<6>   Low water time difference is +2h 47m. SEE CAUTION NOTE ON PAGE FOLLOWING LISTING.

<8>   Values for the Hudson River above the George Washington Bridge are based upon averages for the six months May to October, when the freshwater discharge is at a minimum.

<9>   In Albermarle and Pamlico Sounds, except near the inlets, the periodic tide has a mean range of less than 0.5 foot.

<11>   In Choctawhatchee and Perdido Bays the periodic tide has a mean range of less than 0.5 foot.

<12>   At New Orleans the diurnal range of the tide during low river stages averages 0.8 foot. There is no periodic tide at high river stages.

<13>   For places on the Pacific coast, see "Tide Tables, West Coast of North and South America."

<15>   Spring range is given instead of diurnal range.

<16>   A "Pororoca", a bore, reported to vary from 5 to 15 feet at spring tides, occurs in the Araguary, Guama and Guajara Rivers.

<17>   Predictions will be approximate.

<18>   Diurnal range is given instead of spring range.

<19>   For places in Magellan Strait, on the south coast of Tierra del Fuego and on the Pacific coast, see "Tide Tables, West Coast of North and South America."

<20>   The time differences should be applied only to the higher high and the lower low water times of the reference station.

<21>   From Oak Hill southward in Mosquito Lagoon the periodic tide is negligible.

<22>   In Indian River north of Palm Bay, in Banana River and in Banana Creek, the periodic tides are negligible.

<24>   The periodic tide is negligible, at this location and above.

<26>   The periodic range of the tide is negligible at this location.

<27>   The periodic range of the tide is negligible inside Sugarloaf Sound.

TABLE 3.—HEIGHT OF TIDE AT ANY TIME

EXPLANATION OF TABLE

Although the footnote of Table 3 may contain sufficient explanation for finding the height of tide at any time, two examples are given here to illustrate its use.

Example 1.—Find the height of the tide at 0755 at New York (The Battery), N.Y., on a day when the predicted tides from Table 1 are given as:

Low Water			High Water	
Time	Height		Time	Height
h.m.	ft		h.m.	ft
0522	0.1		1114	4.2
1741	0.6		2310	4.1

An inspection of the above example shows that the desired time falls between the two morning tides

The duration of rise is $11^h 14^m - 5^h 22^m = 5^h 52^m$.

The time after low water for which the height is required is $7^h 55^m - 5^h 22^m = 2^h 33^m$.

The range of tide is $4.2 - 0.1 = 4.1$ feet.

The duration of rise or fall in Table 3 is given in heavy-faced type for each 20 minutes from $4^h 10^m$ to $10^h 40^m$. The nearest tabular value to $5^h 52^m$, the above duration of rise, is $6^h 00^m$; and on the horizontal line of $6^h 00^m$, the nearest tabular time to $2^h 33^m$ after low water for which the height is required is $2^h 36^m$ Following down the column in which this $2^h 36^m$ is found to its intersection with the line of the range 4.0 feet (the nearest tabular value to the above range of 4.1 feet), the correction is found to be 1.6 feet, which being reckoned from low water, must be added, making $0.1 + 1.6 = 1.7$ feet or 52 centimeters which is the required height above mean lower low water, the datum for New York.

Example 2. —Find the height of the tide at 0300 at Somewhere, U.S.A. on a day when the predicted tides are given as:

High Water			Low Water	
Time	Height		Time	Height
h.m.	ft		h.m.	ft
0012	11.3		0638	-2.0
1251	11.0		1853	-0.8

The duration of fall is $6^h 38^m - 00^h 12^m = 6^h 26^m$.

The time after high water for which the height is required is $3^h 00^m - 00^h 12^m = 2^h 48^m$.

The range of tide is $11.3 - (-2.0) = 13.3$ feet.

Entering Table 3 at the duration of fall of $6^h 20^m$, which is the nearest value to $6^h 26^m$, the nearest value on the horizontal line to $2^h 48^m$ is $2^h 45^m$ after high water. Follow down this column to its intersection with a range of 13.5 feet which is the nearest tabular value to 13.3 feet, one obtains 5.3 which, being calculated from high water, must be subtracted from it. The approximate height at $03^h 00^m$ is, therefore, $11.3 - 5.3 = 6.0$ feet or 183 centimeters.

When the duration of rise or fall is greater than $10^h 40^m$, enter the table with one-half the given duration and with one-half the time from the nearest high or low water; but if the duration of rise or fall is less than 4 hours, enter the table with double the given duration and with double the time from the nearest high or low water.

Similarly, when the range of tide is greater than 20 feet, enter the table with one-half the given range. The tabular correction should then be doubled before applying it to the given high or low water

263

TABLE 3.—HEIGHT OF TIDE AT ANY TIME

height. If the range of tide is greater than 40 feet, take one-third of the range and multiply the tabular correction by 3.

If the height at any time is desired for a place listed in Table 2 predictions of the high and low waters for the day in question should be obtained by the use of the difference given for the place in that table. Having obtained these predictions, the height for any intermediate time is obtained in the same manner as illustrated in the foregoing example.

GRAPHIC METHOD

If the height of the tide is required for a number of times on a certain day the full tide curve for the day may be obtained by the *one-quarter, one-tenth rule*. The procedure is as follows:

1. On cross-section paper plot the high and low water points in the order of their occurrence for the day, measuring time horizontally and height vertically. These are the basic points for the curve.

2. Draw light straight lines connecting the points representing successive high and low waters.

3. Divide each of these straight lines into four equal parts. The halfway point of each line gives another point for the curve.

4. At the quarter point adjacent to high water draw a vertical line above the point and at the quarter point adjacent to low water draw a vertical line below the point, making the length of these lines equal to one-tenth of the range between the high and low waters used. The points marking the ends of these vertical lines give two additional intermediate points for the curve.

5. Draw a smooth curve through the points of high and low waters and the intermediate points, making the curve well rounded near high and low waters. This curve will approximate the actual tide curve and heights for any time of the day may be readily scaled from it.

Caution.—Both methods presented are based on the assumption that the rise and fall conform to simple cosine curves. Therefore, the heights obtained will be approximate. The roughness of approximation will vary as the tide curve differs from a cosine curve.

An example of the use of the graphical method is illustrated below. Using the same predicted tides as in example 2, the approximate height at $3^h 00^m$ could be determined as shown below.

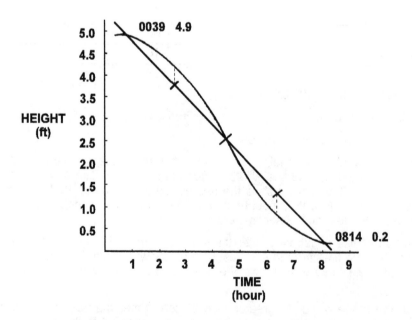

TABLE 3.—HEIGHT OF TIDE AT ANY TIME

Duration of rise or fall, see footnote

Duration h. m.	Time from the nearest high water or low water														
	h. m.	h. m.	h. m.	h. m.	h. m.	h. m.	h. m.	h. m.	h. m.	h. m.	h. m.	h. m.	h. m.	h. m.	h. m.
4 10	0 08	0 16	0 24	0 32	0 40	0 48	0 56	1 04	1 12	1 20	1 28	1 36	1 44	1 52	2 00
4 20	0 09	0 17	0 26	0 35	0 43	0 52	1 01	1 09	1 18	1 27	1 35	1 44	1 53	2 01	2 10
4 40	0 09	0 19	0 28	0 37	0 47	0 56	1 05	1 15	1 24	1 33	1 43	1 52	2 01	2 11	2 20
5 00	0 10	0 20	0 30	0 40	0 50	1 00	1 10	1 20	1 30	1 40	1 50	2 00	2 10	2 20	2 30
5 20	0 11	0 21	0 32	0 43	0 53	1 04	1 15	1 25	1 36	1 47	1 57	2 08	2 19	2 29	2 40
5 40	0 11	0 23	0 34	0 45	0 57	1 08	1 19	1 31	1 42	1 53	2 05	2 16	2 27	2 39	2 50
6 00	0 12	0 24	0 36	0 48	1 00	1 12	1 24	1 36	1 48	2 00	2 12	2 24	2 36	2 48	3 00
6 20	0 13	0 25	0 38	0 51	1 03	1 16	1 29	1 41	1 54	2 07	2 19	2 32	2 45	2 57	3 10
6 40	0 13	0 27	0 40	0 53	1 07	1 20	1 33	1 47	2 00	2 13	2 27	2 40	2 53	3 07	3 20
7 00	0 14	0 28	0 42	0 56	1 10	1 24	1 38	1 52	2 06	2 20	2 34	2 48	3 02	3 16	3 30
7 20	0 15	0 29	0 44	0 59	1 13	1 28	1 43	1 57	2 12	2 27	2 41	2 56	3 11	3 25	3 40
7 40	0 15	0 31	0 46	1 01	1 17	1 32	1 47	2 03	2 18	2 33	2 49	3 04	3 19	3 35	3 50
8 00	0 16	0 32	0 48	1 04	1 20	1 36	1 52	2 08	2 24	2 40	2 56	3 12	3 28	3 44	4 00
8 20	0 17	0 33	0 50	1 07	1 23	1 40	1 57	2 13	2 30	2 47	3 03	3 20	3 37	3 53	4 10
8 40	0 17	0 35	0 52	1 09	1 27	1 44	2 01	2 19	2 36	2 53	3 11	3 28	3 45	4 03	4 20
9 00	0 18	0 36	0 54	1 12	1 30	1 48	2 06	2 24	2 42	3 00	3 18	3 36	3 54	4 12	4 30
9 20	0 19	0 37	0 56	1 15	1 33	1 52	2 11	2 29	2 48	3 07	3 25	3 44	4 03	4 21	4 40
9 40	0 19	0 39	0 58	1 17	1 37	1 56	2 15	2 35	2 54	3 13	3 33	3 52	4 11	4 31	4 50
10 00	0 20	0 40	1 00	1 20	1 40	2 00	2 20	2 40	3 00	3 20	3 40	4 00	4 20	4 40	5 00
10 20	0 21	0 41	1 02	1 23	1 43	2 04	2 25	2 45	3 06	3 27	3 47	4 08	4 29	4 49	5 10
10 40	0 21	0 43	1 04	1 25	1 47	2 08	2 29	2 51	3 12	3 33	3 55	4 16	4 37	4 59	5 20

Range of tide, see footnote

Range Ft.	Correction to height														
	Ft.	Ft.	Ft.	Ft.	Ft.	Ft.	Ft.	Ft.	Ft.	Ft.	Ft.	Ft.	Ft.	Ft.	Ft.
0.5	0.0	0.0	0.0	0.0	0.0	0.0	0.1	0.1	0.1	0.1	0.1	0.2	0.2	0.2	0.2
1.0	0.0	0.0	0.0	0.0	0.1	0.1	0.1	0.2	0.2	0.2	0.3	0.3	0.4	0.4	0.5
1.5	0.0	0.0	0.0	0.1	0.1	0.1	0.2	0.2	0.3	0.4	0.4	0.5	0.6	0.7	0.8
2.0	0.0	0.0	0.0	0.1	0.1	0.2	0.3	0.3	0.4	0.5	0.6	0.7	0.8	0.9	1.0
2.5	0.0	0.0	0.1	0.1	0.2	0.2	0.3	0.4	0.5	0.6	0.7	0.9	1.0	1.1	1.2
3.0	0.0	0.0	0.1	0.1	0.2	0.3	0.4	0.5	0.6	0.8	0.9	1.0	1.2	1.3	1.5
3.5	0.0	0.0	0.1	0.2	0.2	0.3	0.4	0.6	0.7	0.9	1.0	1.2	1.4	1.6	1.8
4.0	0.0	0.0	0.1	0.2	0.3	0.4	0.5	0.7	0.8	1.0	1.2	1.4	1.6	1.8	2.0
4.5	0.0	0.0	0.1	0.2	0.3	0.4	0.6	0.7	0.9	1.1	1.3	1.6	1.8	2.0	2.2
5.0	0.0	0.1	0.1	0.2	0.3	0.5	0.6	0.8	1.0	1.2	1.5	1.7	2.0	2.2	2.5
5.5	0.0	0.1	0.1	0.2	0.4	0.5	0.7	0.9	1.1	1.4	1.6	1.9	2.2	2.5	2.8
6.0	0.0	0.1	0.1	0.3	0.4	0.6	0.8	1.0	1.2	1.5	1.8	2.1	2.4	2.7	3.0
6.5	0.0	0.1	0.2	0.3	0.4	0.6	0.8	1.1	1.3	1.6	1.9	2.2	2.6	2.9	3.2
7.0	0.0	0.1	0.2	0.3	0.5	0.7	0.9	1.2	1.4	1.8	2.1	2.4	2.8	3.1	3.5
7.5	0.0	0.1	0.2	0.3	0.5	0.7	1.0	1.2	1.5	1.9	2.2	2.6	3.0	3.4	3.8
8.0	0.0	0.1	0.2	0.3	0.5	0.8	1.0	1.3	1.6	2.0	2.4	2.8	3.2	3.6	4.0
8.5	0.0	0.1	0.2	0.4	0.6	0.8	1.1	1.4	1.8	2.1	2.5	2.9	3.4	3.8	4.2
9.0	0.0	0.1	0.2	0.4	0.6	0.9	1.2	1.5	1.9	2.2	2.7	3.1	3.6	4.0	4.5
9.5	0.0	0.1	0.2	0.4	0.6	0.9	1.2	1.6	2.0	2.4	2.8	3.3	3.8	4.3	4.8
10.0	0.0	0.1	0.2	0.4	0.7	1.0	1.3	1.7	2.1	2.5	3.0	3.5	4.0	4.5	5.0
10.5	0.0	0.1	0.3	0.5	0.7	1.0	1.3	1.7	2.2	2.6	3.1	3.6	4.2	4.7	5.2
11.0	0.0	0.1	0.3	0.5	0.7	1.1	1.4	1.7	2.3	2.8	3.3	3.8	4.4	4.9	5.5
11.5	0.0	0.1	0.3	0.5	0.8	1.1	1.5	1.8	2.3	2.9	3.4	4.0	4.6	5.1	5.8
12.0	0.0	0.1	0.3	0.5	0.8	1.1	1.5	1.9	2.5	3.0	3.6	4.1	4.8	5.4	6.0
12.5	0.0	0.1	0.3	0.5	0.8	1.2	2.6	1.9	2.6	3.1	3.7	4.3	5.0	5.6	6.2
13.0	0.0	0.1	0.3	0.6	0.9	1.2	1.7	2.2	2.7	3.2	3.9	4.5	5.1	5.8	6.5
13.5	0.0	0.1	0.3	0.6	0.9	1.3	1.7	2.2	2.8	3.4	4.0	4.7	5.3	6.0	6.8
14.0	0.0	0.2	0.3	0.6	0.9	1.3	1.8	2.3	2.9	3.5	4.2	4.8	5.5	6.3	7.0
14.5	0.0	0.2	0.4	0.6	1.0	1.4	1.9	2.4	3.0	3.6	4.3	5.0	5.7	6.5	7.2
15.0	0.0	0.2	0.4	0.6	1.0	1.4	1.9	2.5	3.1	3.8	4.4	5.2	5.9	6.7	7.5
15.5	0.0	0.2	0.4	0.7	1.0	1.5	2.0	2.6	3.2	3.9	4.6	5.4	6.1	6.9	7.8
16.0	0.0	0.2	0.4	0.7	1.1	1.5	2.1	2.6	3.3	4.0	4.7	5.5	6.3	7.2	8.0
16.5	0.0	0.2	0.4	0.7	1.1	1.6	2.1	2.7	3.4	4.1	4.9	5.7	6.5	7.4	8.2
17.0	0.0	0.2	0.4	0.7	1.1	1.6	2.2	2.8	3.5	4.2	5.0	5.9	6.7	7.6	8.5
17.5	0.0	0.2	0.4	0.8	1.2	1.7	2.2	2.9	3.6	4.4	5.2	6.0	6.9	7.8	8.8
18.0	0.0	0.2	0.4	0.8	1.2	1.7	2.3	3.0	3.7	4.5	5.3	6.2	7.1	8.1	9.0
18.5	0.1	0.2	0.5	0.8	1.2	1.8	2.4	3.1	3.8	4.6	5.5	6.4	7.3	8.3	9.2
19.0	0.1	0.2	0.5	0.8	1.3	1.8	2.4	3.1	3.9	4.8	5.6	6.6	7.5	8.5	9.5
19.5	0.1	0.2	0.5	0.8	1.3	1.9	2.5	3.2	4.0	4.9	5.8	6.7	7.7	8.7	9.8
20.0	0.1	0.2	0.5	0.9	1.3	1.9	2.6	3.3	4.1	5.0	5.9	6.9	7.9	9.0	10.0

Obtain from the predictions the high water and low water, one of which is before and the other after the time for which the height is required. The difference between the times of occurrence of these tides is the duration of rise or fall, and the difference between their heights is the range of tide for the above table. Find the difference between the nearest high or low water and the time for which the height is required.

Enter the table with the duration of rise or fall, printed in heavy-faced type, which most nearly agrees with the actual value, and on that horizontal line find the time from the nearest high or low water which agrees most nearly with the corresponding actual difference. The correction sought is in the column directly below, on the line with the range of tide.

When the nearest tide is high water, subtract the correction.

When the nearest tide is low, add the correction.

TABLE 4. - TIME OF SUNRISE AND SUNSET IN SELECT CITIES

EXPLANATION OF TABLE

This table shows information relating to the time of Sunrise and Sunset in select cities on the East Coast of the United States. This replaces what, in previous editions, was based on Mean sunrise/sunset times, accompanied by a conversion table.

NOAA Global Monitoring Laboratory
Global Radiation Group
https://www.esrl.noaa.gov/gmd/grad/solcalc

Boston, MA, 2021
Sunrise Table

Location: Latitude 42.35000 Longitude -71.05000

Time Zone Offset: America/New_York -4.0

All times are in local time. Cells with light green color indicate when daylight savings time is in effect.

Day	Jan	Feb	Mar	Apr	May	Jun	Jul	Aug	Sep	Oct	Nov	Dec
1	07:13	06:57	06:19	06:26	05:39	05:10	05:11	05:37	06:10	06:42	07:18	06:5
2	07:13	06:56	06:17	06:24	05:38	05:09	05:12	05:38	06:11	06:43	07:19	06:5
3	07:13	06:55	06:16	06:23	05:36	05:09	05:12	05:39	06:12	06:44	07:20	06:5
4	07:13	06:54	06:14	06:21	05:35	05:09	05:13	05:40	06:13	06:45	07:22	06:5
5	07:13	06:53	06:13	06:19	05:34	05:08	05:14	05:41	06:14	06:46	07:23	06:5
6	07:13	06:52	06:11	06:18	05:33	05:08	05:14	05:42	06:15	06:47	07:24	06:5
7	07:13	06:51	06:09	06:16	05:31	05:08	05:15	05:43	06:16	06:48	06:25	07:0
8	07:13	06:49	06:08	06:14	05:30	05:07	05:16	05:44	06:17	06:49	06:27	07:0
9	07:13	06:48	06:06	06:13	05:29	05:07	05:16	05:45	06:18	06:50	06:28	07:0
10	07:12	06:47	06:04	06:11	05:28	05:07	05:17	05:46	06:19	06:52	06:29	07:0
11	07:12	06:46	06:02	06:09	05:27	05:07	05:18	05:47	06:20	06:53	06:30	07:0
12	07:12	06:44	06:01	06:08	05:26	05:07	05:19	05:48	06:21	06:54	06:32	07:0
13	07:11	06:43	05:59	06:06	05:25	05:07	05:19	05:50	06:22	06:55	06:33	07:0
14	07:11	06:42	06:57	06:04	05:24	05:07	05:20	05:51	06:23	06:56	06:34	07:
15	07:11	06:40	06:56	06:03	05:23	05:07	05:21	05:52	06:24	06:57	06:35	07:
16	07:10	06:39	06:54	06:01	05:22	05:07	05:22	05:53	06:25	06:58	06:37	07:
17	07:10	06:37	06:52	06:00	05:21	05:07	05:23	05:54	06:27	07:00	06:38	07:
18	07:09	06:36	06:50	05:58	05:20	05:07	05:24	05:55	06:28	07:01	06:39	07:
19	07:08	06:35	06:49	05:57	05:19	05:07	05:24	05:56	06:29	07:02	06:40	07:
20	07:08	06:33	06:47	05:55	05:18	05:07	05:25	05:57	06:30	07:03	06:41	07:
21	07:07	06:32	06:45	05:53	05:17	05:08	05:26	05:58	06:31	07:04	06:43	07:
22	07:06	06:30	06:44	05:52	05:16	05:08	05:27	05:59	06:32	07:06	06:44	07:
23	07:06	06:29	06:42	05:50	05:15	05:08	05:28	06:00	06:33	07:07	06:45	07
24	07:05	06:27	06:40	05:49	05:15	05:08	05:29	06:01	06:34	07:08	06:46	07
25	07:04	06:25	06:38	05:47	05:14	05:09	05:30	06:02	06:35	07:09	06:47	07
26	07:03	06:24	06:37	05:46	05:13	05:09	05:31	06:03	06:36	07:10	06:48	07
27	07:02	06:22	06:35	05:45	05:13	05:09	05:32	06:04	06:37	07:12	06:50	07
28	07:01	06:21	06:33	05:43	05:12	05:10	05:33	06:05	06:38	07:13	06:51	07
29	07:00		06:31	05:42	05:11	05:10	05:34	06:06	06:39	07:14	06:52	07
30	06:59		06:30	05:40	05:11	05:11	05:35	06:08	06:40	07:15	06:53	07
31	06:58		06:28		05:10		05:36	06:09		07:17		07

NOAA Global Monitoring Laboratory
Global Radiation Group
https://www.esrl.noaa.gov/gmd/grad/solcalc

ation: Latitude 42.35000 Longitude -71.05000

Zone Offset: America/New_York -4.0

nes are in local time. Cells with light green color indicate when daylight savings time is in effect.

Jan	Feb	Mar	Apr	May	Jun	Jul	Aug	Sep	Oct	Nov	Dec
16:23	16:59	17:34	19:10	19:44	20:15	20:25	20:03	19:18	18:25	17:37	16:13
16:24	17:00	17:36	19:11	19:45	20:15	20:25	20:02	19:16	18:23	17:36	16:12
16:24	17:01	17:37	19:13	19:46	20:16	20:24	20:01	19:14	18:22	17:35	16:12
16:25	17:03	17:38	19:14	19:47	20:17	20:24	20:00	19:13	18:20	17:33	16:12
16:26	17:04	17:39	19:15	19:49	20:18	20:24	19:58	19:11	18:18	17:32	16:12
16:27	17:05	17:40	19:16	19:50	20:18	20:23	19:57	19:09	18:17	17:31	16:12
16:28	17:07	17:42	19:17	19:51	20:19	20:23	19:56	19:07	18:15	16:30	16:12
16:29	17:08	17:43	19:18	19:52	20:19	20:23	19:55	19:06	18:13	16:29	16:11
16:30	17:09	17:44	19:19	19:53	20:20	20:22	19:53	19:04	18:12	16:28	16:12
16:32	17:10	17:45	19:20	19:54	20:21	20:22	19:52	19:02	18:10	16:27	16:12
16:33	17:12	17:46	19:22	19:55	20:21	20:21	19:51	19:00	18:08	16:26	16:12
16:34	17:13	17:47	19:23	19:56	20:22	20:21	19:49	18:59	18:07	16:25	16:12
16:35	17:14	17:49	19:24	19:57	20:22	20:20	19:48	18:57	18:05	16:24	16:12
16:36	17:16	18:50	19:25	19:58	20:22	20:20	19:46	18:55	18:03	16:23	16:12
16:37	17:17	18:51	19:26	19:59	20:23	20:19	19:45	18:53	18:02	16:22	16:12
16:38	17:18	18:52	19:27	20:00	20:23	20:18	19:43	18:52	18:00	16:21	16:13
16:40	17:19	18:53	19:28	20:01	20:24	20:18	19:42	18:50	17:59	16:20	16:13
16:41	17:21	18:54	19:30	20:02	20:24	20:17	19:40	18:48	17:57	16:19	16:13
16:42	17:22	18:56	19:31	20:03	20:24	20:16	19:39	18:46	17:55	16:19	16:14
16:43	17:23	18:57	19:32	20:04	20:24	20:15	19:37	18:45	17:54	16:18	16:14
16:45	17:25	18:58	19:33	20:05	20:25	20:14	19:36	18:43	17:52	16:17	16:15
16:46	17:26	18:59	19:34	20:06	20:25	20:14	19:34	18:41	17:51	16:17	16:15
16:47	17:27	19:00	19:35	20:07	20:25	20:13	19:33	18:39	17:49	16:16	16:16
16:48	17:28	19:01	19:36	20:08	20:25	20:12	19:31	18:37	17:48	16:15	16:16
16:50	17:29	19:02	19:37	20:09	20:25	20:11	19:29	18:36	17:47	16:15	16:17
16:51	17:31	19:04	19:39	20:10	20:25	20:10	19:28	18:34	17:45	16:14	16:18
16:52	17:32	19:05	19:40	20:11	20:25	20:09	19:26	18:32	17:44	16:14	16:18
16:53	17:33	19:06	19:41	20:12	20:25	20:08	19:24	18:30	17:42	16:14	16:19
16:55		19:07	19:42	20:12	20:25	20:07	19:23	18:29	17:41	16:13	16:20
16:56		19:08	19:43	20:13	20:25	20:06	19:21	18:27	17:40	16:13	16:21
16:57		19:09		20:14		20:04	19:19		17:38		16:22

NOAA Global Monitoring Laboratory
Global Radiation Group
https://www.esrl.noaa.gov/gmd/grad/solcalc

Boston, MA, 2021
Solar Noon Tab

Location: Latitude 42.35000 Longitude -71.05000

Time Zone Offset: America/New_York -4.0

All times are in local time. Cells with light green color indicate when daylight savings time is in effect.

Day	Jan	Feb	Mar	Apr	May	Jun	Jul	Aug	Sep	Oct	Nov	De
1	11:47:58	11:57:51	11:56:26	12:47:55	12:41:15	12:42:07	12:48:10	12:50:31	12:44:05	12:33:44	12:27:44	11:3
2	11:48:26	11:57:58	11:56:14	12:47:37	12:41:09	12:42:17	12:48:22	12:50:27	12:43:46	12:33:25	12:27:43	11:3
3	11:48:54	11:58:04	11:56:01	12:47:20	12:41:03	12:42:27	12:48:33	12:50:22	12:43:26	12:33:06	12:27:43	11:3
4	11:49:21	11:58:10	11:55:48	12:47:02	12:40:57	12:42:37	12:48:43	12:50:16	12:43:06	12:32:48	12:27:44	11:3
5	11:49:47	11:58:14	11:55:34	12:46:45	12:40:52	12:42:48	12:48:54	12:50:10	12:42:46	12:32:30	12:27:46	11:3
6	11:50:14	11:58:18	11:55:20	12:46:28	12:40:48	12:42:59	12:49:04	12:50:04	12:42:26	12:32:12	12:27:48	11:3
7	11:50:40	11:58:21	11:55:06	12:46:12	12:40:44	12:43:10	12:49:13	12:49:56	12:42:06	12:31:55	11:27:52	11:3
8	11:51:05	11:58:24	11:54:51	12:45:55	12:40:41	12:43:22	12:49:22	12:49:48	12:41:45	12:31:38	11:27:56	11:3
9	11:51:30	11:58:25	11:54:36	12:45:39	12:40:38	12:43:33	12:49:31	12:49:40	12:41:24	12:31:21	11:28:01	11:3
10	11:51:54	11:58:26	11:54:20	12:45:23	12:40:36	12:43:45	12:49:40	12:49:31	12:41:03	12:31:05	11:28:07	11:3
11	11:52:17	11:58:26	11:54:04	12:45:07	12:40:34	12:43:57	12:49:48	12:49:21	12:40:42	12:30:49	11:28:14	11:3
12	11:52:40	11:58:25	11:53:48	12:44:52	12:40:34	12:44:10	12:49:55	12:49:11	12:40:21	12:30:34	11:28:22	11:3
13	11:53:03	11:58:24	11:53:32	12:44:37	12:40:33	12:44:22	12:50:02	12:49:00	12:40:00	12:30:20	11:28:30	11:3
14	11:53:25	11:58:21	12:53:15	12:44:22	12:40:33	12:44:35	12:50:09	12:48:48	12:39:38	12:30:06	11:28:40	11:
15	11:53:46	11:58:18	12:52:58	12:44:08	12:40:34	12:44:48	12:50:15	12:48:37	12:39:17	12:29:52	11:28:50	11:
16	11:54:06	11:58:14	12:52:41	12:43:53	12:40:35	12:45:01	12:50:20	12:48:24	12:38:56	12:29:39	11:29:01	11:
17	11:54:26	11:58:10	12:52:24	12:43:40	12:40:37	12:45:14	12:50:25	12:48:11	12:38:34	12:29:27	11:29:13	11:
18	11:54:45	11:58:05	12:52:06	12:43:27	12:40:40	12:45:27	12:50:30	12:47:58	12:38:13	12:29:15	11:29:26	11
19	11:55:03	11:57:59	12:51:49	12:43:14	12:40:43	12:45:40	12:50:34	12:47:44	12:37:51	12:29:04	11:29:39	11
20	11:55:21	11:57:52	12:51:31	12:43:01	12:40:46	12:45:53	12:50:37	12:47:30	12:37:30	12:28:53	11:29:54	11
21	11:55:38	11:57:45	12:51:13	12:42:49	12:40:50	12:46:06	12:50:40	12:47:15	12:37:09	12:28:44	11:30:09	11
22	11:55:54	11:57:37	12:50:55	12:42:38	12:40:55	12:46:19	12:50:42	12:47:00	12:36:48	12:28:34	11:30:25	11
23	11:56:09	11:57:29	12:50:37	12:42:26	12:41:00	12:46:32	12:50:44	12:46:44	12:36:27	12:28:26	11:30:42	11
24	11:56:24	11:57:20	12:50:19	12:42:16	12:41:06	12:46:45	12:50:45	12:46:28	12:36:06	12:28:18	11:31:00	11
25	11:56:37	11:57:10	12:50:01	12:42:06	12:41:12	12:46:58	12:50:45	12:46:11	12:35:45	12:28:11	11:31:18	11
26	11:56:50	11:57:00	12:49:43	12:41:56	12:41:18	12:47:10	12:50:45	12:45:54	12:35:24	12:28:05	11:31:37	11
27	11:57:02	11:56:49	12:49:25	12:41:47	12:41:25	12:47:23	12:50:44	12:45:37	12:35:04	12:28:00	11:31:57	11
28	11:57:14	11:56:38	12:49:07	12:41:38	12:41:33	12:47:35	12:50:43	12:45:19	12:34:44	12:27:55	11:32:18	11
29	11:57:24		12:48:48	12:41:30	12:41:41	12:47:47	12:50:41	12:45:01	12:34:24	12:27:51	11:32:39	11
30	11:57:34		12:48:31	12:41:22	12:41:49	12:47:59	12:50:38	12:44:43	12:34:04	12:27:48	11:33:01	11
31	11:57:43		12:48:13		12:41:58		12:50:35	12:44:24		12:27:45		1

ation: Latitude 40.72000 Longitude -74.02000

Zone Offset: America/New_York -4.0

nes are in local time. Cells with light green color indicate when daylight savings time is in effect.

	Jan	Feb	Mar	Apr	May	Jun	Jul	Aug	Sep	Oct	Nov	Dec
	07:20	07:06	06:30	06:39	05:54	05:27	05:29	05:53	06:23	06:53	07:27	07:01
	07:20	07:05	06:28	06:38	05:53	05:27	05:29	05:54	06:24	06:54	07:28	07:02
	07:20	07:04	06:26	06:36	05:52	05:26	05:30	05:55	06:25	06:55	07:29	07:03
	07:20	07:03	06:25	06:34	05:51	05:26	05:30	05:56	06:26	06:56	07:30	07:04
	07:20	07:02	06:23	06:33	05:49	05:26	05:31	05:57	06:27	06:57	07:31	07:05
	07:20	07:01	06:22	06:31	05:48	05:25	05:32	05:58	06:28	06:58	07:33	07:06
	07:20	06:59	06:20	06:29	05:47	05:25	05:32	05:59	06:29	06:59	06:34	07:07
	07:20	06:58	06:19	06:28	05:46	05:25	05:33	06:00	06:30	07:00	06:35	07:08
	07:20	06:57	06:17	06:26	05:45	05:25	05:34	06:01	06:31	07:01	06:36	07:09
	07:20	06:56	06:15	06:25	05:44	05:25	05:34	06:02	06:32	07:02	06:37	07:09
	07:19	06:55	06:14	06:23	05:43	05:24	05:35	06:03	06:33	07:03	06:38	07:10
	07:19	06:53	06:12	06:22	05:42	05:24	05:36	06:04	06:34	07:04	06:40	07:11
	07:19	06:52	06:11	06:20	05:41	05:24	05:36	06:05	06:35	07:05	06:41	07:12
	07:18	06:51	07:09	06:18	05:40	05:24	05:37	06:06	06:36	07:06	06:42	07:12
	07:18	06:50	07:07	06:17	05:39	05:24	05:38	06:07	06:37	07:08	06:43	07:13
	07:17	06:48	07:06	06:15	05:38	05:24	05:39	06:08	06:38	07:09	06:44	07:14
	07:17	06:47	07:04	06:14	05:37	05:24	05:40	06:09	06:39	07:10	06:46	07:14
	07:16	06:46	07:02	06:12	05:36	05:25	05:40	06:10	06:40	07:11	06:47	07:15
	07:16	06:44	07:01	06:11	05:35	05:25	05:41	06:11	06:41	07:12	06:48	07:16
	07:15	06:43	06:59	06:09	05:34	05:25	05:42	06:12	06:42	07:13	06:49	07:16
	07:15	06:41	06:57	06:08	05:34	05:25	05:43	06:13	06:43	07:14	06:50	07:17
	07:14	06:40	06:56	06:07	05:33	05:25	05:44	06:14	06:44	07:15	06:51	07:17
	07:13	06:39	06:54	06:05	05:32	05:26	05:45	06:15	06:45	07:16	06:52	07:18
	07:13	06:37	06:52	06:04	05:31	05:26	05:46	06:16	06:46	07:17	06:54	07:18
	07:12	06:36	06:51	06:02	05:31	05:26	05:46	06:16	06:47	07:19	06:55	07:18
	07:11	06:34	06:49	06:01	05:30	05:27	05:47	06:17	06:48	07:20	06:56	07:19
	07:10	06:33	06:47	06:00	05:30	05:27	05:48	06:18	06:49	07:21	06:57	07:19
	07:09	06:31	06:46	05:58	05:29	05:27	05:49	06:19	06:50	07:22	06:58	07:19
	07:09		06:44	05:57	05:28	05:28	05:50	06:20	06:51	07:23	06:59	07:20
	07:08		06:42	05:56	05:28	05:28	05:51	06:21	06:52	07:24	07:00	07:20
	07:07		06:41		05:27		05:52	06:22		07:26		07:20

NOAA Global Monitoring Laboratory
Global Radiation Group
https://www.esrl.noaa.gov/gmd/grad/solcalc

New York, NY, 2
Sunset Tabl

Location: Latitude 40.72000 Longitude -74.02000

Time Zone Offset: America/New_York -4.0

All times are in local time. Cells with light green color indicate when daylight savings time is in effect.

Day	Jan	Feb	Mar	Apr	May	Jun	Jul	Aug	Sep	Oct	Nov	De
1	16:40	17:14	17:48	19:21	19:53	20:21	20:31	20:11	19:28	18:38	17:52	16:
2	16:41	17:15	17:49	19:22	19:54	20:22	20:31	20:10	19:26	18:36	17:51	16:
3	16:41	17:17	17:50	19:23	19:55	20:23	20:31	20:09	19:25	18:34	17:50	16:
4	16:42	17:18	17:51	19:24	19:56	20:23	20:31	20:08	19:23	18:33	17:48	16:
5	16:43	17:19	17:52	19:25	19:57	20:24	20:30	20:07	19:21	18:31	17:47	16
6	16:44	17:20	17:53	19:26	19:58	20:25	20:30	20:05	19:20	18:29	17:46	16
7	16:45	17:22	17:54	19:27	19:59	20:25	20:30	20:04	19:18	18:28	16:45	16
8	16:46	17:23	17:55	19:28	20:00	20:26	20:29	20:03	19:16	18:26	16:44	16
9	16:47	17:24	17:57	19:29	20:01	20:26	20:29	20:02	19:15	18:25	16:43	16
10	16:48	17:25	17:58	19:31	20:02	20:27	20:28	20:00	19:13	18:23	16:42	16
11	16:49	17:26	17:59	19:32	20:03	20:27	20:28	19:59	19:11	18:22	16:41	16
12	16:50	17:28	18:00	19:33	20:04	20:28	20:28	19:58	19:10	18:20	16:40	16
13	16:51	17:29	18:01	19:34	20:05	20:28	20:27	19:56	19:08	18:18	16:39	16
14	16:53	17:30	19:02	19:35	20:06	20:29	20:26	19:55	19:06	18:17	16:39	16
15	16:54	17:31	19:03	19:36	20:07	20:29	20:26	19:54	19:05	18:15	16:38	16
16	16:55	17:32	19:04	19:37	20:08	20:30	20:25	19:52	19:03	18:14	16:37	16
17	16:56	17:34	19:05	19:38	20:09	20:30	20:25	19:51	19:01	18:12	16:36	16
18	16:57	17:35	19:06	19:39	20:10	20:30	20:24	19:49	19:00	18:11	16:36	16
19	16:58	17:36	19:07	19:40	20:10	20:30	20:23	19:48	18:58	18:09	16:35	16
20	16:59	17:37	19:08	19:41	20:11	20:31	20:22	19:46	18:56	18:08	16:34	16
21	17:01	17:38	19:10	19:42	20:12	20:31	20:22	19:45	18:54	18:06	16:34	1
22	17:02	17:40	19:11	19:43	20:13	20:31	20:21	19:43	18:53	18:05	16:33	1
23	17:03	17:41	19:12	19:44	20:14	20:31	20:20	19:42	18:51	18:04	16:32	1
24	17:04	17:42	19:13	19:45	20:15	20:31	20:19	19:40	18:49	18:02	16:32	1
25	17:05	17:43	19:14	19:46	20:16	20:31	20:18	19:39	18:48	18:01	16:31	1
26	17:07	17:44	19:15	19:47	20:17	20:31	20:17	19:37	18:46	18:00	16:31	1
27	17:08	17:45	19:16	19:48	20:17	20:31	20:16	19:36	18:44	17:58	16:31	1
28	17:09	17:47	19:17	19:49	20:18	20:31	20:15	19:34	18:43	17:57	16:30	1
29	17:10		19:18	19:50	20:19	20:31	20:14	19:33	18:41	17:56	16:30	1
30	17:12		19:19	19:52	20:20	20:31	20:13	19:31	18:39	17:54	16:30	1
31	17:13		19:20		20:21		20:12	19:29		17:53		1

NOAA Global Monitoring Laboratory
Global Radiation Group
https://www.esrl.noaa.gov/gmd/grad/solcalc

ation: Latitude 40.72000 Longitude -74.02000

Zone Offset: America/New_York -4.0

ies are in local time. Cells with light green color indicate when daylight savings time is in effect.

Jan	Feb	Mar	Apr	May	Jun	Jul	Aug	Sep	Oct	Nov	Dec
11:59:51	12:09:43	12:08:19	12:59:48	12:53:08	12:54:00	13:00:03	13:02:24	12:55:58	12:45:37	12:39:36	11:45:16
12:00:19	12:09:51	12:08:07	12:59:30	12:53:01	12:54:10	13:00:14	13:02:20	12:55:38	12:45:18	12:39:36	11:45:39
12:00:47	12:09:57	12:07:54	12:59:12	12:52:55	12:54:20	13:00:25	13:02:15	12:55:19	12:44:59	12:39:36	11:46:03
12:01:14	12:10:03	12:07:41	12:58:55	12:52:50	12:54:30	13:00:36	13:02:09	12:54:59	12:44:41	12:39:37	11:46:28
12:01:41	12:10:07	12:07:27	12:58:38	12:52:45	12:54:41	13:00:46	13:02:03	12:54:39	12:44:22	12:39:38	11:46:52
12:02:07	12:10:11	12:07:13	12:58:21	12:52:41	12:54:52	13:00:56	13:01:56	12:54:19	12:44:05	12:39:41	11:47:18
12:02:33	12:10:14	12:06:58	12:58:04	12:52:37	12:55:03	13:01:06	13:01:49	12:53:58	12:43:47	11:39:44	11:47:44
12:02:58	12:10:17	12:06:43	12:57:48	12:52:34	12:55:14	13:01:15	13:01:41	12:53:38	12:43:30	11:39:49	11:48:10
12:03:23	12:10:18	12:06:28	12:57:32	12:52:31	12:55:26	13:01:24	13:01:32	12:53:17	12:43:14	11:39:54	11:48:37
12:03:47	12:10:19	12:06:13	12:57:16	12:52:29	12:55:38	13:01:32	13:01:23	12:52:56	12:42:58	11:40:00	11:49:04
12:04:10	12:10:19	12:05:57	12:57:00	12:52:27	12:55:50	13:01:40	13:01:14	12:52:35	12:42:42	11:40:07	11:49:32
12:04:33	12:10:18	12:05:41	12:56:44	12:52:26	12:56:03	13:01:48	13:01:03	12:52:14	12:42:27	11:40:14	11:50:00
12:04:56	12:10:16	12:05:24	12:56:29	12:52:26	12:56:15	13:01:55	13:00:52	12:51:52	12:42:12	11:40:23	11:50:28
12:05:18	12:10:14	13:05:08	12:56:15	12:52:26	12:56:28	13:02:01	13:00:41	12:51:31	12:41:58	11:40:32	11:50:57
12:05:39	12:10:11	13:04:51	12:56:00	12:52:27	12:56:41	13:02:07	13:00:29	12:51:10	12:41:45	11:40:43	11:51:26
12:05:59	12:10:07	13:04:34	12:55:46	12:52:28	12:56:54	13:02:13	13:00:17	12:50:48	12:41:32	11:40:54	11:51:55
12:06:19	12:10:03	13:04:16	12:55:33	12:52:30	12:57:07	13:02:18	13:00:04	12:50:27	12:41:19	11:41:06	11:52:24
12:06:38	12:09:57	13:03:59	12:55:19	12:52:33	12:57:20	13:02:22	12:59:51	12:50:05	12:41:08	11:41:19	11:52:54
12:06:56	12:09:52	13:03:41	12:55:06	12:52:36	12:57:33	13:02:26	12:59:37	12:49:44	12:40:57	11:41:32	11:53:23
12:07:14	12:09:45	13:03:23	12:54:54	12:52:39	12:57:46	13:02:30	12:59:22	12:49:23	12:40:46	11:41:47	11:53:53
12:07:31	12:09:38	13:03:06	12:54:42	12:52:43	12:57:59	13:02:33	12:59:07	12:49:01	12:40:36	11:42:02	11:54:22
12:07:47	12:09:30	13:02:48	12:54:30	12:52:48	12:58:12	13:02:35	12:58:52	12:48:40	12:40:27	11:42:18	11:54:52
12:08:02	12:09:22	13:02:30	12:54:19	12:52:53	12:58:25	13:02:36	12:58:36	12:48:19	12:40:19	11:42:35	11:55:22
12:08:17	12:09:13	13:02:12	12:54:09	12:52:58	12:58:38	13:02:37	12:58:20	12:47:58	12:40:11	11:42:53	11:55:52
12:08:30	12:09:03	13:01:53	12:53:58	12:53:05	12:58:50	13:02:38	12:58:04	12:47:37	12:40:04	11:43:11	11:56:21
12:08:43	12:08:53	13:01:35	12:53:49	12:53:11	12:59:03	13:02:38	12:57:47	12:47:17	12:39:58	11:43:30	11:56:51
12:08:55	12:08:42	13:01:17	12:53:39	12:53:18	12:59:16	13:02:37	12:57:29	12:46:56	12:39:52	11:43:50	11:57:20
12:09:07	12:08:31	13:00:59	12:53:31	12:53:26	12:59:28	13:02:36	12:57:12	12:46:36	12:39:48	11:44:11	11:57:50
12:09:17		13:00:41	12:53:23	12:53:34	12:59:40	13:02:34	12:56:54	12:46:16	12:39:44	11:44:32	11:58:19
12:09:27		13:00:23	12:53:15	12:53:42	12:59:52	13:02:31	12:56:35	12:45:57	12:39:40	11:44:54	11:58:48
12:09:35		13:00:05		12:53:51		13:02:28	12:56:17		12:39:38		11:59:16

NOAA Global Monitoring Laboratory
Global Radiation Group
https://www.esrl.noaa.gov/gmd/grad/solcalc

Washington, DC, 202

Sunrise Tabl

Location: Latitude 38.88000 Longitude -77.03000

Time Zone Offset: America/New_York -4.0

All times are in local time. Cells with light green color indicate when daylight savings time is in effect.

Day	Jan	Feb	Mar	Apr	May	Jun	Jul	Aug	Sep	Oct	Nov	De
1	07:27	07:14	06:40	06:52	06:10	05:45	05:47	06:09	06:37	07:04	07:36	07
2	07:27	07:13	06:39	06:51	06:09	05:44	05:47	06:10	06:38	07:05	07:37	07
3	07:27	07:12	06:37	06:49	06:08	05:44	05:48	06:11	06:39	07:06	07:38	07
4	07:27	07:11	06:36	06:48	06:06	05:44	05:48	06:12	06:40	07:07	07:39	07
5	07:27	07:10	06:34	06:46	06:05	05:43	05:49	06:13	06:41	07:08	07:40	07
6	07:27	07:09	06:33	06:45	06:04	05:43	05:49	06:14	06:42	07:09	07:41	07
7	07:27	07:08	06:31	06:43	06:03	05:43	05:50	06:15	06:43	07:10	06:42	07
8	07:27	07:07	06:30	06:42	06:02	05:43	05:51	06:16	06:44	07:11	06:43	07
9	07:27	07:06	06:28	06:40	06:01	05:43	05:51	06:17	06:44	07:12	06:44	07
10	07:26	07:05	06:27	06:39	06:00	05:42	05:52	06:17	06:45	07:13	06:45	0
11	07:26	07:04	06:25	06:37	05:59	05:42	05:53	06:18	06:46	07:14	06:47	0
12	07:26	07:03	06:24	06:36	05:58	05:42	05:53	06:19	06:47	07:15	06:48	0
13	07:26	07:01	06:22	06:34	05:57	05:42	05:54	06:20	06:48	07:16	06:49	0
14	07:25	07:00	07:20	06:33	05:56	05:42	05:55	06:21	06:49	07:17	06:50	0
15	07:25	06:59	07:19	06:31	05:55	05:42	05:55	06:22	06:50	07:18	06:51	0
16	07:25	06:58	07:17	06:30	05:55	05:42	05:56	06:23	06:51	07:19	06:52	0
17	07:24	06:56	07:16	06:28	05:54	05:42	05:57	06:24	06:52	07:20	06:53	0
18	07:24	06:55	07:14	06:27	05:53	05:43	05:58	06:25	06:52	07:21	06:54	0
19	07:23	06:54	07:13	06:26	05:52	05:43	05:58	06:26	06:53	07:22	06:55	0
20	07:23	06:53	07:11	06:24	05:51	05:43	05:59	06:27	06:54	07:23	06:57	0
21	07:22	06:51	07:10	06:23	05:51	05:43	06:00	06:27	06:55	07:24	06:58	0
22	07:22	06:50	07:08	06:21	05:50	05:43	06:01	06:28	06:56	07:25	06:59	0
23	07:21	06:49	07:06	06:20	05:49	05:44	06:02	06:29	06:57	07:26	07:00	0
24	07:20	06:47	07:05	06:19	05:49	05:44	06:02	06:30	06:58	07:27	07:01	0
25	07:20	06:46	07:03	06:17	05:48	05:44	06:03	06:31	06:59	07:28	07:02	0
26	07:19	06:44	07:02	06:16	05:47	05:45	06:04	06:32	07:00	07:29	07:03	0
27	07:18	06:43	07:00	06:15	05:47	05:45	06:05	06:33	07:01	07:30	07:04	0
28	07:17	06:42	06:59	06:14	05:46	05:45	06:06	06:34	07:02	07:31	07:05	•
29	07:17		06:57	06:12	05:46	05:46	06:07	06:35	07:02	07:32	07:06	•
30	07:16		06:55	06:11	05:45	05:46	06:08	06:36	07:03	07:33	07:07	•
31	07:15		06:54		05:45		06:08	06:36		07:34		

NOAA Global Monitoring Laboratory
Global Radiation Group
https://www.esrl.noaa.gov/gmd/grad/solcalc

Washington, DC, 2021
Sunset Table

ation: Latitude 38.88000 Longitude -77.03000

Zone Offset: America/New_York -4.0

nes are in local time. Cells with light green color indicate when daylight savings time is in effect.

Jan	Feb	Mar	Apr	May	Jun	Jul	Aug	Sep	Oct	Nov	Dec
16:57	17:30	18:01	19:32	20:01	20:28	20:37	20:19	19:38	18:50	18:07	16:46
16:58	17:31	18:02	19:33	20:02	20:28	20:37	20:18	19:36	18:49	18:06	16:46
16:59	17:32	18:03	19:34	20:03	20:29	20:37	20:17	19:35	18:47	18:05	16:46
17:00	17:33	18:04	19:35	20:04	20:30	20:37	20:16	19:33	18:46	18:04	16:46
17:01	17:35	18:05	19:36	20:05	20:30	20:37	20:15	19:32	18:44	18:03	16:46
17:02	17:36	18:06	19:37	20:06	20:31	20:36	20:13	19:30	18:43	18:02	16:46
17:02	17:37	18:07	19:38	20:07	20:32	20:36	20:12	19:29	18:41	17:01	16:46
17:03	17:38	18:08	19:39	20:08	20:32	20:36	20:11	19:27	18:40	17:00	16:46
17:04	17:39	18:09	19:40	20:09	20:33	20:35	20:10	19:26	18:38	16:59	16:46
17:05	17:40	18:10	19:41	20:09	20:33	20:35	20:09	19:24	18:37	16:58	16:46
17:06	17:41	18:11	19:42	20:10	20:34	20:35	20:08	19:22	18:35	16:57	16:46
17:07	17:43	18:12	19:43	20:11	20:34	20:34	20:06	19:21	18:34	16:56	16:46
17:09	17:44	18:13	19:44	20:12	20:34	20:34	20:05	19:19	18:32	16:56	16:47
17:10	17:45	19:14	19:44	20:13	20:35	20:33	20:04	19:18	18:31	16:55	16:47
17:11	17:46	19:15	19:45	20:14	20:35	20:33	20:02	19:16	18:29	16:54	16:47
17:12	17:47	19:16	19:46	20:15	20:36	20:32	20:01	19:14	18:28	16:53	16:48
17:13	17:48	19:17	19:47	20:16	20:36	20:31	20:00	19:13	18:26	16:53	16:48
17:14	17:49	19:18	19:48	20:17	20:36	20:31	19:58	19:11	18:25	16:52	16:48
17:15	17:50	19:19	19:49	20:18	20:36	20:30	19:57	19:10	18:24	16:51	16:49
17:16	17:52	19:20	19:50	20:18	20:37	20:29	19:56	19:08	18:22	16:51	16:49
17:17	17:53	19:21	19:51	20:19	20:37	20:29	19:54	19:06	18:21	16:50	16:50
17:18	17:54	19:22	19:52	20:20	20:37	20:28	19:53	19:05	18:20	16:50	16:50
17:20	17:55	19:23	19:53	20:21	20:37	20:27	19:51	19:03	18:18	16:49	16:51
17:21	17:56	19:24	19:54	20:22	20:37	20:26	19:50	19:01	18:17	16:49	16:51
17:22	17:57	19:25	19:55	20:23	20:37	20:25	19:48	19:00	18:16	16:48	16:52
17:23	17:58	19:26	19:56	20:23	20:37	20:25	19:47	18:58	18:14	16:48	16:53
17:24	17:59	19:27	19:57	20:24	20:38	20:24	19:46	18:57	18:13	16:48	16:53
17:25	18:00	19:28	19:58	20:25	20:38	20:23	19:44	18:55	18:12	16:47	16:54
17:26		19:29	19:59	20:26	20:37	20:22	19:43	18:54	18:11	16:47	16:55
17:28		19:30	20:00	20:26	20:37	20:21	19:41	18:52	18:10	16:47	16:55
17:29		19:31		20:27		20:20	19:40		18:08		16:56

275

NOAA Global Monitoring Laboratory
Global Radiation Group
https://www.esrl.noaa.gov/gmd/grad/solcalc

Washington, DC, 202
Solar Noon Tabl

Location: Latitude 38.88000 Longitude -77.03000

Time Zone Offset: America/New_York -4.0

All times are in local time. Cells with light green color indicate when daylight savings time is in effect.

Day	Jan	Feb	Mar	Apr	May	Jun	Jul	Aug	Sep	Oct	Nov	De
1	12:11:54	12:21:46	12:20:21	13:11:50	13:05:10	13:06:03	13:12:06	13:14:27	13:08:00	12:57:39	12:51:39	11:5
2	12:12:22	12:21:53	12:20:09	13:11:32	13:05:04	13:06:12	13:12:17	13:14:22	13:07:41	12:57:20	12:51:38	11:5
3	12:12:49	12:21:59	12:19:56	13:11:15	13:04:58	13:06:22	13:12:28	13:14:17	13:07:21	12:57:01	12:51:38	11:5
4	12:13:16	12:22:05	12:19:43	13:10:57	13:04:52	13:06:33	13:12:39	13:14:12	13:07:01	12:56:43	12:51:39	11:5
5	12:13:43	12:22:10	12:19:29	13:10:40	13:04:47	13:06:43	13:12:49	13:14:05	13:06:41	12:56:25	12:51:41	11:5
6	12:14:09	12:22:14	12:19:15	13:10:23	13:04:43	13:06:54	13:12:59	13:13:59	13:06:21	12:56:07	12:51:43	11:5
7	12:14:35	12:22:17	12:19:01	13:10:07	13:04:39	13:07:05	13:13:09	13:13:51	13:06:00	12:55:49	11:51:47	11:5
8	12:15:00	12:22:19	12:18:46	13:09:50	13:04:36	13:07:17	13:13:18	13:13:43	13:05:40	12:55:32	11:51:51	12:0
9	12:15:25	12:22:21	12:18:31	13:09:34	13:04:33	13:07:29	13:13:27	13:13:35	13:05:19	12:55:16	11:51:56	12:0
10	12:15:49	12:22:21	12:18:15	13:09:18	13:04:31	13:07:41	13:13:35	13:13:26	13:04:58	12:55:00	11:52:02	12:0
11	12:16:13	12:22:21	12:17:59	13:09:02	13:04:30	13:07:53	13:13:43	13:13:16	13:04:37	12:54:44	11:52:09	12:0
12	12:16:36	12:22:20	12:17:43	13:08:47	13:04:29	13:08:05	13:13:50	13:13:06	13:04:16	12:54:29	11:52:17	12:0
13	12:16:58	12:22:19	12:17:27	13:08:32	13:04:28	13:08:18	13:13:57	13:12:55	13:03:55	12:54:15	11:52:25	12:0
14	12:17:20	12:22:16	13:17:10	13:08:17	13:04:29	13:08:31	13:14:04	13:12:43	13:03:33	12:54:01	11:52:35	12:0
15	12:17:41	12:22:13	13:16:53	13:08:02	13:04:29	13:08:43	13:14:10	13:12:32	13:03:12	12:53:47	11:52:45	12:0
16	12:18:02	12:22:10	13:16:36	13:07:48	13:04:31	13:08:56	13:14:15	13:12:19	13:02:50	12:53:34	11:52:56	12:0
17	12:18:21	12:22:05	13:16:19	13:07:35	13:04:33	13:09:09	13:14:20	13:12:06	13:02:29	12:53:22	11:53:08	12:0
18	12:18:41	12:22:00	13:16:01	13:07:22	13:04:35	13:09:22	13:14:25	13:11:53	13:02:08	12:53:10	11:53:21	12:
19	12:18:59	12:21:54	13:15:43	13:07:09	13:04:38	13:09:35	13:14:29	13:11:39	13:01:46	12:52:59	11:53:35	12:
20	12:19:16	12:21:47	13:15:26	13:06:56	13:04:42	13:09:48	13:14:32	13:11:25	13:01:25	12:52:48	11:53:49	12:
21	12:19:33	12:21:40	13:15:08	13:06:44	13:04:46	13:10:02	13:14:35	13:11:10	13:01:04	12:52:39	11:54:05	12.
22	12:19:49	12:21:32	13:14:50	13:06:33	13:04:50	13:10:15	13:14:37	13:10:54	13:00:42	12:52:30	11:54:21	12.
23	12:20:05	12:21:24	13:14:32	13:06:21	13:04:55	13:10:27	13:14:39	13:10:39	13:00:21	12:52:21	11:54:38	12.
24	12:20:19	12:21:15	13:14:14	13:06:11	13:05:01	13:10:40	13:14:40	13:10:23	13:00:00	12:52:13	11:54:55	12
25	12:20:33	12:21:05	13:13:56	13:06:01	13:05:07	13:10:53	13:14:40	13:10:06	12:59:40	12:52:06	11:55:14	12
26	12:20:46	12:20:55	13:13:38	13:05:51	13:05:14	13:11:06	13:14:40	13:09:49	12:59:19	12:52:00	11:55:33	12
27	12:20:58	12:20:44	13:13:19	13:05:42	13:05:21	13:11:18	13:14:39	13:09:32	12:58:59	12:51:55	11:55:53	12
28	12:21:09	12:20:33	13:13:01	13:05:33	13:05:28	13:11:30	13:14:38	13:09:14	12:58:38	12:51:50	11:56:13	12
29	12:21:19		13:12:43	13:05:25	13:05:36	13:11:42	13:14:36	13:08:56	12:58:18	12:51:46	11:56:34	12
30	12:21:29		13:12:25	13:05:17	13:05:45	13:11:54	13:14:34	13:08:38	12:57:59	12:51:43	11:56:56	12
31	12:21:38		13:12:08		13:05:53		13:14:30	13:08:19		12:51:40		12

NOAA Global Monitoring Laboratory

Global Radiation Group
https://www.esrl.noaa.gov/gmd/grad/solcalc

Sunrise Table

ation: Latitude 25.77000 Longitude -80.18000

Zone Offset: America/New_York -4.0

nes are in local time. Cells with light green color indicate when daylight savings time is in effect.

Jan	Feb	Mar	Apr	May	Jun	Jul	Aug	Sep	Oct	Nov	Dec
07:07	07:04	06:44	07:12	06:44	06:29	06:33	06:47	07:01	07:13	07:29	06:50
07:08	07:04	06:43	07:11	06:43	06:29	06:33	06:48	07:02	07:14	07:30	06:51
07:08	07:03	06:42	07:10	06:42	06:29	06:34	06:48	07:02	07:14	07:31	06:52
07:08	07:03	06:41	07:09	06:42	06:29	06:34	06:49	07:02	07:14	07:31	06:53
07:08	07:02	06:40	07:07	06:41	06:29	06:35	06:49	07:03	07:15	07:32	06:53
07:09	07:02	06:39	07:06	06:40	06:29	06:35	06:50	07:03	07:15	07:32	06:54
07:09	07:01	06:38	07:05	06:40	06:29	06:35	06:50	07:04	07:16	06:33	06:55
07:09	07:00	06:37	07:04	06:39	06:29	06:36	06:51	07:04	07:16	06:34	06:55
07:09	07:00	06:36	07:03	06:38	06:29	06:36	06:51	07:04	07:17	06:35	06:56
07:09	06:59	06:35	07:02	06:38	06:29	06:37	06:52	07:05	07:17	06:35	06:57
07:09	06:58	06:34	07:01	06:37	06:29	06:37	06:52	07:05	07:18	06:36	06:57
07:09	06:58	06:33	07:00	06:36	06:29	06:38	06:52	07:05	07:18	06:37	06:58
07:09	06:57	06:32	06:59	06:36	06:29	06:38	06:53	07:06	07:19	06:37	06:59
07:09	06:56	07:31	06:58	06:35	06:29	06:38	06:53	07:06	07:19	06:38	06:59
07:09	06:56	07:30	06:58	06:35	06:29	06:39	06:54	07:07	07:20	06:39	07:00
07:09	06:55	07:29	06:57	06:34	06:29	06:39	06:54	07:07	07:20	06:39	07:00
07:09	06:54	07:27	06:56	06:34	06:29	06:40	06:55	07:07	07:21	06:40	07:01
07:09	06:53	07:26	06:55	06:33	06:30	06:40	06:55	07:08	07:21	06:41	07:02
07:08	06:52	07:25	06:54	06:33	06:30	06:41	06:56	07:08	07:22	06:42	07:02
07:08	06:52	07:24	06:53	06:33	06:30	06:41	06:56	07:09	07:22	06:42	07:03
07:08	06:51	07:23	06:52	06:32	06:30	06:42	06:57	07:09	07:23	06:43	07:03
07:08	06:50	07:22	06:51	06:32	06:30	06:42	06:57	07:09	07:23	06:44	07:04
07:08	06:49	07:21	06:50	06:31	06:31	06:43	06:57	07:10	07:24	06:45	07:04
07:07	06:48	07:20	06:49	06:31	06:31	06:43	06:58	07:10	07:24	06:45	07:05
07:07	06:47	07:19	06:49	06:31	06:31	06:44	06:58	07:11	07:25	06:46	07:05
07:07	06:46	07:18	06:48	06:31	06:31	06:44	06:59	07:11	07:26	06:47	07:05
07:06	06:45	07:17	06:47	06:30	06:32	06:45	06:59	07:11	07:26	06:48	07:06
07:06	06:45	07:16	06:46	06:30	06:32	06:45	07:00	07:12	07:27	06:48	07:06
07:06		07:15	06:45	06:30	06:32	06:46	07:00	07:12	07:27	06:49	07:06
07:05		07:14	06:44	06:30	06:33	06:46	07:00	07:13	07:28	06:50	07:07
07:05		07:13		06:29		06:47	07:01		07:29		07:07

277

NOAA Global Monitoring Laboratory
Global Radiation Group
https://www.esrl.noaa.gov/gmd/grad/solcalc

Miami, FL, 2021
Sunset Tabl

Location: Latitude 25.77000 Longitude -80.18000

Time Zone Offset: America/New_York -4.0

All times are in local time. Cells with light green color indicate when daylight savings time is in effect.

Day	Jan	Feb	Mar	Apr	May	Jun	Jul	Aug	Sep	Oct	Nov	De
1	17:42	18:05	18:23	19:38	19:52	20:08	20:16	20:07	19:40	19:07	18:39	17
2	17:42	18:05	18:23	19:38	19:53	20:09	20:16	20:06	19:39	19:06	18:38	17
3	17:43	18:06	18:24	19:38	19:53	20:09	20:16	20:05	19:38	19:05	18:38	17
4	17:44	18:07	18:24	19:39	19:54	20:10	20:16	20:05	19:36	19:04	18:37	17
5	17:44	18:08	18:25	19:39	19:54	20:10	20:16	20:04	19:35	19:03	18:36	17
6	17:45	18:08	18:25	19:40	19:55	20:10	20:16	20:03	19:34	19:02	18:36	17
7	17:46	18:09	18:26	19:40	19:55	20:11	20:16	20:02	19:33	19:01	17:35	17
8	17:47	18:10	18:26	19:41	19:56	20:11	20:16	20:02	19:32	19:00	17:35	17
9	17:47	18:10	18:27	19:41	19:56	20:12	20:16	20:01	19:31	18:59	17:34	17
10	17:48	18:11	18:27	19:42	19:57	20:12	20:16	20:00	19:30	18:58	17:34	17
11	17:49	18:12	18:28	19:42	19:57	20:12	20:15	19:59	19:29	18:57	17:33	1
12	17:50	18:12	18:28	19:43	19:58	20:13	20:15	19:59	19:28	18:56	17:33	1
13	17:50	18:13	18:29	19:43	19:58	20:13	20:15	19:58	19:27	18:55	17:32	1
14	17:51	18:14	19:29	19:44	19:59	20:13	20:15	19:57	19:26	18:54	17:32	1
15	17:52	18:14	19:30	19:44	20:00	20:14	20:14	19:56	19:25	18:53	17:32	1
16	17:53	18:15	19:30	19:45	20:00	20:14	20:14	19:55	19:23	18:52	17:31	1
17	17:53	18:16	19:31	19:45	20:01	20:14	20:14	19:54	19:22	18:51	17:31	1
18	17:54	18:16	19:31	19:46	20:01	20:14	20:13	19:53	19:21	18:50	17:31	1
19	17:55	18:17	19:32	19:46	20:02	20:15	20:13	19:52	19:20	18:49	17:30	1
20	17:56	18:17	19:32	19:47	20:02	20:15	20:13	19:52	19:19	18:48	17:30	1
21	17:56	18:18	19:33	19:47	20:03	20:15	20:12	19:51	19:18	18:47	17:30	1
22	17:57	18:19	19:33	19:48	20:03	20:15	20:12	19:50	19:17	18:47	17:30	1
23	17:58	18:19	19:33	19:48	20:04	20:15	20:11	19:49	19:16	18:46	17:30	1
24	17:59	18:20	19:34	19:49	20:04	20:16	20:11	19:48	19:15	18:45	17:29	1
25	17:59	18:20	19:34	19:49	20:05	20:16	20:10	19:47	19:13	18:44	17:29	1
26	18:00	18:21	19:35	19:50	20:05	20:16	20:10	19:46	19:12	18:43	17:29	1
27	18:01	18:22	19:35	19:50	20:06	20:16	20:09	19:45	19:11	18:42	17:29	1
28	18:02	18:22	19:36	19:51	20:06	20:16	20:09	19:44	19:10	18:42	17:29	1
29	18:02		19:36	19:51	20:07	20:16	20:08	19:43	19:09	18:41	17:29	
30	18:03		19:37	19:52	20:07	20:16	20:08	19:42	19:08	18:40	17:29	
31	18:04		19:37		20:08		20:07	19:41		18:40		

NOAA Global Monitoring Laboratory
Global Radiation Group
https://www.esrl.noaa.gov/gmd/grad/solcalc

ation: Latitude 25.77000 Longitude -80.18000

Zone Offset: America/New_York -4.0

nes are in local time. Cells with light green color indicate when daylight savings time is in effect.

Jan	Feb	Mar	Apr	May	Jun	Jul	Aug	Sep	Oct	Nov	Dec
12:24:30	12:34:22	12:32:57	13:24:26	13:17:46	13:18:39	13:24:42	13:27:03	13:20:36	13:10:15	13:04:15	12:09:55
12:24:58	12:34:29	12:32:45	13:24:08	13:17:40	13:18:48	13:24:53	13:26:58	13:20:16	13:09:56	13:04:14	12:10:18
12:25:26	12:34:36	12:32:32	13:23:51	13:17:34	13:18:58	13:25:04	13:26:53	13:19:57	13:09:37	13:04:14	12:10:42
12:25:53	12:34:41	12:32:19	13:23:33	13:17:28	13:19:09	13:25:15	13:26:48	13:19:37	13:09:19	13:04:15	12:11:06
12:26:19	12:34:46	12:32:05	13:23:16	13:17:23	13:19:19	13:25:25	13:26:41	13:19:17	13:09:00	13:04:17	12:11:31
12:26:46	12:34:50	12:31:51	13:22:59	13:17:19	13:19:30	13:25:35	13:26:35	13:18:57	13:08:43	13:04:19	12:11:57
12:27:11	12:34:53	12:31:36	13:22:42	13:17:15	13:19:41	13:25:45	13:26:27	13:18:36	13:08:25	12:04:23	12:12:23
12:27:37	12:34:55	12:31:22	13:22:26	13:17:12	13:19:53	13:25:54	13:26:19	13:18:16	13:08:08	12:04:27	12:12:49
12:28:01	12:34:57	12:31:06	13:22:10	13:17:09	13:20:05	13:26:03	13:26:11	13:17:55	13:07:52	12:04:32	12:13:16
12:28:26	12:34:57	12:30:51	13:21:54	13:17:07	13:20:17	13:26:11	13:26:01	13:17:34	13:07:36	12:04:38	12:13:43
12:28:49	12:34:57	12:30:35	13:21:38	13:17:06	13:20:29	13:26:19	13:25:52	13:17:13	13:07:20	12:04:45	12:14:11
12:29:12	12:34:56	12:30:19	13:21:23	13:17:05	13:20:41	13:26:26	13:25:42	13:16:52	13:07:05	12:04:53	12:14:39
12:29:35	12:34:55	12:30:02	13:21:08	13:17:04	13:20:54	13:26:33	13:25:31	13:16:30	13:06:50	12:05:02	12:15:07
12:29:56	12:34:52	13:29:46	13:20:53	13:17:05	13:21:07	13:26:40	13:25:19	13:16:09	13:06:36	12:05:11	12:15:36
12:30:17	12:34:49	13:29:29	13:20:38	13:17:05	13:21:19	13:26:46	13:25:07	13:15:48	13:06:23	12:05:21	12:16:05
12:30:38	12:34:46	13:29:12	13:20:24	13:17:07	13:21:32	13:26:51	13:24:55	13:15:26	13:06:10	12:05:32	12:16:34
12:30:58	12:34:41	13:28:54	13:20:11	13:17:09	13:21:45	13:26:56	13:24:42	13:15:05	13:05:58	12:05:44	12:17:03
12:31:17	12:34:36	13:28:37	13:19:57	13:17:11	13:21:58	13:27:01	13:24:29	13:14:43	13:05:46	12:05:57	12:17:32
12:31:35	12:34:30	13:28:19	13:19:45	13:17:14	13:22:12	13:27:05	13:24:15	13:14:22	13:05:35	12:06:11	12:18:02
12:31:53	12:34:23	13:28:02	13:19:32	13:17:18	13:22:25	13:27:08	13:24:00	13:14:01	13:05:24	12:06:25	12:18:32
12:32:09	12:34:16	13:27:44	13:19:20	13:17:22	13:22:38	13:27:11	13:23:46	13:13:39	13:05:15	12:06:41	12:19:01
12:32:25	12:34:08	13:27:26	13:19:09	13:17:26	13:22:51	13:27:13	13:23:30	13:13:18	13:05:05	12:06:57	12:19:31
12:32:41	12:34:00	13:27:08	13:18:57	13:17:31	13:23:04	13:27:15	13:23:15	13:12:57	13:04:57	12:07:14	12:20:01
12:32:55	12:33:51	13:26:50	13:18:47	13:17:37	13:23:16	13:27:16	13:22:58	13:12:36	13:04:49	12:07:31	12:20:31
12:33:09	12:33:41	13:26:32	13:18:37	13:17:43	13:23:29	13:27:16	13:22:42	13:12:16	13:04:42	12:07:50	12:21:00
12:33:22	12:33:31	13:26:13	13:18:27	13:17:50	13:23:42	13:27:16	13:22:25	13:11:55	13:04:36	12:08:09	12:21:30
12:33:34	12:33:20	13:25:55	13:18:18	13:17:57	13:23:54	13:27:15	13:22:08	13:11:34	13:04:31	12:08:29	12:21:59
12:33:45	12:33:09	13:25:37	13:18:09	13:18:04	13:24:06	13:27:14	13:21:50	13:11:14	13:04:26	12:08:49	12:22:29
12:33:56		13:25:19	13:18:01	13:18:12	13:24:18	13:27:12	13:21:32	13:10:54	13:04:22	12:09:11	12:22:58
12:34:05		13:25:01	13:17:53	13:18:21	13:24:30	13:27:09	13:21:13	13:10:35	13:04:19	12:09:33	12:23:26
12:34:14		13:24:43		13:18:29		13:27:06	13:20:55		13:04:16		12:23:55

TABLE 6. - CONVERSION OF FEET TO CENTIMETERS

Feet	Tenths of a Foot										Feet
	0.0	0.1	0.2	0.3	0.4	0.5	0.6	0.7	0.8	0.9	
0	0	3	6	9	12	15	18	21	24	27	0
1	30	34	37	40	43	46	49	52	55	58	1
2	61	64	67	70	73	76	79	82	85	88	2
3	91	94	98	101	104	107	110	113	116	119	3
4	122	125	128	131	134	137	140	143	146	149	4
5	152	155	158	162	165	168	171	174	177	180	5
6	183	186	189	192	195	198	201	204	207	210	6
7	213	216	219	223	226	229	232	235	238	241	7
8	244	247	250	253	256	259	262	265	268	271	8
9	274	277	280	283	287	290	293	296	299	302	9
10	305	308	311	314	317	320	323	326	329	332	10
11	335	338	341	344	347	351	354	357	360	363	11
12	366	369	372	375	378	381	384	387	390	393	12
13	396	399	402	405	408	411	415	418	421	424	13
14	427	430	433	436	439	442	445	448	451	454	14
15	457	460	463	466	469	472	475	479	482	485	15
16	488	491	494	497	500	503	506	509	512	515	16
17	518	521	524	527	530	533	536	539	543	546	17
18	549	552	555	558	561	564	567	570	573	576	18
19	579	582	585	588	591	594	597	600	604	607	19
20	610	613	616	619	622	625	628	631	634	637	20
21	640	643	646	649	652	655	658	661	664	668	21
22	671	674	677	680	683	686	689	692	695	698	22
23	701	704	707	710	713	716	719	722	725	728	23
24	732	735	738	741	744	747	750	753	756	759	24
25	762	765	768	771	774	777	780	783	786	789	25
26	792	796	799	802	805	808	811	814	817	820	26
27	823	826	829	832	835	838	841	844	847	850	27
28	853	856	860	863	866	869	872	875	878	881	28
29	884	887	890	893	896	899	902	905	908	911	29
30	914	917	920	924	927	930	933	936	939	942	30
31	945	948	951	954	957	960	963	966	969	972	31
32	975	978	981	985	988	991	994	997	1000	1003	32
33	1006	1009	1012	1015	1018	1021	1024	1027	1030	1033	33
34	1036	1039	1042	1045	1049	1052	1055	1058	1061	1064	34
35	1067	1070	1073	1076	1079	1082	1085	1088	1091	1094	35
36	1097	1100	1103	1106	1109	1113	1116	1119	1122	1125	36
37	1128	1131	1134	1137	1140	1143	1146	1149	1152	1155	37
38	1158	1161	1164	1167	1170	1173	1177	1180	1183	1186	38
39	1189	1192	1195	1198	1201	1204	1207	1210	1213	1216	39
40	1219	1222	1225	1228	1231	1234	1237	1241	1244	1247	40
41	1250	1253	1256	1259	1262	1265	1268	1271	1274	1277	41
42	1280	1283	1286	1289	1292	1295	1298	1301	1305	1308	42
43	1311	1314	1317	1320	1323	1326	1329	1332	1335	1338	43
44	1341	1344	1347	1350	1353	1356	1359	1362	1366	1369	44
45	1372	1375	1378	1381	1384	1387	1390	1393	1396	1399	45
46	1402	1405	1408	1411	1414	1417	1420	1423	1426	1430	46
47	1433	1436	1439	1442	1445	1448	1451	1454	1457	1460	47
48	1463	1466	1469	1472	1475	1478	1481	1484	1487	1490	48
49	1494	1497	1500	1503	1506	1509	1512	1515	1518	1521	49
50	1524	1527	1530	1533	1536	1539	1542	1545	1548	1551	50

Feet to Meters = Centimeters divided by 100 (from above table)
Example: 09.40 feet = (287 centimeters) / (100) = 02.87 meters.

1 Meter = 100 centimeters   1 Foot = 0.30480061 meters
1 Meter = 3.2808399 feet   1 Foot = 30.480061 centimeters

TABLE 7. - TIDE PREDICTION ACCURACY

EXPLANATION OF TABLE

The accuracy of National Ocean Service tide predictions is determined by comparing predicted and observed high and low waters at all stations for which data exists, primarily the U.S. and its territories. Each water-level station is unique; there is no single standard of accuracy when comparing astronomic tide predictions with observed water levels. Water-level station locations are examined on an individual basis to determine if the predictions are adequate. Comparisons are based on 1989 data except for those locations where the stations were not in operation or the data acquired were unacceptable. If a station was not in operation in 1989, the last good year of data was used. Comparisons are made by subtracting the observed times and heights of the high and low waters from the predicted tides to compute a difference.

Table Legend

Station ID—Each water-level station in the United States and dependent territories has a unique seven digit identification number (ID). The ID is unrelated to the four digit station number used in the published prediction tables.

90% Distribution Level—90% of the absolute values of the differences are less than or equal to the values in these columns.

Standard Deviation of Differences—Standard deviation of all the differences.

Average Difference—Average of the signed sum of all the differences.

Notes

Albany—This station, located on the Hudson River, experiences a significant change in river level and corresponding times and heights of high and low waters throughout the year.

Baltimore—Winds greatly affect the times and heights of the high and low tides, owing to the large shallow bay and small tidal range.

Gulf of Mexico locations—Water level is difficult to predict because the Gulf, being large, relatively shallow, and with a small tidal range, is greatly influenced by weather conditions.

TABLE 7. - TIDE PREDICTION ACCURACY

Station ID	Station Name	Year	90% Distribution Level Time Differences High Water (Hours)	90% Time Diff Low Water (Hours)	90% Height Diff High Water (Feet)	90% Height Diff Low Water (Feet)	Std Dev Times High Water (Hours)	Std Dev Times Low Water (Hours)	Std Dev Heights High Water (Feet)	Std Dev Heights Low Water (Feet)	Avg Times High Water (Hours)	Avg Times Low Water (Hours)	Avg Heights High Water (Feet)	Avg Heights Low Water (Feet)
841-0140	Eastport, ME	1998	0.2	0.2	0.7	0.6	0.09	0.11	0.41	0.40	-0.07	-0.10	-0.08	-0.10
841-8150	Portland, ME	1998	0.3	0.2	0.6	0.6	0.14	0.13	0.40	0.39	-0.10	-0.07	-0.11	0.06
844-3970	Boston, MA	1998	0.3	0.3	0.8	0.7	0.14	0.14	0.49	0.48	-0.10	-0.10	-0.10	-0.09
844-7930	Woods Hole, MA	2003	0.5	>1.0	0.7	0.7	0.48	0.77	0.43	0.40	-0.03	0.01	-0.02	-0.01
844-9130	Nantucket,Ma	2003	0.3	0.3	0.6	0.6	0.23	0.21	0.40	0.39	-0.03	0.03	-0.03	0.03
845-2660	Newport, RI	1997	0.3	0.6	0.7	0.7	0.19	0.14	0.41	0.40	-0.06	-0.04	-0.07	-0.05
846-1490	New London, CT	1998	0.4	0.3	0.7	0.7	0.25	0.22	0.47	0.47	-0.11	-0.08	-0.10	-0.09
846-7150	Bridgeport, CT	1998	0.3	0.3	0.8	0.8	0.13	0.13	0.55	0.56	-0.12	-0.15	-0.11	-0.16
841-6945	Kings Point, NY	1999	0.9	>1.0	0.8	0.8	0.59	0.54	0.55	0.56	-0.12	-0.15	-0.11	-0.16
851-8750	The Battery, NY	2003	0.6	0.5	0.9	0.9	0.37	0.31	0.59	0.60	-0.07	-0.06	0.03	-0.02
853-1680	Sandy Hook, NJ	2002	0.4	0.4	0.8	0.9	0.25	0.25	0.51	0.54	-0.13	-0.12	0.19	0.21
853-4720	Atlantic City, NJ	2000	0.3	0.4	0.9	0.9	0.24	0.24	0.57	0.57	-0.02	-0.01	0.02	-0.02
854-5530	Philadelphia, PA	1989	0.5	0.6	1.0	1.0	0.30	0.36	0.72	0.65	0.14	0.11	-0.12	0.28
855-1910	Reedy Point, DE	2002	0.5	0.7	0.9	0.9	0.23	0.31	0.55	0.56	-0.18	-0.35	0.09	-0.02
855-7380	Breakwater Harbor, DE	1998	0.3	0.3	0.9	0.9	0.18	0.18	0.62	0.68	-0.06	-0.03	-0.03	-0.01
857-4680	Baltimore, MD	1998	0.8	1.0	1.0	1.0	1.38	1.43	0.64	0.62	-0.21	-0.09	-0.21	-0.11
859-4900	Washington, DC	1998	0.5	0.8	1.0	1.0	0.33	0.48	0.73	0.83	-0.05	-0.19	-0.03	-0.23
863-8863	Chesapeake Bay Bri Tunnel	2002	0.3	0.4	0.8	0.8	0.25	0.27	0.50	0.52	-0.06	-0.08	-0.07	-0.08
863-8610	Hampton Roads, VA	1995	0.4	0.4	0.8	0.9	0.27	0.25	0.51	0.56	0.07	0.05	0.03	-0.01
865-8120	Wilmington, NC	2003	0.5	0.5	0.6	0.8	0.34	0.29	0.38	0.46	-0.01	-0.08	0.11	0.16
8661070	Myrtle Beach, SC	2003	0.4	0.4	0.8	0.8	0.28	0.29	0.48	0.50	0.00	0.01	0.00	0.00
866-5530	Charleston, SC	2000	0.4	0.4	0.6	0.7	0.19	0.20	0.42	0.47	0.14	-0.10	0.05	-0.02
867-0870	Savannah R. Ent., GA	1995	0.3	0.3	0.7	0.9	0.21	0.19	0.47	0.58	-0.01	-0.07	0.05	0.03
872-0030	Fernandina Beach, FL	1995	0.2	0.3	0.9	0.9	0.15	0.19	0.48	0.56	-0.02	0.06	0.33	0.30
872-0218	Mayport, FL	2003	0.2	0.3	0.6	0.8	0.14	0.21	0.41	0.51	-0.04	0.01	-0.02	0.01
872-3178	Miami, Government Cut, FL	1985	0.3	0.3	0.4	0.4	0.18	0.17	0.25	0.24	-0.07	0.01	-0.02	-0.01
872-4580	Key West, FL	2000	0.5	0.4	0.3	0.3	0.29	0.25	0.19	0.20	-0.18	-0.06	-0.15	-0.10
872-6520	St. Petersburg, FL	2003	0.7	0.7	0.6	0.5	0.56	0.44	0.38	0.34	0.07	0.00	0.01	0.2
872-9840	Pensacola, FL	1995	>1.0	>1.0	0.6	0.9	2.61	2.72	0.48	0.41	0.04	0.10	-0.04	0.07
873-7048	Mobile, AL	1984	>1.0	>1.0	0.8	0.7	2.56	2.49	0.48	0.45	0.05	-0.09	-0.05	0.04
876-1724	Grand Isle, LA	2003	>1.0	>1.0	0.5	0.5	1.21	1.22	0.30	0.30	-0.24	-0.33	0.00	0.00
877-1450	Galveston, TX	1995	>1.0	>1.0	0.7	0.8	1.29	1.25	0.50	0.54	-0.15	-0.12	-0.03	0.00

TABLE 8. - LOWEST/HIGHEST ASTRONOMICAL TIDE AND OTHER TIDAL DATUMS

EXPLANATION OF TABLE

Lowest Astronomical Tide (LAT and Highest Astronomical Tide (HAT are the lowest and highest predicted values for the tides at a given location over a 19 year period. These values were calculated by generating tide predictions for the time period of the latest National Tidal Datum Epoch (1983-2001 using the latest set of tidal harmonic constituents. The highest and lowest values predicted were recorded to the nearest 0.1 foot. It is important to note that the LAT and HAT values are derived solely from predicted tides based on astronomical forces. Observed water levels can be above the HAT level or below the LAT level due to storms, winds, or other meteorological effects which are not accounted for in the tide predictions.

Table Legend

Station - Each water level station in the United States and its territories has a unique seven digit identification number (ID. The ID is unrelated to the four digit indexing number used in the published prediction tables.

LAT - Lowest Astronomical Tide - The lowest predicted tidal level

MLLW - Mean Lower Low Water

MLW - Mean Low Water

MHW - Mean High Water

MHHW - Mean Higher High Water

HAT - Highest Astronomical Tide - The highest predicted tidal level

Notes

All elevations are provided in feet relative to Mean Lower Low Water (MLLW, the reference datum for tide predictions and soundings on NOAA nautical charts. The other tidal datums (Mean Low Water, Mean High Water, and Mean Higher High Water in this table are included to provide additional information.

TABLE 8. - LOWEST/HIGHEST ASTRONOMICAL TIDE AND OTHER TIDAL DATUMS

RELATIVE TO MLLW (feet

Station	Name	LAT	MLW	MHW	MHHW	HAT
8410140	Eastport, Maine	-3.4	0.4	18.8	19.3	22.9
8413320	Bar Harbor, Maine	-2.2	0.4	10.9	11.4	13.7
8418150	Portland, Maine	-2.0	0.3	9.5	9.9	11.9
8443970	Boston, Massachusetts	-2.2	0.3	9.8	10.3	12.4
8449130	Nantucket Island, Massachusetts	-0.8	0.2	3.2	3.6	4.5
8447930	Woods Hole, Massachusetts	-0.7	0.1	1.9	2.2	3.2
8452660	Newport, Rhode Island	-1.0	0.1	3.6	3.9	5.2
8510560	Montauk, Fort Pond, New York	-0.9	0.2	2.2	2.5	3.5
8461490	New London, Connecticut	-0.8	0.2	2.8	3.1	3.9
8467150	Bridgeport, Connecticut	-1.4	0.2	7.0	7.3	8.8
8516945	Kings Point, New York	-1.5	0.3	7.4	7.8	9.7
8518750	New York (The Battery), New York	-1.5	0.2	4.7	5.1	6.4
8519483	Bayonne Bridge, New York	-1.6	0.2	5.2	5.5	6.9
8518995	Albany, New York	-1.1	0.2	5.1	5.5	6.3
8531680	Sandy Hook, New Jersey	-1.4	0.2	4.9	5.2	6.6
8534720	Atlantic City, New Jersey	-1.3	0.2	4.2	4.6	5.8
8557380	Breakwater Harbor, Delaware	-1.1	0.2	4.2	4.7	5.8
8551910	Reedy Point, Delaware	-1.0	0.2	5.5	5.8	6.9
8545530	Philadelphia, Pennsylvania	-0.6	0.2	6.4	6.8	8.0
8570280	Ocean City, Maryland	-1.2	0.2	3.5	3.9	5.1
8574680	Baltimore, Maryland	-0.6	0.2	1.4	1.7	2.3
8594900	Washington, DC	-0.6	0.2	2.9	3.2	3.8
8638863	Chesapeake Bay Bridge Tunnel, Virginia	-0.9	0.1	2.7	2.9	4.0
8638610	Hampton Roads, Sewells Point, Virginia	-0.7	0.1	2.6	2.8	3.6
8651370	Duck Pier, North Carolina	-1.0	0.1	3.4	3.7	4.9
8652587	Oregon Inlet Marina, North Carolina	-0.2	0.1	1.0	1.2	1.7
8654400	Cape Hatteras, North Carolina	-1.0	0.1	3.1	3.5	4.7
8658120	Wilmington, North Carolina	-0.4	0.2	4.4	4.7	5.4
8661070	Myrtle Beach, South Carolina	-1.5	0.2	5.2	5.6	7.2
8665530	Charleston, South Carolina	-1.5	0.2	5.4	5.8	7.3
8670870	Savannah River Entrance, Georgia	-1.7	0.2	7.1	7.5	9.2
8670681	Savannah, Georgia	-1.9	0.3	8.1	8.6	10.1
8720030	Fernandina Beach, Florida	-1.7	0.2	6.2	6.6	8.2
8720218	Mayport, Florida	-1.6	0.2	4.7	5.0	6.4
8721604	Port Canaveral, Florida	-1.2	0.2	3.6	4.0	5.4
8723178	Miami, Government Cut, Florida	-0.9	0.1	2.5	2.5	3.6
8723970	Vaca Key, Florida	-0.5	0.2	0.9	1.0	1.7
8724580	Key West, Florida	-0.8	0.2	1.5	1.8	2.6
8725110	Naples, Florida	-1.4	0.6	2.6	2.9	3.8
8726520	St. Petersburg, Florida	-1.1	0.4	2.0	2.3	3.1
8727520	Cedar Key, Florida	-1.4	0.6	3.5	3.8	4.8
8728130	St. Marks River Entrance, Florida	-1.6	0.6	3.3	3.5	4.5
8728690	Apalachicola, Florida	-1.0	0.4	1.5	1.6	2.1
8729840	Pensacola, Florida	-1.2	0.0	1.2	1.3	2.2
8735180	Dauphin Island, Alabama	-1.0	0.0	1.2	1.2	2.0
8737048	Mobile, Alabama	-1.2	0.1	1.5	1.6	2.4
8760551	South Pass, Louisiana	-1.2	0.0	1.2	1.2	2.2
8761724	Grand Isle, Louisiana	-0.9	0.0	1.1	1.1	1.8
8771450	Galveston, Texas	-1.2	0.3	1.3	1.4	2.0
8773701	Port O'Connor, Texas	-0.9	0.0	0.8	0.8	1.7
8779750	Padre Island, Texas	-1.5	0.2	1.4	1.5	2.4
2695540	Bermuda Esso Pier, Bermuda	-0.8	0.1	2.6	2.9	3.9
9710441	Settlement Point, Grand Bahamas Island	-0.8	0.1	2.8	3.1	4.1
9759110	Magueyes Island, Puerto Rico	-0.5	0.0	0.7	0.7	1.1
9755371	San Juan, Puerto Rico	-0.6	0.2	1.3	1.6	2.2
9751639	Charlotte Amalie, St. Thomas Island	-0.5	0.0	0.7	0.8	1.2
9751401	Lime Tree Bay, St. Croix Island	-0.5	0.0	0.7	0.7	1.1

OFFICIAL U.S. DATUMS

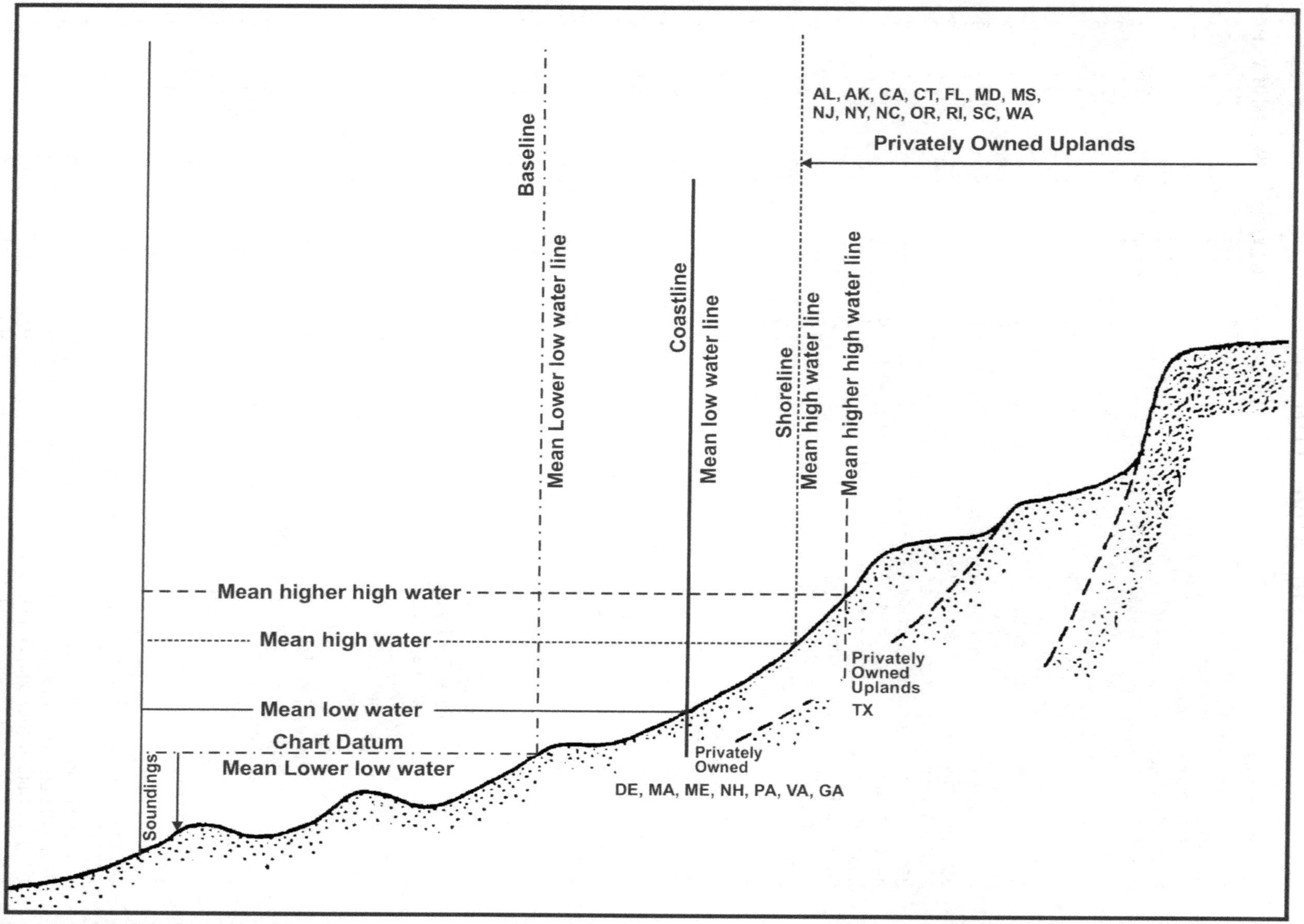

Privately Owned Uplands

AL, AK, CA, CT, FL, MD, MS,
NJ, NY, NC, OR, RI, SC, WA

Mean higher high water line

Mean high water line

Shoreline

Mean low water line

Coastline

Mean Lower low water line

Baseline

Privately
Owned
Uplands
TX

Mean higher high water line

Privately
Owned

DE, MA, ME, NH, PA, VA, GA

Mean higher high water

Mean high water

Mean low water

Chart Datum
Mean Lower low water

Soundings

Sky Events 2021

Source: NASA - SKYCAL - Sky Events Calendar

2021

Jan	01	Fr	02:05	Moon-Beehive: 2.5° S
	01	Fr		Venus: 20.2° W
	02	Sa	03:59	Perihelion: 0.9833 AU
	03	Su	09:47	Quadrantid Shower: ZHR = 120
	06	We	04:37	Last Quarter
	09	Sa	10:39	Moon Perigee: 367400 km
	10	Su	15:14	Moon Descending Node
	11	Mo	15:11	Moon-Venus: 1.5° N
	12	Tu	03:18	Moon South Dec.: 24.9° S
	13	We	00:00	New Moon
	20	We	16:02	First Quarter
	21	Th	08:11	Moon Apogee: 404400 km
	23	Sa	20:59	Mercury Elongation: 18.6° E
	23	Sa	21:26	Saturn Conjunction
	24	Su	16:47	Moon Ascending Node
	26	Tu	10:39	Moon North Dec.: 24.9° N
	28	Th	09:50	Moon-Beehive: 2.4° S
	28	Th	14:16	Full Moon
	28	Th	19:51	Jupiter Conjunction
Feb	01	Mo		Venus: 13° W
	03	We	14:33	Moon Perigee: 370100 km
	04	Th	12:37	Last Quarter
	06	Sa	19:29	Moon Descending Node
	08	Mo	08:39	Mercury Inferior Conj.
	08	Mo	10:34	Moon South Dec.: 25° S
	11	Th	14:06	New Moon
	18	Th	05:22	Moon Apogee: 404500 km
	18	Th	17:47	Moon-Mars: 4.1° N
	19	Fr	13:47	First Quarter
	20	Sa	20:44	Moon Ascending Node
	22	Mo	19:12	Moon North Dec.: 25.1° N
	23	Tu	02:38	Mercury-Saturn: 4° N
	24	We	19:16	Moon-Beehive: 2.5° S
	27	Sa	03:17	Full Moon
Mar	01	Mo		Venus: 6.3° W
	02	Tu	00:19	Moon Perigee: 365400 km
	03	We	18:32	Mars-Pleiades: 2.6° S
	05	Fr	00:11	Mercury-Jupiter: 0.3° N
	05	Fr	19:56	Moon Descending Node
	05	Fr	20:30	Last Quarter
	06	Sa	05:59	Mercury Elongation: 27.3° W
	07	Su	15:45	Moon South Dec.: 25.2° S
	09	Tu	18:02	Moon-Saturn: 3.9° N
	10	We	10:35	Moon-Jupiter: 4.3° N
	10	We	18:36	Neptune Conjunction
	10	We	20:02	Moon-Mercury: 3.9° N
	13	Sa	05:21	New Moon
	18	Th	00:04	Moon Apogee: 405300 km

	19	Fr	12:48	Moon-Mars: 2.1° N
	19	Fr	22:31	Moon Ascending Node
	20	Sa	04:37	Vernal Equinox
	20	Sa	14:15	Mars-Aldebaran: 6.9° N
	21	Su	09:40	First Quarter
	22	Mo	03:35	Moon North Dec.: 25.3° N
	24	We	04:58	Moon-Beehive: 2.7° S
	26	Fr	01:17	Venus Superior Conj.
	28	Su	13:48	Full Moon
	30	Tu	01:12	Moon Perigee: 360300 km
Apr	01	Th		Venus: 2° E
	01	Th	21:41	Moon Descending Node
	03	Sa	21:08	Moon South Dec.: 25.4° S
	04	Su	05:02	Last Quarter
	06	Tu	03:34	Moon-Saturn: 4.2° N
	07	We	02:15	Moon-Jupiter: 4.7° N
	11	Su	21:31	New Moon
	14	We	12:47	Moon Apogee: 406100 km
	16	Fr	00:53	Moon Ascending Node
	17	Sa	07:09	Moon-Mars: 0.1° N
	18	Su	11:02	Moon North Dec.: 25.5° N
	18	Su	20:31	Mercury Superior Conj.
	20	Tu	01:59	First Quarter
	20	Tu	13:25	Moon-Beehive: 3° S
	22	Th	07:16	Lyrid Shower: ZHR = 20
	26	Mo	22:31	Full Moon
	27	Tu	10:24	Moon Perigee: 357400 km
	29	Th	04:17	Moon Descending Node
	30	Fr	16:15	Uranus Conjunction
May	01	Sa	04:37	Moon South Dec.: 25.6° S
	01	Sa		Venus: 9.4° E
	03	Mo	12:02	Moon-Saturn: 4.4° N
	03	Mo	14:50	Last Quarter
	03	Mo	22:01	Mercury-Pleiades: 2.2° S
	04	Tu	16:00	Moon-Jupiter: 4.9° N
	04	Tu	20:30	Eta Aquarid Shower: ZHR = 60
	11	Tu	14:00	New Moon
	11	Tu	16:54	Moon Apogee: 406500 km
	13	Th	05:29	Moon Ascending Node
	13	Th	12:59	Moon-Mercury: 2.4° N
	15	Sa	17:25	Moon North Dec.: 25.6° N
	15	Sa	23:47	Moon-Mars: 1.6° S
	17	Mo	00:59	Mercury Elongation: 22° E
	17	Mo	20:08	Moon-Beehive: 3.1° S
	19	We	14:13	First Quarter
	25	Tu	20:52	Moon Perigee: 357300 km
	26	We	06:14	Full Moon
	26	We	06:19	Total Lunar Eclipse
	26	We	14:38	Moon Descending Node
	28	Fr	14:21	Moon South Dec.: 25.6° S
	28	Fr	22:01	Mercury-Venus: 0.4° N
	30	Su	20:22	Moon-Saturn: 4.3° N
	31	Mo	06:39	Mars-Pollux: 5.3° S
Jun	01	Tu	03:57	Moon-Jupiter: 4.9° N

288

Month	Day	Weekday	Time	Event
	01	Tu		Venus: 17.5° E
	02	We	02:24	Last Quarter
	07	Mo	21:27	Moon Apogee: 406200 km
	09	We	11:42	Moon Ascending Node
	10	Th	05:43	Annular Solar Eclipse
	10	Th	05:53	New Moon
	10	Th	20:06	Mercury Inferior Conj.
	11	Fr	23:11	Moon North Dec.: 25.6° N
	12	Sa	01:44	Moon-Venus: 1.6° S
	13	Su	14:52	Moon-Mars: 3° S
	14	Mo	01:47	Moon-Beehive: 3.1° S
	17	Th	22:54	First Quarter
	20	Su	22:32	Summer Solstice
	21	Mo	10:57	Venus-Pollux: 5.2° S
	22	Tu	15:54	Mercury-Aldebaran: 6.4° N
	23	We	00:21	Mars-Beehive: 0.3° S
	23	We	01:07	Moon Descending Node
	23	We	04:58	Moon Perigee: 360000 km
	24	Th	13:40	Full Moon
	25	Fr	00:49	Moon South Dec.: 25.6° S
	27	Su	04:30	Moon-Saturn: 4.1° N
	28	Mo	13:38	Moon-Jupiter: 4.6° N
Jul	01	Th		Venus: 25.4° E
	01	Th	16:11	Last Quarter
	02	Fr	21:45	Venus-Beehive: 0.1° N
	04	Su	14:59	Mercury Elongation: 21.6° W
	05	Mo	09:48	Moon Apogee: 405300 km
	05	Mo	21:59	Aphelion: 1.0167 AU
	06	Tu	17:41	Moon Ascending Node
	07	We	23:38	Moon-Mercury: 4.1° S
	09	Fr	05:05	Moon North Dec.: 25.6° N
	09	Fr	20:16	New Moon
	12	Mo	04:10	Moon-Venus: 3.5° S
	12	Mo	05:10	Moon-Mars: 4° S
	13	Tu	08:17	Venus-Mars: 0.5° N
	17	Sa	05:11	First Quarter
	20	Tu	08:22	Moon Descending Node
	21	We	05:30	Moon Perigee: 364500 km
	21	We	16:21	Venus-Regulus: 1.1° N
	22	Th	10:12	Moon South Dec.: 25.6° S
	23	Fr	21:37	Full Moon
	24	Sa	11:42	Moon-Saturn: 3.9° N
	25	Su	20:17	Moon-Jupiter: 4.3° N
	27	Tu	22:17	Delta Aquarid Shower: ZHR = 20
	29	Th	09:09	Mars-Regulus: 0.6° N
	31	Sa	08:16	Last Quarter
Aug	01	Su		Venus: 33.1° E
	01	Su	09:00	Mercury Superior Conj.
	02	Mo	00:24	Saturn Opposition
	02	Mo	02:35	Moon Apogee: 404400 km
	02	Mo	21:51	Moon Ascending Node
	05	Th	11:46	Moon North Dec.: 25.7° N
	08	Su	08:50	New Moon
	11	We	02:00	Moon-Venus: 4.4° S

	12	Th	14:11	Perseid Shower: ZHR = 90
	15	Su	10:20	First Quarter
	16	Mo	11:04	Moon Descending Node
	17	Tu	04:23	Moon Perigee: 369100 km
	18	We	17:24	Moon South Dec.: 25.8° S
	18	We	22:03	Mercury-Mars: 0.1° N
	19	Th	18:05	Jupiter Opposition
	20	Fr	17:19	Moon-Saturn: 3.8° N
	21	Sa	23:52	Moon-Jupiter: 4.1° N
	22	Su	07:02	Full Moon
	29	Su	21:22	Moon Apogee: 404100 km
	30	Mo	00:13	Moon Ascending Node
	30	Mo	02:13	Last Quarter
Sep	01	We		Venus: 39.9° E
	01	We	19:23	Moon North Dec.: 25.9° N
	03	Fr	23:07	Moon-Beehive: 3.1° S
	05	Su	09:32	Venus-Spica: 1.6° N
	06	Mo	19:52	New Moon
	09	Th	21:09	Moon-Venus: 4.1° S
	11	Sa	05:06	Moon Perigee: 368500 km
	12	Su	11:35	Moon Descending Node
	13	Mo	15:39	First Quarter
	13	Mo	22:59	Mercury Elongation: 26.8° E
	14	Tu	03:10	Neptune Opposition
	14	Tu	22:48	Moon South Dec.: 26° S
	16	Th	21:37	Moon-Saturn: 3.9° N
	18	Sa	01:50	Moon-Jupiter: 4.1° N
	20	Mo	18:55	Full Moon
	20	Mo	21:03	Mercury-Spica: 1.4° S
	22	We	14:21	Autumnal Equinox
	26	Su	02:33	Moon Ascending Node
	26	Su	16:44	Moon Apogee: 404600 km
	28	Tu	20:57	Last Quarter
	29	We	03:26	Moon North Dec.: 26.1° N
Oct	01	Fr		Venus: 44.9° E
	01	Fr	08:08	Moon-Beehive: 3.3° S
	06	We	06:05	New Moon
	07	Th	22:50	Mars Conjunction
	08	Fr	12:28	Moon Perigee: 363400 km
	09	Sa	11:12	Mercury Inferior Conj.
	09	Sa	13:36	Moon-Venus: 2.9° S
	09	Sa	14:35	Moon Descending Node
	12	Tu	04:09	Moon South Dec.: 26.2° S
	12	Tu	22:25	First Quarter
	14	Th	02:12	Moon-Saturn: 4.1° N
	15	Fr	04:58	Moon-Jupiter: 4.3° N
	16	Sa	08:24	Venus-Antares: 1.5° N
	20	We	09:57	Full Moon
	21	Th	06:30	Orionid Shower: ZHR = 20
	23	Sa	06:47	Moon Ascending Node
	24	Su	10:30	Moon Apogee: 405600 km
	24	Su	23:59	Mercury Elongation: 18.4° W
	26	Tu	11:04	Moon North Dec.: 26.3° N
	27	We	15:40	Moon-Pollux: 2.8° N

	28	Th	15:05	Last Quarter
	28	Th	16:32	Moon-Beehive: 3.6° S
	29	Fr	16:59	Venus Elongation: 47° E
Nov	01	Mo		Venus: 47° E
	01	Mo	20:17	Mercury-Spica: 4.1° N
	04	Th	16:15	New Moon
	04	Th	19:13	Uranus Opposition
	05	Fr	06:59	South Taurid Shower: ZHR = 10
	05	Fr	17:23	Moon Perigee: 358800 km
	05	Fr	22:38	Moon Descending Node
	08	Mo	00:21	Moon-Venus: 1.1° S
	08	Mo	11:27	Moon South Dec.: 26.3° S
	10	We	09:27	Moon-Saturn: 4.2° N
	11	Th	07:46	First Quarter
	11	Th	12:12	Moon-Jupiter: 4.5° N
	12	Fr	06:16	North Taurid Shower: ZHR = 15
	17	We	12:33	Leonid Shower: ZHR = 15
	19	Fr	03:58	Full Moon
	19	Fr	04:04	Partial Lunar Eclipse
	19	Fr	12:59	Moon Ascending Node
	20	Sa	21:14	Moon Apogee: 406300 km
	22	Mo	17:43	Moon North Dec.: 26.3° N
	23	Tu	22:22	Moon-Pollux: 2.8° N
	24	We	23:32	Moon-Beehive: 3.6° S
	27	Sa	07:28	Last Quarter
	28	Su	23:35	Mercury Superior Conj.
Dec	01	We		Venus: 41.4° E
	03	Fr	09:58	Moon Descending Node
	04	Sa	02:34	Total Solar Eclipse
	04	Sa	02:43	New Moon
	04	Sa	05:01	Moon Perigee: 356800 km
	05	Su	21:25	Moon South Dec.: 26.3° S
	06	Mo	19:48	Moon-Venus: 1.9° N
	07	Tu	20:52	Moon-Saturn: 4.2° N
	09	Th	01:07	Moon-Jupiter: 4.6° N
	10	Fr	20:36	First Quarter
	14	Tu	01:44	Geminid Shower: ZHR = 120
	16	Th	19:12	Moon Ascending Node
	17	Fr	21:16	Moon Apogee: 406300 km
	18	Sa	23:36	Full Moon
	19	Su	23:32	Moon North Dec.: 26.3° N
	21	Tu	04:20	Moon-Pollux: 2.9° N
	21	Tu	10:59	Winter Solstice
	22	We	05:28	Moon-Beehive: 3.6° S
	22	We	10:00	Ursid Shower: ZHR = 10
	26	Su	21:24	Last Quarter
	27	Mo	04:17	Mars-Antares: 4.5° N
	28	Tu	23:49	Mercury-Venus: 4.2° N
	30	Th	20:07	Moon Descending Node
	31	Fr	15:13	Moon-Mars: 0.9° N

*All event times are given for UTC-5:00: Eastern Standard Time (EST) **without** Daylight Saving Time (DST) on for part of the year.*

This page may be saved or printed.

All SKYCAL astronomical calculations are by Fred Espenak, and he assumes full responsibility for their accuracy. Special thanks to National Space Club summer intern **Sumit Dutta** for his valuable assistance in developing the Sky Events Calendar (July 2007).

GLOSSARY OF TERMS

ANNUAL INEQUALITY—Seasonal variation in the water level or current, more or less periodic, due chiefly to meteorological causes.

APOGEAN TIDES OR TIDAL CURRENTS—Tides of decreased range or currents of decreased speed occurring monthly as the result of the Moon being in apogee (farthest from the Earth).

AUTOMATIC TIDE GAGE—An instrument that automatically registers the rise and fall of the tide. In some instruments, the registration is accomplished by recording the heights at regular intervals in digital format, in others by a continuous graph in which the height versus corresponding time of the tide is recorded.

BENCH MARK (BM)—A fixed physical object or marks used as reference for a vertical datum. A *tidal bench mark is* one near a tide station to which the tide staff and tidal datums are referred. A *Geodetic bench mark* identifies a surveyed point in the National Geodetic Vertical Network.

CHART DATUM—The tidal datum to which soundings on a chart are referred. It is usually taken to correspond to low water elevation of the tide, and its depression below mean sea level is represented by the symbol Zo.

CURRENT—Generally, a horizontal movement of water. Currents may be classified as *tidal* and *nontidal*. Tidal currents are caused by gravitational interactions between the Sun, Moon, and Earth and are a part of the same general movement of the sea that is manifested in the vertical rise and fall, called *tide*. Nontidal currents include the permanent currents in the general circulatory systems of the sea as well as temporary currents arising from more pronounced meteorological variability.

CURRENT DIFFERENCE—Difference between the time of slack water (or minimum current) or strength of current in any locality and the time of the corresponding phase of the tidal current at a reference station, for which predictions are given in the *Tidal Current Tables*.

CURRENT ELLIPSE—A graphic representation of a rotary current in which the velocity of the current at different hours of the tidal cycle is represented by radius vectors and vectorial angles. A line joining the extremities of the radius vectors will form a curve roughly approximating an ellipse. The cycle is completed in one-half tidal day or in a whole tidal day according to whether the tidal current is of the semidiurnal or the diurnal type. A current of the mixed type will give a curve of two unequal loops each tidal day.

CURRENT METER—An instrument for measuring the speed and direction or just the speed of a current. The measurements are usually Eulerian since the meter is most often fixed or moored at a specific location.

DATUM (vertical)—For marine applications, a base elevation used as a reference from which to reckon heights or depths. It is called a *tidal datum* when defined by a certain phase of the tide. Tidal datums are local datums and should not be extended into areas which have differing topographic features without substantiating measurements. In order that they may be recovered when needed, such datums are referenced to fixed points known as *bench marks.*

DAYLIGHT SAVING TIME—A time used during the summer in some localities in which clocks are advanced 1 hour from the usual standard time.

DIURNAL—Having a period or cycle of approximately 1 tidal day. Thus, the tide is said to be diurnal when only one high water and one low water occur during a tidal day, and the tidal current is said to be diurnal when there is a single flood and single ebb period in the tidal day. A rotary current is diurnal if it changes its direction through all points of the compass once each tidal day.

DIURNAL INEQUALITY—The difference in height of the two high waters or of the two low waters of each day; also the difference in speed between the two flood tidal currents or the two ebb tidal currents of each day. The difference changes with the declination of the Moon and to a lesser extent with the declination of the Sun. In general, the inequality tends to increase with an increasing declination, either north or south, and to diminish as the Moon approaches the Equator. *Mean diurnal high water inequality* (DHQ) is one-half the average difference between the two high waters of each day observed over a specific 19-year Metonic cycle (the National Tidal Datum Epoch). It is obtained by subtracting the mean of all high waters from the mean of the higher high waters. *Mean diurnal low water inequality* (DLQ) is one-half the average difference between the two low waters of each day observed over a specific 19-year Metonic cycle (the National Tidal Datum Epoch). It is obtained by subtracting the mean of the lower low waters from the mean of all low waters. *Tropic high water inequality* (HWQ) is the average difference between the two high waters of the day at the times of the tropic tides. *Tropic low water inequality* (LWQ) is the average difference between the two low waters of the day at the times of the tropic tides. Mean and tropic inequalities as

DOUBLE EBB—An ebb tidal current where, after ebb begins, the speed increases to a maximum called *first ebb*; it then decreases, reaching a *minimum ebb* near the middle of the ebb period (and at some places it may actually run in a flood direction for a short period); it then again ebbs to a maximum speed called second ebb after which it decreases to slack water.

DOUBLE FLOOD—A flood tidal current where, after flood begins, the speed increases to a maximum called first flood; it then decreases, reaching a minimum flood near the middle of the flood period (and at some places it may actually run in an ebb direction for a short period); it then again floods to a maximum speed called second flood after which it decreases to slack water.

DOUBLE TIDE—A double-headed tide, that is, a high water consisting of two maxima of nearly the same height separated by a relatively small depression, or a low water consisting of two minima separated by a relatively small elevation. Sometimes, it is called an agger.

DURATION OF FLOOD AND DURATION OF EBB— Duration of flood is the interval of time in which a tidal current is flooding, and the *duration of ebb* is the interval in which it is ebbing. Together they cover, on an average, a period of 12.42 hours for a semidiurnal tidal current or a period of 24.84 hours for a diurnal current. In a normal semidiurnal tidal current, the duration of flood and duration of ebb will each be approximately equal to 6.21 hours, but the times may be modified greatly by the presence of a nontidal flow. In a river the duration of ebb is usually longer than the duration of flood because of the freshwater discharge, especially during the spring when snow and ice melt are the predominant influences.

DURATION OF RISE AND DURATION OF FALL— *Duration of rise* is the interval from low water to high water, and *duration of fall* is the interval from high water to low water. Together they cover, on an average, a period of 12.42 hours for a semidiurnal tide or a period of 24.84 hours for a diurnal tide. In a normal semidiurnal tide, the duration of rise and duration of fall will each be approximately equal to 6.21 hours, but in shallow waters and in rivers there is a tendency for a decrease in the duration of rise and a corresponding increase in the duration of fall.

EBB CURRENT—The movement of a tidal current away from shore or down a tidal river or estuary. In the mixed type of reversing tidal current, the terms *greater ebb* and *lesser ebb* are applied respectively to the ebb tidal currents of greater and lesser speed of each day. The terms *maximum ebb* and *minimum ebb* are applied to the maximum and minimum speeds of a current running continuously ebb, the speed alternately increasing and decreasing without coming to a slack or reversing. The expression maximum ebb is also applicable to any ebb current at the time of greatest speed.

EQUATORIAL TIDAL CURRENTS—Tidal currents occurring semimonthly as a result of the Moon being over the Equator. At these times the tendency of the Moon to produce a diurnal inequality in the tidal current is at a minimum.

EQUATORIAL TIDES—Tides occurring semi monthly as the result of the Moon being over the Equator. At these times the tendency of the Moon to produce a diurnal inequality in the tide is at a minimum.

FLOOD CURRENT—The movement of a tidal current toward the shore or up a tidal river or estuary. In the mixed type of reversing current, the terms *greater flood* and *lesser flood* are applied respectively to the flood currents of greater and lesser speed of each day. The terms *maximum flood* and *minimum flood* are applied to the maximum and minimum speeds of a flood current, the speed of which alternately increases and decreases without coming to a slack or reversing. The expression maximum flood is also applicable to any flood current at the time of greatest speed.

GREAT DIURNAL RANGE (Gt)—The difference in height between mean higher high water and mean lower low water. The expression may also be used in its contracted form, *diurnal range*.

GREENWICH INTERVAL—An interval referred to the transit of the Moon over the meridian of Greenwich as distinguished from the local interval which is referred to the Moon's transit over the local meri-dian. The relation in hours between Greenwich and local intervals may be expressed by the formula

Greenwich interval = local interval +0.069 L
where L is the west longitude of the local meridan in degrees. For east longitude, L is to be considered negative.

GULF COAST LOW WATER DATUM—A chart datum. Specifically, the tidal datum formerly designated for the coastal waters of the Gulf Coast of the United States. It was defined as *mean lower low water* when the type of tide was mixed and *mean low water* when the type of tide was diurnal.

HALF-TIDE LEVEL—See *mean tide level*.

HARMONIC ANALYSIS—The mathematical process by which the observed tide or tidal current at any place is separated into basic harmonic constituents.

HARMONIC CONSTANTS—The amplitudes and epochs of the harmonic constituents of the tide or tidal current at any place.

HARMONIC CONSTITUENT—One of the harmonic elements in a mathematical expression for the tide-producing force and in corresponding formulas for the tide or tidal current. Each constituent represents a periodic change or variation in the relative positions of the Earth, Moon, and Sun. A single constituent is usually written in the form $y=A \cos (at+\alpha)$, in which y is a function of time as expressed by the symbol t and is reckoned from a specific origin. The coefficient A is called the amplitude of the constituent and is a measure of its relative importance. The angle $(at+\alpha)$ changes uniformly and its value at any time is called the phase of the constituent. The speed of the constituent is the rate of change in its phase and is represented by the symbol a in the formula. The quantity α is the phase of the constituent at the initial instant from which the time is reckoned. The period of the constituent is the time required for the phase to change through 360° and is the cycle of the astronomical condition represented by the constituent.

HIGH WATER (HW)—The maximum height reached by a rising tide. The height may be due solely to the periodic tidal forces or it may have superimposed upon it the effects of prevailing meteorological conditions. Use of the synonymous term, *high tide*, is discouraged.

HIGHER HIGH WATER (HHW)—The higher of the two high waters of any tidal day.

HIGHER LOW WATER (HLW)—The higher of the two low waters of any tidal day.

HYDRAULIC CURRENT—A current in a channel caused by a difference in the surface level at the two ends. Such a current may be expected in a strait connecting two bodies of water in which the tides differ in time or range. The current in the East River, N.Y., connecting Long Island Sound and New York Harbor, is an example.

KNOT—A unit of speed, one international nautical mile (1,852.0 meters or 6,076.11549 international feet) per hour.

LOW WATER (LW)—The minimum height reached by a falling tide. The height may be due solely to the periodic tidal forces or it may have superimposed upon it the effects of meteorological conditions. Use of the synonymous term, *low tide*, is discouraged.

LOWER HIGH WATER (LHW)—The lower of the two high waters of any tidal day.

LOWER LOW WATER (LLW)—The lower of the two low waters of any tidal day.

LUNAR DAY—The time of the rotation of the Earth with respect to the Moon, or the interval between two successive upper transits of the Moon over the meridian of a place. The mean lunar day is approximately 24.84 solar hours long, or 1.035 times as long as the mean solar day.

LUNAR INTERVAL—The difference in time between the transit of the Moon over the meridian of Greenwich and over a local meridian. The average value of this interval expressed in hours is 0.069 L, in which L is the local longitude in degrees, positive for west longitude and negative for east longitude. The lunar interval equals the difference between the local and Greenwich interval of a tide or current phase.

LUNICURRENT INTERVAL—The interval between the Moon's transit (upper or lower) over the local or Greenwich meridian and a specified phase of the tidal current following the transit. Examples: *strength of flood interval and strength of ebb interval,* which may be abbreviated to *flood interval and ebb interval,* respectively. The interval is described as local or Greenwich according to whether the reference is to the Moon's transit over the local or Greenwich meridian. When not otherwise specified, the reference is assumed to be local.

LUNITIDAL INTERVAL—The interval between the Moon's transit (upper or lower) over the local or Greenwich meridian and the following high or low water. The average of all high water intervals for all phases of the Moon is known as *mean high water lunitidal interval* and is abbreviated to high water interval (HWI). Similarly the *mean low water lunitidal interval* is abbreviated to *low water interval* (LWI). The interval is described as local or Greenwich according to whether the reference is to the transit over the local or Greenwich meridian. When not otherwise specified, the reference is assumed to be local.

MEAN HIGH WATER (MHW)—A tidal datum. The arithmetic mean of the high water heights observed over a specific 19-year Metonic cycle (the National Tidal Datum Epoch). For stations with shorter series, simultaneous observational comparisons are made with a primary control tide station in order to derive the equivalent of a 19-year value.

MEAN HIGHER HIGH WATER (MHHW)—A tidal datum. The arithmetic mean of the higher high water heights of a mixed tide observed over a specific 19-year Metonic cycle (the National Tidal Datum Epoch). Only the higher high water of each pair of high waters, or the only high water of a tidal day is included in the mean.

MEAN HIGHER HIGH WATER LINE (MHHWL)—The intersection of the land with the water surface at the elevation of mean higher high water.

MEAN LOW WATER (MLW)—A tidal datum. The arithmetic mean of the low water heights observed over a specific 19-year Metonic cycle (the National Tidal Datum Epoch). For stations with shorter series, simultaneous observational comparisons are made with a primary control tide station in order to derive the equivalent of a 19-year value.

MEAN LOW WATER SPRINGS (MLWS)—A tidal datum. Frequently abbreviated *spring low water*. The arithmetic mean of the low water heights occurring at the time of the spring tides observed over a specific 19-year Metonic cycle (the National Tidal Datum Epoch).

MEAN LOWER LOW WATER (MLLW)—A tidal datum. The arithmetic mean of the lower low water heights of a mixed tide observed over a specific 19-year Metonic cycle (the National Tidal Datum Epoch). Only the lower low water of each pair of low waters, or the only low water of a tidal day is included in the mean.

MEAN RANGE OF TIDE (Mn)—The difference in height between mean high water and mean low water.

MEAN RIVER LEVEL—A tidal datum. The average height of the surface of a tidal river at any point for all stages of the tide observed over a 19-year Metonic cycle (the National Tidal Datum Epoch), usually determined from hourly height readings. In rivers subject to occasional freshets the river level may undergo wide variations, and for practical purposes certain months of the year may be excluded in the determination of tidal datums. For charting purposes, tidal datums for rivers are usually based on observations during selected periods when the river is at or near low water stage.

MEAN SEA LEVEL (MSL)—A tidal datum. The arithmetic mean of hourly water elevations observed over a specific 19-year Metonic cycle (the National Tidal Datum Epoch). Shorter series are specified in the name; e.g., monthly mean sea level and yearly mean sea level.

MEAN TIDE LEVEL (MTL)—Also called half-tide level. A tidal datum midway between mean high water and mean low water.

MIXED TIDE—Type of tide with a large inequality in the high and/or low water heights, with two high waters and two low waters usually occurring each tidal day. In strictness, all tides are mixed but the name is usually applied to the tides intermediate to those predominantly semidiurnal and those predominantly diurnal.

NATIONAL TIDAL DATUM EPOCH—The specific 19-year period adopted by the National Ocean Service as the official time segment over which tide observations are taken and reduced to obtain mean values (e.g., mean lower low water, etc.) for tidal datums. It is necessary for standardization because of periodic and apparent secular trends in sea level. The present National Tidal Datum Epoch is 1960 through 1978. It is reviewed annually for possible revision and must be actively considered for revision every 25 years.

NEAP TIDES OR TIDAL CURRENTS—Tides of decreased range or tidal currents of decreased speed occurring semimonthly as the result of the Moon being in quadrature. The *neap range* (Np) of the tide is the average semidiurnal range occurring at the time of neap tides and is most conveniently computed from the harmonic constants. It is smaller than the mean range where the type of tide is either semidiurnal or mixed and is of no practical significance where the type of tide is diurnal. The average height of the high waters of the neap tides is called *neap high water* or *high water neaps* (MHWN) and the average height of the corresponding low waters is called neap low water or low water neaps (MLWN).

PERIGEAN TIDES OR TIDAL CURRENTS—Tides of increased range or tidal currents of increased speed occurring monthly as the result of the Moon being in perigee or nearest the Earth. The *perigean range* (Pn) of tide is the average semidiurnal range occurring at the time of perigean tides and is most conveniently computed from the harmonic constants. It is larger than the mean range where the type of tide is either semidiurnal or mixed, and is of no practical significance where the type of tide is diurnal.

RANGE OF TIDE—The difference in height between consecutive high and low waters, the *mean range* is the difference in height between mean high water and mean low water. Where the type of tide is diurnal the mean range is the same as the diurnal range.

GLOSSARY OF TERMS

For other ranges, see great diurnal, spring, neap, perigean, apogean, and tropic tides.

REFERENCE STATION—A tide or current station for which independent daily predictions are given in the *Tide Tables and Tidal Current Tables,* and from which corresponding predictions are obtained for subordinate stations by means of differences and ratios.

REVERSING CURRENT—A tidal current which flows alternately in approximately opposite directions with a slack water at each reversal of direction. Currents of this type usually occur in rivers and straits where the direction of flow is more or less restricted to certain channels. When the movement is towards the shore or up a stream, the current is said to be flooding, and when in the opposite direction it is said to be ebbing. The combined flood and ebb movement including the slack water covers, on an average, 12.42 hours for the semidiurnal current. If unaffected by a nontidal flow, the flood and ebb movements will each last about 6 hours, but when combined with such a flow, the durations of flood and ebb may be quite unequal. During the flow in each direction the speed of the current will vary from zero at the time of slack water to a maximum about midway between the slacks.

ROTARY CURRENT—A tidal current that flows continually with the direction of flow changing through all points of the compass during the tidal period. Rotary currents are usually found offshore where the direction of flow is not restricted by any barriers. The tendency for the rotation in direction has its origin in the Coriolis force and, unless modified by local conditions, the change is clockwise in the Northern Hemisphere and counterclockwise in the Southern. The speed of the current usually varies throughout the tidal cycle, passing through the two maxima in approximately opposite directions and the two minima with the direction of the current at approximately 90° from the direction at time of maximum speed.

SEMIDIURNAL—Having a period or cycle of approximately one-half of a tidal day. The predominating type of tide throughout the world is semidiurnal, with two high waters and two low waters each tidal day. The tidal current is said to be semidiurnal when there are two flood and two ebb periods each day.

SET (OF CURRENT)—The direction *towards* which the current flows.

SLACK WATER—The state of a tidal current when its speed is near zero, especially the moment when a reversing current changes direction and its speed is zero. The term is also applied to the entire period of low speed near the time of turning of the current when it is too weak to be of any practical importance in navigation. The relation of the time of slack water to the tidal phases varies in different localities. For standing tidal waves, slack water occurs near the times of high and low water, while for progressive tidal waves, slack water occurs midway between high and low water.

SPRING TIDES OR TIDAL CURRENTS—Tides of increased range or tidal currents of increased speed occurring semimonthly as the result of the Moon being new or full. The *spring range* (Sg) of tide is the average semidiurnal range occurring at the time of spring tides and is most conveniently computed from the harmonic constants. It is larger than the mean range where the type of tide is either semidiurnal or mixed, and is of no practical significance where the type of tide is diurnal. The mean of the high waters of the spring tide is called *spring high water or mean high water springs* (MHWS), and the average height of the corresponding low waters is called *spring low water or mean low water springs* (MLWS).

STAND OF TIDE—Sometimes called a platform tide. An interval at high or low water when there is no sensible change in the height of the tide. The water level is stationary at high and low water for only an instant, but the change in level near these times is so slow that it is not usually perceptible. In general, the duration of the apparent stand will depend upon the range of tide, being longer for a small range than for a large range, but where there is a tendency for a double tide the stand may last for several hours even with a large range of tide.

STANDARD TIME—A kind of time based upon the transit of the Sun over a certain specified meridian, called the *time meridian,* and adopted for use over a considerable area. With a few exceptions, standard time is based upon some meridian which differs by a multiple of 15° from the meridian of Greenwich.

STRENGTH OF CURRENT—Phase of tidal current in which the speed is a maximum; also the speed at this time. Beginning with slack before flood in the period of a reversing tidal current (or minimum before flood in a rotary current), the speed gradually increases to flood strength and then diminishes to slack before ebb (or minimum before ebb in a rotary current), after which the current turns in direction, the speed increases to ebb strength and then diminishes to slack before flood completing the cycle. If it is assumed that the speed throughout the cycle varies as the ordinates of a cosine curve, it can be shown that the average speed for an entire flood or ebb period is equal to $2/\pi$ or 0.6366 of the speed of the corresponding strength of current.

SUBORDINATE CURRENT STATION—(1) A current station from which a relatively short series of observations is reduced by comparison with simultaneous observations from a control current station. (2) A station listed in the *Tidal Current Tables* for which predictions are to be obtained by means of differences and ratios applied to the full predictions at a reference station .

SUBORDINATE TIDE STATION—(1) A tide station from which a relatively short series of observations is reduced by comparison with simultaneous observations from a tide station with a relatively long series of observations. (2) A station listed in the *Tide Tables* for which predictions are to be obtained by means of differences and ratios applied to the full predictions at a reference station.

TIDAL CURRENT TABLES—Tables which give daily predictions of the times and speeds of the tidal currents. These predictions are usually supplemented by current differences and constants through which additional predictions can be obtained for numerous other places.

TIDAL DIFFERENCE—Difference in time or height of a high or low water at a subordinate station and at a reference station for which predictions are given in the *Tide Tables*. The difference, when applied according to sign to the prediction at the reference station, gives the corresponding time or height for the subordinate station .

TIDE—The periodic rise and fall of the water resulting from gravitational interactions between the Sun, Moon, and Earth. The vertical component of the particulate motion of a tidal wave. Although the accompanying horizontal movement of the water is part of the same phenomenon, it is preferable to designate the motion as tidal current.

TIDE TABLES—Tables which give daily predictions of the times and heights of high and low waters. These predictions are usually supplemented by tidal differences and constants through which additional predictions can be obtained for numerous other places.

TIME MERIDIAN—A meridian used as a reference for time.

TROPIC CURRENTS—Tidal currents occurring semimonthly when the effect of the Moon's maximum declination is greatest. At these times the tendency of the Moon to produce a diurnal inequality in the current is at a maximum.

TROPIC RANGES—The *great tropic range* (Gc), or *tropic range*, is the difference in height between tropic higher high water and tropic lower low water. The *small tropic range* (Sc) is the difference in height between tropic lower high water and tropic higher low water. The *mean tropic range* (Mc) is the mean between the great tropic range and the small tropic range. The small tropic range and the mean tropic range are applicable only when the type of tide is semidiurnal or mixed. Tropic ranges are most conveniently computed from the harmonic constants.

TROPIC TIDES—Tides occurring semimonthly when the effect of the Moon's maximum declination is greatest. At these times there is a tendency for an increase in the diurnal range. The tidal datums pertaining to the tropic tides are designated as *tropic higher high water* (TcHHW), *tropic lower high water* (TcLHW), *tropic higher low water* (TcHLW), and *tropic lower low water* (TcLLW).

TYPE OF TIDE—A classification based on characteristic forms of a tide curve. Qualitatively, when the two high waters and two low waters of each tidal day are approximately equal in height, the tide is said to be *semidiurnal*; when there is a relatively large diurnal inequality in the high or low waters or both, it is said to be *mixed*; and when there is only one high water and one low water in each tidal day, it is said to be *diurnal*.

VANISHING TIDE—In a mixed tide with very large diurnal inequality, the lower high water (or higher low water) frequently becomes indistinct (or vanishes) at time of extreme declinations. During these periods the diurnal tide has such overriding dominance that the semidiurnal tide, although still present, cannot be readily seen on the tide curve.

Index of Stations

CPSIA information can be obtained
at www.ICGtesting.com
Printed in the USA
LVHW011354270121
677615LV00009B/293